# MEDICAL PHYSIOLOGY

**A CORE TEXT with CLINICAL CORRELATIONS**



**Prof. (Dr.) A. Das**

Since 1960

*for MBBS / MD / M Sc (Medical) / M Sc / B Sc / BPT / DPT / BHMS*

# MEDICAL PHYSIOLOGY

## *A CORE TEXT with CLINICAL CORRELATIONS*

**Prof. (Dr.) Asis Das**

M D (Physiology), Ph D (Medicine), MNA MS (New Delhi), MAMS (Vienna)

*Professor & Head, Department of Physiology,*
*Institute of Post-Graduate Medical Education and Research*
*& SSKM Hospital, Kolkata, Govt. of West Bengal.*

**BOOKS AND ALLIED (P) Ltd.**

No. 1-E(1) 'Shubham Plaza' (1st Floor)
83/1 Beliaghata Main Road, Kolkata 700010 (India)
*Telefax* : (+91-33)6535-3844, 2241-8573 • *e-mail* : books@cal.vsnl.net.in

# MEDICAL PHYSIOLOGY

*A CORE TEXT with CLINICAL CORRELATIONS*

First Published : 2000
Second Edition : 2001
Third Edition (thoroughly revised) : 2004
**Fourth Edition : 2006**



***Publisher*** : Arunabha Sen
BOOKS & ALLIED (P) LTD.
8/1 Chintamoni Das Lane, Kolkata 700009

***Typesetter*** : BOOKS & ALLIED (P) LTD.
8/1 Chintamoni Das Lane, Kolkata 700009

***Printer*** : SWAPNA PRINTING WORKS PVT. LTD.
52, R. R. Roy Sarani, Kolkata 700009

***Project Team*** : Abhijit Ghoshal and Salil Das

**ISBN** 81-87134-58-5

***Price*** : Rs. **395.00** (Rupees Three hundred ninety-five) only

*Kenesitam patati presitam manah*

*kena pranah prathamah praiti yuktah;*

*Kenesitam vacam imam vadanti*

*caksuh srotram ka u devo yunakti.*

[Disciple] : At whose behest the mind is drawn towards its objects? By whose will the vital lifebreath, which is the first sign of life, functions and sustains the body-mind complex? By whose order do people utter words? Which effulgent god directs the eye, the ear (and other organs)?

*Kenoponisad 1.1*

*Srotrasya srotram manaso mano yad*

*vaco ha cacam sa u pranasya pranah;*

*Caksusascaksuratimucya dhirah*

*pretyasmallokadamrta bhavanti.*

[Teacher] : It [the all pervading, Everexisting Consciousness-Brahman] is the ear of the ear, the thinker of the thought, speech of the speech, the very life of the living and the functions, the real seer behind seeing. Therefore, the wise, through discrimination and detachment to the world and sense objects discovers the Real Being behind all phenomena, the Eternal Truth or Brahman and by experiencing THAT becomes immortal and free from all bondages.

*Kenoponisad 1.2*

**ASIS DAS**

*dedicates this book*
*to his father*

Late Professor JANARDAN DAS, M.D., F.C.C.P.(USA),
for a lifetime devotion in the teaching of Pharmacology,
who first conceived the idea for this book but,
tragically, did not live to see it completed.

# Acknowledgments


## *Acknowledgements*

The author thanks **Dr. Azizul Hai,** Associate Professor, Dept. of Physiology, IPGMER/SSKM Hospital, Kolkata for his thoroughly professional approach. His constant interest and input have had a significant impact on the final structure of this text and thoughtful and meticulous work.

*I gratefully acknowledge the following individuals for their help to this text—*

| | |
|---|---|
| **Prof. (Dr.) Mumtaz Goni** | Principal, Govt. Medical College, Jammu, J&K |
| **Prof. (Dr.) R. D. Sharma** | J.L.N. Medical College, Ajmer, Rajasthan |
| **Prof. (Dr.) K. K. Deepak** | All India Institute of Medical Sciences, N. Delhi |
| **Prof. (Dr.) Asha Gandhi** | Lady Hardinge Medical College, N. Delhi |
| **Prof. (Dr.) Archana Sharma** | Assam Medical College, Dibrugarh |
| **Prof. (Dr.) R. R. Dixit** | MP Shah Medical College, Jamnagar, Gujrat |
| **Prof. (Dr.) S. S. Misra** | N.S.C. Medical College, Jabbalpur |
| **Prof. (Dr.) Sarupa Rani** | Andhra Medical College, Visakapattanam, AP |
| **Prof. (Dr.) Krishna Chaudhury Sinha** | Nalanda Medical College, Patna |
| **Prof. (Dr.) Krishna Singh** | Darbhanga Medical College, Darbhanga, Bihar |
| **Prof. (Dr.) Moromi Datta** | Gauhati Medical College, Assam |
| **Prof. (Dr.) Rajib Ranjan Prosad** | Patna Medical College, Patna |
| **Prof. (Dr.) Anita Devi** | Regional Institute of Medical Sciences, Imphal |
| **Prof. (Dr.) Sukhwanta Bose** | SAIMS, Indore, MP |
| **Prof. (Dr.) Bipin Bihari Prodhan** | MKCG Medical College, Behrampur, Orissa. |
| **Prof. (Dr.) R. R. Mahanti** | SCB Medical College, Cuttock, Orissa |
| **Prof. (Dr.) S. K. Saxena** | Sikkim Manipal Institute of Medical College, Gangtok |
| **Prof. (Dr.) Sudipa Chaudhury** | Agartala Govt. Medical College, Tripura |
| **Prof. (Dr.) Sunita Tewari** | K.G. Medical College, Lucknow |
| **Prof. (Dr.) Udai Prokash** | Institute of Medical Sciences, B.H.U. |
| **Prof. (Dr.) Amal K. Das** | Midnapur Govt. Medical College, West Bengal |
| **Prof. (Dr.) Bedopriya Das** | Gauhati Medical College, Guahati, Assam |
| **Prof. (Dr.) H. N. Jha** | Jaharlal Nehru Medical College, Bhagalpur, Bihar |
| **Prof. (Dr.) Asim Das** | Govt. Medical College, Vadodara, Gujarat |
| **Prof. (Dr.) Sujit K. Chaudhury** | Ex-Professor, Medical College, Kolkata |
| **Dr. Archana Das** | Sr. Chief Medical Officer, CGHS, Central Health Service |

# Preface to Fourth Edition

Aims of this book include, primarily, to help the students (i) studying in MBBS course of Indian Universities (or their quivalents abroad) plus the graduate and master course students of general science streams and (ii) preparing for entrance examinations of different post-graduate medical disciplines. Neverthless it is strongly expected that every student of physiology will perhaps get some benefit out of this book.

Every effort has been made to keep the book lucid yet modern. Clinical applications of physiology have been especially emphasised.

The author thanks everybody who has helped him to prepare this edition. Special thanks are to son Abhisek Das, B.Tech (Computer Engg.), MS (Electrical & Computer Engg.) USA, PhD scholar; daughter Agnideepa; and Sri Arunabha Sen of M/s. Books and Allied (P) Ltd. for various help. Lastly not the least my sincere thanks are to Dr. Archana Das, for her ceaseless helps.

Kolkata
21st June, 2006

**ASIS DAS**
*e-mail :* asis5858@dataone.in

# Preface to First Edition

The book **MEDICAL PHYSIOLOGY**, is written primarily for the medical students, keeping in context with the recent changes in medical education and the advent of the core curriculum. As a student and teacher of Physiology, I have come across some serious deficiencies in many physiology textbooks, and how these books failed to emphasize the crucial and important points, and how little these books allowed the proper understanding of the subject.

Learning **Physiology**, the study of the functions at the molecular, cellular and subcellular levels, is an absolute necessary to appreciate the overall function or dysfunction of an individual. This book provides the core and concise knowledge of Physiology keeping in pace with the latest information and newer understanding of the discipline. The material in this book has been kept up-to-date, and have been supplemented at each step with a number of flow charts, diagrams, illustrations and tables. Special emphasis has been laid on molecular physiology and its clinical significances.

The materials in this book have been arranged in **two volumes**, and each volume is further subdivided into different sections. **Volume One** deals with ***Core text*** and *clinical correlations*. In **Volume Two** the **first section** is concerned with ***Viva voce***, and **section two** discusses the ***Practical*** part, while the **third section** deals with ***Self-assessment***.

In the **Core text** portion I have deliberately devoted special attention to **applied physiology** and **clinical correlations** with the belief that these aspects will be required in the future study of Medicine and the Biomedical sciences. The text has been made up-to-date wherever felt appropriate to include recent advances and latest research findings.

**Viva voce** involves facing examiners across the table. It is often a nerve-wreckling experience. The most important point while answering oral questions is to answer as simply as possible, and leading the examiners into one's own territory.

**MCQs** have become an important part of undergraduate examinations, and especially at the post-graduate entrance level. Without extensive practice, MCQs cannot be answered as they need instant recollection from memory.

**Review questions** may be used as a self-test to evaluate one's comprehension and understanding of the contents of a chapter.

In conclusion, I would advise my students to use the two volumes of this book concurrently and according to their own needs. Their aim should be to understand the concepts and principles involved in Physiology and not mere memorisation of the facts. My efforts will be successful if the students derive real benefit from this book.

Kolkata
3rd July, 2000

**ASIS DAS**

# CONTENTS

## CHAPTER 1 : GENERAL AND CELLULAR PHYSIOLOGY



## CHAPTER 2 : MUSCLE CONTRACTION PHYSIOLOGY



## CHAPTER 3 : AUTONOMIC NERVOUS SYSTEM

*Contents contd.*

*Contents contd.*

## CHAPTER 6 : PULMONARY PHYSIOLOGY



## CHAPTER 7 : CARDIOVASCULAR PHYSIOLOGY

*Contents contd.*

## CHAPTER 8 : RENAL PHYSIOLOGY



## CHAPTER 9 : ENDOCRINE PHYSIOLOGY

Contents contd.

## CHAPTER 10 : REPRODUCTIVE PHYSIOLOGY



## CHAPTER 11 : NEUROPHYSIOLOGY



## CHAPTER 12 : THE SPECIAL SENSES

# General and Cellular Physiology

**AGENDA :**



1

## ➤ 1.1 CHAPTER OVERVIEW

Ions, nutrients and waste material are transported across cell membrane by diffusion, osmosis, and active transport. Simple diffusion is described by the **Fick equation**. Carrier-mediated diffusion, called **facilitated diffusion**, is described by Michaelis – **Menton equation**. Active transport process may be primary or secondary. **Primary active transport** processes such as Na-K pump, use the energy derived from the hydrolysis of ATP to transport materials against their electrochemical gradient. **Secondary active transport** processes, such as those that transport glucose and aminoacids into renal or intestinal epithelial cells, use the energy from the $Na^+$ electrochemical gradient. In resting state, the membrane is primarily permeable to $K^+$ and therefore the **resting membrane potential** is close to the equilibrium potential for $K^+$. **Action potentials** are produced by voltage and time dependent gates covering ion selective channels. Nerve and skeletal muscle membranes contain $Na^+$ and $K^+$ ion selective channels.

## ➤ 1.2 Molecular Structure of Cell Membrane and Physical Principles of Transport Across them and Capillary Wall

The cell is the building block of all forms of life on earth. The fundamental plan of construction of an animal is : ***cells → multiple cells form tissues → combination of tissues form organs → multiple organs form organ systems → assembly of organ systems, entire physique*** (Fig. 1.1).

Bodies of mammals like human being are composed of an astronomical number of microscopic cells, vastly differentiated and mutually interdependent. In spite of that, there remains some features common to each cell. All the cells are surrounded by a limiting membrane enclosing within it a **nucleus** (absent in RBC and platelets) and other organelles like ***mitochondria, endoplasmic reticulum, chromosomes, Golgi bodies, lysosomes, peroxisomes, various inclusion bodies, cytoskeletal elements etc.*** (Fig. 1.2).

The surrounding limiting membrane, called **plasmalemma** or **plasma membrane** or simply **cell membrane** separates a cell from its neighbours. Properly drawn and anticoagulated blood separates on standing into straw colored plasma and red colored cellular layers. This proves that there must be something (cell membrane) enclosing the hemoglobin- containing cytosol of RBCs. If the membranes of some RBC get disrupted (hemolysis) then the color of plasma becomes reddish. Differences in the composition of extracellular and intracellular constituents eg, $Na^+$, $Ca^{2+}$ (more in extracellular fluid) and $K^+$ and $Mg^{2+}$ (more in intracellular fluid) indicate that the membrane is **selectively permeable**. It is flexible as well, allowing the cell to change its shape as is evident in contracting muscles. Not only the entire cell, but also the boundaries of most cellular organelles are covered by similar type of membrane.

***Under light microscope*** the plasma membrane cannot be distinguished from cytosol, but ***under electron microscope*** it can be observed; where it appears thin, with thickness being 7.5 nm. The chemical structure of cell membrane varies among cell types, but the basic pattern is similar. It consists of double layers of lipid studded with protein molecules. Phospholipids form the basic structural fabric of the membrane. Important **phospholipids** are *phosphatidylcholine* and *phosphatidylethanolamine,* but *glycolipids* and *cholesterol* are also found (Fig.1.3). The phospholipids comprise a glycerol backbone bearing hydrophilic phosphate and hydrophobic long-chain fatty acyl moieties besides nitrogenous bases like choline or ethanolamines. The polar or hydrophilic part of the molecule is relatively soluble in water and faces the extracellular and intracellular compartments, whereas the hydrophobic non-polar portion of molecules of outer and inner laminae face each other in the interior of the membrane.

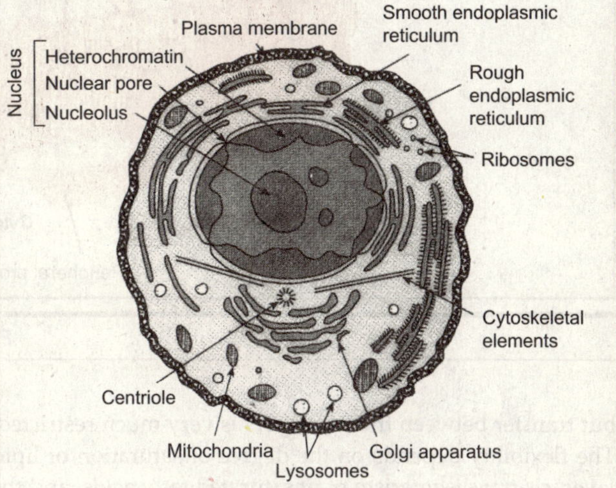


**Fig. 1.1 :** A typical cell, showing the major organ cells

There are differential distributions of membrane lipids in the lipid layers, eg, *glycolipids exist only on the outer layer,* the sprouting sugar residue may take part in cell-cell interactions. *Phosphatidyl choline* is present on the *outer layer* and *phosphatidyl ethanolamine* is present on the *inner layer.* There occurs lateral movement of molecules in each layer

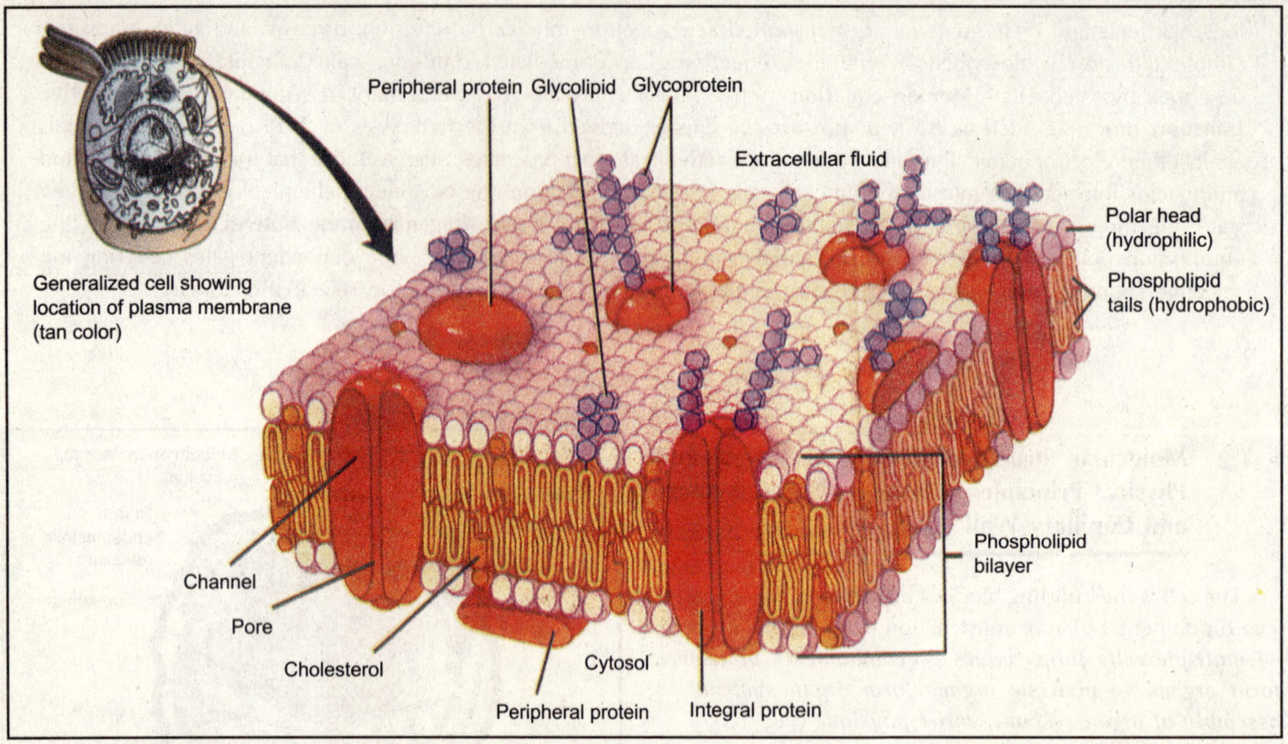


Fig. 1.2

but transfer between the two layers is very much restricted. The flexibility depends on the degree of saturation of lipid layer, *cis-trans* isomerism of unsaturated fatty acids, and the content of cholesterol.

Membrane proteins have been separated and studied in different cell types, but RBC membranes are more conveniently utilized after hemolysis. The protein molecules may pass deep in the membrane **(integral proteins)**, but some may remain attached to either side of the membrane **(peripheral proteins) (Fig. 1.4)**. Some proteins traverse the membrane and get exposed on both sides **(transmembrane proteins)**. The peripheral proteins can be separated from the membrane by mild treatment but separation of integral and transmembrane proteins requires vigorous measures (detergents, organic solvents). In the RBC membrane, peripheral proteins are **spectrin** and **actin** and integral proteins are **bands 3 and 7**.

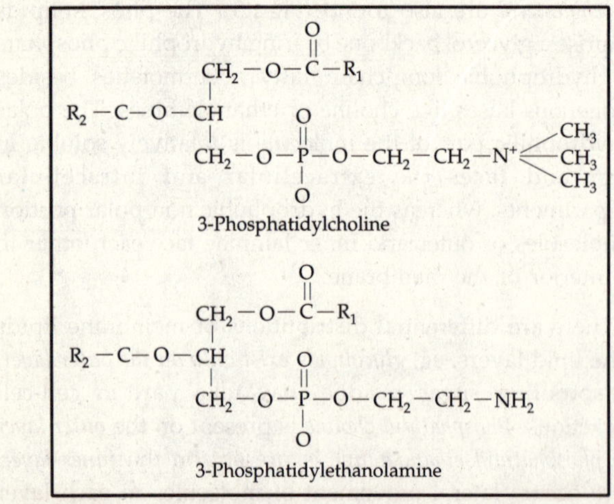


Fig. 1.3 : Structure of major membrane lipids

The mass of membrane lipids and that of proteins are similar, but as lipids are of low molecular weight, they are more numerous. The proteins, like phospholipids, bear hydrophilic portions which face ECF or ICF and hydrophobic moieties which penetrate deep in the membrane. Peripheral proteins get connected to membrane layers by different ways — they may unite to surface proteins or carbohydrate part of glycolipids. Membrane proteins like lipids can move laterally but transfer of berth is very much restricted.

## Functions of cell membrane

1. The *membrane separates a cell* from its neighbours so that each cell *can function independently* but at the same time get influenced appropriately by signals from cells near at hand or lying at distance.

2. Within a cell, the membrane around organelles *maintains their unique composition* so that they have their appropriate functions.

3. **Other functions can be attributed to the membrane proteins** which can be classified functionally into : (Fig. 14.)

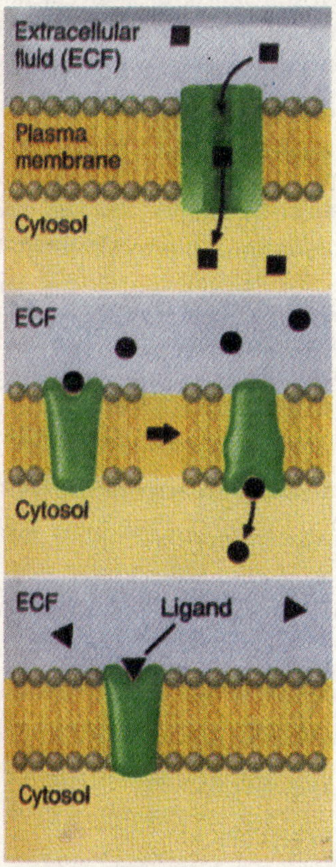


**1 Channel :** Allows specific substance (■) to move through water-filled passageway (pore). Most plasma membranes include specific channels for several ions, most commonly $K^+$ and $Cl^-$.

**2 Transporter (Carrier) :** Transports specific substance (●) across membrane by changing shape. For example, amino acids, needed to synthesize new proteins, enter body cells via transporters.

**3 Receptor :** Recognizes specific ligament (▲) and alters cell's function in some way. For example, antidiuretic hormone binds to receptors in take kidneys and changes in water permeability of certain plasma membranes.

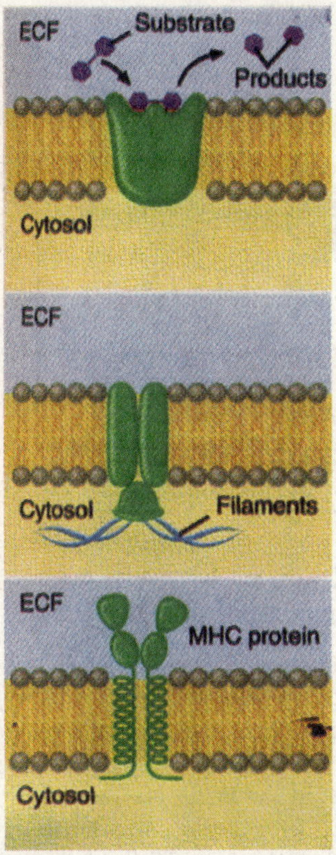


**4 Enzyme :** Catalyzes reaction inside or outside cell (depending on which direction the active site faces). For example, lactase protruding from epithelial cells lining your small intestine splits the disaccharide lactose in the milk you drink.

**5 Cytoskeleton Anchor :** Anchors filaments and tubules of the cytoskeleton inside cell to the membrane to provide structural stability and shape for the cell. May also participate in movement of the cell.

**6 Cell Identity Marker :** Distinguishes your cells from anyone else's (unless you are an identical twin). An important class of such markers are the major histocompatibility (MHC) proteins.

Fig. 1.4 : Structure of cell membrane and mechanism of transport

(a) ***Structural proteins*** : They are part and parcel of membrane structure eg, glycophorins of RBC membrane.

(b) ***Pumps*** : They transfer substances against concentration and/or electrical gradients across the membrane, eg, $Na^+$-pump ($Na^+$– $K^+$– ATPase).

(c) ***Channel proteins*** : Charged particles cannot traverse the lipid layers; they require membrane channels for their transport. Some channels (membrane proteins) may remain continuously open **(leak channels)** but in others their patency can be changed by ligands **(ligand-gated channel)** or changed potential **(voltage-gated channel)**. Some of $K^+$ and $Cl^-$ channels are leak channels, acetylcholine receptors are ligand-gated channels, and voltage-gated $Na^+$, $K^+$ or $Ca^{2+}$ channels in excitable tissues are classic examples of voltage-gated channels.

(d) ***Carriers*** are protein molecules involved in transport across the membrane. They bind to the substance on one side of the membrane, change configuration and expose it to opposite side from where it gets dissociated. Molecules may move passively following concentration and/or electrical gradients by **faciliated diffusion** eg, transport of glucose across the membrane. In others, expenditure of energy is required to transport molecules against concentration and/or electrical gradient **(active transport)**; the carriers are called **pumps**, eg, *$Na^+$– $K^+$– ATPase*. **Carrier proteins** are called **'uniports'** when they carry one particular substance, **'symports'** when they ferry two or more molecules of different substances in one direction, eg, $Na^+$-glucose transporter in GI tract and renal tubules, or **'antiports'** when two (or more molecules) of different substances are transported in opposite directions simultaneously, eg, $Ca^{2+}$– $Na^+$ transporter (Fig. 1.5).

(e) ***Enzyme proteins*** take part in reactions in the membrane, eg, adenylate cyclase responsible for formation of cAMP from ATP. $Na^+$– $K^+$– ATPase is also an example of enzyme protein.

(f) ***Receptor proteins*** : Some membrane proteins bear appropriate site for recognition of specific ligands like peptide hormones, neurotransmitters etc. and trigger physiological responses.

(g) ***Membrane proteins*** can also act as antigens. Membrane proteins like cell adhesion molecules (CAM) are responsible for cell-cell adhesion.

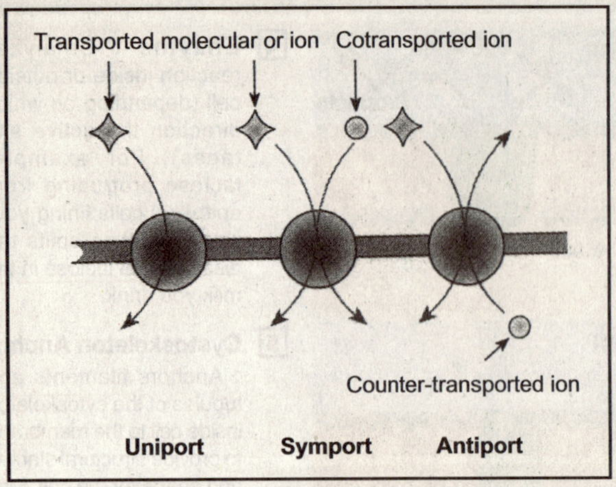


Fig. 1.5

## Forces moving substances across cell membrane and epithelium

The concentration of substances differ between intracellular and extracellular fluids. In different compartments of extracellular space the composition differ to considerable extent. As for example, in ICF $K^+$ and $Mg^{2+}$ concentrations are higher; on the other hand, in the ECF, $Na^+$ and $Ca^{2+}$ concentrations are higher. In plasma, the protein concentration is higher than that of interstitial fluid. These differences are possible due to the barriers separating them behaving selectively and utilizing forces appropriately to maintain the composition of each compartment constant.

Forces operating in the transport across cell membrane and epithelium are the same. They are *diffusion, facilitated diffusion, active transport, exocytosis, endocytosis, osmosis, filtration* and *solvent drag*. Their relative importance varies from place to place according to requirement, eg, diffusion is the primary force in the transfer of molecules across lung alveoli, but, in the renal glomeruli, filtration is the principal driving force.

## Diffusion

Molecules in the gaseous state or in solution move randomly and reach the same concentration everywhere. Within a room without any obvious air movement smell of a flower will spread everywhere; it is not due to bulk flow, but due to motion of individual molecules. If crystals of copper sulphate are taken under water in a long test tube and kept as such, within a few days to weeks the water will be found to be coloured by the solute everywhere. The copper sulphate, though heavier than water, moves upwards by its molecular movement by diffusion and overcomes the force of gravity. When the concentration of molecules in solution or gaseous phase is the same everywhere it does not mean absence of motion, but motion of individual molecules in the same net rate in different directions. Even when there is concentration difference, the movement of molecule is not one-way but the net movement occurs from an area of high concentration to an area of low concentration.

If the particles concerned are charged ones, they will move following **electrical gradient.** This is the process by which negatively charged particles (anions) move towards the anode and the positively charged ones (cations) move to the cathode during electrolysis. Within cells there are impermeable negatively charged protein molecules, this causes movement of permeable positively charged $K^+$ inside the cell and repulsion of negatively charged $Cl^-$ outside. This process is also diffusion and it occurs across many barriers occurs both due to electrical and concentration gradients.

**Fick's law of diffusion** takes into account the factors mediating the magnitude of diffusion of a substance across a barrier.

Mass of substance moving per unit time ($\dot{Q}$) = Diffusion coefficient (D) × surface area available (A) × concentration difference between two sides ($C_1 - C_2$)

$$\times \frac{1}{\text{thickness of barrier (t) or diffusion distance}}, \text{ i.e.,}$$

$$(\dot{Q}) = \frac{D \times A \times (C_1 - C_2)}{t} \text{ at a particular temperature.}$$

In case of gases, diffusion coefficient is inversely proportional to the square root of MW (molecular weight) of the gas concerned and directly to solubility (S) when **diffusion** involves gas fluid interface as in pulmonary capillaries and alveolar air

$$\text{i.e., } D \propto \frac{S}{\sqrt{MW}}$$

In case of membranes separating two compartments, if permeability (P) replaces $\frac{D}{t}$, the equation becomes ($\dot{Q}$)= P × A × ($C_1$–$C_2$). In case of lungs concentrations are replaced by partial pressures, because partial pressure of a gas is the function of its concentration in a gas mixture and permeability along whole surface area (P × A) is replaced by diffusion capacity of lung ($D_L$). Then the volume of gas transferred $\dot{Q} = D_L \times (P_1 - P_2)$.

## Donnan effect

When a barrier, cell membrane or epithelium separates two compartments in such a way that in one of them charged particles are of such large size that they cannot diffuse to the other, then the distribution of permeant ions will be influenced by electrical and chemical gradients, and at equilibrium their concentrations will differ in two compartments. This behaviour of permeable ions in presence of non-diffusible ions is called **Gibbs-Donnan effect**.

Let us think that at a hypothetical time zero, a cell is separated from ECF by membrane which is permeable to $K^+$ and $Cl^-$ ions, so their concentrations will be equal on both sides. Now, some negatively charged protein molecules will be synthesized, they will unite with equivalent amount of $K^+$ and push an equal number of $Cl^-$ to outside. So, initially, $Cl^-$ concentration within the ICF falls, and due to concentration difference $Cl^-$ will diffuse from ECF to ICF (along with some $K^+$ to maintain electrical neutrality) opposite to the direction favoured by electrical force, and at equilibrium, $[K^+]_I > [K^+]_E$ and $[Cl^-]_I < [Cl^-]_E$ and the total number of particles, $[K^+]_I+[Cl^-]_I+[Pr^-]_I > [K^+]_E+[Cl^-]_E$ and osmotic imbalance will occur to some extent.

Now, according to the **Gibbs-Donnan membrane equilibrium distribution**, in case of permanent anions and cations of same valence, product of their concentrations in one compartment is equal to that on the other, eg, $[K^+]_E \times [Cl^-]_E = [K^+]_I \times [Cl^-]_I$.

Plasma protein anions also have **Donnan effect** because the endothelium of capillaries are impermeable to protein ions. At the alkaline pH of plasma, proteins behave as anions and will attract $Na^+$ and repel $Cl^-$, so in the interstitial fluid and lymph, $Na^+$ concentration will be lower and $Cl^-$ concentration higher than that of plasma.

Gibbs-Donnan effect of cellular protein and large organic anions are responsible for the differential distribution of permeant ions like $K^+$ and generation of membrane potential (diffusion potential), whose magnitude can be calculated by Nernst equation.

### Filtration

**Filtration** is the bulk movement of fluid (not movement of individual molecules as in diffusion) as a result of pressure difference on two sides of a barrier, containing pores, through which the fluid (but not the suspended solute particles) can pass. The particles which are smaller than the holes can pass through, retaining the larger ones. In the capillaries that are non-fenestrated, small molecules like $Na^+$, $Cl^-$ come out of the gaps between endothelial cells but the corpuscles and large colloidal molecules are retained.

The amount of filtrate formed per unit time will depend upon the pressure difference across the membrane, the surface area available, the permeability of the membrane, and inversely to the viscosity of the fluid concerned.

Filtration occurs across capillaries everywhere, but in the kidneys the rate of *filtration is enormous* because of large pressure gradient and increased permeability. In every site of filtration, it is opposed by the osmotic forces due to non-permeant particles called **colloid osmotic pressure** or **oncotic pressure**. The *net filtration* is determined by their *counter balancing effects.*

In tissues where capillary surface area is unknown and viscosity remains same, rate of filtration is calculated from capillary filtration coefficient of a particular tissue $K_f$ = ml/min/100 g of tissue/mm of Hg.

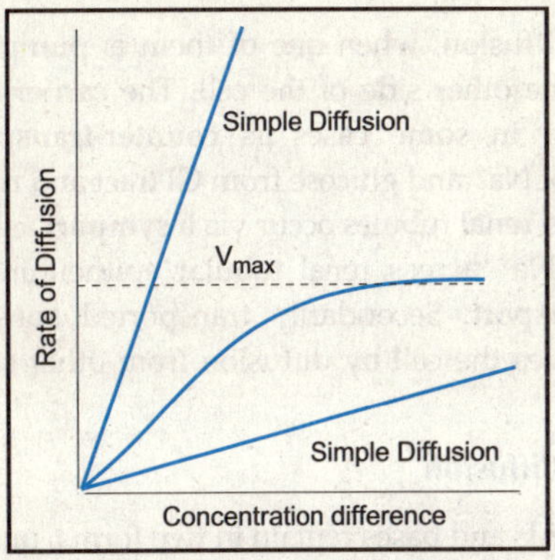


**Fig. 1.6 : Facilitated diffusion**

The term **ultrafiltration** is used, where colloidal particles, eg, plasma proteins, lipoproteins are held back, but the fluid part along with small non-colloidal particles are allowed to pass. It depends on pore size. If anticoagulated blood is filtered with filter paper, only cells are retained, whereas in renal glomeruli, colloids along with cells are retained.

### Facilitated diffusion (Fig. 1.6)

**Facilitated diffusion** is a carrier mediated diffusion where the molecules move along concentration gradient, but is facilitated by protein molecules which unite with a ligand and change configuration to transport it to the other side. *It is a physical process, no cellular energy expenditure* is required. The carrier is essential as other molecules of same dimension have low rate of diffusion. Entry of fructose from lumen to enterocytes in the small gut and glucose from interstitial fluid to cell interior are examples of **facilitated diffusion.**

### Active transport

When transport of molecules cannot be explained by its diffusion along concentration and electrical gradients, cells must consume energy and employ carriers to carry the molecule uphill. $Na^+$-$K^+$-ATPase is a membrane protein responsible for uphill movement of $Na^+$ from ICF to ECF and of $K^+$ from ECF to ICF. Another example is the transport of $Ca^{2+}$ from cytosol to sarcoplasmic reticulum of muscle cells. The energy expended is derived mostly from breakdown of ATP to ADP, Pi and energy.

**Active transport** may be **primary,** as in above examples, (expended energy is utilized directly for the transport of a substance concerned) or **secondary** (uphill movement of one substance is coupled to primary active transport of another). It is due to a carrier at one face of a cell combining with both the substances and transporting them inside the cell by facilitated diffusion, when one of them is pumped actively outside at the other side of the cell. The carrier may act as *symporter* or in some cases as **counter-transporter**. The absorption of $Na^+$ and glucose from GI tract and reabsorption of them from renal tubules occur via a **symport** and exchange of $H^+$ and $Na^+$ across renal tubular epithelium occurs by **counter-transport**. Secondarily transported substance, e.g. glucose, leaves the cell by diffusion from other side.

### Non-ionic diffusion

Weak acids and bases remain in two forms, undissociated and dissociated (or ionic) forms. The undissociated forms are lipid soluble and can diffuse across the membrane following concentration gradient, but when it appears on the other side, depending on the pH of the media, it dissociates to ions which are not permeable, and there is simultaneous lowering of undissociated forms and the gradient is maintained.

When a weak acid eg, salicylates, enters the renal tubular epithelial cells by the process of diffusion its elimination through urine depends on non-ionic diffusion. If the tubular luminal fluid is alkaline the diffused salicylate at lumen gets dissociated and prevented from reuptake, the maintained concentration gradient favours further diffusion and its ultimate elimination by the kidneys. So elimination of weak acidic compounds via urine is facilitated by alkalinizing urine.

Ammonia is produced by renal tubular epithelial cells from glutamine. Ammonia, when it diffuses to lumen, unites with $H^+$ there to form ammonium ion ($NH^+_4$) which is impermeable. $NH_3$ unites with $H^+$ with great affinity and helps to eliminate increased $H^+$ as $NH^+_4$; $NH_3$ production is increased in acidosis.

### Solvent drag

Whenever there occurs bulk flow, dissolved substances naturally follow the solvent from one compartment to another. Bulk flow occurs when there occurs filtration of fluid across tissue capillaries and renal glomerular membrane. Along with watery part of plasma small molecules like $Na^+$, $K^+$, $Cl^-$ etc. come out of capillaries at the arterial end because net hydrostatic pressure > net oncotic pressure, but at the venous end, fluid is taken back inside vessels, as net oncotic pressure > net hydrostatic pressure, but small solutes also return back. As filtration exceeds reabsorption, the remaining fluid along with dissolved constituents is drained by the lymphatics. *Net effect of solvent drag is thus not very significant.*

### Osmosis

**Osmosis** is a form of diffusion. If a solution is separated from the solvent by a semipermeable membrane which allows only solvent to pass, it is seen that the solvent flows to the solution side. This is due to the fact that when a solution is prepared its volume is sum of volumes of solvent and solute, so the concentration of solvent molecules in solution will be less than that in the pure solvent. So solvent molecules will diffuse along the concentration gradient from solvent to solution or from dilute solution to concentrated solution. Fluid molecules move bidirectionally, but net transfer of fluid is from diluted to concentrated side. This tendency of solvent to move can be prevented by applying pressure over the solution, this pressure is the measure of osmotic pressure.

**Osmosis** is one of colligative property of solutes, like freezing point depression, boiling point elevation or vapour pressure lowering, i.e., *it depends upon the number of particles.* Small or large, charged or not, *each particle will have the same effect.* In dilute solution, solute molecules behave like gas, intermolecular attraction is low and the osmotic pressure can be deduced by the formula

$$P = \frac{nRT}{V} = CRT$$

where n is the number of moles (i.e., number of particles), R is the gas constant, T is the absolute temperature and C is the molar concentration, where $C = \frac{n}{V}$ (moles/liter). However, in highly concentrated solution, this equation is not applicable.

*If the solute is a non-ionizable compound, then its molar concentration will indicate the number of particles.* But in ionizable compounds every ion will contribute its share of osmotic tension eg, a molar solution of NaCl which splits into $Na^+$ and $Cl^-$ will give twice the number of particles compared to molar solution of glucose or urea, as compared to $Na_2SO_4$ will give rise to thrice the number of particles as compared to glucose or urea when ionization is complete. But the ionization of the solute may be incomplete, or the interaction between ions make the effective concentration lower. So the effective concentration or activity is less than the electrical equivalents in these solutions, eg, 1 mmol/L of NaCl have less than twice the number of particles in comparison to 1 mmol/L of glucose solution in water. The more the concentration, the more the deviation from ideal dilute solution.

### Osmolality and Tonicity

**One osmol** is the number of osmotically active particles present in a gram mole of a non-dissociable solute eg, glucose, urea etc. So 1 osmol of glucose = 180 g = 1 mol of glucose. But in case of electrolytes it depends on the number of ions each molecule dissociates into, 1 mol of NaCl = (23 + 35.5)g = 58.5 g = 2 osmoles if the dissociation of NaCl is complete ($NaCl \rightarrow Na^+ + Cl^-$). Similarly, 1 mol of $Na_2SO_4$ = 3 osmoles. But incomplete dissociation and ionic interaction precludes the exact derivation from chemical concentrations.

**Osmolality** is determined from the freezing point depression, 1 mosmol/L of solute will depress the freezing point by 0.00186°C. The freezing point of human plasma is –0.54°C, which corresponds to osmolality of 290 mosmol/L. This concentration will exert 7.3 atmosphere against pure water. But if one takes in consideration equivalents of all ions and non-dissociable particles it exceeds 300 mosmol/L for reasons explained above.

**Osmolality :** When *1 osmol of a solute is present in 1 kg of solvent*, the concentration in osmolality is 1 osmol/kg. In case of water (density is 1 kg/L) 1 osmol/L of solvent or water is equal to 1 osmol/kg.

**Osmolarity :** When *1 osmol of a solute is present in a liter of solution*, then it is said that the **osmolarity** of the solution is *1 osmol/L of solution*. As solute occupies some volume in solution and as temperature affects volume, not weight, *osmolality is more precise* than osmolarity. But in physiology, body fluids in solution are obtained, so *osmolarity is used extensively*. In fact, in dilute solution, the differences are insignificant and the terms are used exchangably.

**Tonicity :** The term tonicity is used to compare the osmotic pressure of a solution with the plasma. The osmolality of plasma is normally about 300 mosmol/kg of water, the solutions with equal osmolality are **isotonic**, eg, 5% glucose or 0.9 g/dl of NaCl solution. Those above are called **hypertonic**, those below are called hypotonic solutions. In vivo, 5% glucose is initially isotonic, but decline in concentration takes place due to consumption of glucose by cells and its tonicity falls. But as $Na^+$ is excluded from cells, *0.9% NaCl maintains its isotonicity in plasma* and *interstitial fluid*. RBCs suspended in isotonic solution maintains normal size and shape. In hypertonic solution, RBCs become crenated, but in hypotonic solution, they swell or rupture (**hemolysis**).

### Osmolar gap

$Na^+$ is the predominant cation of the extracellular fluid including plasma; the major non-electrolytes are glucose and urea. It is known that effective concentration or activity of solutes declines due to their incomplete ionization and mutual interactions and normal molar concentration of protein and other cations are normally low. For this reason if it is considered that effective concentration of particles is equal to $[Na^+]$ + its associated univalent anion + [BUN] (blood urea nitrogen) + [Glucose] which make up the osmolarity if not accurate, remain close to measured osmolality as obtained from freezing point depression. So the predicted osmolarity (mosmol/L)

$$\text{mOsm/L} = (1.86 \times \text{Serum Na}) + \left(\frac{\text{Serum glucose}}{18}\right) + \left(\frac{\text{BUN}}{2.8}\right) + 9$$

(in mg/dl)

*or,*

in SI units = (1.86×Serum Na) + Serum glucose (mmol/L) + BUN (mmol/L)+9

Rise of plasma osmolality due to hyperglycemia or retention of nitrogenous products in renal diseases can be explained by the raised level of glucose and urea respectively. But in some cases, the observed osmolality of plasma by freezing point depression differs widely from the predicted osmolality obtained from the equation noted above. *It indicates the presence within plasma of unmeasured substances like mannitol (an osmotic diuretic), toxicants like ethanol, methanol etc.*

## ➤ 1.3 Transport across the epithelia

Transport across epithelial surfaces occur at different sites; glucose, other monosaccharides, amino acids, glycerol, short and long chain fatty acids, vitamins, minerals and water are all absorbed from GI tract. Capillaries are the sites where these substances are transported to interstitial spaces to be collected by the cells. In the kidneys, along with glomerular filtrate all non-colloids enter the renal tubules, which helps in reabsorption of wanted ingredients while the wastes are eliminated, even by secretion. In the alveoli, gaseous exchange occurs. In all the glands, including the sweat glands, substances pass bilaterally across their acini and ducts.

The physical processes behind the transport are same as transport across the cell membrane. ***Glucose and amino acids are absorbed by secondary active transport process in GI tract and renal tubules.***

Absorption of water from GI tract and its reabsorption across renal tubules occur passively by the process of osmosis created by the transport of osmotically active particles like $Na^+$, $Cl^-$, glucose etc. The **tight junctions** between the epithelial cells (paracellular route) and through the cells (transcellular) routes are taken by water to seep in. The tight junctions in some sites are leaky, so that ions, small molecules can diffuse back to some extent to lumen, but in some cases, the junctions are really tight, preventing the back flow as in colon, gall bladder.

The permeability to water in some instances is variable, depending on humoral factors. The epithelium of collecting tubule becomes very permeable to water in presence of antidiuretic hormone of posterior pituitary; its absence makes collecting duct almost impervious to water. Active reabsorption of $Na^+$ along with water is increased from distal nephron, sweat gland and elsewhere by mineralocorticoid hormone aldosterone secreted from adrenal cortex. *Active forms of vitamin D enhances active absorption of* $Ca^{2+}$ and $PO_4$ *from GI tract and renal tubules, whereas parathormone inhibits reabsorption of phosphate at renal tubules.*

## Oncotic pressure

In the transport across the epithelium, hydrostatic force (blood pressure) is the driving force for filtration, but along with water, small molecules get out of the capillaries, and their distribution is the same in intravascular and extravascular spaces and the osmotic pressure due to them gets neutralized. But the capillary endothelium is impermeable to proteins (colloids) which exert osmotic tension, by means of which water tries to percolate from interstitial space to intravascular space. So the net transfer of water across a capillary depends upon balance between filtration and reabsorption.

In the kidney ***the glomeruli are the sites of net filtration*** ($P_{cap}$–$P_B$) – ($P_{cap}$–$P_B$) is positive almost all through the capillary length, $P_{cap}$ and $\Pi_{cap}$ are hydrostatic and oncotic pressures of glomerular capillaries and $P_B$ and $\Pi_B$ are those of fluid in Bowman's space. But in peritubular capillaries; osmotic pressure gradient is more than hydrostatic pressure gradient ***so net reabsorption of fluid occurs.***

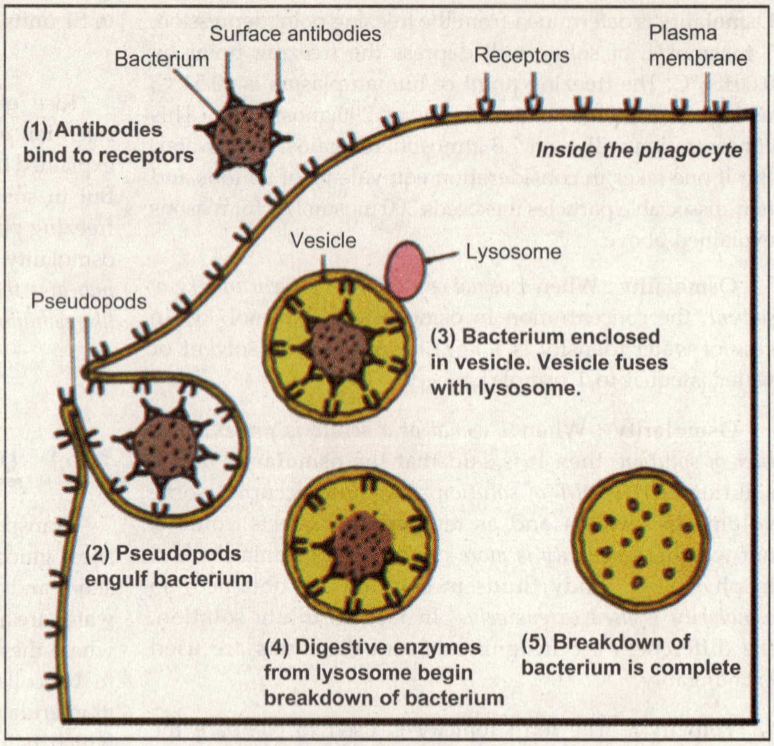


Fig. 1.7 : Phagocytosis and exocytosis

## Exocytosis and Endocytosis

The epithelium is the site of transfer of large molecules. In endocrine organs, fenestrated capillaries are seen, where attenuation of cytoplasm of endothelium makes fenestrations 20-100 nm in diameter which allows large protein molecules to pass. In liver, sinusoids provide holes between endothelial cells and also fenestrations to allow proteins of various dimensions to enter them or leave them to be drained by lymphatics. But protein molecules are seen to be taken up from luminal side of the endothelium by *endocytosis* or *pinocytosis* and delivered to the other side by the process of *exocytosis*. Not only endothelial cells, but also other cells take up or give up large molecules by the processes of endocytosis and exocytosis (Fig. 1.7).

When a cell like polymorphonuclear leukocyte comes across a microbe, part of the cell membrane near it produces pseudopodia, the microbe is surrounded by the pseudopodia and, ultimately, there is fusion of membrane around it. In this type of transport, where the material taken is visible under microscope, the process is called **phagocytosis**. On the other hand, when the engulfed material is in dissolved state and cannot be identified by microscope, the process is called **pinocytosis** (cell drinking). The membrane bound space in phagocytosis or pinocytosis is called **phagocytic** or **pinocytic vacuoles**. Commonly, lysosomes fuse with them to form **phagolysosome** and the lysosomal enzymes cause degradation of microbe. If undigested residue remains it is eliminated by the cell by the process of **exocytosis**.

There are two types of endocytosis : (1) **constitutive endocytosis**, (2) **receptor-mediated endocytosis**.

**Constitutive endocytosis** is a process of endocytosis, described above which is non-specific and not induced by any particular ligand.

**Receptor-mediated endocytosis** is triggered by ligands with their appropriate receptors; the ligand-receptor complex moves laterally to coated pits, the pits themselves contain receptors. The coating is due to clathrin, a membrane protein of MW 18,000. The coated pits, along with the receptor-ligand combinations, are taken in by the process of endocytosis to form coated vesicles that are acted upon by lysosomal enzymes. The process is rapid and specific. But the *importance* of this process of *endocytosis* is not clear as this type of engulfment is not essential for survival of a cell. Insulin, low density lipoprotein, epidermal growth factor etc. are taken up by receptor-mediated endocytosis and provide the important way of degradation of insulin and cellular metabolism of cholesterol. Endocytosis is an active process.

**Exocytosis** is the reverse of endocytosis by which proteins synthesized within a cell are extruded; protein synthesized in rough surfaced endoplasmic reticulum travel through Golgi vesicles to bud off as secretory vesicles before *exocytosis*. The vesicle membrane fuses with plasma membrane and the place of fusion breaks down. It *requires* $Ca^{2+}$ *and energy*.

It is also of 2 types — **constitutive** and **non-constitutive exocytosis**. The process described above is constitutive which is a *rapid process*, no processing of protein molecules occur in the secretory vesicles.

In non-constitutive exocytosis, secretory vesicles are coated with ***clathrin***, and there is processing of proteins within these vesicles as in the formation of mature hormones from pro-hormones. Before exocytosis, the clathrin coat is lost and the vesicle fuses with cell membrane.

## 1.4 Membrane Potential and Action Potential in Excitable Tissues, Conduction of Nerve Impulses in Medullated and Nonmedullated Nerves

### Membrane potential

Every cell is surrounded by a lipid bilayer (plasma membrane), which separates intracellular fluid (ICF) from extracellular fluid (ECF) as a semipermeable barrier. In ECF and also in ICF — the distribution of charge is the same everywhere but there remains potential difference across the membrane of all living cells with the inside negative in relation to outside. The magnitude of the potential is different in different cells and in a particular cell varies according to its functional state. As for example, a mammalian nerve cell has a membrane potential of –70 mV (inside negative) at rest, but when it gets excited, it reverses to +30 mV.

### Generation of the membrane potential

The nature of the membrane in respect of permeability to different ions is responsible for separation of charges across it. The membrane allows some ions to move readily through it, restricts some and prevents others to cross it. Within the cell are organic ions (proteins, phosphate) which are not at all permeable, but $Cl^-$ and $K^+$ are permeable and $Na^+$ has variable permeability, low to high.

The impermeable (fixed) anions will attract the positively charged particles ($K^+$ or $Na^+$ or $Ca^{2+}$) and the permeable cations will accumulate within the cell ($K^+$). So $K^+$ concentration which was (assumed) initially equal on both sides of membrane, becomes more on the inside and a concentration gradient develops between the inside and outside of the membrane. Following this chemical or concentration gradient $K^+$ will try to diffuse back to ECF from ICF, but it is counteracted by electrostatic attraction of fixed anions. The fixed anions will repel permeable anions like $Cl^-$ to outside of the cells. At equilibrium there will be excess negative charge inside the cell and equal excess positive charge outside. These excess negative charges will attract positive charges across the membrane to generate the membrane potential. So during resting state an equilibrium takes place at which both the forces are equal. The concentrations of $K^+$ is adjusted in ICF and ECF in such a way that the membrane potential attains a fixed value (equilibrium potential). The potential can be derived by **Nernst equation** which considers both the chemical and electrical forces across the membrane.

$$E_{K^+} = -\frac{RT}{FZ_{K^+}} \log_e \frac{[K^+ \text{ inside}]}{[K^+ \text{ outside}]}$$

where

$E_{K^+}$ = Equilibrium potential for $K^+$;

R = Gas constant;

T = Absolute temperature;

F = Faraday, no. of coulombs per mole of charge;

$Z_{K^+}$ = Valence of $K^+$ (+1);

[$K^+$ inside] = Molar concentration of $K^+$ inside the cell;

[$K^+$ outside] = Molar concentration of $K^+$ outside the cell.

The equation is derived by considering the electrochemical potential for $K^+$ outside and that for $K^+$ inside, which are equal at equilibrium.

$$\underset{\text{(chemical potential)}}{RT \log_e[K^+ \text{ outside}]} + \underset{\text{(electrical potential)}}{ZFK^+ \psi_{outside}} = RT \log_e[K^+ \text{ inside}] + ZFK^+ \psi_{inside},$$

where ψ (psi) is absolute potential in ECF or ICF.

Rearranging [$\psi_{inside} - \psi_{outside}$]

$$E_{K^+} = -\frac{RT}{FZ_{K^+}} \log_e \frac{[K^+ \text{ inside}]}{[K^+ \text{ outside}]}$$

On simplification

$$E_{K^+} = -61 \log_{10} \frac{[K^+_i]}{[K^+_o]}$$

In case of a neuron [$K^+_i$] is more than [$K^+_0$] and $E_{K^+}$ is near –90 mV. This differential distribution of an ion inside and outside of a membrane predictable due to presence of an impermeable ion on one side of a semipermeable membrane is called **Donnan effect**. If the impermeable ions are negative at equilibrium it is evident that inside the membrane there is excess of negative charge opposed on the outside by equal number of positive charges. In this way a membrane potential develops, whose magnitude will depend on the concentrations and permeabilities of diffusing ions in modified form of Nernst equation.

In neurons the $E_{K^+}$ is near –90 mV, $E_{Cl^-}$ is –70 mV and $E_{Na^+}$ is +60 mV. But experimental finding shows the resting membrane potential (r.m.p.) is –70 mV i.e., equal to chloride equilibrium potential, so the differential distribution of $Cl^-$ can be explained on the basis of physical (diffusion) forces. But the $E_{K^+}$ is more negative than the observed r.m.p. and it is possible due to entry of excess positive charge from outside the membrane to inside. Ubiquitous $Na^+$–$K^+$–ATPase is responsible for transport of $K^+$ ion inside in exchange of $Na^+$ with the ratio of 2 : 3. $K^+$ and $Cl^-$ diffusion potentials thus contribute largely in the generation of the resting membrane potential. Of course it is modified by active transport systems. $E_{Na^+}$ differs to a great extent from r.m.p as its permeability at resting state in a neuron is very low.

The integrated role of different ions in the generation of r.m.p. is taken into account in Goldman constant field equation :

$$\text{R.M.P.} = \frac{RT}{F}\log_e\left(\frac{P_K[K_o^+]+P_{Na}[Na_o^+]+P_{Cl}[Cl_o^-]}{P_K[K_i^+]+P_{Na}[Na_i^+]+P_{Cl}[Cl_i^-]}\right)$$

where R, T, F bear usual meanings, $P_K$, $P_{Na}$, $P_{Cl}$ are their respective permeabilities.

The equation ignores the bivalent ions like $Ca^{2+}$, $Mg^{2+}$ etc. but, as their concentrations are low, their exclusion does not affect the accuracy to a sensible extent.

In *skeletal muscle*, the ***r.m.p is –90 mV***. The cell membrane acts as a capacitor separating opposite charges across it. Thus at rest the cell membrane remains in a polarized state, inside negative to exterior. When the cell is activated, there occurs a change in polarity or there may be reversal of resting polarity, that is, depolarization. In a living cell, forces responsible for generation of r.m.p. always tries to bring the altered level back to normal.

## Action potential

*Resting membrane potential of a mammalian neuron is –70 mV*. The function of a neuron is to send signal to another nerve or a gland cell or a muscle fiber, where the appropriate response occurs. Now the signal is a wave of spontaneously spreading massive depolarization which is initiated at the site of stimulus and spreads with undiminished amplitude to termination – this runaway potential is called **action potential (AP)**. When the action potential involves a muscle fiber, action potential will spread along its membrane from myoneural junction to entire extent, that, ultimately, will lead to its contraction. Action potential is an all-or-none type of response.

## Generation of action potential in a neuron

When any point of a nerve cell gets stimulated by electrical, mechanical, chemical or thermal stimuli, at the site of stimulation there occurs depolarization. But the stimulus must be of sufficient strength and duration so that the depolarization reaches a particular level (firing level) when there is abrupt change in membrane potential. This strength of the stimulus is then called **threshold stimulus**.

In an experimental setting when an axon, even of a non-vertebrate, is connected with a cathode ray oscilloscope (CRO), it is seen that there occurs a membrane potential, inside negative. When graded stimulus is given at a site and membrane potential is recorded by a neighouring – electrode depolarization is observed to progresses in stages :

1. *Local non-propagated change in potential, electrotonic potential, depolarizing at cathode (catelectrotonus)* but hyper- polarizing at anode (anelectrotonus), up to a few mV. It is a physical property of the membrane concerned.
2. *Local response to cathode stimulation* — the depolarization is greater in magnitude than expected from physical forces due to involvement of membrane, but non-propagative and transient, a few mV above electrotonic level.
3. *When the stimulus reaches a particular strength, the depolarization will attain the firing level* and abrupt depolarization with propagation occurs (action potential).

An action potential shows the following features (fig.1.8) :

1. **Latent period** : The interval between the application of stimulus and the onset of action potential. It depends upon the distance between the site of stimulation and the point of recording and on the velocity of action potential along an axon.
2. **Spike potential** : The depolarization proceeds relatively slowly up to firing level, at which point there is abrupt reversal of potential and it may reach above +30 mV. After reaching this peak, it descends quickly near firing level. This is called *spike potential*. Its duration is a few ms in an axon. The part of it above zero line is overshoot.
3. **After-depolarization** : The process of repolarization after the spike is slower up to the level of r.m.p. This part is called after depolarization.
4. **After-hyperpolarization** : The membrane potential on attaining r.m.p. level goes below, i.e, remains hyperpolarized 1-2 mV for a prolonged period after which the r.m.p. level is regained. This phase is called after hyperpolarization.

## Ionic basis of action potential (Fig. 1.9)

At the onset of action potential up to firing level, the rate of depolarization is slower. During the phase of local response, some fast $Na^+$ channels begin to open. If the stimulus strength is sub-threshold, the repolarizing tendency due to $K^+$ efflux and $Cl^-$ influx will quickly restore the r.m.p. when the stimulus is withdrawn.

But when firing level is reached, voltage gated $Na^+$ channels will open simultaneously and as the concentration gradient and electrical gradient of this ion are directed inward, rapid entry of $Na^+$ is sufficient to overwhelm the repolarizing forces and the membrane potential is carried

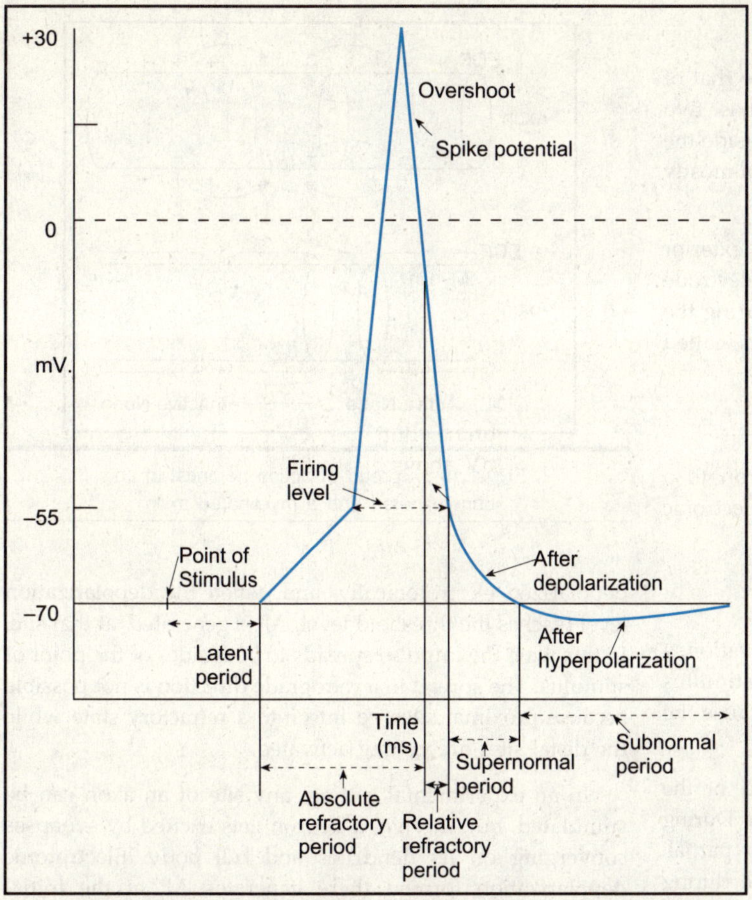


Fig. 1.8 : Monophasic action potential in a neuron with one electrode intracellular

towards the equilibrium potential of $Na^+$ (+60 mV). But this level is not attained for some reasons :

(a) *The opening of $Na^+$ channels are short-lasting*, the $Na^+$ channels get inactivated quickly after transient opening.

(b) *The concentration gradient diminishes* and during overshoot the electrical gradient reverses.

(c) *The voltage gated potassium channels begin to open.*

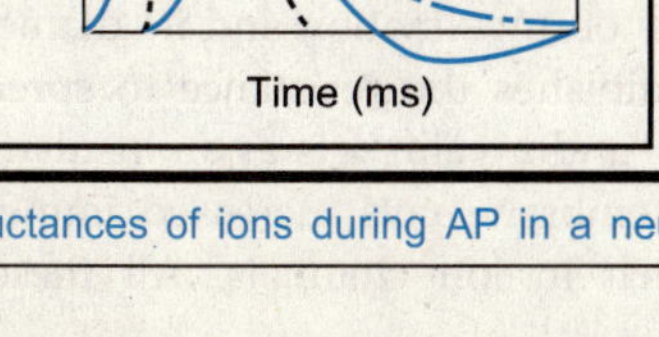


Fig. 1.9 : Conductances of ions during AP in a neuron

The repolarization is due to exit of $K^+$ ions through the voltage gated $K^+$-channels which open later than $Na^+$-channels but remain activated for prolonged period. As $Na^+$-channels get inactivated, efflux of $K^+$-channel brings the membrane potential to r.m.p.

During after-depolarization the rate of $K^+$ exit is slower as the electrical gradient responsible for initial rapid diffusion declines.

The efflux through $K^+$-channel at a slow rate continues even after the r.m.p. is reached, resulting in the prolonged phase of after-hyperpolarization. After this phase, the $K^+$-channels become inactivated and r.m.p. is restored.

The ionic distribution is brought to resting state by the action of $Na^+$-$K^+$-ATPase and the leak channels ($K^+$, $Cl^-$).

As the permeability of the membrane to $K^+$ is much higher than that of $Na^+$, r.m.p. is affected readily by changing the concentration of $K^+$. More is the ECF $K^+$, the less negative is the r.m.p. But as timely entry of $Na^+$ is responsible for generation of action potential, lower concentration of $Na^+$ in ECF diminishes the magnitude of action potential as its concentration gradient goes down.

If a stimulus of sufficient strength is applied quickly, then action potential is regularly obtained, but if the stimulus strength is raised slowly during application, no action potential may be generated **(accommodation)**. Generation of action potential requires abrupt opening of voltage-gated $Na^+$-channels, but with slow rate of depolarization the opening of long-lasting $K^+$-channels — which occur normally later than that of $Na^+$-channel —can make the membrane resistant to potential fluctuation, even if $Na^+$-channels open and, as a result, action potential is not generated. Hypocalcemia (as in hypoparathyroidism) is associated with tetany—spontaneous contraction of skeletal muscles. The excitability of neurons supplying them gets increased. $Ca^{2+}$ stabilizes the membrane, limiting the permeability to $Na^+$.

$Na^+$-channels can be blocked selectively by *tetrodotoxin* (TTX), *saxitoxin* (STX) and some $K^+$-channels are blocked by *tetraethyl ammonium (TEA)*. By means of labelled TTX and TEA, the surface distribution of $Na^+$-and $K^+$-channels in a neuron has been known. The channels are concentrated at the nodes of Ranvier in myelinated axons, but uniform (lower) conc. is seen over unmyelinated axons. In the soma or cell body of a neuron they are few but they are densely seen at the initial segment, the very early part of the axon, where the runaway action potential is normally generated.

### Monophasic and biphasic action potential

The particulars of action potential described are that of monophasic action potential, as the recorder has two exploring electrodes — one inside and the other outside the axon— and the deviation during action potential is mostly on one side of the isopotential line (r.m.p.)

But if both the exploring electrodes are placed exterior to the membrane of an axon, the excitation of one electrode will cause deflection opposite to that of another during the passage of impulse. This alternate deflection is called **biphasic action potential.**

### Refractory period

There occurs changes in threshold of a neuron to a stimulus during various phases of action potential, electronic potential and local response.

### Absolute refractory period

From the firing level up to one-third of repolarization, a neuron is resistant to stimulation by a second stimulus whatever may be the strength of that stimulus, because the $Na^+$-channels remain inactivated up to this point.

**Relative refractory period starts** from the end of the absolute one to the beginning of after-depolarization. During this period stronger stimulus may elicit response, even partial, as $Na^+$-channels are coming out of inactivated state during this phase, but voltagegated potassium channels are still open.

*During after-depolarization,* the $Na^+$-channels have come out of inactivated state but the $K^+$ channels (voltage gated) are mostly closed and the membrane potential is nearer to the firing level, so less intense stimulus will be able to generate action potential in this stage, that is, threshold is diminished.

*During after-hyperpolarization* the membrane potential goes further away from the firing level and so the threshold of stimulation has increased. Underneath the anode, the membrane potential gets more negative (hyperpolarized), so the threshold rises. But, under the cathode, membrane potential is less negative, so a catelectrotonic potential lowers the threshold.

## ➤ 1.5 Propagation of action potential along an unmyelinated axon (Fig. 1.10)

When an unmyelinated axon is stimulated at one site, the membrane at that site undergoes depolarization, i.e., outside negative and inside positive, but the neighbouring areas uptil now is in polarized state, i.e., outside positive and inside negative. As ECF and ICF are both conductors of electricity, current will flow from positive polarized area to negative activated area through ECF and in the reverse direction in the ICF. In this way, the nearby areas will get depolarized electrotonically, and, when the depolarization level reaches the threshold level, AP is generated at that site. In this way, the impulse spreads to both sides of the point of stimulus. The spread in a retrograde direction is not possible because proximal sites go into into a refractory state while the distal sites are getting activated.

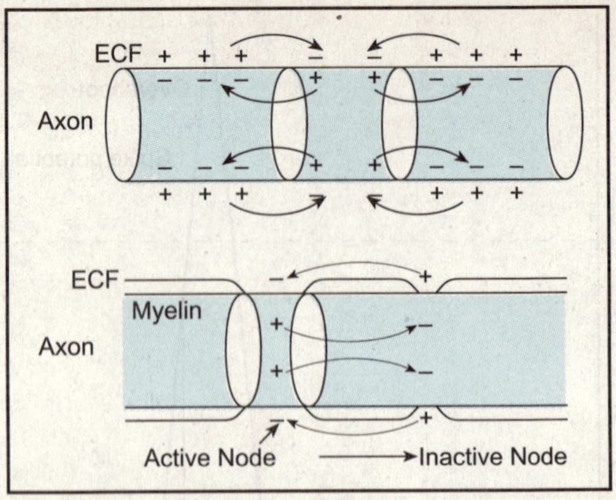


Fig. 1.10 : Spread of action potential in an unmyelinated and a myelinated axon

In an experimental setting, any site of an axon can be stimulated, but, in vivo, a neuron gets excited by synapses converging on its dendrites and cell body. Electrotonic depolarization formed there generates AP at the initial segment of the axon. The axon then carries the AP to its site of termination.

### Propagation along a myelinated axon

Myelinated axon has a wrapping of lipid (myelin) substance over its surface and there are gaps at regular intervals devoid of myelin – **nodes of Ranvier** which bears densely packed ion-channels. The initial segment of a neuron, and in case of insulated receptor, the 1st node of Ranvier, are the sites of origin of AP. Action potential spreads by electrotonic depolarizaton similar to unmyelinated axon by circular current flow in ECF and ICF, but here the sites involved are nodes of Ranvier. The myelin acts as an insulator resisting spread of charge across it. When local response at node of Ranvier reaches firing level, AP develops in it and AP involves nodes in front, so the impulse jumps from node to node – **saltatory conduction.**

***This conduction is rapid, may be 100 times faster than that of unmyelinated axon.***

The speed of propagation of action potential along an axon depends on myelination and its diameter. Increase in diameter diminishes the resistance to spread of potential along the ICF and myelin acts as an insulator; so resistance across the membrane gets increased immensely, whereas nodes are rich in ion channels. All these factors work together to increase the speed of impulse conduction in large myelinated axons.

*For carrying of proprioceptive sensations, sense of balance and equilibrium, impulse for contraction of skeletal muscles* — nature has provided heavily myelinated large neurons, both sensory and motor. But where no such urgency is there, like movement of smooth muscle and secretion of most glands, unmyelinated or thin myelinated axons with low conduction velocity serve the functions.

## ➤ 1.6 KEY CONCEPTS

1. The physiologic processes have evolved to maintain the constancy or stability of the internal environment. The term **'homeostasis'** was coined by the American physiologist Walter B. Cannon and involves all regulatory mechanisms by which stability of the internal environment of biologic systems necessary for their survival is maintained. Normal cell function depends on appropriate environmental conditions (eg. temperature, pH, ionic concentration, $O_2$ and $CO_2$ levels in the extra cellular fluid). Body temperature regulation is a good example of homeostasis.
2. **Distribution of body water** : Total body water is distributed within two major compartments :
   - Intracellular compartment — (a) about 25 L which is about 35% of total body weight. (b) Low $Na^+$ and $Cl^-$ concentration and high $K^+$ concentration.
   - Extracellular compartment — (a) Plasma (3L). (b) Interstitial fluid (12L). [Characterised by high $Na^+$ and $Cl^-$ concentration and low $K^+$ concentration].
3. **Concept of second messenger** : Cell surface receptors are activated by hormones or similar substances and information from them is transmitted to intracellular effectors by molecules called **second messengers**. These molecules initiate biochemical responses within the cell and its organelles. The resultant effects are the change in the protein manufacturing of the cell and not to the activator or inhibitor of cellular responses.
4. **Diffusion** of non-electrolytes takes place from a higher concentration to a lower concentration and its rate is directly proportionate to the concentration difference. However, diffusion rate of charged particles, besides being dependent on concentration gradient, also depends on the electrical field.
5. **Active transport** involves movement against the **electrochemical potential gradient. Primary active transport** involves carrier-mediated processes directly coupled to a source of chemical energy i.e., in this, consumption of metabolic energy and the movement of solutes are directly coupled together. All primary active transporters in animal cells are ATPases.
6. The carrier-mediated processes that are indirectly coupled to a source of energy like an ionic gradient are classified as **secondary active transport.**
7. The resting permeability of $K^+$ is greater than that of $Na^+$ and this gives rise to resting membrane potential.
8. **Action potential** involves very short electrical changes essentially involving $Na^+$ (especially for nerve action potential). The opening of voltage gated $Na^+$ channels initiate action potential. Closure of $Na^+$ channels and delayed opening of $K^+$ channels underlie repolarization phase of action potential. The slow closure of these $K^+$ channels underlies the after hyperpolarization. Action potential can be recorded by placing electrodes near the surface of the nerve.
9. **Communication** between cells is maintained either by locally diffusible **neurotransmitters, paracrine and autocrine secretions or by blood-carried chemical signals.** Small organic molecules (such as acetylcholine and epinephrine) as well as larger molecules (proteins and steroids) may be involved in the process.
10. Cells may also communicate with their immediate neighbours through gap junctions transmitting both electrical and chemical signals. Voltage, pH and intracellular messengers regulate mainly the permeability of gap junctions.
11. **Neurotransmitters** alter membrane permeability via ligand gating and activate internal metabolic processes via signal transduction within cell. They also alter receptor number.

## ➤ 1.6 KEY CONCEPTS

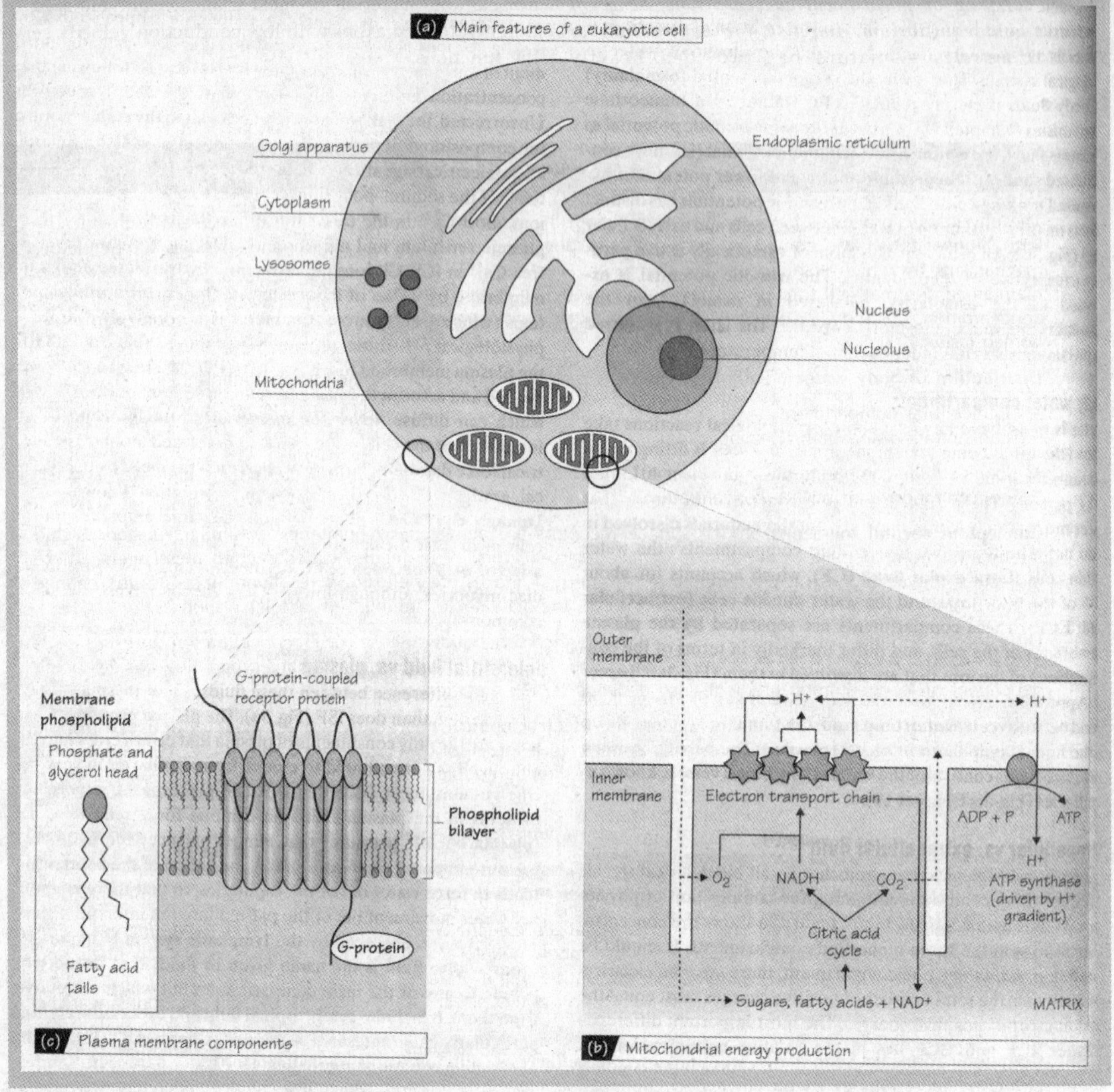


(c) Plasma membrane components

(b) Mitochondrial energy production

# Muscle Contraction Physiology

**AGENDA :**



2

## ➤ 2.1 CHAPTER OVERVIEW

**Muscle cells** are cells that can be excited by chemical, electrical or mechanical stimuli to produce a propagated action potential leading to contraction brought about by actin and myosin (the contractile proteins) with the help of $Ca^{2+}$. Other important proteins involved in muscle contraction are *troponin* and *tropomyosin.* The basic mechanism of contraction is binding of actin and myosin with their overlapping that causes shortening. Energy for contraction is provided by ATP utilized via myosin ATPase in case of skeletal muscle and myosin light chain kinase (MLCK) in case of smooth muscle.

**Muscle** is generally classified as striated (skeletal and cardiac) and smooth muscle, based on ultrastructural differences. **Skeletal muscle** forms most of the body's musculature and has well-developed cross-striations and is under voluntary control. **Cardiac muscle** is also striated but it has the property of spontaneous discharge producing rhythmic contractions. **Smooth muscle** does not have cross-striations and is functionally syncitial in most cases. Smooth muscle also contains pacemakers but the discharge is irregular.

## ➤ 2.2 Morphology of Skeletal Muscle

Each skeletal muscle is composed of innumerable microscopic units, muscle cells or fibers (for elongated shape), arranged in parallel. Each muscle cell or fiber is separated anatomically from its neighbour but connected by connective tissue. Each muscle cell is surrounded by **endomysium,** fascicles formed of groups of muscle fibers are surrounded by **perimysium,** the whole muscle is covered by **epimysium** (Fig. 2.1).

Each muscle fiber is an elongated structure, multinucleated, of average length 25 mm, and is packed with longitudinal structures called **muscle fibrils** besides cellular organelles like mitochondria, extensive endoplasmic reticulum etc. The muscle fibrils are made of filaments while the latter are composed of contractile proteins (molecules).

The filaments of a muscle fibril have regular arrangement, that is in register with all other fibrils of a single muscle cell and those of a cell remain in register with all the muscle cells which lie parallel to it. For this reason a whole muscle preparation, a single fiber or a fibril, show, transverse striations when examined under microscope. The striations are alternate light, isotropic (I) bands and dark anisotropic (A) bands. It is produced by disposition of filaments making the refraction of light different at different regions of muscle fiber (Fig. 2.2).

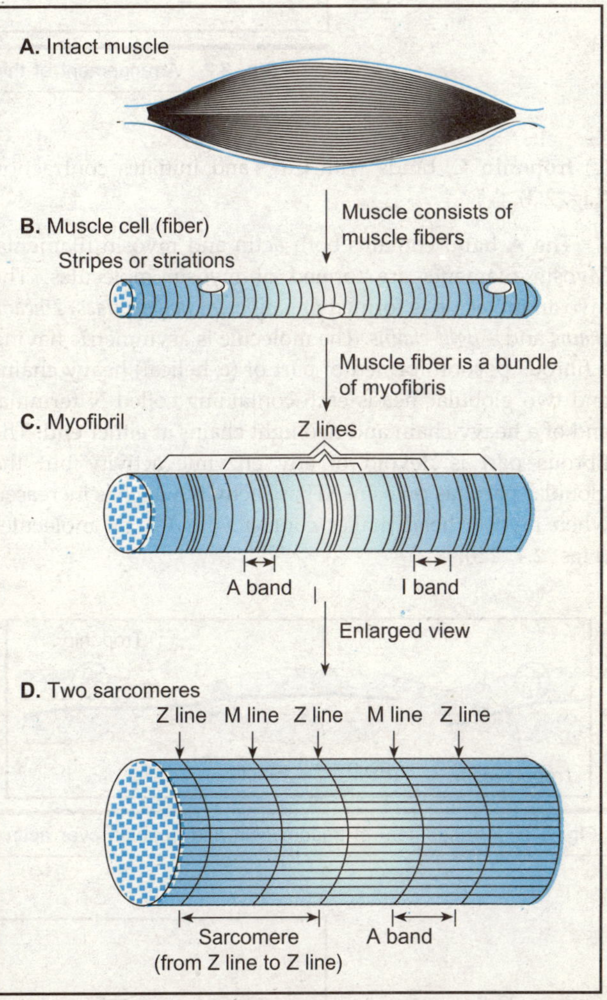


Fig. 2.1 : Microscopic structure of a skeletal muscle.

In the region of light (I) band only actin filaments are present. Actin filament is thin, composed primarily of actin molecules (G-actin), a globular 43 K protein which unite linearly in a double helical pattern (300-400 molecules) to form the actin (F-actin) filament, 6-7 nm thick . The actin molecules contain specific sites for attachment to myosin heads. Along the groove of double helical actin filament are elongated tropomyosin molecules (40-60) attached end-to-end in double helical pattern. At regular distances along the tropomyosin filament are placed troponin molecules. *The troponin molecules are globular units, each made of 3 subunits,* (a) **troponin T** binds with tropomysin filament, (b) **troponin I** binds with actin and inhibits binding of actin with myosin,

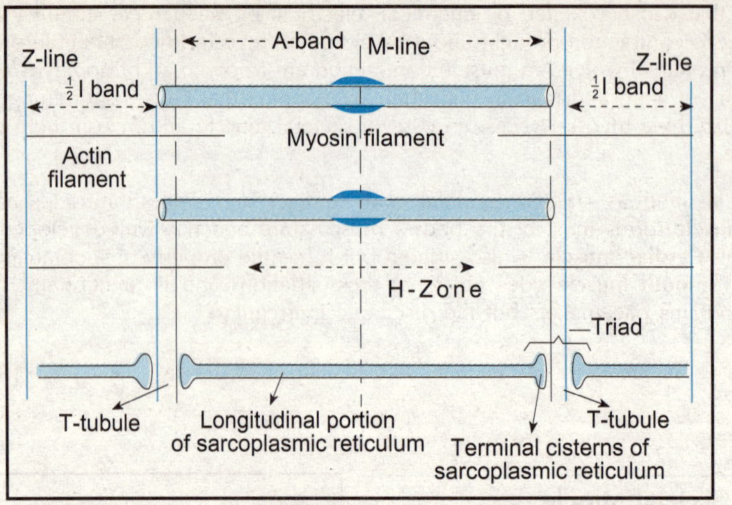


**Fig. 2.2 : Arrangement of thick and thin filaments in a myofibril**

(c) **troponin C**, binds with $Ca^{2+}$ and initiates contraction (Fig. 2.3).

The **A band** contains both actin and myosin filaments. Myosin filaments are formed of myosin molecules. The myosin molecule is formed of *6 different polypeptides, 2 heavy chains* and *4 light chains*. The molecule is asymmetric having a fibrous portion formed of part of (α-helical) heavy chains and two globular heads each containing coiled N terminal end of a heavy chain and two light chains at either end. The fibrous part is devoid of any enzymic activity but the globular part has myosin-ATPase activity which is increased when myosin head makes contact with F-actin molecules (Figs. 2.4, 2.5).

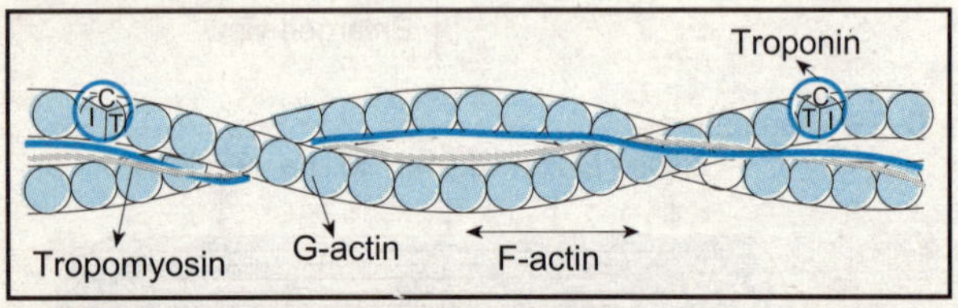


**Fig. 2.3 : Arrangement of tropomyosin and troponin over actin**

The light I band contains in its middle a dark transverse Z line. Z line contains α-actinin protein molecules which hold actin filaments projecting to both sides of Z-line. **A-band** contains a *lighter H-band* in its center. The **H-band** is due to non-extension of actin filaments in myosin filaments when the muscle is relaxed. So this band shorters or disappears when actin filaments slide past myosin filaments during contraction. The **H-band** is divided transversely at its middle by a **M line**. This line together with narrow relatively light areas on both sides constitutes the **pseudo-H zone.**

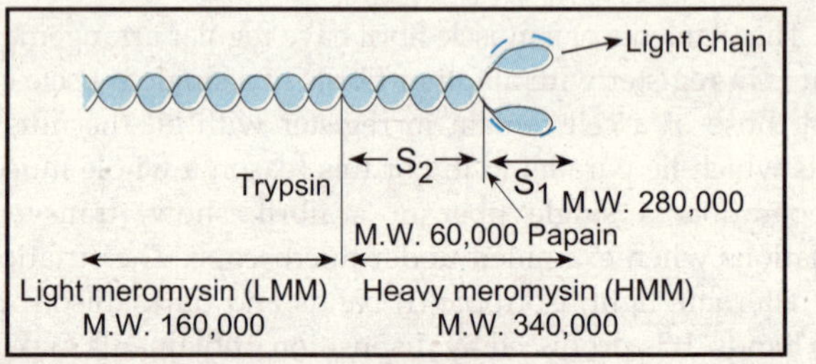


**Fig. 2.5 : Myosin molecule**

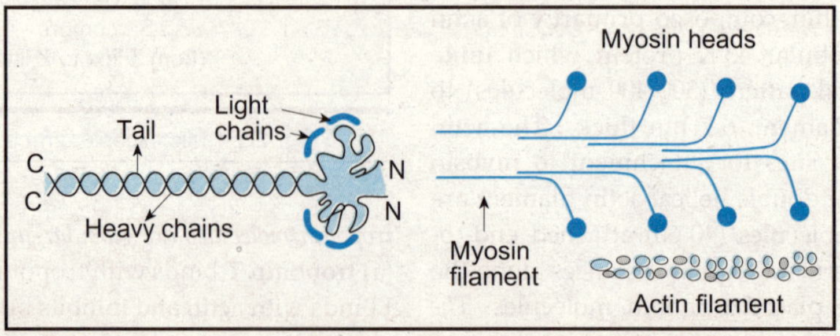


**Fig. 2.4 : Myosin molecule and filament**

The segment of a fibril between two successive Z-lines forms the sarcomere, the contractile unit of a fibril or muscle fiber. **Sarcomeres** shorten during contraction and elongates during relaxation.

Besides these contractile proteins, there are numerous other structural proteins which help to hold the filaments in proper array and take important indirect role for contraction of muscle.

### Sarcotubular system (Fig. 2.1)

The muscle fibrils are surrounded by *endoplasmic reticulum* **(sarcoplasmic reticulum)**. The sarcoplasmic reticulum is the store house of $Ca^{2+}$ which is needed for contraction. It consists of a central longitudinal part (L-tubules) and expanded on both ends (terminal cisterns). The terminal cisterns of sarcoplasmic reticulum abut against transverse tubules, **T tubules,** which are invagination of sarcolemma inside the muscle cell at the A-I junctions, i.e., twice in a sarcomere. The **T-system** forms an invaginated disk like double wall structure at regular intervals at A-I junctions of muscle cell and is perforated through and through by the myofibrils. T tubules provide the surface required to carry the action potential inside the cell. **Each T tubule** and apposed terminal cisterns on its either side constitute the **'triad'**, the anatomical site for excitation-contraction coupling.

## 2.3 Molecular Basis of Contraction (see Chart 2.1)

Physiologically, contraction of skeletal muscle always occurs in response to its excitation carried by a motor nerve. Contraction of a whole muscle is due to simultaneous contraction of some or all of its fibers. The electrical activity (action potential) reaches the myoneural junction and it causes release of acetylcholine molecules into the myoneural cleft (50-100 nm) and acetylcholine molecules unite with nicotinic cholinergic receptors and increase permeability of $Na^+$ at the end-plate. Action potential is regularly generated and spreads to adjacent muscle membranes (sarcolemma).

The impulse (action potential) then enters the depth of the muscle by the T tubules. At the triads it will activate the ***dihydropyridine receptors of the T tubule membrane.*** The *dihydropyridine receptor* is a voltage-gated slow $Ca^{2+}$ channel increasing permeability to $Ca^{2+}$ to some extent. Either this $Ca^{2+}$ ion itself itself or interaction of this receptor with another in terminal cistern, **the ryanodine receptor**, leads to release of large amounts of $Ca^{2+}$ from the cisterns into sarcoplasm which unite with troponin C.

**In the resting muscle** *troponin I binds to* actin tightly and tropomyosin covers the active site of action which attaches with myosin. When $Ca^{2+}$ unites with troponin C, the binding of troponin I with actin gets loosened and the tropomyosin molecule gets displaced laterally exposing the active site of actin. Now myosin heads unite with actin and at the same time there is splitting of ATP molecules to ADP, Pi and liberation of energy by myosin-ATPase activity which is accelerated by contact with actin. Seven myosin binding sites are uncovered by binding of a single $Ca^{2+}$ to troponin C. Before attachment myosin head lodges ADP & Pi, split products of ATP, but when contact with actin mole-cule takes place, energy as well as ADP & Pi are liberated from myosin.

**Chart 2.1 : Sequence of events in contraction**

1. Motor neuron discharge.
2. Release of neurotransmitter acetylcholine at myoneural junction.
3. Acetylcholine binds to nicotinic receptor at motor end plate.
4. Increased conductance of $Na^+$ and $K^+$ through the ligand gated receptors.
5. Generation of action potential in the muscle.
6. Action potential enters cells through T-tubules.
7. At the triad, release of $Ca^{2+}$ from the cisterns of E.R. via dihydropyridine and ryanodine receptors.
8. $Ca^{2+}$ diffuses to bind to troponin C, lateral movement of tropomyosin exposing the active site of actin.
9. Formation of cross-linkages between myosin heads and actin, liberation of energy and sliding of actin filaments over myosin producing contraction.

**Steps in relaxation :** 1. $Ca^{2+}$ is pumped back to T-tubules. 2. $Ca^{2+}$ gets released from troponin. 3. Troponin I firmly unites with actin and tropomyosin returns to the resting state, thus covering the myosin binding site of actin.

With the liberation of energy, the myosin head, which engages with actin filament at a right angle, undergoes bending (swivelling) and gets detached from it. Due to this movement, the actin filament is pulled nearer the centre of the sarcomere causing sliding of actin filaments over myosin filaments. After detachment the myosin head springs back to erect position to connect at a new site of actin filament and same events are repeated. Each cycle of union, bending to the centre of sarcomere and re-union shortens the muscle by one percent (Fig. 2.6). Detachment requires union of ATP with myosin head.

**During muscle contraction** thin filaments from either side of sarcomere slide past the myosin filaments and there occurs shortening of sarcomeres and the H-zone diminishes. During extreme shortening, the thin filaments overlap, the H-zone disappears and the Z-lines may abut the myosin filaments, which may get bent. When a muscle cell contracts, its length diminishes but it becomes rounder. If the myosin filaments, i.e., A bands, maintain distances among them constant, it is not possible for a whole cell to shorten.

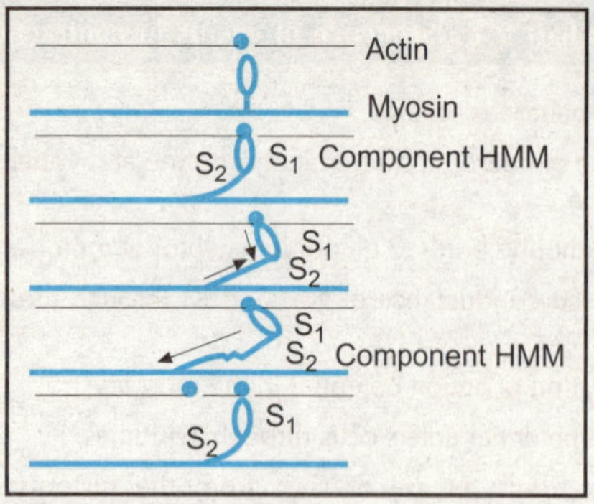


**Fig. 2.6 :** Sliding of actin filament over myosin

During contraction, noncontractile protein molecules definitely help to bring the A band or myosin filaments closer to each other making the contractile process shorten the whole cell.

**Relaxation requires** the intracellular $Ca^{2+}$ to fall to normal level of $10^{-7}$ mol/L. This low level is maintained by its sequestration within the sarcoplasmic reticulum. When the contraction is over, the excess $Ca^{2+}$ is pumped back into the longitudinal portion of tubules. It is an active process and requires splitting of ATP. So, both the contraction and relaxation are active processes requiring expenditure of energy. When the cytosolic $Ca^{2+}$ concentration is low enough, then $Ca^{2+}$-troponin C, actin-myosin interaction all cease, tropomyosin comes back to its original place covering active sites of actin and the muscle relaxes. **Tropomyosin-troponin complex** is thus relaxing protein of muscle. After repeated stimulation of a muscle, the energy source (ATP) may get depleted and complete relaxation after each contraction cannot take place and residual contraction remains (contracture).

**Rigor mortis** is a state of stiffness of skeletal muscles after death. It develops some time after death depending upon the state of antemortem contraction. The muscle becomes completely depleted of ATP and creatine phosphate, sequestration of $Ca^{2+}$ in sarcoplasmic reticulum is not possible, actin binds with myosin and remains attached making the muscle stiff and rigid. This is entirely different from persistent contractile state or contracture.

## 2.4 Mechanism of Neuromuscular Transmission, Molecular Basis of Muscular Contraction and Relaxation : Concept of Tetanus, Clonus, Fatigue and Myasthenia Gravis

### Neuromuscular transmission in skeletal muscle

***Myoneural junction*** : The axon of a neuron supplying a skeletal muscle loses myelin sheath and divides into branches which end in dilated ends — terminal boutons. Each terminal bouton connects with a single muscle fiber or cell at a specialised site to form a **myoneural junction**. Each fiber bears only one junction. The muscle fibers supplied by a single axon form a **motor unit**. Number of muscle fibers in a unit vary from a few (as in extraocular muscles where accuracy of movement is required) to hundreds (in postural muscles made for gross, crude movement). The end feet contain neurotransmitter-containing vesicles. In contrast to dense core granules containing catecholamines, the granules here are clear and small. The membrane of skeletal muscle at myoneural junction, the motor end-plate, is thick and form folds — called the **palisades**. It helps to increase the surface area so that both the action of the neurotransmitter and its removal can be hastened (Fig. 2.7).

***Transmission through the junction*** : Physiologically, the skeletal muscle is stimulated only through its nerve. Action potential travelling along the motor nerve (axon) will reach its terminal buttons. The terminal buttons contain voltage-gated $Ca^{2+}$ channels and $Ca^{2+}$ enters from ECF into the cytosol and $Ca^{2+}$ brings about fusion of vesicles with cell membrane causing exocytosis of granule contents at the myoneural junction. The acetylcholine molecules then diffuse to the motor end plate and unite with nicotinic cholinergic receptors, which are ligand-gated ion channels and conductance to $Na^+$ and also to $K^+$ are increased. $Na^+$ enters the muscle fiber following its electrochemical gradient causing depolarization (end-plate potential).

Now this potential electrotonically depolarizes neighbouring areas and when the firing level is attained there is generation of an action potential which is propagated on both sides of the end-plate. The end-plate potential is similar to EPSP at a synapse, a depolarizing forerunner of action potential. In the myoneural junction the number of

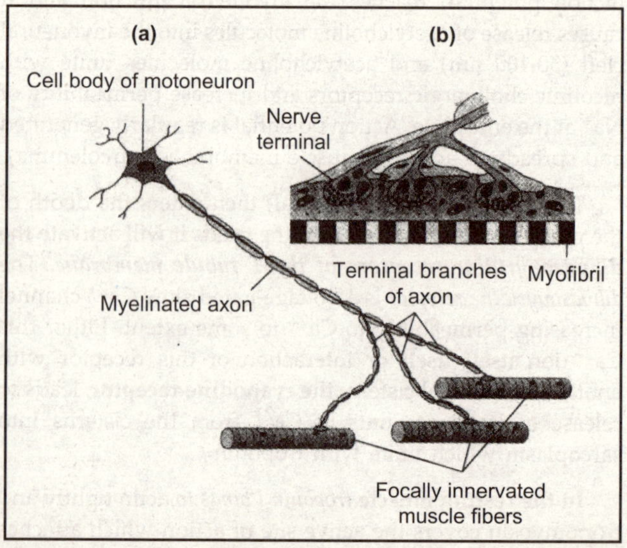


**Fig. 2.7**

acetylcholine molecules liberated in response to a single action potential is adequate to initiate action potential regularly in the muscle fiber concerned. So its demonstration requires blocking of some nicotinic receptors by curare so that graded end-plate potential can be recorded near the motor end-plate. The **end-plate potential** is localized, non-propagated, and decays exponentially away from the plate. As a muscle fiber bears only one end-plate, spatial summation is impossible, but temporal summation can be demonstrated by trepeated stimuli.

## Myoneural junction of smooth muscle and cardiac muscle

Smooth muscles are supplied by post-ganglionic autonomic neurons (sympathetic and parasympathetic) which are small and unmyelinated. The myoneural junction is much simpler than that of skeletal muscle and no specialization in the form of motor end-plate is evident. The nerve fibers during their course come in close contact with muscle cells; at these sites the nerve fibers contain dilated parts called **varicosities**. The varicosities contain granules of different morphology, eg, clear vesicles of acetylcholine or dense core granules of norepinephrine.

A single fiber bear multiple varicosities and contacts with multiple muscle cells one after another. This pattern of junction is called **synapse-en-passant**. In the heart the junctional tissues receive both parasympathetic (cholinergic) and sympathetic (adrenergic) fibers. Ventricles are innervated by sympathetic fibers. Myoneural junctions here are similar to that of smooth muscle. Transmission of impulse across the myoneural junction is similar to myoneural junction of skeletal muscle. Neurotransmitter released will bind to its appropriate receptors and may excite — or in some cases inhibit — the muscle it supplies. The excitation and inhibition are sequel to **excitatory junctional potential (EJP)** and **inhibitory junctional potential (IJP)**, respectively.

## Muscle twitch

When a nerve muscle preparation of a frog is stimulated via nerve, a brief contraction and relaxation seen in response to a single induction shock (single action potential) is called a **muscle twitch**. The twitch duration varies from muscle to muscle. **Fast muscle fibers** have short twitch durations. They are used for fine, rapid, precise movements. **Slow muscle fibers** have long twitch durations and are involved in gross, sustained movements. They also differ in other aspects (Table 2.1).

In submammalian species, the muscles are not of the twitch type but slow type which exhibits prolonged contraction in response to neural stimulus. The muscle fiber has multiple sites of innervation and poorly developed T-tubule system.

**Table 2.1 : Types of fibres in skeletal muscles**

| | *Type I* | *Type II* |
|---|---|---|
| **Synonyms** | Red, slow oxidative | White, fast glycolytic |
| **Myosin ATPase activity** | Slow | Fast |
| **Diameter** | Moderate | Large |
| **Glycolytic activity** | Moderate | High |
| **Myoglobin content, Mitochondria, Vascularity, Oxidative activity** | High | Low |
| **Twitch duration** | Long | Short |
| **Type of movement** | Slow, sustained contraction as in maintaining posture | Fine, skilled, short lasting |

## Summation of contraction (Tetanus and Clonus)

When the excitation, i.e., action potential, of a skeletal muscle and its mechanical response, i.e., muscle twitch, are plotted on a same time scale, the twitch begins to take place about 2 milliseconds after the onset of action potential (Fig. 2.8). The action potential is over in around 5 milliseconds but the twitch continues beyond that, depending upon twitch duration of the muscle concerned. The muscle is electrically refractory during the action potential (absolute and relative refractory period); but the mechanical event depends upon chemical reactions and is not subject to refractoriness. So if a second stimulus falls after the refractory period, a second action potential is generated and contraction due to the 2nd stimulus will ride upon the contraction of the 1st stimulus and **summation of contraction** occurs. If the tensions are recorded in isometric preparations, the tension developed during summation is much greater than that of muscle twitch. Depending upon the twitch duration, if repeated stimuli are applied, each after expiry of refractory period, but before the height of contraction is reached, i.e., end of contraction, then

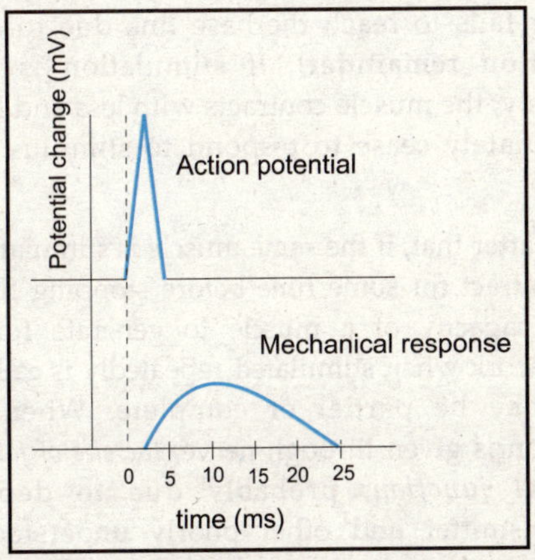


**Fig. 2.8 :** Skeletal muscle AP and mechanical events

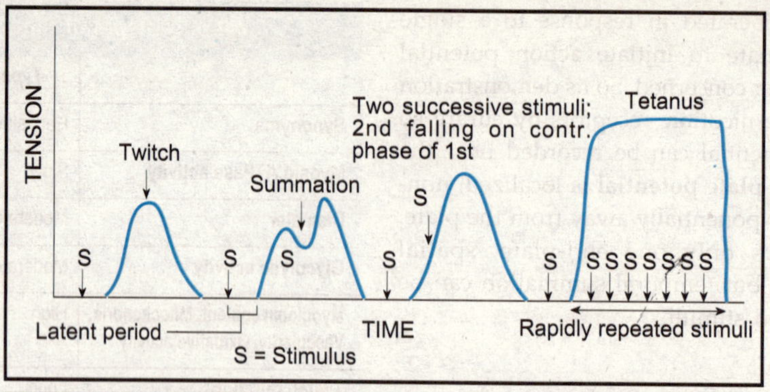


**Fig. 2.9 :** Single muscle twitch, summation and tetanus

summation of contraction will give rise to a powerful sustained contraction – **complete tetanus**. But if the train of stimuli causes excitation at the relaxation phase of the each previous contraction then forceful continuous contraction with trembling occurs due to partial relaxation between stimuli **incomplete tetanus** or **clonus** (Fig. 2.9).

The term **tetanus** is used to mean both summation of contrac-tions and complete tetanus, as explained before. The term **clonus** is also used clinically in conditions of involuntary state of alternate contraction and relaxation of a group of muscles, eg, ankle clonus, patellar clonus, involving triceps surae and quadriceps femoris muscles in spastic paralysis.

## Fatigue

If a nerve muscle preparation is stimulated repeatedly with maximal stimuli (involving all the motor units), initial few contractions become larger in amplitude due to beneficial effect of previous contractions (raised $Ca^{2+}$, temperature, diminished viscosity), but after that the height of contraction diminishes and all the phases of isotonic contraction, i.e., **latent period, contraction period, relaxation period,** gradually increase and then the lever fails to reach the base line due to *contracture* **(contraction remainder)**. If stimulation is continued relentlessly, the muscle contracts with less and less vigour and ultimately cease to respond to stimulus (complete fatigue).

Even after that, if the same muscle is stimulated directly it can contract for some time before stopping finally. This reduced capacity of a muscle to generate force i.e., to perform work when stimulated repeatedly is called **fatigue** which may be partial or complete. When repeated stimulation is given through nerve, *the site of fatigue* is the *myoneural junction*, probably due to depletion of neurotransmitter and other poorly understood factors preventing propagation across the junction. When the muscle is stimulated directly then fatigue occurs due to depletion of ATP, creatine phosphate, glycogen and accumulation of $H^+$ ions, anoxia etc.

## Myasthenia gravis

It is an auto-immune disease common in women producing antibodies against acetylcholine receptors at skeletal muscle. The receptors are either destroyed or taken into the cell after aggregation by receptor mediated endocytosis. The clinical feature is the development of extreme **weakness of skeletal muscles.** Muscles of face and neck are primarily involved, causing difficulty in chewing, swallowing and talking. Symptoms aggravate at evening. Involvement of respiratory muscles make the state worse. Marked improvement occurs with drugs with anticholinesterase activity.

**In Eaton-Lambert syndrome,** there also develops skeletal muscle weakness which improves rather than deteriorates (as in **myasthenia gravis**) with repeated exercise. There is usually lower limb weakness and it may be associated with oat cell bronchial carcinoma and autoimmunity. In this syndrome the antibody to voltage-gated $Ca^{2+}$ channels in the terminal bouton of myoneural junction causes their damage. Less neurotransmitter is released due to diminished influx of $Ca^{2+}$ during excitation.

## Duchenne muscular dystrophy (pseudohypertrophic muscular dystrophy)

X-linked recessive disease causes apparent muscular hypertrophy, but in reality there is weakness of the muscles the muscle fibers being replaced by fibrous and adipose tissues. Pelvic girdle muscles are commonly affected.

The disorder is due to absence or production of abnormal form of dystrophin, a 400 K protein, having its gene on the short arm of the X-chromosome. **Dystrophin** is a structural component of sarcolemma and T-tubules. The protein is present also in smooth muscle. Its role in muscle contraction is not yet clear. Function of sarcolemma gets defective in its absence and permeability to $Ca^{2+}$ increases.

**Becker's muscular dystrophy** is also an X-linked recessive disorder, having the genetic defect at the same locus as **Duchenne muscular dystrophy**. Here dystrophin is present, but of larger molecular size and is deficient quantitatively.

**Myotonic dystrophy,** on the other hand, is an autosomal dominant disease due to mutation on chromosome 19. The patient complains of muscle stiffness, often foot drop; myotonia i.e. delayed relaxation of muscle after contraction is observed.

## Smooth muscle

This type of muscle is distinguished from skeletal and cardiac muscle by lack of transverse striations. For this reason, they are also known as unstriped, unstriated or plain muscle. This muscle is found in most of the viscera except heart.

Histologically, the structural and functional units of smooth muscle are the muscle cells or fibers which are fusiform or spindle shaped, each containing a central nucleus. In walls of the viscera like intestine, bladder and uterus they are arranged either in distinct layers or in fasiculi running in various directions. Smooth muscle cells contain contractile proteins *actin* and *myosin*, but they *are not organized in a paracrystalline fashion as in skeletal muscle.* **Tropomyosin is present but troponin is absent,** its role is played by another protein, called **calmodulin**. *Instead of Z-lines* the smooth muscle contains structures called **'dense bodies'**, present both in the cytosol and cell membrane and actin filaments radiate from it. A myosin filament is placed between two dense bodies with actin filaments radiating from both sides. Contraction occurs due to sliding of actin filaments over myosin. Smooth muscle contains fewer mitochondria than skeletal muscle and depends more on anerobic glycolysis, its energy requirement is much lower than skeletal muscle (Fig. 2.10).

Smooth muscle is involuntary, supplied by autonomic nervous system; parasympathetic and sympathetic system have opposite effects in most cases. Contraction of smooth muscle is modified by neural stimulation, but it can contract without neural impulse i.e., they can depolarize spontaneously. Smooth muscle can be divided into two types, **single unit or visceral type of smooth muscle and multiunit type of smooth muscle** (Fig. 2.11).

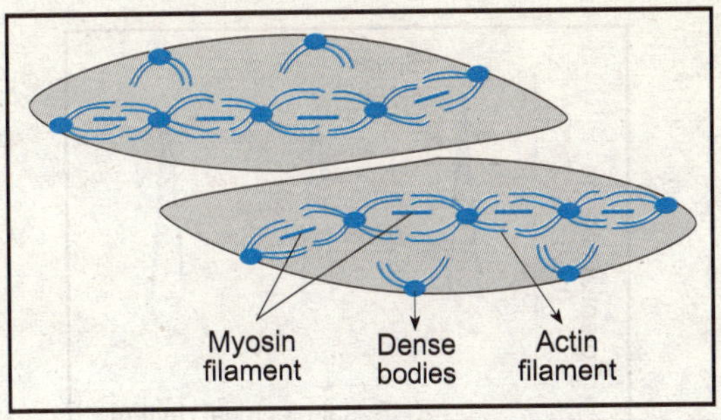


Fig. 2.10 : Arrangement of contractile proteins in smooth muscle

**The visceral or single unit type** has wide distribution throughout the body, all the viscera and blood vessels contain this type. Here the cells are connected to one another by gap junctions which form low resistance bridges. Not all the cells of this type of smooth muscle receive innervation, only the superficial layers have such innervation, and electrical activity reaches the deeper layer by gap junctions, i.e., they behave like a syncytium.

**The multiunit variety** has limited distribution as in iris, ciliary body, piloerector muscles. In this variety, the cells are not connected by gap junctions. Every cell has its innervation and though the cells respond to humoral factors, normally they respond by neural stimulation similar to skeletal muscle. They mediate through involuntary, fine, precise contractions like regulating entry of right amount of light through the pupil or accurate change in the refraction as in accommodation. Norepinephrine tends to persist at the neuromuscular junction of multiunit smooth muscle causing repeated stimulation, with summation of contraction, i.e., tetanic contraction, rather than single twitch as in skeletal muscle. *The excitation-contraction coupling process is much slower than that of skeletal muscle.*

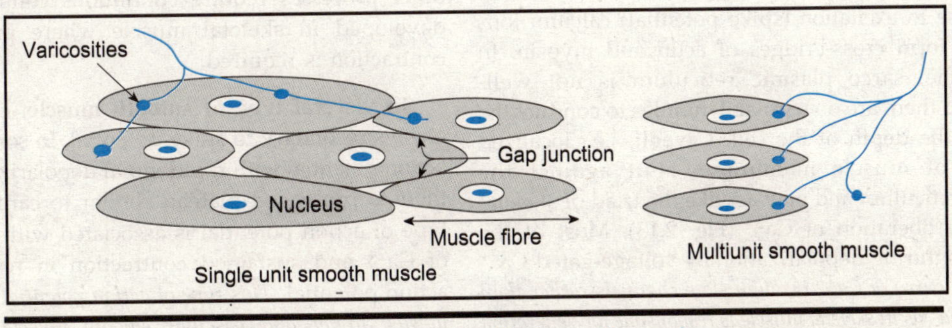


Fig. 2.11 : Single and multiunit smooth muscles

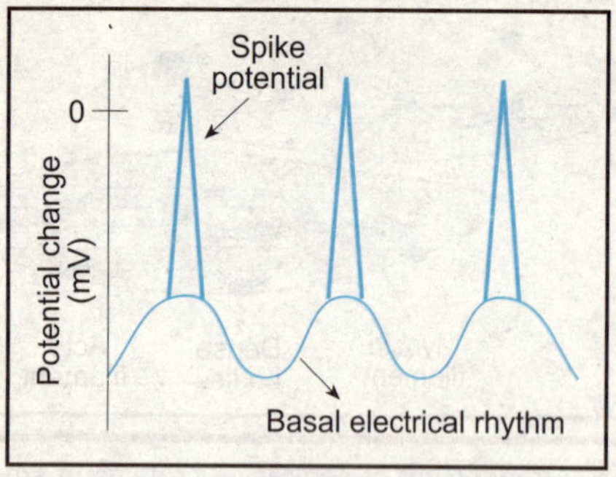


Fig. 2.12 : Basal electrical rhythm and spike potential in smooth muscle

## 2.5 Excitation-contraction coupling in smooth muscle

The visceral smooth muscle is found to contract spontaneously without any external neural stimulation. This type of continuous contractile state is called **tonus** or **tone of visceral smooth muscle.** When the potential of relatively inactive preparations are recorded, it is seen that there is no true resting membrane potential, fluctuating around an average –50 mV.

These almost sine wave like fluctuations are not attended by contraction and are called the basal electrical rhythms. *It is due to fluctuation of activity of $Na^+$ pump or alternate changes in $Na^+$ permeability.* Superimposed on this basal electrical rhythm, spike potentials occur either at the peak or in descending or in ascending phase of the basal electrical cycles (Fig. 2.12). Some areas of smooth muscle acts as a pacemaker, and electrical potential spreads from it. The site is not fixed, there occurs shifting of the site, as and when required. The spike potential is of much longer duration than action potential of skeletal muscle, about 50 milliseconds. Contraction of muscle occurs in response to this potential, contraction starts after 200 milli seconds from beginning of action potential and contraction can continue up to seconds; the peak contraction is reached 500 ms after the spike is over. It is apparent from the duration of excitation and contraction that the periods are much more prolonged than skeletal muscle in which action potential lasts for few milli- seconds and twitch duration lasts for 10 milliseconds or more.

In response to excitation (spike potential) calcium ions contribute to form cross-bridges of actin and myosin. In smooth muscle, sarco plasmic reticulum is not well-developed and there are no regular T-tubules to conduct the impulse into the depth of the cell. **Caveoli**, i.e., localized depressions of muscle membrane, abut against the endoplasmic reticulum and may act like the triad of skeletal muscle in the liberation of $Ca^{2+}$ (Fig. 2.13). Most of the calcium enters during depolarization by voltage-gated $Ca^{2+}$ channels and *entry of $Ca^{2+}$ through slow channels rather than quick entry of $Na^+$ as in skeletal muscle is responsible for generation of spike potential in smooth muscle.*

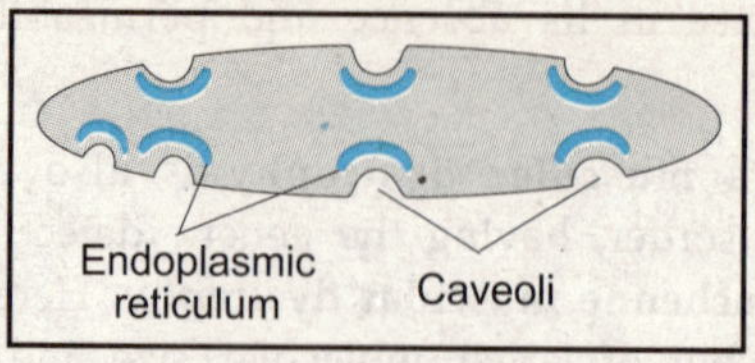


Fig. 2.13 : Caveoli

The $Ca^{2+}$ in the cytosol then unites with **calmodulin** to form calcium-calmodulin complex. This complex causes activation of **myosin light chain kinase** which causes phosphorylation of myosin light chain present on its head activating its myosin ATPase activity. Actin then binds with myosin and sliding of actin past myosin occurs along with breakdown of ATP.

### Relaxation of smooth muscle

When the contraction is over and there is no electrical activity, $Ca^{2+}$ level within the cells falls and myosin phosphatase enzyme causes dephosphorylation of myosin light chain, myosin-ATPase activity is lost and dissociation of actin-myosin bond occurs. $Ca^{2+}$ is actively pumped into ER but more is extruded to ECF.

### Latch phenomenon

Viscera containing smooth muscle can remain in a contracted state for prolonged periods. This maintenance of tone is possible with very small expenditure of energy. When some segment of smooth muscle contracts vigorously, there is rapid formation and breakdown of cross-bridges as in skeletal muscle and it requires enhanced expenditure of energy. But this heightened tone can be maintained for prolonged period by minimal consumption of energy by **latch phenomenon**. It appears that due to slow excitation–contraction coupling in smooth muscle, though the rate of formation and break down of bridges fall, the number of cross-bridges making attachment and detachment in respect of time remains the same. The process is slow and economical in energy requirement. It is the number of cross-bridges involved per unit time that determines the force of contraction. This is advantageous because digestive and other processes require continuous contraction. It is not developed in skeletal muscle where precise measured contraction is required.

**In visceral type of smooth muscle,** contraction is not always secondary to spike potential. In some cases, there is action potential with rapid initial depolarization after which there is prolonged plateau similar to cardiac muscle. This type of action potential is associated with prolonged entry of $Ca^{2+}$ and sustained contraction in response to single action potential. *This type of action potential is seen in cases of uterus, ureter and vascular smooth muscle, when prolonged contraction is required.*

**In multiunit smooth muscle** *action potential is not generated.* Probably due to small size of the fibers, electrotonic depolarization produced by the neurotransmitters (acetylcholine and norepinephrine) at myoneural junction is sufficient to involve the whole muscle cell in time and $Ca^{2+}$ entry secondary to this depolarization via voltage-gated channels is sufficient to initiate contraction. *Molecular mechanism of contraction and relaxation is the same as that of single unit smooth muscle.*

## Factors influencing smooth muscle contraction

Smooth muscles may contract spontaneously without any apparent stimuli, but their rate and force of contraction are influenced by a number of factors :

(a) ***Local stretch*** when a segment of smooth muscle containing viscera become dilated by its contents, then stretch is responsible for generation of spike potential with higher frequency and forceful contraction follows. This is best seen in GI tract and in ureters; contractions may be so strong as to cause colicky pain.

(b) ***Neurotransmitters*** acetylcholine and norepinephrine have reciprocal effects in most tissues. There may be excitation with increase in the frequency of spike potential or in some cases inhibition caused by hyperpolarization, either by blocking $Na^+$ channels or by opening $K^+$ channels.

(c) ***Hormones*** like vasopressin, angiotensin, oxytocin, serotonin, histamine and also catecholamines have stimulating and inhibiting effects at appropriate sites. The effect depends upon particular receptors. When the hormone receptor complex increases $Ca^{2+}$ concentration in cytosol by cyclic AMP, phosphoinositide or any other mechanism, contraction occurs. In some cases phosphorylation of enzyme proteins by cAMP or cGMP mechanisms activate them to pump $Ca^{2+}$ into ER or outside the cell causing its inhibition.

(d) ***Lack of O2***, increased $CO_2$ level, raised $H^+$ and adenosine cause vasodilation in systemic circulation, but hypoxia causes vasoconstriction in pulmonary vessels and lack of $CO_2$ causes contraction of bronchial smooth muscle. These type of responses may be due to changes of membrane potential, $Ca^{2+}$ permeability or by other poorly understood mechansims.

Smooth muscle has properties like stress relaxation or plasticity, eg, when urinary bladder is filled with water at **steps**, wall tension rises initially, but falls to previous level or below with time till the bladder is sufficiently distended. So the intravesical pressure remain more or less constant — it is similar to latch mechanism — myosin and actin form cross- bridges of equal numbers in a new orientation. It is different from active contraction of the muscle.

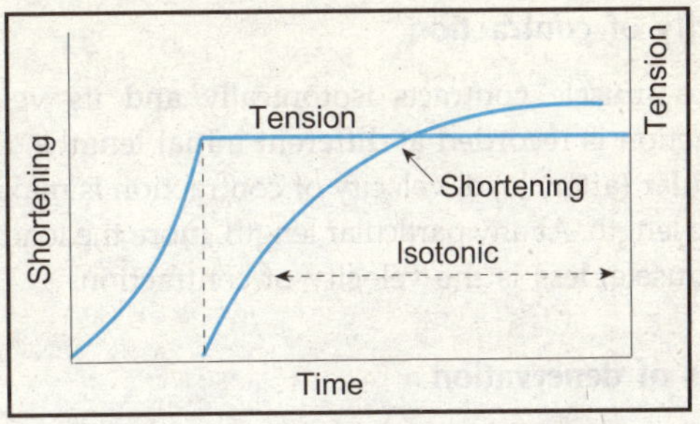


Fig. 2.14 : Isotonic and isometric contractions

**Relation between muscle length, tension and velocity of contraction (2.14).**

When a muscle contracts isometrically, i.e., length remains unaltered, and the force or tension is recorded, the tension here is **total tension**. A muscle also shows change in tension when it is stretched without external stimulation – **passive tension**. Both total tension and passive tension varies with length of the muscle. So **active tension** is the difference between total tension and passive tension (2.15).

The particular length at which the active tension developed is maximum is called **resting length** because this length is seen to be maintained by muscles at rest. The length of a muscle cut free from its attachments is **equilibrium length**. A muscle is seen to rupture if it is passively stretched to about 3 times its equilibrium length. The resting length is explained by the number of actin-myosin cross-bridges; at this length the number is optimal, at higher length the number of cross-linkages are less, and at shorter length hindrance by over-lapping actin filaments lowers tension. The passive tension is due to viscoelastic properties of contractile as well as non-contractile elements of muscle.

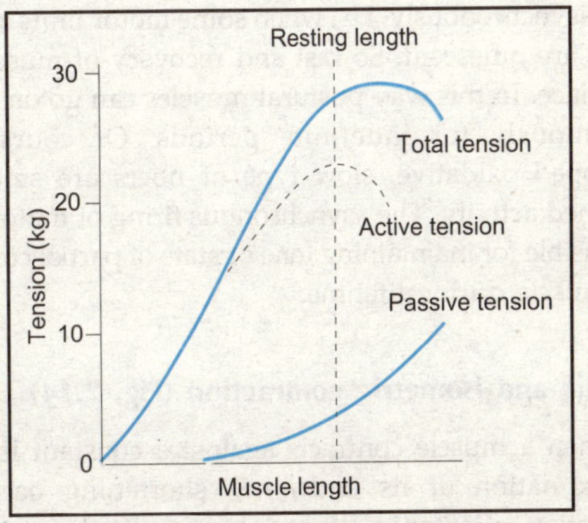


Fig. 2.15 : Length-tension relationship of skeletal muscle

### Velocity of contraction

If a muscle contracts isotonically and its velocity of contraction is recorded at different initial lengths, then at a particular (after) load, velocity of contraction is maximum at resting length. At any particular length, more the load applied to a muscle, less is the velocity of contraction.

### Effects of denervation

Destruction of motor nerve to a muscle leads to atrophy **(lower motor neuron type of lesion)** and there is denervation hypersensitivity to circulating acetylcholine (probably the number and affinity of receptors increase). **Fibrillation** (fine, irregular contraction of individual fibers), an electromyographic finding, is seen in denervation. It disappears if reinnervation takes place.

**Fasciculation** : Jerky, visible spontaneous contraction of groups of muscle fibers is seen with abnormal discharge of lower motor neurons. It can *be elicited by tapping a denervated muscle.*

### Strength of skeletal muscle

The tension a skeletal muscle in human can develop is 3-4 kg/sq.cm of cross-sectional area. Similar values are found in all mammals. The muscles with large cross-sectional areas like gluteus maximus, quadriceps and gastrocnemius can exert great force. The gastrocnemius can support the whole body during climbing and resists several times the weight of the body during jumping.

The force of contraction of a muscle can be changed voluntarily. The graded increase in strength of muscle is due to involvement of more and more motor units. In different movements all or part of a muscle bulk can be put into action. When maximal motor units are recruited, further increase in force of contraction is due to increase in the rate of firing, i.e., by tetanization. *Length-tension relation shows that tension also depends on the initial length of muscle.* When a muscle is utilized for a length of time the muscle fibers work asynchronously, i.e., when some motor units are firing, others are quiescent. So rest and recovery of muscle fibers take place. In this way postural muscles can go on working continuously for indefinite periods. Of course, well-developed oxidative, slow type of fibers are suitable for sustained activity. The asynchronous firing of motor units is responsible for maintaining tone or state of partial contraction of a muscle during lifetime.

### Isotonic and isometric contraction (Fig. 2.14)

When a muscle contracts against a constant load with approximation of its ends, i.e., shortening occurs, the contraction is **isotonic.** When a load is lifted, force exerted to overcome the weight (i.e., the initial part of contraction) is **isometric**, but when the load is above the surface, the rest

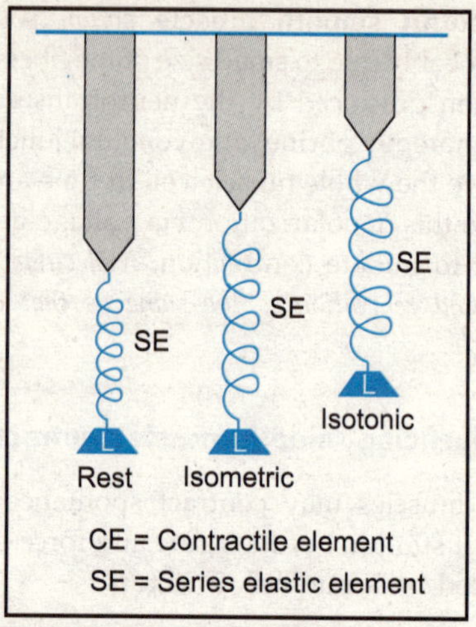


**Fig. 2.16**

of contraction is isotonic as the tension is equal to the gravitational pull of the load. When we are standing, postural muscles are producing force, but there is no obvious shortening. Similarly, when one pushes a wall with hand, there is no movement of the wall, no shortening of muscle, but there are contraction and generation of force as there is formation of actinmyosin cross-links and breakdown of ATP to liberate energy.

*During **isotonic contraction,*** active work is done, but in isometric contraction no work is performed. Heat liberated during isometric contraction is more than that of isotonic contraction. **Isometric contraction** is possible due to the fact that in series with contractile elements there are elastic elements in the muscle and they elongate along with contraction of contractile element making the length of the muscle constant (Fig. 2.16). In isotonic contraction work is positive when the shortening takes place in the intended direction, but when a contracting muscle elongates (as if supporting a heavy load by the hand) the work is negative.

### Heat production in a muscle

**Resting heat** : Heat liberated by a muscle due to basal metabolic process at rest.

**Initial heat** : During contraction additional heat is produced. This initial heat comprises :

(a) **activation heat**, the heat that is produced by a muscle whenever it is contracting, isotonic or isometric, Activation heat is the heat evolved prior to formation and cycling of cross-bridges. It is heat produced due to (i) liberation of $Ca^{2+}$ from sarcoplasmic reticulum, (ii) the molecular motion of tropomyosin over actin and orientation of myosin heads prior to the attachment-detachment cycle, (iii) activation of myosin ATPase.

(b) **shortening heat** in isotonic contraction is proportionate to the distance the muscle shortens. It is not generated in isometric contraction. It is due to movement of cross bridges and myosin heads and breakdown of glycogen.

(c) **heat generated in addition** to activation and shortening heats are:

**Recovery heat** is prolonged heat production in excess of resting heat after contraction is over. It is approximately equal to the initial heat and is due to metabolic processes to bring the muscle to its precontraction state.

These include $Ca^{++}$ ATPase activity which pumps back calcium into the sarcsplasmic reticulum and also regenerated of ATP and other energy substrates.

**Fenn effect :** Fenn effect states that the heat produced is directly proportional to the work done. When the work done is more, the expenditure of ATP will also be more.

**Relaxation heat** : An isotonically contracted muscle, if restored to its previous length, liberates extra heat (in addition to recovery heat). This relaxation heat is liberated passively by the viscoelastic elements in a muscle.

## ➤ 2.6 KEY CONCEPTS

Muscle contraction is produced by repetitive cycling of the myosin cross-bridges on thin filaments. The cross bridges attach to actin molecules on the thin filaments and cause the thin filaments to slide over the thick filaments towards the center of the sarcomere (skeletal or cardiac muscle) or cell. The initiation of contraction is called excitation contraction coupling. In striated muscle, excitation contraction coupling is initiated when $Ca^{2+}$ binds to troponin. Troponin causes tropomyosin to move, thereby exposing the actin binding site to myosin. In skeletal muscle, $Ca^{2+}$ is released from the sarcoplasmic reticulum (SR) when the muscle fiber depolarizes. In smooth muscles, excitation-contraction coupling is initiated when $Ca^{2+}$ binds to calmodulin. The $Ca^{2+}$ calmodulin complex activates myosin light chain kinase (MLCK) which in turn, phosphorylates the 20,000 Da myosin light chain. Cross-bridge cycling begins when the myosin light chains are phosphorylated. When dephosphorylated, the cross-bridges stay attached called **latch bridges** which allow smooth muscle to maintain force while minimizing energy expenditure.

## ➤ 2.7 DISORDERS/CLINICAL CORRELATIONS

➤ **Rigor mortis :** Some chemical changes occur in the muscle tissue following death. Myosin cross-bridges remain attached to the actin myofilaments due to the lack of ATP and, as a result, the muscles are in a state of rigidity. This condition is called **rigor mortis.**

ATP is essential for dissociating actin and myosin and producing relaxation. After death, muscle cells can no longer synthesize ATP as oxygen and substrates are not supplied any more to the tissues. Due to the fall in the concentration of muscle ATP, the actomyosin–ADP bonds that formed are not broken due to the lack of ATP.

➤ **Tetany :** A disorder marked by intermittent tonic muscular contraction, accompanied by fibrillary tremors, paresthesias and muscular pains; the hands are usually first affected, the spasms occurring later in the face, trunk and sometimes the laryngeal muscles. There is increased irritability of the motor and sensory nerves to electrical and mechanical stimuli. It is a pathologic condition where *low extracellular $Ca^{2+}$* is present. Low $Ca^{2+}$ reduces chemical transmitter release and also the threshold for initiating action potentials. The most prominent feature of hypocalcaemia is tetany which occurs *when serum calcium level falls below 1.75 mmol/litre.* This causes *paresthesia* and *numbness* in the limbs and face. Muscle cramps are also prominent.

Tetany may also be seen in alkalotic conditions such as that produced by hyperventilation and occasionally in hypokalemia and hypomagnesemia.

A positive **Chvostek's** or **Trousseau's** sign is usually considered to be fairly good clinical evidence of hypocalcemia. A positive Chvostek's sign is a twitch at the corner of the mouth when the examiner taps over the facial nerve just in front of the ear. However, it is present in about 10% to 38% of normal individuals. Neverthless eyelid muscle contraction with the Chvostek maneuver is said to be almost diagnostic of hypocalcemia.

**Trousseau's sign**, which is generally a more reliable indicator of hypocalcemia, is positive if carpopedal spasm is produced when the examiner wraps a blood pressure cuff to the upper arm and maintains a pressure above systolic for 3 minutes. The fingers are spastically extended at the interphalangeal joints and flexed at the metacarpophalangeal joints. The wrist is flexed and forearm is pronated.

➤ **Myasthenia gravis** : A chronic progressive muscular weakness, beginning usually in the face and throat, unaccompanied by atrophy.It is a neuromuscular disease accompanied by weakness and fatiguability of skeletal muscle. The bulbar, respiratory and proximal limb muscles are maximally affected.

The primary cause of myasthenia is not known. Immunological factors are clearly important. There are a reduced number of functioning acetylcholine receptors in skeletal muscle and this probably results from immunological damage provoked by circulating antibodies. *Anticholinesterase therapy* is indicated in all but the mildest cases; *thymectomy* is indicated. Steroids and immunosuppressive therapy are also necessary. Severe myasthenia is characterized by dysphagia, a weak cough and poor respiratory reserve.

*The molecular cause of myasthenia gravis* is a decreased number of ACh receptors in post-synaptic membrane → EPP are smaller → AP cannot be generated sufficiently → muscle contraction cannot occur.

Pyridostigmine and neostigmine are the drugs of choice in the treatment of myasthenia gravis. Neostigmine blocks the action of AChE, as such, more ACh is available to bind with postsynaptic ACh receptors.

## ➤ 2.7 DISORDERS/CLINICAL CORRELATIONS

Immunosuppressant drugs are used to decrease the production of antibodies. Plasmapheresis may also be adopted in this disease. In some individuals, surgical removal of thymus gland is indicated.

**In short**, myasthenia gravis results from anti-ACh receptor antibodies that attach on postsynaptic membrane of the neuromuscular junction. Consequently, there is diminished force of contraction of the muscles involved with repeated stimuli. It is usually mediated by auto-immunity. **Test :** (a) clinical counting of receptor number, normally 30 or more. (b) **Tensilon** (edrophonium) **Test :** Edrophonium 10 mg (an antichdinesterase) in injected I/V as a bolus after a test dose of 1-2 mg. Improvement in weakness occurs within seconds and last for 2-3 minutes when it is positive. To be certain it is wise to have an observer present and to perform a control test using an injection of saline occasionally the test itself causes bronchoconstriction and syncope and needs resuscitation.

➤ **Marfan's Syndrome :** Autosomal dominant disorder. There is mutation in extra cellular matrix glycoprotein fibrillin. Marfan's syndrome is a group of clinically heterogeneous familial disorders of connective tissue. The characteristic features are the combination of long fingers, hyperextensible joints and a high arched palate in a tall individual. Generally, children and adolescents are affected. **CVS :** Aortic and mitral in competence and aortic aneurysm. **Eye :** Dislocation of ocular lens is common.

➤ **Lambert-Eaton myasthenic syndrome :** Resembles myasthenia gravis clinically. It does not involve extraocular muscles. Therefore, patients with Lambert-Eaton syndrome do not have ptosis and diplopia.

➤ **Muscular dystrophy :** It is defined as primary degenerative myopathy which is genetically determined . It is characterised by progressive muscular weakness and replacement of muscle tissue by fibrous one. Voluntary muscles are involved bilaterally symmetrically. *The diaphragm is not affected.*

It is thought that a protein named *dystrophin* is totally absent in almost all cases of **Duchenne muscular dystrophy** and much reduced in **Becker's dystrophy**. The absence or deficiency of dystrophin renders the plasma membrane incompetent leading to uncontrolled entry of calcium. This leads to areas of hypercontraction of myofibrils and activation of calcium activated neutral proteases leading to muscle fibre necrosis.

Muscular dystrophies are diagnosed by means of serum creatinine kinase (CK) estimation, radioimmunoassay of serum myoglobin, quantitative EMG and muscle biopsy.

## ➤ 2.7 DISORDERS/CLINICAL CORRELATIONS

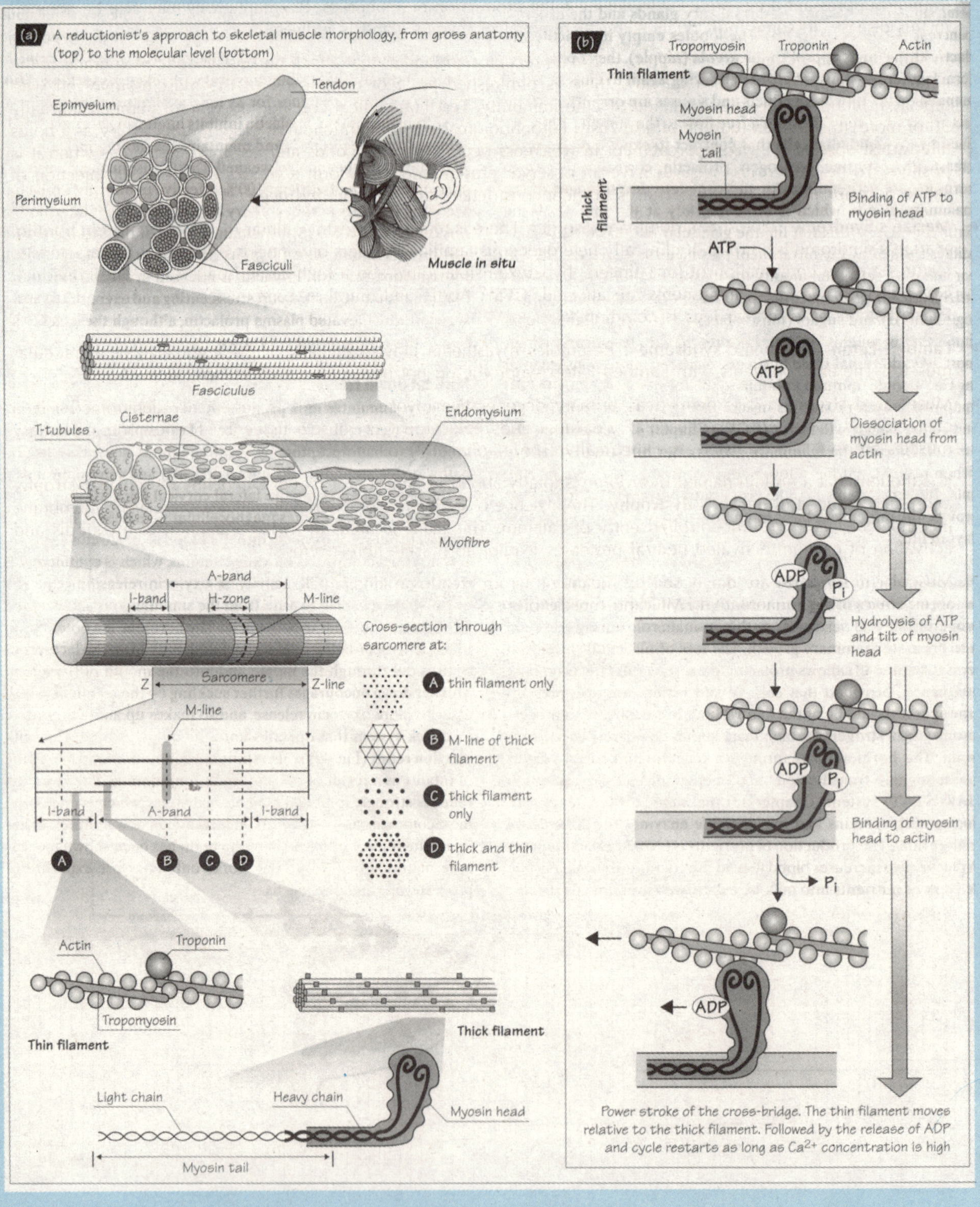

# Autonomic Nervous System

AGENDA :



3

## ➤ 3.1 CHAPTER OVERVIEW

**Autonomic nervous system (ANS)** regulates the functions of heart, smooth muscles, glands and viscera. It works below the level of consciousness and thus enjoys some degree of autonomy. It has **two broad divisions**, the **sympathetic** and **the parasympathetic**. These two systems are in a state of dynamic equilibrium. The **sympathetic nervous system** enables the individual to adjust against stress and prepare the body for flight or fight. **The parasympathetic nervous system** is concerned with tissue-building reactions. Each division has two sets of fibers :

- *Pre-ganglionic fiber* — nerve fiber running from spinal cord to ganglion;
- *Post-ganglionic fiber*— nerve fiber running from ganglion to effector organs.

**Synapse** — structure that is formed by close apposition of a neuron either with another neuron or with effector cell. The synapse between the pre-ganglionic and post-ganglionic fibers is termed ganglion while that between the post-ganglionic fibers and the receptor is termed neuroeffector junction.

**Sympathetic origin** — $T_1$-$T_{12}$ and $L_1$- $L_3$ or $L_4$ segments.

**Parasympathetic origin** — Cranial nerves (III, VII, IX, X) and sacral nerves ($S_2$, $S_3$, $S_4$).

**Neurotransmitter for sympathetic nervous system** is noradrenalin and that of parasympathetic nervous system is acetylcholine (ACh). Noradrenalin acts through adrenergic receptors $\alpha(\alpha_1, \alpha_2)$ and $\beta(\beta_1, \beta_2, \beta_3)$. Acetylcholine acts through two sets of receptors (i) muscarinic receptors ($M_1$, $M_2$, $M_3$) and (ii) Nicotinic receptors ($N_N$, $N_M$).

## ➤ 3.2 Introduction

**Autonomic nervous system**

(*autos* = self, *nomos* = law)

The part of the peripheral nervous system that works mostly independent of consciousness and voluntary control is called ***autonomic nervous system (ANS)***.

It innervates and regulates the activities of *heart, vascular and visceral smooth muscle, exocrine and endocrine glands,* and *parenchymal cells.* This system is responsible for distribution of blood flow, maintenance of tissue perfusion, control of blood pressure, gastrointestinal motility and secretion, urinary bladder emptying, regulation of volume and composition of ECF, maintenance of body temperature, utilization of metabolic energy and many other activities related to visceral smooth muscle and various glands. It responds rapidly within a millisecond to any changes in the internal environment to maintain the homeostasis.

## ➤ 3.3 Centers of Autonomic Nervous System

**Centers of autonomic nervous system** are located in the ***spinal cord, brain stem*** and ***hypothalamus.*** *Extrapyramidal area of cerebral cortex and limbic system are also functionally related to autonomic nervous system.*

### Divisions of autonomic nervous system

**ANS** is composed of afferent and efferent fibers with central connection for integration.

**Afferent fibers** : ***Visceral afferent fibers*** are carried by vagus nerve. ***Sensory fibers*** from carotid sinus and carotid body (via IX N), and aortic arch and aortic body (Vth and Xth) regulate respiratory vasomotor reflexes and co-ordinate all other autonomic reflexes.

**Efferent fibers** : The efferent fibers are of two types : (1) ***sympathetic fibers*** and (2) ***parasympathetic fibers.*** They differ from each other anatomically, physiologically and according to their pharmacological responses to drugs (see table 3.4) [some physiologists now consider ENS (enteric nervous system) as the 3rd division of ANS]. Most organs are supplied by both sympathetic and parasympathetic fibers except **sweat gland** and **vascular smooth muscle.** These two systems are in a state of dynamic equilibrium.

### Anatomy of sympathetic nervous system (Fig. 3.1)

The efferent sympathetic fibers originate in the intermediolateral column of the spinal cord that extends from ***1st* thoracic** to ***3rd*** or ***4th* lumbar** segments. That is why this division is also known as ***thoracolumbar division.*** Each sympathetic pathway from each spinal segment to the stimulated tissue is composed of two neurons, a preganglionic neuron and a postganglionic neuron. The cell body of preganglionic neuron lies in the lateral horn of spinal cord. Two lateral or paravertebral sympathetic chain are situated on either side of spinal cord.

Each of these chains extends from cervical region to the coccyx and is made up of 22 ganglia, interconnected by nerve fiber. The first three ganglia, i.e., superior, middle and inferior cervical ganglia, are bigger in size. Inferior cervical ganglia may be fused to the 1st thoracic ganglia to form ***stellate ganglia.*** A few ***prevertebral ganglia*** or

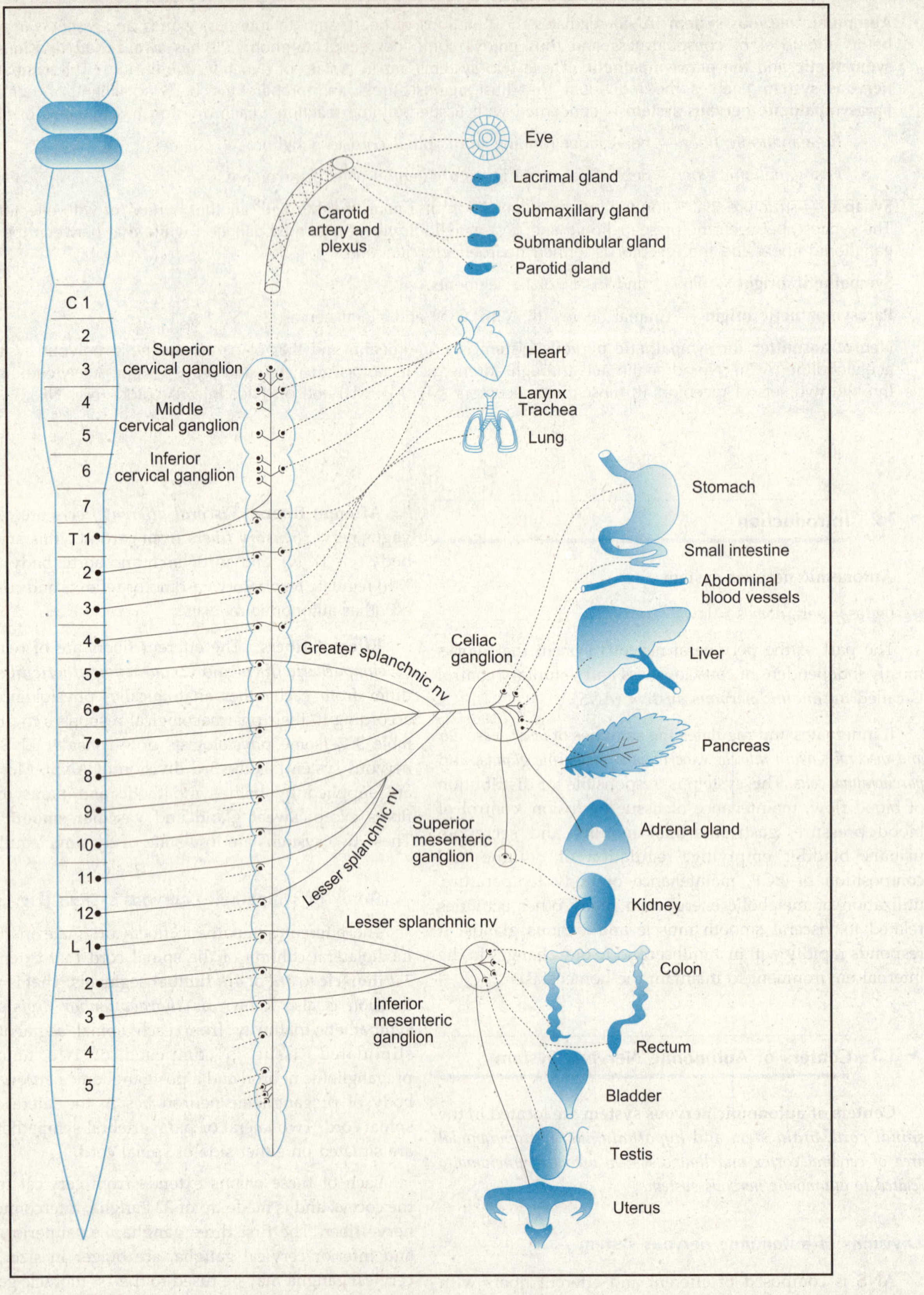


**Fig. 3.1 :** Sympathetic nervous system *(Courtesy : Dr. Asim K. Ghosh)*

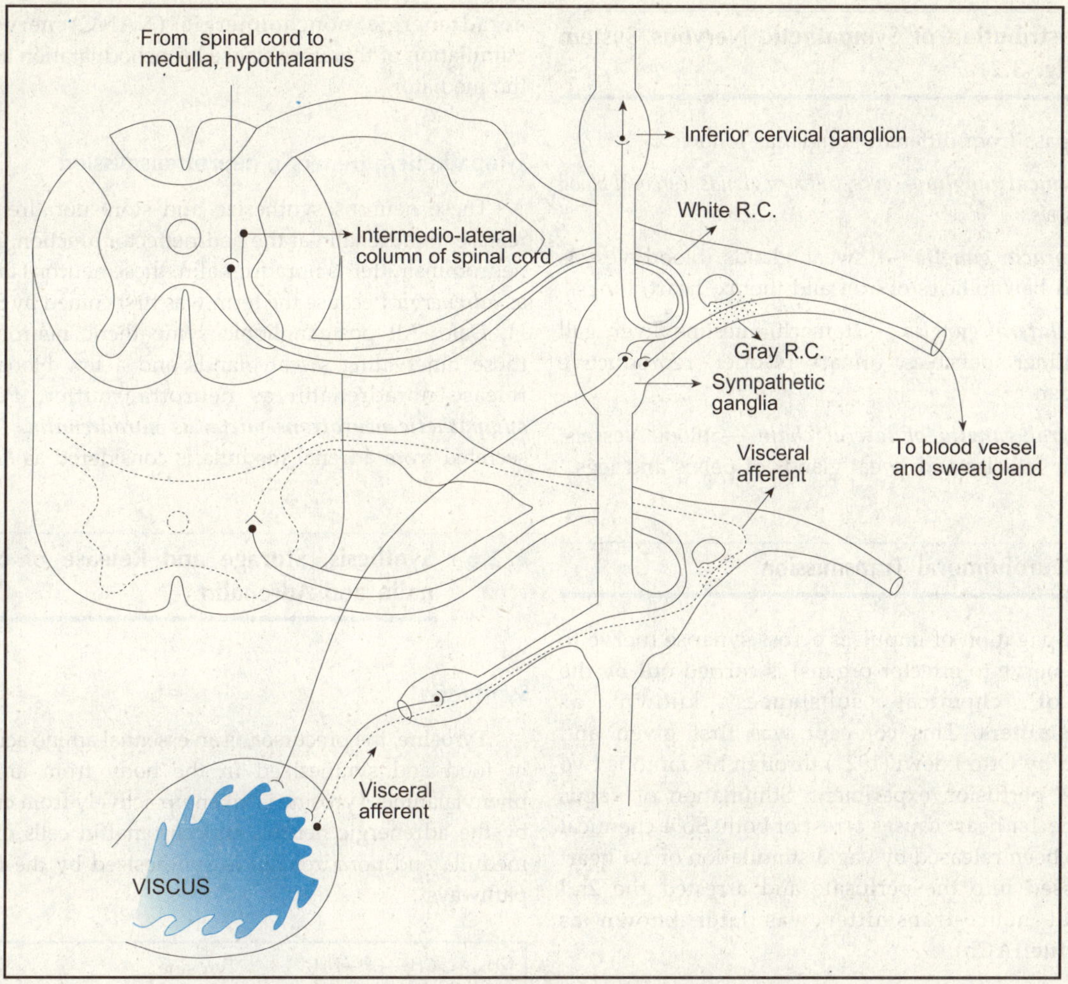


**Fig. 3.2 : Distribution of sympathetic nervous system**

***collateral ganglia*** are situated outside the lateral chains, eg, celiac, hypogastric, superior and inferior mesenteric ganglia.

The myelinated preganglionic sympathetic fibers come out of the spinal cord through ventral spinal nerve root as fine white nerve cord called ***white rami communicantes*** which enter into one of the ganglia of sympathetic chain. The course of the fiber can be one of the following :

(a) *Most of the sympathetic preganglionic fibers* terminates in ganglia located in the paravertebral chain/ sympathetic chain.

(b) It *can pass upward or downward in the chain* and synapse in one of the other ganglia of the chain.

(c) *Some sympathetic preganglionic fibers pass through paravertebral ganglion terminate* in prevertebral ganglia or collateral ganglia and terminal ganglia in located it or near the viscera supplying sex organs.

(d) *Preganglionic sympathetic nerves* supplying the adrenal medulla pass through the sympathetic chain but do not synapse there. It directly innervates chromaffin cells of adrenal medulla which are considered as postganglionic neuron that secrete neurotransmitter in circulation. So adrenalin is known as a hormone as well.

From the ganglia, postganglionic sympathetic fibers run to the tissues innervated. Some of the postganglionic fibers pass back from the sympathetic chain to spinal cord through gray rami communicantes and supply to all parts of the body through skeletal nerves and control the blood vessels, sweat glands and piloerector muscles. Recently, it has been shown in animal experiments that there are intrinsic cardiac adrenergic cells. Cells are probably essential for normal development of heart.

## 3.4 Distribution of Sympathetic Nervous System (Fig. 3.2)

Fibers pass from different ganglia as follows :

(i) *Cervical ganglia — eyes, salivary glands, cerebral blood vessels.*

(ii) ***Thoracic ganglia*** — sweat glands, blood vessels and hair follicles of arm and thorax, heart, lungs.

(iii) ***Collateral ganglia*** — stomach, intestine, liver, gall bladder, pancreas, urinary bladder, reproductive organ.

(iv) ***Sacral ganglia of lateral chain*** — blood vessels, hair follicles and sweat glands of pelvis and legs.

## 3.5 Neurohumoral Transmission

The propagation of impulses across synapse (nerve to nerve and nerve to effector organs) is carried out by the release of chemical substances known as **neurotransmitters**. This con-cept was first given and established by Otto Loewi (1921) through his famous two frog hearts perfusion experiment. Stimulation of vagus nerve in the 1st heart causes arrest of both. So a chemical must have been released by vagal stimulation of 1st heart which passed into the perfusate and arrested the 2nd heart—that neuro-transmitter was later known as **acetylcholine (ACh)**.

### Transmission in sympathetic ganglion

Responses produced in post ganglionic neuron by stimulation of preganglionic neuron include the following events.

(a) Fast EPSP — which generate action potential. It is of short duration, only 30 ms mediation is by Ach.

(b) Slow IPSP — probably produced by dopamine, which is secreted by an interneuron within the ganglia.

(c) Slow EPSP — a prolonged excitatory post synaptic potential duration is 30 s and mediator is Ach.

(d) Late slow EPSP — duration 4 min. It is produced by GnRH or a peptide closely resembling it.

### Chemical transmission at autonomic junctions

Transmission at ganglia and neuro effector junction is chemically mediated. The transmitters are Acetylcholine, norepinephrine, dopamine and GnRH. Other than these there are some cotransmitters in the neuron such as VIP, ATP, neuropeptide Y etc. Bronchioles are supplied by noradrenergic noncholinergic (NANC) nerve fibres. Stimulation of therefore, cause bronchodilatation and VIP is the mediator.

### Sympathetic/adrenergic neurotransmission

These neurons synthesize and store noradrenalin and release noradrenalin at the neuroeffector junction. Although neurotransmitter is noradre-nalin, these neurons are known as ***adrenergic*** because the term was first coined by Sir Henry H. Dale. All postganglionic sympathetic neurons except those innervating sweat glands and a few blood vessels, release noradrenalin as neurotransmitter. ***Peripheral sympathetic neurotrans-mitter is noradrenalin.*** Adrenalin secreted from adrenal medulla is considered as ***hormone.***

## 3.6 Synthesis, Storage and Release of Noradrenalin and Adrenalin

### Synthesis

**Tyrosine,** the precursor, is an essential amino acid present in food and synthesized in the body from amino acid phenylalanine. Tyrosine is taken up actively from circulation by the adrenergic neuron and chromaffin cells of adrenal medulla and noradrenalin is synthesized by the following pathways :

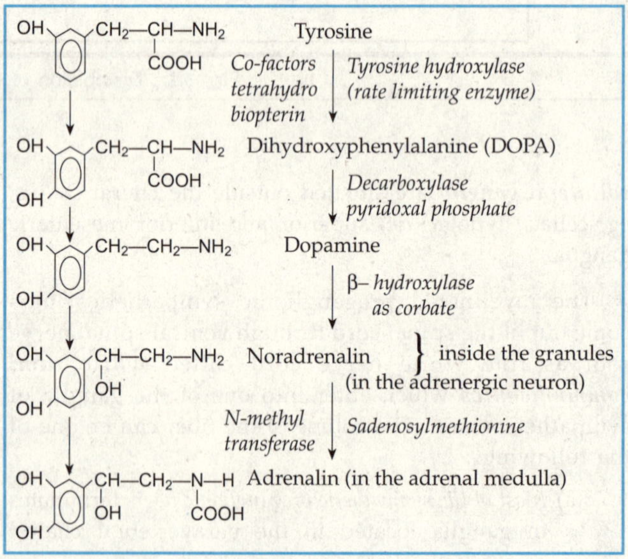


### Storage and release

Noradrenalin is stored in vesicles and when an impulse arrives there is depolarization of nerve terminal causing an increased calcium permeability which causes fusion of storage vesicles to the inner surface of neuronal membrane

**Table 3.1 : Different types of adrenergic receptors, their location, response, agonist and antagonist**

| Receptors | Location | Response | Agonist | Antagonist |
|---|---|---|---|---|
| $\alpha_1$ | Vascular smooth muscle | Contraction | Phenylephrine, methoxamine | Prazosin, terazosin |
| | Genitourinary muscle | Contraction | — | — |
| | Intestinal smooth muscle | Relaxation | — | — |
| | Heart | Contraction | — | — |
| $\alpha_2$ | Prejunctional postganglionic sympathetic nerve terminals | Decreased release of noradrenalin | Clonidine, α-methyldopa | Yohimbine |
| | Platelets | Aggregation | — | — |
| | Pancreatic B-cells | Decreased insulin secretion | — | — |
| $\beta_1$ | Heart | Increased contractility and heart rate, increased AV nodal conduction velocity | Prenalterol, dobutamine | Atenolol, metoprolol |
| | JG cells of kidney | Increased renin secretion | — | — |
| $\beta_2$ | Smooth muscles of blood vessels supplying the skeletal muscle, bronchus, GIT, uterus | Relaxation | Salbutamol, terbutaline | Butoxamine |
| $\beta_3$ | Adipose tissue | Lipolysis | Noradrenalin, isoprenaline | ICI 11855 |

and release of its contents into the synaptic cleft by exocytosis and acts on postjunctional receptors.

### Termination of action of catecholamines

Noradrenalin, adrenalin and dopamine are called **endogenous catecholamines** because they contain catechol nucleus (benzene ring with OH group at 3, 4 position with side chain). After release into the synaptic cleft, it is removed by :

(i) 75-90% active re-uptake into the noradrenergic neuron (uptake I), active uptake is blocked by cocaine.

(ii) Diffusion in the body fluid.

(iii) Less importantly, metabolized by the enzyme monoamine oxidase (MAO) inside the neuronal cells and catechol-O-methyl transferase (COMT) in other cells (liver, kidney). Catecholamines released into the circulation from adrenal medulla are inactivated primarily by MAO and COMT. Process (i) + (ii) + (iii) cause lowering of concentration of noradrenalin in the neuroeffector junction.

## 3.7 Physiology of Sympathetic Nervous System (Fig. 3.1)

This system is known as the system for ***fight, fright and flight.*** Under normal circumstances, the importance of the system is not felt. It is essential when there is stress. *Sympatho-adrenal system acts as a unit.* When this system is activated there is a rise in blood pressure, increase in heart rate; more RBCs are poured into the circulation from spleen, rise of blood glucose concentration, bronchioles and pupils are dilated, blood flow is shifted from skin and splanchnic areas to skeletal muscles. Noradrenalin discharge also lowers threshold in the reticular formation leading to increased alertness and wakefulness.

These things are done to prepare the organism for fight or flight. Though more importance is given on the discharge of noradrenalin in stressful situation, it also subserves other normal functions such as maintenance of normal arterial blood pressure through the carotid sinus reflex. *Sympathetic nervous system* performs its physiological actions through various receptors which are known as ***adrenergic receptors*** (Table 3.1).

## 3.8 Dopaminergic System

### Dopamine receptors

***$D_1$ receptor*** — mediates vasodilation in the renal, mesenteric, coronary and cerebral blood vessels. Fenoldopam is the selective agonist of $D_1$ receptor.

***$D_2$ receptor*** — inhibits transmission in the sympathetic ganglia, inhibits release of noradrenalin from sympathetic neuron, inhibits prolactin release and causes vomiting.

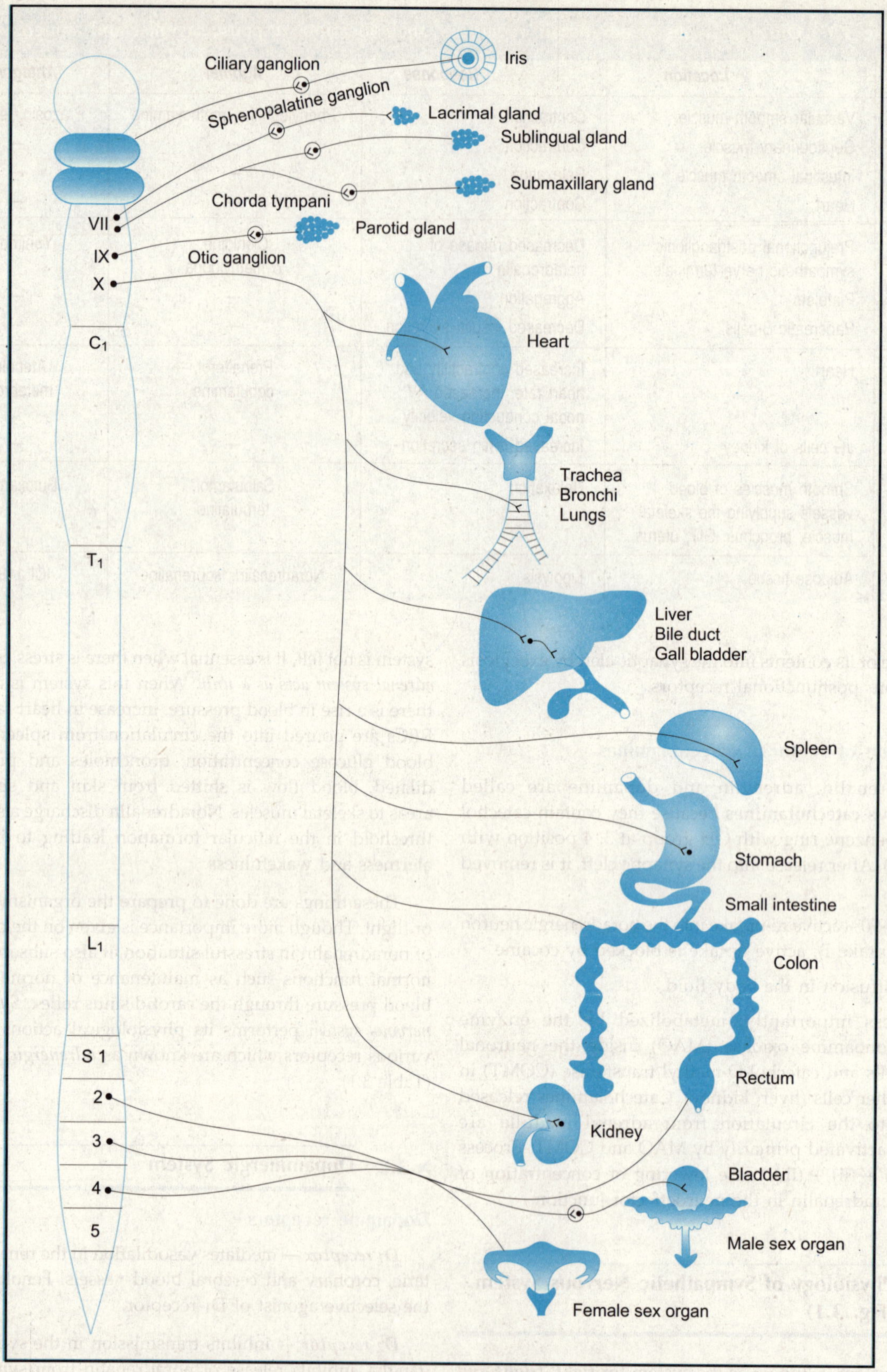


**Fig. 3.3 :** Parasympathetic Nervous System with visceral innervations

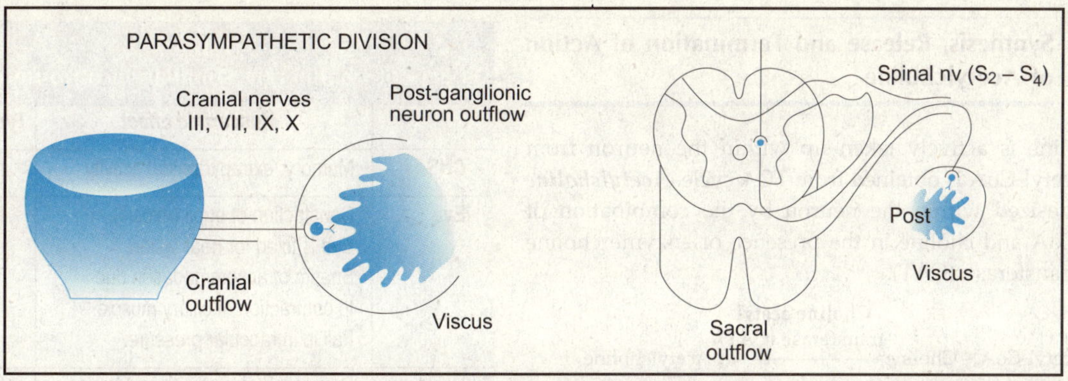


**Fig. 3.4 :** Parasympathetic nervous system

Selective agonist for $D_2$ receptor are bromocriptine, apomorphine, lergotrile. $D_2$ receptor can be blocked selectively by haloperidol, domperidone.

## 3.9 Parasympathetic Nervous System

This branch of autonomic nervous system may be considered as the ***anabolic nervous system*** because it promotes digestion and absorption of food, reduces catabolic changes and heat production. Therefore it is related to conservation of energy. Without this nervous system animals cannot survive. Due to its origin it is also known as ***craniosacral outflow*** because preganglionic fibers emerge from midbrain, pons, medulla and sacral spinal segments.

***Cranial outflow of parasympathetic preganglionic fibers*** arise from midbrain, pons and medulla and come out along with III CN, VII CN, IX CN and X CN cranial nerves to supply the head, thorax and bulk of the abdominal viscera. Sacral outflow arises from 2nd, 3rd and sometimes 4th sacral segments and come out through sacral spinal nerves to supply the pelvic viscera. Parasympathetic ganglia are scattered and located near the respective target organs. Myelinated preganglionic parasympathetic fibers are long while nonmyelinated postganglionic fibers are short. Preganglionic parasympathetic fibers of 3rd cranial nerve terminates in the ciliary ganglion from where postganglionic fibers go to supply the ciliary muscles of the eye and the constrictor muscle of pupil.

**Preganglionic fibers of VIIth cranial nerve** terminate in submaxillary ganglion from where postganglionic fibers supply the lacrimal, submaxillary and sublingual glands. The *preganglionic fibers of IXth nerve* end in otic ganglion where–from postganglionic fibers supply the parotid gland (Fig. 3.4).

Vagus nerve (Xth CN) carries approximately 75% of preganglionic parasympathetic fibers. The preganglionic fibers of vagus nerve terminate and form synapse in many ganglia close to different thoracic and abdominal organs and the respective postganglionic fibers supply heart, lungs, stomach, pancreas, small intestine, liver and proximal part of colon. Sacral preganglionic fibers pass through the pelvic nerve and terminate in several fibers supplying distal colon, rectum, urinary bladder, ovary and fallopian tubes. Neurotransmitter of parasympathetic nervous system is acetylcholine (ACh). Nerves that release acetylcholine are said to be cholinergic. Following are the sites where acetylcholine is the neurotransmitter (Table 3.2) :

**Table 3.2 : Location, function and response of acetylcholine**

| *Sites of release* | *Acts on* | *Response* |
|---|---|---|
| Preganglionic autonomic nerve terminals (both parasympathetic and sympathetic) | Autonomic ganglia | Development of action potential in postganglionic nerve terminals |
| Postganglionic parasympathetic nerve terminals | Effector organs | Stimulatory/ Inhibitory |
| From somatic motor nerve terminals | Striated muscle end plate | Contraction of muscles |
| From postganglionic sympathetic nerve endings | Sweat glands | Sweating |
| Postganglionic sympathetic vasodilatory nerve terminals | Vascular smooth muscle | Vasodilatation |
| Preganglionic sympathetic nerve terminals | Chromaffin cells of adrenal medulla | Release of adrenalin |

## 3.10 Synthesis, Release and Termination of Action of Acetylcholine

Choline is actively taken up within the neuron from ECF. Acetyl-CoA is obtained from TCA cycle. ***Acetylcholine is*** synthesized within the neuron by the combination of acetyl-CoA and choline in the presence of enzyme choline acetyl transferase (CAT).

$$\text{Acetyl-CoA + Choline} \xrightarrow[\textbf{transferase (CAT)}]{\textbf{Choline acetyl}} \text{Acetylcholine}$$

Acetylcholine is stored in synaptic vesicles and released in response to nerve impulses that depolarize the nerve terminal. Due to depolarization there is increase in calcium influx which causes fusion of synaptic vesicles with neuronal membrane and release of acetylcholine by exocytosis. Released acetylcholine combines with cholinergic receptors and produces its effect. But its action is very short lived because it is rapidly metabolized by acetylcholine esterase in the synaptic cleft and by the butynyl choline esterase/ serum choline esterase in plasma and in nonneuronal tissue.

### Cholinergic receptors

Two types of receptors (i) ***muscarinic receptors*** (predominantly stimulated by alkaloid muscarine), (ii) ***nicotinic receptor*** (predominantly by nicotine).

***Muscarinic receptors are*** further subdivided into three Types :

1. **$M_1$ receptors** ⟶ located in CNS, parasympathetic ganglia ⟶ stimulated by oxotremorine, MCN-A-343 and blocked by pirenzipine, atropine. Post receptor mechanism → ↑$IP_3$, DAG.
2. **$M_2$ receptors** ⟶ located in heart, nerves, smooth muscle ⟶ blocked by atropine, AF DX 115. Post receptor mechanism → ↓Cyclic AMP.
3. **$M_3$ receptors** ⟶ located in smooth muscle, glands, endothelium ⟶ blocked by atropine, hexahydrosiladifenidol. Post receptor mechanism → ↓Cyclic AMP.

**All muscarinic receptors can be blocked by atropine sulphate.**

**Nicotinic receptors are** subdivided into two types :

1. **$N_M$ (M – muscle type)** ⟶ location – skeletal muscle, neuromuscular junction ⟶ agonist – PTMA (phenyltrimethyl ammonium) ⟶ antagonist – d-tubocurarine. Post receptor mechanism → ↑Na & K.
2. **$N_N$ (N – neuronal type)** ⟶ present in autonomic ganglion ⟶ DMPP (dimethyl phenylpiperazine) selective agonist ⟶ antagonist — trimethaphan. Post receptor mechanism → increased sodium and other small ions.

**Table 3.3**
**Effects of cholinergic stimulation on different organs**

| | Muscarinic effect | Type of receptor |
|---|---|---|
| CNS | Memory, extrapyramidal activity | $M_1$ receptor |
| Eye | Constriction of pupil (miosis). Eye is fixed for near vision. Spasm of accommodation due to contraction of ciliary muscle. Fall in intraocular pressure. | $M_3$ receptor |
| Heart | Decrease in heart rate and force of contraction | $M_2$ receptor |
| Respiration | Smooth muscle contraction leading to bronchospasm | $M_3$ receptor |
| GIT | Contraction of intestinal smooth muscle causing increase in peristalsis but sphincter is relaxed | $M_1$ receptor |
| Secretory glands | Increased secretion (saliva, gastric, sweat, bronchial) | $M_3$ receptor |

## 3.11 Physiology of Parasympathetic Nervous System

This system is concerned with regulation of cardiovascular system, GI system and genitourinary system. The role of cholinergic nervous system on metabolism is not well understood. But important organs like liver, pancreas, kidney and thyroid are supplied by parasympathetic nerves. So parasympathetic nervous system might play a role in metabolism also (Table 3.3).

### Nicotinic effect

Autonomic ganglion stimulated through ($N_N$) and neuromuscular junction, skeletal muscle stimulation via $N_M$ receptor (on continued stimulation there is stimulation followed by paralysis).

### Presynaptic receptors

These are also called ***autoreceptors***. These are present in both adrenergic and cholinergic nervous system. They are usually inhibitory in nature. The best example is $\alpha_2$-receptor located on prejunctional membrane of postganglionic sympathetic nerve terminals. Activation of $\alpha_2$-receptor inhibits further release of noradrenalin from the nerve terminal. Conversely, stimulation of presynaptic β-receptor may increase release of norepinephrine. Adrenergic

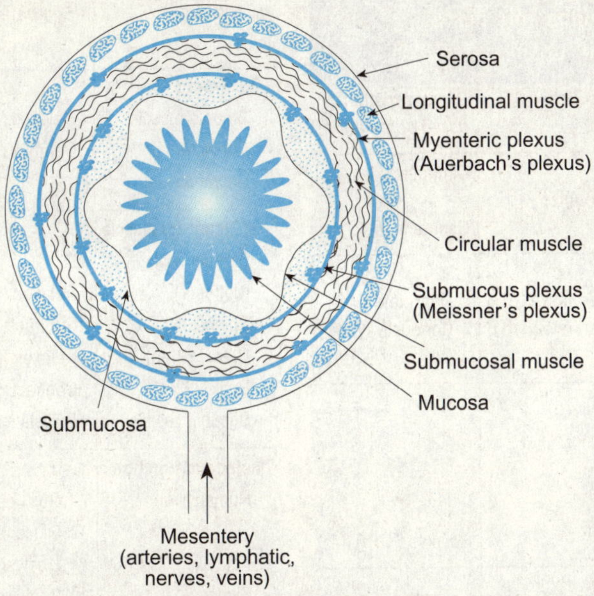


**Fig. 3.5 :** Enteric nervous system

$\alpha_2$-receptor stimulants are clonidine and alpha-methyldopa. They are used as antihypertensives as they stimulate $\alpha_2$-receptor present in VMC (main function) and thereby inhibit noradrenalin release. Cholinergic fibers — especially somatic motor fibers — contain excitatory autoreceptors for acetylcholine.

## ➤ 3.12 Enteric Nervous System (Fig. 3.5)

To some physiologist it is the ***3rd division of autonomic nervous system***. It consists of large and highly organized collection of neurons located in the walls of gastrointestinal system. It includes ***myenteric plexus*** (plexus of Auerbach) and the ***submucous plexus*** (plexus of Meissner). These plexuses within gastrointestinal system are indispensible in the control of gastrointestinal motility, secretion and transport. ***The enteric nervous system is innervated by the sympathetic and parasympathetic divisions*** of the ANS.

These sympathetic and parasympathetic innervations appear to play a modulatory role because deprivation of these fibers does not halt activity of the enteric nervous system. Probable neurotransmitters of ENS are encephalins, endorphins, 5HT, vasoactive intestinal peptide (VIP), somatostatin, adenosine, and ATP.

**Table 3.4**
**Difference between sympathetic and parasympathetic nervous systems**

| *Sympathetic* | *Parasympathetic* |
|---|---|
| **Origin** – $T_1$ – $T_{12}$ and $L_1$– $L_3$/$L_4$ | CN – III, VII, IX, X and Sacral – $S_2$, $S_3$, $S_4$ |
| Thoracolumbar outflow | Craniosacral outflow |
| **Distribution** – Wide | Diffuse |
| **Ganglia** | |
| (a) Paravertebral ganglia – 22 pairs on each side of spinal cord | Located very close to the tissue innervated |
| (b) Prevertebral ganglia (celiac, superior and inferior mesenteric ganglia, hypogastric ganglia) | – |
| (c) Terminal ganglia to urinary bladder and rectum | – |
| **Preganglionic fiber** — they are short, myelinated | Long, myelinated |
| **Postganglionic fiber** — long, nonmyelinated | Short, nonmyelinated |
| Neurotransmitter — noradrenalin (major) | Acetylcholine |
| **Result of stimulation** — generalized reaction | Localized reaction |
| **Physiological function** — preparing the body for stress (for fight or flight) | Conserve energy of the body |
| Catabolic function | Anabolic function |

*Table contd. next page*

**Table 3.5 : Effect of autonomic nerve stimulation on different organ system**

| *System* | *Sympathetic stimulation* | *Parasympathetic nerve stimulation* |
|---|---|---|
| Eye-circular muscle | --- | Contracts ($M_3$) |
| Radial muscle | Contracts (dilatation) $\alpha_1$ | --- |
| Ciliary muscle | Relaxes ($\beta$) | Contracts ($M_3$) |
| **Heart :** | | |
| S. A. Node | Accelerates ↑ heart rate ($\beta_1\beta_2$) | ↓ Heart rate ($M_2$) |
| A. V. Node | Accelerates ↑ heart rate ($\beta_1\beta_2$) | ↓ Conductivity ($M_2$) |
| S. A. Node | Increases ($\beta_1\beta_2$) | ↓ Contractility ($M_2$) |
| **Blood vessels :** | | |
| Skin, splanchnic vessels | Contracts ($\alpha_1$) | --- |
| Skeletal muscle vessels | Relaxes ($\beta_1$) | --- |
| Endothelium | --- | Relaxes EDRF ($M_3$) |
| **Lungs :** | | |
| Bronchial smooth muscle | Relaxation ($\beta_2$) | Contracts ($M_3$) |
| Blood vessels supplying lungs | Contracts ($\alpha_1$) decongestion effects | --- |
| **G.I. Tract :** | | |
| Smooth muscle | Relaxes ($\alpha_2\beta_2$) | Contracts ($M_3$) |
| Sphincters | Contracts ($\alpha_1$) | Relaxes ($M_3$) |
| Secretion | --- | Increases ($M_3$) |
| **Genitourinary muscle :** | | |
| Bladder wall (detrusor) | Relaxes ($\beta_2$) | Contracts ($M_3$) |
| Sphincter | Contracts ($\alpha_1$) | Relaxes ($M_3$) |
| Uterus (Preg) | Relaxes ($\beta_2$) | --- |
| Penis | Contracts ($\alpha$) | Contracts ($M_3$) |
| Seminal vesicles | Ejaculation ($\alpha$) | Erection (M) |
| **Metabolic function :** | | |
| Human liver | ↑ Glycogenolysis ($\beta_2\alpha$) | --- |
| | ↑ Gluconeogeneris ($\beta_2\alpha$) | --- |
| Fat cells | ↑ Lipolysis ($\beta_3$) | --- |
| Kidney | ↑ Renin release ($\beta_1$) | --- |
| **Skin :** | | |
| Pilomotor muscle | Contracts ($\alpha_1$) | --- |
| Sweat glands | Secretion ($\alpha$) (mainly cholinergic) | --- |

*Table contd. next column*

## ➤ 3.13 KEY CONCEPTS

1. **Autonomic nervous system** innervates heart, smooth muscle, exocrine glands, parenchymal cells and endocrine glands. Thus it controls smooth muscle contraction and relaxation, force of contraction of heart, heart rate and certain metabolic processes (eg, glucose utilization).
2. It has **two main divisions – sympathetic** and **parasympathetic**. According to some physiologists enteric nervous system is its 3rd division. Usually parasympathetic nervous system is inhibitory and sympathetic nervous system is excitatory. Most autonomic organs are supplied by both sympathetic and parasympathetic fibers. Sympathetic and parasympathetic system are in a dynamic balance. In majority of cases they have opposing actions (eg, control of heart rate, gastrointestinal smooth muscle activities) but this may not be true in some situations (eg, salivary glands, ciliary muscles).
3. **Sympathetic activity tends** to predominate in stress (fight or flight response) whereas **parasympathetic** activity predominates during satiation and repose. ENS (enteric nervous system) is concerned with GI motility, secretion and transport.
4. Sympathetic ganglia are paravertebral or prevertebral in location. The parasympathetic ganglia are in or near the organs they innervate. The neurotransmitters of the postganglionic sympathetic neurons are noradrenaline except those for sweat glands and piloerection muscles which are cholinergic. ACh = acetylcholine. NE = norepinephrine (noradrenalin).

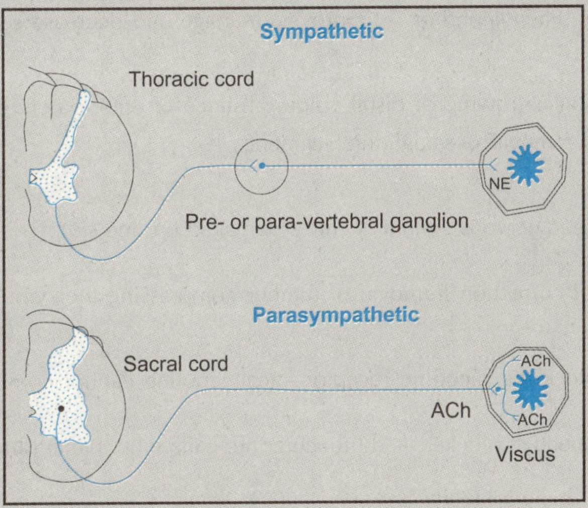


5. The myenteric and submucous plexuses are shown in the figure. The sites of known transmitters are shown as are sites of synaptic excitation (+) and inhibition (–). NE = Norepinephrine. ACh = Acetyl choline.

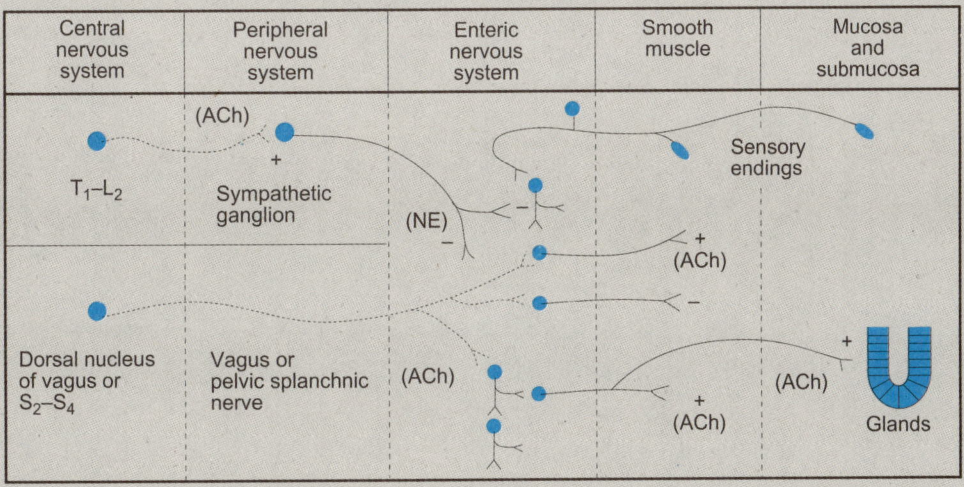

## ➤ 3.14 DISORDERS/CLINICAL CORRELATIONS

➤ **Anaphylactic shock :**

*Pathophysiology* — Release of histamine and SRS from mast cells cause bronchoconstriction and hypotension.

*Clinical measures* — Adrenalin antagonizes the laryngeal oedema, bronchoconstriction and hypotension.

➤ **Bronchial asthma :**

*Pathophysiology* — Bronchoconstriction due to various allergens.

*Clinical measures* — $\beta_2$ stimulant salbutamol, terbutaline, isoprenaline, adrenalin cause direct bronchodilation.

➤ **Diabetic autonomic neuropathy :**

*Pathophysiology* — Loss of pre- and post-ganglionic autonomic nerve fibers – hypotension on standing, diarrhea, constipation, decreased gastric emptying, impotence, abnormal sweating.

*Clinical measures* — Diarrhea can be controlled by $\alpha_2$-stimulant, clonidine.

➤ **Glaucoma :**

*Pathophysiology* — Increase in intraocular pressure more than 20 mm of water due to blockade in the drainage of aqueous humor through the iridocorneal angle (canal of Schlemm) or there is increase formation of aqueous humor.

*Clinical measures* — 1. Pilocarpine (cholinomimetic alkaloid) improves drainage. 2. β-blocker timolol decreases aqueous humor formation. 3. Phenylephrine → improves drainage and decrease secretion.

➤ **Hirschprung's disease :**

*Pathophysiology* — Congenital narrowing of distal colon, absence of enteric nerves.

*Clinical measures* —Surgical removal of ganglionic segments.

➤ **Horner's syndrome :**

*Pathophysiology* — Sympathetic nervous system is cut or damaged on one side. Triad of miosis, ipsilateral ptosis and anhydrosis.

*Clinical measures* — Surgical correction (removal of tumour compressing the sympathetic chain).

➤ **Neuromuscular paralysis :**

*Pathophysiology* — Drugs block the nicotinic receptor—acetylcholine cannot combine with nicotinic receptor, paralysis of muscle.

*Clinical measures* — 1. Competitive blocker — d-tubocurarine, gallamine, pancuronium. 2. Depolarising blocker – succinylcholine.

# Gastrointestinal and Digestive Physiology

AGENDA :



4

## ➤ 4.1 CHAPTER OVERVIEW

Nutritive substances, vitamins, minerals, and fluids enter the body through gastrointestinal system. The gastrointestinal system comprises the gastrointestinal tract (from mouth cavity through esophagus, stomach, small and large intestines, rectum, and anal canal to the anus) and the associated glands (salivary glands, liver and pancreas). Food that is swallowed is temporarily stored in the stomach where the food particles are crushed and mixed. Gastric acid helps in protein digestion but, in addition, it protects the G.I. tract by killing ingested bacteria. Intrinsic factor secreted by the stomach is essential for life because it is required for absorption of Vitamin $B_{12}$. The chyme of food which reaches the duodenum is acidic. Alkaline pancreatic juice neutralizes the acidity of chyme. Powerful amylolytic , proteolytic and lipolytic enzymesare present in the exocrine pancreatic secretion; the major part of digestion (breaking down of complex carbohydrates, proteins and fats in food to simpler absorbable molecules) occurs in the proximal part of the small intestine with the help of these enzymes. However, enzymes present in the intestinal brush border also play a significant role. Digestion and absorption of fat requires bile salts which are produced by the liver and secreted in bile. Gall bladder is the storehouse of bile. Bile salts help fat digestion by emulsifying large fat droplets into smaller fragments. They help fat absorption by packaging fat into water-soluble particles called **micelles. Monosaccharides** are the principal form in which carbohydrates are absorbed. **Proteins** are principally absorbed as amino acids. Fat absorption is a bit complicated. Small chain fatty acids and glycerol can be absorbed as such but long chain fatty acids need to be reesterified and packaged into chylomicrons before they can be absorbed. Unlike absorption of monosaccharides, amino acids, short chain fatty acids and glycerols, chylomicrons (being large in size) enter the blood stream indirectly via lymph. Folding of the intestinal mucous membrane, formation of villi, and microvilli present on enterocytes greatly increase the absorptive surface of the small intestine. A large amount of water along with electrolytes are absorbed by the intestine in addition to the absorption of other nutritive substances. The function of the colon is mainly absorptive (water and electrolytes). Colon contains a large number of bacteria (commensals) which live symbiotically. Rectum is the part of the G.I. tract where fecalmatter is accumulated. Feces is passed from time to time by defecation which is a reflex phenomenon with some voluntary control.

The functions of the G.I. system is regulated by chemical mediators (gut hormones, paracrines and neurocrines) and nerves (enteric nervous system and extrinsic nerves). Gut hormones are released from enteroendocrine cells found throughout the mucosa of the G.I. tract. Intrinsic nerves of the G.I. tract regulates G.I. motility and secretion and is influenced by the extrinsic nerves (parasympathetic and sympathetic). Highly coordinated motility of the G.I. tract is crucial for optimal digestion and absorption of nutritive substances and maintenance of water and electrolyte balance. Parasympathetic nerves generally stimulate motility of the wall of the G.I. tract with relaxation of sphincters. Sympathetic nerves have an opposite effect.

## ➤ 4.2 Introduction

### Structure and Organisation (Fig. 4.1)

The **gastrointestinal system** is comprised of gastro intestinal tract (mouth, pharynx, esophagus, stomach, small intestine, large intestine, rectum and anal canal) and accessory organs which drain into alimentary tract. ***Three pairs of salivary glands, pancreas, liver and biliary tract*** are the accessory organs of digestion.

### Structure of digestive tract

There are four histological subdivisions in a cross-section of the gastrointestinal tract — ***(a) mucosa; (b) submucosa; (c) muscularis and (d) adventitia.***

(a) ***Mucosa*** — protection, secretion and absorption are the functions of mucosal layer.

(b) ***Submucosa*** — connective tissue layer.

(c) ***Muscularis*** — smooth muscle cells are arranged in inner circular layer and outer longitudinal layer. The spindleshaped smooth muscle cells in each layer are electrically coupled by means of *gap junctions* and form functional syncytium.

  (i) *Esophagus* : Striated muscle is present in the upper one-third. Mixed, striated and smooth muscles are present in the middle one-third.

  (ii) *Stomach* : Muscularis layer is reinforced by an innermost oblique layer.

  (iii) *Colon* : The outer longitudinal muscle layer forms three bundles (tenia coli).

(d) ***Adventitia*** : formed by peritoneum and underlying connective tissue :

### Nerve supply of the gastrointestinal tract (Fig. 4.2)

The gastrointestinal system has got its own **enteric nervous system** (ENS). The enteric nervous system is made of neural plexuses within the walls of esophagus, stomach, and large and small intestines. Two major types of plexuses constitute the enteric nervous system.

(a) ***Submucosal (Meissner's) plexus*** — located within the submucosal layer and controls secretion.

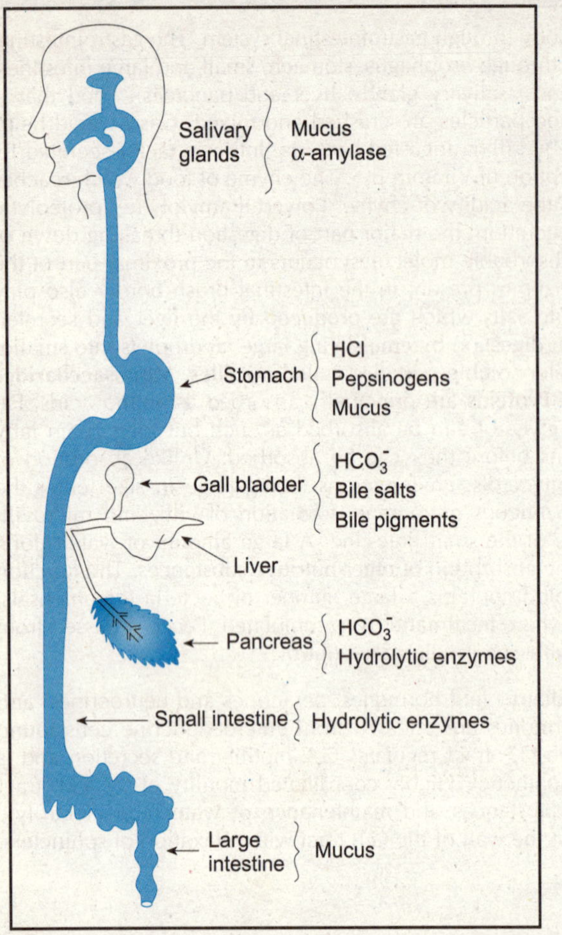


**Fig. 4.1 :** Schematic diagram of the GI tract showing its different parts along with major constituents of their secretions

(b) ***Myenteric (Auerbach's) plexus*** — located between the circular and longitudinal muscle layers and regulates motility.

**ENS** has an intrinsic pattern of activity which is responsible for the ***control of most of the functions of the gastrointestinal tract*** (motility, secretion and transport) (Fig. 4.3. These intrinsic neurons receive input from extrinsic neurons and form an extensively integrated network. The extrinsic neurons which synapse on these plexuses include :

(i) *Voluntary nervous system* : These fibers are from alpha motor neurons that travel via vagus nerve to esophagus and to the external anal sphincter via pudendal nerve, and regulate swallowing and defecation.

(ii) *Sympathetic nervous system* : All portions of the GI tract are innervated by postganglionic sympathetic nerve fibers. Its effect is mediated by the release of norepinephrine. Sympathetic nerves are inhibitory to the smooth muscle lining the wall of G.I. tract but stimulatory to the sphincters.

(iii) *Parasympathetic nervous system* :

- Preganglionic parasympathetic fibres pass via vagus and sacral outflows
- Postganglionic neurons are in the submucous and myenteric plexuses

In general, the parasympathetic system is stimulatory to muscle lining wall of G.I. tract but inhibitory to the sphincters.

(iv) *Sensory pathways* : Sensation (sometimes conscious) arises out of irritation of mucosa and distension of the intestine. The afferent neurons have their cell bodies in prevertebral ganglia, dorsal root ganglia of sacral nerves and afferent ganglia of vagus nerves.

**Neurotransmitters** found in the G.I. tract include acetylcholine, norepinephrine, enkephalins and endorphins, serotonin, vasoactive intestinal peptide, somatostatin, ATP and adenosine.

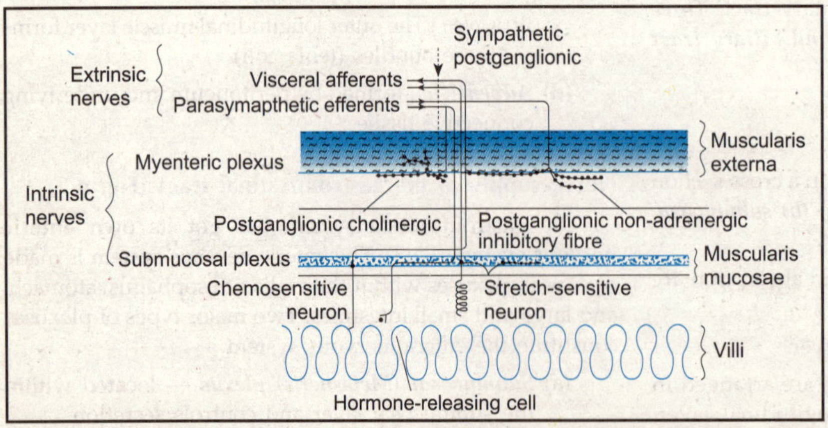


**Fig. 4.2 :** Intrinsic and extrinsic nerves of gastrointestinal tract

## Regulation of gastrointestinal processes

The gastrointestinal tract has extensive nerve plexuses within its wall (**enteric nervous system**). The intramuscular (myenteric/Auerbach's) and submucous (Meissner's) plexuses do function autonomously, yet they are controlled by parasympathetic and sympathetic divisions of ANS. ***The parasympathetic fibers are all preganglionic but sympathetics are postganglionic.*** CNS can influence motor and secretory activities of G.I. tract via these pathways. The hormones which control the gastrointestinal system are secreted mainly by endocrine cells which are distributed throughout epithelium of stomach and small intestine. ***Secretin, cholecystokinin (CCK), gastrin and gastric inhibitory peptide (GIP)*** are mainly responsible for regulation of gastrointestinal processes.

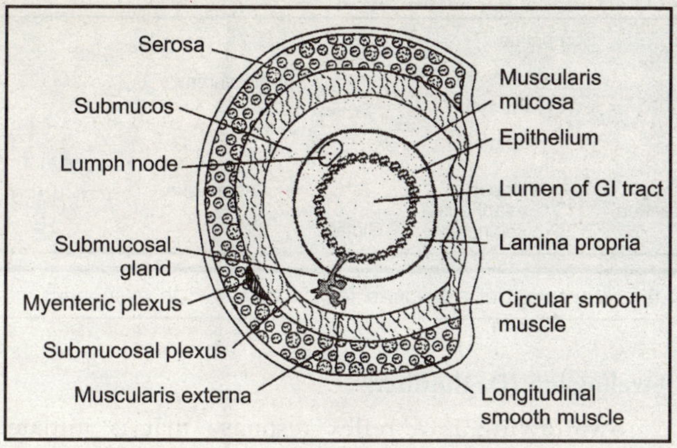


Fig. 4.3

## 4.3 Motility

When a part of the wall of the G.I. tract is stretched by the contents in its lumen, a reflex called **peristalsis** is initiated, which is responsible for propelling food along the G.I. tract. Peristalsis is found in all parts of the G.I. tract from the esophagus to the rectum. The local stretch leads to contraction of the part of gut wall proximal to the stretched part and relaxation distal to it. This propels the content in an oral to aboral direction. The contents of the lumen now stretches another part of the gut wall and the same sequence of events occur again. These sequential events occuring along the gut wall sets up a continuous wave of contraction (peristalsis) that moves the contents of the gut towards the rectum. The rate of this movement varies from 2 to 25 cm/s in different parts of the G.I. tract. Occurrence of peristaltic movements is dependent on the enteric nervous system but they can be modulated by extrinsic autonomic nerves. The exact neural mechanism for peristalsis has not yet been settled but the following sequence of events seems to be responsible for occurrence of peristalsis (Fig. 4.4, 4.5) :

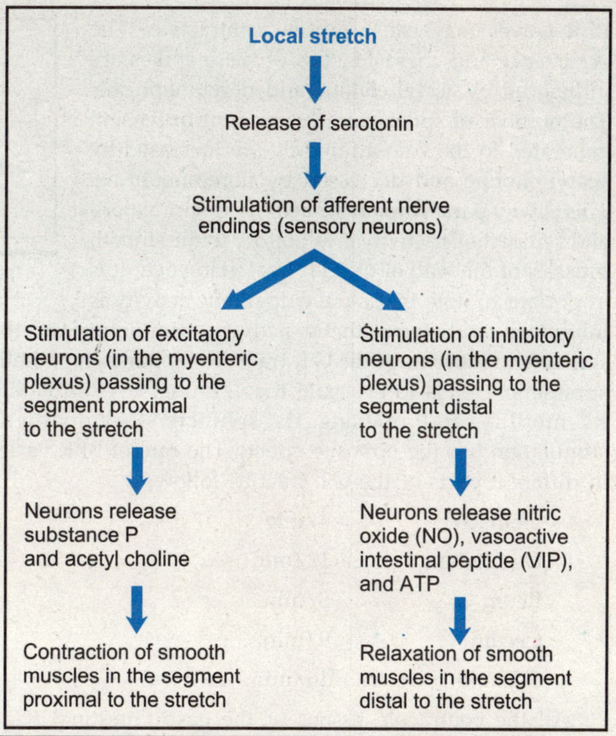


Fig. 4.4

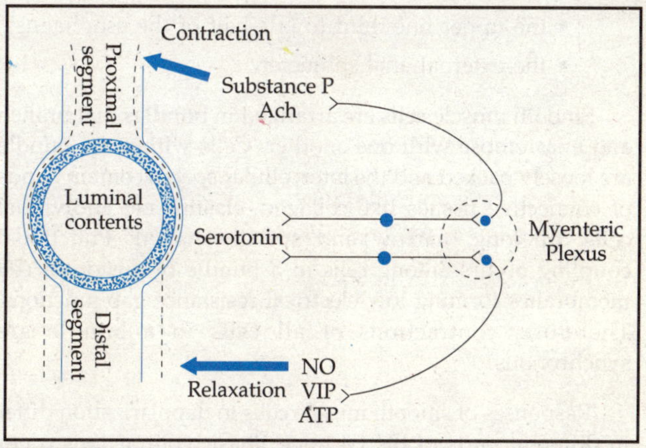


Fig. 4.5

Spontaneous rhythmic fluctuations in membrane potential (between –65 mV and –45 mV) of the smooth muscle cells of the G.I. tract is known as **basal electrical rhythm (BER)**. BER is found in all parts of the intestine except the esophagus and the proximal stomach, and it coordinates peristaltic and other motor activity of the G.I. tract. The cells responsible for generation of BER appear to be stellate, muscle-like pacemaker cells (interstitial cells of Cajal) located in between the longitudinal and circular muscle layers. Influx of $Ca^{2+}$ into the cell is responsible for the depolarizing portion of each wave of BER while $K^+$ efflux is responsible for repolarization. BER itself does not usually cause muscle contraction; spike potentials arising on the most depolarizing parts of

**Table 4.1 : The volumes, osmolarity, pH and ionic concentration of plasma and gastrointestinal secretions**

| | Volume (liters/day) | pH | $Na^+$ mmol/L | $K^+$ mmol/L | $Cl^-$ mmol/L | $HCO_3^-$ mmol/L |
|---|---|---|---|---|---|---|
| **Saliva** | 1.5 | 7.5 | 40 | 15 | 25 | 30 |
| **Gastric juice** | 3 | 1.0 | 50 | 10 | 100 | 0 |
| **Pancreatic juice** | 1.5 | 7.8 | 140 | 10 | 70 | 80 |
| **Bile** | 0.5 | 7.5 | 140 | 5 | 80 | 20 |

BER waves may cause muscle contraction. The occurrence and characteristics of these spikes are influenced by acetyl choline and norepinephrine. The number of spikes and the amount of tension generated in the smooth muscle are increased by acetyl choline and decreased by norepinephrine. This is why parasympathetic activity is stimulatory and sympathetic activity is inhibitory to the smooth muscles of the wall of the G.I. tract. (However it is important to note that parasympathetic activity is inhibitory and sympathetic activity stimulatory to the sphincteric muscles of the G.I. tract. Thus, parasympathetic stimulation tends to evacuate the G.I. tract by stimulating its motility and opening its sphincters; sympathetic stimulation has the opposite effect). The rate of BER varies in different parts of the G.I. tract as follows :

| | |
|---|---|
| Stomach | 4/min |
| Duodenum | 12/min |
| Ileum | 8/min |
| Cecum | 9/min |
| Sigmoid colon | 16/min. |

All the contractile tissues of the gastrointestinal (G.I.) tract contain smooth muscle cells with the following exceptions which contain striated muscle :

- the pharynx;
- the upper one-third to one-half of the esophagus;
- the external anal sphincter.

Smooth muscle cells are arranged in bundles that branch and anastomose with one another. Cells within the bundle are loosely packed and the intercellular spaces contain bands of connective tissues like collagen, elastin etc. Individual cells are long, narrow and spindle-shaped. Functional coupling occurs among cells in a bundle by fusion of cell membranes forming low electrical resistance gap junctions. Therefore, contractions of all cells in a bundle are synchronous.

Responses of smooth muscle cells to depolarization differ in different parts of the GI tract. Phasic contractions occur rapidly in a matter of seconds followed by rapid relaxation. This type of contractions are found in ***the musculature of the esophagus, the distal stomach*** (antrum) and the ***small intestine***. Tonic contractions may last for minutes to hours and are found in the lower esophageal sphincter (LES), the proximal stomach, the ileocecal sphincter and the internal anal sphincter.

The resting membrane potential of the smooth muscle in some parts of the GI tract oscillates to produce slow waves that have different frequencies (3-12 cycles/min) in different parts of the GI tract. These slow waves originate probably in the interstitial **cells of Cajal** and determine the pattern of spike or action potential produced. This activity may be modified by the activity of extrinsic nerves as well as the hormones including the local hormones.

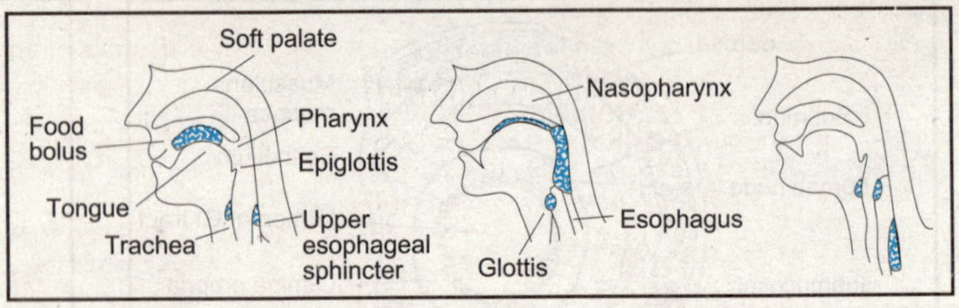


Fig. 4.6 : Movement of a bolus of food from mouth to esophagus

## Swallowing (Deglutition)

**Swallowing** is a reflex response that is initiated voluntarily by propelling the oral contents, collected on the tongue, backward into the pharynx. The afferent impulses that trigger swallowing pass through the trigeminal, glossopharyngeal and vagus nerves. The efferent fibers pass to the pharyngeal musculature and tongue via trigeminal, facial and hypoglossal nerves. The reflex response consists of involuntary contraction of the pharyngeal musculature, inhibition of respiration, closure of the glottis and relaxation of the upper esophageal sphincter (UES). **Peristaltic contraction** that begins in the superior constrictor muscle of the pharynx proceeds through the middle and inferior constrictors. This propels the bolus of food through the pharynx. Relaxation of UES allows the pharyngeal contractions to move the bolus of food into the esophagus (Fig. 4.6).

## Esophageal motility

**Primary peristaltic contraction** of the esophagus begins just below the *upper esophageal sphincter*. Coordinated and sequential contractions produce a high pressure zone within the esophagus that moves down with the bolus in front of it. The speed of esophageal peristalsis is ***2-6 cm/sec***. When the bolus reaches the LES, relaxation of the sphincter allows the bolus to enter the stomach. The time taken for a bolus to reach the stomach depends also on gravity and the physical nature of the material swallowed. Liquids and semisolid foods, when taken in an upright position, usually falls by gravity ahead of the peristaltic contraction.

If the esophagus cannot be emptied by the primary peristaltic contractions initiated by the swallow (which is not infrequent), secondary peristaltic contractions triggered involuntarily due to the distension produced by residual material **"sweeps"** the esophagus clean.

Tone and elasticity of the cricopharyngeal muscle determines the closure of the UES. Resting tone of the LES is mainly myogenic. Its relaxation upon swallowing is neurally mediated. Vagal stimulation leads to decrease in sphincter tone and pressure. Vasoactive intestinal peptide (VIP) has been suggested as the mediator of this response. Nitric oxide (NO) may also be responsible.

**In achalasia,** relaxation of LES during swallowing fails to occur and the primary esophageal peristalsis is weak and

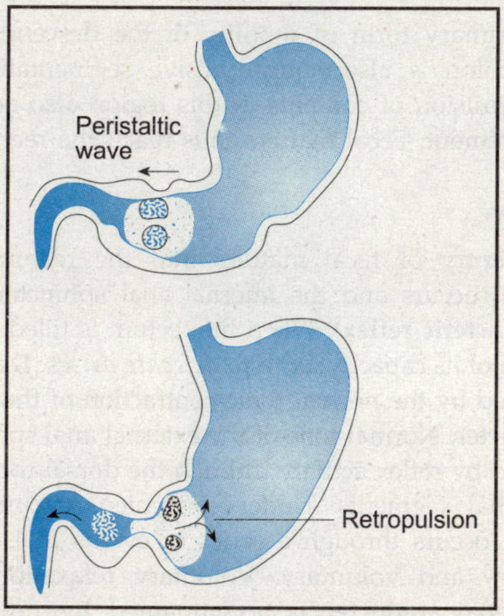

Fig. 4.7 : Movement of peristaltic wave of stomach

nonpropulsive. Thus, food accumulates in the esophagus producing dilatation of lower esophagus. Pneumatic dilatation or surgical incision (myotomy) of the LES is done to treat achalasia.

Incompetence of the LES leads to **gastroesophageal reflux disease (GERD)** due to reflux of acidic gastric contents into the esophagus. Inflammation of the esophagus (esophagitis) and, sometimes, ulceration occurs. *Heartburn* and *water brash* are common symptoms in these patients. ***Treatment*** is aimed at inhibition of gastric acid secretion (by using antacids, $H_2$-blockers or proton pump inhibitors) and decreasing gastric emptying time (by using prokinetic agents like metoclopramide, domperidone or cisapride). In severe cases, surgery (fundoplication) may be needed.

## Gastric motility

Based on patterns of motility, the stomach may be divided into ***two regions*** (a) ***the proximal or orad region*** (accommodates a meal); (b) ***the distal or caudad region*** (mixing and propulsion).

### Motility of the proximal stomach (Fig. 4.7)

The proximal stomach relaxes simultaneously with the LES and accommodates the bolus of food. This active relaxation of gastric smooth muscle is referred to as receptive relaxation and can accommodate a volume change of upto 1,500 mL without significant increase in intragastric pressure. Receptive relaxation is a vagovagal reflex (both afferent and efferent impulses pass through the vagus nerve) and is abolished after vagotomy. The neurotransmitter involved appears to be nitric oxide (NO). Cholecystokinin (CCK) may have some role in facilitating this process — possibly by making the proximal stomach more distensible.

### Motility of the distal stomach

In the fasting state, the stomach remains quiescent for most of the time. However, at intervals of about 90 minutes, contractions called **migrating motility complex** or **migrating myoelectric complex (MMC)** start in the mid-portion of the stomach and move distally. ***These contractions last for 3-5 minutes and propel residue*** of the previous meal and accumulated mucus into the duodenum. MMC is abolished by eating. **Motilin,** a gastrointestinal hormone is responsible for MMC.

After taking a meal, more frequent contractions of varying strength occur depending on the nature of the ingested food. These peristaltic contractions also originate in the mid-portion of the stomach. They occur usually at a rate of 3-5 per minute and each contraction persists for 2-20 seconds. The velocity of contraction increases towards the pylorus so that it overtakes most of the gastric contents moving in front of it and almost closes the distal antrum. Thus, some of the stomach contents are squirted into the duodenum while most are propelled back into the stomach. This facilitates mixing of the contents and reduces the size of the solid particles.

Smooth muscle cells in the distal stomach have unstable resting membrane potentials giving rise to the **"slow waves"**. A contraction is triggered if a threshold level of depolarization is reached. These slow waves are referred to as the **"basal electric rhythm"** (BER) of the stomach because the timing and patterns of the contractions of the distal stomach are determined by the slow waves. These waves, having a frequency of 3-5 per minute, originate in the **"gastric pace maker"** situated in the middle of the stomach. The mechanism of origin of **gastric slow wave** is uncertain. Interstitial **cells of Cajal** (specialized nonmuscle cells) may be the pacemaker cells. Oscillations of electrogenic activity of the $Na^+$ pump and intracellular $Ca^{2+}$ release may also be responsible.

The force and frequency of these contractions are increased by vagal stimulation. Sympathetic stimulation has an opposite effect.

After a normal mixed meal, the gastric contents are emptied into the duodenum in 3 hours approximately. Liquids are more rapidly emptied. Fatty food delays gastric emptying via release of CCK. Hyperosmolality and low pH of the duodenal contents also inhibit gastric emptying. **Prokinetic agents** (like *metoclopramide, domperidone and cisapride) hastens gastric emptying time.*

## Small intestinal motility

**MMC** is also found in ***small intestine in the fasting state.*** Each MMC takes about *90 minutes* to sweep the entire length of the small intestine. **MMC** clears *undigested residue and accumulated secretions from the bowel.*

After a meal, **two types of contractions occur in the small intestine — segmentation contractions** and **peristaltic waves** (Fig. 4.8). **Segmentation contractions** are isolated

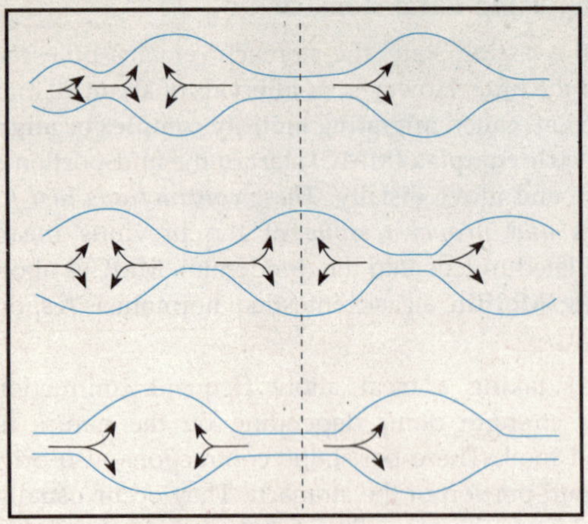

**Fig. 4.8 :** Alternate relaxation and contraction of segments of small intestine

involving short lengths (1 to 5 cm) of bowel and are not coordinated with movement above or below. They are responsible for *to and fro movement* of the intestinal contents (chyme) *without net propulsion*. This aids in mixing of intestinal contents and exposing them to the mucous membrane due to alternate contraction and relaxation of adjacent segments of intestine.

**Slow wave** or **BER** similar to that in the stomach is also found in the small intestine. Its frequency *is 11-12 per minute in the duodenum and 8-9 per minute in the terminal ileum.*

The frequency and amplitude of intestinal contractions are generally enhanced by parasympathetic stimulation and decreased by sympathetic stimulation.

Distension produced by a bolus within the lumen of intestine triggers contraction of the muscle above and relaxation of the muscle below the bolus resulting in its propulsion for a short distance. This is a ***reflex phenomenon*** (**peristaltic reflex**) dependent on ***the intrinsic (enteric) nervous*** system and is referred to as **the law of the intestine**. Contractile activity in the remaining bowel is inhibited if one portion of the bowel is severely distended. This **intestinointestinal reflex** requires intact extrinsic innervation. Gastric secretion and emptying is accompanied by increased motor activity of the ileum and relaxation of cecum resulting in the movement of ileal contents into the large intestine. This reflex response is known as **gastroileal reflex.**

## Large intestinal motility

Movements of the proximal colon are mainly segmental and serve the purpose of mixing the colonic contents back and forth, and exposing them to absorptive surfaces. These segmental contractions appear to be partly responsible for the colonic haustrations. One to three times a day, contents are moved in a narrow tubular length of bowel (at least 20 cm long) by peristaltic contractions referred to as **"mass movement"**. During mass movement, segmentation ceases and haustrations disappear.

The primary form of motility of the descending and sigmoid colon is also nonpropulsive segmentation. Net distal propulsion of contents in this region also occurs by mass movement. Fecal matters thus reach the rectum.

## Defecation

With entry of fecal matters into the rectum, rectal contraction occurs and the internal anal sphincter relaxes (**rectosphincteric reflex**). When the rectum is filled to about one-fourth of its capacity, urge ***to defecate arises***. **Defecation** is prevented by the normal tonic contraction of the external anal sphincter. Normal tone of the external anal sphincter is maintained by reflex activity through the dorsal roots in the sacral spinal segments. Under convenient circumstances, defecation occurs through a series of events that are both involuntary and voluntary. Voluntary relaxation of the external anal sphincter is accompanied by involuntary contraction of the longitudinal muscles of the rectum and distal colon. In normal individuals, the external anal sphincter remains closed if defecation is inconvenient. The urge to defecate subsides due to accommodation of the rectal receptors to distension. The tonic contraction of the external anal sphincter is absent in paraplegics and the rectosphincteric reflex results in defecation.

Gastric distension by food triggers contraction of the rectum and often an urge to defecate. This is called **gastrocolic reflex.**

Increased or decreased transit time through the colon may lead to constipation or diarrhea. **Diarrhea** may result from many diseases or conditions unrelated to colonic motility. Severe diarrhea causes debility and may even be fatal, especially in children. The **cause of death** is *usually shock and cardiovascular collapse due to dehydration, electrolyte depletion (especially $Na^+$ and $K^+$) and hypovolemia.* Severe hypokalemia is an insidious complication of chronic diarrhea.

## Vomiting (emesis)

Forceful expulsion of intestinal and gastric contents through the mouth is referred to as **vomiting**. Generalized autonomic discharge usually precedes and accompanies vomiting. ***Vomiting*** usually (but not necessarily) starts with the sensation of nausea. The sequence of events that leads to vomiting is as follows :

Reverse peristalsis begins in the distal small intestine moving the intestinal contents into the stomach.

↓

Glottis is closed and breath is held in mid-inspiration; muscles of the abdominal wall contract increasing intra-abdominal pressure.

↓

LES and UES relax allowing gastric contents to be ejected out through the mouth.

**Vomiting is** reflexly controlled by the **vomiting center** in the medulla which integrates all the events in a coordinated fashion. The vomiting center may be activated by afferent impulses initiated by diverse stimuli from different parts of the body which include —

- tickling the back of the throat
- gastric or duodenal distension
- dizziness
- unequal vestibular stimulation (as occurs in motion sickness)
- pain from urogenital system or injuries.

**Vomiting** may be stimulated by various chemicals by their action on *central or peripheral receptors*. The **chemoreceptor trigger zone (CTZ)** is a group of such receptors located in the floor of the fourth ventricle of the brain. ***The CTZ may be activated by emetics in the blood or CSF as well as in radiation exposure and motion sickness.*** Peripheral chemoreceptors responsible for vomiting are found primarily in the GI tract (mostly duodenum) and respond to emetics like ipecac. Emotional stimuli also may initiate vomiting through the afferents from the diencephalon and the limbic system.

Prolonged and severe vomiting may cause *electrolyte imbalance (metabolic alkalosis and hypokalemia) due to loss of $H^+$ and $K^+$.*

## 4.4 Salivary Glands and Salivary Secretion

The main salivary glands are three paired structures that deliver their secretions into the mouth through ducts. Histologically each gland contains acini (made up of a group of cells called acinar cells), intercalated duct (myoepithelial cells) and striated ducts (lined by columnar epithelial cells). (The secretory unit or **salivon** of the salivary gland = acinus + intercalated duct + striated duct) (Fig. 4.11). The salivary glands have a high blood flow with respect to their weight. The direction of the arterial flow is opposite to the flow of saliva through the salivon. The salivary glands are innervated by both sympathetic and parasympathetics nerves which regulate secretion, blood flow and growth of the salivary glands.

### Composition of saliva

Amount Approximately 1500 ml per day

pH 7.0 (saliva from resting glands)

8.0 (saliva from actively secreting glands)

**Organic constituents**

Enzymes (salivary α-amylase, lingual lipase)

Mucins (glycoproteins)

| | |
|---|---|
| IgA (immunoglobulin A) | Kallikrein |
| Lysozyme | Blood group |
| Lactoferrin | Substances of the A B O system (in some individuals) |

Some proline-rich proteins

**Inorganic constitutents** Water

$Na^+$, $K^+$

$Cl^-$, $HCO_3^-$

Striated ducts (and probably intercalated ducts) modify ionic composition of saliva whichcomes to the ducts from the acini. Acinar saliva is almost isotonic with electrolyte ($Na^+$, $K^+$, $Cl^-$, $HCO_3^-$) composition similar to those in plasma. But $Na^+$ and $Cl^-$ are actively reabsorbed from saliva in the striated ducts. These ducts add $K^+$ and $HCO_3^-$ to saliva. As the ducts are somewhat impermeable to water, saliva in the ducts contains relatively more water and hence is hypotonic (Fig. 4.11). The electrolyte exchange in the striated ducts is more prominent at low salivary flow (more time for electrolyte exchange to occur). Therefore, saliva coming out of the ducts is hypotonic, alkaline (due to $HCO_3^-$), and rich in $K^+$ when the flow rate is low. The exchange of $K^+$ with $Na^+$ at salivary ducts is dependent on aldosterone, which also has a similar action in the distal renal tubules. Aldosterone is deficient in Addison's disease and therefore, $Na^+$ content of saliva coming out of the ducts is high (a high $Na^+/K^+$ ratio) in this condition.

### Functions of saliva

Water and mucin act as *lubricants* which moisten and lubricate the food. The lubricating action is due mainly to its mucus content. It also helps in *swallowing* and *speech*. Adequate flow of saliva is responsible *for cleansing the mouth* and keeps its tissues soft, moist and pliable. Lysozyme, immunoglobulins and clotting factors *combat invading microbes*. Dental caries is prevented by salivary $HCO_3^-$. The digestion of carbohydrates is initiated by the **salivary α-amylase** (ptyalin) which is present in the mouth. It is capable of ***breaking alpha 1, 4 glycosidic linkages*** of glycogen. Lingual lipase is responsible for digestion of triglycerides. Saliva protects the mouth by diluting and buffering harmful substances. Saliva contains lysozyme which attacks bacterial cell wall. IgA present in saliva is active against bacteria and viruses, and lactoferrin chelates iron and is bacteriostatic.

### Formation of saliva (Figs. 4.9, 4.10 and 4.11)

**The salivary glands** are made up of *acini* and *ducts*. Two types of salivary acini are there — ***serous acini*** containing ***alpha amylase*** and the other is ***mucinous acini*** containing ***viscous secretion*** (e.g. mucoprotein). The acinar cells contain enzymes, mucoproteins and electrolytes at concentrations similar to those in plasma. The acinar cells secrete the initial salivary fluid consisting of electrolytes, mucus and enzymes. From the acinus, saliva passes to striated duct via intercalated duct. The serous secretion reaching the mouth is hypotonic when compared to plasma and has less $Na^+$ and $Cl^-$ but more $K^+$ than plasma. When the primary secretion passes through the ducts, $Na^+$ is actively reabsorbed accompanied by $Cl^-$, and less amount of $K^+$ is secreted. The striated ducts

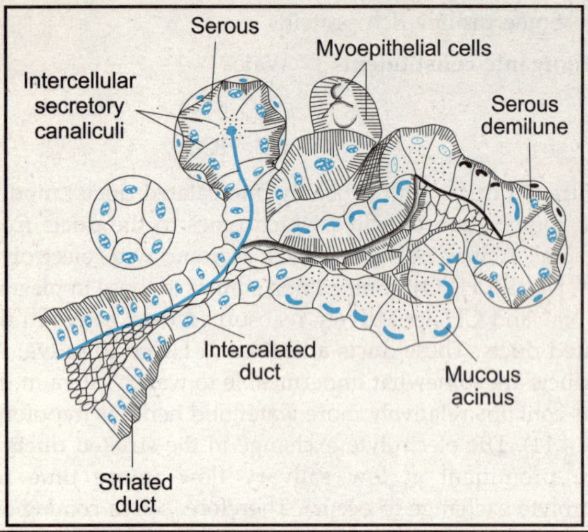


Fig. 4.9 : Structure of a salivary gland

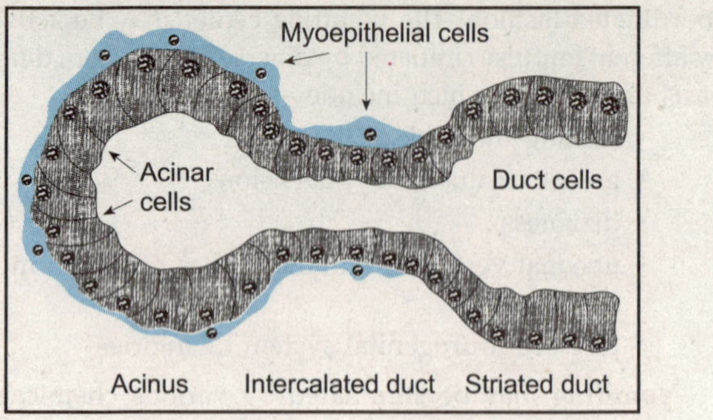


Fig. 4.11 : Functional histology of the salivon, the secretory unit of the salivery glands

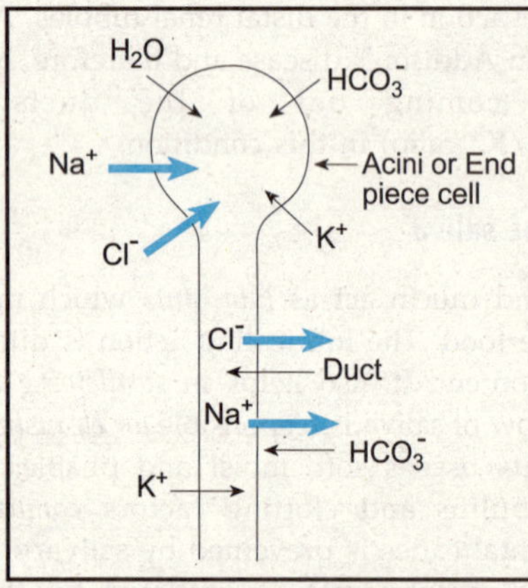


Fig. 4.10 : Movement of ions and water in the acinus and duct of a salivary gland

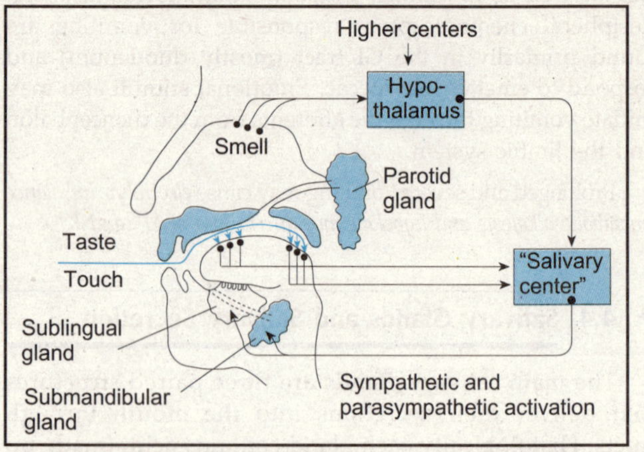


Fig. 4.12 : Reflex pathways in salivary secretion

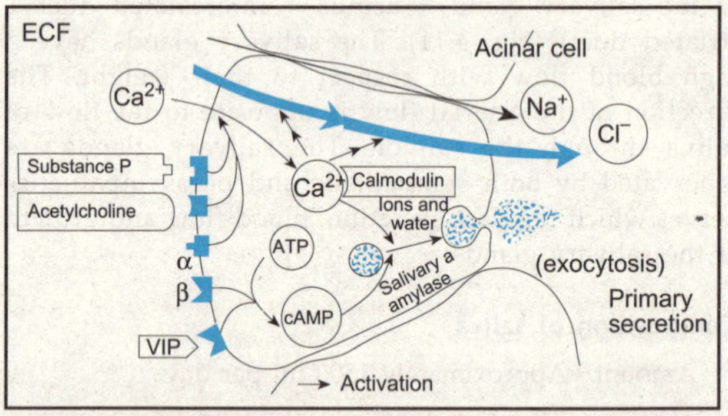


Fig. 4.13 : Control of formation of salivary secretion

change the electrolytic composition of the primary acinar secretion (see above).

### Control of salivary secretion (Figs. 4.12 and 4.13)

(a) **Autonomic nervous system reflexes** are responsible for regulation of salivary secretion. When there is **parasympathetic nerve stimulation,** there is secretion of large volume of watery fluid which is high in electrolytes but low in proteins. When there is *sympathetic nerve stimulation* there is less volume of fluid containing *high concentration of mucus.* Afferent sensory fibers carry information to salivary centers in the pons and medulla of the brain while efferent autonomic fibers supply the glands. Salivary centers receive impulses from higher centers of the brain. Sight, smell and thought of food cause salivation. Salivation is inhibited by sleep, fatigue, dehydration and fear. The intracellular effects of autonomic stimulation on secretory cells are regulated by the second **messengers cyclic adenosine monophosphate** (cAMP), **$Ca^{2+}$** and **diacylglycerol (DAG)**. *Acetylcholine* released by parasympathetic fibers initiate the secretion of electrolytes and water via $Ca^{2+}$ dependent process which is further initiated by **phosphoinositide system. Sympathetic system** increases enzyme secretion by stimulating β-adrenoceptors and causing elevation of cyclic adenosine monophosphate (cAMP) in cells.

(b) The stimulation of salivary output is a reflex response set off by taste, smell and touch receptors in the mouth as well as by chewing. Conditioned reflexes may also be involved.

(c) The secretion, metabolism, contraction of myoepithelial cells and growth of salivary glands are mediated by the parasympathetic system. **The parasympathetic mediator is ACh** which acts on muscarinic receptors → ↑formation of inositol triphosphate → ↑release of $Ca^{2+}$, **VIP** and **substance P** from neurons within salivary glands → ↑$Ca^{2+}$ release. The main sympathetic mediator is **norepinephrine** which binds to α-adrenergic receptors → formation of 3'5' cyclic monophosphate → protein phosphorylation and enzyme activation → ↑salivary secretion.

**Paralytic secretion :** When the sympathetic nerve to the salivery glands is cut—an increase in secretion of saliva occurs after 2 to 3 weeks. It stops after 6 weeks. This is known as Paralytic salivary secretion. It is due to increased sensitivity of the myoepithelial cells to circulating catcholamines, which results is an increase in the flow of saliva.

## 4.5 Gastrointestinal Hormones

**Gastrointestinal hormones** are peptides and are produced by ***enterochromaffin cells*** in the gastrointestinal mucosa. They regulate gastrointestinal motility and secretion. Gastrointestinal peptides can also be found in central and peripheral neurons. In those cases they act as neurotransmitters or neuromodulators.

Previously it was believed that all GI peptides were hormones. Now it is known that GI peptides can be hormones, or, paracrine or neurocrine effectors.

**Hormones** are released into the portal circulation → liver → all tissues of the body. **Paracrine** substances are released from endocrine cells within the mucosa → extracellular space → target cells. Histamine is a key agent in the stimulation of gastric acid secretion that acts in a paracrine fashion. **Neurocrine substances** are produced in the cell bodies of neurons → axonal ending → released by action potential → synaptic cleft → target cells. Acetylcholine is the best example of a neuroregulator in the GI tract. The **GI peptides** regulate water and electrolyte secretion, enzyme secretion from stomach, pancreas, liver and gut, contraction and relaxation of smooth muscles of stomach, small and large bowel, gall bladder and various sphincters. They also regulate insulin, glucagon and calcitonin secretion.

For a peptide to be a **GI hormone** it must satisfy the following criteria (a) must be produced in response to a physiologic stimulus; (b) the response should be specific, unequivocal and related to the hormone; (c) the substance must be isolated, purified, identified and synthesized chemically.

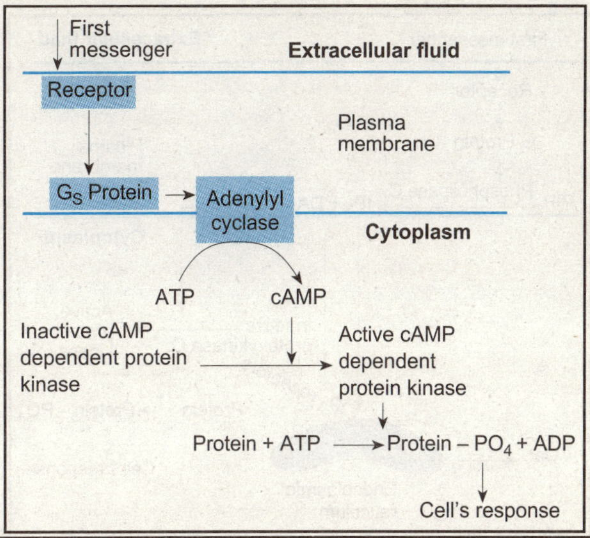


**Fig. 4.14 :** G protein mediated signal transduction

**Candidate hormones** are those located in endocrine cells of the GI tract, which for one reason or another, have failed to satisfy one of the above criteria of GI hormones.

### History of GI hormones

Edkins, in 1905, discovered Gastrin. The existence of gastrin was controversial for about 45 years due to the presence of histamine in large quantities in the gastric mucosa. In 1938, Komaror showed that gastrin was a peptide different from histamine. The word 'hormone' was first coined by W.B. Hardy and used by Starling in 1905. In 1928 Ivy and Oldberg showed that fat in the duodenum stimulated gall bladder contraction. In 1943, Harper and Raper showed that a hormone released from the mucosa of the small intestine stimulates pancreatic enzyme secretion – they called it pancreozymin. In 1969, Brown described GIP in intestinal mucosa. In early 1970, Brown and his co-workers described motilin found mainly in proximal small intestine.

**Gastrointestinal hormones** are proteins synthesized and released primarily by ***enteroendocrine cells*** which line the gut. Gastrointestinal hormones are generally released into the blood stream and the effect is at some distant place, usually another organ in the gastrointestinal system. There are other proteins described as gastrointestinal peptides and their mode of action is **paracrine** or **neurocrine**. Generally gastrointestinal hormones and peptides bind to receptors and act via two possible signal transduction mechanisms — (i) *G proteins* and (ii) *activation of $Ca^{2+}$ channels.*

(i) **G proteins (see Fig. 4.14)**

(ii) **Activation of $Ca^{2+}$ channels (see Fig. 4.15)**

The **gastrointestinal hormones and peptides** are classified in two groups : **(a) Cholecystokinin (CCK)/Gastrin family; (b) Secretin family.**

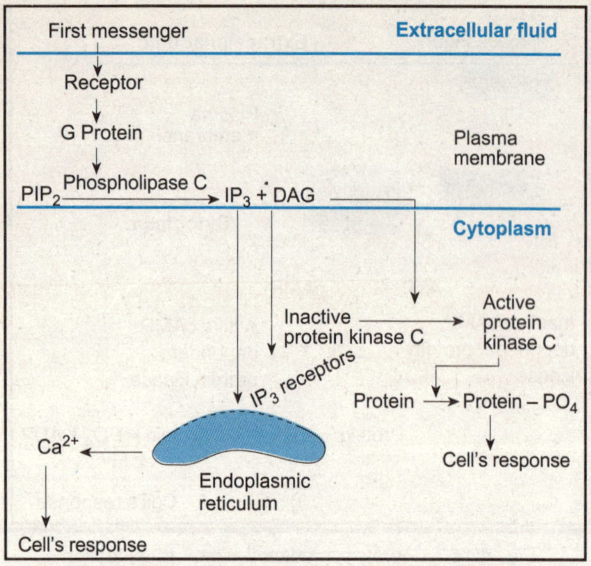


**Fig. 4.15 :** Signal transduction by activation of $Ca^{2+}$ channels. $PIP_2$ = Phosphatidylinositol biphosphate; IP3 = Inositoltriphosphate

**Cholecystokinin and gastrin** share identical carboxy–terminal sequence but unique amino-terminal sequences. Preprogastrin (the precursor) is synthesized by G cells in gastric antrum. The **secretin family** comprises ***secretin, vasoactive intestinal peptide* (VIP), *gastric inhibitory peptide (GIP), enteroglucagon* and *growth hormone releasing factor.***

| Functions of gut peptide neurotransmitters | |
|---|---|
| ***VIP*** | Concerned with smooth muscle relaxation<br>Regulate the peristaltic reflex<br>Regulate intestinal blood flow<br>Transport of ions |
| ***Bombesin (GRP)*** | Regulate smooth muscle contraction<br>Regulate gastric secretion |
| ***Tachykinins*** | Smooth muscle contraction<br>Regulate peristaltic reflex |
| ***Opioids*** | Modulate the activity of VIP<br>Regulate peristaltic reflex<br>Inhibit the secretions of the intestine |
| ***Somatostatin*** | Modulate VIP release in myenteric plexus<br>Control peristaltic reflex<br>Regulation of water balance in intestine |

The principal action of gastric hormones is on the motility and secretion of the digestive system. Gastrin, CCK, secretin and GIP are likely to stimulate the release of insulin. It is also believed that GI hormones play an important trophic effect on the target glands, e.g., CCK accelerates the growth of acinar cells in the pancreas while the growth of gastric mucosa is stimulated by gastrin.

**Gastrin** : Gastrin is secreted by G cells in the mucosa of the gastric antrum. Gastrin secreting cells are found in the islets of the pancreas in fetal life. Interestingly, gastrinomas (tumor of gastrin-secreting cells) commonly occur in pancreas.

Structurally, gastrin is a polypeptide with various numbers of amino acid residues in it. The preprogastrin is the gastrin precursor molecule which is processed to produce at least three major types of gastrin-G34, G17 and G14-containing 34, 17 and 14 amino acid residues respectively.

Gastrin has been demonstrated to have various actions in experimental conditions but the functions of gastrin which appear to be physiologically important are —

- Stimulation of gastric acid and pepsin secretion
- Trophic action (stimulation of growth) on the gastric and intestinal mucosa.
- Stimulation of gastric motility.

Function of gastrin found in the pituitary gland, and central and peripheral nervous systems is not known.

Secretion of gastrin in the G.I. tract is regulated by the contents of the stomach, vagal activity and humoral (blood-borne) factors. Gastrin secretion is increased by gastric distension and the presence of products of protein digestion (particularly amino acids like phenylalanine and tryptophan) in the stomach. Vagal activity stimulates gastrin production by secretion of a neurotransmitter-gastrin-releasing peptide (GRP)-at postganglionic vagal fibers innervating the G.cells.

The inhibitory effect of acid in the gastric antrum on gastrin secretion may occur by either of the two mechanisms-(a) by direct action of acid on G cells, and (b) by release of somatostatin from interneurons of the ENS which is an inhibitor of gastrin secretion. This is an example of negative feedback control.

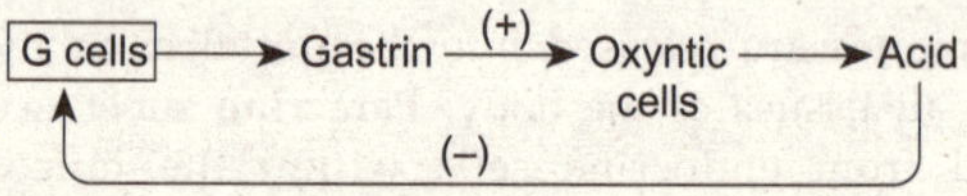


Therefore, hyperchlorhydria (excessive gastric acid secretion) is usually associated with hypogastrinemia (low serum levels of gastrin) whereas hypochlorhydria or achlorhydria (low or absent gastric acid secretion) is usually associated with hypergastrinemia (high serum levels of gastrin). However, patients with gastrinomas have both hyperchlorhydria and hypergastrinemia because excessive gastrin secretion is the reason for hyperchlorhydria in these patients.

**Factors causing increased gastrin/secretion -**

| | |
|---|---|
| Luminal factors — | Gastric distension/Peptides/ amino acids in stomach |
| Neural factor — | Increased vagal discharge, Blood bone factors, Epinephrine, calcium |

Factors causing inhibition of gastrin secretion—

Luminal factors — Acid, Somatostatin (from interneurons of the ENS)

Blood-borne factors — Secretin, GIP, VIP, Glucagon, Calcitonin.

CCK also has structural heterogeneity like that of gastrin. Processing of prepro-CCK may give rise to CCK with different numbers of amino acids residues- CCK 4, CCK 8, CCK 12, CCK 33 and CCK 58. CCK secreted in the intestine mainly consists of CCK 8 and CCK 12. In the brain, CCK 8 and CCK 58 are mainly present.

The **principal physiologic actions of CCK are :**

- Contraction of gall bladder
- Relaxation of sphincter of Oddi thus helping in passage of bile into the intestine following food intake especially food rich in fat
- Secretion of enzyme-rich juice from pancreas
- Augmentation of the action of secretin in producing $HCO_3^-$-rich pancreatic secretion.
- Inhibition of gastric emptying
- Trophic action on pancreas
- Increase in secretion of enterokinase.

Two types of CCK receptors have been identified-CCK-A and CCK-B. Both are found in the brain whereas peripheral CCK receptors are mainly CCK-A receptors.

CCK secretion is stimulated by the presence of products of digestion (particularly peptides, amino acids and fatty acids with more than 10 carbon atoms) in the upper part of the intestine. The amount of these products of digestion increase in the upper intestine as digestion proceeds resulting in a positive feedback loop for secretion of CCK. Secretion of CCK decreases when the products of digestion move distally.

*Secretin* : It is ***produced from S cells*** of the mucosa lining the duodenum and jejunum. Its secretion is stimulated by increased acidity of the chyme and also by protein digestion products in the duodenum and jejunum. ***It acts directly on the cells and indirectly via local nerve reflexes.*** Secretin contains 27 amino acids. Out of these, 14 occupy the same position as in glucagon. It is transported in blood. Duct cells in the pancreas and liver are stimulated by secretin via cAMP $\rightarrow$ volume of $HCO_3^-$ is increased by potentiation of the effects of CCK and ACh via the effects of phosphoinositide system and $Ca^{2+}$. Secretin inhibits gastric acid secretion by acting directly on parietal cells and thereby inhibiting release of gastrin. It also stimulates the growth of acinar cells and pepsinogen secretion.

*GIP* : It contains 9 amino acids. It has got some structural similarity with secretin. ***GIP is produced by K cells in the mucosal lining of the duodenum and upper intestine.*** Release of GIP in the blood is stimulated by fat, amino acids and glucose present in the upper small intestine. Principally, it releases insulin from β-cells of islets of Langerhans of the pancreas. Gastric acid secretion and gastric motility can be inhibited by GIP but these effects appear to be physiologically unimportant. GIP is the only hormone which is released by all the three major food-stuffs.

*Enteroglucagon* : It is **structurally similar** to glucagon. It is secreted **from L cells of the distal ileum and colon.** Presence of glucose and fats in the ileal lumen stimulate the release of enteroglucagon. It inhibits gastric and intestinal motility. It may also inhibit gastric secretion and emptying. Some A-cells (like these in pancreatic islets) found in the mucosa of stomach and duodenum secrete glucagon.

*Somatostatin* : It is **produced by D cells in the intestinal epithelium** and in **the pancreatic islets**. The release of somatostatin is stimulated by the presence of fats, glucose and bile salts in the lumen of the intestine. It inhibits release of gastrin, enzymes of pancreas, glucagon and insulin. It acts as a paracrine agent.

*Neurotensin* : ***Produced by N cells found in the mucosa lining the ileum.*** Release of neurotensin is enhanced by presence of fat. It also regulates gastric motility. It inhibits motility of G.I. tract. Ileal blood flow is increased by neurotensin.

*Pancreatic polypeptide* : *Synthesized by F cells of the **islets of Langerhans of pancreas.*** Protein meals stimulate pancreatic polypeptide secretion in the blood. It is responsible for inhibition of pancreatic enzyme and bicarbonate secretion.

*Motilin* : It is ***produced by M cells located in the mucus lining of duodenum.*** Presence of fat and acid in the duodenum **stimulates motilin** release. It stimulates gastric emptying. Motilin is released approximately every 90 minutes during fasting and is responsible for the migrating motility complex.

*Peptide YY* : Peptide YY is present in ileal and colonic mucosa. It ***inhibits neural stimulation of the stomach.*** It does not inhibit gastrin or histamine release.

*Histamine* : It is not a peptide and is present throughout the mucosa in endocrine-like cells. When histamine is released, it ***stimulates the gastric parietal cells to secrete acid.*** Histamine augments the effecs of gastrin and acetylcholine on acid secretion.

*Vasoactive intestinal peptide (VIP)* : It belongs to the member of secretin-glucagon family. ***It is present in nerves and responsible for GI smooth muscle relaxation.*** It inhibits gastric secretion but stimulates pancreatic fluid and bicarbonate secretion. VIP secreting tumors (VIPomas) can cause severe diarrhea.

*Bombesin or gastrin-releasing peptide* : It was first isolated from the skin of a frog but, in mammals, ***bombesin is GRP which is present in the nerves of the gastric mucosa.*** It is released by vagal stimulation.

*Enkephalins* : They are present in the nerves of mucosa and smooth muscles of GI tract. They are ***responsible for smooth muscle contraction*** and may have some role in peristalsis.

**Table 4.2 (a)**
**Summary of the gastrointestinal hormones**

| *GI hormones* | *Functions* |
|---|---|
| **Gastrin** G-cells in the gastric antrum. | (a) HCl secretion ↑; (b) Pepsinogen secretion ↑; (c) IF secretion ↑; (d) Growth of gastric mucosa ↑. |
| **CCK** I-cells lined in the duodenum and jejunum | (a) It stimulates the secretion of pancreatic digestive enzymes; (b) Contraction of gall bladder ↑; (c) It inhibits gastric emptying; (d) Growth of exocrine pancreas. |
| **Secretin** S-cells of duodenum and jejunum | (a) It stimulates $H_2O$ and $HCO^-$ secretion by pancreas and bile ducts; (b) It potentiates the action of CCK; (c) ↑ pepsin secretion; (d) Growth of exocrine pancreas. |
| **VIP** Neurons in the enteric nervous system and in the body | (a) It is responsible for secretion of ions, $H_2O$ and $HCO^-$ from intestine and pancreas; (b) It increases intestinal blood flow; (c) Relaxes GI smooth muscle |
| **GIP** K-cells in the small intestine | (a) It initiates insulin secretion; (b) It inhibits water and electrolyte absorption in the small intestine; (c) Inhibits gastric acid secretion; |
| **Somatostatin** • D-cells in intestine, • Neurons in the enteric system | (a) It inhibits HCl secretion in the stomach and decreased release of gastrin; (b) It inhibits enzyme secretion in the pancreas; (c) Decreases release of insulin and glucagon. |
| **Enteroglucagon** L-cells in distal ileum and colon | Gastric and intestinal motility are decreased |
| **Motilin** Duodenum, Jejunum | (a) It stimulates gastric motility; (b) It stimulates intestinal motility. (c) It is responsible for movement. |

**Table 4.2 (b)**
**Summary of the candidate (putative) gastrointestinal hormones**

| *Peptide* | *Functions* |
|---|---|
| **Pancreatic polypeptide** | Inhibits pancreatic bicarbonate and enzyme secretion |
| **Peptide YY** | Inhibits gastric emptying and secretion |
| **Glucagon-like peptide-I or enteroglucagon** | Stimulates insulin release. Inhibits gastric emptying and secretion |

**Table 4.2 (c)**
**Summary of the paracrine secretions**

| *Substance* | *Functions* |
|---|---|
| Somatostatin | Inhibition of gastric acid secretion, gastrin and other peptide hormones |
| Histamine | Stimulates gastric acid secretion |

**Table 4.2 (d)**
**Summary of the neurocrine secretions**

| *Peptide* | *Functions* |
|---|---|
| VIP (Vasoactive intestinal peptide) | ↑ Pancreatic secretion<br>↑ Intestinal secretion<br>Relaxes sphincters and gut circular muscle |
| Bombesin or GRP (Gastrin releasing peptide) | ↑ Gastrin release |
| Enkephalins | ↑ Smooth muscle contraction<br>Inhibition of intestinal secretion |

## 4.6 Stomach and Gastric Secretion

The **proximal part** of stomach may be considered as a reservoir of food and the **distal part** is involved in mixing and breakdown of food. Stomach secretes gastric juice which has four important components of physiological relevance-hydrochloric acid (HCl), pepsinogen, mucus and intrinsic factor (IF). HCl is necessary for activation of pepsinogen to pepsin, an important proteolytic enzyme. In addition, HCl is bacteriostatic. Therefore, most of the ingested bacteria are killed in stomach. Mucus forms a protective coating on the wall of the stomach and acts as lubricant. IF binds vitamin $B_{12}$ so that it can be absorbed from the ileum. It is essential for life.

### Functional anatomy of stomach (Fig. 4.16)

According to its secretory function, the stomach is divided into two regions. The proximal portion is ***acid secreting oxyntic gland mucosa*** and the distal portion contains **endocrine cells** which are responsible ***for synthesis and release of the hormone gastrin.*** The glands which are located in the gastric mucosa open into the pits in the mucosal surface. The pits of the oxyntic glands are shallow and covered with mucus or surface epithelial cells. The glands open at the bases of the pits. The **oxyntic glands** contain acid producing parietal or oxyntic cells and **chief or peptic cells** (secrete pepsinogen). **Pyloric glands** contain G cells and mucus cells. The pits of pyloric glands are much deeper than those of oxyntic glands (Fig. 4.18).

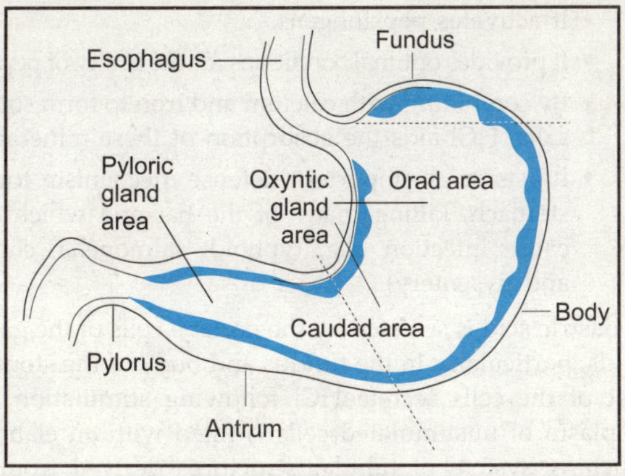


**Fig. 4.16 :** Anatomic and functional divisions of the stomach

In short,

(a) ***Fundus and body glands :***

(i) *mucus cells* — mucus

(ii) *parietal cells* — HCl, IF

(iii) *chief cells* — pepsinogen (see Fig. 4.17).

(b) ***Antral glands :***

(i) *mucus cells* — mucus

(ii) *G cells* — gastrin (see Fig. 4.19).

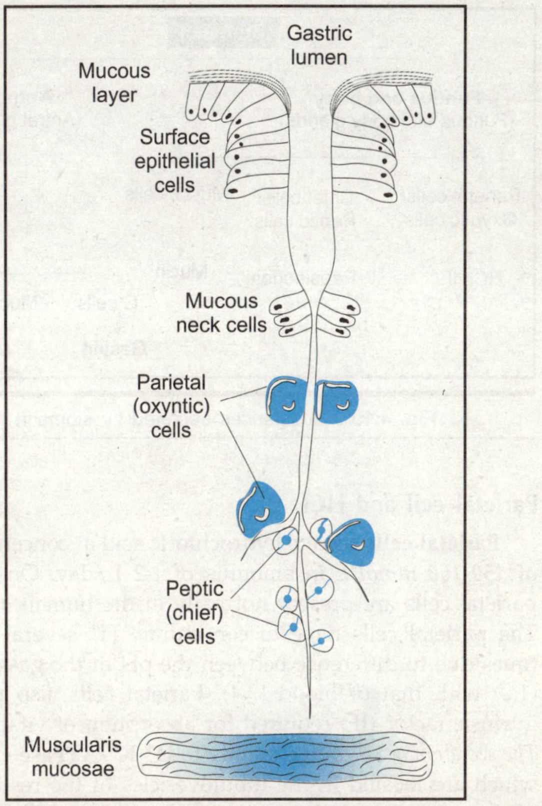


**Fig. 4.17 :** The position of the various cell types in gastric gland

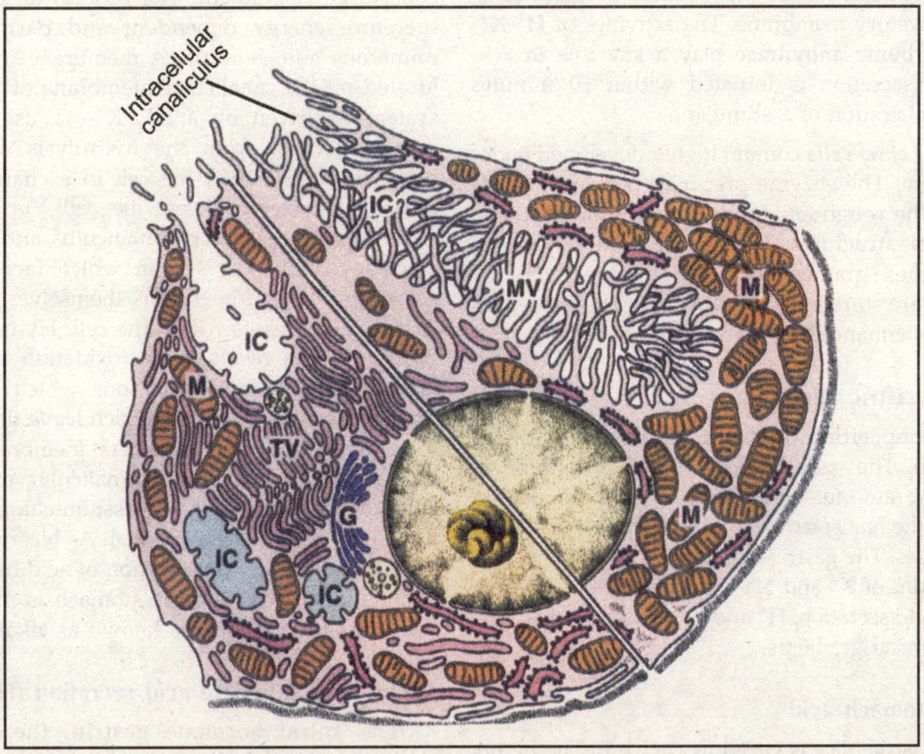


**Fig. 4.18 :** Composite diagram of a parietal cell, showing ultrastructural differences between a resting cell (Left) and an active cell (Right). Note that the tubulovesicles (TV) in the cytoplasm of the resting cell fuse to form microvilli (MV) that fill up the intracellular canaliculi (IC). G, Golgi complex; M, mitrochondria. (Based on the work of Ito S, Schofield GC. J Cell Biol 1974:63:364)

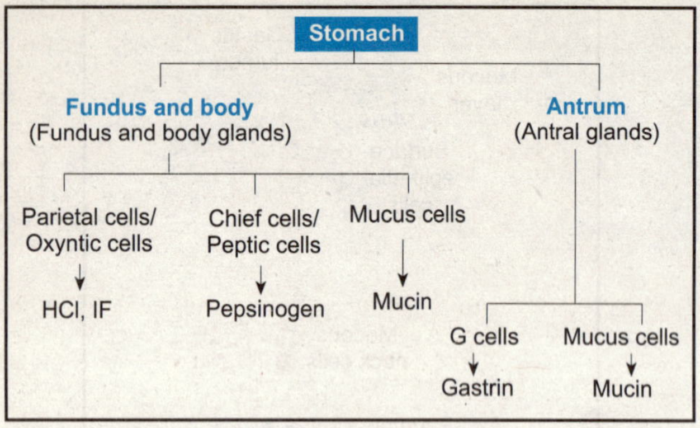


**Fig. 4.19 :** Substances secreted by stomach

## Parietal cell and HCl

**Parietal cells** secrete hydrochloric acid at concentrations of ***150-160 mmol/L*** in amounts of 1-2 L/day. One billion parietal cells are present normally in the human stomach. The parietal cells have to concentrate $H^+$ several million times due to difference between the pH of the gastric juice (1.0) with that of blood (7.4). Parietal cells also produce intrinsic factor (IF) required for absorption of vitamin $B_{12}$. *The secretion of* $H^+$ is due mainly to **$H^+$-$K^+$-ATPase enzymes** which are located in the tubulovesicles of the resting cell. The cytoplasm of the resting cell contains tubular and vesicular membranous structures — **tubulovesicles**. During the stimulation of secretion, $H^+$–$K^+$–ATPase is relocated to the apical or secretory membrane. The activities of **$H^+$-$K^+$-ATPase** and **carbonic anhydrase** play a key role in acid secretion. Acid secretion is initiated within 10 minutes following administration of a stimulant.

The ***peptic or chief cells*** contain highly developed endoplasmic reticulum. The enzyme precursor pepsinogens are synthesized in the rough endoplasmic reticulum → transported to Golgi structures → packaged into zymogen granules. Then these granules reach the apical region of the cell where they are stored in the cytoplasm. The exocytosis of pepsinogen is enhanced by a secretory stimulus.

## Electrolytes of gastric juice (Fig. 4.20)

The **ionic composition** of gastric juice varies with the rate of secretion. The gastric juice contains a solution of **NaCl** with some amount of **$H^+$** and **$K^+$** at *basal rates of secretion*. When the *rate of secretion increases*, $[Na^+]$ decreases and $[H^+]$ increases. The gastric juice primarily contains HCl with small amount of $K^+$ and $Na^+$ at peak rate of secretion. During gastric acid secretion, $H^+$ and $Cl^-$ are secreted against their electrochemical gradients.

## Formation of stomach acid

The pH of gastric juice is very low (pH 1-3). The highly acidic environment is important for several reasons :

- It helps in the breakdown of connective tissue and muscle fibers of ingested meat.
- It activates pepsinogens.
- It provides optimal conditions for the actiity of pepsins.
- By combining with calcium and iron to form soluble salts, HCl aids the absorption of these minerals.
- It acts as an important defense mechanism for the stomach, killing many of the bacteria which may cause infection (e.g. typhoid, salmonella, cholera and dysentery).

Gastric acid is secreted by the parietal cells of the gastric glands, particularly in the fundus and body of the stomach. Most of the cells secrete HCl following stimulation. The cytoplasm of unstimulated cells is filled with an elaborate branching system of tubular structures derived from the endoplasmic reticulum. These are lined by microvilli and possess the hydrogen ion secretory apparatus. When the parietal cells are stimulated to secrete (i.e. following a meal), the tubular structures fuse to form deep invaginations of the apical membrane known as secretory canaliculi. The formation of a canaliculus results in a large increase in the surface area of the parietal cell membrane and brings large number of hydrogen ion pumping sites into close proximity with the luminal fluid.

The metabolic steps involved in the production of acid by a parietal cell is shown in the figure 4.20.

Chloride ions are moved out of the cell against both a chemical and an electrical gradient. Hydrogen ions move down an electrical gradient but against a massive concentration gradient. The process of acid production is therefore energy dependent and parietal cells contain numerous mitochondria. A membrane transport system is located on the canalicular membrane of parietal cells. The system is driven by a $H^+$, $K^+$–ATPase pump and uses energy derived from the hydrolysis of ATP to pump hydrogen ions out of the cell in exchange for potassium ions. Chloride ions leave the cell Via — (i) a chloride channel in the secretory canaliculus and (ii) a potassium-chloride cotransport system which facilitates the exit of chloride. The hydrogen ions themselves are derived from oxidative processes within the cell. Hydroxyl ions are also produced as a result of this oxidation and with carbonic acid, generate bicarbonate ions which leave the cell in exchange for chloride ions which leave the cell in exchange for chloride ions at the basolateral membrane. These chloride ions leave the cell at the canalicular membrane via the chloride channel and the potassium-chloride co-transporter $K^+$ leaves the cell via a channel. As bicarbonate is added to the plasma during the secretion of acid by the stomach, the venous blood draining the stomach is more alkaline than the arterial blood. This is known as alkaline tide.

## Agents that stimulate acid secretion (Fig. 4.21)

The antral hormone **gastrin**, the parasympathetic mediator **acetylcholine** and paracrine agent **histamine** directly stimulate acid secretion from the parietal cells. These three main stimulants are known as **enterooxyntin**.

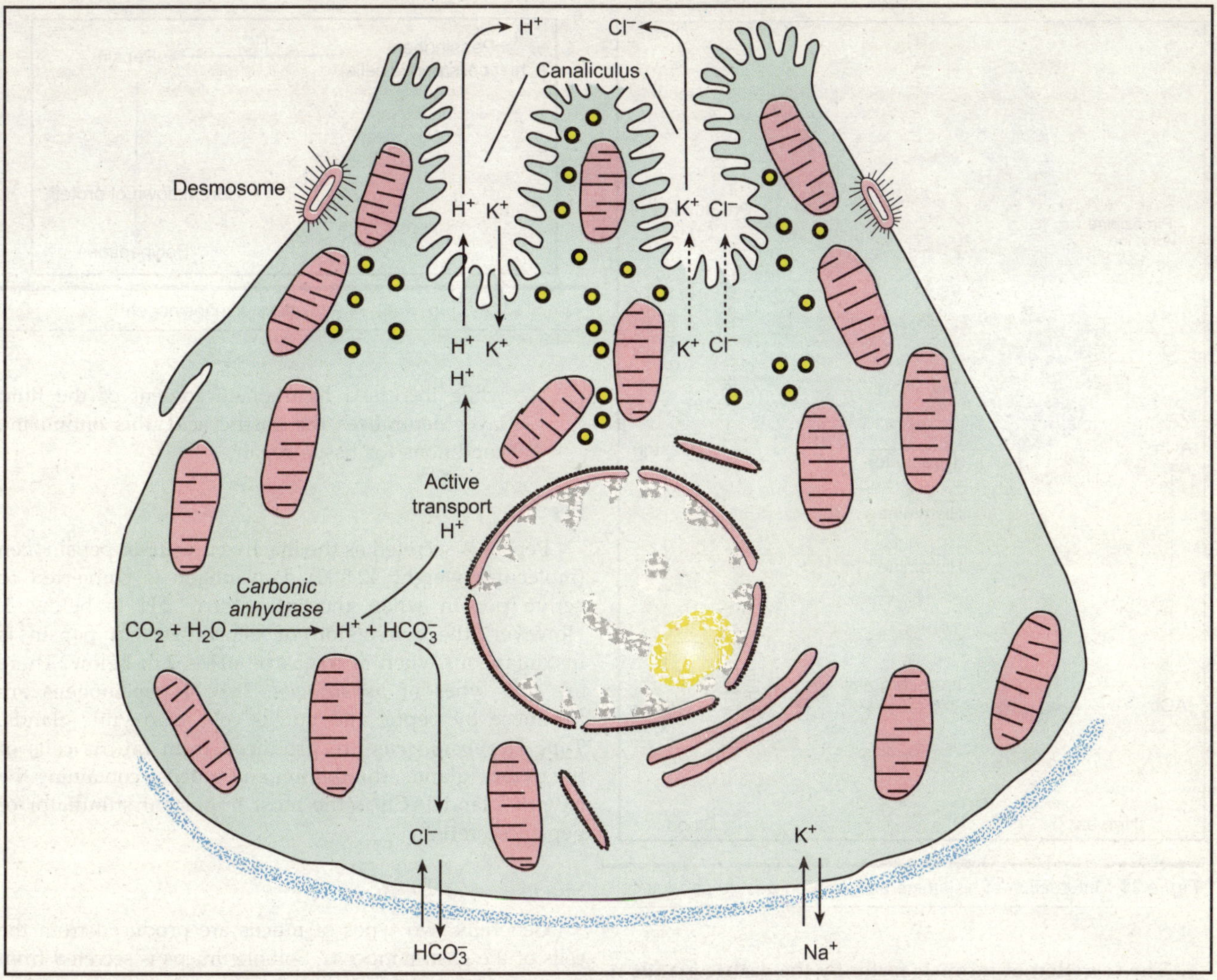


**Fig. 4.20 :** Diagram of a parietal cell, showing the main steps in the synthesis of hydrochloric acid. Active transport by ATPase is indicated by arrows and diffusion is indicated by dotted arrows. Under the action of carbonic anhydrase, blood $CO_2$ produces carbonic acid. Carbonic and dissociates into a bicarbonate ion and a proton $H^+$, which is pumped into the stomach lumen in exchange for $K^+$. A high concentration of intracellular $K^+$ is maintained by the $Na^+$, $K^+$ ATPase, while $HCO^-{}_3$ is exchanged for $Cl^-$ by an antiport. The tubulovesicles of the cell apex are seen to be related to hydrochloric acid secretion, because their number decreases after parietal cell stimulation. The bicarbonate ion returns to the blood is in responsible for a measurable increase in blood pH during digestion.

**Histamine** is produced from the ***enterochromaffin like*** (ECL) cells within the propria lamina and diffuses ***to parietal cells*** via ***extracellular fluid***. Histamine functions in a paracrine fashion to enhance the acid secretion.

The **ECL cells** have **gastrin** and **ACh receptors**. Gastrin stimulates release of histamine from ECL cells as well as histamine synthesis by enhancing the activity of histidine decarboxylase. ACh also stimulates the ECL cells.

The **parietal cell membrane** has got different receptors for **histamine, gastrin** and **ACh**. The final rate of secretion depends on the interactions of ***histamine, gastrin*** and ***acetylcholine.***

Histamine potentiates the action of gastrin and ACh at the oxyntic cell. Potentiation also occurs between gastrin and acetylcholine. The exact intracellular events resulting in potention are unknownThis is why antihistamines which block acid secretion stimulated by histamine ($H_2$ receptor blockers like cimetidine) also block the secretory responses to ACh and gastrin.

However atropine, the specific antagonist of muscarinic actions of ACh, blocks secretion stimulated by histamine and gastrin. Pirenzipine is a more specific antagonist of the $M_3$ muscarinic receptors.

**ACh** binds to the muscarinic receptor → formation of inositol triphosphate and accumulation of intracellular $Ca^{2+}$. **Histamine** binding enhances the action of adenylate cyclase → formation of cAMP. The second messenger for gastrin is not clear; $Ca^{2+}$ probably is involved.

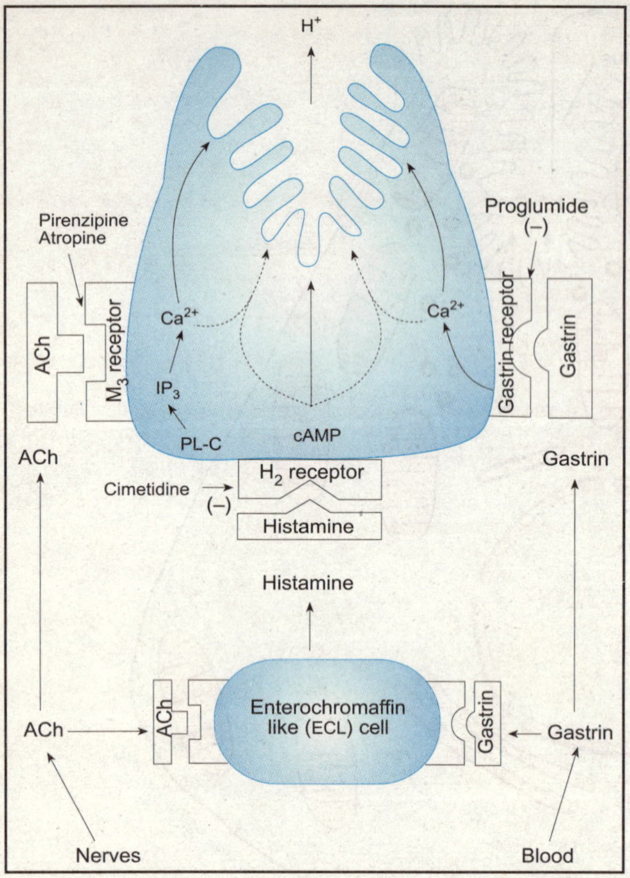


Fig. 4.21 : Interaction of histamine and ACh on gastric parietal cells

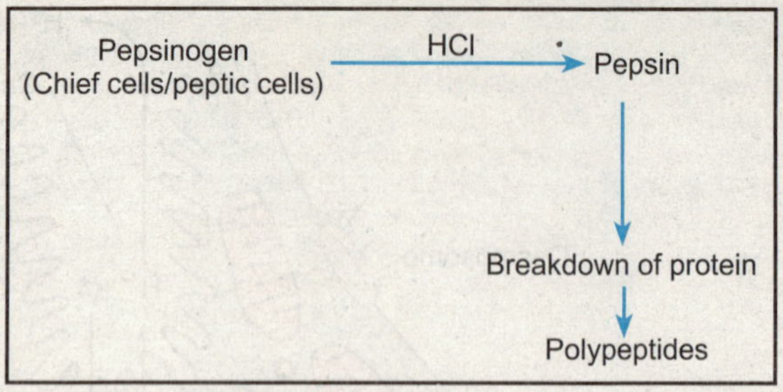


Fig. 4.22 : Activation of pepsinogen

**The secretion of intrinsic factor by the gastric glands :** The secretion of the glycoprotein intrinsic factor by the parietal cells of the stomach is essential for life. Intrinsic factor is secreted in response to the same stimuli which promote acid secretion. It binds to vitamin $B_{12}$ in food in the upper small intestine and protects it from the enzymatic actions of the gut. Vitamin $B_{12}$ is needed for the production of mature red blood cells and its absence results in pernicious anemia.

Gastric juice is corrosively acidic and contains proteolytic enzymes. Stomach creates a mucosal Barrier to protect itself.

- The tight junctions between the cells of the mucosal epithelium help to prevent the gastric juice from leaking into the underlying layers of tissue.
- Mucosa secreted by the surface epithelial cells and the neck cells of gastric glands adheres to the gastric mucosa and forms a protective layer.
- Prostaglandin E plays an important role inthe protection of gastric mucosa. It increases the thickness of the mucus gel layer, stimulates the production of bicarbonate, and causes vasodilatation of the vessels of the mucosa. This improves the supply of nutrients to any damaged areas of mucosa while increased bicarbonate content of the fluid layer neutralizes the gastric acid, this optimizing conditions for tissue repair.

## Pepsin

Pepsin is secreted as the inactive precursor pepsinogen (molecular weight 42,500). Pepsinogen is converted to active pepsin when the intragastric pH is below 5. However, the conversion of pepsinogen to pepsin is instantaneous when intragastric pH is 2 or below. There are two types of ***pepsinogen. Type I*** pepsinogens are produced by peptic and mucus cells of oxyntic glands. ***Type II pepsinogens*** are produced from mucus cells of the pyloric glands, duodenum and mucosa containing the oxyntic gland. ACh is the most important stimulator of pepsin secretion.

## Mucus

Generally two types of mucus are produced from the cells of the gastric mucosa. Soluble mucus is secreted from mucous neck cells due to stimulation of vagus nerve and acetylcholine. Soluble mucus mixes with different types of secretions of the glands and lubricates gastric chyme.

Visible mucus is secreted by mucus secreting cells thoughout the entire gastric mucosa. It forms a gel-like coat over the mucosa. Along with mucus, bicarbonate ($HCO^-_3$) ions are also secreted by there cells. These $HCO^-_3$ ions raise the pH of the mucus to about 7.

## Intrinsic factor

**Intrinsic factor** is produced by the **parietal cells.** It is a mucoprotein having a molecular weight of 55,000. It combines with dietary vitamin $B_{12}$ for the absorption of the vitamin by an active process. The ***absorption*** takes place in ***ileal mucosa.*** Pernicious anemia occurs when intrinsic factor is absent. This disease is manifested by achlorhydria and absence of parietal cells. The etiology of this disease is not clear but recent evidences suggest that autoimmunity may be responsible.

**Factors that inhibit gastric acid secretion :**

- **Luminal pH :** When pH of the lumen becomes 3 or less, gastrin secretion is inhibited.

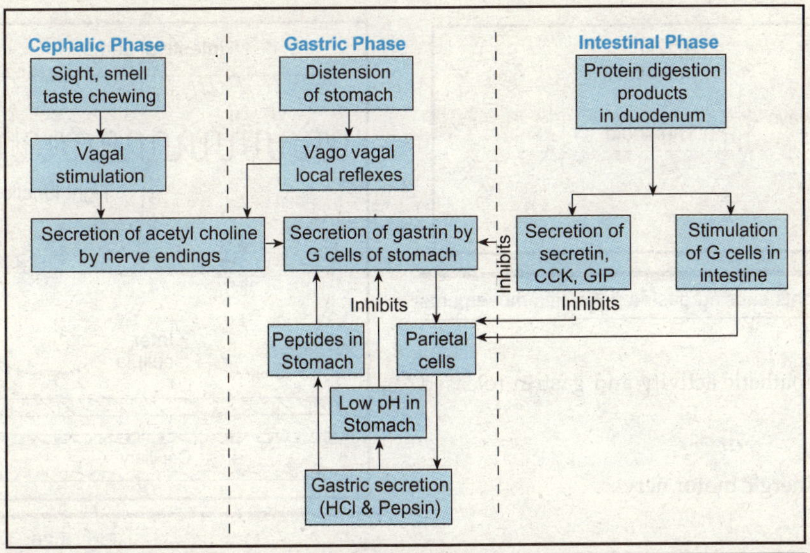


**Fig. 4.23 :** Regulation of gastric secretion during different phases of secretion.

- **Cholecystokinin :** Gastrin secretion is inhibited by CCK, secretion of which, in turn, is enhanced by presence of fat, protein or acid in small intestine.
- **Enterogastric reflex :** Vagal output to stomach is decreased by mechanical distension of small intestine.

## Gastric emptying

The rate at which the stomach empties is regulated by its contents and motility. Solid particles empty more slowly than liquids. The stomach contains about 1.5 L of solids, ingested liquids and gastric juice, which take 3 hours to empty into duodenum following a normal mixed meal.

Regulation of gastric emptying

When the stomach is distended and partially digested proteins are in the stomach.

↓

*Gastrin* is produced and gastric secretion is increased.

↓

*Gastric motility* is increased.

↓

*Gastric emptying* is stimulated.

Factors inhibiting gastric emptying are schematically represented in fig. 4.24.

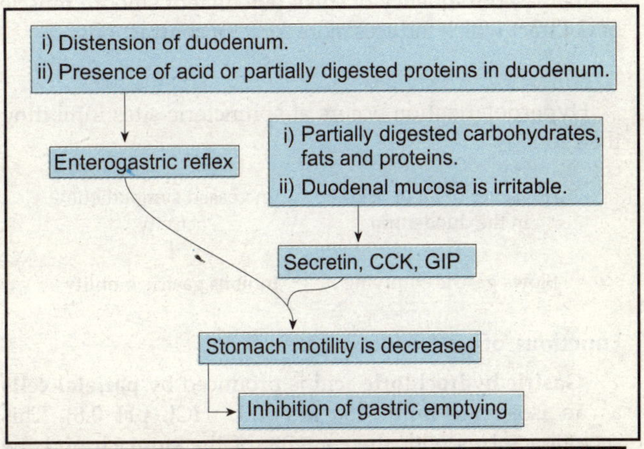


**Fig. 4.24 :** Inhibition of gastric emptying

## Gastric motility

*Continuous peristaltic waves* are generated at the distal stomach at the *rate of 3 per minute* and sweep along pyloric sphincter. These peristaltic waves become more powerful and the progress is more rapid when the contractions reach the antrum and pylorus. The pressure in the antrum may be 30 mm Hg or more. Movement of a peristaltic wave into the pyloric part of the stomach pushes a small quantity of chyme (1-2 ml of fluid containing small particles of food) into duodenum and remainder back into the antrum referred to as retropulsion.

## Control of gastric motility

The gastric motility is regulated by myogenic, neural and hormonal mechanisms. The contraction rate is about 3 per minute in the distal stomach. The coordination of contraction depends upon the slow wave of depolarization throughout smooth muscle layers. The rhythmic depolarization is known as **basic electrical rhythm** (Fig. 4.25).

The *slow waves* are normally *larger in amplitude* and *spikes are smaller than in small intestine*. The ionic basis of the slow waves is not clear. It is supposed to be due to electrogenic pump and permeability changes of the plasma membrane of the smooth muscles. The force of gastric contractions is regulated by the following :

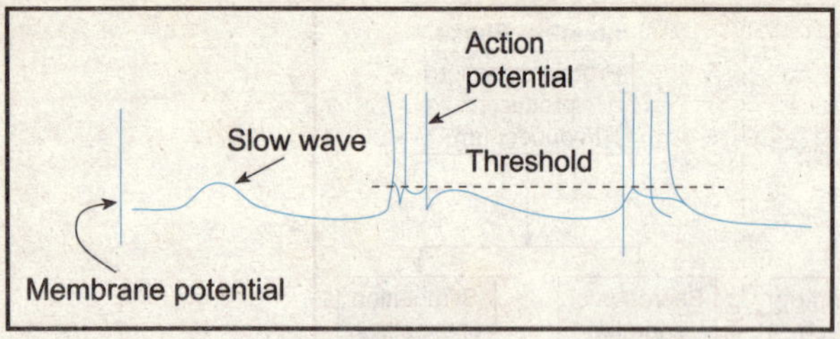


Fig. 4.25 : Electrical events causing gastric peristaltic movements

Increased parasympathetic activity and gastrin released from antral mucosa

*or*

Stimulation of cholinergic motor nerves.

↓

Decreased membrane potential of smooth muscle cell.

↓

Increased frequency of spike potential of smooth muscle of G I tract which induces more forceful contractions.

↓

Hyperpolarization occurs at sphincteric sites inhibiting their tone

| Presence of fat or acid in the duodenum | Increased sympathetic activity |
|---|---|
| ↓ | ↓ |
| Slows gastric emptying | Inhibits gastric motility |

### Functions of gastric secretions

**Gastric hydrochloric acid** is produced by **parietal cells** as an isosmotic fluid (150 mmol/L. HCl, pH 0.8). This secretion mixes with the contents of the stomach and the final acid concentration of gastric contents becomes lower. This acid environment is necessary for the activation of gastric proteolytic enzymes. The pepsin has got maximum proteolytic activity between pH 2 and 3.

Mucus is produced from the mucus cells of the stomach which forms a viscid unstirred layer on the surface of the epithelial cells which trap $HCO^-_3$ ions. Intrinsic factor is an essential component of gastric juice. It is a heat labile glycoprotein (molecular weight 60,000) which is responsible for absorption of vitamin $B_{12}$ (extrinsic factor) in the ileum. The amount of intrinsic factor produced in 24 hours is enough to bind 50-200 mg of vitamin $B_{12}$.

It is important to note that gastric mucosa is normally not irritated or digested by acid and pepsin present in gastric juice because of the following reasons —

- Mucus secreted by stomach forms a flexible gel coating the gastric mucous membrane.
- Some of the mucus-secreting cells (surface mucus cells) also secrete $HCO_3^-$, which is trapped within the mucus gel increasing the pH near the epithelial cells to 6-7.
- The luminal membranes of gastric mucosal cells and the tight junction between these cells form a physical barrier to acidpeptic digestion.
- Recently identified trefoil peptides may also have some role.

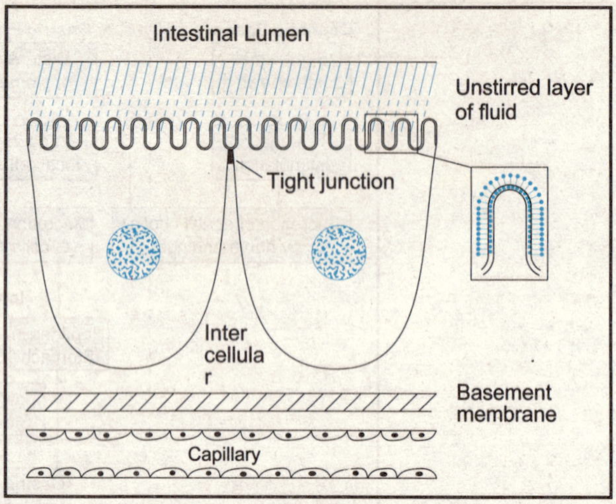


Fig. 4.26

Ethanol, vinegar, bile salts and nonsteroidal anti-inflammatory drugs (NSAIDs) like aspirin tend to damage the gastric mucosal barrier and may cause peptic ulcer. Prostaglandins have a protective role because they stimulate mucus secretion and inhibit acid secretion. NSAIDs inhibit prostaglandin synthesis. Misoprostol, a synthetic prostaglandin analogue, when coadministered with NSAIDs has been found to protect the gastric mucosa from acid-peptic digestion.

## ➤ 4.7 Pancreas and Pancreatic Secretion

The exocrine secretion of the *uman* pancreas (100 gm) is ***approximately 1,000 ml*** which is poured into the duodenum daily. The pH of pancreatic secretion is 6.7-9.0. The basic secretory unit of exocrine pancreas, like salivary glands, is composed of acini and ducts. The acinar cells secrete digestive enzymes for digestion of proteins, carbohydrates, fat and nucleic acid. Centroacinar cells and small ductule cells secrete $HCO_3^-$ and water.

Pancreatic exocrine secretion has got two components — ***an aqueous or bicarbonate component and an enzymatic or protein component. Aqueous component*** is composed mainly of water and $NaHCO_3$ and is secreted by the cells lining the pancreatic ducts. *The function of the aqueous component* is to neutralize the duodenal contents, prevent injury of the duodenal mucosa and maintain the pH range necessary for enzymatic digestion of nutrients. The **enzymatic** or **protein component** is a low volume secretion

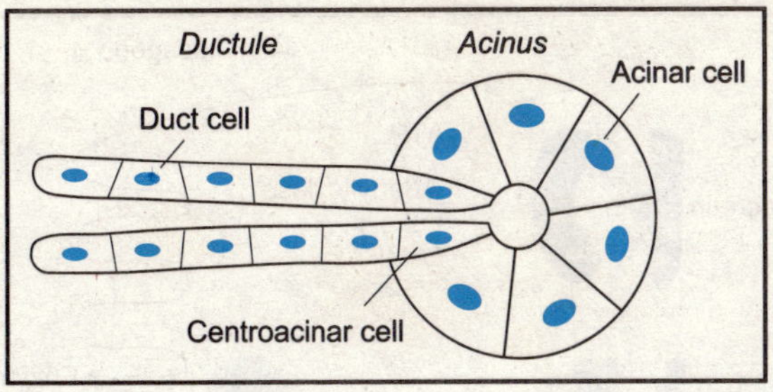


**Fig. 4.27 :** Histology of a functional unit of pancreas

produced by the pancreatic acinar cells which contain enzymes for digestion of all food stuffs.

## Functional anatomy of pancreas (Fig. 4.27)

The structure of exocrine pancreas is like a cluster of grapes and its functional units are similar to that of salivary glands. The acinar cells are pyramidal with the apices toward the lumen to form an acinus. The groups of acini are separated by areolar tissue. The acinar cells form about 80% of the pancreas by volume. Ductule cells occupy about 4% of the gland along with centroacinar cells that secrete the aqueous component containing a large volume of water and $NaHCO_3$.

***The endocrine cells of the pancreas*** include only 2% of its mass and islets of Langerhans cells are distributed throughout the pancreatic parenchyma. The islets include both insulin-secreting ***β-cells*** and glucagon secreting ***α-cells.*** The islet also contains ***δ-cells*** (D-cells) that produce somatostatin (functions as paracrine) to inhibit the release of both insulin and glucagon. ***The pancreas (F-cells)*** produces **pancreatic polypeptide** (candidate hormone) which inhibits pancreatic exocrine secretion.

**Composition of pancreatic secretion**

(a) Isoosmotic $Cl^-$ secretion by acinar cells;

(b) Isoosmotic $HCO_3^-$;

(c) $Cl^-$ and $HCO_3^-$.

Pancreatic secretion varies between 40 mmol/L of $HCO_3^-$ and 110 mmol/L of $Cl^-$ under basal conditions to 120 mmol/L of $HCO_3^-$ and 30 mmol/L of $Cl^-$ at high flow rate.

***Aqueous component of pancreatic secretion*** : The aqueous component is produced by the ductule and centroacinar cells and contain $HCO_3^-$ at a concentration equal to several times its concentration in plasma. $HCO_3^-$ is produced against both its chemical and electrical gradients as the lumen of the pancreatic ducts is 5-9 mV negative with respect to the blood.

The relationship between the principal ions in pancreatic juice is represented in Fig. 4.28.

The enzymes are produced in the acinar cells as precursors and stored in these zymogen granules. CCK

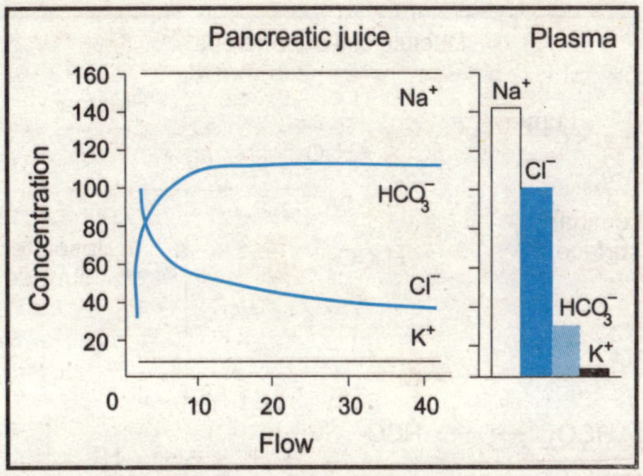


**Fig. 4.28 :** The principal ions in pancreatic juice

activates the release of granules and enhances the rate of synthesis of new proenzymes. This primary secretion is modified in the duct due to influence of secretin. CCK and Secretin concentrations control enzyme and bicarbonate.

## Pancreatic enzymes

The pancreatic enzymes are ***trypsinogen, chymotrypsinogen, procarboxypeptidase A, procarboxypeptidase B, elastase, lipase, phospholipase A, α-amylase, cholesterol ester hydrolase, ribonuclease and deoxyribonuclease.*** Pancreatic enzyme secretion increases abruptly after the chyme enters the duodenum.

## Mechanism of $HCO_3^-$ secretion by pancreatic ductule cells (Figs. 4.29 and 4.30)

Carbonic acid is produced from $CO_2$ and $H_2O$ in presence of carbonic anhydrase. It is then dissociated into $H^+$ and $HCO_3^-$ at the luminal surface of the ductule cells of the

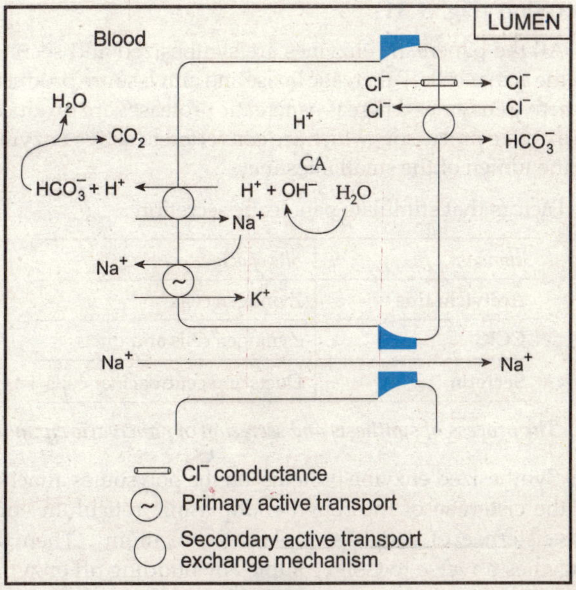


**Fig. 4.29 :** The cellular mechanism for the secretion of $HCO_3^-$ by pancreatic ductule cells. CA = Carbonic anhydrase

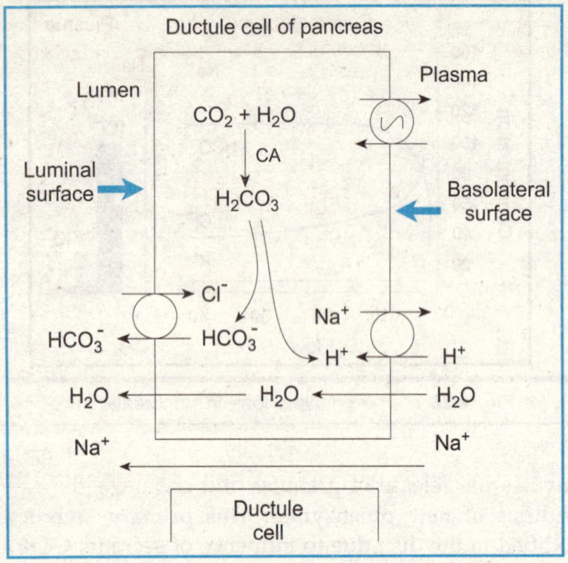


Fig. 4.30 : Proposed mechanism for secretion of electrolytes by cells of pancreatic ductules

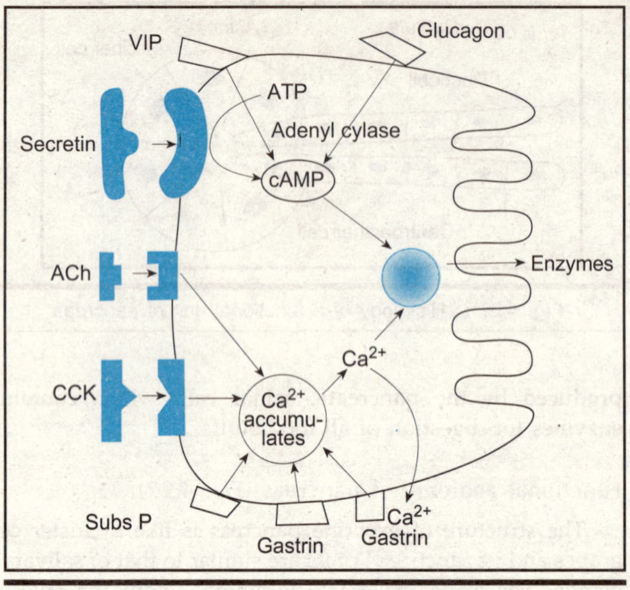


Fig. 4.31 : Potentiation of enzyme secretion from pancreatic acinar cells

pancreas. $HCO_3^-$ is exchanged for $Cl^-$ and $Na^+$ is exchanged for $H^+$ at the basolateral surface due to the generation of gradient by $Na^+$-$K^+$-ATPase at basolateral membrane. There is some evidence that a $H^+$-ATPase may actually pump $H^+$ out of the cell. Much of the $Na^+$ diffuses via intercellular (or paracellular) pathways. Water passes into the lumen along its osmotic gradient. The rate of $HCO_3^-$ secretion depends on luminal $Cl^-$ and the activity of $Cl^-$ channel in the apical membrane. This conductance is regulated by cAMP.

## Enzymic component of pancreatic secretion (Fig. 4.31)

All the pancreatic enzymes are synthesized and secreted by the acinar cells. Pancreatic lipase and amylase are produced as active enzymes whereas pancreatic proteases are produced as inactive precursors which are converted to active enzymes in the lumen of the small intestine.

Factors that stimulate pancreatic secretion :

| *Stimulant* | *Site of action* |
|---|---|
| **Acetylcholine** | Zymogen cells |
| **CCK** | Zymogen cells and ducts |
| **Secretin** | Ducts and centroacinar cells |

***The process of synthesis and secretion of pancreatic enzymes.***

Synthesized enzyme proteins on the polysomes attached to the cisternae of the rough endoplasmic reticulum enter the cisternae of rough endoplasmic reticulum . Then the enzymes traverse to Golgi complex by budding off enzyme-containing transition elements from RER → transported to condensing vacuoles where they form zymogen granules. The enzymes are collected in the zymogen granules until a secretory stimulus triggers their expulsion into the lumen of the acinus.

## Regulation of secretion (Fig. 4.32 & Fig. 4.33)

The secretion of the aqueous component (fluid and bicarbonate) is controlled by the amount of acid entering the duodenum. ***The main agents*** which are responsible for stimulation of the pancreatic cells are ***secretin, CCK*** and ***acetyl-choline*** acting via vagovagal reflexes. Pancreatic secretions are controlled by neural and hormonal regulation.

### Cephalic phase

Vagal efferents to the pancreas release acetylcholine at both ductule and acinar cells. This results in the production of a low volume of secretion with high enzyme content. The

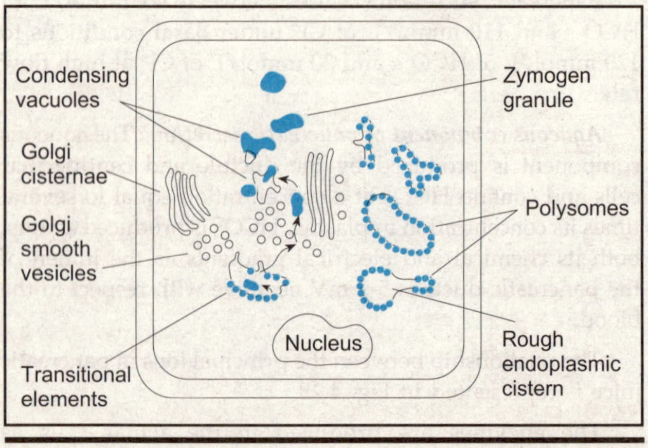


Fig. 4.32 : Synthesis and secretion of enzymes

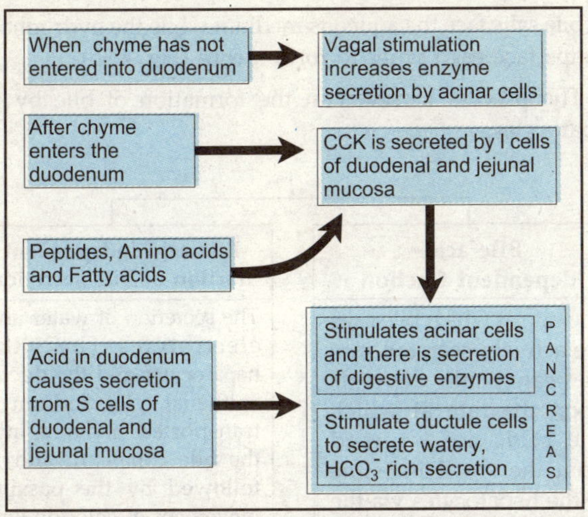


**Fig. 4.33 :** Control of pancreatic secretion

pancreatic secretion due to cephalic phase is about 20% of the total amount.

**Gastric phase** : When proximal or distal regions of the stomach is distended, there is stimulation of pancreatic secretion by initiating vagovagal reflexes which are mediated by Acetylcholine and Secretin. The percentage of pancreatic secretion due to gastric phase is small and is only 5% to 10% of the total volume.

**Intestinal phase** : Acid releases secretin from S cells of duodenal mucosa. Secretin is responsible for stimulation of the aqueous component. CCK from duodenal I cells is released due to fat and protein digestion. CCK is the main humoral stimulant for enzymatic component. Further enzymatic component is stimulated by acid, fatty acids, peptides and amino acids.

***The mechanism of pancreatic secretion during intestinal phase is as follows :***

Glycylphenylalanine, glycyltryptophan, phenylalanylglycine are the effective releasers of CCK. Lauric, palmitic, stearic and oleic acids also help release of CCK.

***Secretin*** binds with membrane receptors resulting in increase in cAMP formation. ***Acetylcholine*** binds with differ-ent membrane receptors and increases the formation of inositol triphosphate which, in turn, moblizes $Ca^{2+}$ from intracellular stores. *CCK* binds with different distinct receptors and increases intracellular free $Ca^{2+}$ through the inositol triphosphate pathway. Interaction between secretin and acetylcholine or secretin and CCK results in potentiation. The mechanism of the interaction is not clear.

**VIP** and **glucagon** also increase cAMP levels in the acinar cells. **Substance P, GRP** and **gastrin** increase $Ca^{2+}$ levels in acinar cells.

## 4.8 LIVER

- The **key role of liver in digestion** is the secretion of bile. Bile salts are essential for the digestion and absorption of fat and fat soluble vitamins.
- The liver plays a vital role in the **maintenance of normal plasma glucose level**. It stores glycogen when plasma glucose levels are high and releases glucose to the blood by glycogenolysis when plasma glucose is low. It can also synthesize glucose from non carbohydrate precursors (gluconeogenesis).
- The liver plays an important part in **the formation and destruction of red blood cells**. It removes the bilirubin formed by the breakdown of red cells and excretes it in the form of bile pigments.
- **Detoxification** — inactivation of hormones. Conjugation of various drugs and toxins for excretion, conversion of ammonia to urea.
- **Storage of vitamin $B_{12}$** — required for normal erythropoiesis.
- Steroid hormones including estrogens, progesterone, testosterone, glucocorticoids and aldosterone, are also **metabolized by** the liver.
- The hepatocytes manufacture the **majority of the plasma proteins** including clotting factors such as prothrombin, fibrinogen and Factors V, VII, IX and X. The liver is also involved in the catabolism of proteins and converts the ammonia formed by deamination of excess aminoacids to urea.

### Structure of the liver

The liver is composed of 50,000 and 1,00,000 lobules, separated by septa. These are hexagonal structures. Each lobule consists of a central vein which empties into the hepatic vein, from which single rows of hepatocytes radiate towards the surrounding layer of thin connective tissue. Bile canaliculi is located in between the hepatocytes. Portal triad (a branch of the hepatic artery, a branch of the portal vein, and a bile duct) is located at each of the six corners of a lobule (Fig. 4.34).

### The production of bile

The hepatocytes secrete a fluid known as **hepatic bile** into lobe canaliculi. It is an isotonic fluid with a pH between 7 and 8 that resembles plasma in its ionic composition. **Composition of hepatic bile :** bile salts, bile pigments, cholesterol, lecithin and mucus. When it passes along the bile ducts, the ductal epithelial cells modify this primary secretion by secreting a watery, bicarbonate rich fluid. This adds considerably to the volume of the bile so that overall the liver produces 500-1000 ml. of bile each day. The bile may be discharged continuously into the duodenum or stored in the gall bladder during which time its composition changes.

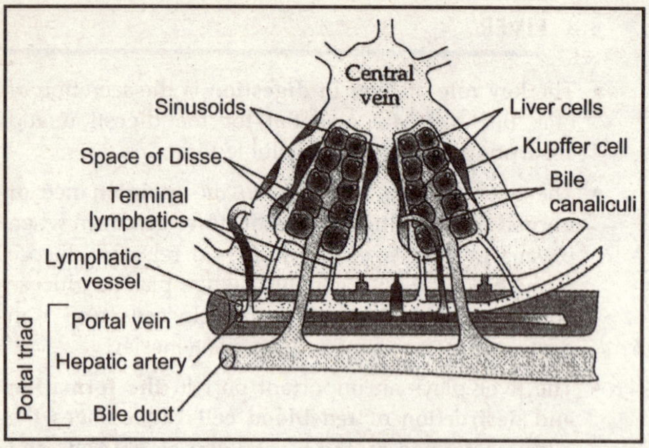


Fig. 4.34 : Histological structure of liver

## The chemical nature of bile acids and bile salts

The bile acids are derived from the metabolism of cholesterol. Cholic acid and chenodeoxycholic acid are formed in the hepatocytes themselves and are known as the ***primary bile acids***. In the intestine, the secondary bile acids, deoxycholic acid and lithocholic acid, are formed in small amounts from the primary acids by the *dehydroxylating action* of bacteria : The primary bile acids are conjugated to amino acids such as glycine and taurine in a complex with sodium, to form water soluble bile salts prior to secretion into bile.

Bile salts are amphipathic (have both hydrophobic and hydrophilic regions). The bile salts form aggregates called ***micelles*** when they reach a certain concentration in the bile. The micelles are organized so that the hydrophilic groups of the bile salts face the aqueous medium while the hydrophobic groups face each other to form a core (Fig. 4.35).

The process involved in the formation of bile by the hepatocytes.

| Bile acid-dependent fraction | Bile acid independent fraction of bile secretion |
|---|---|
| The rate at which bile salts are actively secreted into the canaliculi depends upon the rate at which bile acids are returned from the small intestine to the hepatocytes via the *enterohepatic circulation*. | The secretion of water and electrolytes by the hepatocytes and the ductal epithelial cells. Sodium is transported actively into the bile canaliculi and is followed by the passive movement of chloride ions and water. Bicarbonate ions are actively secreted into the bile by the ductal cells and are followed by the passive movement of sodium and water. |

## The Enterohepatic circulation

Bile salts (94%) which enter the intestine in the bile are reabsorbed into the portal circulation by active transport from the distal ileum. Most of the bile salts return to the liver unaltered and are recycled. Some are first deconjugated in the gut lumen and returned to the liver for reconjugation and recycling. A small number are deconjugated and then undergo modification by intestinal bacteria to secondary bile acids. Some of these, particularly lithocholic acid, are relatively insoluble and are excreted in the feces.

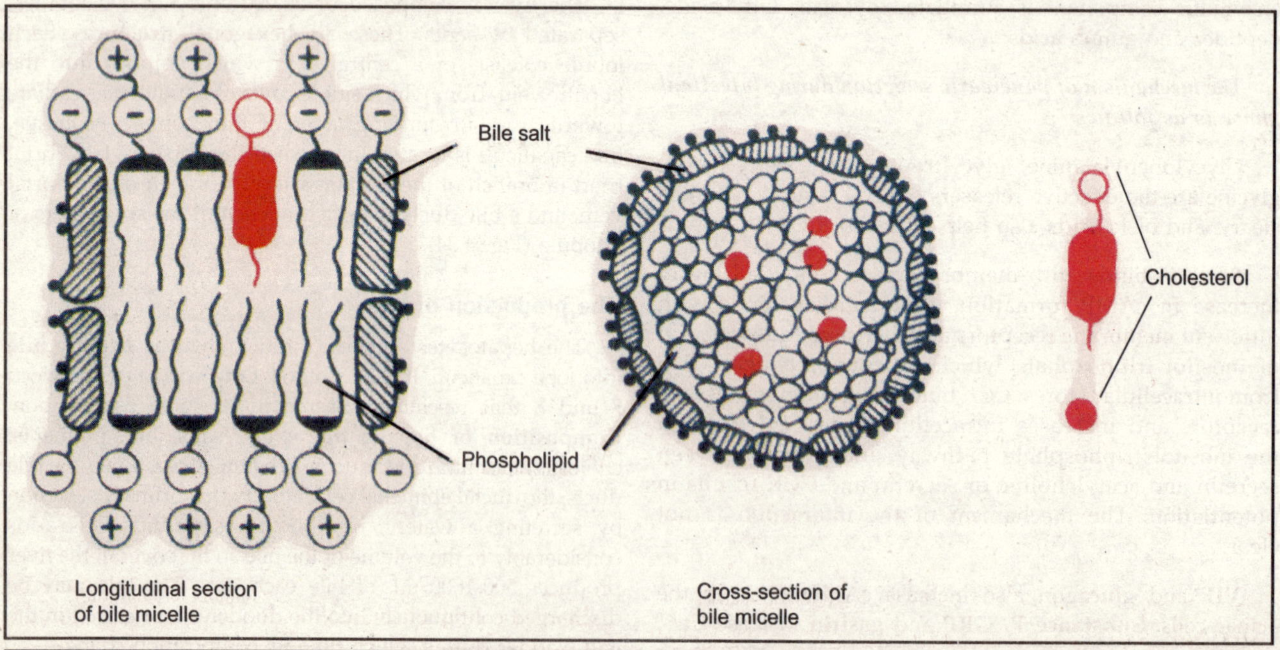


Fig. 4.35 : The structure of the bile micelle.

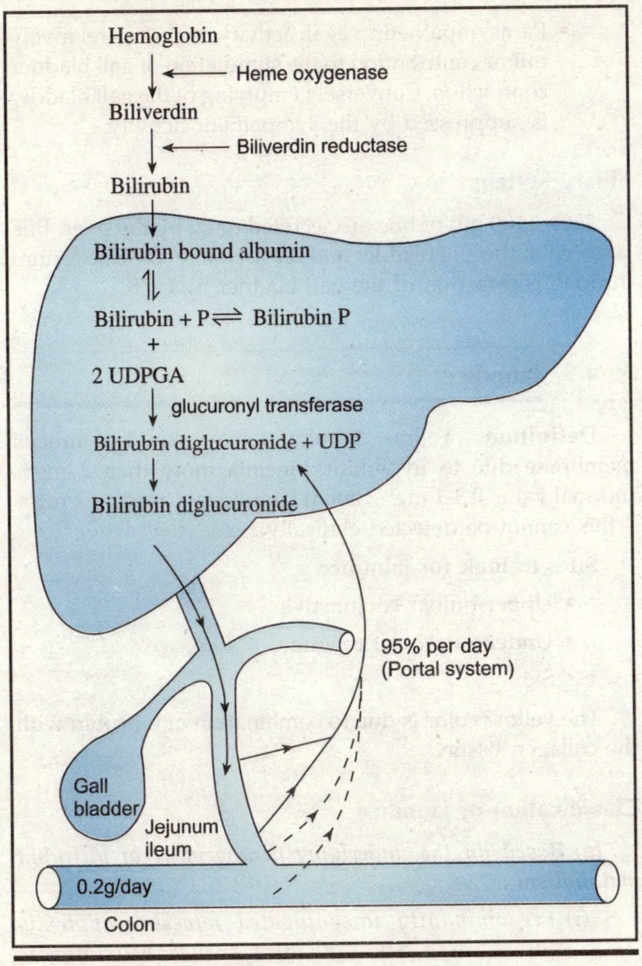


Fig. 4.36 : Bilirubin excretory pathways

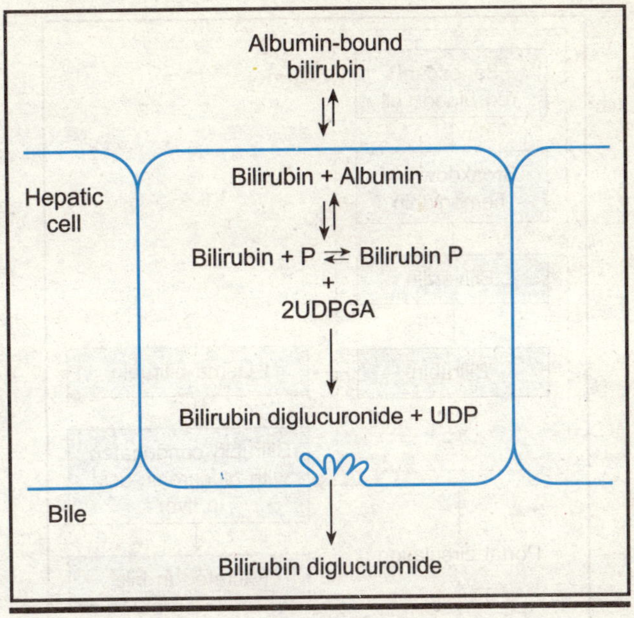


Fig. 4.37

**The Regulation of bile secretion :** Substances that increase the rate of bile secretion are known **choleretics. Cholagogues** are substances (CCK) that increase the flow of bile by stimulating the emptying of the gall bladder. The main factor in the production of hepatic bile is the return of bile salts to the hepatocytes via the enterohepatic circulation.

This produces the driving force for the fluid transport into the biliary system. The production of hepatic bile is not under hormonal control. The secretion of bicarbonate rich watery fluid by the ductal epithelial cells is enhanced by secretin and to a lesser extent, glucagon and gastrin.

**Haem and Bilirubin catabolism (Fig. 4.36) :**

- Worn out red blood cells are phagocytosed by reticulo endothelial cells in the spleen. The free hemoglobin released is bound to haptoglobin. This complex is transported in the blood stream to the liver where hepatic reticuloendothelial cells split off the hemoglobin portion converting it to its haem and globin moieties.
- The globin is hydrolysed into its component amino acids which are added to the hepatic pool for reuse.
- Bilirubin is formed fromthe catabolism of the haem moiety and transported to the liver bound to albumin. The iron released from haem in this process is stored in the liver for reuse.
- Bilirubin is conjugated with glucuronic acid catalysed by glucuronyl transferase to form water soluble bilirubin diglucuronide which is excreted in bile. Bacterial metabolism of bilirubin in the bowel leads to the formation of urobilinogen some of which undergoes as enterohepatic circulation and mass be found in the urine (Fig. 4.38).

**The Gall bladder** (Fig. 4.38) :

- The gall bladder is a green, thin walled muscular sac. 10 c.m. long. Capacity of the gall bladder is 30-50 ml.
- It stores bile that is not required immediately for digestion and concentrates it by absorbing water and electrolytes.
- Between meals, most of the bile produced by the liver is diverted into the gall bladder because of the relatively high level of tone in the splincter of oddi.
- The gall bladder concentrates the bile by absorbing sodium, chloride, bicarbonate and water from it.

Composition of Hepatic bile and gall bladder bile :

| | *Hepatic Duct Bile* | *Gall bladder Bile* |
|---|---|---|
| Percentage of Solids | 2—4 | 10—12 |
| Bile Salts (m mol/L) | 10—20 | 50—200 |
| pH | 7.8—8.6 | 7.0—7.4 |

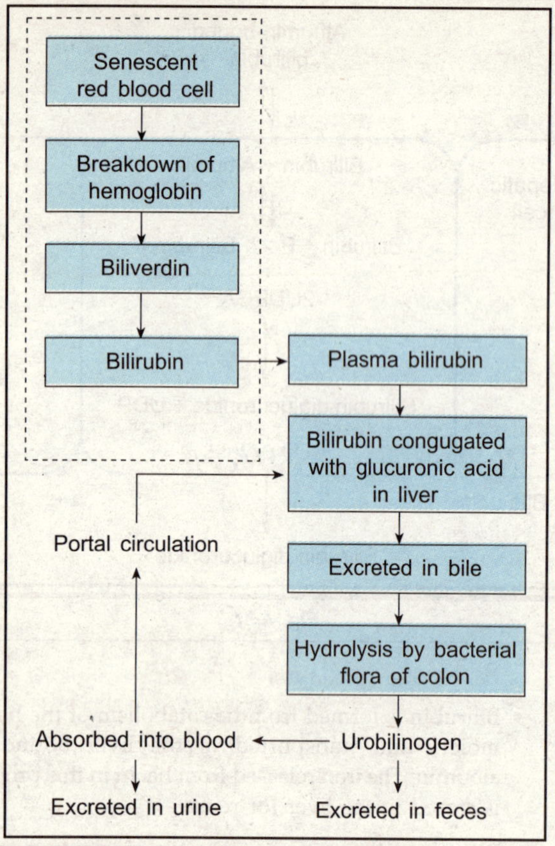


Fig. 4.38

**Composition of human hepatic duct bile :**

| | |
|---|---|
| Water | 97.0% |
| Bile salts | 0.7% |
| Bile pigments | 0.2% |
| Cholesterol | 0.06% |
| Inorganic Salts | 0.7% |
| Fatty acids | 0.15% |
| Lecithin | 0.1% |
| Fat | 0.1% |
| Alkaline phosphatase. | |

**Contraction of the gall bladder forces bile into the duodenum :**

- Within a few minutes of starting a meal (particularly rich in fats), the muscle of the gall bladder contracts. As a result pressure forces bile towards the duodenum.
- The initial response is mediated via the vagal nerves but major stimulus for contraction is CCK. (CCK is secreted in response to the presence of fatty and acidic chyme in the intestine.
- CCK also stimulates pancreatic secretion and relaxes the sphincter of oddi so that bile and pancreatic juice can enter the duodenum.
- Parasympathetic vagal activity makes a relatively minor contribution to the stimulation of gall bladder contraction. Conversely emptying of the gall bladder is suppressed by the sympathetic activity.

### Biliary System

250—1100 ml. of bile are secreted daily by the liver. Bile is stored in the gall bladder and released into the duodenum through contraction of the gall bladder by CCK.

## 4.9 Jaundice

**Definition** : Yellow discoloration of skin and mucus membrane due to hyperbilirubinemia more than 2 mg% (normal value 0.3-1 mg%; latent jaundice > 1 mg% < 2 mg% – this cannot be detected clinically).

**Sites to look for jaundice :**

- Upper bulbar conjunctiva
- Under surface of tongue
- Skin.

The yellow color is due to combination of bilirubin with the collagen tissue.

### Classification of jaundice

(a) ***Based on the underlying derangement of bilirubin metabolism :***

(i) *Predominantly unconjugated hyperbilirubinemia* (more than 80% of total serum bilirubin is unconjugated).

- Overproduction : Hemolysis
- Decreased hepatic uptake : (a) sepsis, (b) starvation

(ii) *Impaired conjugation due to transferase deficiency* :

- Hereditary —
  - (a) Gilbert's syndrome — mild deficiency
  - (b) Crigler-Najjar Type II — moderate deficiency
  - (c) Crigler-Najjar Type I — absence of enzyme
- Transient deficiency as in neonates.
- Drug induced, breast milk induced and hepatocellular disease.

(iii) *Predominantly conjugated hyperbilirubinemia* (more than 50% of total serum bilirubin is conjugated)

- Hereditary :
  1. Dubin-Johnson syndrome,
  2. Rotor syndrome
- Acquired diseases :
  1. Hepatocellular : viral, drug induced and alcoholic hepatitis
  2. Intrahepatic cholestasis : drugs, viral hepatitis
  3. Biliary cirrhosis.

Table : 4.6 : Difference between hemolytic, hepatocellular and obstructive jaundice

| Source | Hemolytic | Hepatocellular | Obstructive |
|---|---|---|---|
| I. **Color of urine** | Golden yellow bilirubinuria) | Dark | Dark |
| II. **Color of stool** (more urobilinogen) | Golden yellow (less urobilinogen) | Clay coloured | Clay-colored (less urobilinogen) |
| III. **Urine for bile pigment** | Absent | Present | Present |
| IV. **Liver function test :** | | | |
| 1. Serum bilirubin — | | | |
| (i) Total | Increased | Increased | Increased |
| (ii) Unconjugated | 80% | 50% | 20% |
| (iii) Conjugated | 20% | 50% | 80% |
| 2. Van den Bergh Reaction | Indirect positive | Biphasic | Direct positive |
| 3. ALT (SGPT) | Normal | Markedly raised | Normal or slightly raised |
| 4. Alkaline phosphatase | Normal | Slightly raised | Markedly elevated |
| 5. Prothombin time | Normal | Prolonged and not corrected by vit. K injection | Prolonged and can be corrected by vit. K injection |
| V. **Ultrasonography** of liver, gall bladder and pancreas | Normal | Intrahepatic biliary radicles are not dilated | Intrahepatic biliary radicles are dilated |

- Extrahepatic biliary obstruction :
  1. Stone in CBD
  2. Malignancy of bile duct or head of the pancreas
  3. Pancreatitis.

(b) ***Practical disease oriented classification :***

I. **Hemolytic** : Leads to over–production of and rise of unconjugated bilirubin in serum. This variety is to be differentiated from other causes of unconjugated hyperbilirubinemia like Gilbert's, Crigler-Najjar, etc.

II. **Hepatocellular** : Jaundice caused by hepatocellular damage (necrosis) like viral hepatitis, alcoholic hepatitis, cirrhosis, drug-induced hepatitis etc. There will be predominant rise of conjugated bilirubin.

III. **Obstructive** : 1. ***Intrahepatic cholestasis :*** In this condition bile is inspissated within the intrahepatic biliary canaliculi causing obstruction to the flow of bile. The biliary canaliculi are not dilated. This may be caused by viral hepatitis and many drugs. 2. ***Extrahepatic*** **:** The common bile duct is mechanically obstructed by stone, growth etc. The bile stagnates within the intrahepatic biliary canaliculi which are, therefore, dilated (Table 4.6).

**It should be remembered that —**

1. In any single disease, more than one mechanism may operate for causing jaundice, e.g., in cirrhosis there may be hemolysis of RBC as well as hepatocellular jaundice.
2. In hepatocellular disease, although all three phases of bilirubin metabolism (uptake, conjugation, excretion) is likely to be impaired, it is the excretory function which is most seriously impaired (due to intrahepatic cholestasis) and, therefore, it has features like obstructive jaundice. Jaundice is more common in acute hepatocellular disorder like viral hepatitis than in chronic hepatic diseases like cirrhosis.

## 4.10 Intestinal Secretion (Fig. 4.39)

### Small intestine

Small intestine (in life) is a tube about 4 m long and diameter is 2.5 cm. and is divided into three segments; the duodenum (25 cm long), jejunum, and ileum. The ducts which deliver bile and pancreatic secretions unite close to the duodenum at the hepato-pancreatic ampulla, which opens in to the duodenum at major duodenal papilla. The sphincter of Oddi controls the entry of bile and pancreatic

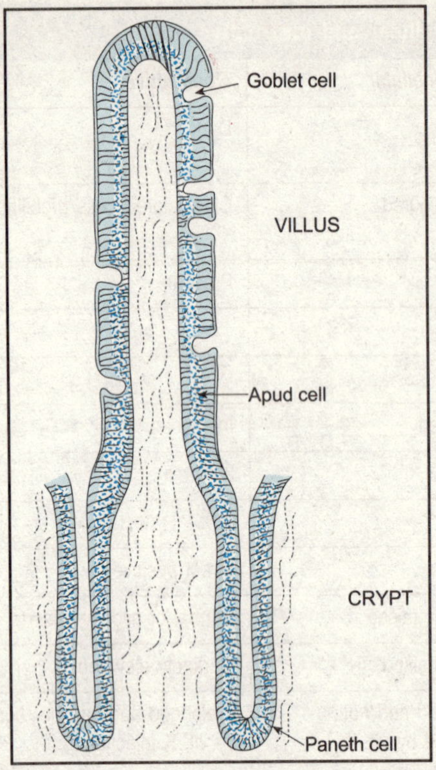


**Fig. 4.39 :** Intestinal villus and crypt

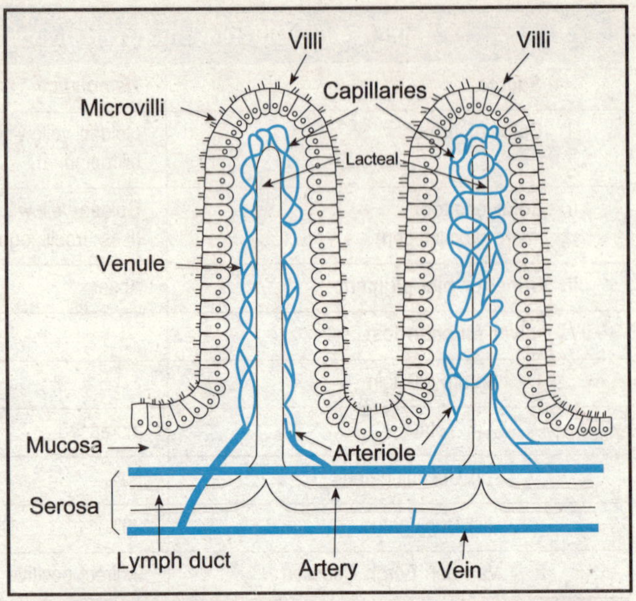


**Fig. 4.40 :** Blood and lymphatic vessels around the villi

juice into the small intestine. The jejunum is about 1.5 m long and extends from the duodenum to the ileum, a coiled tube about 2.5 m in length.

Significant digestion and absorption occur in the small intestine. The macroscopic surface area of human small intestine is about 2.5 $m^2$. The surface of the small intestine is thrown up into longitudinal folds, termed as **folds of Kerckring**. Five million finger-like projections (villi) project from these folds into lumen. A villus is lined by columnar epithelial cells called ***enterocytes***, interpersed with ***goblet cells*** *(Fig. 4.39)*. Tiny processes, ***microvilli***, are present on the apical surface of an enterocyte. The appearance of the tiny processes (the microvillus surface) is called ***brush border***. In between the **villi** are scattered numerous simple tubular, intestinal glands, called the **crypts of Leiberkuhn**. These glands open into the spaces between neighbouring villi and are composed of cells similar to the columnar epithelial cells of the villus. Tube-like crypts project down along the surface of each villus. Crypts are about 0.3 to 0.5 mm deep, with the deepest ones located in the duodenum and the shallowest ones in the terminal ileum (Fig. 4.41).

**Brunner's glands** are present in the most proximal segment of the duodenum (submucosal glands) and produce a highly viscid secretion. They secrete alkaline mucus. ***The function of the Brunner's glands*** is to protect the duodenum from the acid chyme entering from the stomach. Daily secretion of Brunner's gland is less than 100 ml.

The function of the intestinal mucus is not clearly understood. However it plays a key role in physical, chemical and probably immunological protection.

**Paneth cells** have some important immunological role in protecting against infection from ingested organisms. They secrete bacteriolytic enzymes. There are some cells termed **APUD cells** located along the villi which are very specialized to secrete hormones. **APUD cells** are the gut endocrine cells which are believed to be of neural crest origin. They secrete Secretin, CCK, gastrin, motilin, substance P, enteroglucagon and neurotensin.

A number of different types of endocrine and paracrine cells have also been identified in the crypts and on the villi.

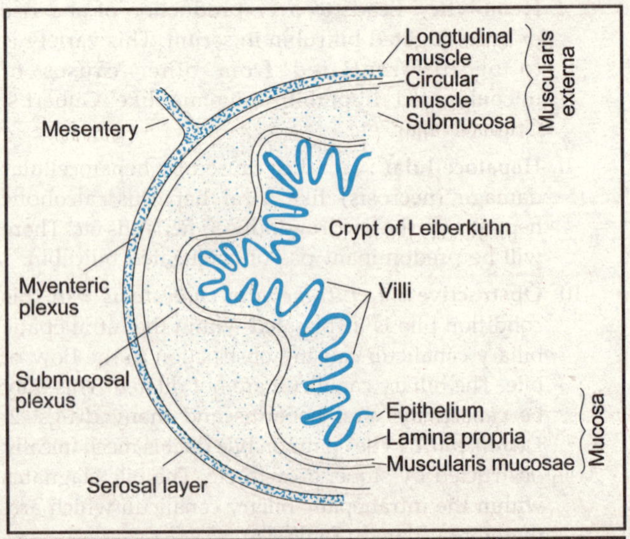


**Fig. 4.41 :** Cross-section through small intestine

These cells have been shown to produce somatostatin (D cells), secretin (S cells), Neurotensin (N-cells). CCK and 5HT. CCK and secretin are secreted by cells in the wall of the duodenum in response to the presence of fat digestion products and acid respectively.

**Secretion of fluid and enzymes by the small intestine** : Crypt cells secrete 2-3 litres of isotonic fluid each day. Chloride is transported out of the cells and sodium and water follow passively by paracellular route. In the duodenum, Brunner's glands contribute to the secretion of alkaline fluid which helps to protect the epithelium from the corrosive effects of acidic chyme arriving from the stomach. Secretion is stimulated by vagal neurons and by CCK, secretin, gastrin and endogeneous prostaglandin.

The secretion of the small intestine.

| *Hormone* | *Cells of origin* |
|---|---|
| Cholecystokinin(CCK) | I-cells |
| Neurotensin | N-cells |
| Secretion | S-cells |
| Serotonin(5HT) | Enterochromaffin cells |
| Somatostatin | D-cells |

## ➤ 4.11 Large Intestine

The lower part of the alimentary canal bears the name large intestine because its diameter is noticeably larger than that of small intestine. Length is 1.5 to 1.8 m (5 or 6 feet).

The large intestine is divided into cecum, colon and rectum.

**Wall of large intestine :**

- Presence of intestinal mucous glands which produce the lubricating mucus that coats the feces as they are formed.
- In the wall of the colon, there is uneven distribution of fibers in the muscle layer.
- The longitudinal muscles are grouped into tapelike strips called taeniae coli and the circular muscles are grouped into ring that produce pouch like **haustra** between them.

**Mucosa of large intestine :**

- Crypts of Lieberkulin present but no villi.
- Epithelial cells contain no enzymes.
- Surface epithelium contains large number of mucous cells dispersed among the other epithelial cells.

The large intestinal juice contains 99.5% of water and 0.5% of solids. *Organic Substances* — albumin, globulin, mucin, urea and debris of epithelial cells. *Inorganic Substances* — sodium, potassium, chloride and bicarbonate.

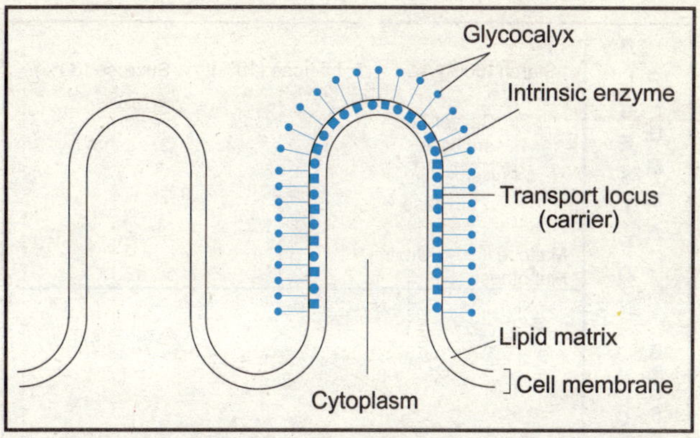


**Fig. 4.42 :** The pathways traversed by absorbed substances

**Functions of large intestine :**

(1) Secretory function — mucin; chlorides and bicarbonates.

(2) Synthetic function — bacterial flora of large intestine synthesizes folic acid, vit. $B_{12}$ & K.

(3) Excretory function — excretes mercury, lead, bismuth and arsenic through feces.

(4) Absorptive function — absorbs water, glucose, alcohol, sedatives and steroids.

(5) Formation of feces — The unwanted substances after absorption of nutrients, water, form feces which is excreted out.

## ➤ 4.12 Carbohydrate Digestion and Absorption

Carbohydrate assimilation such as in the form of polysaccharides (eg, starch, glycogen), disaccharides (eg, sucrose, lactose) and monosaccharides (eg, glucose, fructose) involve the following steps :

**• Luminal digestion • Surface digestion • Cell transport**

Enzymes present in salivary, gastric and pancreatic secretions are responsible for luminal digestion. The enzymes which are synthesized by enterocytes are responsible for membrane or brush border digestion (Fig. 4.42 & 4.43).

The major form of carbohydrate present in diet is starch, which may be of plant or animal origin. Dietary starch comprises polysaccharides in different forms. Polysaccharides contain monosaccharides like glucose linked to each other by α-1.4 and/or α-1.6 glycosidic linkages. Dietary carbohydrate also includes disaccharides (sucrose, lactose and maltose) and monosaccharides (glucose, fructose and trehalose). Cellulose is a polysaccharide of plant origin containing β-1.4 linkages, which cannot be broken by enzymes in human G.I. tract. Hence, it is a primary constitutent of 'fiber' in our diet.

Dietary carbohydrates need to be broken down to monosaccharides for their absorption. Digestion of starch

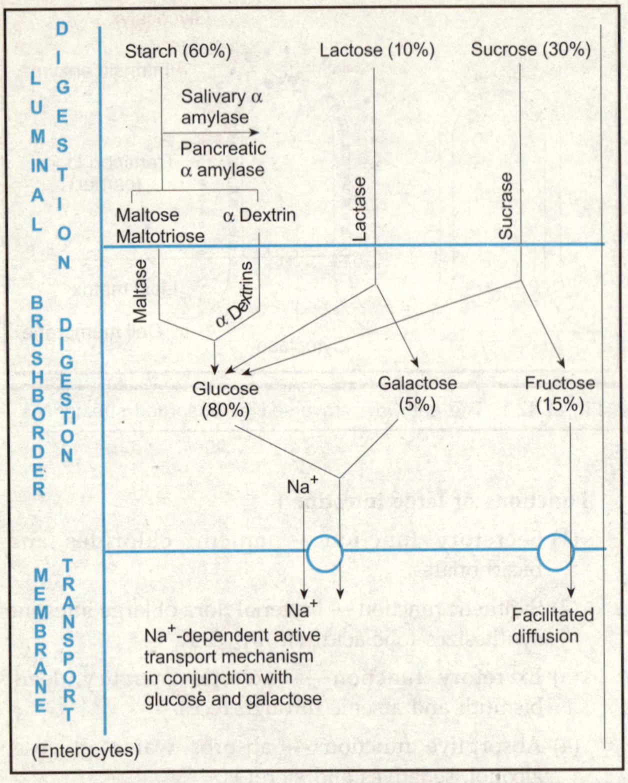


Fig. 4.43 : Schematic representation of carbohydrate digestion and absorption

begins in the mouth cavity where it is attacked by salivary α-amylase and ends in the small intestine with the help of pancreatic amylolytic enzymes and enzymes from enterocytes. The α-amylase (both salivary and pancreatic) acts on α-1.4 glycosidic linkages to hydrolyze them sparing α-1.6 glycosidic linkages (i.e., branch points), terminal α-1.4 linkages, and α-1.4 linkages next to the branch points. As a result, maltose (disaccharide) maltotriose (trisaccharide), some slightly larger straight chain polymers of glucose, and α-dextrins (glucose polymers with an average of 8 glucose molecules having α-1.6 glycosidic linkages) are formed.

The oligosaccharides thus formed are further digested by oligosaccharidases (α-dextrinase or isomaltase, maltase and sucrase) to monosaccharides. Lactase and trehalase are two disaccharidases which hydrolyze lactose and trehalose respectively. All these oligosaccharides and disaccharidases are present in the outer portion of the brush border of the small intestine.

If one or more of the brush border oligosaccharidases is deficient, diarrhoea and flatulence may occur after ingestion of a carbohydrate rich diet. Undigested oligosaccharides increase the number of osmotically active particles within the lumen of the intestine, increasing the amount of water in the intestinal lumen. This is the reason for diarrhoea.

The disaccharidase lactase is often deficient in adults particularly those from Africa, Asia and Mediterranean. Lactase deficiency is less common in Europeans and Americans. In all these populations, lactase activity within the intestine of newborns and infants is good enough to digest lactase in milk. However, lactase activity begins to decline in childhood to reach a lower level in adulthood. The adult level of lactase activity varies from population (see above). Persons with lactase deficiency suffer from milk intolerance manifested by diarrhoea and flatulence following ingestion of milk. Curd or yogurt is better tolerated by persons with lactase deficiency because curd and yogurt contain lactase produced by **Lactobacillus**.

Monosaccharides, the breakdown products of carbohydrate digestion are rapidly absorbed from the small intestine. Glucose is taken up by the enterocytes by $Na^+$ glucose cotransporter present in the luminal surface of these cells. This is an example of secondary active transport the energy for which is derived from the activity of $Na^+$–$K^+$ ATPase present in the basolateral membrane membrane of enterocytes. Glucose requires SGLT 1(sodium-dependent glucose transporter 1) for its absorption. On the basolateral surface of the enterocytes. GLUT 2(glucose transporter 2) transports glucose out of the calls by facilitated diffusion to enter the capillaries (Fig. 4.45). Galactose shares the same pathway as glucose for its absorption. Congenital deficiency of SGLT causes severe diarrhoea due to malabsorption of glucose and galactose. Fructose is absorbed by facilitated diffusion with the help of GLUT 5 present in the luminal surface of the enterocytes, it is transported out of the small intestinal cells by GLUT 2. Pentose sugars-derived mainly from digestion of nucleic acids-are absorbed by simple diffusion.

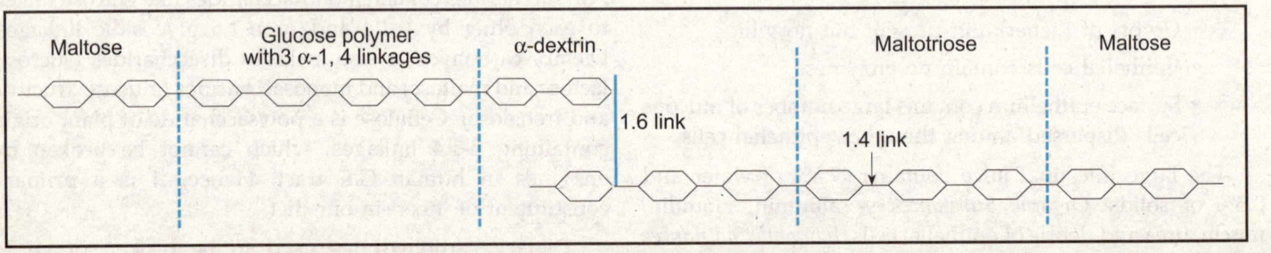


Fig. 4.44 : Products of starch digestion.

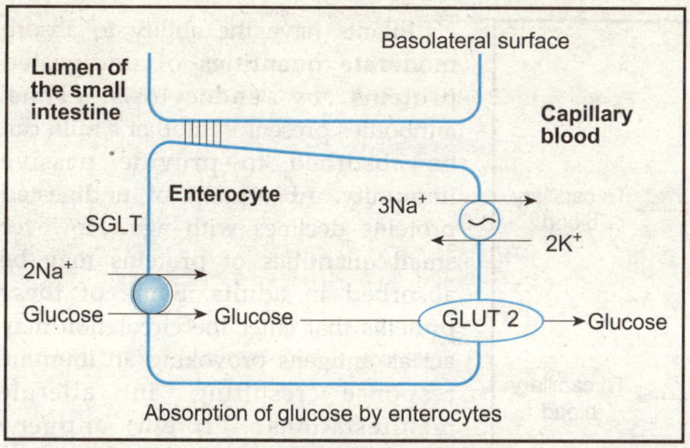


Fig. 4.45

**Table : 4.7**
**Digestion and absorption of carbohydrate**

| Location | Enzyme | Substrate | End products |
|---|---|---|---|
| Salivary glands | α-amylase | Starch | Oligosaccharides and amylopectin |
| Exocrine pancreas | Pancreatic amylase | Starch | Oligosaccharides |
| Brush border of enterocytes | Amylase | Starch, Oligosaccharides | Maltose and glucose |
| | Sucrase | Saccharose, Sucrose | Fructose and glucose |
| | Maltase | Maltose | Glucose |
| | Lactase | Lactose | Galactose and glucose |

## ➤ 4.13 Protein Digestion and Absorption (Fig. 4.46)

**Protein digestion is** initiated in the stomach by the action of ***pepsin and gastric acid***. The **main enzymes** involved in protein digestion are secreted by the **pancreas** as inactive zymogens eg, ***trypsinogen, chymotrypsinogen, proelastase,*** and ***procarboxypeptidase A and B. Trypsinogen is activated to trypsin by enterokinase,*** a duodenal brush border peptidase.

Apart from dietary protein, about 35 to 55g. of protein is added to the lumen of the digestive tract every day by way of protein present in gastrointestinal secretions and desquamation of cells. Almost all the protein in the GI tract is digested and absorbed. Absorption of protein is normally complete before the end of jejunum.

Protein digestion begins in the stomach with the action of pepsin on bonds between aromatic amino acids (e.g. phenylalanine, tyrosine) and a second amino acid producing polypeptides of various sizes. Gelatinase present in the stomach liquefies gelatin. Chymosin (also known as rennin)- a gastric enzyme present in the stomach of young animals makes milk clot. In human stomach its presence is doubtful.

Action of pepsin is terminated in the duodenum where the pH of the intestinal contents gradually become less acidic due to alkaline pancreatic juice. Further digestion of protein continues with the help of proteolytic enzymes from pancreas and enterocytes. Two classes of proteolytic enzymes (proteases) are secreted into the lumen of the intestine-Endopeptidases (hydrolyze peptide bonds in the interior of the protein molecules) and Exopeptidases (remove one amino acid at a time from the C-terminal ends of proteins). Endopeptidases include trypsin, chymotrypsin and elastase (as well as pepsin from stomach). Carboxypeptidases A and B are exopeptidases.

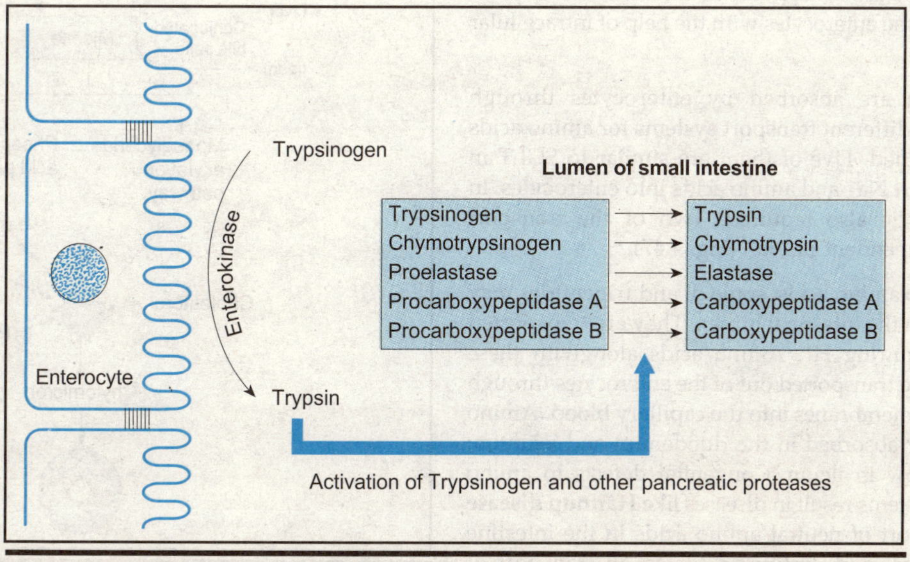


Fig. 4.46

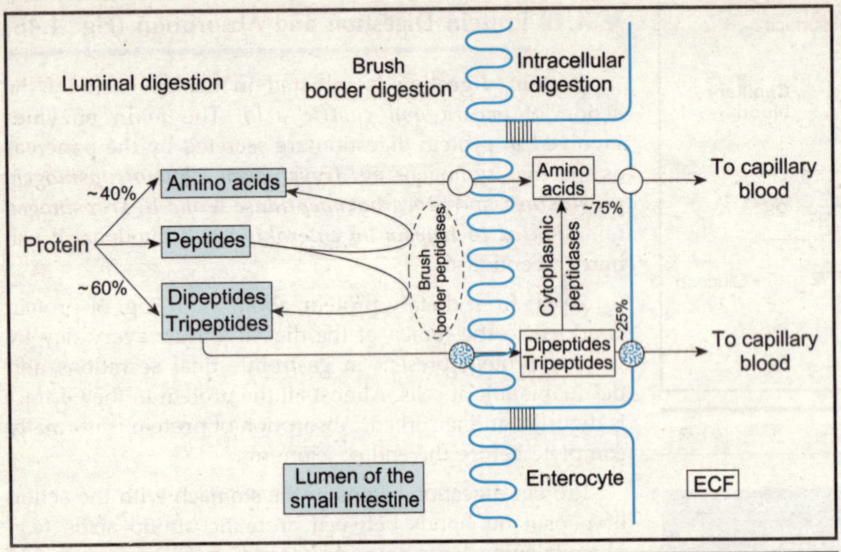


Fig. 4.47

Pancreatic proteases are secreted as inactive precursors. Trypsinogen is the precursor of trypsin. The enzyme enterokinase present in the brush border of enterocytes converts trypsinogen to trypsin. Trypsin also has the ability to activate trypsinogen. Besides, trypsin acts on chymotrypsinogen, proelastase and procarboxypeptidase A and B to convert them to their active forms chymotrypsin, elastase and procarboxypeptidases A and B.

In addition to luminal digestion of protein, some digestion occurs at the brush border of enterocytes as well. Aminopeptidases, dipeptidases, endopeptidases and exopeptidases are present in the brush border of the enterocytes, which aid in protein digestion. Some di-or tripeptides can be absorbed intact by the mucosal cells of the intestine; these are broken down to amino acids within the cytoplasm of the enterocytes with the help of intracellular peptidases.

Amino acids are absorbed by enterocytes through symports. Seven different transport systems for amino acids have been identified. Five of them are similar to SGLT in that they transport $Na^+$ and amino acids into enterocytes. In some cases, $Cl^-$ is also required. Two of the transport systems are independent of $Na^+$ (Fig. 4.47).

In addition to amino acids, some di and tripeptides may be absorbed from the intestinal lumen. They are transported by a system requiring $H^+$. Amino acids alongwith these small peptides are transported out of the enterocytes through their basolateral membranes into the capillary blood. Amino acids are rapidly absorbed in the duodenum and jejunum; absorption is slow in ileum. Congenital defects in amino acid transport systems result in diseases like **Hartnup disease** (defect in transport of neutral amino acids in the intestine and renal tubules) and **cystinuria** (defect in transport of basic amino acids).

Infants have the ability to absorb moderate quantities of undigested proteins by endocytosis. Thus, antibodies present in mother's milk can be absorbed to provide passive immunity. Absorption of undigested proteins declines with age. However small quantities of proteins may be absorbed in adults. Some of these proteins that enter the circulation may act as antigens provoking an immune response resulting in allergic manifestations. Protein antigens (particularly bacterial and viral proteins) are usually absorbed through M cells (microfold cells) which overlie Peyer's patches. Peyer's patches are aggregates of lymphoid tissue in the wall of the intestine, which can mount an immune response to the antigens. The immune response leads to production of IgA which is secreted by the mucosal cells and provides surface immunity.

## 4.14 Fat Digestion and Absorption (Fig.4.48)

More than 90% of dietary fat is triglycerides, phospholipids, cholesterol and cholesterol esters, while the fat soluble vitamins A, D, E and K make up the rest. The absorption of lipid is an efficient process. As the lipids are not water soluble, digestion and absorption of lipids are more complicated.

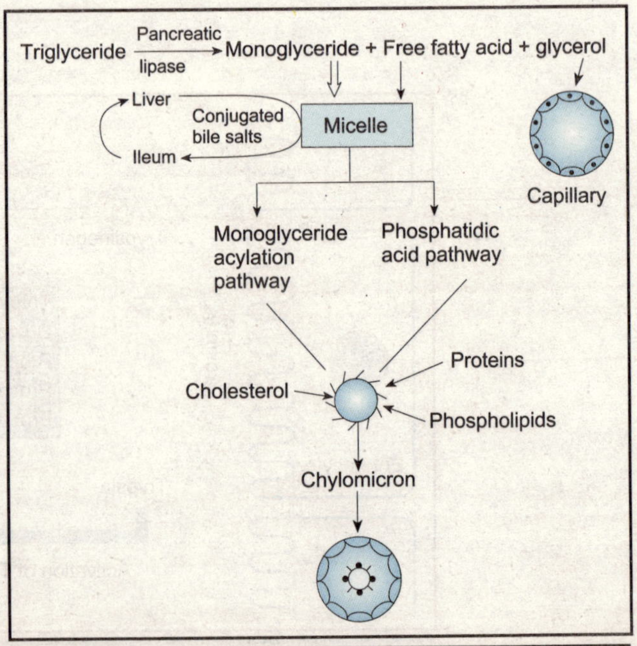


Fig. 4.48 : Digestion and absorption of fat

**Table 4.8**
**Major events in protein digestion**

| Location | Enzyme | Mode of action |
|---|---|---|
| **Chief cells of stomach** | **Pepsin (pepsinogen)** | Endopeptidases cleave bonds between $NH_2$ groups of other amino acids (optimum pH 1.5-3.5) |
| **Exocrine pancreas** | **Trypsin (trypsinogen)** | Endopeptidases cleave mainly between COOH groups of lysine or arginine and $NH_2$ group of other amino acids |
| | **Chymotrypsin (chymotrypsinogen)** | Endopeptidases split between COOH of aromatic amino acids and $NH_2$ groups of other amino acids except glutamic acid and asparagine |
| | **Carboxypeptidase A, B (procarboxy peptidases)** | Exopeptidase (A) splits aromatic amino acids at C-terminal end and exopeptidase (B) splits off basic amino acids in same position |
| **Duodenal mucosa** | **Enterokinase** | Endopeptidase cleaves between isoleucine and lysine |
| **Brush border of enterocytes** | **Tripeptidase** | Exopeptidase cleaves N-terminal or C-terminal amino acids |
| | **Aminopolypeptidase** | Exopeptidase |
| | **Aminopeptidase** | Exopeptidase cleaves amino bond |

The principal constituents of dietary fat are triglycerides (triacylglycerols), cholesterol esters and phospholipids. Digestion of fat starts with lingual lipase secreted by Ebner's glands of the tongue. Lingual lipase retains its activity even inside the stomach. A lipase is present in stomach as well. These two lipase together can digest about 30% of dietary triglycerides.

Pancreatic lipolytic enzymes are mainly responsible for most of the digestion of dietary fat. Bile acids help in fat digestion by emulsifying large fat globules into a fine suspension of droplets of 0.5-1.0mm diameter. This increases the surface area available for enzyme action. **Pancreatic lipase**, with the help of a colipase secreted by pancreas, hydrolyzes triglycerides to fatty acids, 2-monoglycerides. Hydrolysis of 2-monoglycerides into fatty acid and glycerol requires cholesterol ester hydrolase, which is probably identical to nonspecific esterase. **Cholesterol ester hydrolase** also hydrolyses cholesterol esters as well as ester linkages of vitamins A and B. Bile salt-activated lipase is a variety of pancreatic lipase which is activated by bile salts. This enzyme can catalyze the hydrolysis of cholesterol esters, esters of fat-soluble vitamins, phospholipids and triglycerides. Milk lipase found in human milk has a similar action. Phospholipids are digested by phospholipase A2 of the pancreatic juice. Phospholipase A2 releases fatty acids from phospholipids to form lysopholipids.

Bile salts form micelles to solubilize products of fat digestion. This greatly helps in transport of fat-digestion products across the unstirred layer of fluid lining the brush border of enterocytes. Thus lipids come in contact with the luminal surface of enterocytes, wherefrom they are mainly absorbed by passive diffusion. However, carrier-mediated transport may also be involved.

Short-chain fatty acids and some medium-chain fatty acids pass unaltered through enterocytes to the portal blood. Fatty acids with longer chains (more than 10-12 carbon atoms) are required to be reesterified and incorporated into chylomicrons for their passage through lymph to blood. Triglycerides (90%), cholesterol (2%) and phospholipid (7%) are other constituents of chylomicrons (Fig. 4.49 and Fig. 4.50).

Some 2-monoglycerides are also absorbed by enterocytes. These and fatty acids are carried to the smooth endoplasmic reticulum (SER) of enterocytes with the help of fatty acid binding proteins (FABP). Within the SER, fatty acids combine with coenzyme A(CoA) to form acyl CoA, which in turn combines with monoglycerides to generate diglycerides. Triglycerides are formed when diglycerides

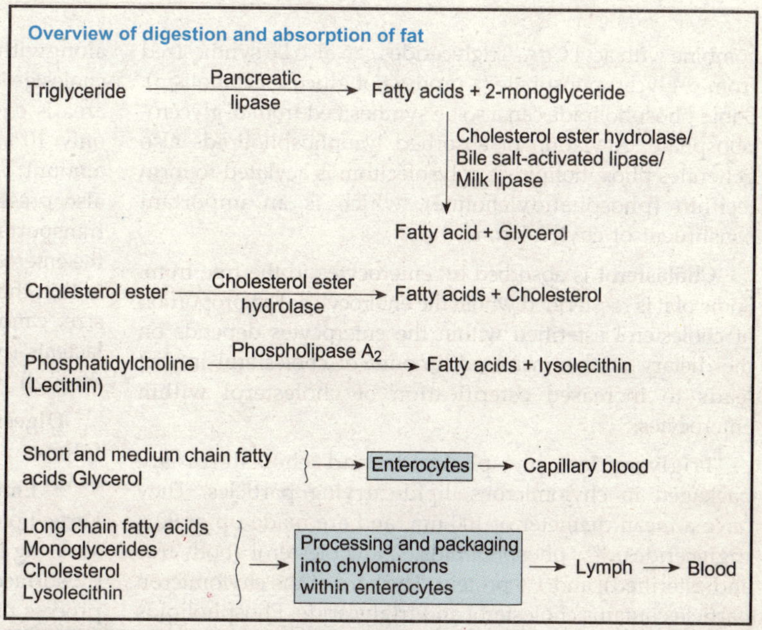


Fig. 4.49 : Fat digestion & absorption

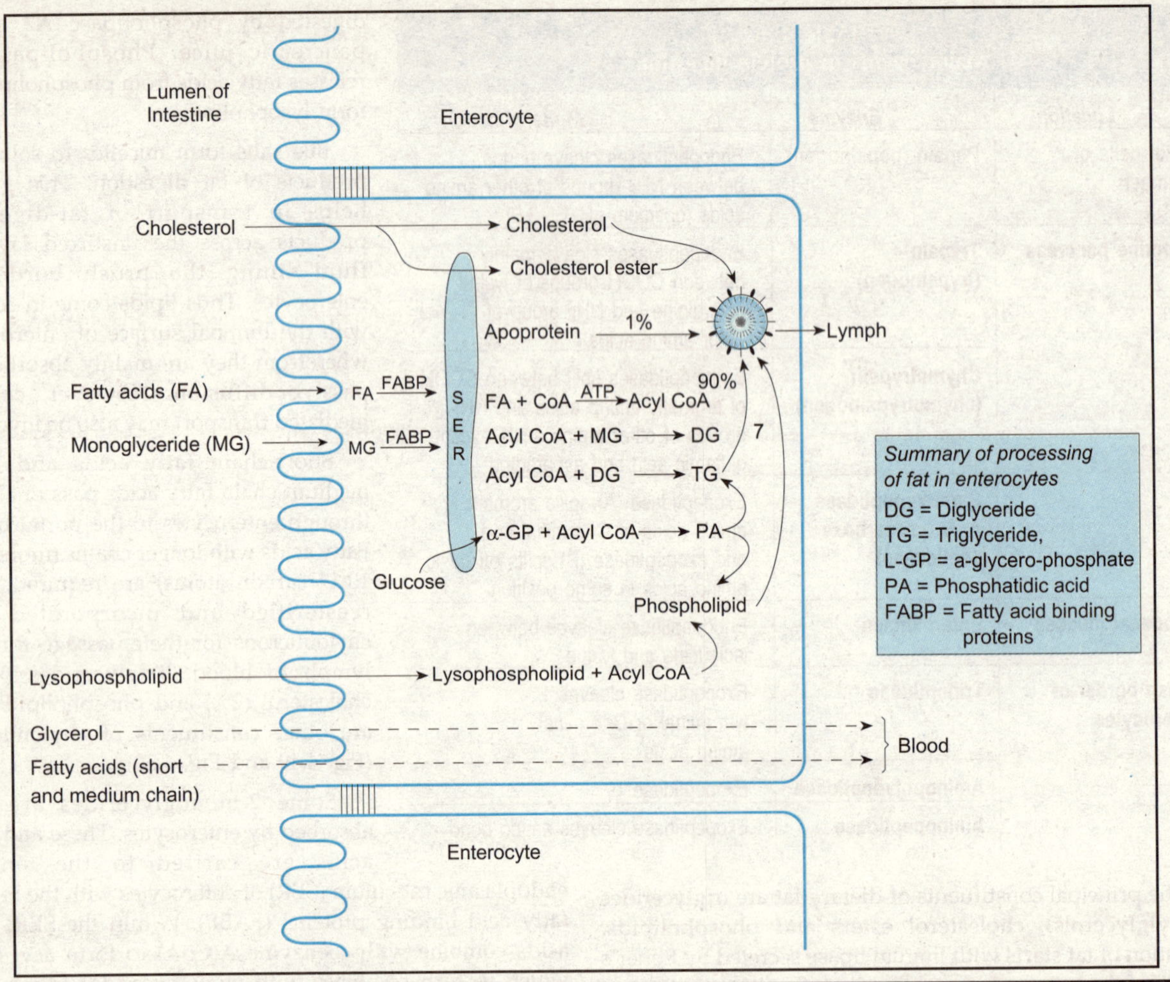


Fig. 4.50 : Summary of processing of fat in enterocytes

combine with acyl CoA. Triglycerides can also be synthesized from α-glycerophosphate (a product of glucose catabolism). Some phospholipids can also be synthesized from α-glycerophosphate. Acylation of absorbed lysophospholipids also generates phospholipids e.g. lysolecithin is acylated to form lecithin (phosphatidylcholine), which is an important constituent of chylomicrons.

**Cholesterol** is absorbed by enterocytes in the free from. Some of it is reesterified within the enterocytes. The proportion of cholesterol esterified within the enterocytes depends on the dietary intake; increased amount of cholesterol in diet leads to increased esterification of cholesterol within enterocytes.

Triglycerides, phospholipids and cholesterol are packaged in chylomicrons, lipid-carrying particles. They have a mean diameter of 100 nm, and are made up of 90% triglycerides, 7% phospholipids, 2% cholesterol (both free and esterified), and 1% protein. The core of the chylomicron particle contains cholesterol and triglyceride. Phospholipids alongwith apoproteins form a monolayer around the cholesterol-triglyceride core. About 80% to 90% of the surface area is covered by phospholipids while apoproteins cover only 10% to 20" of the surface of chylomicrons; a small amount of free cholesterol and saturated triglycerides are also present on the surface. Apoproteins are essential for transport of chylomicrons through basolateral membrane of the enterocytes; lack of apoproteins causes lipid accumulation within the enterocytes. Chylomicrons, because of their large size, cannot enter capillary blood. Indeed, they enter the lacteals (lymph vessels) in the intestinal villi to be carried through lymph to the blood.

**Digestion and absorption of fat can be summarized as follows :**

- **Emulsification, digestion and micelle formation** : Large lipid droplets are converted to small lipid droplets. A shearing force exerted by intestinal movements and assisted by surface lowering effect of bile salts is necessary for the process of emulsification.

**Fat Digestion**

| Stomach | Duodenum |
|---|---|
| Fat digestion occurs by lingual lipase and gastric lipase | **Emulsification** is enhanced by combination of bile salts and lecithin resulting in *a wider surface area.* Procolipase (from pancreas) and trypsin colipase, which bind pancreatic lipase to act at the oil-water interface of the emulsion, convert triglycerides to free fatty acids and 2 monoglycerides. **Micelle** is formed with bile salts, lecithin, cholesterol and fat soluble vitamins. |

- **Way to cell from lumen** : The micelles pass to the luminal cellular membrane. Free fatty acids and monoglycerides diffuse across the luminal membrane. Mechanism of absorption of bile salts is by two ways :

| In the duodenum and jejunum – by passive diffusion | In the terminal ileum – by active carrier mediated process |
|---|---|

- **Synthesis of chylomicrons** : At the brush border of epithelial cells, the long chain fatty acids bind to a soluble protein. Fatty acids are reesterified to triglycerides. **Chylomicrons** are composed of triglycerides (87%), cholesterol esters (3%) and fat soluble vitamins. It is about 100 nm in diameter.

- **Way to interstitium from cell** : *Chylomicrons* are released form the cell by the process of exocytosis along the basolateral membrane.

- **Fate of chylomicron** : *Chylomicrons* pass into lymphatic lacteals located in villi. Chylomicrons enter systemic circulation through lymphatic system via thoracic duct.

### Absorption

2 monoacylglycerol, free fatty acids, free cholesterol plus bile salts

↓

Mixed micelles

[Clusters of amphipathic lipids that coalesce with their hydrophobic groups on the inside and their hydrophilic groups on the outside of the cluster. They are soluble in aqueous environment of intestinal lumen.]

↓

Approach towards brush border membrane of intestinal mucosal cells

↓

Short chain fatty acids are absorbed by blood but medium and long chain fatty acids, after leaving the micelles, enter the enterocytes to be incorporated in chylomicrons to be carried ultimately by lymphatics.

### Hormonal control of lipid digestion

**CCK** (also called pancreozymin), a small peptide hormone in the mucosa of jejunum and lower duodenum is produced when there is presence of lipids and partially digested proteins in the upper part of small intestine. ***It causes contraction of gall bladder and ejects bile. It also decreases gastric motility.*** Another small peptide hormone, secretin, is produced when low pH chyme enters into the intestine. It releases a watery solution rich in bicarbonate which helps to neutralize the pH of intestinal contents. Pancreatic lipase removes the fatty acids at carbons 1 and 3. Primary products of hydrolysis are 2-monoacylglycerol and free fatty acids.

## ➤ 4.15 Absorption in the Electrolytes, Water, Minerals and Vitamins

Approximately 9 litres of water is presented to the intestine everyday. 2 litres comes from water that is consumed and 7 liter comes from G.I. secretion. Almost 98% of this water is absorbed by the intestine to excrete only 200 ml. in stool. The small intestine has a large absorptive capacity only 40% of which is usually utilized. The **normal rate of absorption** is **200-400 ml/hour**. Apart from water, electrolytes like $Na^+$, $K^+$, $Cl^-$ and $HCO_3^-$ are also transported across the intestine. In the intestine, there are two routes for the transport of water and electrolytes across the epithelium. The transcellular route involves passage of the substance through the apical membrane of the enterocytes the cytoplasm of the enterocyte; and the basolateral membrane of the enterocytes. Substances transported via the paracellular route bypass the cytoplasm of the enterocytes; they pass through the extracellular space in between the basolateral membranes of the enterocytes (Fig. 4.51). The magnitude of the paracellular route is determined by the permeability of the tight junction (zonulae occludens).

### Absorption of sodium (Fig. 4.52)

Sodium can be absorbed from the intestine by four mechanisms: by passive diffusion through water-filled channels, by cotransport with a solute like glucose or amino acid, by cotransport with $Cl^-$, and by countertransport with $H^+$. Sodium that enters the enterocytes by any of these routes is extruded through the basolateral membrane of the enterocytes with the help of $Na^+$–$K^+$ ATPase. Each $Na^+$–$K^+$ ATPase allows two $K^+$ to enter the enterocytes for every three $Na^+$ pumped out. Thus, $K^+$ concentration within enterocytes is high. Excess $K^+$ leaks out of the enterocytes through $K^+$ leak channels present in the basolateral (as well as apical) membrane of these cells.

In colon, $Na^+$ entry occurs mainly via passive diffusion through water-filled channels. On the other hand, the other

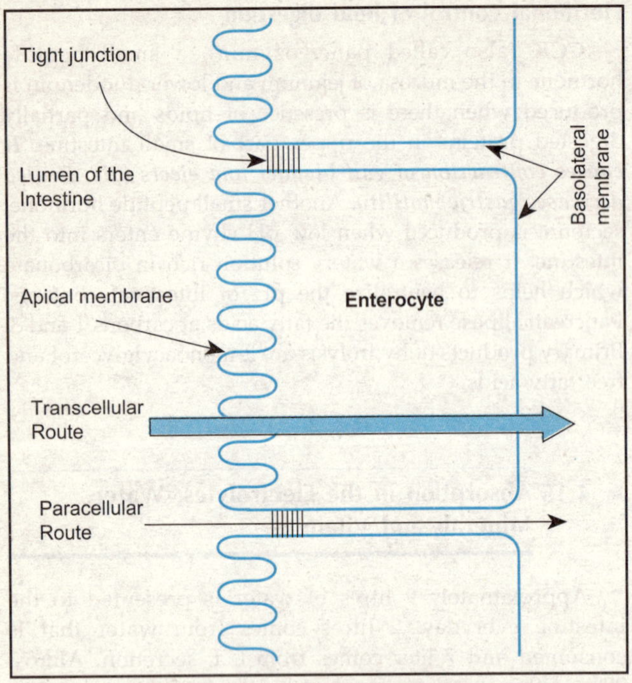


Fig. 4.51 : Transcellular and paracellular routes of transport across intestinal epithelium

three mechanisms predominate in the small intestine. The number of $Na^+$ channels in the apical membrane of colonic epithelial cells appears to be regulated by aldosterone (mineralocorticoid secreted by adrenal cortex); increase in aldosterone (in conditions such as hypovolemia) causes increase in $Na^+$ channel density and thereby increase in $Na^+$ absorption.

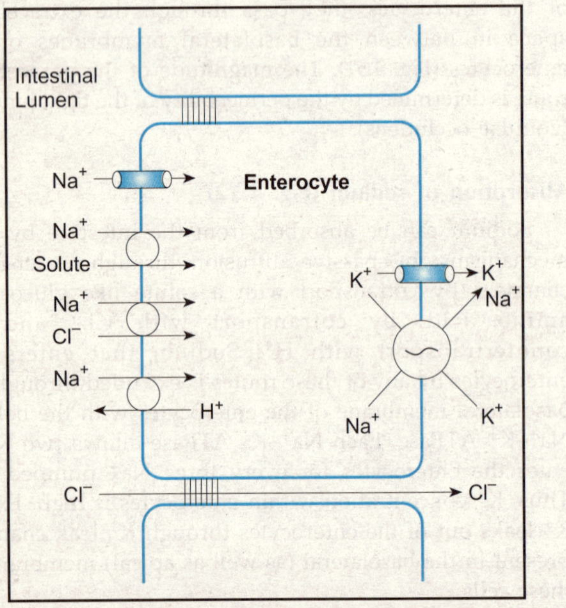


Fig. 4.52 : Mechanisms of $Na^+$ transport across intestinal epithelium on ⊖ Active transport

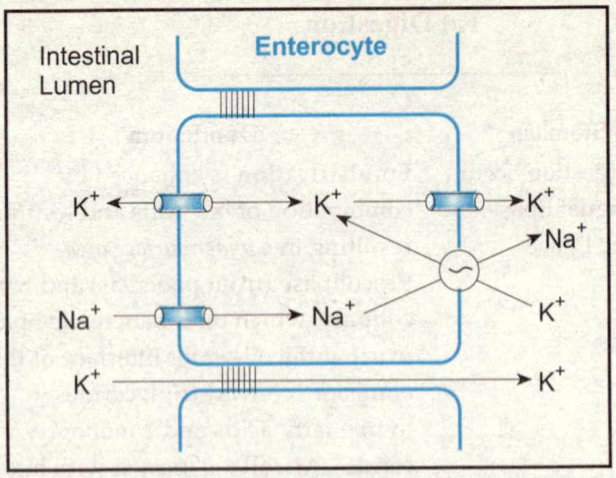


Fig. 4.53 : Absorption and secretion of $K^+$ in the intestine. ⊖ Active transport

## Transport of potassium by the intestine

Potassium in the intestine comes from two sources-diet and G.I. secretions. Potassium is both absorbed and secreted by the intestine (Fig. 4.53). Absorption occurs mostly in the small intestine and the primary mechanism responsible for absorption is probably diffusion through paracellular pathways. Secretion of $K^+$ occurs in the colonic epithelium. Some of the $K^+$ that enters colonocytes (colonic epithelial cells) through $Na^+ - K^+$ ATPase in their basolateral membranes exit into the colonic lumen via $K^+$ channels present in the apical membranes of the colonyctes. Therefore fecal water contains a high concentration of $K^+$. As the amount of water lost in feces is only about 100-200 ml/day, the absolute quantity of $K^+$ lost is not significant. In diarrohea, especially when it is chronic, $K^+$ loss through colon may be significant enough to cause hypokalemia. Aldosterone has an effect on colonic $K^+$ loss (and $Na^+$ reabsorption) similar to that it has on distal nephron, i.e., **aldosterone promotes** $Na^+$ **reabsorption and** $K^+$ **secretion by the colonocytes.**

## Transport of chloride and bicarbonate by the intestine

Absorption of $Na^+$ in the intestine creates an electrical potential difference across the intestinal epithelium driving $Cl^-$ through paracellular pathways (Fig. 4.54). Absorption of $Cl^-$ also occurs via transcellular pathways. Entry of $Cl^-$ into enterocytes through their apical membranes may occur either by cotransport with $Na^+$ or by counter transport with $HCO_3^-$. Exit of $Cl^-$ out of enterocytes through their basolateral membranes possibly occur by diffusion.

Some $Cl^-$ may enter enterocytes via $Na^+$–$K^+$ – $2Cl^-$ cotransporters in the basolateral membrane of enterocytes and it can be secreted into the lumen of the intestine via $Cl^-$ channels regulated by protein kinases. Secretion of $Cl^-$ by these channels is augmented by the toxin produced by *Vibrio cholerae* (bacteria causing cholera).

## Absorption of water by the intestine

Absorption of water by the intestine is a passive process. It is dependent on an proportional to the total solute

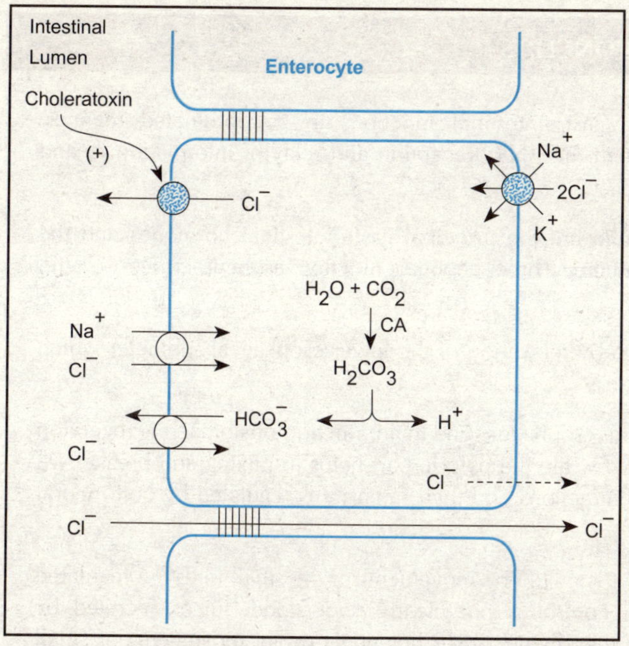


Fig. 4.54 : Chloride and bicarbonate transport by the intestine

absorption. The apical and basolateral membranes of the enterocytes are highly permeable to water; the tight junctions also allow to permeate through them.

## $Ca^{2+}$ absorption by intestine

It is dependent on $Ca^{2+}$ binding protein in mucosal epithelial cells. Most of the $Ca^{2+}$ is absorbed by primary active transport in the duodenum. Absorption of $Ca^{2+}$ is controlled by 1, 25 dihydroxy cholecalciferol (DHCC) which stimulates $Ca^{2+}$ entry to the cells from the lumen. Absorption of $Ca^{2+}$ is disturbed at an alkaline pH and if there is presence of fat in the gut. $Ca^{2+}$ entry may be carrier mediated. $Ca^{2+}$ is transported along the basolateral membrane by $Ca^{2+}$-ATPase and $Na^+$ $Ca^{2+}$ exchange protein. The rate of $Ca^{2+}$ absorption is increased when vitamin D is increased.

## Phosphate absorption

***1 gm of inorganic phosphate (Pi) is absorbed from the small intestine daily.*** This is mediated by coupled Pi cotransport at the luminal membrane and further stimulated by 1, 25 DHCC. It is not known how Pi leaves the cell along the basolateral membrane but definitely there is an involvement of carrier mediated process.

## Absorption of Vitamins by the Intestine

Fat-soluble vitamins (A, D, E and K) are absorbed with lipids in which they are dissolved. Most of the water-soluble vitamins depend on $Na^+$ for their absorption. Intrinsic factors secreted by gastric parietal cells is essential for absorption of vitamin $B_{12}$. While most of the vitamins are absorbed in the upper small intestine, vitamin $B_{12}$ is absorbed in the ileum.

## Iron absorption

1 mg of iron is absorbed daily. Iron is required for the synthesis of hemoglobin, myoglobin, cytochrome, catalase and peroxidase. $Fe^{2+}$ is readily absorbed in the duodenum and jejunum by an active process. Ionized form of iron enters cells directly via membrane transport. Absorption depends on the rate of erythropoiesis. Ascorbic acid enhances iron absorption by reducing $Fe^{3+}$ to $Fe^{2+}$. Acid in stomach breaks insoluble iron complexes apart and helps iron absorption. Iron is important in oxygen storage, transfer and metabolism.

## Transport of iron from intestine to the plasma

Iron is carried to apical membrane of enterocyte by a specific iron carrier system. Iron binds to apoferritin to form ferritin. Subsequently, iron is transported to the plasma by transferrin (β-globulin). ***The total body content of iron is about 4 gm. 65% is in the form of hemoglobin, 5% is in the form of myoglobin and 1% is in enzymes.*** The rest is stored in the liver (primarily) in the form of ferritin and hemosiderin. Normal adult male absorbs approximately 1 mg/day. Iron is absorbed in the duodenum and upper jejunum :

**Forms of absorption of iron**

| Bound to hemoglobin, myoglobin (known as heme iron) | Free ionized iron in the ferric ($Fe^{3+}$) or ferrous state ($Fe^{2+}$) |
|---|---|

Some heme traverses membrane directly due to lipophilic action. Heme binds with heme oxygenase within the cell, thereby releasing free iron. Then, iron binds with ferritin and reaches the basolateral surface. Most of the iron in the enterocyte binds with storage protein known as apoferritin yielding ferritin. The iron present in the plasma is bound to a β-globulin, called **transferrin**.

## ➤ 4.16 KEY CONCEPTS

1. **Both neural and hormonal mechanisms** regulate the gastrointestinal functions in a coordinated manner. Information to and from the GI tract is transmitted through the ANS. Reception and relay of information to and from the ANS is carried by enteric nervous system (ENS).

2. **Gastrin, cholecystokinin (CCK), secretin, GIP** and **motilin** are the principal gastrointestinal hormones and the main paracrine agents include somatostatin and histamine. Three peptides function as neurocrines — VIP, bombesin and enkephalins.

3. From the esophagus the bolus of food enters the stomach by relaxation of the lower esophageal sphincter which is otherwise closed.

4. **Swallowing** produces primary peristaltic movements in the esophagus. The main function of stomach is reception of food. However, cardiac part of stomach stores the food while the pyloric part helps in mixing and breakdown of food. The slow depolarization waves evoke gastric contractions and their intensity is regulated by both neural and hormonal mechanisms.

5. The **chyme** from the stomach enters the intestine where it is mixed by movements of the small intestine regulated by intrinsic and extrinsic nerves. However, hormonal control is not clearly understood. Juices secreted by pancreas and liver help in digestion and in mixing of the chyme. Spike potentials evoke movements of small intestine. Movements of first part of large intestine are weak and help in storage of contents and absorption of water.

6. **Saliva** is secreted from the salivary glands and its total secretion amounts to 1.5 litres per day of which $^1/_3$ is secreted by the parotid gland and rest by the submandibular and other glands. Saliva is mainly composed of water with mucus, ions and enzymes like α-amylase and lingual lipase. Primary saliva is produced in the acinar (endpiece cell) cells of salivary glands. Saliva is hypotonic containing high concentration of $K^+$.

7. The **total gastric secretion** amounts to *2-3 litres daily* and is composed of water, mucus, ions, HCl, enzymes (pepsin and gastric lipase) and intrinsic factor necessary for vitamin $B_{12}$ absorption. Parietal cells secrete hydrochloric acid amounting to about 150 mmol/L. Parietal cells have protein pumps ($H^+$– $K^+$ATPase) in their apical membrane by help of which $H^+$ is secreted into gastric lumen. Gastrin, histamine and acetylcholine are some of the gastric acid secretion stimulators.

8. **Pancreatic secretion** is approximately 1.5 litres per day and contains water, $HCO_3^-$ ions and enzymes like pancreatic amylase, lipase and proteolytic enzymes like trypsin and chymotrypsin. Secretin is the principal stimulator of pancreatic secretion whose action is increased by CCK and acetylcholine.

9. **Bile** is produced continuously by the liver, stored in the gall bladder and secreted intermittently after the meals. Bile contains bile acids, cholesterol, phospholipids, bile pigments, water and different ions. Of these bile salts and bicarbonate ions are specially important in digestion (Fig. 4.55).

10. **Hepatocytes** produce the primary bile acids from cholesterol. A large part of it is absorbed in the intestine and is brought back to liver by portal vein.

11. The **greatest part of digestion and absorption** occurs in the small intestine. Disaccharides are broken down by specific enzymes present in the brush border membranes. Glucose and galactose are absorbed in the intestine actively by $Na^+$ dependent co-transport system.

12. **Trypsinogen is activated by enterokinase to form trypsin, which helps in digestion of protein.** There are several transporters in the brush border membrane for the absorption of di and tri-peptides as well as for different free amino acids. Fat digestion is carried out by the pancreatic enzymes such as lipase, phospholipase A and cholesterol ester hydrolase.

13. **Triglycerides,** by the action of lipid hydrolases, are broken down into free fatty acids and monoglycerides. The products of lipid digestion form micelles with the help of bile salts and diffuse across the surface of enterocytes.

## ➤ 4.16 KEY CONCEPTS

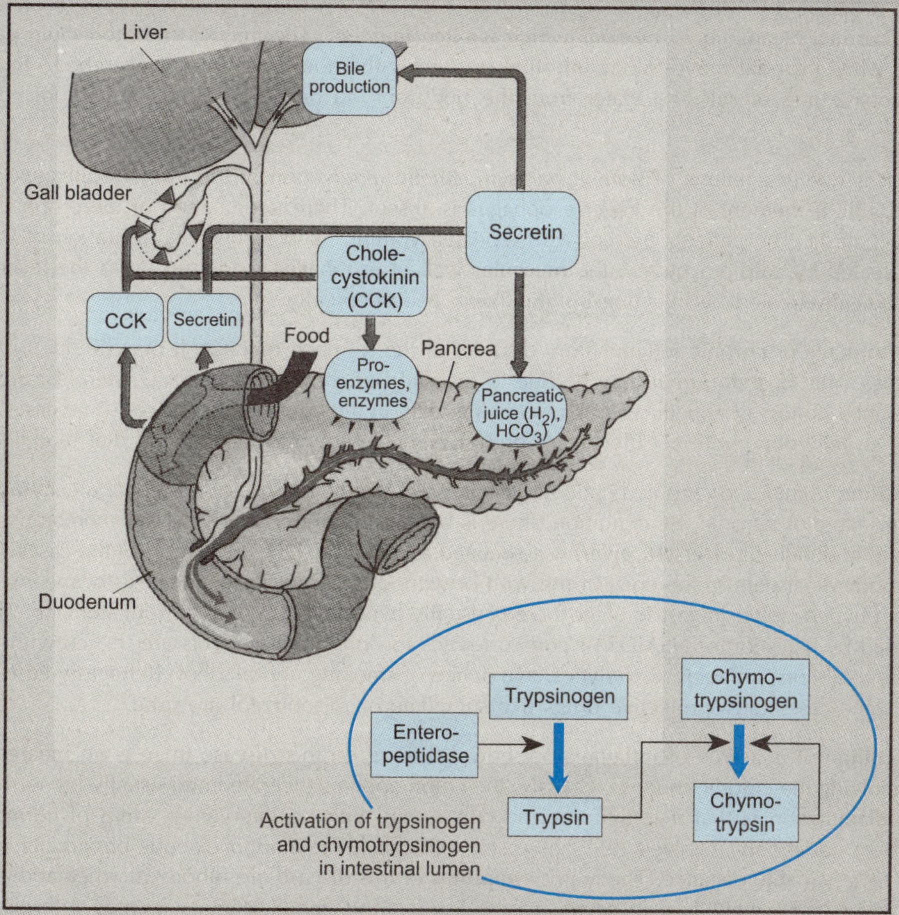


Action of bile and pancreatic juice

14. **Triglycerides** and **phospholipids** are resynthesized inside the enterocytes and they then form **chylomicrons**. These chylomicrons come out of the enterocyte by exocytosis to enter the lymphatic circulation through the lacteals.
15. **Minerals** are mainly absorbed in the small intestine. *90% of the* **sodium** *is absorbed in small intestine and about 10% is absorbed in the colon.* ***Potassium*** absorption in the small intestine involves diffusion through paracellular pathway. ***Water*** is absorbed both through cellular and paracellular pathways influenced by the surrounding osmotic gradients. Absorption of ***calcium*** and ***inorganic phosphate*** is stimulated by active vitamin D (1, 25 dihydroxycholecalciferol).

## ➤ 4.17 DISORDERS/CLINICAL CORRELATIONS

➤ **Diarrhea :** Diarrhea means liquid motions which is often frequent. The frequent and too rapid passage of loose feces results when material moves along intestine so quickly that too little water is absorbed. In acute diarrhea, there is excessive loss of salt and water from the body and so dehydration results. Chronic diarrhea causes malnutrition.

➤ **Achalasia :** It is due to agenesis of normal parasympathetic innervation of the lower esophagus. As a result the normal peristaltic movement of the lower esophagus is absent. There is dilatation of the esophagus proximal to the site of achalasia. The patients present with repeated vomiting and sometimes aspiration of vomitus into the lungs. It is treated by cardiomyotomy (the muscular wall of esophagus is incised up to the level of esophageal mucosa). Medically treated by injecting Botulin Toxin endoscopically.

➤ **Gastritis :** An acute or chronic inflammatory disorder of the stomach mucosa. It may be due to infection of the gastric mucosa with ***H. pylori*** or it may be due to ingestion of some drugs (NSAID, steroids, doxycycline). The patients present with loss of appetite, nausea, vomiting, pain in the epigastrium and, in some cases, hematemesis. Treatment is usually done with $H_2$ blocker or proton pump inhibitor, antacids, and diet modifications.

➤ **Peptic ulceration** (Acute and chronic peptic ulcer) : It may be either gastric or duodenal ulceration both of which can be either acute or chronic. By definition, there is breach in continuity of mucous membrane of the stomach or duodenum. In duodenal ulcers ***H. pylori*** is associated as a causative agent in most of the cases. Patient presents with upper abdominal pain in the epigastrium with or without vomiting, haematemesis or melena. There may be complaints of hyperacidity. In gastric ulcer there is usually hyposecretion of acid from stomach. These ulcers can also be caused by ingestion of NSAIDS or corticosteroids for long time. Patients are treated with $H_2$ antagonists, proton pump inhibitors, antacids, anxiolytics, avoidance of smoking and alcohol. Refractory cases are treated by surgery. In some cases mucoprotective drugs like sucralfate or misoprostol are used.

➤ **Ulcerative colitis :** It is a type of inflammatory bowel disease. In this disease there is an inflammatory reaction primarily involving the colonic mucosa. Grossly, the colon appears ulcerated and usually hemorrhagic. A striking feature of inflammation is that it is uniform and continuous with no intervening areas of normal mucosa. The rectum is most commonly involved (95% of cases) and the inflammation extends proximally in a continuous fashion but for a variable distance. The major **symptoms** of this disease are bloody diarrhea and abdominal pain, often with fever and weight loss in severe cases. Extracolonic manifestations include arthritis, skin changes, evidence of liver disease etc.

➤ **Cirrhosis of liver :** It is defined as irreversible chronic injury of the liver with extensive fibrosis and regenerative nodule formation. The **causes of cirrhosis** can be enumerated as (i) alcoholic; (ii) cryptogenic and postviral or postnecrotic; (iii) biliary; (iv) cardiac; (v) metabolic, inherited and drug related; (vi) miscellaneous.

**Clinical features** of cirrhosis derive from the morphological alterations and often reflect the severity of hepatic damage rather than the etiology of cirrhosis. Loss of functioning liver tissue may lead to jaundice, edema and a variety of metabolic abnormalities; fibrosis and distorted vasculature lead to portal hypertension and its sequelae including gastroesophageal varices and splenomegaly. Ascites and hepatic encephalopathy result from both hepatocellular insufficiency and portal hypertension.

➤ **Tumors of the pancreas :** A variety of tumors are found in the pancreas. They are named according to the hormones they produce eg, **gastrinoma** (gastrin); **insulinoma** (insulin); **VIPoma** (VIP); **glucagonoma** (glucagon); **somatostatinoma** (somatostatin). There may be nonfunctioning islet cell tumours which are not associated with any definable hormone mediated syndrome.

➤ **Gastrinoma or Zollinger-Ellison Syndrome :** This is a gastrin secreting tumor of the pancreas. These gastrinomas produce high serum gastrin levels leading to hypersecretion of gastric acid and consequent duodenal and jejunal ulcers. They are the most common of the hormone secreting tumors of the pancreatic islets. Ulcer disease develops in almost all patients with gastrinoma. More than half of the patients experience diarrhea and approximately 30 percent present with diarrhea alone. **Treatment** of Zollinger-Ellison syndrome is directed at the sequelae of excess gastric secretion and at the tumor itself. The availability of $H_2$ antagonists and proton pump inhibitors has reduced the need for surgery in these patients. The rare patient who fails to respond to medical therapy should be treated surgically.

## ➤ 4.17 DISORDERS/CLINICAL CORRELATIONS

➤ **Gall stone :** These are crystalline structures formed by concretion or accretion of normal or abnormal bile constituents. These stones are usually of three types. ***Cholesterol*** and ***mixed stones*** account for 80% of total with ***pigment*** stones comprising the remaining 20%. Mixed and cholesterol gall stones usually contain more than 70% cholesterol monohydrate plus an admixture of calcium salts, bile acids and bile pigments, proteins, fatty acids and phospholipids. **Pigment stones** are composed of calcium bilirubinate and they contain less than 10 per cent cholesterol. The **symptoms of gall stones** are either due to inflammation or obstruction following their migration into the cystic duct or common bile duct. They may be asymptomatic. The most specific and characteristic symptom of gall stone disease is **biliary colic**. **Gall stone** disease can be treated by surgical methods. Medical therapy, though available, is usually not very effective (nowadays gall stones can be fragmented by lithotripsy and then removed). In recent times laparoscopic cholecystectomy is preferred.

➤ **Cholecystitis (Acute and chronic) :** It is, by definition, inflammation of the gall bladder. This inflammatory response can be acute or chronic. It is usually **provoked by three factors** (i) mechanical inflammation; (ii) chemical inflammation; (iii) bacterial inflammation, which usually accounts for 50-85 percent of patients with acute cholecystitis. **Acute cholecystitis** often begins as an attack of biliary colic which progressively worsens. The right upper quadrant of abdomen is almost invariably tender on palpation. The triad of sudden onset of right upper quadrant tenderness, fever and leukocytosis is highly suggestive. Chronic inflammation of the gall bladder wall is almost always associated with the presence of gall stones and is thought to result from repeated bouts of subacute or acute cholecystitis or from persistent mechanical irritation of the gall bladder wall. **Chronic cholecystitis** is treated by surgical removal of the gall bladder considering the natural course of the disease. Acute cholecystitis is also best treated by early surgery whenever possible.

➤ **Acute pancreatitis :** It is an acute inflammatory disorder of the pancreas where there is a possibility that normal function of the pancreas may be restored. Approximately 80% of cases of acute pancreatitis are due to alcohol and gallstones. Another 10% of cases one due to metabolic abnormalities (e.g. hyperlipidemia), drugs (e.g. steroids, thiazide diuretics) and trauma. And 10% of cases are idiopathic, with a small role for hereditary pancreatitis (approximately 1%). Autodigestion is one pathogenic theory which proposes that proteolytic enzymes are activated within the pancreas rather than in the intestinal lumen. A recent hypothesis to explain the intrapancreatic activation of zymogens is that they become activated by lysosomal hydrolases within the pancreatic acinar cell itself.

The patient usually **presents** with upper abdominal pain, nausea, vomiting, abdominal distension, low grade fever, tachycardia and hypotension. The **diagnosis** of acute pancreatitis is usually suggested by the presence of an increased **serum amylase**. Three-fold rise virtually clinches the diagnosis. Lipase is more specific for pancreatitis. Radiological investigations (straight X-ray abdomen, USG or CT scan of abdomen) are also of value in the diagnosis of acute pancreatitis.

➤ **Chronic pancreatitis :** It is a **chronic inflammatory disorder of the pancreas**. It may present as an episode of acute inflammation superimposed on a previously injured pancreas or as chronic damage with persistent pain or malabsorption. The causes of chronic relapsing pancreatitis are similar to those of acute pancreatitis except that there is a sizeable proportion of cases of undetermined origin. Patients with chronic pancreatitis who develop extensive destruction of the pancreas will demonstrate steatorrhea. Patients may present with upper abdominal pain, weight loss, abnormal stool and often signs or symptoms of malabsorption.

➤ **Viral hepatitis :** It is a viral infection of the liver. It is caused by hepatitis virus A, B, C, D, E, F and G. The patient comes with history of anorexia, fever and malaise followed by yellowish discoloration of urine and eyes. The liver may be enlarged and some patients may complain of discomfort in right upper abdomen. Splenomegaly is present in 20% of cases. The **diagnosis** is confirmed by **serum bilirubin, SGPT, SGOT** and **serological tests**. Treatment is usually strict bed rest and ingestion of high carbohydrate diet. Hepatitis B, D and C can be associated with serious and fatal complications.

➤ **Malabsorption :** By definition, it means defective absorption of one or more constituents of food. Depending on the constituent whose absorption is defective, the patient presents with different clinical features. **Malabsorption disorders** can be due to a **variety of causes**. It can be due to **inadequate digestion** (eg, post-gastrectomy steatorrhea or deficiency/inactivation of pancreatic lipase), **reduced intestinal bile salt concentration** (eg, parenchymal liver disease); inadequate absorptive surface (eg, intestinal resection or bypass), **primary mucosal absorptive defects** (eg, inflammatory or infiltrative disorders, regional enteritis) or endocrine and metabolic disorders (eg, diabetes mellitus).

## ➤ 4.17 DISORDERS/CLINICAL CORRELATIONS

➤ **Gastric carcinoma :** 90% of the gastric cancers are adenocarcinoma whereas the rest 10% is contributed by non-Hodgkins lymphoma and leiomyosarcoma. Blood group A persons have a higher incidence of gastric carcinoma as compared with those with blood group 'O'. Patients usually present with vague upper abdominal discomfort, post-prandial fullness of abdomen, anorexia and, sometimes, dysphagia. The presence of iron deficiency anemia and occult blood in the stool of both sexes should mandate a search for an occult lesion in the GI tract. Usual clinical features of gastric adenocarcinoma includes migratory thrombophlebitis. The best treatment of gastric carcinoma is complete surgical removal of the tumor with resection of the adjacent lymph nodes. These tumors are relatively radioresistant but cytotoxic chemotherapy can cause reduction in tumor mass by more than 50%.

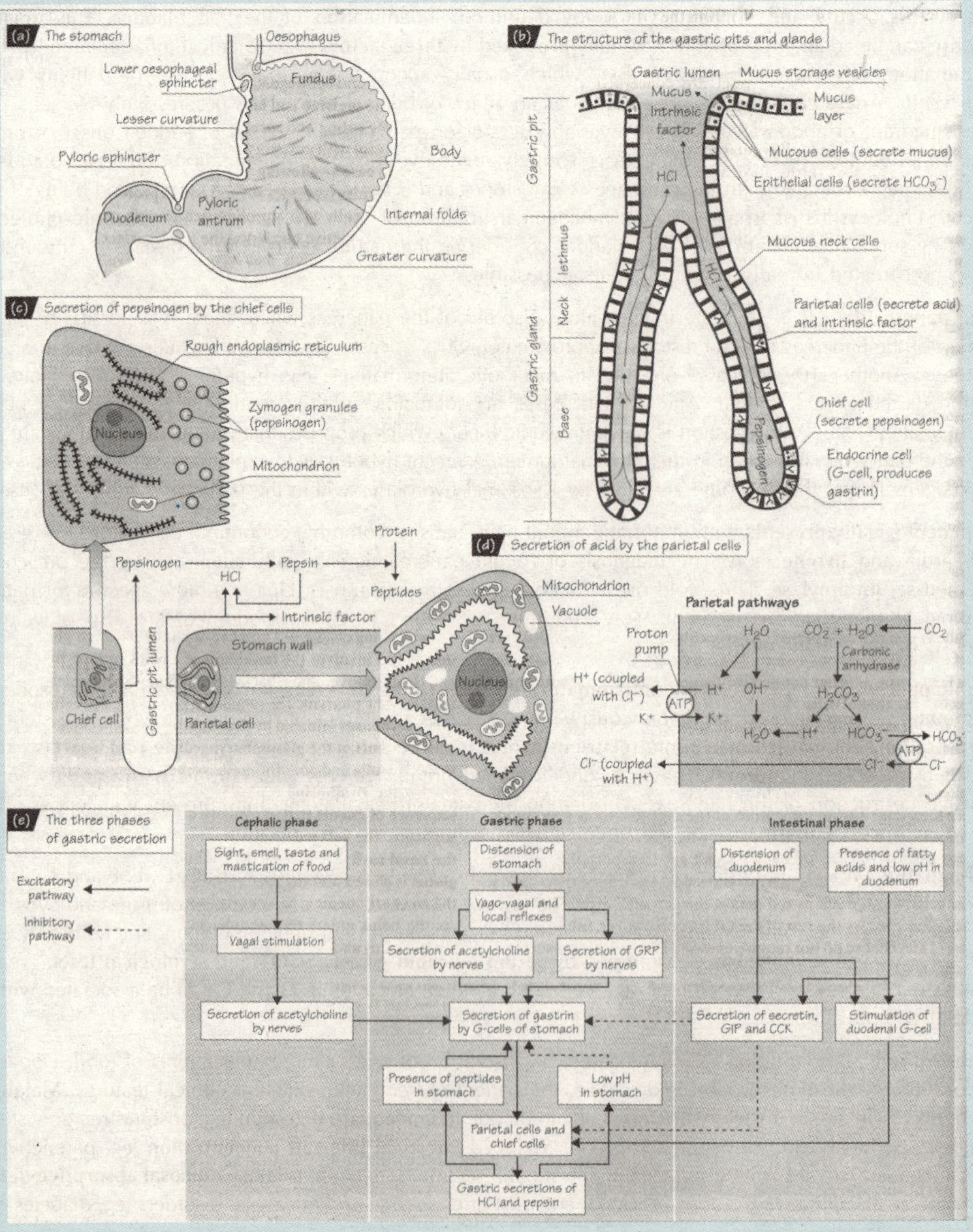

# Blood and Related Physiology

AGENDA :



5

## ➤ 5.1 CHAPTER OVERVIEW

**Blood** is composed of cellular part (erythrocytes, leukocytes and platelets) and non-cellular part (plasma). Plasma is about 55% and cells are about 45% of blood volume.

The **plasma proteins** are synthesized and secreted by liver and some are produced and secreted by lymphocytes.

**Red cells** are non-nucleated biconcave discs having a diameter of about 7.2 μm that carry hemoglobin in the circulation. RBCs are derived from pluripotent hematopoietic stem cells in the red bone marrow. The cellular elements of blood are responsible for gas transport, immunity and some aspects of hemostasis.

**The membranes of human RBCs** contain over 300 different antigenic determinants dictated by genes at different chromosomal loci. The term blood group refers to any well-defined system of RBC antigen. Over twenty blood group systems have been recognized so far.

**Erythropoietin** is a circulating glycoprotein that increases the number of erythropoietin-sensitive committed stem cells in the bone marrow and, thereby, facilitates erythropoiesis.

**Anemia** is said to be present when the hemoglobin level in the blood is below the lower extreme of the normal range for the age and sex of the individual. Anemia may be due to loss of blood, underproduction of RBCs or lysis of RBCs (hemolysis).

**Platelets** are very small non-nucleated discs, 2-4 μm in diameter, derived from the cytoplasm of megakaryocytes in red bone marrow. **Plasma proteins** are the most abundant dissolved substances in plasma.

**The white cells** differ from red cells in that they contain no hemoglobin and have nuclei. The most of white cells are considerably larger than the erythrocytes.

## ➤ 5.2 Introduction

Blood is composed of cells (erythrocytes, leukocytes and platelets) and plasma (water and dissolved solutes). ***Plasma is about 55% and cells are about 45%*** of blood volume. The ***plasma*** contains water (90%) and dissolved substances such as plasma proteins (albumin, globulin, fibrinogen etc.), inorganic salts (sodium chloride, sodium bicarbonate, K, Mg, P, Fe, Ca, Cu, I, Co), monosaccharides (from carbohydrates), amino acids (from proteins), fatty acids and glycerol (from fats), vitamins (from foods), hormones, immunoglobulins and gases ($O_2$, $CO_2$, $N_2$).

### Functions of blood :

- Nutrients are delivered from gut to tissues.
- The carriage of oxygen from the lung to the tissues to the lungs.
- Waste products of metabolism are transported from the sites of production to the sites of disposal.
- Hormones are carried from endocrine glands to specific target tissues.
- Immunological role protection against invading organisms.

## ➤ 5.3 Blood Cell Production

### Cellular elements of blood

**Blood cells** are not born in the blood. Blood cells are produced in the red bone marrow from cells called ***stem cells*** (Table 5.1). Blood cell production is regulated by cytokines which are released by supporting cells in the marrow. **Cytokines** are proteins that control many activities of cells nonspecifically.

**Table 5.1**
**Bone marrow production pathways of blood cells**

| | Erythroid | Granulocytic | Monocytic | Megakaryocytic |
|---|---|---|---|---|
| Marrow | Proerythroblast<br>↓<br>Erythroblasts<br>↓<br>Reticulocyte<br>↓ | Myeloblast<br>↓<br>Promyelocyte<br>↓<br>Myelocyte (neutrophil, eosinophil and basophil)<br>↓<br>Metamyelocyte (neutrophil, eosinophil and basophil)<br>↓ | Monoblast<br>↓<br>Promonocyte<br>↓<br>Monocyte<br>↓ | Megakaryoblast<br>↓<br>Promegakaryocyte<br>↓<br>Megakaryocyte<br>↓<br>Platelet<br>↓ |
| Blood | Reticulocyte<br>↓<br>**Erythrocyte** | **Neutrophil**<br>**Eosinophil**<br>**Basophil** | **Monocyte**<br>↓ | **Platelet** |
| Tissue | | | **Macrophage** | |

Hematopoietic growth factors (eg, cytokines) stimulate multipotent and committed stem cells. ***Megakaryocyte colony*** stimulating factor is responsible for the production of ***platelets***. Similarly interleukin-3, insulin-like growth factor-1 and erythropoietin are responsible for the production of red cells.

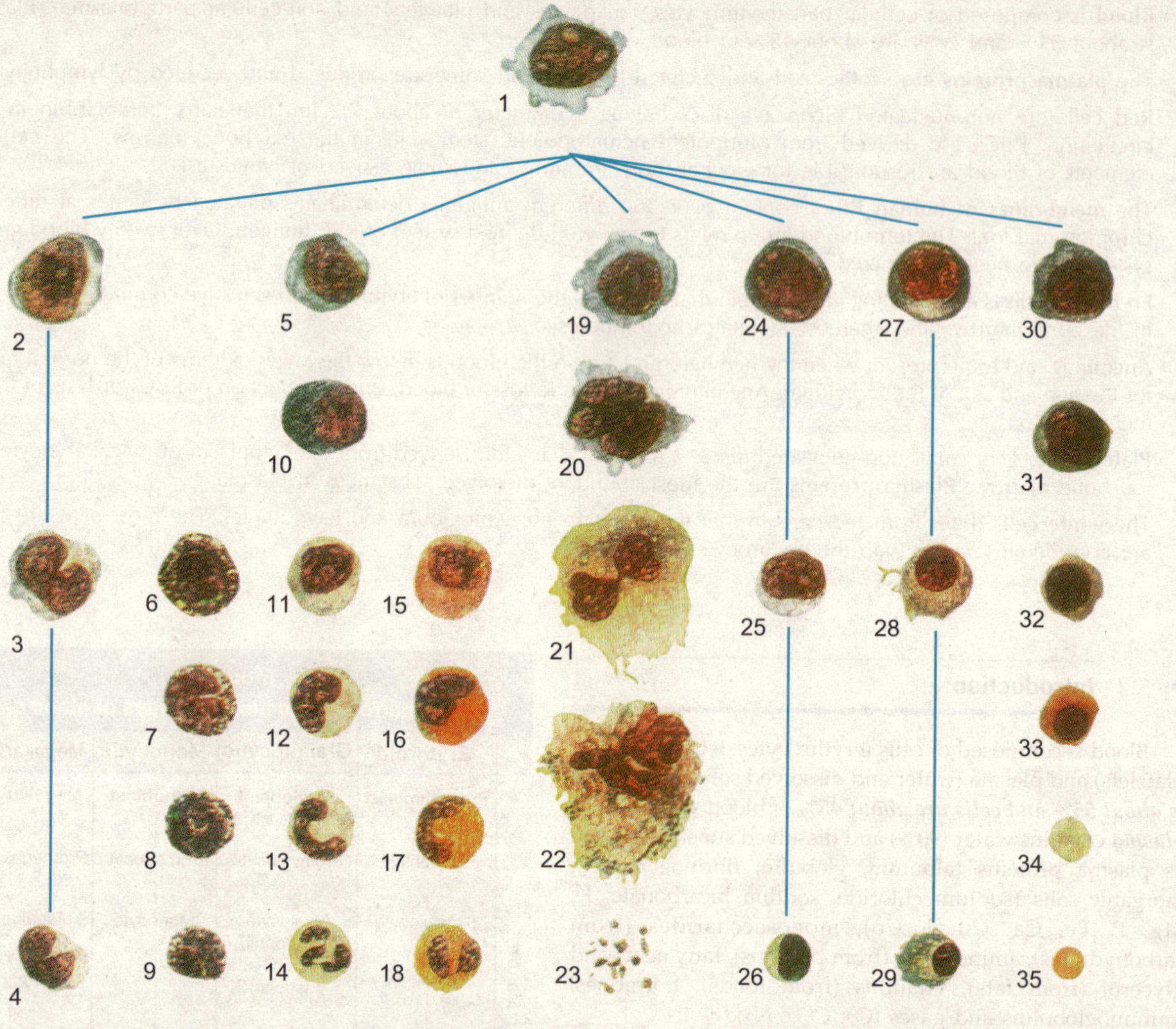


1. Stem cell; 2. Monoblast; 3. Promonocyte; 4. Monocyte; 5. Myeloblast; 6. Progranulocyte; 7. Basophilic myelocyte; 8. Basophilic metamyelocyte; 9. Basophilic band; 10. Basophilic segmented; 11. Neutrophilic myelocyte; 12. Neutrophilic metamyelocyte; 13. Neutrophilic band; 14. Neutrophilic segmented; 15. Eosinophilic myelocyte; 16. Eosinophilic metamyelocyte; 17. Eosinophilic band; 18. Eosinophilic segmented; 19. Megakaryoblast; 20. Promegakaryocyte; 21. Megakaryocyte; 22. Metamegakaryocyte; 23. Thrombocytes; 24. Lymphoblast; 25. Prolymphocyte; 26. Lymphocyte; 27. Plasmoblast; 28. Proplasmocyte; 29. Plasmocyte; 30. Rubriblast; 31. Prorubricyte; 32. Rubricyte; 33. Metarubricyte; 34. Diffusely basophilic erythrocyte; 35. Erythrocyte

Fig. 5.1 : Haematopoiesis

### Hematopoiesis

Blood cells originate in the yolksac in the initial weeks (3rd week) of gestation. All types of blood cells develop mainly in the liver but also in the spleen from about 6 weeks to 7 months of fetal life. ***At birth the marrow is the main site of hematopoiesis.***

**Blood cells** are produced in the bone marrow from precursors known as *pluripotent stem cells.* **T- and B-lymphocytes** are produced from stem cells via lymphoid stem cells. Platelets, erythrocytes, monocytes, neutrophils, eosinophils and basophils all originate from hemopoietic stem cell via megakaryocytes, erythroid stem cells, myeloid stem cells and granulocyte stem cells. ***The three stimulating factors thrombopoietin, erythropoietin and colony stimulating factors*** are necessary for cell production. Though mast cell is similar to basophil, it has different origin. At an early stage of life, the thymus gland guides T-cells to distinguish between self and non-self (Fig. 5.1).

## ➤ 5.4 Red Blood Cell

**Red blood cells** (RBCs) are non-nucleated, biconcave discs having a diameter of ***about 7.2 μm*** that carry

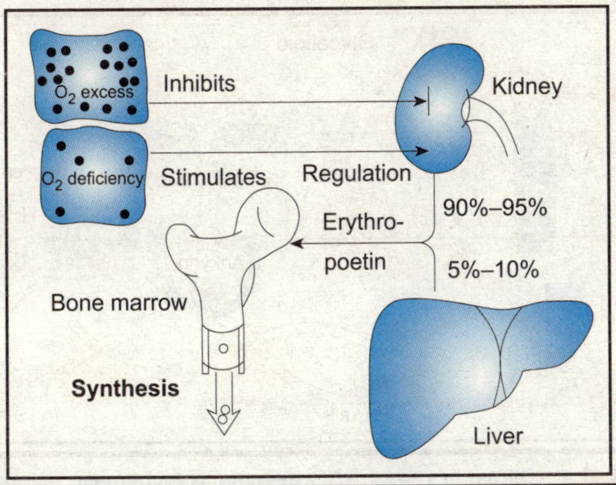


**Fig. 5.2 :** Synthesis of erythrocytes in adults

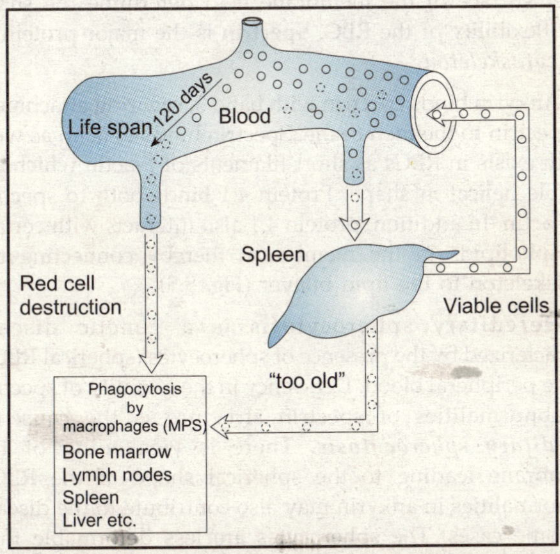


**Fig. 5.3 :** Destruction of erythrocytes in adults

hemoglobin in the circulation. They are produced in the *red bone marrow* in adult life and survive in the circulation for about 120 days. On an average, a normal adult male contains ***5.4 million RBCs per cubic mm*** of blood whereas the total RBC count in a normal adult female is ***about 4.8 million/cu.mm.***

## Erythropoiesis (Fig. 5.4)

RBCs are derived from the pluripotent hematopoietic stem cell in the red bone marrow. The most primitive erythroid pro-genitor is called the **erythroid burst-forming unit (BFU-E).** From BFU-E erythroid ***colony-forming unit (CFU-E)*** is formed. CFU-E is very sensitive to erythropoietin, a glycoprotein hormone produced primarily by the endothelial cells of the peritubular capillaries of the renal cortex in response to hypoxia. Erythropoietin induces differentiation of CFU-E into proerythroblasts. **Proery-throblasts**

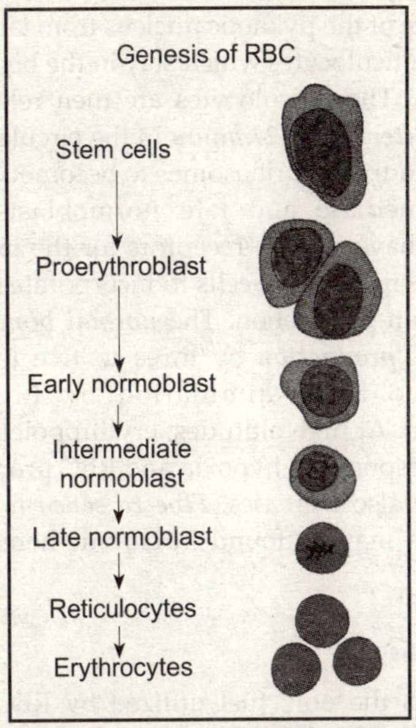


**Fig. 5.4 :** RBCs at various stages of development

undergo three or four cell divisions to produce ***early, intermediate and late normoblasts*** over a 4-day period. During this period, increasing amount of hemoglobin appears in the cytoplasm and the nucleus becomes smaller.

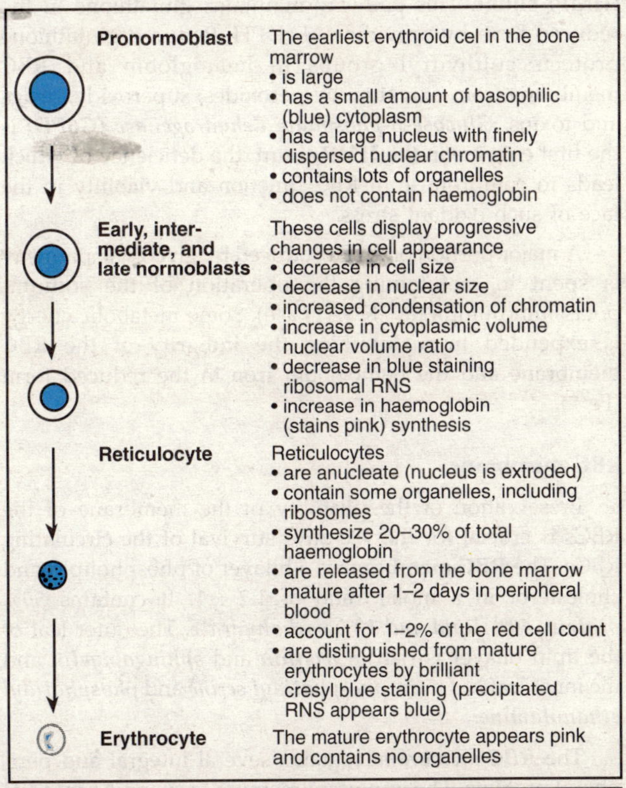


**Fig. 5.4(a) :** Red cell precursors and sequence of erythropoiesis. The appearance is that seen with the routine Romanowsky stain unless otherwise specified

Disappearance of the pyknotic nucleus from late normoblasts gives rise to reticulocytes which stay in the bone marrow for 2.5 to 3 days. The reticulocytes are then released into the circulation. ***After about 24 hours*** in the circulation they lose their mitochondria and ribosomes to become a **mature RBC**. Early, intermediate and late normoblasts as well as reticulocytes have surface receptors for the iron-transferrin complex that enable these cells to incorporate sufficient iron for hemoglobin production. The ***normal bone marrow can increase RBC production*** by three to five times within a week or two after stimulation by high levels of erythropoietin. At high altitudes, erythropoietin production increases in response to hypoxia and RBC production by the bone marrow also increases. ***Five-to seven-fold*** increase in erythropoiesis may be found in chronic hemolytic anemia (Fig. 5.4).

## RBC metabolism

**Glucose** is the only fuel utilized by RBCs. Glucose is taken up by facilitated diffusion and is converted to ***glucose-6-phosphate.*** 80-90% of glucose-6-phosphate is converted to lactate by the ***glycolytic (Embden-Meyerhoff)*** pathway that generates two moles of ATP from each mole of glucose. 2, 3-diphosphoglycerate (2, 3-DPG), the intracellular mediator of hemoglobin function, is synthesized in a side-reaction in the glycolytic pathway. About 10% of the glucose-6-phosphate is oxidized via the **hexose-monophosphate (HMP) shunt**. This pathway maintains glutathione in the reduced form by providing NADPH. Reduced glutathione protects sulfhydryl groups in hemoglobin and RBC membrane from oxidation by peroxides, superoxide, drugs and toxins. ***Glucose-6-phosphate dehydrogenase (G6PD)*** is the first enzyme in the **HMP shunt,** the deficiency of which leads to compromise of RBC function and viability in the face of such oxidant stress.

A major portion of ATP produced by glycolytic pathway is spent in maintaining the operation of the sodium-potassium pump ($Na^+$-$K^+$-ATPase). Some metabolic energy is expended in maintaining the integrity of the RBC membrane and the hemoglobin iron in the reduced form ($Fe^{2+}$).

## RBC membrane

Preservation of the pliability of the membrane of the RBCs is crucial for the 120-days survival of the circulating RBCs. The **RBC membrane** is a bilayer of phospholipid and cholesterol in a molar ratio of 1.2 : 1. It contains ***50% protein, 40% lipid and 10% carbohydrate***. The outer leaf of the lipid bilayer is rich in ***lecithin*** and ***sphingomyelin*** and the inner leaf has more ***phosphatidyl serine*** and ***phosphatidyl ethanolamine***.

The ***RBC membrane*** contains several integral and peripheral proteins. The important membrane spanning integral proteins include an anion exchange protein (band 3) and glycophorins (which contain a number of polysaccharide blood group antigens) among others. Peripheral membrane

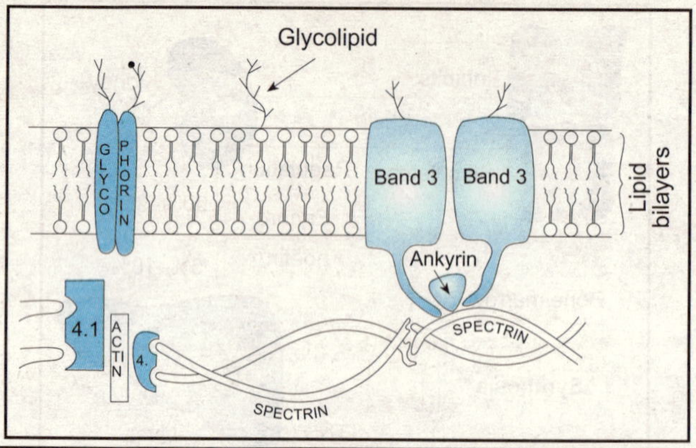


Fig. 5.5 : Ultrastructure of RBC membrane (*schematic diagram*)

proteins like ***spectrin, ankyrin*** and ***actin*** present on the inner surface of the membrane help determine the shape and flexibility of the RBC. **Spectrin** is the major protein of the ***cytoskeleton***.

Ankyrin binds spectrin with band 3, securing attachment of spectrin to the membrane. Spectrin binds to actin as well. Actin exists in RBCs as short filaments of F-actin which are double helical in shape. Protein 4.1 binds both to spectrin and actin. In addition, protein 4.1 also interacts with certain phospholipids in the membrane, thereby connecting the cytoskeleton to the lipid bilayer (Fig. 5.5).

**Hereditary spherocytosis** is a genetic disease characterized by the presence of spherocytes (spherical RBCs) in the peripheral blood. Deficiency in the quantity of spectrin or abnormalities of spectrin structure is the cause of ***hereditary spherocytosis***. There is weakening of the membrane leading to the spherical shape of the RBCs. Abnormalities in ankyrin may also contribute to the disease in some cases. The spherocytes are less deformable than normal RBCs and have higher surface-to-volume ratio. Hence, they are destroyed in the spleen giving rise to ***hemolytic anemia***. The spherocytes are more susceptible to osmotic lysis than normal RBCs. Susceptibility of RBCs to osmotic lysis is tested in vitro by osmotic fragility test in which RBCs are exposed to decreasing concentration of sodium chloride. 50% of spherocytes are lysed at a NaCl concentration of 0.50 g/dL while very few normal RBCs are lysed at this concentration.

**Hereditary elliptocytosis** is also a genetic disease similar to hereditary spherocytosis, but the affected RBCs are elliptical in shape. The defect lies in ***spectrin*** but, in some cases, defects in band ***4.1 or glycophorin C*** may be present as well.

## Fate of RBCs

The life of a RBC comes to an end possibly due to a loss of the flexibility of its membrane preventing it from negotiating the narrow channels of the microcirculation including the splenic sinusoids. The senescent RBCs are

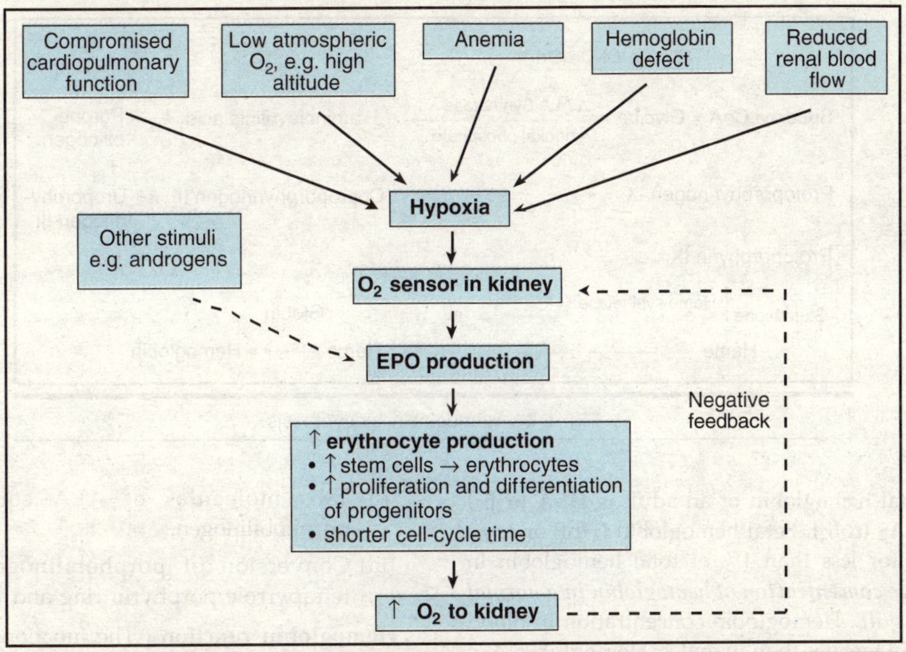


**Fig. 5.6 : Regulation of RBC and erythropoietin (EPO) production**

sequestered mainly in spleen and are engulfed by the macrophages. Hemoglobin is readily catabolized. Amino acids that are generated by proteolytic digestion of hemoglobin are subsequently metabolized. The heme group is catabolized by a microsomal oxidizing system to iron and porphyrin. Iron that is released is first incorporated into ferritin (the iron storage protein). Later on, iron is transported to bone marrow erythroid precursor cells by transferrin (the iron-transport protein in the plasma). The porphyrin ring is converted to bile pigments (biliverdin, bilirubin) which are excreted by the liver. During catabolism of the heme group, one mole of carbon monoxide is generated per mole of heme. Endogenous production of carbon monoxide correlates well with erythroid cell destruction.

### Erythropoietin

**Erythropoietin** is a circulating glycoprotein that increases the number of erythropoietin-sensitive committed stem cells in the bone marrow and, thereby, facilitates ***erythropoiesis*** (Fig. 5.6). The source of erythropoietin during fetal and neonatal life is the liver. ***In adults, erythropoietin*** is mainly (about 85%) produced by the ***endothelial cells of the peritubular capillaries in the renal cortex.*** The liver generates the rest. In renal disease or nephrectomy (removal of kidney by surgery), the liver cannot compensate for the reduction in erythropoietin production and anemia results. This type of anemia responds to treatment with recombinant erythropoietin (erythropoietin produced by recombinant DNA technology). ***Erythropoietin secretion is stimulated by hypoxia, cobalt salts, androgens, alkalosis, catecholamines*** (via β-adrenoceptors) and ***adenosine***. Erythropoietin production is inhibited by theophylline, an adenosine antagonist.

## ➤ 5.5 Hemoglobin : Blood Pigments

**Hemoglobin** is a tetramer consisting of two pairs of polypeptide chains (globin) designated α, β, γ and δ, each of which is linked covalently to an iron-containing porphyrin (heme). Thus each molecule of hemoglobin contains four globin chains attached with four heme groups. About 98% of the protein in the cytoplasm of the circulating RBCs is hemoglobin. ***The main function of hemoglobin is to carry oxygen ($O_2$).*** Each hemoglobin molecule can bind four molecules of $O_2$.

**Table 5.2 : Types of hemoglobin present during different stages of development. Hb, hemoglobin, HbA, adult hemoglobin, HbF, fetal hemoglobin.**

| Development stages | Haemoglobin type | Chains | Note |
|---|---|---|---|
| Embryonic | Hb Gower I<br>Hb Gower II<br>Hb Portland | $\zeta_2\varepsilon_2$<br>$\zeta_2\varepsilon_2$<br>$\zeta_2\varepsilon_2$ | |
| Fetal | HbF | $\alpha_2\gamma_2$ | Main Hb in later two-thirds of fetal life and in the newborn; higher affinity for $O_2$ than HbA |
| Adult | HbA | $\alpha_2\beta_2$ | Principal Hb; 6800kDa |
| | $HbA_2$ | $\alpha_2\delta_2$ | –2% of adult Hb |

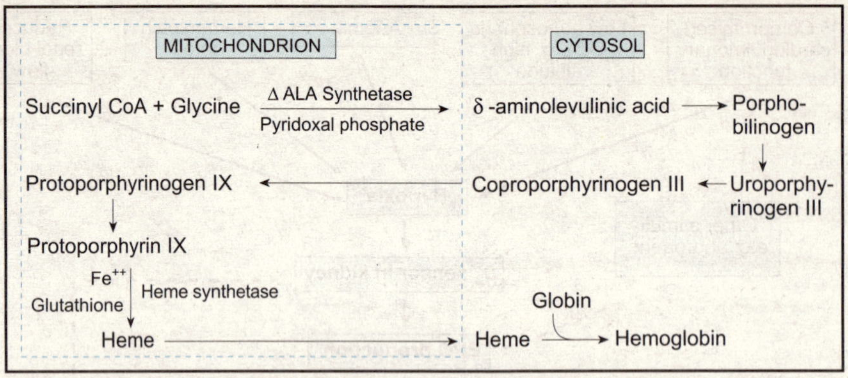


Fig. 5.7 : Hemoglobin biosynthesis

97% of the total hemoglobin of an adult is **HbA ($\alpha_2\beta_2$)** while 2.5% is **HbA$_2$ ($\alpha_2\delta_2$)**. Fetal hemoglobin (HbF or $\alpha_2\gamma_2$) usually accounts for less than 1% of total hemoglobin in adults. The ***average concentration of hemoglobin in a normal adult is 12 to 16 g/dL***. Hemoglobin concentration in blood is somewhat less in females than in males. **Hemoglobin A$_{1C}$** or **glycosylated hemoglobin** or **glycated hemoglobin** (HbA with a glucose attached to each of its β-chains) is a minor hemoglobin component that is present in normal persons but increases in the presence of hyperglycemia. The amount of **glycated hemoglobin** (expressed as %; normal value is **around 6%**) gives an estimate of glycemic control in diabetics for the preceding 3-month period.

**Hemoglobin in the human fetus** is usually **HbF** ($\alpha_2\gamma_2$). In young embryos, two other varieties of hemoglobin may be found — **Gower 1** ($\zeta_2\varepsilon_2$) and **Gower 2** ($\alpha_2\varepsilon_2$) hemoglobin and portland. HbF binds 2, 3-DPG less avidly and, consequently, the ***$O_2$ affinity of HbF is more***. The γ-chain synthesis switches to β-chain synthesis during the last 3 months of gestation. Adult hemoglobin replaces fetal hemoglobin soon after birth.

**Hemoglobin biosynthesis** : The first and the rate-limiting step in the ***synthesis of heme*** in the precursors of RBCs is the condensation of ***succinyl coenzyme A (CoA) and glycine to form δ-aminolevulinic acid (δ-ALA)***. This reaction, catalyzed by δ-ALA synthetase, occurs inside ***mitochondria*** and requires activation of glycine by pyridoxal phosphate. The subsequent steps (except the last three reactions) of heme synthesis occur in the ***cytosol***. Two δ-ALA molecules fuse to form a ring structure, porphobilinogen (a pyrrole) which is converted to protoporphyrin IX in several steps through intermediates. Iron is incorporated into protoporphyrin IX to form heme. The last three reactions take place inside mitochondria. Heme combines with globin in the cytosol to form **hemoglobin**. Other heme-containing proteins in the body are myoglobin ($O_2$-binding pigment in red muscles) and cytochrome C (a respiratory chain enzyme). (Fig. 5.7).

**The key step of haem synthesis :**

(i) Biosynthesis of δ-amino levulinic acid (ALA) from the precursors, glycine and succinyl CoA.

(ii) Two molecules of ALA condense to form porphobilinogen.

(iii) Conversion of porphobilinogen to the cyclic tetrapyrrole porphyrin ring and haem.

**Hemoglobin function** : The function of hemoglobin is to transport $O_2$ from lungs to tissues and carbon dioxide from tissues to lungs. *Each gram of hemoglobin can take up 1.34 mL of $O_2$*. The sigmoid shape of the oxygen dissociation curve makes efficient unloading of $O_2$ at relatively high $O_2$ tension possible (Fig. 5.8). Factors that modify the affinity of hemoglobin for $O_2$ are hydrogen ion, carbon dioxide and 2, 3-DPG. Increase in concentration of any of these factors causes the oxygen dissociation curve to shift to the right and, thereby, increase $O_2$ release. Increase in temperature also has a similar effect. 2, 3-DPG decreases $O_2$ affinity of hemoglobin by binding to the β-chains of deoxyhemoglobin. In various states of hypoxia, 2, 3-DPG levels are elevated resulting in enhanced $O_2$ release from hemoglobin due to decrease in $O_2$ affinity.

**Reactions of hemoglobin :** $O_2$ atta-ches to the ferrous iron ($Fe^{2+}$) of heme to form ***oxyhemoglobin.*** The affinity of hemoglobin for carbon monoxide is much greater than that of $O_2$. Hence, carbon monoxide can displace $O_2$ from hemoglobin to form carbon monoxy-hemoglobin ***(carboxyhemoglobin)***. When the ferrous iron ($Fe^{2+}$) of hemoglobin is converted to ferric iron ($Fe^{2+}$) by drugs such as sulphonamides, nitroglycerine or other oxidizing agents such as aniline dyes, ***methemoglobin*** is formed. The NADH-methemoglobin reductase system in the RBCs converts methemoglobin back to hemoglobin.

**Hemoglobin abnormalities** : Hemoglobin increases the capacity of the blood to transport oxygen; each gram of hemoglobin is capable of combining with approx. 1.34 ml of oxygen. Inherited disorders of hemoglobin in humans result either in defect in the structure of hemoglobin or in quantitative diminution in hemoglobin (globin chain, to be specific) production.

Qualitative defects in globin chains are referred to as **hemoglobinopathies. Sickle cell anemia** occurs due to the presence of an abnormal hemoglobin called **HbS**. In HbS,

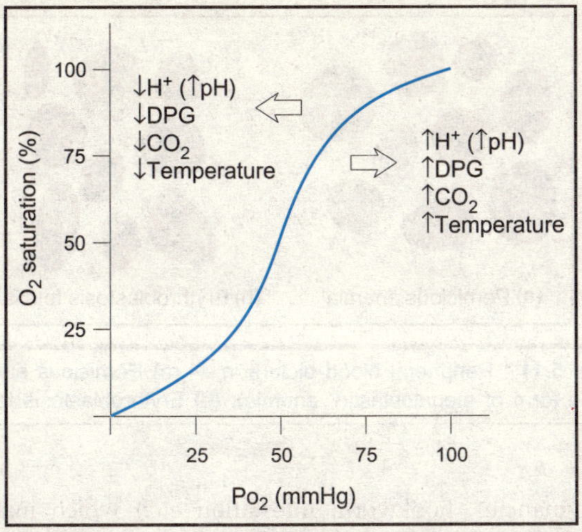


**Fig. 5.8 :** Oxyhemoglobin dissociation curve

the glutamic residue at the 6th position of the β-globin chain is replaced by valine because of a genetic defect in the β-globin gene. HbS polymerizes at low $O_2$ concentrations producing long crystals of HbS and, thereby, deforming the RBCs to assume a sickle shape. Sickle cells are readily destroyed in spleen and they may occlude the capillaries. This results in hemolytic anemia and vasoocclusive signs and symptoms. Individuals heterozygous for the HbS gene have less severe disease (sickle cell trait). HbS confers resistance to falciparum malaria.

Quantitative decrease in globin chain production may also occur due to genetic defects giving rise to diseases referred to **as thalassemias.** In *α-thalassemia, production of α-globin chain is reduced* and *in β-thalassemia, production of β-globin chain is deficient.* When the deficiency is absolute, the thalassemia is referred to as major **(thalassemia major).** In **thalassemia minor,** the deficiency is partial. **Thalassemia major** is found in individuals homozygous for the genetic defect and thalassemia minor in heterozygous individuals. In normal fetal development, dominant pattern of fetal hemoglobin (HbF, $\alpha_2\gamma_2$) is gradually switched over to adult hemoglobin (HbA, $\alpha_2\beta_2$) due to changing pattern of synthesis of β and γ chains (Fig. 5.9). This switch over takes place between 6 months of intra-uterine life to 6 months after birth. The intersection of the synthetic curve takes place at around $1^1/_2$ – 3 months postnatal (Fig. 5.9).

In case of thalassemia (say β thalassemia), due to moderate to severe deficiency of β chain synthesis, this switchover does not take place and, in affected infants, HbF concentration remains, high, and HbA concentration remains low (Fig. 5.10).

## Haemoglobinopathies

**Definition :** When biological properties of Hb is altered due to mutation in Hb molecule, the condition is called Hb-pathy.

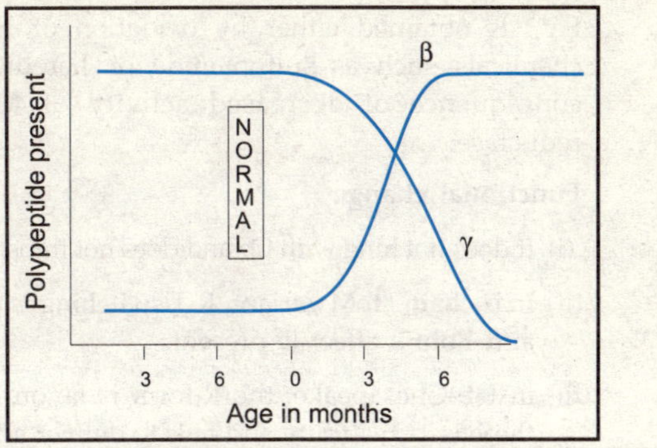


**Fig. 5.9 :** Switch over of polypeptide synthesis takes place at about $1^1/_2$ – 3 months postnatal life

(1) **Thalasaemic Hb :** Here the synthesis of α and β chains is reduced. In α-thalassemia, α-chain and in β-thalassemia, β-chain is absent. The defect lies at the genetic level. The genetic expression of the α-chain or β-chain is absent.

**Function result :** Thalassemia.

**Glycosylated Hb or HbA1C :** This type of Hb is useful in clinical laboratories for management of Diabetes mellitus and this Hb forms in certain pathological condition.

**Hb is non-enzymatically glycosylated when blood glucose enters the RBC.**

Normal, glycosylated Hb is 5%. Therefore increased conc. of HbA1C indicates increased blood glucose level. Measurement of HbA1C is useful in management of DM. HbA1C level reflects average blood glucose conc. over preceeding 6-8 weeks since mean life span of RBC 60-80 days.

**Met Hb : Structural change :** In this Hb, tyrosine replaces histidine F8 (numeric indicates the position of α-helix in the molecule). Hence Fe is stabilized in the $Fe^{+3}$ forming a complex with phenolate anion.

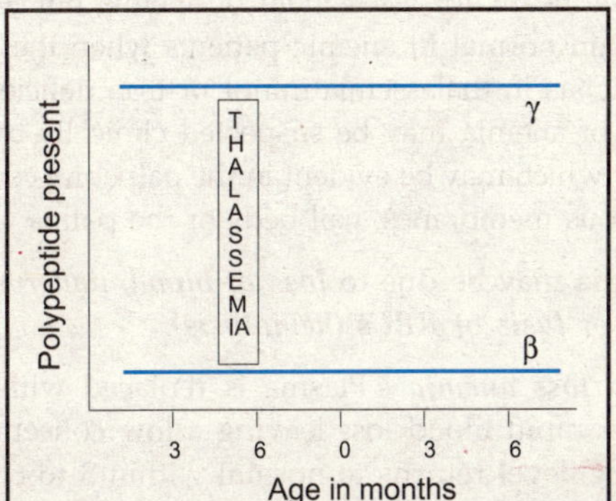


**Fig. 5.10 :** Absence of β to γ switchover in case of β-thalassemia. Compare with Fig. 5.9.

$Fe^{+3}$ is obtained either by oxidation of $Fe^{+2}$ by chemicals such as sulfonamide or hereditary or consequence of decreased activity of Met Hb reductase.

**Functional change :**

(i) It does not bind with $O_2$ and does not transport $O_2$.

(ii) In α-chain HbM variant, R-T switching is present and Bohr's effect is present.

(iii) in Hb-Chesapeake, the R-form is favoured and there is ↑$O_2$ affinity and fails to deliver adequate $O_2$ to peripheral tissue leading to polycythemia as a result of hypoxia.

(iv) In β-chain, HbM variant, R-T switching is present and Bohr's effect is present.

(2) **HbS :** In this Hb, valine replaces glutamate at $F_6$, located on surface of Hb and exposed to water. Hydrophilic glutamate in β-chain is replaced by valine. This change produces sticky hydrophobic patch on the surface and results in abnormal quaternary association of Hb molecule.

In low $O_2$ concentration, the subunits polymerise into linear array of fibre, that disturb the cell shape and result in the sickling of RBC. The sickling of RBC takes place in deoxy HbS. Sickling can be prevented by maintaining Hbs in oxygenated state. T-form of HbS polymerises, deoxy HbA has receptor site for sticky patch of oxy and deoxy Hb. So, the binding of Hbs to deoxy HbA terminates polymerisation of Hbs → condition is **sickle cell anaemia**.

## ➤ 5.6 Anemia

**Anemia** is said to be present when the hemoglobin level in the blood is below the lower extreme of the normal range for the age and sex of the individual. In pregnancy, the lower limit of normality is reduced. The RBC count provides an alternative means for assessment of anemia but RBC count may remain normal in anemic patients when the RBCs are microcytic (as in thalassemia minor or iron deficiency). The presence of anemia may be suspected clinically by looking for pallor which may be evident in the palpebral conjunctiva, oral mucous membranes, nail beds or the palms.

**Anemia** may be due to ***loss of blood, underproduction of RBCs or lysis of RBCs (hemolysis).***

***Blood loss anemia*** : Plasma is replaced within 1 to 3 days after rapid blood loss leaving a low concentration of RBCs. RBC level returns to normal within 3 to 6 weeks in the absence of a second hemorrhage. Chronic blood loss results in ***microcytic hypochromic anemia*** due to ***iron deficiency*** (more iron is lost than can be absorbed). Chronic gastrointestinal bleeding (as in peptic ulcer, gastrointestinal

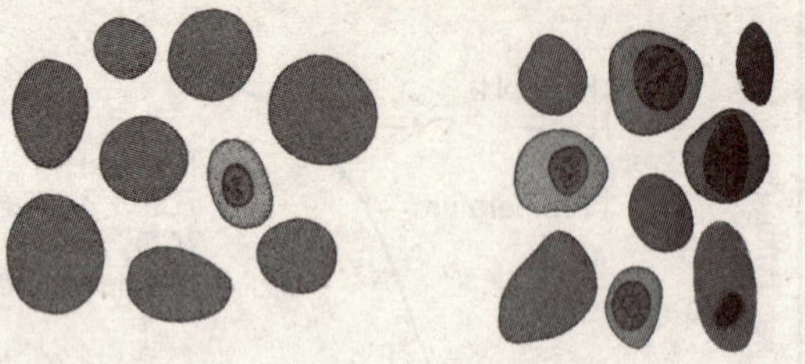


Fig. 5.11 : Peripheral blood picture in — (a) Pernicious anemia (one form of megaloblastic anemia); (b) Erythroblastosis fetalis

malignancies, hookworm infestation etc.) which may be occult (not visible to the naked eye) is a common cause of this type of anemia.

***Megaloblastic anemia*** : Deficiency of vitamin $B_{12}$ and folic acid results in **megaloblastic anemia** characterized by pre-sence of *megaloblasts* (large blast cells) *in the bone marrow* and macrocytes in the peripheral blood. In **pernicious anemia** (one form of megaloblastic anemia Fig. 5.11a), there is ***atrophy of gastric mucosa*** (probably autoimmune) leading to deficiency of intrinsic factor required for absorption of vitamin $B_{12}$. Gastrectomy (surgical resection of stomach) may also lead to megaloblastic anemia. Another cause of this type of anemia is intestinal sprue, a disease in which intestinal absorption of folic acid and vitamin $B_{12}$ (as well as other B vitamins) is poor.

**Aplastic anemia** : Bone marrow aplasia i.e., lack of funct-ioning bone marrow leads to *decreased production of all types of blood cells* causing aplastic anemia characterized by **pancytopenia** in the peripheral blood. Exposure to radioactivity, certain industrial chemicals and some drugs such as chlo-ramphenicol may cause this type of anemia.

**Hemolytic anemia** : This type of anemia results from different red cell abnormalities (some hereditary) that increase RBC fragility. As a result, RBCs rupture easily while passing through capillaries especially in the spleen. RBC production is normal but life span of RBC is reduced. In hereditary spherocytosis, there is abnormality in the RBC membrane making the cell spherical (instead of the normal biconcave disc); that is why the cells are easily ruptured.

**In sickle cell anemia**, an abnormal hemoglobin called ***hemoglobin S (HbS)*** is produced due to substitution of the glutamic acid residue at position 6 of β-globin chain by valine. At low oxygen concentration, HbS polymerizes to form long crystals that alter the shape of the RBCs to make them sickle-shaped. Sickle-shaped RBCs are easily ruptured in the capillaries and may block the capillaries. **In thalassemias, *production of globin chains is deficient.*** Quantitative deficiency of α-chain production leads to α-thalassemia while in β-thalassemia, β-chain production is deficient. *When the deficiency is complete,* the thalassemia is designated as **"major"**.

The globin chains that cannot combine to form hemoglobin are precipitated within the RBCs forming inclusion bodies that damage the RBC membrane rendering them vulnerable to rupture during passage through the capillaries as well as to phagocytosis by macrophages. **Erythroblastosis fetalis** is a condition in which antibodies from Rh-negative mother (sensitized by Rh-positive RBCs from a previous pregnancy with a Rh-positive fetus) bind to Rh-positive RBCs of the fetus and lyse them leading to hemolytic anemia (Fig. 5.11b).

Significant jaundice may be produced due to overproduction of bilirubin and may lead to **kernicterus** (deposition of bilirubin in the CNS). A large number of blast cells of erythroid series are found in the fetal blood due to rapid production of RBCs. In **immunohemolytic anemia,** hemolysis occurs by immune mechanisms, eg, transfusion reactions, drug reactions etc. In malaria, a parasite called plasmodium grows inside RBCs and ultimately comes out by lysing the RBCs.

Reticulocyte count in peripheral blood (normally < 1% of RBCs) is an useful laboratory test to distinguish between underproduction of RBCs from hemolysis. **A significant rise of reticulocytes in peripheral blood is, in most cases, suggestive of hemolysis.** Unconjugated hyperbilirubinemia is another useful guide to the presence of hemolysis.

### Physiological adaptations in anemia

Several mechanisms come into play in anemia to make more effective delivery of oxygen to the tissues by the available hemoglobin.

**Cardiac output** increases in anemia. The increase is mainly due to increased stroke volume which, in turn, is a result of increased venous return to the heart. ***Venous return*** increases in anemia due to fall in resistance to blood flow in peripheral vessels as a result of lowering of blood viscosity which is dependent on the concentration of RBCs in blood. ***Hypoxia*** is another factor that causes peripheral vasodilation and, thereby, increases blood flow and venous return. Therefore, the work load on the heart is greatly increased in severe anemia and, understandably, severe anemia is often accompanied by heart failure. The high output state in anemia tends to increase oxygen delivery to the tissues by increasing blood flow.

Release of oxygen from hemoglobin is increased in anemia *due to* **rise in 2, 3-DPG concentration** in RBCs shifting the oxygen dissociation curve of hemoglobin to the right. This shift to the right results in release of a greater proportion of oxygen from hemoglobin at the partial pressure of oxygen of venous blood.

**Blood flow is redistributed** in anemia. Cerebral and muscle blood flow is increased while cutaneous blood flow is reduced. This maintains the perfusion of vital organs with greater oxygen requirements.

When anemia develops rapidly, the compensatory adjustments may not get adequate time to develop.

### Polycythemia

An increase in hemoglobin concentration usually indicates an absolute increase in the number of circulating RBCs but, in some individuals, the apparent increase in hemoglobin may be due to hemoconcentration (reduction is plasma volume) that may occur in dehydration. A true increase in the number of circulating RBCs is referred to as **polycythemia** or **erythrocytosis**. Polycythemia may be secondary or primary. A common cause of ***secondary polycythemia*** is residence at high altitudes (physiologic polycythemia). Hypoxia at high altitudes stimulates erythropoietin secretion which leads to increased RBC production. ***Causes of secondary polycythemia*** may be summarized as follows :

(a) **Increased erythropoietin production due to hypoxia—**

(i) High altitude;

(ii) Lung disease;

(iii) Congenital cyanotic heart disease;

(iv) Smoking;

(v) Hemoglobins with high $O_2$ affinity.

(b) **Inappropriate production of erythropoietin**

Tumors of kidney, liver, lung, uterus and cerebellum.

**Polycythemia vera or primary proliferative polycythemia** belongs to a group of disorders involving the pluripotent hematopoietic stem cells called **myeloproliferative disorders.** Hematocrit as well as blood volume increase in this condition. Increase in blood viscosity tends to form plugs in the capillaries producing vascular occlusion. Cardiac output remains more or less normal because the effect of increased blood viscosity (causing sluggish blood flow → diminished venous return) and the effect of increased blood volume (causing increased venous return) on heart tend to neutralize each other.

## 5.7 Platelets

**Platelets** are very small nonnucleated discs, 2-4 μm in diameter, derived from the cytoplasm of ***megakaryocytes*** in red bone marrow. The normal platelet count is between ***200 × 10⁹/L and 350 × 10⁹/L.*** The role of platelets is to prevent or stop bleeding. This process is known as **hemostasis**. The cytoplasm stains blue and contains small red purple granules which are located in the central area of the platelet. ***Platelet contains a number of organelles including mitochondria, glycogen granules and lysosomes.*** It also contains α granules and electron dense granules. α ***granules*** contain some proteins — fibrinogen, clotting factors V and VIII, β-thromboglobulin, PDGF and PF-4 etc. ***Dense granules*** contain nonprotein substances — ADP, 5 HT etc.

The megakaryocytes push processes through bone marrow sinusoids into the blood. These processes break off to form tiny platelets. The platelet production is controlled by a hormone ***thrombopoietin***. The platelets contain ATP, 5HT, phospholipids and are rich in enzymes. The platelets form platelet plug to arrest bleeding and also play an important role in the clotting mechanism.

## Production of platelets

The precursor cells which give rise ultimately to the platelets are known as **megakaryoblasts**. Megakaryoblasts are formed from CFU-M under the influence of thrombopoietin. These cells are 15-20 μm in diameter and posser a large avoid or kidney-shaped nucleus. Differentiation of the megakaryoblasts ives rise to the megakaryocytes, which are giant cells (35-150 μm dimeter) whose cytoplasm contains numerous mitochondria, rough endoplasmic reticulum and golgi complex. As these cells mature within the bonemarrow, invagination of the plasma membrane become evident, eventually branching throughout the entire cytoplasm. These form the demarcation membranes which define the areas that will be shed as platelets. The factors that control the rate of production of platelets are pourly understood although it is known that the maturation of megakaryocytes and the budding off of their platelets and the budding off of their platelets is stimulated by a hormone called **thrombopoietin** (Fig. 5.11c).

## The role of platelets

Within seconds of a vascular injury, platelets start to build up and adhere to the site of damage. This process is self perpetuating as the adhering platelets secrete ADP and 5-Hydroxytryptamine. They also synthesize arachidonic acid and thromboxane $A_2$. These factors trigger a change in the surface characteristics of the platelets which causes them to adhere to the walls of damaged vessels and to each other. This process results in the formation of a platelet plug which may be sufficient to stem the flow of blood from minor wounds.

## Fate of platelets

Platelets reside in the spleen for a short period prior to circulation in the blood stream. They are attracted to the injury site of blood vessel. Average life span of platelets is about ***10 days*** (Table 5.3).

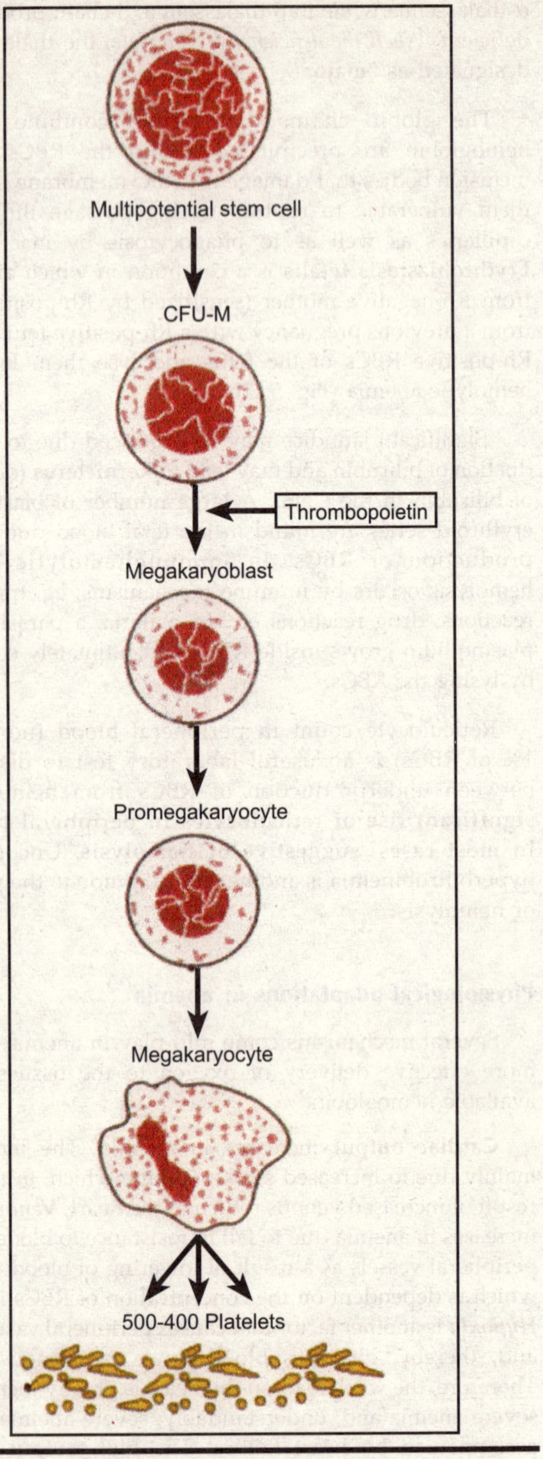


Fig. 5.11(c) : Maturation of megakaryocyte

## Von Willebrand factor (vWF)

***von Willebrand factor (vWF)*** is a plasma protein which is secreted by platelets and endothelial cells. This factor helps platelets to adhere to a damaged vessel wall. This protein helps to form a bridge between the vessel wall and

**Table 5.3**
**Substances produced by platelets**

| Substance | Function |
|---|---|
| Serotonin (5 HT) | Vasoconstriction |
| Adenosine diphosphate | Enhances platelet aggregation |
| Thromboxane | Platelets are aggregated and there is vasoconstriction |
| Clotting factors | Coagulation |
| Platelet derived growth factor (PDGF) | Wound healing |

first layer of platelets. Platelet aggregation is essential for clotting. If there is any abnormality or absence of vWF, there may be delay in clotting.

## 5.8 Plasma Proteins

Plasma contains a variety of proteins with different functions. There are many characterized proteins whose functions remains to be determined. **The total plasma protein concentration is 7.4 gm%** (average **5.4 gm% – 8.3 gm%**)

CHEMICAL COMPOSITION OF PLASMA

- **Water**
  - 91.5%
  - About 90% of water is from absorption through G.I. Tract and 10% from cellular respiration
- **Solute**
  - **Proteins**
    - *Albumin*
      - produced by liver
      - maintenance and regulation of colloidal osmotic pressure
      - maintains water balance
      - regulates blood volume
    - *Globulins*
    - *Fibrinogen*
      - produced by liver
      - plays an important role in clotting
  - **Nonprotein nitrogeneous substances**
    Nitrogen, urea, uric acid, creatinine and ammonium salts.
  - **Regulatory substances**
    Enzymes and hormones
  - **Electrolytes**
    $Na^+$, $K^+$, $Mg^{2+}$, $Ca^{2+}$, $Cl^-$
    $HPO_4^-$, $HCO_3^-$
  - **Protein, amino acids and glucose**

Fig. 5.12 : Chemical composition of plasma

**serum** is the fluid part of blood after clotting. It contains only serum albumin and serum globulin. Composition of serum is almost (but not totally) same as plasma. **Plasma** contains the fibrinogen and other procoagulant factors. Serum does not contain them.

### Classification of plasma proteins

***Classical method or the Howe method :***

- Introduced by Howe in 1922.
- Clinical importance
- Easy operation
- Major classes of plasma proteins, albumin, globulins and fibrinogens are isolated.

***Paper electrophoretic method :***

- Introduced in 1946
- Five classes of plasma proteins can be separated (albumin; $\alpha_1$ globulin; $\alpha_2$ globulin; β-globulin and Y-globulin).

***The normal level of plasma proteins***

**Albumin** : 3.5 – 5.2 g/100 ml.
**Globulin** : 1.7 – 3.2 g/100 ml.
**Fibrinogen** : 0.2 – 0.4 g/100 ml.

### Composition of blood plasma proteins :

| Plasma protein | % of total protein | Function |
|---|---|---|
| **Albumin** | 50-70% | • Plasma volume is maintained.<br>• Distribution of ECF is maintained. |
| **$\alpha_1$-globulins** | 2-6% | • Transport of thyroid hormones and lipid.<br>• Concentration increases in inflamma-tion.<br>• e.g., Cortisol binding globulin.<br>• Inhibits proteolytic enzymes (trypsin and plasmin)<br>• In acute illness.<br>• In emphysema and neonatal hepatitis. |
| **$\alpha_2$-globulins** | 5-11% | • Binds to hemoglobin released from damaged red cells and hence prevents loss of iron in the urine.<br>• Transport of copper.<br>• Lipid transport. |
| **β-globulins** | 7-16% | • Transport of lipid and iron.<br>• Fibrinolysis.<br>• Sensitive indicator of connective tissue disorders.<br>• ↑In glomerulonephritis and infections diseases.<br>• Used as an index of renal tubular function. |

**The clinical value of estimation of the plasma proteins :**

- Estimation of total plasma protein concentration has value only when the patient has lost every type of plasma proteins which occurs, for example, as a result of burns or hemorrhage.

- Estimation of plasma proteins should be done in all cases of liver disease, in nephrotic syndrome, and for the investigation of the collagen diseases.
- The plasma protein pattern on electrophoretic analysis may be diagnostic in multiple myeloma, nephrosis, cirrhosis of the liver and agammaglobulinemia.
- Estimation of plasma fibrinogen is usually not necessary except in the investigation of hemorrhagic diseases of uncertain etiology.

## Properties of the individual plasma proteins

(a) ***Albumin :***

- Molecular weight is 70,000.
- Albumin is responsible for the carriage in the plasma of most of the bilirubin and of nonionized calcium.
- Albumin is synthesized in the liver and has a half-life of about 10 days.
- When plasma albumin level falls below 2.0-2.5 g/ 100 ml, edema is likely to develop.
- Increase in plasma albumin : An increase in the plasma concentration of albumin occurs when there is loss of plasma water (hemoconcentration), for example, burns.
- Decrease in plasma albumin : The possible causes of fall in the plasma albumin concentration are low protein intake, inadequate digestion or absorption of protein, increased protein catabolism, diminished albumin synthesis, increased protein loss and hemodilution.
- **Applied** :
  - (i) *Hypoproteinemia* : This is accompanied by low albumin level and occurs due to low protein diet, deficiency of essential amino acids, viral hepatitis, cirrhosis of liver, nephrotic syndrome.
  - (ii) *Hereditary analbuminemia* : An inborn defect at genetic level where there is no synthesis of albumin.

(b) ***Globulins :***

- Molecular weight is 90,000-1,56,000.
- These plasma proteins are glycoprotein in nature.
- Often found to be conjugated with lipid fractions to form VLDL, HDL etc.
- This protein fraction comprises $\alpha_1$, $\alpha_2$, $\beta_1$, $\beta_2$, $\gamma_1$ and $\gamma_2$ globulin fractions.
- **Site of synthesis :** $\gamma$-globulin is synthesized in plasma cells whereas other globulins are synthesized in liver cells.
- **Increase in total plasma globulin** : This occurs in most acute or chronic bacterial or parasitic infections (but not generally in viral infections) especially in those of long duration. In chronic liver disease and in metastatic carcinoma there is a variable increase in the total plasma globulin. Marked increase occurs in collagen disease, multiple myeloma and sarcoidosis.
- **Decrease in total plasma globulin** : This is seen when there is loss of plasma protein, for example burns or cachexia associated with severe malnutrition or disease of gastro-intestinal tract.
- **Applied** : Lymphogranuloma venerum is a disease manifested by increased lymphoid tissue activity resulting in high concentration of serum immunoglobulin.

  Additional information of clinical value may be obtained by electrophoretic studies of separate globulin groups.

  **$\alpha$-globulin** : They carry lipids and carbohydrates. Increased $\alpha$-globulins (principally $\alpha_2$) are obtained when there is tissue destruction, in acute inflammatory conditions and, occasionally, in chronic infections. In nephrosis, typically only $\alpha_2$ globulin is increased.

  **$\beta$-globulin** : The $\beta$-globulin group contains specific proteins which can bind metals and are responsible for the transport in the plasma of iron (transferrin) and copper (ceruloplasmin), $\beta$-globulin combines with lipid and carries fat soluble vitamins and hormones. Increase of $\beta$-globulins is found in conditions where there is increased plasma lipid, eg, diabetes mellitus, nephrosis and biliary cirrhosis.

  **$\gamma$-globulin** : They consist of the antibodies. Increase in $\gamma$-globulin is seen in chronic infective states (parasitic disease, collagen disease, certain types of liver disease).

(c) ***Fibrinogen :***

- Fibrinogen is produced in the liver.
- Molecular weight 500,000.
- Chemical structure : Protein part of the molecule is made up of six polypeptide chains ($\alpha_2$, $\beta_2$, $\gamma_2$) joined by disulfide bonds.
- The plasma fibrinogen concentration is raised in almost all diseases in which raised ESR is found, particularly in acute infections and in pregnancy.
- **Applied** : Afibrinogenemia is a rare congenital abnormality. There may be a marked fall in the plasma fibrinogen in severe liver disease or in pregnancy as a complication of detachment of placenta.

(d) ***Prothrombin :*** The liver is also the site for the synthesis of prothrombin. This synthesis is promoted by vitamin K. Dietary vitamin K is not absorbed from the intestine unless bile salts are present (Fig. 5.13).

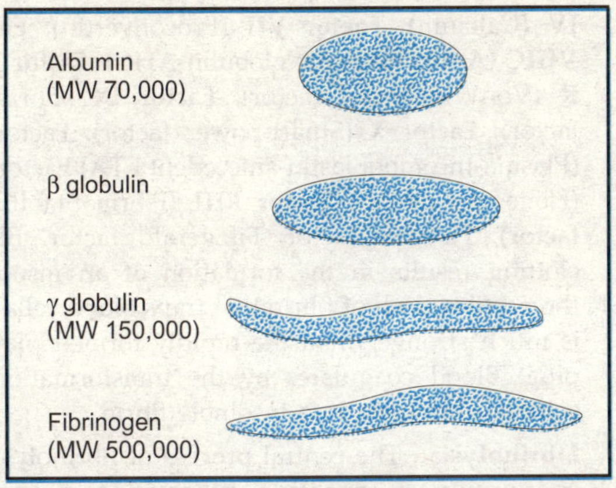


Fig. 5.13 : Relative size of different plasma proteins

(e) ***Abnormal proteins :***

- ***Bence-Jones protein and myeloma globulin*** : In multiple myeloma, abnormal proteins are formed in the bone marrow and may be found in the plasma. They are excreted in the urine.
- ***Cryoglobulin*** : Rarely, an insoluble protein separates from plasma when it is cooled. This phenomenon has been observed in periarteritis nodosa and, occasionally, in multiple myeloma and leukemia. The abnormal globulin is, electrophoretically, usually a γ-globulin.
- ***Acute phase protein*** : This abnormal globulin is also called **C-reactive protein** because it forms a precipitate with the somatic C-polysaccharide of the pneumococcus and estimated by serological method. It appears in the serum when there is acute inflammation or acute tissue destruction as in myocardial infarction.

### Functions of plasma proteins

(a) Plasma proteins maintain **colloidal osmotic pressure (COP)** across the capillary wall. It is normally *25-30 mm Hg.* The capillary wall is relatively impermeable to plasma proteins. The colloid osmotic pressure of plasma proteins play a vital role in the distribution of water between the blood and tissues. Plasma albumin plays an important role for this function because of low molecular weight and making the greatest contribution to the colloid osmotic pressure of plasma.

(b) Plasma proteins contain a large *number of proteins called* **clotting factors** (fibrinogen, prothrombin). Fibrinogen is converted to fibrin during the process of coagulation.

(c) Plasma proteins maintain ***viscosity of blood***. Viscosity of blood is one of the key factors to maintain peripheral vascular resistance and blood pressure. Plasma proteins and blood cells contribute mainly in maintaining viscosity of blood.

(d) Immunoglobulin (γ-globulin) and complement system are the plasma proteins responsible for ***body defence mechanism.***

(e) The serum proteins can combine with acids or bases to ***maintain the pH of blood.*** They act as acids and combine with cations (mainly sodium) at the normal pH of blood.

(f) Plasma proteins act as **carriers of metals, hormones, lipids and drugs.** The binding of hormones, metals and drugs with the plasma proteins limits their free diffusion into ECF.

(g) Plasma contains ***several enzymes of diagnostic importance*** in some diseases.

(h) Albumin acts as a ***nonspecific transport protein*** for a number of substances having low solubility in water eg, bilirubin.

(i) Plasma proteins ***transport lipids*** and the fat soluble vitamins (A, D and E).

### Changes in the plasma proteins in health and disease

In infants, the total protein level is low due to low γ-globulin.

In old age, there is a tendency for the albumin level to fall and the total globulin level to rise.

During pregnancy, the total protein level falls mainly because of water retention. The albumin level may fall by as much as 20 per cent at the eighth month of gestation. However, α and β-globulin as well as fibrinogen fractions may rise. In detachment of the placenta and in certain other complications of pregnancy, placental thromboplastin may be released into the maternal circulation to cause a dangerous depletion of plasma fibrinogen.

## ➤ 5.9 Physiology of Hemostasis

Mechanisms of hemostasis : When a blood vessel is damaged by mechanical injury of somekind, excessive blood loss from the wound is prevented by a process called **Hemostasis**. This involves a series of events-vasoconstriction platelet aggregation and blood coagulation (clot formation). Later, blood vessel repair, clot retraction and dissolution complete the healing process.

### Blood Coagulation and Fibrinolytic System

**Hemostasis :** Hemostasis is the spontaneous arrest of bleeding from damaged blood vessels. The process of blood clotting and then the subsequent dissolution of the clot, following repair of the injured tissue, is termed as **hemostasis**. Hemostasis comprises 4 major events that occur in a set order following the loss of vascular integrity.

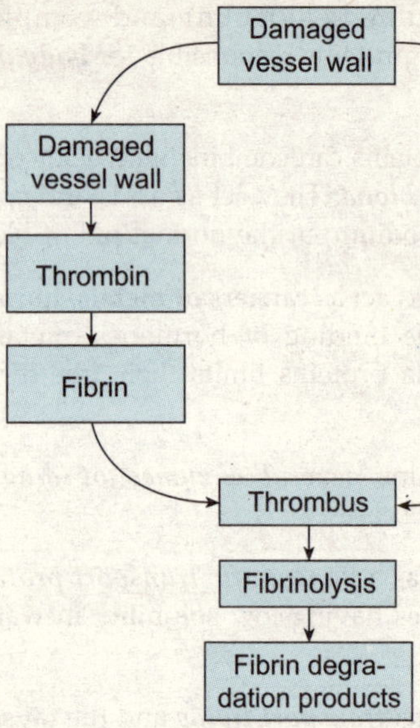


**Events in Hemostasis :**

1. **Vasoconstriction :** The initial phase of the process is vascular constriction. This limits the flow of blood to the area of injury.

   When plaelets come in contact with a damaged blood vessel, their surface becomes sticky and they adhere to the damaged vessel wall. Then they release serotonin (5-HT), which constricts the vessel, reducing blood flow through it. The damaged vessel releases other chemicals that cause vasoconstriction.
2. **Platelet plug formation :** The platelets beeome activated by thrombin and aggregate at the site of injury, forming a temporary, loose platelet plug. The adherent platelets clump to each other and release other substances, including ADP, which attracts more platelets to the site. Passing platelets stick to those already at the damaged vessel and they too release their chemicals. This is a positive feed back system by which many platelet rapidly arrive at the site of vascular damage and quickly form a temporary seal i.e. platelet plug. The protein fibrinogen is primarily responsible for stimulating platelet clumping. Platelet clump by binding to collagen which get exposed following rupture of the endothelial lining of vessels. Upon activation, platelets release adenosine 5' diphosphate (ADP) & TXA2 (which activate additional platelets), serotonin, phospholipids, lipoproteins and other proteins important for coagulation cascade.
3. **Blood clotting :** To ensure stability of the initially loose platelet plug a fibrin mesh (also called the clot) forms and entraps the plug. This is a complex feedback system and factors numbered I–XII are involved. These **clotting factors** are numbered accending to the order in which they were discovered. **Factor I** (Fibrinogen), **Factor II** (Prothrombin) **Factor III** (Thromboplastin), **Factor IV** (Calcium); **Factor VII** (Proconvertin); **Factor VIIIC** (Antihemophilic globulin AHC); **Factor VIII R** (VonWillebrand factor); **Factor IX** (Christma factor); **Factor X** (Stuart-power factor); Factor **XI** (Plasma-thromboplastin-antecedent PTA) **Factor XII** (Hageman factor); **Factor XIII** (Fibrin Stabilizing factor); Fletcher factor; Fitzgerald factor. Blood clotting results in the formation of an insoluble thread like mesh of fibrin that traps blood cells and is much stronger than the rapidly formed platelet plug. Blood coagulates by the transformation of soluble fibrinogen into insoluble fibrin.
4. **Fibrinolysis :** The central process of fibrinolysis is conversion of **inactive plasminogen to the proteolytic enzyme plasmin**. Injured cells release activators of plasminogen. Plasmin remodels the thrombus and limits the extension of thrombus by proteolytic digestion of fibrin.

## 5.10 Mechanism of Blood Coagulation

More than 50 important substances affect blood coagulation, some that promote coagulation are called as **procoagulants** and others that inhibit coagulation are called as **anticoagulants.**

When a vessel is ruptured, procoagulants in the area of damage become activated and override the anticoagulants and then a clot does develop. Scheme for conversion of prothrombin and polymerization of fibrinogen to form fibrin fibers.

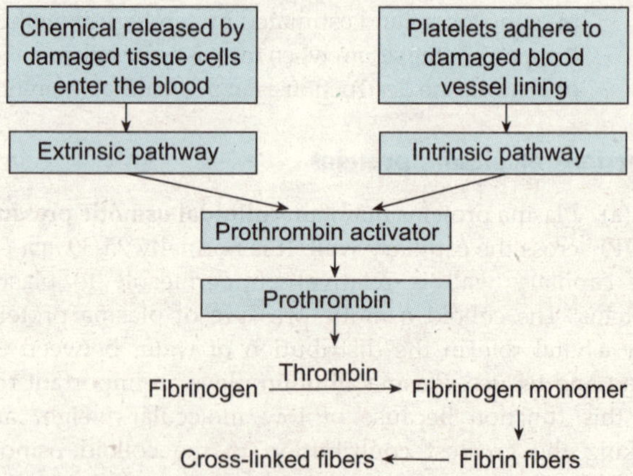


Two pathways lead to the formation of a fibrin clot : **the intrinsic** and **extrinsic** pathway.

**Extrinsic pathway :** Begins with a traumatized vascular wall or extravascular tissues. The traumatic tissue releases tissue factor. This is followed by activation of factor VII & X and formation of thrombin.

**Intrinsic pathway :** Begins with trauma to the blood itself or exposure of the blood to collagen in a traumatized blood vessel wall. Blood trauma causes activation of factor XII and release of platelets phospholipids. This is followed by activation of factor XI, IX, VIII & X and formation of thrombin.

**Interaction of Extrinsic and Intrinsic pathways :** Although they are initiated by distinct mechanisms, the two converge on a common pathway that leads to clot formation. The formation of a red thrombus or a clot in response to an abnormal vessel wall in the absence of tissue injury is the result of the **intrinsic pathway**. Fibrin clot formation in response to tissue injury is the result of the **extrinsic pathway**. Both pathways are complex and involve numerous different proteins termed clotting factors. After a blood vessel ruptures, clotting is initiated by both pathways simultaneously. **Difference between the extrinsic and intrinsic pathways—**

The **extrinsic pathway** can be explosive in nature. With severe tissue trauma, clotting can occur in as little as 15 seconds. The **intrinsic pathway** is slower to proceed usually requiring 1–6 minutes to cause clotting.

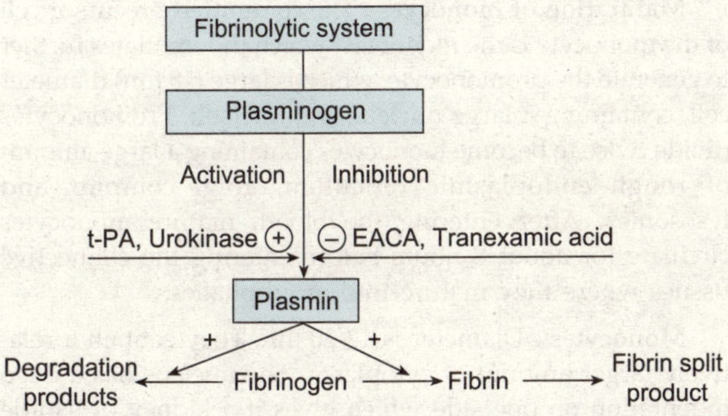


**Fibrinolysis** is mediated through the activation of plasminogen, the plasma precursor of the proteolytic enzyme plasmin. Plasminogen binds to lysine residues on the surface of the fibrin and is converted to plasmin by an activator released from endothelial cells (t–PA) that simultaneously binds to fibrin. Plasmin then degrades fibrin into large fragments known as X and Y. These are subsequently broken down into soluble fibrin degradation products.

***The most interesting thing in this phenomenon is that both of the above pathways include the final common pathway*** which consists of— (a) Activation of prothrombin and (b) Conversion of fibrinogen to fibrin momomer and formation of polymeric fibrin.

- **Prothrombin is** a monomeric $\alpha_2$-globulin with molecular weight 66,000. It contains 14 Gla residues in its structure. After activation, factor X binds with the anionic phospholipid layer of platelet membrane by means of Va and Xa in turn causes cleavage of prothrombin to produce thrombin as indicated in the figure 5.15. Two chains (A and B) are cleaved but are still connected with each other by disulfide bonds that remain intact to produce dimeric thrombin.

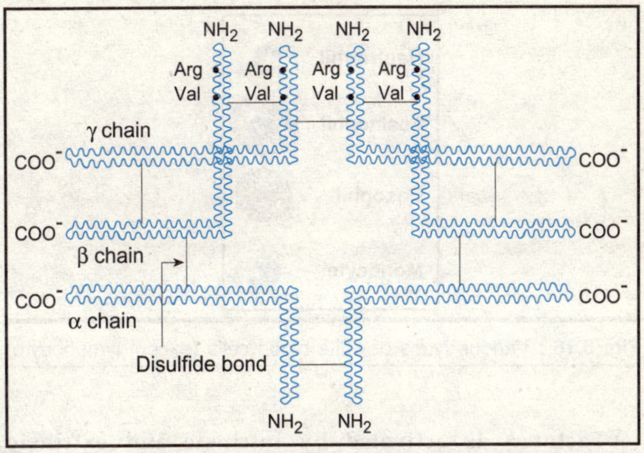


Fig. 5.14 : Structure of fibrinogen

- **Structure of fibrinogen shows** that it consists of three polypeptide chains namely α, β and γ (Fig. 5.14).

Each of the α- and β-chains is cleaved towards N-terminal end. The cleavage of 2α and 2β chains at their amino terminals gives off fibrin monomer and 2 fibrinopeptides. **Fibrino-peptide A** and **Fibrinopeptide B** contain excess negative charges due to aspartate and glutamate residues which make fibrinogen soluble. But fibrin monomer is insoluble. So they precipitate. Fibrin monomer, by combining with each other through disulfide bond, produces fibrin. This fibrin, by making glutamyllysine linkage between each other, produces fibrin mesh.

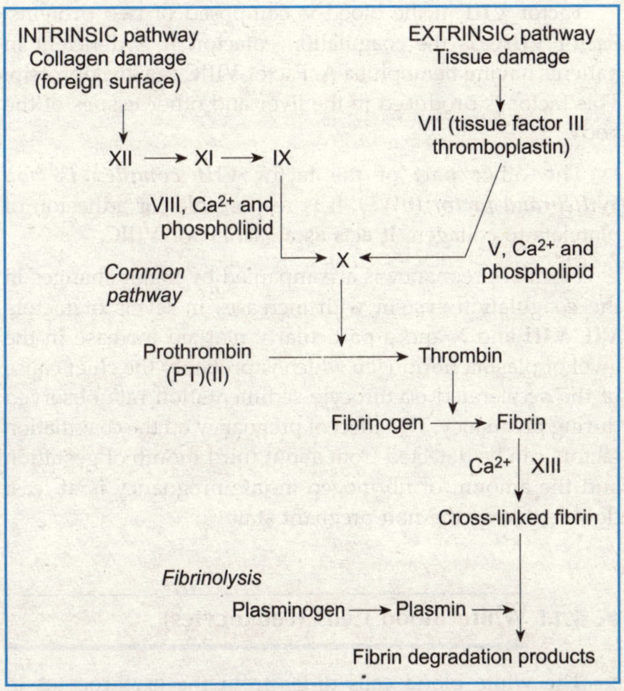


Fig. 5.15 : The coagulation cascade and fibrinolytic pathway

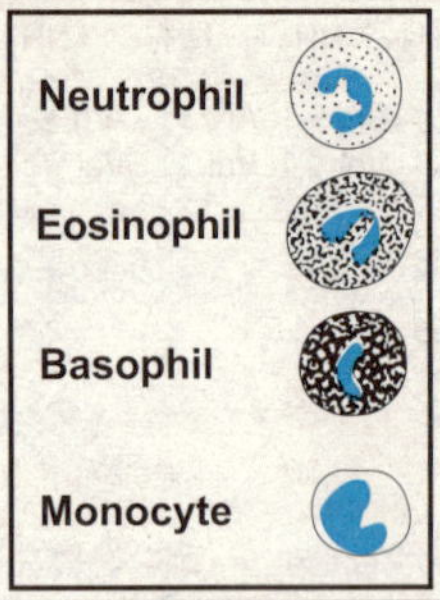


Fig. 5.16 : Various types of white blood cells (except lymphocyte)

**Factor X is activated by intrinsic and extrinsic pathways.** ***The components of intrinsic pathway*** are present in the circulating blood. Tissue factor, which is required for extrinsic pathway, is released from damaged cells. ***Factor X is also activated by extrinsic pathway.*** A complex (factor VII, tissue factor and $Ca^{2+}$) directly activates **factor X**. Tissue factor is a lipoprotein located in microsomal preparations of various tissues and is also found in the membrane of injured endothelial cells. The **factor VII-tissue factor** activates factor IX; a product of activation of **factor XII can** produce VIIa. Platelet can directly activate factor XI without the intervention of factor XII, HMWK or prekallikrein.

Contact factors **XIIa, kallikrein with HMWK accelerate** fibrinolytic system. Kallikrein cleaves from HMWK. Bradykinin is one of the group of kinins that increases vascular permeability. It causes smooth muscle contraction and initiates chemotactic activity in leukocytes.

**Factor VIII** in the blood is composed of two proteins. Factor ***VIIIC is*** the coagulation cofactor. It is deficient in patients having hemophilia A. Factor VIIIC is a glycoprotein. This factor is produced in the liver and other tissues of the body.

The other part of the factor ***VIII complex is von Willebrand factor (vWF).*** It is responsible for adhesion of platelets to collagen. It acts as a carrier for VIIIC.

Normal pregnancy is accompanied by major changes in the coagulation system with increases in levels of factors **VII, VIII** and **X** and a particularly marked increase in the level of plasma fibrinogen which is probably the chief cause of the accelerated erythrocyte sedimentation rate observed during pregnancy. The effect of pregnancy on the coagulation factors can be detected from about third month of gestation and the amount of fibrinogen in late pregnancy is at least double that of the non-pregnant state.

## 5.11 White Blood Cells (Leukocytes)

The white blood cells differ from the erythrocytes in that they contain no hemoglobin and have nuclei. Most of the white cells are considerably larger than the erythrocytes. Their diameter is 6-20 µm. The size depends upon the particular variety.

On the basis of histological differences, five main types of leukocytes may be isolated. They fall into two **morphological groups**. ***Polymorphonuclear granulocytes*** irregular, multilobed nuclei and a high density of cytoplasmic granules. Neutrophils, eosinophils and basophils are included in this group. But lymphocytes and monocytes lack granules and contain large and regular nuclei. They are termed *mononuclear agranulocytes.*

### Mononuclear agranulocytes

**Maturation of lymphocytes :** Circulating lymphocytes originate mainly in the thymus and peripheral lymphoid organs (spleen, lymph nodes, tonsils etc.). The first identifiable progenitor is the lymphoblast. These cells divide several times to become smaller prolymphocytes. These subsequently synthesize the cell-surface receptors that distinguish them as T or B lymphocytes.

**Maturation of monocyes :** The committed precursor cell of the monocyte is the monoblast which differentiates further to generate the promonocyte, which is large (18 µm) diameter cell, containing a large nucleus and nucleoli. Promonocytes divide twice to become monocytes containing a large amount of rough endoplasmic reticulum, golgi complex and lysosomes. After entering the blood, mature monocytes circulate for about 8 hours before entering the connective tissues where they mature into macrophages.

**Monocytes :** Diameter is 12-20 µm. They contain a relatively larger amount of cytoplasm. The nucleus has a deep indentation on one side which gives it a kidney or saddle bag shape. The monocytes are actively motile and phagocytic. Monocytes constitute 2-8% of leukocytes. These monocytes then leave the blood and enter the tissues where they are known as "**tissue macrophages**". Tissue macrophages are considered to be monocytes which have migrated into connective tissues. The monocytes and macrophages form the core of the reticuloendothelial system (Fig. 5.16).

### Polymorphonuclear leukocyte (granulocytes) (Fig. 5.17)

**Maturation of granulocytes :** There are three types of granulocytes— Neutrophils, Basophils, and Eosinophils. Multipotential progenitor cells (promyelocytes) in the hematopoietic tissue give rise to three kinds of precursor cells : neutrophilic, basophilic, and eosinophilic myelocytes. These mature further with condensation of the nucleus and an increase in specific granule content over the next 10 days or so, before appearing in the circulation. During an infection, the rate of granulocyte production (especially of neutrophils) increases considerably.

They are classified into three groups according to the staining reactions of their granules. The eosinophils stain with acid dyes, eg, eosin. The basophils stain with basic dyes, eg, methylene blue. The neutrophils stain with neutral dyes, (i.e., mixtures of acid and basic dyes). The nucleus of an adult granulocyte is composed of two or more lobes connected together by strands of chromatin.

**Eosinophils :** They include not more than 1-4% of the total white cell count. The cell is slightly larger and the nucleus is bilobed. The cytoplasmic granules are large and coarse and stain deeply red with eosin. They are phagocytic and are particularly involved in the destruction of parasitic worms. They also play an important role in allergic responses.

**Neutrophils :** Diameter is 12-15 μm. They comprise 50-70% of total number of white cells present in blood. Cytoplasmic granules are lysosomal in nature. They liberate enzymes to kill bacteria (Fig. 5.18). Their nuclei show a variable number of lobes depending upon the age of cells. Their granules are fine and are stained with a violet tint when stained by neutral dye.

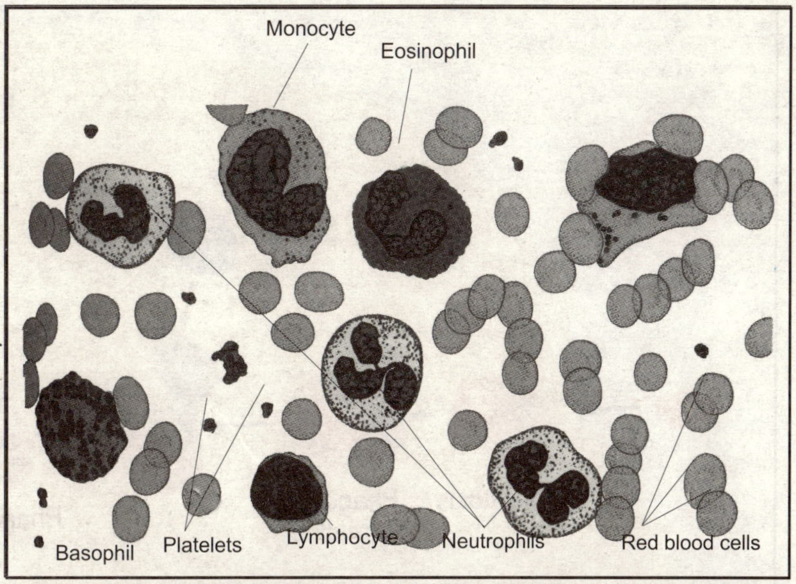


Fig. 5.17 : Different types of cells in blood

**Basophils :** The granules are large and coarse and stain deeply with methylene blue. Nucleus is often 'S' shaped. It accounts for under 1% of leukocytes.

Table 5.4
Different types of white cells

| Cell | Diameter(μm) | Nucleus | Cytoplasm | % of total |
|---|---|---|---|---|
| Neutrophil | 12-15 | 2-5 lobes | Pink and granular | 50-70% |
| Lymphocytes | 6-10 (small) 12-16 (large) | Round, chromatin is heavy | Pale blue, Deep blue | 20-40 |
| Monocyte | 12-20 | Large, fine chromatin | Pale blue, grey | 2-8 |
| Eosinophil | 12-15 | Two lobes | Orange, red granules | 1-4 |
| Basophil | 12-15 | Large, irregular lobes | Dark blue granules | 0.5-1 |

## Leukocyte production

**Leukocytes** originate from pluripotential stem cells in the bone marrow. Subsequently, they divide and mature giving two separate leukocyte stem cell lines

**Myeloid line**
- Three types of granulocytes
- Monocytes
- Macrophages
- Large multinucleated megakaryocytes

**Lymphoid line**

*Lymphocytes*
- B cells mature in marrow prior to the distribution to the lymphoid tissues of the body (eg, spleen, thymus, lymph nodes, Peyer's patches).
- T lymphocyte precursor cells migrate initially to thymus and mature fully.

## Granulocyte production

Granular leukocytes originate in the red bone marrow (myeloid tissue) but agranular leukocytes are produced in both myeloid and lymphoid tissues. Granulocytes and monocytes develop in the red bone marrow from a common progenitor, the myeloid stem cell.

The **myeloid stem cell** gives rise to red cells, granulocytes (neutrophils, eosinophils, basophils), monocytes or platelets.

**Neutrophils** are born in the **stem cell** also called **pluripotent stem cell** (Red bone marrow) → **committed stem cell** → colony forming unit, granulocyte–monocyte CFU–GM → **Myelo-blasts**/monoblasts (first identified by Leishman's stain, seen only in RBM but never in peripheral blood) → **Promyelocyte** (primary lysosomal/azurophilic granules appears in this stage and contains chemicals eg hydrolase; myeloperoxidase, cationic proteins, lysozyme and also defensins. Function is to kill microbes by different mechanisms. It contains cytoplasm and nucleolus) → **Myelocyte** (Nucleus indented; abundant of cytoplasm; absence of nucleolus; secondary granules appear at this stage. It contains lactoferrin; different types of receptor molecules and vit $B_{12}$ binding protein) → **band form** (nucleus is horse shoe shaped) → **mature neutrophils**.

**Eosinophils :** CFU–Eo → myeloblast → promyelocyte → myelocyte → metamyelocyte → band form → mature

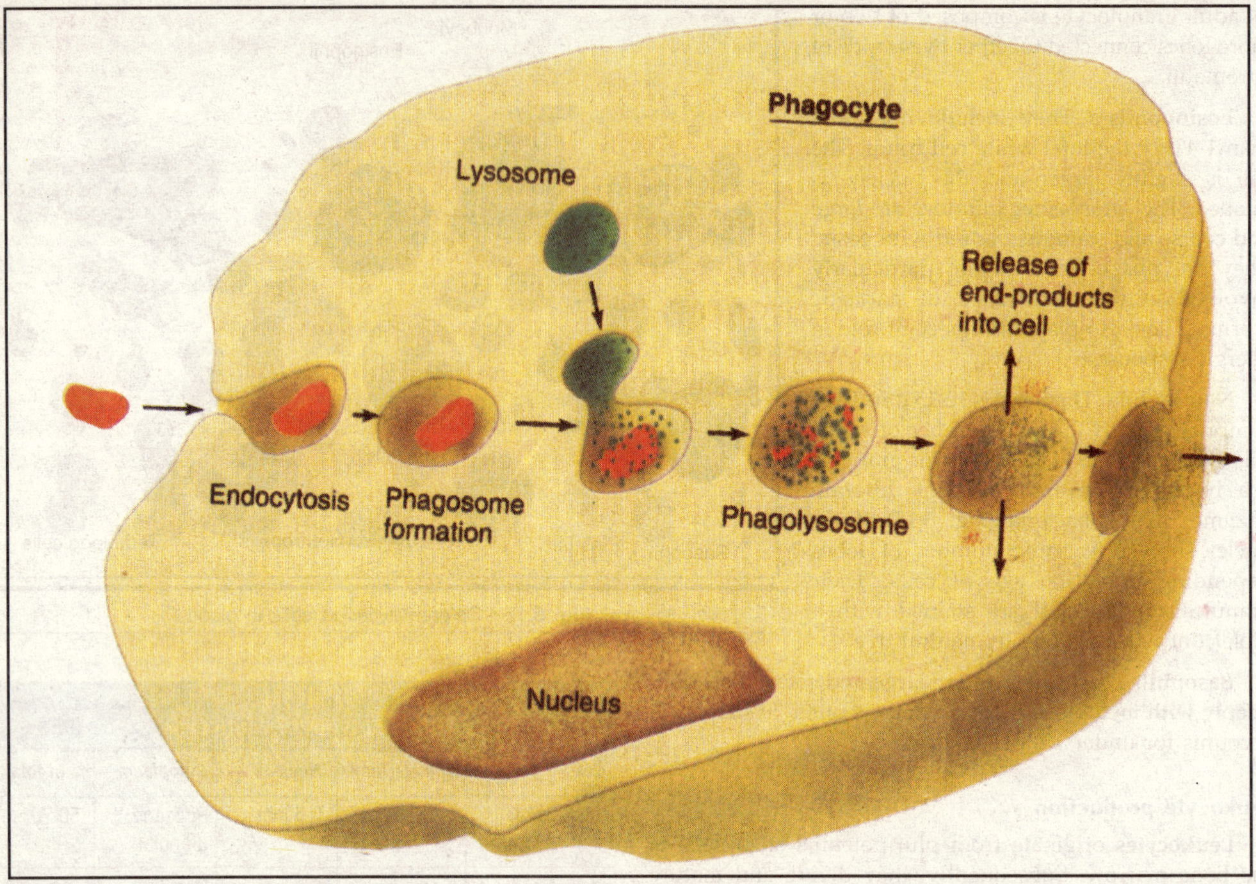


Fig. 5.18 : Phagocytosis

eosinophil. Eosinophilic granules contain major basic protein, eosinophil peroxidase and cationic proteins.

**Monocytes :** Granulocyte–monocyte colony stimulating factor (CFU, GM) [RBM] → blast cell (Monoblast) → monocyte → enters peripheral blood (stay about 48-72hours) → enters the tissue (tissue macrophage). They can remain alive for about three months.

**Lymphocytes :** Lymphocytes are born in the stem cells of the RBM. One type of daughter cells matures in thymus and forms T lymphocytes. The other type of daughter cells are matured in RBM and subsequently become B lymphocytes. T and B lymphocytes enter peripheral blood → lymph nodes → blood → lymph nodes.

## Control of leukocyte production in RBM

Granulocyte production depends upon a number of growth factors. **Growth factors** are cytokines, small proteins with paracrine activity. They are produced by various cells (eg, endothelium, macrophages, fibroblasts and lymphocytes) in the bone marrow. A number of growth factors have been isolated by recombinant DNA technology. **These growth factors** are (i) Erythropoietin (ii) Interleukins (iii) SCF (↑pluripotent and committed stem cells; ↑number of B lymphocytes) (iv) granulocyte-monocyte colony stimulating factor (GM-CSF) (v) M–CSF (↑precursor of monocyte) (vi) thrombopoietin.

***Cytokines*** **:** Proteins of low molecular mass which control different types of cellular activities nonspecifically —

- accelerate the inflammatory response
- initiate the growth and differentiation of the cells of the immune system
- responsible for cellular and antiviral activity (interferon).

## Life span and number

A leukocyte can phagocytize only a certain number of substances before they interfere with the leukocyte's normal metabolic activities and bring on its death. Life span of most leukocytes is very short. Some white blood cells can live up to several months in healthy body. Most live only a few days. During the time of infection, they may live only a few hours.

Leukocytes are less in number than red blood cells, averaging from 4,000 to 11,000 cells per cubic millimeter of blood.

## Functions of the leukocytes

The white cells of the blood perform two functions mainly (a) phagocytic function — engulf and destroy bacteria and (b) lymphocytes are responsible for immunity.

The neutrophilic polymorphonuclear leukocytes and monocytes and other reticuloendothelial elements play an important role in the defence mechanism against invading microorganisms.

**Neutrophil :** Their key function is to attack and destroy the invading bacteria. When bacteria enters the body, there develops an inflammation which produces effects by which neutrophils emigrate : Neutrophils → bacteria (chemotaxis) → phagocytose them → digest the bacteria. For the movement of neutrophils, they take the help of **pseudopods** by contraction of actin filaments.

**Eosinophils** contain lysosomal enzymes and a protein, major basic protein which neutralizes heparin. They play an important role to combat parasitic infestations and modulate the effects of histamine, leukotrienes in allergic reactions and also in phagocytosing antigen-antibody complexes.

**Basophils** contain heparin and histamine in their granules and its cell membrane has receptors for immunoglobulin E (IgE).

Basophils and mast cells release histamine. **Mast cells** are located in connective tissue and brain. Mast cells release histamine; which may cause anaphylactic shock manifested by arteriolar dilatation and bronchospasm.

**Monocytes** and **macrophages :** (1) They are important for performing phagocytic functions. (2) Secretion. (3) Important role in tissue repair and (4) are responsible for stimulation of the immune system by antigens. Their phagocytic action is very powerful. It emigrates into tissues following acute bacterial invasion (generally one day after neutrophil emigration). **Monocytes** are the **second line of defence**.

Table 5.5

| *T cell* | *B cell* |
|---|---|
| 1. 80% blood lymphocytes are T cell. | 1. 15% blood lymphocytes are B cell. |
| 2. T cells cannot be identified by Leishman's stain. Special technique is necessary. | 2. B cells also cannot be identified by Leishman's stain. Special methods are required. |
| 3. T cells kill virus and bacteria also. | 3. B cells convert into plasma cells which produce chemicals (immunoglobulin also called antibodies) neutralize antigens. |
| 4. T cells are responsible for cell mediated immunity (CMI). | 4. B cells involve humoral immunity where antigens are attacked by immunoglobulins (antibodies) |

## Lymphocyte circulation

**Lymphocytes** are present in large numbers in spleen and lymph nodes. They are present also in mucosal lymphoid aggregations in the gastrointestinal and respiratory tracts (tonsils, Peyer's patches). Lymphocytes do not remain confined to a particular site. They travel through blood and lymph to various lymphoid and nonlymphoid organs.

The ***lymphocytes*** in circulation are ***immunocompetent cells.*** They may be memory cells or virgin lymphocytes that respond to antigens entering the body by any route.

Both the T and B-lymphocytes respond to antigens by primary and secondary responses. In case of primary response, the antigen is to be processed by macrophages or equivalent cells or, in some cases, somatic cells. Part of the antigen is then expressed by the antigen presenting cells (mostly macro-phages) along with appropriate MHC gene coded products to T-lymphocytes ($CD_4$ and $CD_8$). Now sensitized $T_4$ and $T_8$ lymphocytes are responsible for different aspects of cell mediated and humoral immunity. In case of humoral immunity, B-lymphocytes respond to antigenic determinants to produce corresponding antibodies, but their function can be facilitated or inhibited by appropriately sensitized $T_4$ and $T_8$ cells.

## Variations in the number of leukocytes in the blood

*Neutrophilia*

**Increase in neutrophil count occurs in**

(i) **Physiologic :** Exercise, excitement, stress, excess epinephrine secretion.

(ii) **Pathologic :** Infections (mainly bacterial), burns, tissue necrosis (as in myocardial or pulmonary infarction), myelocytic leukemia, glucocorticoid administration.

*Neutropenia*

**Decrease in neutrophil count occurs in**

(i) Hematologic diseases like aplastic anemia

(ii) Drugs like cytotoxic agents used in cancer chemotherapy

(iii) Myelofibrosis

(iv) Infections like tuberculosis, enteric fever, measles, viral hepatitis, malaria, leishmaniasis.

*Eosinophilia*

**Increase in eosinophil count occurs in**

(i) Parasitic infestations

(ii) Allergic diseases

(iii) Collagen vascular diseases

(iv) Malignancies like Hodgkin's disease, chronic myelogenous leukemia (CML).

*Eosinopenia*

**Decrease in eosinophil count occurs in**

(i) Stress

(ii) Infections (nonparasitic)
(iii) Corticosteroid administration.

*Lymphocytosis*

**Increase in lymphocyte count occurs in**

(i) Chronic lymphatic leukemia (CLL)
(ii) Infections like infectious mononucleosis, viral hepatitis, pertussis, tuberculosis, brucellosis, syphilis
(iii) Thyrotoxicosis, Addison's disease.

*Lymphocytopenia*

**Decrease in lymphocyte count occurs in**

(i) Congenital immunodeficiency syndromes
(ii) Stress
(iii) Radiation injury
(iv) Cytotoxic drugs
(v) Corticosteroid therapy
(vi) Lymphoma
(vii) Aplastic anemia.

*Monocytosis*

**Increase in monocyte count occurs in**

(i) Chronic inflammation like tuberculosis, bacterial endocarditis, malaria, leishmaniasis (kala-azar)
(ii) Sarcoidosis, Crohn's disease
(iii) Some collagen vascular diseases
(iv) Myeloproliferative syndromes.

*Monocytopenia*

**Decrease in monocyte count occurs in**

(i) Stress
(ii) Acute infections
(iii) Glucocorticoid administration
(iv) Acute myelogenous leukemia (AML)
(v) Immunosuppressive and myelotoxic drugs.

### Proliferative disorders of the white blood cells

Malignant proliferative diseases of the blood include the leukemias, lymphomas, and myelomas. Self-limiting proliferative disorders such as infectious mononucleosis can also occur.

**Leukemia :** Increased numbers of abnormal white blood cells circulating in the blood. **Lymphocytic leukemias** are most commonly seen in children and involve the lymphoid precursors that originate in the bone marrow. Cancerous production of lymphoid cells then spreads to other tissues such as spleen, lymph nodes and CNS.

Myelocytic disease, which is more common in adults, involves the pluripotent myeloid stem cells in the bone marrow. The maturation of all the blood cell types, including granulocytes, erythrocytes and thrombocytes is affected.

## 5.12 Lymphocytes

### Introduction

The conventional morphological classification of leukocytes is granulocytes (containing granules in their cytoplasm) and agranulocytes (no granules in the cytoplasm). Granulocytes include neutrophils, eosinophils and basophils while agranulocytes comprise monocytes and lymphocytes (small lymphocyte and large lymphocyte).

But the **WBCs** can also be functionally grouped into **phagocytes** and **immunocytes**. Phagocytes are those WBCs who have active role in phagocytosis, i.e., engulfing foreign substances such as bacteria, virus etc. Phagocytes include neutrophils, eosinophils, basophils and monocytes. Immunocytes are those which play a major role in immune mechanism of the body. Immunocytes are small and large lymphocytes.

### Structure

The cells of the immune system are morphologically quite similar but shows a functional diversity. The diversity is due to variations in the expression of immunoglobulin and histocompatibility genes which makes the immunocytes competent for a vast number of immune interactions and immune responses.

### Cell morphology

In stained blood and bone marrow films the small lymphocyte is a round cell measuring about 9 µm in diameter with a thin rim of pale blue cytoplasm and may contain a few azurophilic granules. Its nucleus has a chromatin pattern arranged in bluish purple blocks :

**Small lymphocytes** 

The large lymphocyte has a more generous cytoplasm that stains a deeper shade of blue. Its nucleus is also larger with chromatin blocks spaced further apart in looser arrangements. Nucleoli may be seen :

**Large lymphocytes** 

The **lymphoblast** is a large lymphocyte in which the nuclear chromatin no longer exhibits a block-like character but instead is finely divided into a grainy texture in the midst of which are one or two nuclei. Cell size is related to cell division.

**Small lymphocytes** are non-dividing lymphocytes and lymphoblasts are in the process of a transformation associated with active cell poliferation.

**Plasma cells** are identified by eccentrically placed nucleus with densely stained compact chromatin blocks and deep bluish-green cytoplasm indicative of a high level of secretory activity. Golgi apparatus is located adjacent to the nucleus :

**Plasma cells** 

The immunoblasts (plasmablasts) contain large blast-like nuclei along with the secretory cytoplasm of the plasma cells although there may be cell variants.

## 5.13 Immunity

Immunity refers to the body's defense mechanisms to fight against foreign proteins (e.g. bacteria, virus etc.) and altered self proteins (e.g. cancer cells).

An antigen is anything that can trigger immune response. Antigens are usually high molecular weight proteins. Some low molecular weight proteins or carbohydrates may also act as antigens when associated with some other proteins.

Immunity may be non specific (or innate) and specific (or acquired)

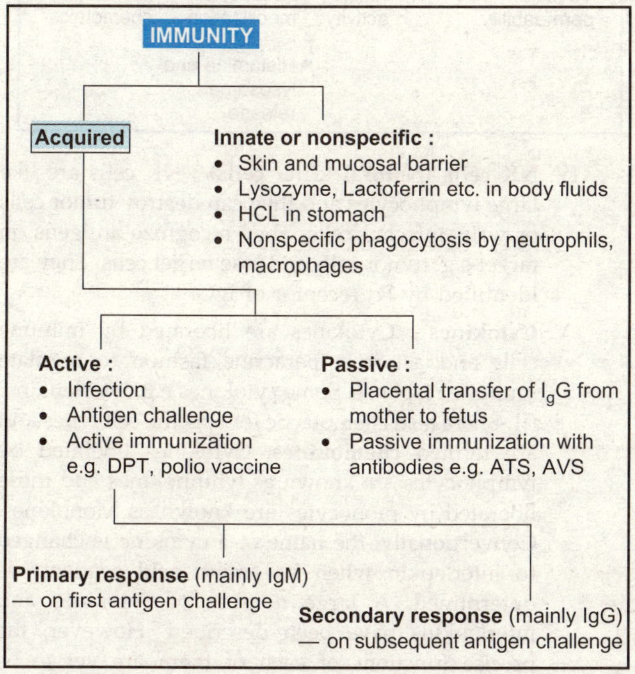


### Nonspecific or innate immunity

This kind of immunity comprises interrelated mechanisms that nonspecifically act against any foreign or abnormal cell. These mechanisms do not require previous exposure to the foreign material which is why this type of immunity is also called innate immunity.

The mechanisms are as follows :

I. **Mechanical and chemical barrier :** Skin and mucus membrane lining the gastro intestinal, genito urinary, and respiratory tracts provide mechanical barriers against infective organisms. Mucus secretion and ciliary movements rather aid in this barrier function. This is particularly remarkable in the respiratory tract. Acidic pH of gastric and vaginal secretion have role in preventing invasion by micro organism.

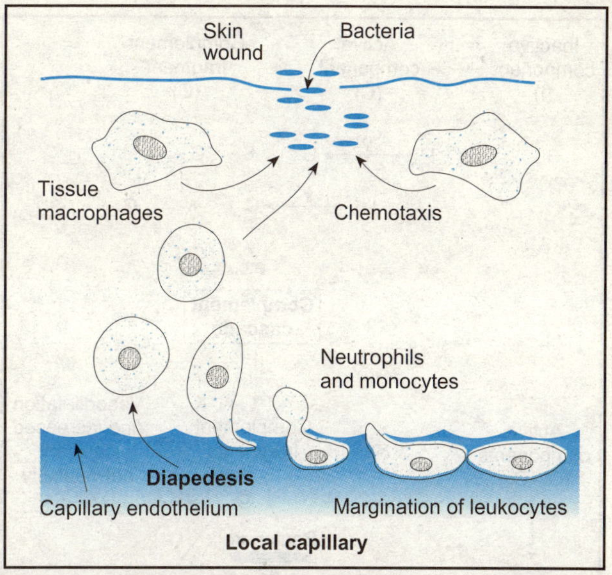


**Fig. 5.19 : Diapedesis of blood granulocytes and monocytes**

II. **Inflammation and Phagocytosis :** Inflammation is the response of tissue to sublethal injury. It almost always accompany infection. The hallmark of acute inflammation is increase in capillary permeability allowing migration of inflammatory cells (mainly neutrophils and macrophages). The enzymes of the system are named as C1 to C9.

Neutrophils phagocytize the invading micro organisms. In chronic inflammation, the inflammatory response tries to keep the invading foreign material within a granuloma formed by lymphocytes and modified macrophages. Fever that often accompanies inflammation may help in attenuating the infective organisms (Fig. 5.19).

III. **Activation of the Complement System :** Comprises atleast nine plasma proteins and some regulatory factors, that modulate several functions of the inflammatory process.

It is synthesized by macrophages or hepatocytes.

**Functions :**

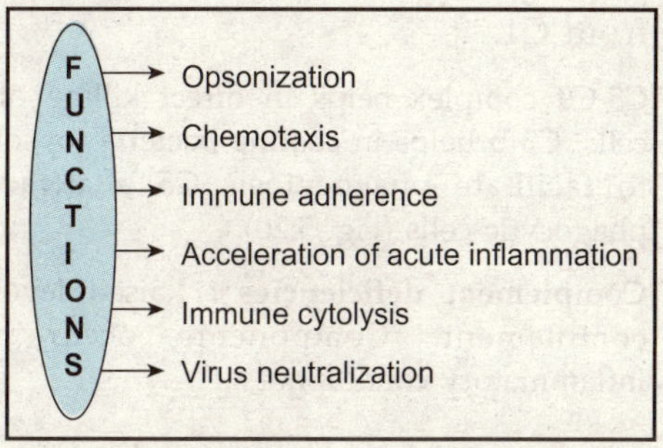

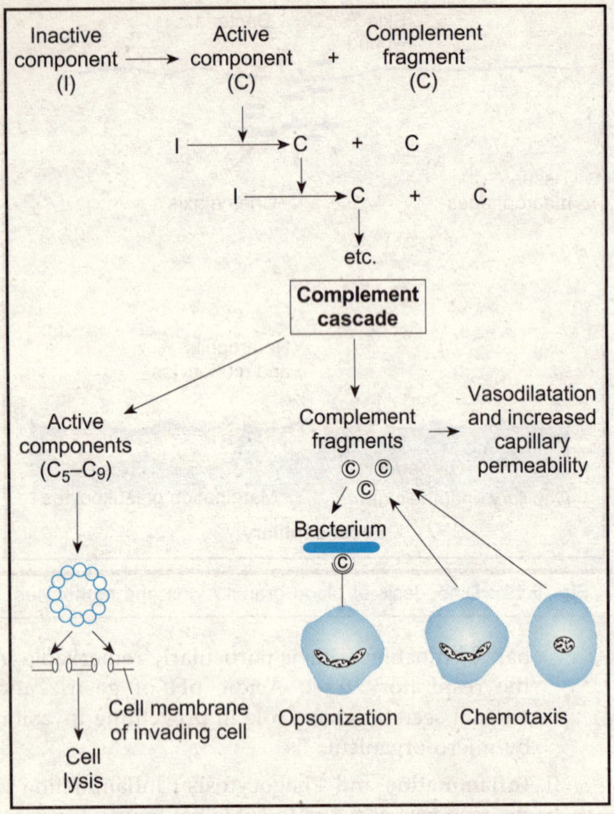


**Fig. 5.20 :** Non specific activation of the complement cascade by alternate pathway.

A system of enzymes found in plasma that help in immune mechanism is known as the complement system (Fig. 5.20). The system can be activated by two different pathways — classical pathway mediated b, IgG, IgG2, IgG3 or and IgM antibody (initiated by certain antigens and IgA complexes) Alternative pathway.

The classical pathway is triggered by antigen antibody complexes and starts from C3. Activation then proceeds sequentially till terminal component (The lytic complex i.e. C5–C9) is formed. Lytic complex and some other intermediate products of activation are important in fighting against foreign antigens. Activation via the Alternative pathway is similar to classical pathway except that the alternate pathway starts from C1.

C5-C9 complex helps in direct killing of foreign cells. C3 b helps in coating bacteria (opsonization) to facilitate phagocytosis C5 a attracts more phagocytic cells (Fig. 5.20).

**Complement deficiencies :** Raised levels of all complement. Components occur in any inflammatory condition.

Decreased levels occur —

- Post-streptococcal glomerulo nephritis
- SLE nephritis
- Infective endocarditis
- Nephritis
- Liver disease
- Disseminated intravascular coagulation

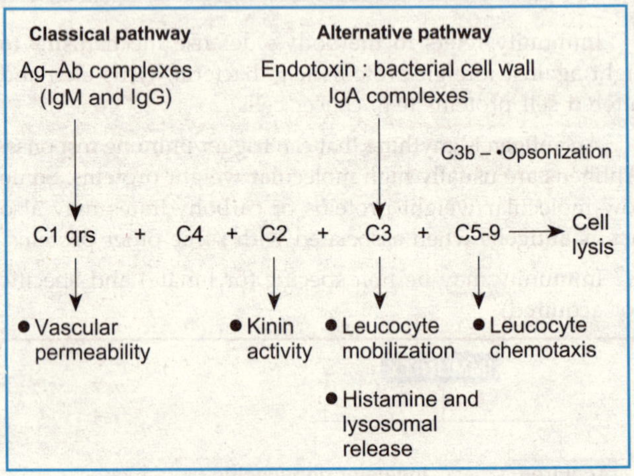


IV. **NK cells (Natural killer cells) :** NK cells are like large lymphocytes and they can destroy tumor cells or virus infected cells. They recognize antigens on target e.g. tumor cells and lyse target cells. They are identified by Fc receptor of IgG.

V. **Cytokines :** Cytokines are liberated by immune cells and act in a paracrine fashion to regulate immune response. Some cytokines e.g. interleukin 8 (IL-8) are also chemotactic for specific cell types and are termed **chemokines**. Cytokines liberated by lymphocytes are known as lymphokines and those liberated by monocytes are known as Monokines. Convertionally, the name of a cytokine is changed to interleukin when its amino acid sequence is determined. A large number of cytokines and interleukins have been described. However, the precise functions of each of them are yet to be determined.

The interrelationship of immune cell population.

**Interferon**

| Cytokine | Immune cells | Immunological effects |
|---|---|---|
| IFN–α,β | T and B cells, monocytes or macrophages. | • Antiviral activites<br>• Stimulation of macrophages and large granular lymphocytes (LGL). |
| IFN–γ | T and LGL (large granular) | • Antiviral activity<br>• Stimulation of macrophages<br>• Enhanced HLA Class I |

**Interleukins**

| Cytokine | Immune cells | Immunological effects |
|---|---|---|
| IL-1α,β | Monocytes/ Macrophages | Activation of T and B cells. |
| IL-2 | T cells | Proliferation or activation of T, B and LGL |
| IL-4 | T and B cells, mast cells basophil | Activation of B cells |
| IL-5 | T cells, mastcells | Development, activation and chemoattraction of eosinophils |
| IL-6 | T cells, monocytes or macrophage | Activation of hemopoietic stem cells. Differentiation of B and T cells. |
| IL-8 | T cells, mono-cytes Neutrophils | Chemoattraction of Neutrophil, T cells, basophils |
| IL-10 | T and B cells macrophages | Suppression of macrophage function. Activation of B cells |

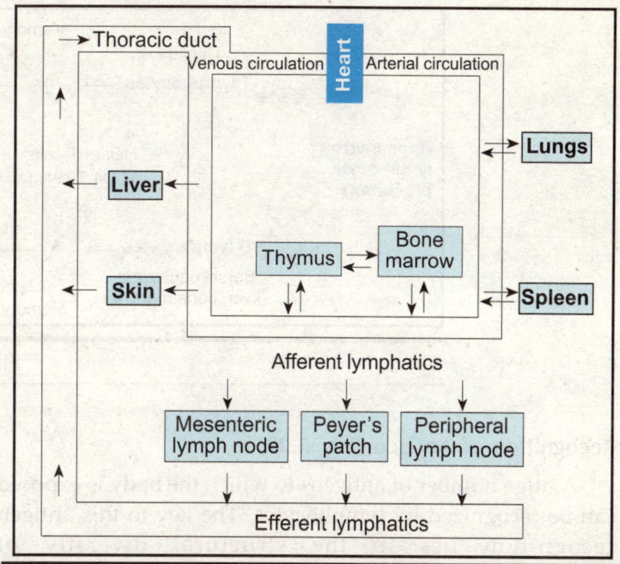


**Fig. 5.21 : Production and recirculation of lymphocytes in the body**

### Specific or Acquired immunity

Specific immunity refers to the ability of the body to respond to foreign molecules called antigens. Antigens are usually proteins and have molecular weight > 10,000. Some smaller molecules (hapten) when attached to a protein, can also act as antigens. Specific immunity depends on lymphocytes and may be humoral (mediated by B lymphocytes) or cell mediated (T-lymphocytes).

### Development of lymphocytes

The bonemarrow is the source of lymphocyte precursors during fetal development. The uncommitted lymphoid stem cells originate from pluripotent stem cells in the bonemarrow. The uncommitted lymphoid stem cells differentiate into two different types of committed lymphoid stem cells — B stem cell and T stem cell. These committed stem cells migrate to primary lymphoid organs — bonemarrow (B stem cells) and Thymus (T-stem cells). These cells are processed in the environment of these organs into lymphocytes responsible for cellular immunity (T lymphocytes, processed in thymus) and lymphocytes responsible for humoral (antibody mediated) immunity (B lymphocytes, processed in bonemarrow). The B lymphocytes derive their name originally from the Bursa of Fabricius (a lymphoid structure found near the cloaca of birds) where B lymphocytes are processed in birds. In humans, B lymphocytes are processed in bursal equivalents (liver in fetal life and bonemarrow after birth). After residing in the processing organs for sometime, the lymphocytes migrate to the lymph nodes, bonemarrow and other lymphoid structures like Peyer's patches (Fig. 5.21).

### Development of B lymphocytes

Within the bone marrow, B stem cells divide into two functional stages — Pre B cell (lymphoblasts) and mature B cell (resting). Pre B cells have μ chains of immunoglobulin molecules (see later) in their cytoplasm but lack surface immunoglobulin (Ig). These cells express IgM on their surface with further differentiation. They may contain IgM only or IgM in combination with IgA or IgG or IgD on their surface. These are mature B lymphocytes which may be called Virgin cells as long as they are not exposed to antigens. Once challenged with antigen these cells get activated and differentiate into secretory B cells (Plasma cells) and memory B cells.

**Plasma cells** secrete only a particular type of antibody specifically targetted against the antigens that activated the B cells. **Memory B cells** are quiescent cells capable of secreting the same kind of antibody during future challenges with the same antigen.

### Development of T lymphocytes

Committed T stem cells differentiate into pre T cells (lymphoblasts) and mature (resting) T cells. With processing of pre T cell in the thymus, two different subgroups of T lymphocytes develop. They derive their names from the cluster differentiating (CD) molecules expressed on their surface. T lymphocytes that express CD 4 molecules on their surface are known as CD 4+ T lymphocytes (helper-inducer T cells). T lymphocytes expressing CD 8 molecules from their surface are known as **CD 8+** T lymphocytes (suppressor—Cytotoxic T cells). CD 4+ T cells can be further subdivided into TH1 and TH2 cells. **TH1 cells** are primarily concerned with cell mediated immunity while **TH2 cells** are responsible for interaction with B cells. With antigenic challenge, virgin T cells become activated to mount cellular immune response against the antigen. Some T cells become memory cells for utilization during further challenges with the same antigen. Both B and T memory cells can remain in the body for months or years. They may persist even lifelong (Fig. 5.22).

It is important to note that during subsequent antigenic challenges memory cells can evoke an immune response very rapidly which is characteristic of acquired immunity.

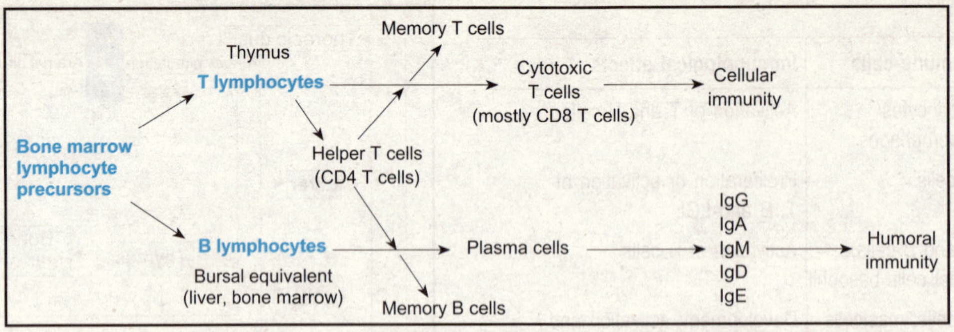


Fig. 5.22

### Recognition of Antigen (Fig. 5.23)

A huge number of antigens to which the body is exposed can be recognized by lymphocytes. The key to this antigen recognition lies in the structural diversity of immunoglobulinsand T cell receptors. The lymphoid stem cells can differentiate into millions of different types of B and T lymphocytes expressing different types of immunoglobulins and T cell receptors (Fig. 5.24).

### Immunoglobulins : Humoral mediators of immunity

Immunoglobins or antibodies, are proteins produced by the plasma cells of the bone marrow as part of the immune response. The plasma cells are B lymphocytes transformed after exposure to a foreign antigen.

#### Structure

All **immunoglobulins** have the same basic structure and consist of two identical **'light'** and two identical **'heavy'** polypeptide chains, held together by disulphide bridges.

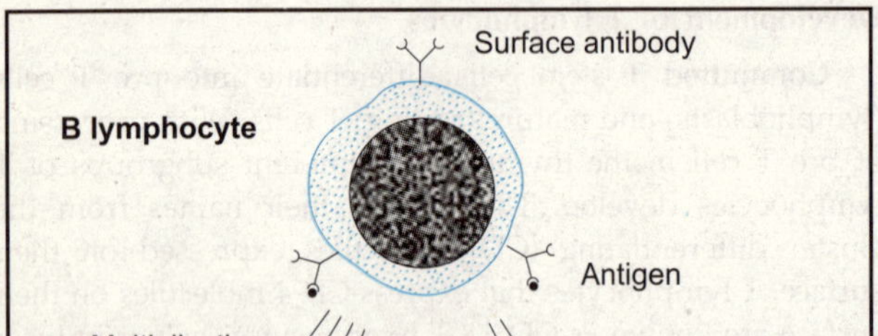


Fig. 5.23 : B lymphocyte activation by antigen binding leads to formation of antibody secreting cells and antigen sensitive memory cells.

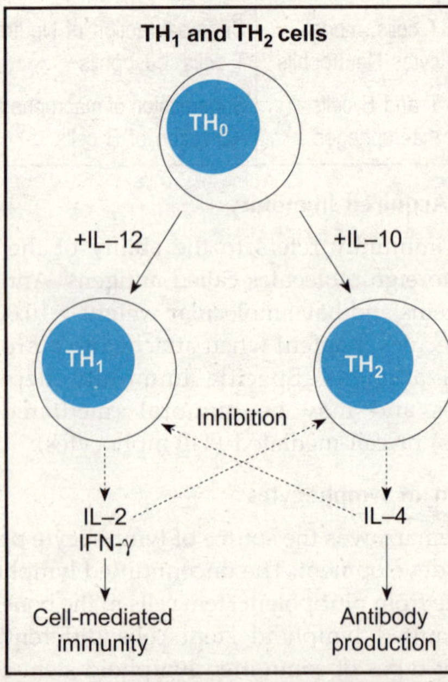


Fig. 5.24 : T-cell antigen receptor

The 'light' chains may be either of two types : Kappa or lambda. The heavy chains may be of five types : alpha, gamma, delta, epsilon and mu. The immunoglobulins are named after their heavy chain type as IgA; IgG, IgD, IgE and IgM (Fig. 5.25).

The molecules are characterized by two functional areas :

- The **Fab** or **variable mend** is the area which recognizes and binds to the antigen.
- The Fc end is responsible for interaction with other components.

### Classes of immunoglobulin

*IgM* : IgM (molecular weight about 9,600,000 daltons) antibodies exist as pentamer and consist of 5 units linked together by a small polypeptide J chain (Fig. 6.39) and normally circulate in blood. IgM is the first immunoglobulin to appear in the immune response (primary antibody response) and is the initial type of antibody made by

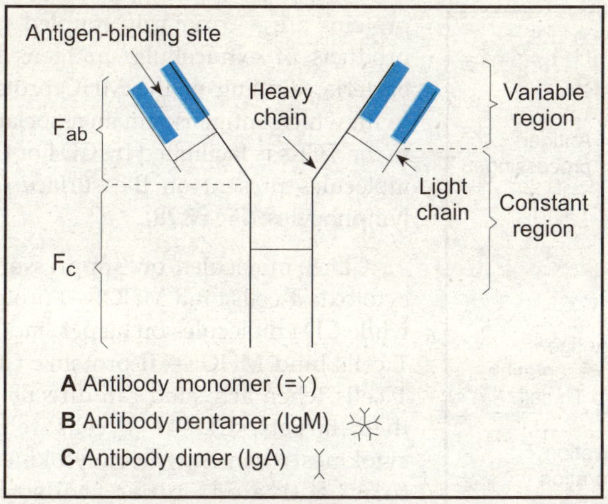


**Fig. 5.25 : Immunoglobulin structure**

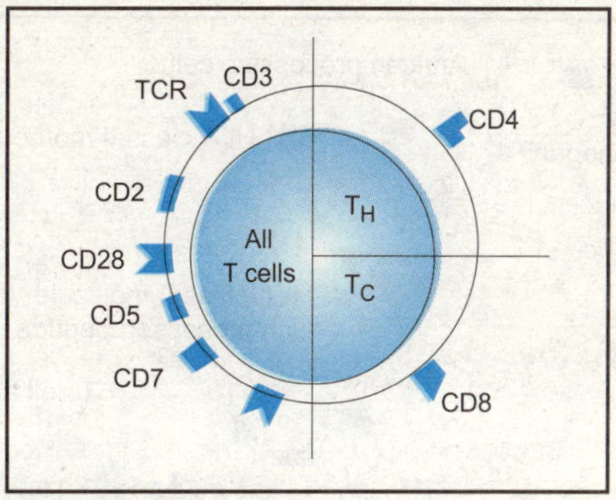


TS = Suppressor T-cells.
TC = Cytotoxic T-cells.
CD = Cluster of differentiation.
MHC = Major histo compatibility complex.
TH = Helper T-cells.
TDH = Delayed hypersensivity T-cells.

**Fig. 5.26 : T-cell surface antigen and CD markers**

neonates. IgM is an important component of immune complexes of autoimmune disease.

*IgG* : IgG (molecular weight about 190,000 daltons) comprises about 75% of the total serum immunoglobulins. There are four IgG subclasses. Of the immunoglobulins, only IgG crosses the placenta.

*IgA* : IgA (molecular weight about 160,000 daltons) comprises only 10-15% of the total serum immunoglobulins. IgA secretion occurs in tear, saliva, nasal secretion, GI tract fluids and human milk in the form of secretory IgA.

*IgD* : IgD (molecular weight is about 175,000 daltons) found in small quantity in serum and along with IgM is a major receptor for antigens on B-cell surface.

*IgE* : IgE (molecular weight is about 190,000 dalton) is present in serum in very low concentrations. IgE is the major class of immunoglobulin which binds to mast cells and basophils via its Fc region.

**Summary of classes of immunoglobulin**

| *Immunoglobin* | *Location* | *Action* |
|---|---|---|
| IgG | ECF | Neutralizes toxins, activates complement |
| IgA | ECF + secretions | Antimicrobial |
| IgM | ECF + cell membrane | First to be made in immune response |
| IgD | ECF + cell membrane | Uncertain |
| IgE | ECF | Anti allergic, antiparasitic |

**Complement**

**Complement system** is a complex biological amplifying system. The term 'complement' refers to serum proteins involved in a complicated sequence of reactions. These reactions (complement cascade) have amplifying effect upon the antigen-antibody interaction and support or mediate a number of immunological functions and have an effector function in cell destruction.

There are two pathways to the activation of complement system – **the classical and alternate pathways**. These pathways meet at $C3_a$ and the rest of the cascade is then the same regardless of the mode of initiation. Initiation of classical pathway usually requires an antigen-antibody reaction. IgM and three of the four subclasses of IgG can activate complement. Once the cascade is initiated, each step involves activation of an inactive precursor molecule present in the serum and is enzyme mediated. Complement activation itself involves release of serotonin and kinin activation, with one or both associated with local changes of classic inflammation.

**T-cell receptors (TCR)**

T cell receptors are present on the surface of T lymphocytes. Structurally, they may be considered analogous to immunoglobulin. Functionally they are similar to immunoglobulins as far as antigen recognition is concerned. However a remarkable difference between Ig and TCR is that TCR is never secreted.

TCRs are heterodimers composed of two polypeptide units (a and b). They are associated with other polypeptides like CD3 molecules. TCRs together with CD3, MHC (Major Histocompatibility complex, see below), and CD4 or CD8 recognise antigens (Fig. 5.26).

For recognition, antigen need to be processed and presented to the lymphocytes by antigen presenting cells (APC) (Fig. 5.27).

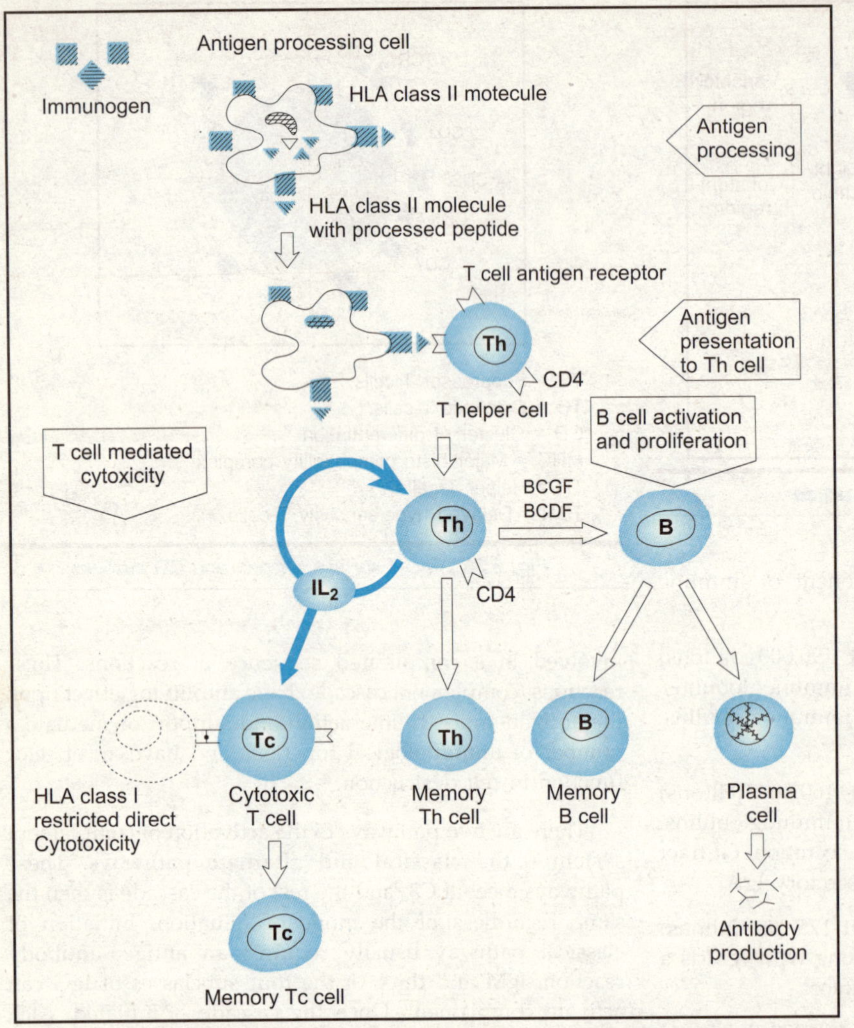


**Fig. 5.27 : Cellular interactions and effects in adaptive immune system**

### Presentation of Antigen

Before being presented to lymphocytes, antigens are processed by antigen presenting cells (APC). APC include various types of specialized cells such as dendritic cells (spleen and lymph nodes), Langerhan cells (Skin), Macrophages, and sometimes B lymphocytes themselves. Inside the APCs, the antigens are digested and the products of digestion are coupled to human leukocyte antigen (HLA) which are the products of the major histocompatibility complex (MHC) genes. The antigens along with the HLA is expressed on the surface of the APC.

The MHC genes are located on the short arm of the 6th chromosome. Their products can be divided into two classes — class I antigens (MHC — I proteins) and class II antigens (MHC — II proteins) MHC — I proteins are associated with β2 microglobulin and are found on all nucleated cells except RBC. These proteins are primarily responsible for coupling antigens formed from intracellular proteins. MHC — II antigens are found in APCs as well as in B cells. These proteins are — primarily coupled with products of extracellular antigens like bacteria. Binding of the MHC proteins (with which antigens remain associated) to the TCRs is facilitated by CD4 or CD8 molecules present on the surface of T lymphocytes (Fig. 2.28).

CD 8 molecules on suppressor — cytotoxic T cells bind MHC — I proteins while CD4 molecules on helper -inducer T cells bind MHC — II proteins. $CD8^+$ T cells when activated can directly kill their targets. CD $4^+$ T cells release cytokines when activated; cytokines in turn activated other cells like macrophages for the ultimate response (Fig. 5.27 & 5.28).

### Self–recognition by the immune system

Why the immune system does not mount an immune response to proteins that are present within our body is an unsettled question. The possible mechanisms may be as follows :

(1) **Clonal deletion :** It may be that the body proteins (self antigens) are presented to the immune system like nonself antigens. However the clones of lymphocytes sensitized against self antigens are selectively destroyed in the thymus very early in life. This is known as clonal deletion but the exact events that are responsible are unknown.

(2) **Clonal anergy :** This theory postulates that the lymphocytes exposed to a large quantity of antigens in the absence of lymphokines undergo a state of prolonged hyporesponsiveness (clonal anergy)

(3) **Suppressor T cells may also be responsible.**

### Autoimmunity

Inspite of the body's effort to avoid immune response to self antigens, the mechanisms may sometimes fail due to various reasons. In many cases, their exact reason is unclear. Diseases that result from immune response against self antigens (autoimmunity) are known as **autoimmune diseases**. Autoimmune diseases can be mediated by B or T lymphocytes. they can be organ specific (affecting a particular organ or tissue) or systemic (nonspecific diffuse involvement of the organs and tissues). Examples include myasthenia gravis (occurring due to production of antibodies against nicotinic cholinergic receptors, Graves' disease (occurring due to production of antibodies against TSH receptors), pernicious anemia (occurring due to production of antibodies against intrinsic factor). etc. Sometimes antibodies produced

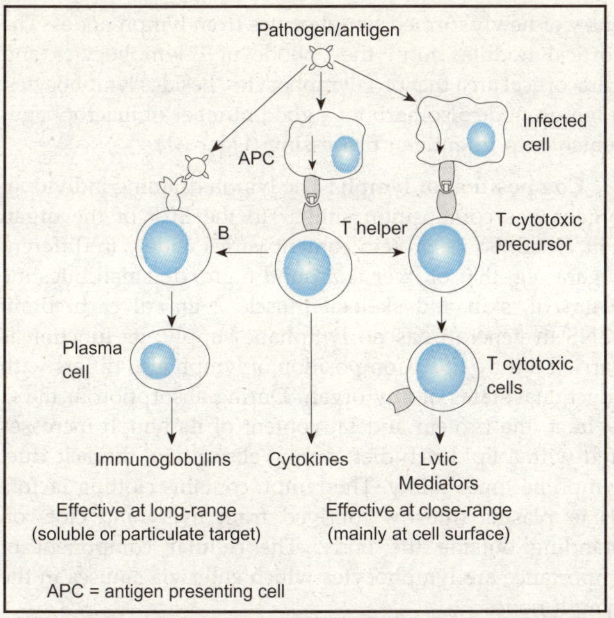


Fig. 5.28

against foreign protein (e.g. Streptococcal antigen) may cross react with body proteins (e.g. heart valves) resulting in autoimmune disease (e.g. rheumatic fever). This is known as molecular mimicry.

**Transplant rejection**

Transplantation of organs and tissues is increasingly becoming a mode of treatment in diseases which earlier had no treatment. But a real challenge in tissue transplantation is transplant rejection. Transplant rejection is mediated by T lymphocytes. The immune response occurs against the HLAs (MHC proteins) of the donor's tissue cells.

Hence a perfect HLA match between the donor and acceptor (Host) is necessary before transplantation. However a perfect HLA match is possible only if the host has an identical twin to act as a donor. This is rarely found in practice. Therefore the usual practice is to find out a donor whose HLA matches as closely as possible with that of the host. After transplantation, efforts are taken to avoid rejection. The various approaches that can be employed to prevent rejection without life threatening immune suppression are as follows :

1. Killing T lymphocytes by cytotoxic drugs like azathioprine. The disadvantage is that the drug can kill all rapidly dividing cells in the body.
2. Administration of glucocorticoids to inhibit proliferation of CD 8 + T cells.
3. To use antilymphocyte globulin to suppress cytotoxic T cells.
4. Preventing T cell differentiation and proliferation with the help of drugs like Cyclosporine, Tacrolimus, and rapamycin.

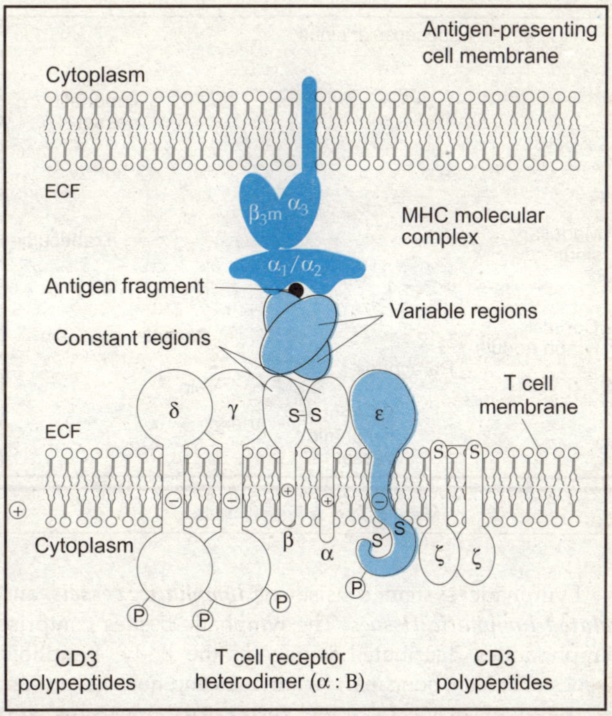


Fig. 5.29 : Interaction between antigen presenting cell and T-lymphocyte. The MHC proteins and their peptide antigen fragment bind to the α and β units that continue to form T-cell receptor.

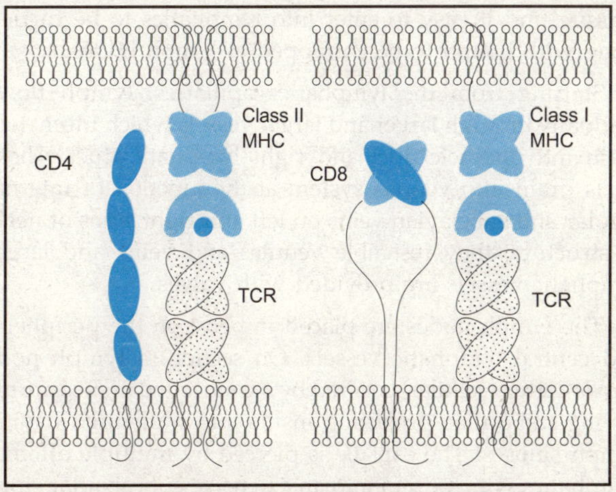


Fig. 5.30 : Structure of CD4 and CD8 and their relation to MHC-I and MHC-II proteins.

## 5.14 Circulation of Lymph

**Lymph** is the fluid flowing through the lymphatic vessels for draining into venous system. The lymph is formed in the tissues by the filtration through the capillaries — the redundant of the filtrate after reabsorption at the venous end of capillaries.

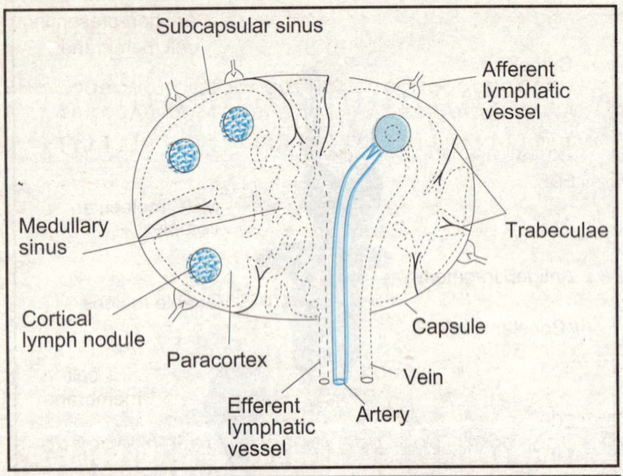


**Fig. 5.31 : A lymph node**

Lymphatic system consists of ***lymphatic vessels*** and ***related lymphatic tissues***. The lymphatic tissues comprise lymph nodes distributed widely in the body, lymphoid tissues of spleen, bone marrow, thymus and nodules present in the wall of G I tract, respiratory passages and genitourinary tract. The lymphatic vessels begin as blind network of endothelial tubes almost deficient in basement membrane. The terminal lymphatics are highly permeable allowing large molecules and blood corpuscles to enter their lumen through intercellular spaces. So infecting microbes in a tissue find it easy to enter into lymphatics to be carried along with lymph to be entrapped at lymph nodes.

Starting from the lymphatic capillaries, lymph flows gradually through larger and larger vessels which ultimately drain into thoracic duct and right lymphatic duct. These ducts drain into venous system at the junction of internal jugular and subclavian veins on left and right sides of neck. In structure, they resemble venules and veins and larger lymphatic vessels are provided with valves.

The lymph nodes are placed in between the peripheral and central lymphatic vessels. On section, a lymph node shows cortex (cellular) covered by a connective tissue capsule having trabeculae projecting inside and a medulla having lymph sinuses. The capsule is pierced by multiple afferent lymphatics which drain into an extensive subcapsular sinus from which centrally directed sinuses project to converge into a plexus of sinuses at the medulla. An efferent lymphatic vessel drains the medullary sinuses and subcapsular sinus. Lymphocytes aggregate to form nodules in the cortex. Lymphocytes are diffusely scattered at the medulla and in between medulla and cortex (paracortex). A small artery supplies nutrition to the lymph node that is drained by a vein. The supporting element of the cellular constituents is formed by reticular tissue.

Lymphocytes can enter and leave the substance of the node through sinuses and post-capillary venules. In this way, there takes place recirculation of lymphocytes and entry of newly formed lymphocytes from lymph nodes. The cortical nodules form the abode of B-lymphocytes and paracortical area that of T-lymphocytes. Besides lymphocytes, a lymph node also harbors a good number of macrophages which help in antigen processing (Fig. 5.31).

**Composition of lymph :** The lymph draining individual organs has composition similar to the ECF of the organ concerned. So its protein content varies widely in different organs, eg. that of liver is around 6 gm/dl; small intestine 3 gm/dl, skin and skeletal muscle 2 gm/dl each. Brain (CNS in general) has no lymphatic supply; its function is carried out by CSF. Composition of lymph also differs with functional states of any organ. During absorption in the G I tract, the protein and fat content of its lymph increases and with a lipid-rich diet, during absorption, thoracic duct lymph becomes milky. The lymph contains clotting factors as in plasma (mostly derived from liver) and clots on standing outside the body. The cellular component of importance are lymphocytes which enter via sinuses in the lymph nodes.

Filtration of plasma occurs at the arterial end of most of the capillaries (least in lungs) but more than 90% is reabsorbed at the venous end and the remaining 10% is returned by the lymphatics, around 2.5 liters/day. The flow through thoracic duct contributes more than 80% of this.

Forces that operate in the movement of lymph through the lymphatics generate hydrostatic pressure gradient starting from interstitial space up to its termination. Normally, the hydrostatic pressure at most interstitial spaces is subatmospheric. In different physiological and pathological states (eg. edema) the ISF pressure increases above atmospheric pressure. It has been seen that when the ISF pressure rises from negative (– 6 mm Hg) to higher values, lymph flow increases almost linearly up to atmospheric level (0 mm Hg) pressure. Further increment in pressure does not generally increase the flow much.

The lymphatic capillaries are tethered to tissue cells by fibrils which prevent their collapse and maintain the gaps between neighbouring cells. So whenever interstitial fluid pressure increases in any organ the lymph formation increases. Interstitial fluid pressure increases whenever there is rise in capillary filtration rate. The Starling forces favoring filtration like (a) increased capillary hydrostatic pressure (b) heightened permeability of capillaries (c) diminished oncotic pressure gradient between plasma and ISF—all increase the rate of lymph formation. Working muscles and absorbing intestine have increased lymph formation due to above factors (see Figs. 5.32 and 5.33).

Moreover, larger lymphatic vessels are provided with muscles and valves. Contraction of muscle in their walls, when distended, push lymph proximally. The portion between successive valves distend till the pressure generated by muscle contraction is sufficient to push fluid across the proximal valve to distend the proximal segment and the process continues.

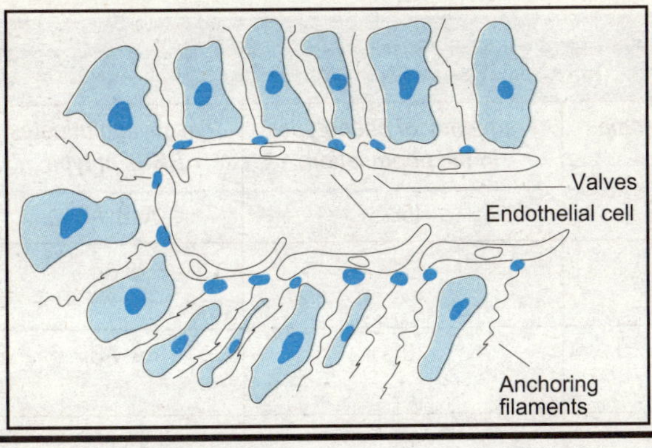


Fig. 5.32 : Structure of lymphatic capillaries

Besides these factors, the same factors that facilitate venous drainage also favors lymph flow, e.g., muscular contractions, respiratory movements, suction effect of cardiac relaxation also operate in lymph return. Pulsation of neighbouring large arteries like abdominal and thoracic aorta also contribute.

***The functions of lymphatic system*** is (a) to return fluid from tissue spaces, (b) to absorb lipid from the intestines and carry proteins and other constituents of plasma leaking to exterior, (c) to carry antigens to lymph nodes and mount appropriate immune response against it by generating effector T-lymphocytes (cellular immunity) and B-lymphocyte-plasma cell (humoral immunity), (d) production of majority of lymphocytes in postnatal life and antibodies, (e) by removing proteins and fluid from interstitial space they prevent accumulation of excess fluid in tissue spaces (edema).

In conformity to functions the lymph nodes show enlargement (lymphadenopathy) in microbial infections and neoplastic conditions, but also in some immunological reactions (obscure etiology). A few examples are (a) *infective* —pyrogenic, tuberculous, Epstein-Barr virus etc. (b) *neoplastic* —Hodgkin's and non-Hodgkin's lymphomas, metastatic tumors, (c) *immunological reactions* — connective tissue disorders like systemic lupus erythematosus, histiocytosis etc.

Chronic obstruction of the lymphatics may occur after surgical removal of lymphatics, eg. radical mastectomy or their destruction after radiotherapy of malignancies or, more commonly, due to filariasis. Impairment of lymphatic drainage of the affected area causes accumulation of interstitial fluid and subsequent proliferation of connective tissues leading to firm (non-pitting) edema (lymphedema). In some cases, specially in filariasis, chronic obstruction of the lymphatics and recurrent inflammation of the affected parts (legs, scrotum, arm, vulva etc.) may lead to gross swelling and thickening of tissues, known as **elephantiasis.**

## 5.15 Blood Groups and Blood Transfusion

The membrane of human RBCs contain over 300 different antigenic determinants (blood group antigens or agglutinogens) dictated by genes at different chromosomal loci. The term blood group refers to any well-defined system of RBC antigens. Over twenty blood group systems have been recognized so far. The term blood type is applied to the antigen phenotype (serologic expression of the blood group genes). Over 500 billion blood group phenotypes are possible based on the known antigens. **Alloantibodies** (agglutinins) specific for the blood group antigens may occur naturally or may be formed in response to exposure to the antigen (eg, blood transfusion). Naturally occurring antibodies are usually of IgM type. Antibodies that form in response to exposure to blood group antigens are initially IgM but within a few weeks or months IgG antibodies are produced.

### ABO blood group system

A, B and O are the major allelic genes in the ABO system. They are inherited as Mendelian dominants and their locus is on the long arm of chromosome 9. There are four major blood types in this system **A, B, AB and O.** The genotypes and phenotypes of this system may be summarized as in Table 5.6.

The **A and B antigens** are complex oligosaccharides with different terminal sugar residue (Fig. 5.34). **A antigen**

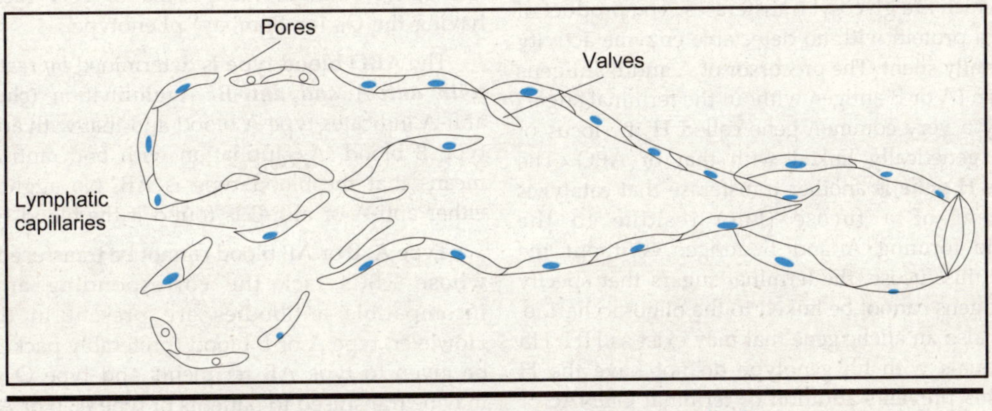


Fig. 5.33 : Lymphatic capillaries showing pores and valves

Table 5.6
ABO blood group system

| Genotype | Phenotype | Antigen(s) on RBC | Antibodies in plasma | Frequency of phenotypes in the popoulation | Plasma agglutinates RBCs of type |
|---|---|---|---|---|---|
| OO | O | H | Anti-A, Anti-B | 45% | A, B, AB |
| AA<br>AO | A | A | Anti-B | 41% | B, AB |
| BB<br>BO | B | B | Anti-A | 10% | A, AB |
| AB | AB | A, B | None | 4% | None |
| hh | $O_h$ | None | Anti-A, Anti-B, Anti-H | Very rare | O, A, B, AB |

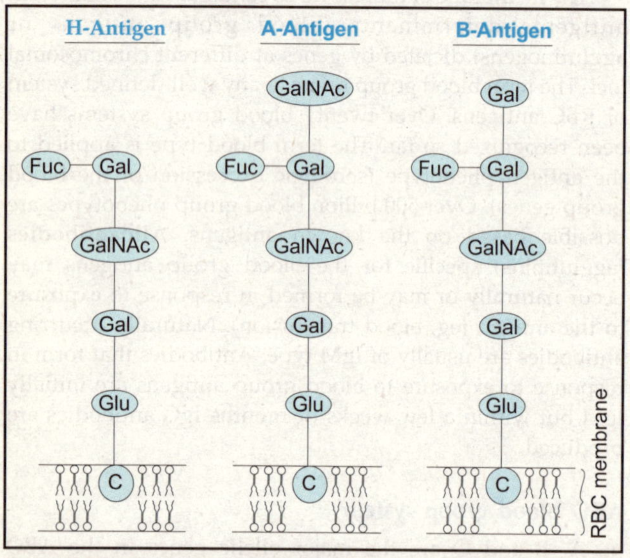


Fig. 5.34 : Antigens of the ABO system
© = Ceramide; Glu = glucose; Gal = Galactose;
GalNAc = N–acetylgalactosamine; Fuc = Fucose

contains a terminal N-acetylgalactosamine (GalNAc) and B antigen contains a terminal galactose (Gal). Attachment of these terminal sugars is catalyzed by the products of the A and B genes which are glycosyl transferases. The product of the O gene is a protein with no detectable enzyme activity and is functionally silent. The precursor of A and B antigens is the H antigen (A or B antigen without the terminal sugar) determined by a very common gene called **H** the locus of which is not genetically linked with that of ABO. The product of the **H gene** is another transferase that catalyzes the attachment of a fucose (Fuc) residue to the oligosaccharide forming A and B antigen. Without the attachment of this fucose, the terminal sugars that specify the A or B antigens cannot be linked to the oligosaccharide. The H gene is also an allelic gene that may exist as HH, Hh or hh. Individuals with hh genotype do not have the H transferase. This prevents addition of terminal GalNAc or Gal by A or B transferases to the precursor molecule. Hence A or B antigens cannot be formed even if the A or B genes are present in these individuals and their sera contain anti-A, anti-B and anti-H antibodies. These rare individuals are said to have the $O_h$ (or Bombay) phenotype and they can be transfused blood only from the same rare $O_h$ type of blood.

The antigens of the ABO system are *also found in salivary glands, saliva, pancreas, kidney, liver, lungs, testes, semen and amniotic fluid.* ABO system antigens are found in the body fluids of individuals having the secretor or Se gene. Nonsecretors have an apparently inactive allele se. About 80% of the population are secretors.

**Type A blood** can be subdivided into two types **$A_1$** and **$A_2$**. $A_1$ and $A_2$ transferases perform the same function of adding GalNAc to the H antigen but they have different rate constants. As a result, people having $A_1$ gene (i.e., people having type $A_1$ blood) have more A-reactive sites than those having $A_2$ gene (i.e., people having type $A_2$ blood).

***Antibodies against A or B antigens (Anti-A or Anti-B) occur naturally in the plasma.*** This is probably due to the fact that antigens very similar to A and B are often found in intestinal bacteria and some foods to which individuals are exposed after birth. The antibody or antibodies present in one's plasma are against the antigen(s) that are not present on his/her cells. Anti-H antibody (in addition to anti-A and anti-B) is found in the plasma of very rare individuals having the $O_h$ (or Bombay) phenotype.

The **ABO blood type** is determined ***by testing the RBCs with anti-A and anti-B.*** Agglutination (clumping) with anti-A indicates type A blood and that with anti-B indicates type B blood. Agglutination with both anti-A and anti-B means that the blood type is AB. No agglutination with either anti-A or anti-B is found if the blood type is O.

Type A, B or AB blood cannot be transfused into patients whose RBCs lack the corresponding antigens since incompatible antibodies are present in their plasma. However, type A or B blood (preferably packed RBCs) may be given to type AB recipients and type O packed RBCs may be transfused to patients of type A, B or AB if the type-specific blood is not available or there is emergency.

## Rh blood group system

The Rh system derives its name from the Rhesus monkey in which it was first studied. There are three tandem Rh loci on chromosome 1. The **Rh alleles** dictate the structure of a set of epitopes (antigenic determinants) that are : C or c, D or d (d = absence of D) and E or e. They are inherited from each parent as a haplotype , eg, CDE, cDe, cde, cDE etc. The D ($Rh_o$) antigen is the most immunogenic. ***Rh-positive individuals have D antigen.*** Rh-negative individuals do not have D antigen and form anti-D antibody when exposed to D-positive cells. ***Anti-D antibodies do not occur naturally in the plasma.*** Rh-negative patients should always be given Rh-negative blood. About 99% of Asians are Rh-positive while Rh-positivity in Caucasians is 85%.

## Other blood group systems

*Apart from ABO and Rh systems,* other blood group systems include ***Lewis, P, I, MNSs, Kidd, Kell, Duffy, Lutheran*** etc.

## Biologic significance of blood groups

- **Immune reactions :** Transfusion reaction leading to lysis of donor's RBCs occurs when blood transfused is incompatible. Moreover, antigens of the ABO system play a role in histocompatibility (tissue match) by virtue of their presence in other tissues. Transplantation of ABO-incompatible kidneys or other organs carries the risk of rejection.
- **Infertility and early fetal loss** : ABO incompatibility may be responsible for both of these.
- **Disease-related changes in phenotype** : Acquired changes may occur in A and B determinants due to the action of some bacterial enzymes or due to acute myelocytic leukemia. In the early hypoplastic phase of leukemia, this change in phenotype may occasionally be diagnostic.
- **Other disease relationships** : The incidence of some diseases is associated with the blood type. Incidence of duodenal ulcer is more in type O nonsecretors. Tumors of salivary glands, stomach and pancreas are more common in persons with type A blood. Duffy negative individuals are protected against *Plasmodium vivax* (a malarial parasite) possibly because the major Duffy antigens ($Fy_a$ and $Fy_b$) act as specific recognition or acceptor sites for the merozoites of the parasite.
- **Chromosome mapping** : Blood genetic markers are very useful for the mapping of the human chromosomes.

**Medicolegal significance** : RBC antigens may be used as genetic markers for ruling out paternity, maternity and monozygosity.

**Anthropological significance** : By studying prevalance of various blood group systems in different communities, racial and population groups; valuable information regarding racial mixing and population migration can be obtained.

## Blood transfusion

Blood for transfusion is collected from donors into a sterile plastic bag containing either citrate-phosphate-dextrose (CPD) or citrate-phosphate-dextrose-adenine (CPD-A) solution as anticoagulant and preservative.

Before transfusion, blood is to be cross-matched. In **cross-matching,** donor RBCs are mixed with recipient plasma and donor plasma with recipient RBCs. If there is no agglutination, donor blood is compatible with the recipient. Before planned surgery, blood may be collected from the patient few weeks prior to surgery for transfusion during the operation. This is called **autologous transfusion**. There is no risk of transfusion reaction and transmission of disease in autologous transfusion.

**Summary of principles of blood transfusion :** Blood group O is the universal donor group because there are no A or B antigens on the red cell membrane. Therefore blood transfusion may be given thus—

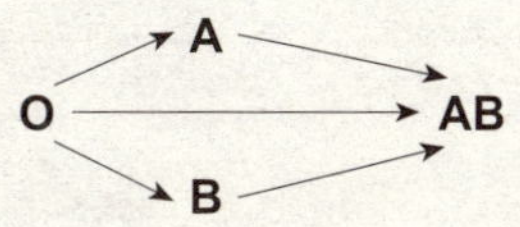


## Hazards of transfusion

Excess blood transfusion in a relatively short time would lead to volume overload on the heart and may precipitate ***cardiac failure***.

The hazards of heterologous transfusion are ***transfusion reactions*** and ***transmission of diseases*** like hepatitis, malaria, syphilis, AIDS etc.

Incompatible blood transfusion leads to ***hemolytic transfusion reaction***. Blood is incompatible for transfusion if the recipient's blood has antibodies against the RBCs of the donor's blood. Antibodies in the recipient's blood combine with the antigens on the donor's RBCs and there is agglutination and hemolysis. This may result in jaundice and renal tubular damage which may lead to anuria and death. Antibodies in the donor's plasma are so much diluted by the recipient's plasma that they are rarely, if ever, the cause of transfusion reaction.

## Result of storage of blood

Changes in blood due to storage includes inhibition of $Na^+$-$K^+$ ATPase which leads to

(a) ↑ in cell $Na^+$; ↓ cell $K^+$ with net increase in cell $Na^+$

(b) cell becomes more spherocytic

(c) plasma becomes hyponatremic, hyperkalemic and hypocalcemic.

### Hemolytic disease of the newborn

***Rh-incompatibility*** is said to be present when Rh-negative mother carries a Rh-positive fetus. Leaking of fetal blood into maternal circulation (fetomaternal bleeding) usually at the time of delivery leads to production of anti-D antibodies in maternal blood in significant quantities. In subsequent pregnancies with Rh-positive fetus, the anti-D antibodies cross the placenta to the Rh-positive fetus and cause hemolysis of the fetal RBCs. This leads to various forms of **hemolytic disease of the newborn (erythroblastosis fetalis)**. In severe cases, the fetus dies in utero. Otherwise, the baby is born with anemia, jaundice and edema (**hydrops fetalis**) of varying severity. Immature blast cells of erythroid series are found in the blood (**erythroblastosis**).

Sensitization of the mother in the first pregnancy may be prevented by administration of anti-D antibodies immediately after delivery in order to destroy the Rh-positive fetal cells in maternal circulation before they can trigger an immune response.

**ABO hemolytic disease** may also occur in the newborn. This is usually found in A or B infants of O mothers. This is because of the fact that while most of the anti-A and anti-B are IgM which cannot cross placenta, some O type mothers have much of the anti-A and anti-B as IgG which can cross placenta.

## ➤ 5.16 KEY CONCEPTS

1. **Blood** confined in the cardiovascular system constitutes a major part of the extracellular fluid of our body. It consists of straw colored liquid matrix plasma in which the formed elements (red cells; white cells and platelets) are suspended. The red cells help in transport of gases between the tissues and the lungs, thereby increasing the efficiency of gas exchange.

2. **Red bone marrow** gives origin to the blood cells. **Cytokines** are produced by the supporting cells of the bone marrow and they control the blood cell production. Red cell production is also stimulated by the glycoprotein hormone **erythropoietin** secreted by kidney. **Erythropoiesis** involves a number of overlapping stages of mitosis and maturation that gives rise to reticulocytes which are released into the blood.

3. **The red cells** contain $Fe^{2+}$ having respiratory pigment **hemoglobin**. It is a metalloprotein consisting of four polypeptide chains of the protein globin, each containing a molecule of heme. Red cells lack enzymes of aerobic respiration and so 95% of the glucose utilized by them undergoes anaerobic glycolysis and the rest is metabolised through the pentose phosphate pathway.

4. **White blood cells** or **leukocytes** are important for the protection of body from diseases and in disposal of damaged and aging tissues. They defend the body from infections and cancer cell proliferation by initiating immune responses.

5. **Pluripotent stem cells** in the bone marrow give origin to leukocytes as follows :

**Myeloid line :**

- Three types of granulocytes
- Monocytes
- Macrophages
- Large muiltinucleate megakaryocytes from which plateles are produced

**Lymphoid line :**

- Lymphocytes are produced
- From bone marrow some cells go to lymphoid tissues of the body (lymph nodes, spleen, thymus and Peyer's patches) to produce B-lymphocytes.
- Some cells are matured in thymus to form T-lymphocytes and then distributed to other lymphoid tissues

6. **Platelets** help in hemostasis and originate from the giant multinucleate megakaryocytes produced through myeloid stem cell line. **Hemostasis** means a process by which platelets help to stop bleeding by vascular spasm, platelet plug formation and clot formation.

7. The **total concentration of plasma proteins** is about 6-8 g/dl. Electrophoresis separates plasma proteins into albumin, $\alpha_1$, $\alpha_2$, $\beta$ and $\gamma$-globulin. Albumin is the principal constitutent (65%) of plasma proteins with a concentration of 3.5 to 5.0 g/dl. It is mainly produced in the liver. Albumin has nutritive functions. The complement system is composed of about 20 plasma proteins that complement the functions of antibodies in defending the body from invading antigens. The complement system helps the body immunity in different ways — promoting phagocytosis, clearance of antigen-antibody complexes.

8. **Blood clotting** is the body's major defence mechanism against blood loss. The extrinsic and intrinsic pathways lead to the formation of factor Xa which then participates in the final common pathway to activate prothrombin to thrombin. Fibrinogen is then converted to fibrin clot (Fig. 6.35).

9. **Immunoglobulins** are specialized proteins to defend the body against the foreign substances. They are associated with $\gamma$-globulin fraction of plasma proteins. The immunoglobulins essentially consist of two identical heavy chains and two identical light chains, held together by disulfide linkage.

There are five classes of immunoglobulin — **IgG, IgA, IgM, IgD** and **IgE. IgG** is most abundant and is mainly responsible for humoral immunity. **IgA** protects body surfaces, IgM acts as a first line of defence for

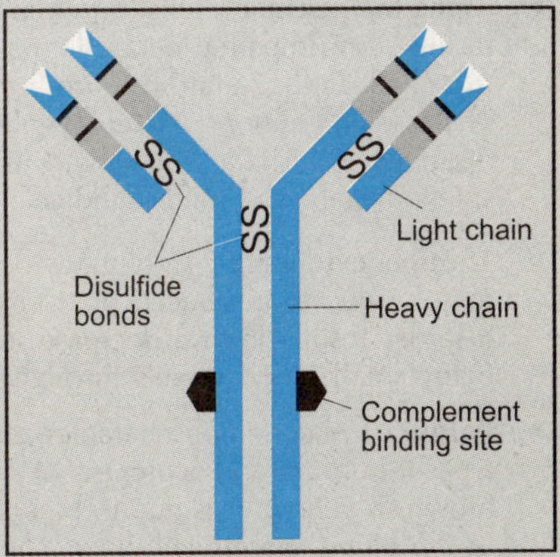


**Fig. 5.35 :** Structure of an antibody molecule. An antibody is a protein made of four polypeptide chains linked by disulfide bonds. The antigen binding site is specific for one foreign antigen.

## ➤ 5.16 KEY CONCEPTS

humoral immunity while **IgE** is associated with allergic reactions. Lymphocytes are of two functionally distinct types : T-lymphocytes and B-lymphocytes. Lymphocytes are produced from hemocytoblast in red bone marrow → spread in the blood to lymphoid tissue elsewhere in the body where they are activated. **T-lymphocytes** are activated by thymosin in the thymus gland and **B-lymphocytes** are activated in red bone marrow and in the lymphoid tissue elsewhere in the body, possibly the wall of the intestine.

10. The **B-cells** bind with the specific antigens. The formation of antigen-antibody complexes on their surfaces provokes activation, proliferation and further differentiation into antibody-secreting plasma cells.

    **T-cells** exert important regulatory function upon B-cell activity. These are carried out by separate T-cell subsets, augmentation by the helper T-cells and inhibition by the suppressor T-cells.

## ➤ 5.17 DISORDERS / CLINICAL CORRELATIONS

➤ **Erythrocytosis :** Increased level of hemotocrit well above the normal range. It may be secondary to tissue hypoxia due to any reason (high altitude – low atmospheric oxygen tension, ventilatory disorder, alveolar membrane disorder → impaired oxygenation, cyanotic heart disease, drugs blocking the respiratory chain at the tissue level.

➤ **White blood cell disorders :**

- Leukemia — by definition, it means malignant disorder of the white blood cell. More widely speaking, malignant monoclonal proliferation of hematopoietic stem cell. It may be acute or chronic. It may be myeloid or lymphocytic leukaemia. Here the WBCs are found in increased number in peripheral blood.
- Leukopenia — It is a condition when the WBC count is reduced. It is due to aplasia of bone marrow or it may be secondary to drug reaction.
- *Neutropenia* — It is a condition where the neutrophil count is reduced in peripheral blood. It may be secondary to bone marrow aplasia or due to drug reaction.

➤ **Thalassemia :** Thalassemia develops due to lack or diminishes level of synthesis of α or β globin chain of HbA. A complex group of genetically transmitted disorders in which there is an intracorpuscular type of hemolytic anemia associated with three abnormalities in the synthesis of hemoglobin i.e. (1) the presence of hemoglobin F (2) the suppressed formation of hemoglobin A and (3) an increased proportion of hemoglobin $A_2$; none of these is invariably present and in some instances, there are morphologic abnormalities in the erythrocytes.

➤ **Alpha thalassemia** results from impaired synthesis of the alpha chain in the hemoglobin molecule. Beta thalassemia results from impaired beta chain synthesis. The diagnosis of α-thalassemia is made by demonstrating a reduced α/β chain ratio. Failure to form β chain (β chain thalassemia) is the commonest type. **Types of β-thalassemia–** (i) Thalassemia minor : Heterozygotes presents as hypochromatic microcytic anaemia with little or no clinical disability. (ii) Thalassemia major (Cooley's amaemia) — Homozygotes develop serious hemolytic anaemia with splenomegaly and mild jaundice.

➤ **Thrombocytopenia :** Thrombocytopenia occurs when blood platelet count below 150 × 10 g/L (150,000/$mm^3$). It may be due to a reduced platelet production or increased rate of destruction. A more common type of clotting disorder results from a decrease in the platelet count—thrombocytopenia. It is Characterized by bleeding from many small blood vessels through out the body most visibly in the skin and mucous membrane.

➤ **Purpura :** A condition characterized by hemorrhage into the skin. The appearance of the lesions varies with the type of purpura and acuteness of onset. The colour is first red, becoming gradually darker, then purple, fading to brownish yellow. It is due to bleeding caused by an abnormally low platelet count (< 40,000/cu mm) or a defect in the blood vessel wall.

➤ **Hemophilia :** A type of X-linked inherited disorder called hemphilia results from a failure to form blood clotting factor VIII, IX or X. This clotting process are necessary to complete the clotting process. Thus hemophilia is characterized by a relative inability to form blood clots.

**Hemophilia A :** due to deficiency of factor VIII; a sex linked recessive condition affecting males.

**Hemophilia B :** due to deficiency of factor IX.

## ➤ 5.17 DISORDERS / CLINICAL CORRELATIONS

➤ **von Willebrand's disease :** It is inherited as an autosomal dominant character. It affects both sexes. There is defective synthesis of the part of the factor VIII molecule which carries immunological determinants. This factor is required for normal platelet function. The characters of this disease are low factor VIII clotting and immunological activity, a prolonged bleeding time, diminished platelet aggregation and defective platelet adhesiveness.

➤ **AIDS (Acquired Immune Deficiency Syndrome) :** Identification of an unusual opportunistic infection (*Pneumocystis carinii* pneumonia) in five previously healthy young homosexual men in the Los Angeles area of USA in 1981 marked the beginning of an epidemic of a retroviral disease characterized by severe immunosuppression associated with opportunistic infections, secondary neoplasms and neurologic manifestations. Later on, the disease was named acquired immunodeficiency syndrome (AIDS). The association between infection with human immunodeficiency virus (HIV) and the development of AIDS was established in 1984. Between five to ten million people are now thought to be HIV infected, worldwide. The HIV epidemic is now continuing globally with increasing number of cases being reported from Central Africa, South America and South-East Asia including the Indian subcontinent.

Retroviruses are RNA-viruses having the unique property of transcribing a DNA copy of the RNA genome with the help of the enzyme RNA dependent DNA polymerase also known as **reverse transcriptase**. This DNA is integrated into the host cell DNA to provide a proviral copy. Viral replication occurs through transcripton of the proviral copy of the viral DNA. Two closely related forms of HIV (called HIV-1 and HIV-2), which are genetically different, have been isolated from patients with AIDS. Infection with HIV requires exchange of infected body fluids like semen, vaginal secretions, breast milk or blood. Thus transmission of HIV may occur through three possible routes :

- Sexual contact
- Parenteral inoculation
- Mother-to-fetus and mother-to-infant transmission

**Sexual transmission** is the predominant mode of infection worldwide. Recipient of penetrative sex (anal or vaginal) is more vulnerable. Risk of infection is more if there is genital trauma during intercourse and/or there is pre-existing genital ulceration. **Parenteral transmission** is most common in intravenous drug abusers who share contaminated needles and syringes. Recipients of blood and blood-products are also at risk of HIV infection if the blood or blood-products contain HIV. Transmission through blood and blood-products may be avoided by testing the blood for HIV and rejecting the HIV-infected units as well as by using recombinant clotting factors whenever possible. Majority of the paediatric AIDS cases are either due to transplacental transmission or to exposure to maternal blood and other infected fluids during birth. Transmission through breast milk is also possible.

The major targets of HIV are the immune system and the central nervous system (CNS).

The hallmark of AIDS is profound immunosuppression primarily affecting cell-mediated immunity (CMI) which results mainly from a severe loss of $CD4^+$ T-lymphocytes as well as an impairment in the function of helper T cells that survive. The selective tropism of HIV for $CD4^+$ T-lymphocytes and its ability to infect other $CD4^+$ cells like macrophages may be explained by the fact that the CD4 molecule is a high-affinity receptor for HIV. As $CD4^+$ helper T-cells are responsible for the initiation of almost all immunological responses, attrition of the $CD4^+$ cell population following HIV infection results in gradual and increased failure of nearly all aspects of immune function. The number of circulating $CD4^+$ cells gradually decrease leading to an inversion of the ratio of $CD4^+$ cells to $CD8^+$ cells (CD4-CD8 ratio). Normal CD4-CD8 ratio is about 2 which may be close to 0.5 in AIDS.The disease progression may be assessed by laboratory measurement of $CD4^+$ cell count in peripheral blood using special techniques employing monoclonal antibodies. $CD4^+$ cell count is also used to guide therapeutic measures to be taken in AIDS. The immunological abnormalities in AIDS are :

- **$CD4^+$ T helper lymphocytes —**

  Decrease in number

  Functional abnormality :

  ↓ response to antigen/mitogen ↓ response to interleukin-2 (IL-2) ↓ production of IL-2 and interferon-γ(IFN-γ)

## ➤ 5.17 DISORDERS / CLINICAL CORRELATIONS

- **B-lymphocytes** —

  Functional abnormality :

  - response to antigen/mitogen
  - immunoglobulins due to polyclonal activation

- **Macrophages and dendritic cells** —

  - Defect in antigen presentation • Defect in cytokine secretion • Defect in phagocytosis/killing

Depressed CMI in AIDS predisposes to infections by intracellular parasites like viruses, protozoa and mycobacteria as well as to secondary neoplasms like Kaposi's sarcoma. Defects in humoral immunity results in infection with capsulated bacteria.

Cells in the CNS are also affected by HIV which may result in direct damage to the CNS.

Confirmation of HIV infection requires demonstration of the presence of antibodies to HIV in the patient's serum. ELISA (Enzyme Linked Immuno Sorbent Assay) is simple and cheap. All positive results obtained by ELISA are usually confirmed by the more precise Western blot test.

AIDS is an invariably fatal disease in spite of all available treatment. Hence the mainstay for control of this disease is measures to prevent spread of HIV (eg, advice on safe sex, use of disposable needles/syringes, routine HIV-testing of blood/blood-products for transfusion). Anti-retroviral drugs currently in clinical use are zidovudine (azido dideoxy- thymidine, AZT), dideoxyinosine (DDI) and dideoxycytidine (DDC). These dideoxynucleosides, acting on the viral DNA polymerase (reverse transcriptase), inhibit the synthesis of viral DNA and thereby markedly decrease viral replication.

➤ **Plasmapheresis :** An experimental procedure in animals in which blood is removed and the corpuscles separated by centrifuging, suspended in Ringer's solution and returned to the circulation, the plasma proteins of the animal being thus depleted.

➤ **Thrombolytic (clot dissolving) agents :** These agents are used to lyse any clot within the blood vessels. Commonly used thrombolytic agents are *streptokinase, urokinase, tPA* etc. They are mainly used in acute myocardial infarction where a coronary artery is occluded by an athero-thrombus.

➤ **Sickle-cell anaemia :** The adult hemoglobin molecule (HbA) is made of two alpha chains and two beta chains bound together in a tetramer. Fetal hemoglobin (HbF) which is normally gradually replaced by the adult type after birth is made of two alpha chains and two gamma chains. This recessive disorder is due to abnormal beta chain formation (called on S chain) in the hemoglobin molecule. The result is an abnormal hemoglobin molecule made of two alpha chains bound to two S chains.

➤ **Hodgkin's disease :** It is marked by chronic inflammatory enlargement of the lymph nodes, first the cervical and then the axillary, inguinal, mediastinal, mesenteric etc. together with enlargement of the spleen and often of the liver and kidneys with lymphoid infiltration along the blood vessels. There is no pronounced leukocytosis.

➤ **Tissue rejection :** It is a process whereby a graft tissue is rejected from the host body. For example, after kidney trans-plantation.

➤ **Immunotherapy :** It means modulation of the immune status of the body and thereby changing the disease process. It can be done by drugs or by infusion of immunoglobins.

➤ **Aplastic anemia :** An abnormally low number of red blood cells. Although most cases result from destruction of bone marrow by drug, toxic chemicals or radiation.

➤ **Pernicious anemia :** Low no. of RBC. Results from a dietary deficiency of **vit. $B_{12}$** and also result from the failure of stomach lining to produce intrinsic factor—the subs that allows vit. $B_{12}$— to be absorbed. It is an autoimmune disease in which auto-antibodies destroy parietal cells.

# Pulmonary Physiology

AGENDA :



6

## ➤ 6.1 CHAPTER OVERVIEW

The major function of the respiratory system is to exchange gases with the environment. The essential role is mechanical which is performed by the muscles of respiration. The diaphragm is the principal muscle of inspiration. Quiet expiration is a passive process. The air that is inhaled during inspiration is distributed to the lung alveoli via the tracheobronchial tree which branches extensively to terminate as alveoli. The **lung alveoli** are richly supplied by capillaries arising from pulmonary arteries. Oxygen ($O_2$) from inspired air reaching the alveoli diffuses through the alveolo capillary membraneto reach capillary blood while carbon dioxide ($CO_2$) from blood diffuses to alveolar air. $CO_2$ is exhaled during expiration. The **four main processes** related to gas exchange in the lungs include ventilation (movement of air in and out of the lungs), distribution of ventilated gases into various lobes, segments and lobules, diffusion of gases back and forth between the alveoli and plasma and perfusion of blood through the pulmonary capillaries.

During normal quiet breathing, an average adult inhales or exhales **about 500 ml of air** with each breath (tidal volume, VT). Out of the 500 ml of inspired air, 350 ml. reaches the alveoli to take part in gas exchange while the remaining 150 ml, occupies the "dead space" with no gaseous exchange. Assuming a respiratory rate of 12/minute, the alveolar minute ventilation is thus (350 ml × 12) = 4200 ml. Ventilatory lung function can be assessed by measuring various lung volumes and capacities by spirometry and other techniques.

The state of **lung inflation** is mainly determined by the balance between the tendency of the lungs to collapse towards their hila and the tendency of the chest wall to recoil outwards. Stiffness of any of these two (the lungs or the chest wall) can cause impairment of ventilation. **Gaseous exchange** at alveolocapillary membrane is dependent on several factors which include alveolar ventilation and perfusion as well as the thickness of the alveolocapillary membrane. Mismatch between ventilation and perfusion, and thickening of the alveolocapillary membrane both can give rise to impairment of gaseous exchange.

**Oxygen** that reaches pulmonary capillary blood is transported to tissues mainly carried by **hemoglobin** present in RBCs. **One gram of hemoglobin can carry 1.34 ml $O_2$.** $CO_2$ generated as a result of tissue metabolism is carried in blood in various forms but the major form is $HCO_3^-$, which is produced by combination of $CO_2$ and $H_2O$ catalyzed by carbonic anhydrase.

Rhythmic discharge from respiratory centers in the brain produces spontaneous respiration. Some voluntary control over respiration is also there. The neural discharges from the brain that regulate respiration are in turn regulated by changes in partial pressures of $O_2$, $CO_2$, and $H^+$ concentration ($PO_2$, $PCO_2$, and pH) of arterial blood. This chemical control is supplemented by some nonchemical factors.

In addition to its respiratory functions, the respiratory system carries out some metabolic and endocrine functions.

### Table of Symbols

| | | | |
|---|---|---|---|
| $V_T$ | — tidal volume. | $\dot{V}A$ | — alveolar ventilation per minute |
| **FRC** | — functional residual capacity | $VCO_2$ | — rate of Carbon dioxide elimination per minute |
| **ERV** | — expiratory reserve volume | **FVC** | — Forced expired vital capacity. |
| **RV** | — residual volume | $P_A$ | — alveolar pressure |
| **IC** | — inspiratory capacity | $PO_2$ | — partial pressure of oxygen |
| **IRV** | — inspiratory reserve volume | $P_{CO2}$ | — partial pressure of Carbon dioxide |
| **TLC** | — total lung capacity | $P_{aO2}$ | — partial pressure of oxygen in arterial blood |
| **VC** | — vital capacity | $PACO_2$ | — partial pressure of Carbondioxide in alveolar gas. |
| **VD** | — dead space volume | $\dot{Q}$ | — blood flow |
| $V_A$ | — alveolar gas volume | $\dot{Q}s$ | — shunt blood flow |
| $V_E$ | — expired volume | $\dot{V}A/\dot{Q}$ | — alveolar ventilation ferfusion ratio |
| $\dot{V}$ | — volume of ventilation per minute | | |
| $\dot{V}_I$ | — inspired volume of ventilation per minute | | |
| $\dot{V}E$ | — expired volume of ventilation per minute | | |

## 6.2 Introduction and Functional Anatomy

**Respiration** involves the processes by which $O_2$ is carried to and utilised by the cells and $CO_2$ is produced and eliminated. These are mediated by the respiratory system, the red cells in the blood and the circulatory system. ***The main structures involved in the respiratory system are*** — (a) airways, (b) lungs, (c) thoracic cage and respiratory muscles, (d) pulmonary vasculature.

**The respiratory processes consist of :**

- Ventilation of the lungs with air
- Exchange of gas between air and blood.
- Perfusion of the lungs with blood (Fig. 6.1).

**Breathing** is an automatic, rhythmic, centrally regulated mechanical process by which the contraction and relaxation of the skeletal muscles of the diaphragm, abdomen and rib cage result in gas movement into and out of the terminal respiratory units of the lungs.

**Respiration** is the overall process of controlled oxidation of metabolites for the production of energy by living organisms. It includes breathing. Oxygen ($O_2$) and other nutrients must come in close contact with respiring cells while $CO_2$ and waste products must be taken away.

The **process of breathing** is measured by ventilation (rate and depth of breathing). The exchange of $O_2$ and $CO_2$ in the lung is measured by their concentration differences between inspired and expired gas.

The *main function of the lung* is to distribute inspired air and pulmonary blood so that the *exchange of $O_2$ and $CO_2$* between the alveolar gas and pulmonary capillary blood occurs efficiently. ***The pulmonary blood flow is regulated by the pulmonary vascular resistance [(pulmonary arterial to left atrial pressure difference)/cardiac output].*** The exchange of $O_2$ and of $CO_2$ in pulmonary blood is measured by their concentration differences between blood in pulmonary artery (mixed venous blood) and blood in the systemic artery. The differences between the $O_2$ and $CO_2$ partial pressures between alveolar gas and systemic arterial blood are important to determine overall lung function efficiency.

**Ventilation** is the process of getting air into and out of the lungs. This is **regulated by respiratory muscles** which is further mediated by nervous signals generated in the brain. The airways present in the lungs are bronchioles, terminal bronchioles, respiratory bronchioles and alveolar ducts. After air gets into mouth and nose it reaches the lungs via pharynx, larynx and trachea. The **trachea** is subdivided into left and right main bronchus which are further divided into lobar and segmental bronchi (Fig. 6.2).

### Respiratory epithelium

A ciliated layer of cells, termed *respiratory epithelium* lines, the internal surface of the airways. **Goblet cells** and **glands** (Fig. 6.3) are also present in the respiratory epithelium which secrete mucus. Mucus is moved upwards at the rate of 1-2 cm/hour.

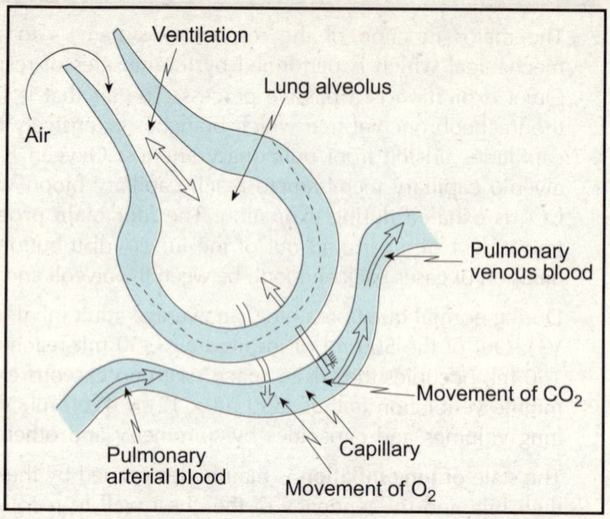


**Fig. 6.1 :** Perfusion of the lungs with blood

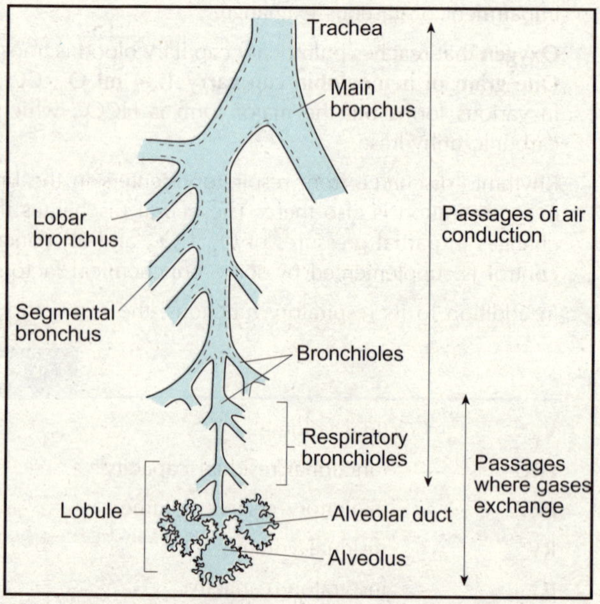


**Fig. 6.2 :** Lower respiratory tract

**External respiration** is the process by which gas is exchanged between the blood and the lungs, gas exchange between the blood and the cells is **internal respiration**. The organs which are involved in the respiratory system are —

- **nasal cavity**
- **pharynx**
- **larynx**
- **trachea**
- **two bronchi**
- **bronchioles**
- **lungs with their covering (pleura)**
- **muscles of respiration** – intercostal muscles and the diaphragm, and some other accessory muscles.

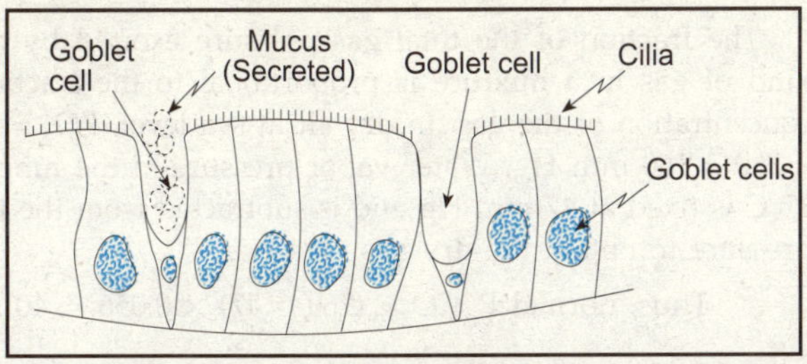


**Fig. 6.3 :** Ciliated columnar epithelium with goblet cells

**Nasal cavity :** It is the first respiratory organ. It is a large irregular cavity divided into two equal parts by a septum.

### Larynx or voice box

It is located in front of the laryngopharynx at the level of 3rd, 4th, 5th and 6th cervical vertebrae. The larynx is composed of several hyaline cartilages and elastic fibrocartilages.

- Corniculate cartilage – two
- Cuneiform cartilage – two

} elastic fibrocartilage

Apical part of arytenoid is elastic fibrocartilaginous.

Several ligaments attach the cartilages to each other and to the hyoid bone. Functions of the larynx are enumerated below (Fig. 6.4) :

Larynx is also provided with extrinsic muscles (sternohyoid, sternothyroid, omohyoid etc.) and intrinsic muscles (cricothyroid, transverse and oblique arytenoids, external and internal thyroarytenoids etc.).

**Trachea :** Trachea begins where larynx ends. It is a musculocartilaginous pipe like structure allowing air to flow down to the lungs. It bifurcates at the level of sternal angle into two main bronchi.

### Bronchi

When the trachea divides, two main bronchi (right and left) originate at the level of 5th thoracic vertebra. The right bronchus is shorter and wider than the left bronchus. It is about 2.5 cm long. The left bronchus is about 5 cm long and is narrower than the right bronchus. Bronchi are lined by ciliated columnar epithelium. Bronchi → bronchioles → terminal bronchioles → respiratory bronchioles → alveolar ducts and alveoli.

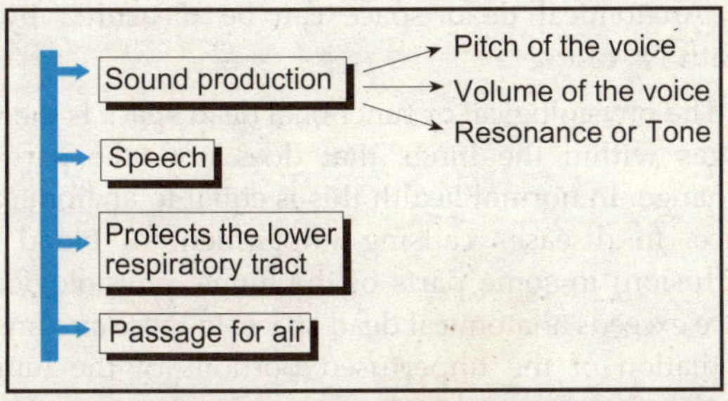


**Fig. 6.4 :** Functions of larynx

**Respiratory muscles**

**Inspiratory muscles**

- *Diaphragm*: Exerts a direct influence on lung volumes by contracting (inspiration) and relaxing (expiration). It also maintains adequate ventilation at rest.
- *Intercostals*: Indirect influences on inspiration are exerted when the thorax enlarges by contraction of the scalene and external intercostal muscles.
- *Accessory muscles*: Used in inspiration only when breathing is vigorous.

**Expiratory muscles**

When the thoracic cavity is expanded by the contraction of the muscles of inspiration, the lungs also expand. The powerful muscles used in the abdominal wall are:

- Rectus abdominis
- Internal and external oblique muscles.
- Transverse abdominis.

**Fig. 6.5 :** Respiratory muscles

### Respiratory bronchioles and alveoli

Lobules are the terminal end of respiratory tract distal to terminal bronchioles. It contains respiratory bronchioles, alveolar ducts and alveoli. The alveoli are surrounded by a network of capillaries. The exchange of gases during respiration takes place along the alveolar and capillary membranes.

**Lungs :** The lungs are composed of millions of alveoli. The diameter of each alveolus is 1/3 mm . The alveoli are bounded by elastic connective tissue. Each lung is covered by a thin epithelium externally known as ***visceral pleura or pulmonary pleura.*** This layer doubles back on itself and is continued to form ***parietal pleura***. Pleural space is located in between the parietal and pulmonary pleura. It is filled with a thin film of liquid which produces strong cohesive forces that prevent the separation of the pleurae.

During quiet breathing, inspiration occurs due mainly to contraction of the diaphragm depressing the floor of the thorax and raising the rib cage at its point of origin. Muscles of respiration (see fig. 6.5).

### Airways

The **conducting airways** are of two types—(a) **cartilaginous bronchi** and (b) **membranous bronchioles.** The alveolar ducts (final branches of the bronchioles) together with the alveoli in their walls form the gas exchange part of the lung. Air in these conducting airways is wasted **(anatomical dead space).**

### Function of the airways

- Passage of gases
- Protection from foreign matters
- Warming and humidifying gases.

### Passage of gases

The airways conduct atmospheric air to the alveoli. The rate of airflow (V) in or out of the lungs depends on the pressure gradient ($\Delta P$) between the alveoli and the atmosphere and the airway resistance :

$$\text{Airflow } (\dot{V}) = \frac{P}{R} = \frac{(P_{ALV} - P_{ATMOS})}{R}$$

Small pressure gradients (1-2 cm of $H_2O$) are necessary for gas exchange in and out of the lungs during ventilation. Smooth muscles present in the bronchi and bronchioles can alter this resistance when they contract and relax.

Bronchoconstriction increases the airway resistance and bronchodilation decrease the airways resistance. These are regulated by autonomic nervous system. Adrenergic sympathetic nerves cause bronchodilatation while cholinergic parasympathetic nerves cause bronchoconstriction.

### Protection of the lungs

Lungs are protected from the entry of foreign matter by various mechanisms. The motile cilia present in the trachea, bronchi and bronchioles transport the bacteria and particles of atmospheric pollutants (which are trapped by mucus lining of the airways) towards the larynx and then into the pharynx. The vocal folds in the larynx play an important role in protecting the lungs from inhalation of food by reflexly closing the glottis during swallowing.

***Warming and humidifying gases*** : When inhaled air traverses the airways, it is warmed and humidified. Prior to reaching the alveoli, gases are fully saturated with water vapor and water vapor pressure of 6.3 KPa (47 mm Hg) at 37°C (body temperature) is produced at this moment.

### Composition of air

The air inside the alveoli is not the same as that of atmosphere. It is gains water from the moist epithelial lining of the respiratory tract, and picks up $CO_2$ and loses $O_2$ within the alveoli (Table 6.1).

**Table 6.1**
**Composition of inspired and expired air**

| | Inspired air % | Expired air % |
|---|---|---|
| Oxygen | 21 | 16 |
| $CO_2$ | 0.04 | 4 |
| Nitrogen | 78 | 78 |
| Water vapor | Variable | Saturated |

Partial pressures of gases : The composition of air containing a mixture of gases can be described as :

- per cent composition
- partial pressures of the constituent gases (KPa)

The fraction of the total gas pressure exerted by each kind of gas in a mixture is proportional to the fractional concentration of the gas. In dry air at sea level, $PO_2 = 0.21 \times 760 = 160$ mm Hg. Water vapor pressure in the lungs at 37°C is fixed at 47 mm Hg and is subtracted from the total pressure to obtain the dry gas pressure.

Thus, normal $P_ACO_2 = (760 - 47) \times 0.056 = 40$ mm Hg

and $P_AO_2 = (760 - 47) \times 0.143 = 102$ mm Hg.

**Table 6.2**
**Total and partial pressures of respiratory gases in ideal alveolar gas and blood at sea level barometric pressure (760 mm Hg)**

| | Ambient air (dry) | Moist tracheal air | Alveolar gas | Systemic arterial blood | Mixed venous blood |
|---|---|---|---|---|---|
| $Po_2$ | 160 | 150 | 102 | 102 | 40 |
| $Pco_2$ | – | – | 40 | 40 | 46 |
| $P_{H_2O}$ 37°C | – | 47 | 47 | 47 | 47 |
| $P_{N_2}$ | 600 | 563 | 571 | 571 | 571 |
| P Total | 760 | 760 | 760 | 760 | 704 |

## 6.3 Ventilation, Gas exchange and Alveolar gases

### Ventilation

The purpose of external respiration is to inhale oxygen—rich atmospheric air into lungs and to drive away $CO_2$—rich gas from lungs to exterior, i.e., **ventilation**. To execute the entry and exit of gases to and from lungs, the chest wall is provided with muscles which contract to create a pressure difference between atmosphere and lung.

All the gas that enters during inspiration cannot take part in diffusion. Like water within a garden hose pipe is not within sprayed, some volume occupies conducting zones of the air ways proximal to the site of gas exchange, i.e., respiratory bronchioles. This volume is **anatomical dead space** (150 ml in adult individual) corresponding roughly to a volume equal to the body weight in pounds expressed in ml. Anatomical dead space can be measured by single breath $N_2$ test.

The physiological or functional dead space is the volume of gas within the lungs that does not take part in gas exchange. In normal health this is equal to anatomical dead space. In diseases causing impairment of blood supply (perfusion) to some parts of the lungs, physiological dead space exceeds anatomical dead space. In these circumstances, ventilation of the unperfused portions of the lungs gets wasted increasing the dead space over and above the anatomical dead space. The volume of gas that takes part in gas exchange in the lungs is useful ventilation, this is 'alveolar ventilation'.

In an adult, the ***tidal volume*** is about ***500 ml***. So with each breath (500 – 150) ml = 350 ml only reaches alveoli.

Hence, ***minute ventilation*** = respiratory frequency × tidal volume = 14/min × 500 ml = *7,000 ml/min.*

But ***alveolar ventilation*** = respiratory frequency × [tidal volume – dead space (physiological) volume] = 14/min × 350 ml = 4,900 ml/min.

So, ventilation wasted = respiratory frequency × dead space = 14/min × 150 ml = 2,100 ml/min.

## Measurement of dead space

All of the $CO_2$ of the expired air comes from the alveoli. The amount of $CO_2$ in any volume of gas is simply the fractional content of $CO_2$ in the sample (F) times of volume. Since the volume of air expired ($V_E$) is the su of the air displaced from the dead space ($V_D$) plus that expelled from the alveoli ($V_A$) :

$$V_E = V_D + V_A \quad (1)$$

and $$F_E \bullet V_E = F_D \bullet V_D + F_A \bullet V_A \quad (2)$$

Since there is no $CO_2$ in the dead space (as it is filled with atmospheric air which has a negligible $CO_2$ content) $F_D = 0$ and Equation (2) becomes :

$$F_E \bullet V_E = F_A \bullet V_A \quad (3)$$

which can be rewitten as :

$$V_A = \frac{V_E F_E}{F_A} \quad (3a)$$

but since $V_A = V_E - V_D$ (from Equation 1) :

$$V_A - V_D = \frac{V_E F_E}{F_A} \quad (4)$$

which can be rewritten as the **Bohr** equation :

$$V_D = V_E\left(1 - \frac{F_E}{F_A}\right) \quad (4a)$$

The physiological dead space can therefore be calculated from the volume and fractional $CO_2$ content of the expired gas and the fractional concentration of $CO_2$ in the alveolar air.

The volume and $CO_2$ content of the expired air can be readily measured and a sample of alveolar air can be obtained by asking a subject to expire fully through a long, thin tube. The last part of the expired volume will have the same composition as the alveolar air. This gas can be sampled and its $F_{CO_2}$ determined. This will give an average for the composition of the alveolar air. A more accurate estimate of the $CO_2$ content of alveolar air can be obtained by measuring the $P_{CO_2}$ of arterial blood.

**A worked example :**

If the percentage of $CO_2$ in the expired and alveolar air were to be 3.6 per cent and 5.2 per cent and the tidal volume was 500 ml what is the physiological dead space?

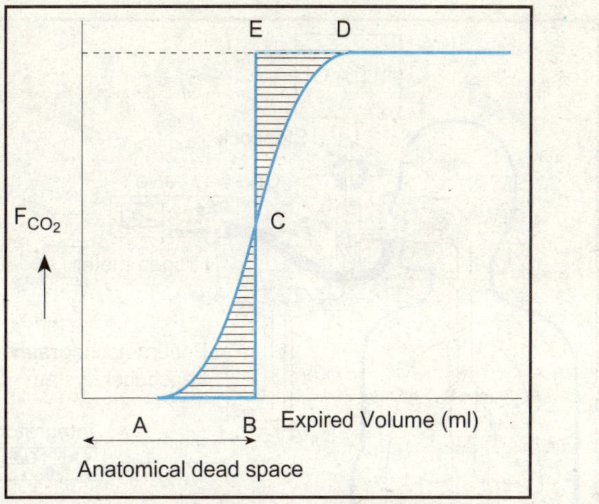


Fig. 6.6 : Anatomical dead space

Using the Bohr equation :

$$V_D = 500 \times [1 - (3.5 \div 5.2)]$$
$$= 500 \times (1 - 0.69)$$
$$= 155 \text{ ml.}$$

In health, $P_ACO_2 = P_aCO_2$, in disease, $P_aCO_2 > P_ACO_2$

2. ***Anatomical dead space*** : It can be measured by —

(a) **Fowler's method** (Fig. 6.6a) : The $CO_2$ content is continuously measured during expiration after a normal inspiration and $CO_2$ fraction is plotted against volume. Initially, the $CO_2$ content is negligible but when the alveolar gas begins to mix with dead space gas its concentration gradually rises till a plateau of alveolar fraction is attained. The anatomical space is the volume opposite to the vertical line B equating the area between it and the line from the onset of the slope to its alveolar plateau, i.e., area DCE = area ABC (Fig. 6.6).

(b) **Single breath $N_2$ test** : Here $N_2$ concentration is continuously recorded at the lips and is plotted against volume. The principle is same as $CO_2$ fraction in Fowler's method but this method also demonstrates the unevenness of ventilation.

## Properties of gases

As the volume of gases varies substantially with changes of temperature and pressure, some standards have been set up for comparing their values measured at varying states, they are —

(i) STPD — Standard emperature and pressure, dry (0°C, 760 mm Hg, dry);

(ii) ATPD — ambient temperature and pressure, dry;

(iii) BTPS — body temperature and pressure, saturated with water vapour;

(iv) ATPS — ambient temperature and pressure saturated with water vapour.

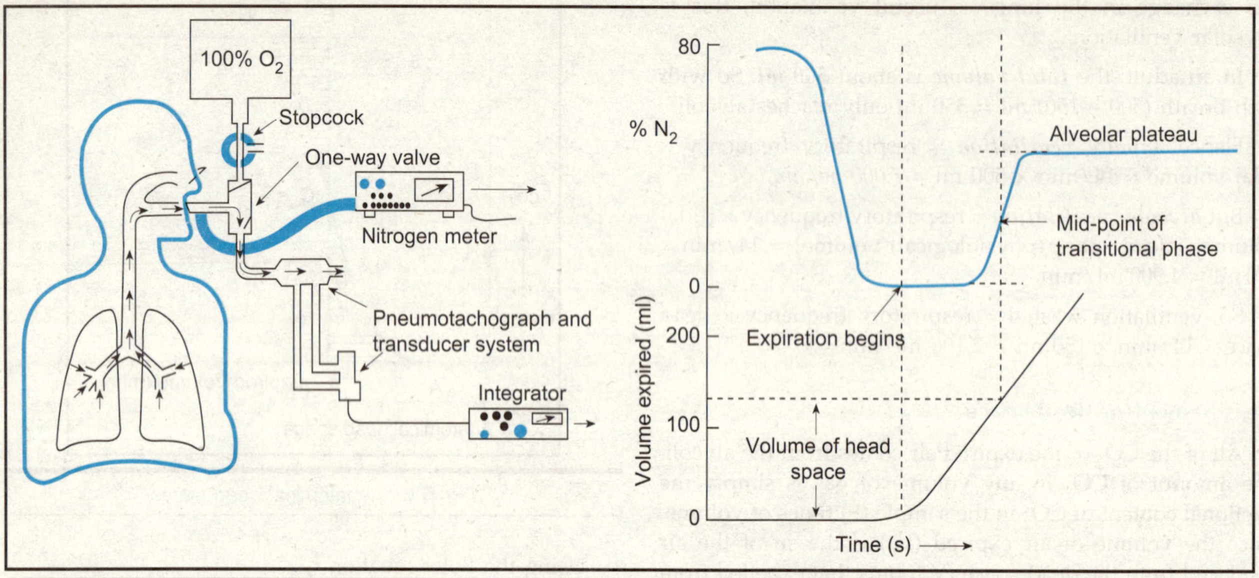


**Fig. 6.6(a) :** Fowler's method for determination of the anatomical dead space. The subject of asked to take a breath of pure oxygen and then breathe out. The concentration of nitrogen in the expired air is measured continuously. The flat portion of the $N_2$ trace presents the alveolar gas. The expired volume at the mid-point of the transition from pure $O_2$ to alveolar gas is taken as the volume of the dead space.

Not only ***volumes***, but also the ***partial pressure of gases*** are important in the consideration of their transport across respiratory membrane. In case of ***dry gas*** mixture, the ***partial pressure of a gas*** is the total pressure multiplied by its fraction, i.e., $P_{gas} = P_B$ (barometric pressure) $\times F_{gas}$ (fraction of the gas). But in case of gas containing ***water vapour***, the partial pressure due to vapour is to be substracted beforehand in the calculation; here $P_{gas} = (P_B – P_{H2O}) \times F_{gas}$. As for example, if an individual has alveolar gas $O_2$ fraction of 0.14 (14%) and the barometric pressure is 760 mm Hg and $P_{H2O}$ at 37°C is 47 mm Hg, the $P_{AO2} = (760 – 47) \times 0.14 = 713 \times 0.14 = 100$ mm Hg (approx).

Gases dissolved in liquid (air/blood) exert partial pressures that are equal at equilibrium with that of the gas of the environment in contact. The absolute volume dissolved will depend on partial pressure and its solubility. It may differ widely between gases, as for example, 0.3 ml of $O_2$/dl of arterial blood exerts partial pressure near 100 mm of Hg, whereas 2.6 ml of $CO_2$/dl will have only 40 mm Hg partial pressure (at same temperature).

The lung volume or capacity measured at any state may have to be converted to another standard. As for example, if the vital capacity of an individual measured at ATPS be 5 litres (where temperature is 22°C, pressure 750 mm Hg, $P_{H2O}$ 20 mm Hg) this volume (V) at STPD can be derived from following equation

$$\frac{V \times (760 - 0)}{273 + 0} = \frac{5 \times (750 - 20)}{273 + 22}$$

so, V can be calculated.

During indirect measurement of BMR, oxygen consumption per unit time obtained from recording by **Benedict-Roth spirometer** is to be routinely converted to at STPD volume before multiplying it with energy equivalent of oxygen.

## 6.4 Regional differences in Ventilation and Perfusion

In the upright position there is unevenness of ventilation and perfusion (blood flow) per unit lung volume along the vertical direction. It has been seen that ***ventilation per unit lung volume is more in the dependent than the in non-dependent portions of the lung.*** This is due to the action of gravity. The weight of the lung in the erect position is responsible for lowering the negativity of intrapleural pressure at the basal region. So at resting end–expiration, the low negativity at dependent region is responsible for more inflation of this part compared to apical part. From the intrapleural pressure-volume plot (Fig. 6.7) it is apparent that $\Delta V/\Delta P$ becomes more as the negativity increases.

***During inspiration, the intrapleural pressure change is same everywhere. So the volume change at dependent part is more due to its initial low negativity,*** i.e., it accommodates more air per unit lung tissue. Moreover, the lung is voluminous at basal part (conical shape). So the ventilation is more at dependent part, i.e., ventilation is uneven. This is the reason why patients with unilateral lung disease lie with healthy one in the dependent position. But if one expires forcefully to residual volume and then takes a small breath, most of the inhaled air will go to upper zones.

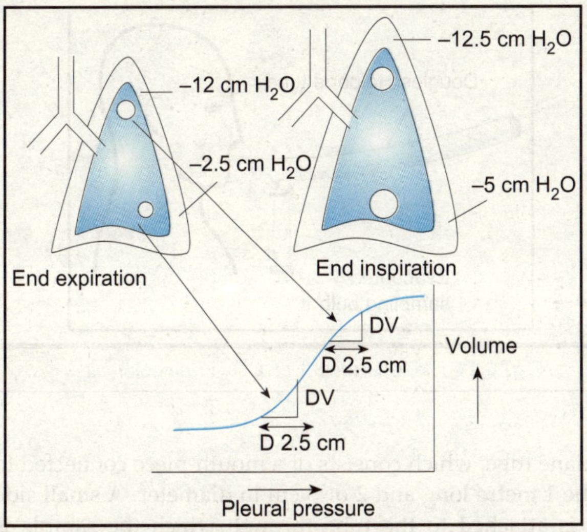


**Fig. 6.7 : Regional distribution of ventilation**

At very low lung volumes, the small airways in the dependent part remain closed and will not allow any air to enter in the very early part of inspiration. However the patent airways at upper zones will allow ventilation. After forceful expiration, if an individual inhales $O_2$ up to end inspiration and exhales slowly, and $N_2$ concentration is measured continuously at lips, the plot of $N_2$ concentration against volume (Fig. 6.8) will have four phases :

(i) Gas exclusively from dead space;
(ii) Mixed gas;
(iii) Alveolar gas from all zones;
(iv) Gas from non-dependent part as the small airways in the dependent part begins to close (closing volume).

The rise in $N_2$ concentration is due to the fact that during forceful expiration, pressure that mounts up outside small airways at dependent parts is sufficient to close them. So, during inhalation of $O_2$, though the initial part of ventilation goes to non-dependent parts (patent airways) the major part goes to dependent parts diluting its nitrogen more than in the apical part. So at the end of forced expiraton, when airways at the dependent part closes, the $N_2$ rich air from apical part comes out to raise the $N_2$ concentration abruptly.

This phenomenon also points to unevenness of ventilation. ***The closing volume also indicates*** functions of small airways. It may increase in diffuse disorders like chronic bronchitis, when functions of medium or large sized airways are yet to be compromised to the extent of detection by conventional testing eg, $FEV_1$, PEFR etc.

Gravity also affects blood flow in the lungs above the level of the heart. The pulmonary capillaries are surrounded by alveoli and they are pressed upon by alveolar pressure. The capillary pressure at the extreme apex of the lung is subatmospheric, i.e., lower than alveolar pressure throughout

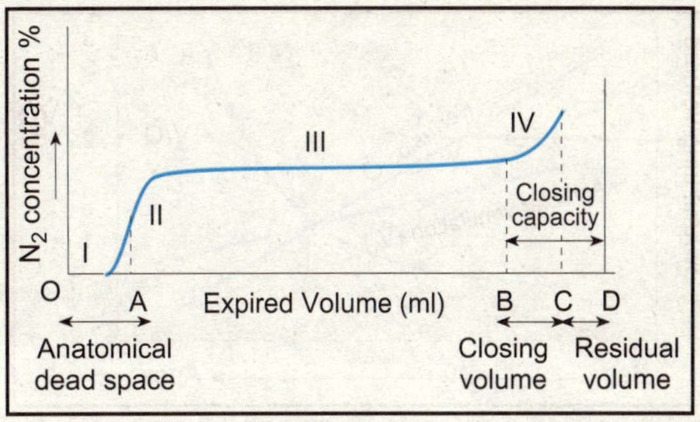


**Fig. 6.8 : Single breath $O_2$ test**

cardiac cycle and the respiration. So there is practically no perfusion $P_{alv} > P_{cap} > P_v$. Somewhat below that level there is a zone where $P_{cap} > P_{alv} > P_v$. Here the perfusion depends on the difference between alveolar and venous pressure. So during inspiration, when alveolar pressure falls during part of the cardiac cycle, $P_v > P_{alv}$ — blood flows intermittently. Further downwards, everywhere $P_{cap} > P_v > P_{alv}$, and flow is continuous and independent of alveolar pressure (Fig. 6.9).

Depth of breathing has its effect on lung perfusion. During forceful expiration, the alveolar pressure becomes high enough to compress and occlude the pulmonary capillaries at non-dependent areas of lung due to low hydrostatic pressure in capillaries there. The same thing takes place during positive pressure artificial respiration.

Normal inspiration increases perfusion by reducing alveolar pressure, but during forced inspiration the expanding alveoli stretch the capillaries along with their walls actually narrowing their lumen and reducing blood flow. Perfusion across the lungs increases in left to right shunts eg, interatrial septal defect, patent ductus arteriosus. Perfusion becomes low when there is fall in blood pressure due to any cause or obstruction due to embolus, thrombus or destruction of vessels along with lung parenchyma.

**Regional distribution of ventilation** can be detected by ***inhalation of radioactive xenon***–containing gas mixture.

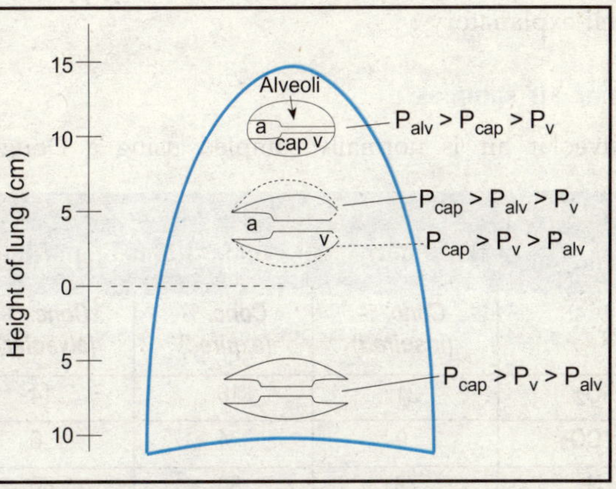


**Fig. 6.9 : Regional distribution of perfusion**

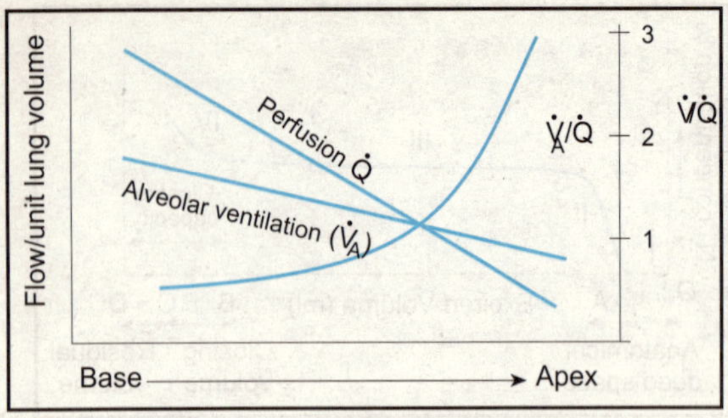


Fig. 6.10 : Distribution of VA/Q

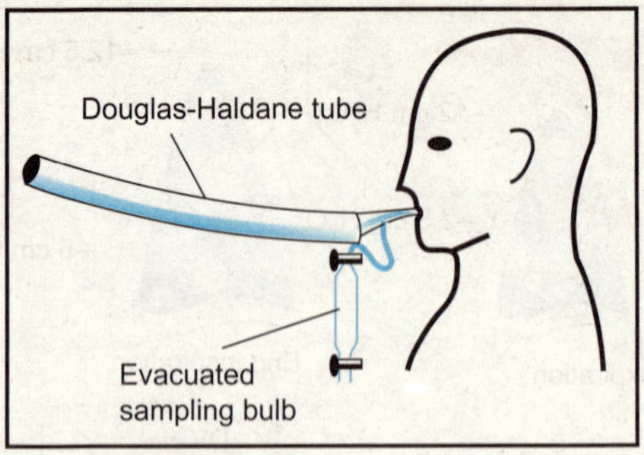


Fig. 6.11 : Measurement of $CO_2$ in alveolar air

Similarly, the perfusion can also be monitored by injecting radioactive xenon in saline solution intravenously. It has been observed that in the upright position, there occurs gradual increase in ventilation and perfusion from top to bottom, but the differences were more marked in blood flow than in air flow. So, per unit lung volume, the ratio between $\frac{\dot{V}}{\dot{Q}}$ is more in the apical part than in the dependent part (Fig. 6.10). Due to this regional $\frac{\dot{V}}{\dot{Q}}$ ratio differences, the apical part had their alveoli more oxygenated than the basal parts. This, along with less perfusion, makes the apical parts abode for growth of tubercle bacilli which require an aerobic environment for growth. This also explains, to some extent, besides physiological shunt, the alveolar-arterial oxygen partial pressure difference.

## 6.5 Determination of Alveolar Gas Composition

In the measurement of anatomical dead space, diffusion capacity etc. it is necessary to sample alveolar air. During expiration, there takes place a mixture between alveolar and dead space air, so the terminal part of expired air can be considered as the best representative of alveolar air.

Different ingenious techniques are adapted to collect terminal sample of expired air. Diagram of two apparatuses are self-explanatory :

### Alveolar air samples :

Alveolar air is normally sampled using a Douglas-Haldane tube, which consists of a mouth-piece connected to a tube 1 metre long and 2 or 3 cm in diameter. A small side arm is attached to the tube through which the sample is taken as required. This is a sample of alveolar air because the dead space is increased, i.e. the interface between alveolar air and expired air occurs distal to thesampling tube attached to the side arm. Only a small number of breaths should be taken, otherwise there will be time for $CO_2$ to accumulate in the lungs and circulation and hence, alter the composition of alveolar air. (Fig. 6.11)

The gas sample is analyzed by manual or automated gas analyzers. The approximate composition and partial pressures of gases of physiological importance are tabulated below (Table 6.3). Atmospheric pressure is assumed to be 760 mm Hg, temperature 37°C saturated with water vapor. Concentrations of gases are that of dry portion excluding the contribution of moisture. $P_{gas} = (P_B - P_{H2O}) \times$ fraction of the gas.

## 6.6 Lung Mechanics

The expansion of lungs are secondary to generation of negative (i.e., subatmospheric) pressure around them by inspiratory muscles. So ***inspiration*** is always an ***active process***. The lungs are covered by a thin membrane — **visceral pleura**. On the other hand the chest wall is lined by **parietal pleura**. The space in between the pleurae is called **interpleural space;** it contains a few ml of interstitial fluid. It (along with negative pressure in the intrapleural space) is responsible for close apposition of two layers of pleurae, so

Table 6.3
Approximate composition and partial pressures of gases of physiological importance

| | Conc. % (inspired) | Conc. % (expired) | Conc. % (alveolar) | Partial pressure (inspired) mm Hg | Partial pressure (expired) mm Hg | Partial pressure (alveolar) mm Hg |
|---|---|---|---|---|---|---|
| $O_2$ | 21 | 16 | 14 | 150 | 114 | 100 |
| $CO_2$ | 0 | 4 | 6 | 0 | 29 | 43 |
| $N_2$ | 79 | 80 | 80 | 563 | 570 | 570 |
| $H_2O$ | – | – | – | 47 | 47 | 47 |

that only a potential space is maintained there. The cohesion of fluid molecules in between the layers allow the surfaces to slide easily one over the other, but opposes separation. A similar thing is seen in case of two moist slides, they can be moved one over the other, but extremely difficult to pull them from apart. The cohesive force is responsible for keeping the lungs expanded. ***The negativity in the interpleural (or intrapleural space) is created by two processes —***

(i) ***Tendency of lungs to collapse*** towards the hila and that of the chest wall to expand outside at normal lung volumes.

(ii) ***Lymphatic drainage of transudate*** (pleural fluid) continuously being formed by filtration from neighbouring capillaries. It forms the fluid in the pleural cavity.

Respiratory movements have been organized in such a way that every dimension of the thoracic cage: vertical, antero-posterior and transverse, can be increased simultaneously.

Simple elevation of the thorax will not increase its capacity. The roof of the thorax along with first rib is more or less fixed. Descent and flattening of the floor will definitely increase its capacity. But movement of ribs can add to it. Lower ribs move upward and come closer to first rib, their anterior ends push the sternum forward to increase antero-posterior distance while their bucket-handle movement expands thorax transversely.

**Inspiration** is due to expansion of the thoracic cavity by different inspiratory muscles. During normal inspiration it is due towards the contraction of (a) ***the diaphragm***, (b) ***external intercostals***. The diaphragm is a sheet of muscle separating thoracic and abdominal cavities. It is dome-shaped, i.e., convex towards the thoracic side. It is supplied by phrenic nerve (cervical 3, 4, 5). When it contracts, the vertical dimension of the chest cavity enlarges and, at the same time, the elevation and flaring of lower ribs by contraction of costal fibers (when the tendinous central part is supported by abdominal viscera) also expands the chest — to some extent side by side. ***The diaphragm is the principal muscle during tidal respiration*** and 75% change in the lung volume can be accounted for by its action.

The diaphragm has its origin from anterior surface of lumbar vertebrae (crural part) and lower six ribs (costal part). The fibers converge to the central tendinous part. During normal inspiration, downward movement is only $^1/_2$ an inch (1.25 cm) but, during forceful inspiration, the deviation can be up to 3 inches (6.5 cm). Movement of the diaphragm is not for inspiration only. It descends to some extent whenever there is need to raise the intra-abdominal pressure like straining during defecation, parturition or vomiting. During vomiting, the costal part contracts but the crural part that surrounds the esophagus are kept relaxed so that the stomach contents can be forced out.

The second important group of muscles responsible for **normal inspiration** are *external intercostals* which run downwards and forwards from rib to rib. Their contraction is responsible for elevation of thoracic cage and pushing forward of the sternum so that the antero-posterior and side to side depth of thoracic cage is increased. 25% change of intrathoracic volume during normal inspiration can be attributed to the contraction of this group of muscles. They are supplied by intercostal nerves.

When the intercostal muscles of both sides are paralyzed, the movement of the diaphragm is sufficient to maintain respiration. On the other hand, when there occurs bilateral phrenic nerve lesion, the increased activity of intercostal muscles is adequate for ventilation at rest. ***Normal expiration is a passive process.*** The lungs, when expanded during inspiration, has a tendency to collapse. So, after normal inspiration, when the diaphragm and intercostals relax, the elastic property of lung tissue is sufficient to drive out air during normal expiration by its recoil; no additional energy is required.

During forceful inspiration, besides diaphragm and external intercostals, other muscles like scaleni and sternocleidomastoids are involved in raising the thoracic cage. Elevation of the thoracic cage increases the antero-posterior and lateral dimensions of thorax. The movement of ribs is described as pump-handle type which elevates anterior ends of them increasing the antero-posterior depth of chest and also bucket-handle movement which is responsible for expansion in the side-to-side dimension of the thorax. Different sets of fibers of external intercostals are put into action in these movements. More anterior fibers are involved in pump-handle movement which occurs around a side to side axis at the posterior aspect of ribs. The posterior fibers are responsible for bucket-handle motion which takes place around an oblique antero-posterior axis.

In **men,** diaphragm is the muscle mostly used during normal respiration and during its descent the abdominal muscles lose tension to prevent rise in intraabdominal pressure; during expiration the opposite phenomenon occurs. This makes alternate bulging and retraction of the anterior abdominal wall — **abdominal type of respiration.**

During extreme **forceful inspiration,** scapula is fixed by trapezius, rhomboids etc. and muscles connecting it to chest wall (eg. serratus anterior, pectoralis minor) contracts to raise the chest cage. If upper limbs can be fixed, even pectoralis major may come into action.

**Forceful expiration** requires active participation of expiratory muscles. They are the internal intercostals and abdominal muscles. The internal intercosrtal muscles run from rib to rib in downward and posterior direction. They contract to pull down the thoracic cage decreasing its antero-posterior and lateral dimensions. The abdominal muscles pull down the chest wall as in internal intercostals. Moreover, it raises the intraabdominal pressure which push liver and other viscera to force diaphragm into thorax. The abdominal muscles are most important muscles during forced expiration. Latissimus dorsi are also expiratory muscles and can be tested by holding the posterior axillary folds during coughing.

In **women**, intercostal muscles are brought into action (along with the diaphragm) more actively than men, so their chest wall moves appreciably during normal respiration — **thoracic type of respiration.**

## Pressure changes during respiration

Pressure changes in the interpleural (or intrapleural) space and in the intraalveolar (or intrapulmonary) space are important for movement of air during different phases of resting and forced breathing.

***During normal inspiration,*** the contraction of the appropriate muscles results in increased negativity of the intrapleural space. Though the negativity is different at different zones (more in non-dependent regions), at some level near lung base in erect posture, it is ***taken to be –2.5 mm of Hg*** at the end of normal expiration. During normal inspiration it ***goes down to –6 cm $H_2O$. During normal expiration*** there occurs steady (but not abrupt) relaxation of muscles and the intrapleural pressure rises to reach the basal level of –2.5 cm $H_2O$ at the end of normal expiration. The intrapulmonary pressure is affected by intrapleural pressure but is substantially different from the latter due to elasticity of lung tissue, communication of the alveoli to atmosphere, airway resistances at all levels and frictional (viscous) resistance within lung parenchyma.

As alveoli remain in connection with the exterior, at the end of normal expiration, the intrapulmonary pressure is equal to that of atmosphere (zero). But during inspiration, along with increased negativity in intrapleural space, the pressure within the alveoli gets subatmospheric but to a lower level (– 1 mm Hg, maximum) due to reasons already mentioned. This pressure difference is sufficient for ***entry of air from exterior to the lung***. The lowest pressure level along with maximum air flow is attained prior to the middle of inspiratory phase after which the negativity subsides steadily to reach the atmospheric or zero level at the end of inspiration (though the intrapleural pressure is at the highest negative value then).

In the expiratory phase, the intrapleural pressure begins to lose negativity along with contraction of thoracic cavity. The lung recoil raises intrapulmonary pressure to above atmospheric, (to +1 mm Hg, maximum); the peak level along with maximum flow is attained prior to middle of expiratory phase. This pressure difference is sufficient to push air from the lungs to exterior. At the end of expiration the pressure in the alveoli falls and the intra-alveolar pressure again becomes zero.

During forceful inspiration, the intrapleural pressure can be as low as –30 mm Hg or less than that. At the time of forced expiration, the intrapleural pressure becomes positive; it may be more than +30 mm Hg as in straining, coughing and forced expiration with closed glottis (**Valsalva's maneuver**).

During normal respiration, expiration outlasts inspiration because expiration here is a passive process, the relaxation of diaphragm is not abrupt, some contraction of the inspiratory muscles extends to early expiratory phase. During expiration narrowing of glottic opening increases resistance to airflow to some extent **(braking effect)**. But with increased respiratory rate **(tachypnea)** this difference is obscured by the enhanced neural discharge affecting both inspiratory and expiratory muscles; respiration becomes active in both the phases during exercise.

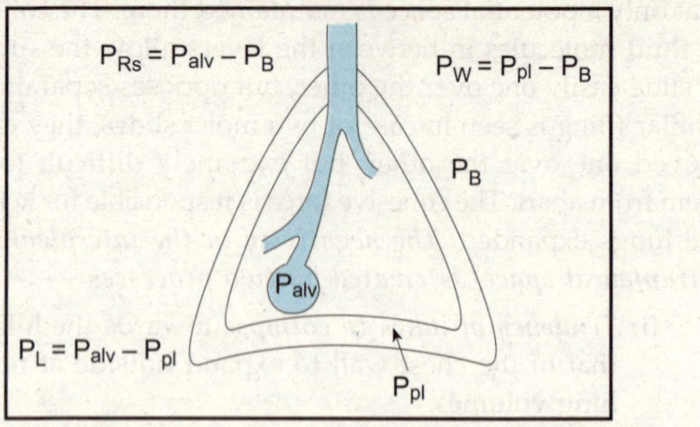


Fig. 6.12 : Pressure in relation to respiration

## Pressures in relation to respiration (Fig. 6.12)

To have an understanding of the elastic properties of the lungs and chest wall, the transmural pressures related to lungs are to be considered. They are

(i) **Trans-respiratory pressure ($P_{RS}$)** is the differ-ence between the alveolar pressure and atmospheric pressure at body surface

(ii) **Trans-chest wall pressure ($P_W$)** is the difference between interpleural pressure and atmospheric pressure of body surface

(iii) **Trans-lung pressure ($P_L$)** is the difference between alveolar pressure and interpleural pressure.

Now, if body surface pressure ($P_B$) is assumed to be zero then

$$P_{RS} = + P_{alv},\ P_W = P_{pl} \text{ but } P_L = P_{alv} - P_{pl} = (P_{RS} - P_W)$$

at any value of $P_B$. The transmural pressure is the effective force that is responsible for change in size of any structure concerned, along with flow of fluid (gas) in appropriate direction.

As there are regional differences in intrapleural pressure, the transmural pressures have also regional variaiton. At functional residual capacity (FRC) (the end of tidal expiration), ***the whole respiratory system has attained a quiescent stage***. But the lungs have an expanding force counteracting its inherent collapsing tendency and the chest wall has an equal compressive force from outside opposing its natural expanding propensity. So at FRC, it is apparent that (in static condition) no force is acting over the total respiratory system (lungs + body wall), indicating the resting state of the system.

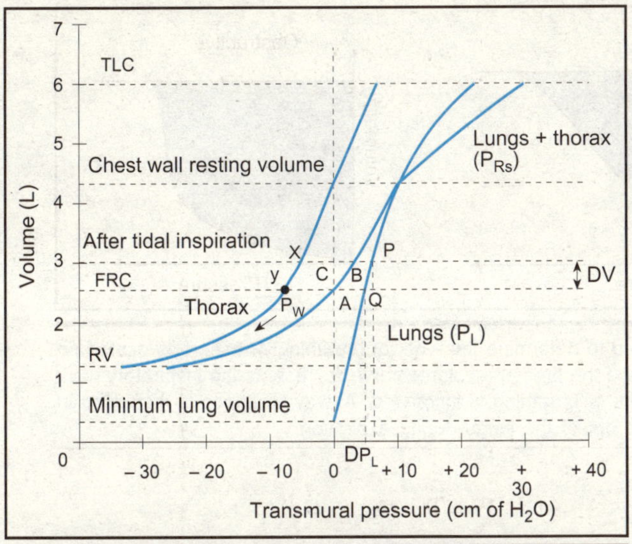


**Fig. 6.13 :** Relaxation pressure-volume curves for lungs, chest wall and the respiratory system (Lungs and thorax)

Elastic properties of lungs, chest wall and the respiratory system can be understood by studying the static pressure-volume relationships with each of the three structures. This can be determined by special tests that measure intrapleural pressure either from pleural space (or esophagus) and mouth pressure (that equals to intrapulmonary or alveolar pressure) :

$$P_{RS} = P_{alv} - P_B \qquad = P_{mouth} - 0 \quad = P_{mouth}$$
$$P_W = P_{pl} - P_B = P_{pl} - 0 \qquad = P_{pl}$$
$$P_L = P_{pl} - P_{alv} \qquad = P_{pl} - P_{mouth}$$

In the experiment, the subject is asked to inhale (or exhale) a volume of gas from spirometer. He bears a mouth-piece which has a one-way valvular system so that gas cannot escape. After each breath he is instructed to relax all respiratory muscle and keep his glottis open and the pressure at the mouth can be read from a meter attached to the mouth-piece. As the muscles are relaxed, no force is active and as the glottis is open the mouth pressure is equal to the alveolar pressure. As the pressure is recorded at the time of stopped respiration, airway resistance and dynamic component of viscous resistance will have no effect on transmural pressure. So the transmural pressure associated with each structure will speak for its elastic properties (static) almost exclusively. The different transmural pressures along with the volumes at which they were measured are plotted (pressures in abscissa and volumes over the ordinate). (See Fig. 6.14).

It is apparent from the curve, that *at FRC the respiratory system is at rest* (zero pressure). In case of lungs, the resting volume is not the residual volume, but the 'minimal volume' which cannot be attained in vivo. The resting value of the chest wall is above 4L, about 70% of the total lung capacity (TLC). So in case of lungs, the relaxation pressure all throughout the excursion (RV to TLC) is positive which indicates that the lungs have a tendency to collapse at any lung volume.

In case of chest wall, the relaxation pressure is positive beyond 70% of TLC; it is negative at all volumes below that volume. So, only at high lung volumes, the chest wall tries to collapse, but during physiological range it tends to expand out ward. At FRC, the relaxation pressures of chest wall and lungs are equal in magnitude but opposite in direction, so their combined pressure is zero :

$$P_{RS} = P_{alv} - P_B = (P_{alv} - P_{pl}) + (P_{pl} - P_B) = P_L + P_W$$

At resting volume of thorax, it loses all tendency to expand or contract, but relaxation pressure of lungs is near +10 cm $H_2O$ and it tries to collapse which must be opposed actively by muscles of inspiration. But when the lungs collapse after entry of air within pleural space to make the intrapleural pressure equal to atmospheric pressure, $P_W = P_{pl} - P_B = 0$. Therefore the chest wall will spring up to attain its resting volume above 4 litres.

Compliance and elastance of lungs and thorax can be appreciated by examining the relaxation pressure curves. **Elastance of a structure** is the pressure required to change its volume by one unit, i.e., elastance in case of lungs is $\Delta P_L/\Delta V$. Near FRC it is 5 cm $H_2O$/L and the value is same in case of chest wall. But near residual volume the elastance of the chest wall increases many times.

**Compliance** is the reciprocal of elastance. It is a measure of distensibility, i.e., volume change in response to unitary transmural pressure change. So compliance is $\Delta V/\Delta P_L$; in case of lungs near FRC. The compliance is 200 ml/cm $H_2O$, same in the case of thorax (slopes are equal). At high lung volumes, near TLC the compliance reduces as the less stretchable (high elastance) connective tissues resist distention.

In case of total respiratory system $P_{RS} = P_L + P_W$, so $\Delta P_{RS} = \Delta P_L + \Delta P_W$. Now $(\Delta P_{RS}/\Delta_V) = (\Delta P_L/\Delta_V) + (\Delta P_W/\Delta_Y)$, i.e., $E_{RS} = E_L + E_W$. Hence, $(1/C_{RS}) = (1/C_L) + (1/C_W)$, when E indicates elastance, C compliance. So, near FRC, the compliance of respiratory system, $(1/C_{RS})$ = (1/0.2 L/cm $H_2O$) + (1/0.2 L/cm $H_2O$ or 0.1 L/cm of $H_2O$ and elastance is 10 cm $H_2O$/L. Compliance of lung is different at various lung volumes. As the pressure changes are related to lung volume changes that vary in different animals and with different body sizes in a species. The compliance of lungs is much smaller in small than in large animals. In men with one lung the compliance get halved. So for comparative and more meaningful interpretation of stretchability of lungs, specific compliance that takes into consideration of lung volume is considered. Specific compliance is compliance/FRC, i.e., in normal individuals it is 0.2 L/cm of $H_2O$/2.5 L, i.e., 0.08/cm $H_2O$. This value is comparable in all mammals irrespective of their sizes.

Compliance of the chest wall and, more commonly, of the lungs may be diminished in different diseases. Severe kyphoscoliosis and muscular weakness may affect chest wall. Pulmonary fibrosis, edema, compression and collapse

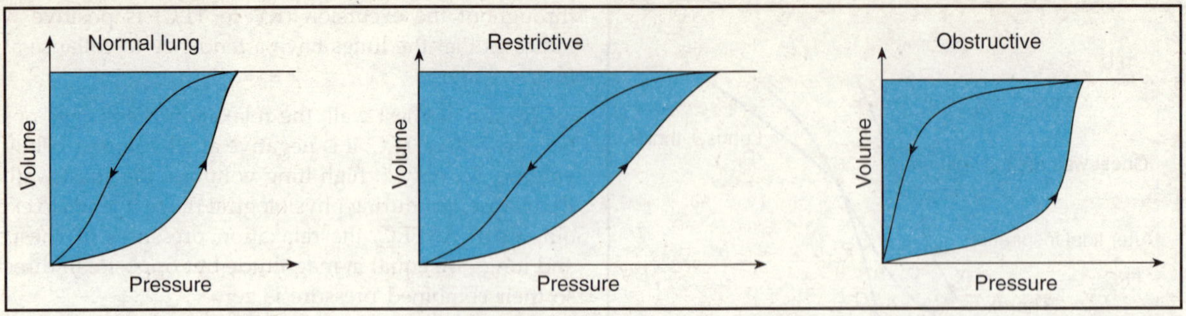


Fig. 6.14 : Work of Breathing : A pressure volume curve is used to determine the work of breathing. Pressure is plotted on the x-axis, and volume is plotted on the y-axis. The red area above the pressure-volume curve represents the inspiratory work of breathing. Note that with a restrictive disorder, inspiratory work of breathing is increased. Airway resitance is increased in an obstructive disorder, which requires more energy to force air out of the lungs during expiration.

(following pneumothorax, pleural effusion) involve lung parenchyma. They are grouped under the term **'restrictive lung diseases'**. Work of breathing increases as more force is required to inflate the lungs (decreased compliance). As airways remain unaffected, the patients take rapid shallow breaths to overcome the diminished distensibility. In cases of asthma or chronic bronchitis where the airway resistance has increased immensely, but the lung parenchyma is normal, slow deep breaths are taken which is less energy-consuming than rapid shallow breaths. Patients suffering from either variety adapt to appropriate breathing pattern to gain adequate alveolar ventilation at the expense of minimal energy expenditure.

The elastic behavior of the lungs within the physiologic range of movement is due to two components—(i) ***elastic fibers in the lung interstitium,*** and (ii) ***surface tension of the fluid film lining the alveoli.*** If in an experimental animal the lungs, after removal, are filled with saline to abolish the air-water interface, the surface active forces are removed it and is seen that elastance falls to 1.25 cm/L from normal gas filled value of 5 cm $H_2O$/L. So the major share of resistance in expansion of the lungs is borne by the surface active forces rather than the elastic structural components.

## 6.7 Work of Breathing

Work Is Required to Expand the Lungs and Overcome Airway Resistance.

During inspiration, muscular work is involved in expanding the thoracic cavity, inflating the lungs, and overcoming air way resistance. Since work can be measured as force times distance, the amoiunt of work involved in breathing can be expressed as a change in lung volume (distance) mulciplied by the change in transpulmonary pressure (force).

Thus, work (W) is equal to the product of pressure (P) and volume (V). With a volume change, the work involved in takings breath is defined by this equation :

$$W = P \times V.$$

where P equals transpulmonary pressure and V ecuals change in lung volume.

During work, energy is expended with muscular contraction to create a force (transpulmonary pressure) to inflate the lungs. When a greater transpulmonary pressure is required to bring more air into the lungs, more muscular work and, hence, greater energy are required. There pressure volume line during inspirationis different from that during expiration. This phenomenon is called **hysteresis**. It indicates involvement of non-elastic resistances, which change in equality and magnitude during different phases of respiration.

Figure 6.14 shows how a pressure volume curve can be used to determine the work required for breathing. The shaded area represents the inspiratory work of breathing. In healthy individuals at rest, the energy needed for breathing represents approximately 5% of the body's total energy expenditure. During heavy exercise, about 20% of the total energy expenditure is involved in breathing. Breathing is efficient and is most economical when elastic and resistive forces yield the lowest work. The total inspiratory work of breathing in a restrictive lung disorder, compared with the normal lung, is increased and is a result of a greater inspiratory effort required. It is important to remember that lungs with a marked decrease in lung copliance (i.e., restrictive lung disorder) requires more work to overcome increase in elastic recoil and surface forces. Patients with a restrictive disorder economize their ventilation by taking rapid and shallow breaths. In contrast, patients with severe airway obstruction tend to do the opposite; they take deeper breaths and breathe more slowly, to reduce their work due to the increased airway resistance. Despite this tendency, patients with obstructive disease still expend a considerable portion of their basal energy for breathing. The reason for this is the expiratory muscles must do additional work to overcome the increased airway resistance. These different breathing patterns help minimize the amount of work required for breathing.

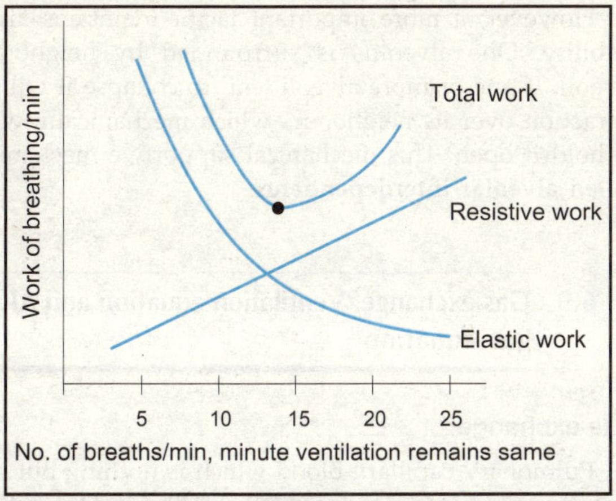


Fig. 6.15 : Relationship between work of breathing and respiratory rate

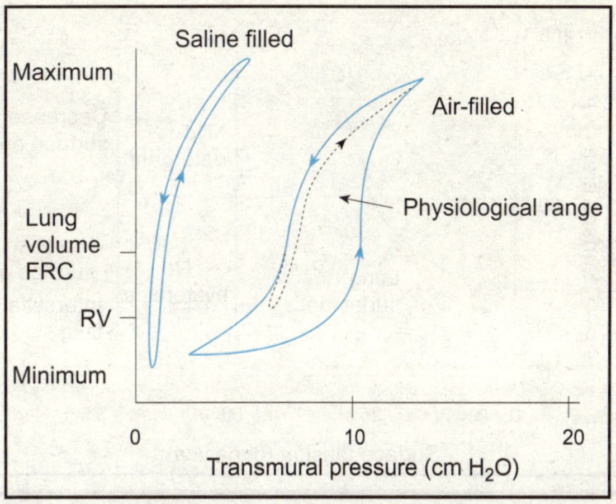


Fig. 6.16 : Pressure volume curve of saline and air filled lungs

## 6.8 Alveolar Surface Tension–Surfactant

In course of our discussion regarding the elastance of the lungs, it was held that 75% of the total elastance is due to surface tension of the fluid film lining the alveoli. Within the liquid phase, every molecule is equally attracted in all possible directions by neighbouring molecules, but at the air-liquid interface, the surface molecules experience unbalanced forces. The attraction of liquid molecules on one of them is much more than the attraction by gas molecules so that the surface appears to be under some force. This is **surface tension**, which operates parallel to the surface and measured as force (dynes) acting at right angles to a line 1 cm from the surface, i.e., dynes/cm. It is surface tension that makes drops of mercury spherical, raindrops rounded, flow of fluid through glass capillaries, umbrellas impervious to rain and flow of ink from pens.

The surface film lining the inner surface of lung alveoli exerts surface tension that is directed to the center of the spherical alveolus. This force tries to collapse the alveolus. To make it stable it is required that force should act in opposite direction to neutralize the tension. The effect of the surface active force in determining compliance can be studied by removing the lung from an experimental animal and inflating it by graded increase in transmural pressure first filled with air and then with saline. ***When the pressure-volume curve is plotted, the saline-filled lung with obliterated air-fluid interface shows only the compliance of elastic structural component and little hysteresis on gradual deflation. The saline-filled lung is more compliant than air filled lung which shows a right shifted curve.***

The air filled curve shows marked hysteresis on deflation— specially at low lung volumes near residual volume—but much reduced hysteresis near FRC. The air-filled curve shows compliance when both elastic tissues and surface tension are operative. At low lung volumes, the air-filled lung shows much less compliance compared to saline-filled state, including enhanced surface active force when the alveoli gets smaller. The hysteresis seen in air-filled lung shows that surface active forces vary at same lung volume in different phases of respiration (Fig. 6.16).

**Law of Laplace** for a spherical thin-walled structure describes the surface force (T) relating to the pressure generated or opposing it (P) as P = 2T/R, where R is the radius. The intrapleural pressure is secondary to collapsing tendency of lungs and expanding tendency of the thorax. If the surface lining film is pure interstitial fluid, having a surface tension of 70 dyne/cm, the pressure developed within it becomes

$$\frac{2 \times 70 \text{ dynes / cm}}{\frac{1}{2} \times 10^{-2} \text{ cm}}$$

(taking the average alveolar diameter at FRC as 0.1 mm or 0.01 cm) or 28,000 dynes/cm$^2$ — it is equal to 28 cm $H_2O$. So the transmural pressure of lung should be kept at this level with the intrapleural pressure of –28 cm taking alveolar pressure as zero. But the experimental value is near –5 cm $H_2O$, which corresponds to surface active force

$$\frac{5 \times 10^3 \times \frac{1}{2} \times 10^{-2}}{2}, \text{i.e. } \frac{50}{4} \text{ or dynes / cm.}$$

So the surface force is much lower than expected It is the presence of surface active compounds (surfactant) — secreted by type II epithelial cells in the surface film — that reduces the surface tension force considerably. Washing of alveolar fluid obtained in an experimental animal also shows much reduced surface tension compared to interstitial fluid by direct measurement (Wilhelmi balance).

**Surfactant is responsible for lowering surface tension** six times at air-liquid interface of alveoli. Detergents also lower surface tension of the fluid in which they get dissolved so that dust particles entrapped by fluid films are easily

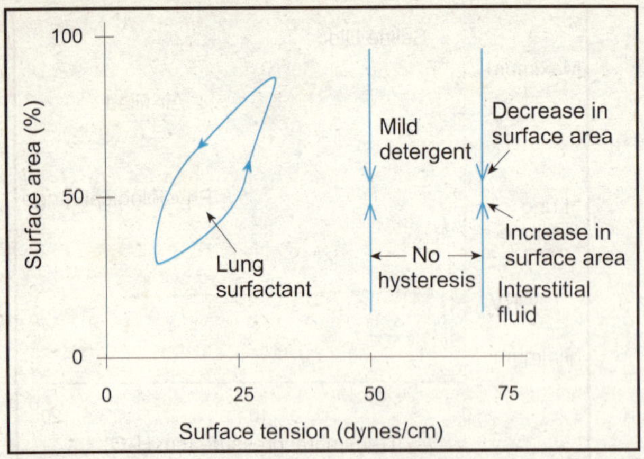


**Fig. 6.17 :** Surface active behaviours of pulmonary surfactant, mild detergent and interstitial fluid

dislodged mechanically. But, in case of pulmonary surfactant, the surface tension lowering property is dependent on the surface area available. For a certain number of surface active molecules, less surface area is associated with more reduction of tension; the smaller an alveolus becomes, the greater is the surface active property. ***The surfactant not only shows area dependence but also shows hysteresis during alternate increase and decrease in surface area*** (Fig. 6.17).

### Functions of surfactant

By reducing the surface tension of the alveolar fluid lining, ***the surfactant has the following functions*** :

(1) **Compliance of the lungs** is increased several-fold. This reduces the work load for respiration.

(2) **Reduces the possibility of accumulation of fluid** within lung alveoli (pulmonary edema). The surface force of alveoli acts towards the center, so it acts on the capillaries surrounding the alveoli favouring fluid transudation from the capillaries to interstitium. This is counteracted by the surfactant. In fact, in cases of surfactant deficiency fluids do accumulate in the interstitium and alveoli.

(3) **Helps to stabilize the alveoli** preventing their collapse. In case of soap bubbles, it is seen that small bubbles discharge their gas to communicating nearby large bubbles and merge into it. It is due to the fact that smaller bubbles with smaller radius will generate more force (pressure) compared to large bubbles when the surface tension is the same in all the bubbles ($P = 2T/R$). As alveoli are in communication they should follow suit specially at low lung volumes after expiration as the size of alveoli are different. This is prevented by the property of surfactant. Their efficacy in lowering tension increases when the surface area is small. So the small alveoli will have lower surface tension than the large ones. Therefore the pressure generated within them becomes equal so that alveoli do not merge into one another and, ultimately, collapse by letting air through the airways.

However, a more important factor maintains alveolar stability. One alveolus is surrounded by neighbouring alveoli. If one or more alveoli tend to collapse it will exert a traction over its neighbours which mechanically will try to hold it open. This mechanical supportive mechanism is called **alveolar interdependence**.

## 6.9 Gas exchange, Ventilation equation and Alveolar gas equation

### Gas exchange

Pulmonary capillary blood which is nothing but mixed systemic venous blood has a $PO_2$ of 40 mm Hg and $PCO_2$ of 46 mm Hg at rest and those of alveolar air are 100 mm Hg ($P_AO_2$) and 40 mm Hg ($P_ACO_2$) respectively. Gases diffuse across the respiratory membrane, 250-300 ml of $O_2$ enters the blood and 200-250 ml of $CO_2$ goes into air per minute at rest. Respiratory exchange ratio (R) becomes about 0.8 ($V_{CO2}/V_{O2}$) and is the same as respiratory quotient which varies with the composition of foodstuff consumed. But during hyperventilation (voluntary or during exercise) $CO_2$ is blown off at higher rate than metabolic production rate and (R) value outstrips the respiratory quotient value.

**Measurement of $O_2$ consumption :** $O_2$ consumption can be calculated by subtracting the amount exhaled (volume of expiration/time × fraction of $O_2$ in expired air) from the amount inhaled (volume of inspiration/time × fraction of $O_2$ in air) In symbols $V_{O2} = V_i \times F_iO_2 - V_E \times F_eO_2$.

$V_E$ is not exactly equal to $V_i$ because the volume of $CO_2$ evolved is less than oxygen consumed. But for practical purposes $V_E$ is taken to be same as $V_i$. So the equation reduces to $V_{O_2} = V_E\ \mathbf{(F_iO_2 - F_eO_2)}$.

**$CO_2$ production :** By the same principle $CO_2$ produced can be calculated as $V_{CO2} = V_E \times F_eCO_2 - V_i \times F_iCO_2$ and approximated as $V_{CO2} = V_E\ (F_eCO_2 - F_iCO_2)$. Now, as $F_iCO_2$ is negligible, the equation gets further simplified, $V_{CO_2} = V_E \times F_eCO_2$.

### Ventilation-perfusion ratio

In the lungs, the blood flow and air flow are matched in such a way that diffusion of oxygen and carbon dioxide takes place adequately. Pulmonary venous blood that returns to left atrium is a mixture of blood draining from millions of alveoli. Each alveolus after diffusion has its gas tension that equals the dissolved gases of blood leaving it.

**The ventilation-perfusion ratio** ($\dot{V}_A/\dot{Q}$) of the lungs is 0.8 on average; **alveolar ventilation** 4.0 L/min and **perfusion** 5.0 L/min. If an alveolus receives no ventilation, the perfusing blood will remain unchanged when it flows across it. On the other hand, when the perfusion becomes very low, the alveolar gas concentrations will change little. It will approach that of inspired air and the draining blood will attain partial gas pressure equal to the alveolus. In extreme

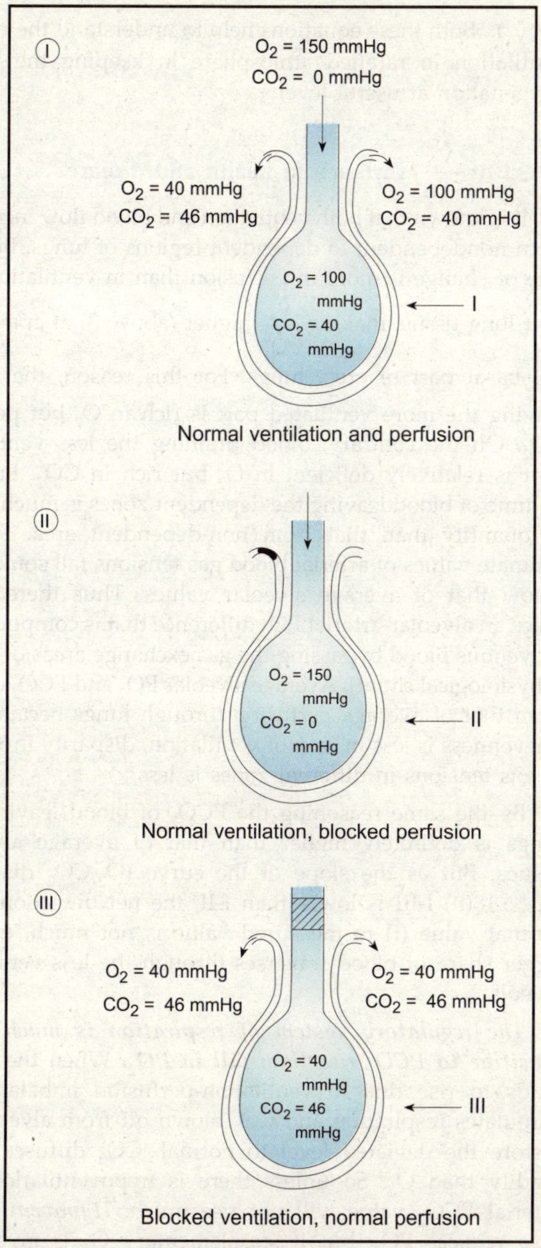


**Fig. 6.18 a :** $O_2 - CO_2$ diagram showing alveolar ($P_AO_2$ and $P_ACO_2$) $O_2$ and $CO_2$ tensions between the points II $\dot{V}_A/\dot{Q}$ = a and III $\dot{V}_A/\dot{Q}$= 0. I is the normal state. When perfusion is blocked partially, alveolar gas pressure will be between I and II. When ventilation is partially reduced, the values lie between I and III. The state of II can be regarded as dead space (inspired air values) and state III as shunt (mixed venous values)

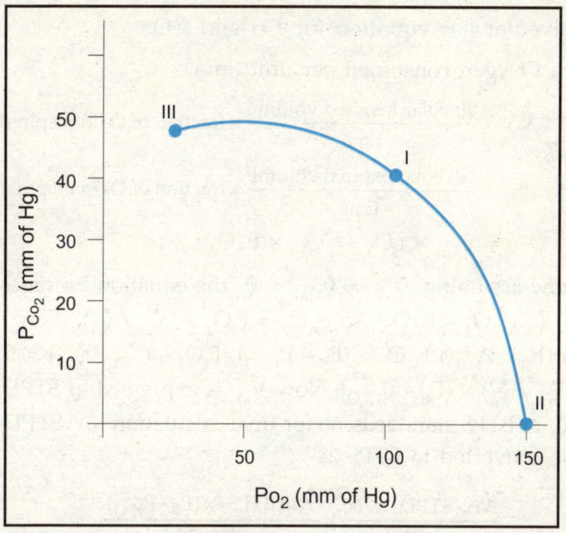


**Fig. 6.18 b :** Concentrations and partial pressures of $O_2$ and $CO_2$ in arterial blood

conditions of $\dot{V}_A/\dot{Q}$ between zero and infinity, there is no scope of gas exchange in the lungs; there will be accumulation of carbon dioxide **(hypercapnia)** and depletion of oxygen **(hypoxia)** within body fluids including blood in general. The condition is fatal in no time and is of theoretical considerations only. But in healthy lungs, mismatching of ventilation and perfusion occurs to some extent (invariably in most disease conditions). Its severity will ultimately dictate the concentrations and partial pressures of $O_2$ and $CO_2$ in arterial blood and the resultant effects over the system. The diagrams (Figs. 6.18 a, b) will explain the situation. The air we breathe from the atmosphere has a partial pressure that is different from inspired air as humidification occurs during transport through the airways. ***Within the alveoli there is addition of $CO_2$ from pulmonary capillaries and removal of $O_2$ away from it continuously,*** and it is always being replenished partially by (alveolar) ventilation. So the partial pressure of $O_2$ and $CO_2$ within the alveoli remains somewhat midway between inspired air and systemic venous blood.

## Alveolar ventilation equation

**$CO_2$ produced per minute** is $\dot{V}_{CO2} = \dot{V}_E \times F_eCO_2$. As $CO_2$ in alveoli is in equilibrium with the perfusing blood, blood leaving the lungs has partial pressure of $CO_2$, i.e., $P_ACO_2$ equal to that of alveolar $P_{ACO2}$. $\dot{V}_{CO2}$ can also be expressed as alveolar ventilation per minute × fraction of $CO_2$ in alveolar gas. In symbols $\dot{V}_{CO2} = \dot{V}_A \times F_ACO_2$. Now $P_ACO_2 = (P_B - P_{H2O}) \times F_ACO_2$, so

$$\dot{V}_{CO_2} = \dot{V} \times \frac{PA_{CO_2}}{P_B - P_{H_2O}}$$

$P_{ACO_2} = [(P_B - P_{H_2O})/\dot{V}_A] \times \dot{V}_{CO_2}$; so in a steady state where $\dot{V}_{CO_2}$ production is constant, $P_B - P_{H_2O}$ is also a constant. Therefore $P_{ACO_2} = P_{aCO_2}$ a $1/\dot{V}_A$. This is **alveolar ventila-tion equation** which relates ventilation (alveolar) to partial pressure of $CO_2$ in arterial blood. ***If metabolic activity within the body remains unaltered, hypoventilation will increase $P_aCO_2$ and hyperventilation will decrease it.***

### Alveolar gas equation for O2 and CO2

Oxygen consumed per unit time

$$\dot{V}_{O_2} = \frac{\text{alveolar inspired volume}}{\text{time}} \times \text{fraction of } O_2 \text{ in inspired air}$$

$$\frac{\text{alveolar expired volume}}{\text{time}} \times \text{fraction of } O_2 \text{ in inspired gas}$$

$$= \dot{V}_{A(i)} \times f_iO_2 - \dot{V}_{A(e)} \times F_AO_2,$$

now assuming $\dot{V}_{A(i)} = \dot{V}_{A(e)} = \dot{V}_A$ the equation becomes $\dot{V}_{O_2} = \dot{V}_A (F_iO_2 - F_AO_2)$, so $F_AO_2 = F_iO_2 - (\dot{V}_{O_2}/\dot{V}_A)$. Now $P_AO_2 = (P_B - P_{H_2O}) F_AO_2 = (P_B - P_{H_2O}) [F_iO_2 - (\dot{V}_{O_2}/\dot{V}_A)] = P_iO_2 - (\dot{V}_{O_2}/\dot{V}_A) \times (P_B - P_{H_2O})$. Now $\dot{V}_{O_2}$ is expressed at STPD and $\dot{V}_A$ at BTPS standards, so for final calculation $\dot{V}_{O_2}$ STPD is to be converted to BTPS as

$$\frac{\dot{V}_{O_2}(STPD) \times 760}{273} \times \frac{\dot{V}_{O_2}(BTPS) \times (P_B - P_{H_2O})}{273 + 37}$$

So $\dot{V}_{O_2}$ (BTPS) = $\dot{V}_{O_2}$ (STPD, i.e., measured) × (310/273) × $[760/(P_B - P_{H2O})]$ = $\dot{V}_{O_2}$ (STPD, i.e., measured) × $[863/(P_B - P_{H_2O})]$

Finally,

$$P_AO_2 = P_iO_2 - \frac{\dot{V}_{O_2}(STPD/\text{measured}) \times 760}{\dot{V}_A} \times \frac{863}{(P_B - P_{H_2O})} \times (P_B - P_{H_2O})$$

$$P_iO_2 - \frac{\dot{V}_{O_2}(STPD/\text{measured}) \times 760}{\dot{V}_A} \times 863 \quad \text{(alveolar gas equation for } O_2)$$

This equation indicates that with increased ventilation (alveolar) the $P_AO_2$, which is equal to $P_aO_2$ will approach $P_iO_2$. Similar approach will give $P_ACO_2 = P_iCO_2 + (\dot{V}_{CO_2}/\dot{V}_A) \times 863$ ignoring $P_iCO_2$, $P_ACO_2 = \dot{V}_{CO_2} \times (863/V_A)$, it is alveolar gas equation for $CO_2$, a precise form of alveolar ventilation equation as $P_ACO_2 \propto (1/\dot{V}_A)$, when metabolic status remains stable.

Simplified forms of alveolar gas equation for $CO_2$ is

$$P_ACO_2 = \frac{\dot{V}_{CO_2}}{\dot{V}_A} \times (P_B - P_{H_2O})$$

and that of oxygen is

$$P_AO_2 = P_iO_2 - \frac{\dot{V}_{CO_2}}{\dot{V}_A} \times (P_B - P_{H_2O})$$

In both cases we ignore correction for temperature, pressure standards. Now R (respiratory exchange ratio) = $\frac{\dot{V}_{CO_2}}{\dot{V}_{O_2}}$, so

$$P_AO_2 = P_iO_2 - \frac{\dot{V}_{CO_2}}{R} \times (P_B - P_{H_2O}) \times \frac{1}{\dot{V}_A}$$

$$= P_iO_2 - \frac{\dot{V}_A CO_2}{R}$$

For more accuracy, nitrogen correction to consider the differences in volumes of inspired and expired gases is put into the equation, as $P_AO_2 = P_iO_2 - (P_ACO_2/R) + F$, where F is the $N_2$ correction factor. During breathing air it is only 1-3 mm Hg. Now, in steady metabolic state, $P_ACO_2 \propto (1/\dot{V}_A)$. Both these equations help to understand the role of ventilation in rarefied atmosphere in keeping the tissue oxygenation at useful level.

### Effect of $\frac{\dot{V}_A}{\dot{Q}}$ variance in health and disease

It is known that both ventilation and blood flow increases from nondependent to dependent regions of lungs. But the rate of change is more in perfusion than in ventilation per unit lung tissue, making $\frac{\dot{V}_A}{\dot{Q}}$ higher (above 3) at apex than the basal part of erect lungs. For this reason, the blood leaving the more ventilated part is rich in $O_2$ but poor in $CO_2$. On the contrary, blood draining the less ventilated part is relatively deficient in $O_2$ but rich in $CO_2$. But the volume of blood leaving the dependent zones is much more in quantity than that from non-dependent area. So the ultimate values of arterial blood gas tensions fall somewhat below that of average alveolar values. Thus there takes place an alveolar-arterial $PO_2$ difference that is compounded by venous blood bypassing the gas exchange areas of lungs (physiological shunt). Average alveolar $PO_2$ and $PCO_2$ differs from that of average perfusion through lungs because the unevenness is less in case of ventilation, disparity in values of gas tensions in different zones is less.

By the same reasoning the $PCO_2$ of blood leaving the lungs is definitely higher than that of average alveolar values. But as the slope of the curve ($O_2$-$CO_2$ diagram) Fig. 6.18(b) I-III is lower than I-II, the net deviation from normal value (I) to measured value is not much, even if larger share of blood traverses through the less ventilated alveoli.

***The regulatory system of respiration is much more sensitive to $PCO_2$ rise than fall in $PO_2$.*** When the $PCO_2$ tends to rise due to ventilation-perfusion imbalance, it stimulates respiration and $CO_2$ blown off from alveoli can restore the deviated level to normal. $CO_2$ diffuses more readily than $O_2$. So unless there is hypoventilation, the arterial $PCO_2$ value will not rise much. ***Hypoventilation also reduces*** $PO_2$, but if supplementary $O_2$ is given the hypoxia is eliminated because $P_AO_2$ can be elevated to ($P_B - P_{H_2O} - PCO_2$), eg, (760 − 47 − 40) mm Hg. But there remains no alternative to decrease $P_ACO_2$ other than to stimulate ventilation by any means (drugs or artificial respiration).

The ***average alveolar $PO_2$ is 100 mm Hg, that of inspired air is 150 mm Hg and of mixed venous blood is 40 mm Hg.*** So the range 40-100-150 mm Hg is considered. But from the $O_2$-Hb dissociation curve, it is apparent that content of $O_2$ does not increase much with increase of $PO_2$ above 40 mm Hg. So when blood of high $O_2$ content from non-dependent regions mixes with more blood draining dependent regions having much lower $PO_2$, the mixture has minimal change in $O_2$ content. But considering the upper flat part of $O_2$ dissociation curve, the change in $PO_2$ tension is substantial in the blood from better aerated alveoli. So the blood having

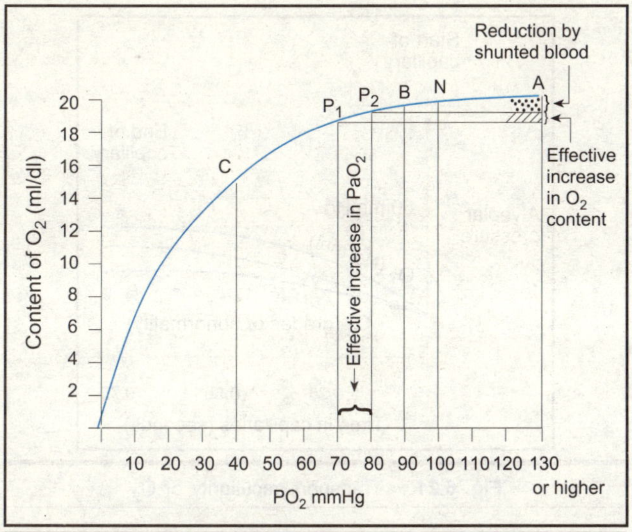


**Fig. 6.19 :** Ventilation-perfusion inequality curve

higher $PO_2$ cannot compensate for the lower $PO_2$ containing blood of greater quantity. This makes alveolar-arterial $PO_2$ difference considerable. In lung diseases when there is hypoventilation — or more prominent ventilation-perfusion mismatch — the difference increases.

## Measurement of ventilation-perfusion inequality

**Ventilation-perfusion inequality can be measured** (a) *with the help of radioactive isotopes*, eg, xenon-133, gas mixture for ventilation, saline solution for perfusion; (b) *pattern of excretion of foreign gases* introduced intravenously which diffuses into alveoli from blood and eliminated by ventilation; (c) *alveolar-arterial $PO_2$ difference.*

Whenever there occurs abnormal anatomical shunt through which venous blood gets mixed with oxygeneted blood passing across the lungs, there occurs definite fall in $P_aO_2$. This fall in $O_2$ tension can be distinguished from $PO_2$ fall in ventilation- perfusion mismatch by inhaling 100% oxygen.

When 100% $O_2$ is breathed, the alveolar and arterial $PO_2$ are corrected in mismatched states, but not in abnormal anatomic shunts as added $O_2$ (mostly due to dissolved state as the hemoglobin is almost cent per cent saturated at normal alveolar $PO_2$ near 100 mm of Hg) cannot raise the $P_aO_2$ much due to the shape of the $O_2$-Hb dissociation curve. In the Fig. 6.19 if the $P_1$ is the original $P_aO_2$ in a case of abnormal anatomic shunt, then, even if 100% of $O_2$ is inhaled, the rise of $P_aO_2$ is to point $P_2$. This is because the $O_2$ content of blood coming from lungs cannot increase much due to flat terminal part of the curve and the shunted blood will decrease the $O_2$ content so that the arterial blood will attain a somewhat elevated $O_2$ content corresponding to $P_aO_2$ at $P_2$.

From this curve (Fig. 6.21) it is evident that if some amount of blood from high $\frac{\dot{V}_A}{\dot{Q}}$ area in upper zone ($PO_2$ 130 mm Hg) mixes with blood draining from dependent zone ($PO_2$ 80-90 mm Hg) there is little increase in content of $O_2$ and small rise in $PO_2$ of the latter).

## Pulmonary gas exchange

It is already known that during ***rest in an adult 200-250 ml of CO2 is eliminated per minute in exchange of 250-300 ml O2 taken in.*** The gaseous exchange occurs through the physical process of diffusion. The partial pressures of O2 and CO2 in the alveoli are 100 mm Hg and 40 mm Hg at rest, and that of pulmonary capillaries are 40 mm Hg and 46 mm of Hg, respectively. To facilitate the process of diffusion the surface area of pulmonary membrane (alveolar-capillary barrier) is enormous — 50-100 square meters.

**Fick's law of diffusion states** that ***the volume of gas transported by the process of diffusion through a barrier is influenced by factors described by the equation $V_{gas}$ = area/ thickness × (pressure difference) × diffusion constant.*** Now, the area and thickness of the pulmonary membrane cannot be known definitely in an individual and the diffusion constant of a gas depends upon physical properties like solubility and molecular weight.

**Diffusion constant,** $D \propto \frac{\text{Solubility(S)}}{\sqrt{\text{Mol. weight}}}$

So when in case of a particular gas volume transported across the pulmonary membrane is calculated taking all the factors together except pressure difference, it reduces to $V_{gas}$ = diffusion capacity × pressure difference. This diffusion capacity is expressed by the symbol $D_L$ :

$$D_{LO_2} = \frac{\text{area}}{\text{thickness}} \times D_{O_2} \text{ and } D_{LCO_2} = \frac{\text{area}}{\text{thickness}} \times D_{CO_2}.$$

Now,

$$\frac{D_{CO_2}}{D_{LO_2}} = \frac{D_{CO_2}}{D_{O_2}} = \frac{\text{solubility of } \frac{CO_2}{\sqrt{MW}} \text{ of } CO_2}{\text{solubility of } \frac{O_2}{\sqrt{MW}} \text{ of } O_2}$$

at 37°C (solubility of CO2/solubility of O2) = 24 ·

$$\frac{D_LCO_2}{D_LO_2} = 24 \times \sqrt{\frac{32}{44}} = 20 \text{ (approx.)}$$

Thus, for a particular pressure difference, $CO_2$ is twenty (20) times more diffusible than $O_2$. For this reason only 6 mm Hg of pressure difference of $O_2$ across alveolo-capillary barrier eliminates volume of $CO_2$ almost equal to the volume of $O_2$ intake (pressure difference in case of $O_2$ is 60 mm Hg).

## Diffusion and perfusion limitations

The amount of any gas diffusing across the pulmonary membrane in a unit time depends not only on the factors underlying diffusion but also on the volume of blood bathing the respiratory membrane. If the surface area, thickness and ventilation remain constant, the volume of some gases traversing the bed will be perfusion limited, i.e., further increase in the uptake of the gas will require only increase in blood flow, because gases in blood will quickly equilibrate

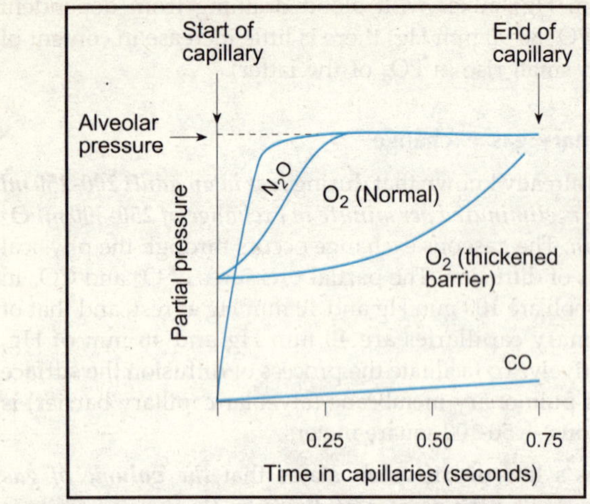


Fig. 6.20 : Alveolar uptake of gases in relation to time

with the alveolar gas pressure. On the other hand some gases require changes in the diffusing properties to increase its rate of transport (Fig. 6.20) at a particular rate of blood flow.

In Fig. 6.20, it is apparent that $N_2O$ or $O_2$ (normal) attains the partial pressure of their alveolar level in one-fourth to one-third of their travel time through the capillary. During the rest of the path there cannot be any further addition of the gases. To increase their transport, one has to increase blood supply per unit time. Thus the transport of these gases is not diffusion limited and common abnormalities relating to diffusion cannot change their transport much. Their uptake is perfusion-limited.

But in case of CO it is seen that it does not attain the alveolar partial pressure value at the end of the capillary. So by increasing perfusion CO transport cannot be increased much. It can however be increased if the time for transport is prolonged (theoretically) or by increasing the factors ***facilitating diffusion***. The transport of CO is thus diffusion-limited. The behaviour of CO is due to the fact that CO combines over 200 times more rapidly with hemoglobin than $O_2$. So when the RBCs at the beginning of a capillary are exposed to CO, they quickly mop up the gas in the form of carbonmonoxyhemoglobin so that during their short transit time (0.75 sec) it is not possible for capillary blood to attain the alveolar level.

If the thickness of the barrier reduces or the pressure gradient of CO increases, more CO can be absorbed. Normal transport of $O_2$ is perfusion-limited, but in abnormal conditions the transport may be diffusion-limited, specially so during exercise, because during exercise the transit time may reduce to one-third of normal (from 0.75 to 0.255). With a rapid transit time in healthy lungs, transport is not hampered (Fig. 6.22), but when there is some abnormality, the transport becomes more retarded and becomes more diffusion limited.

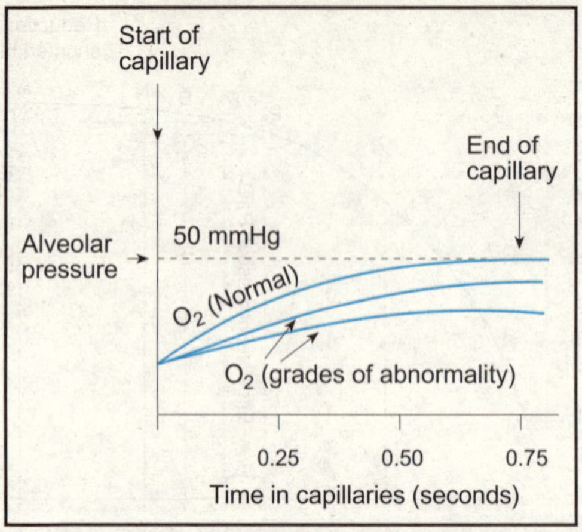


Fig. 6.21 : Transport peculiarity of $O_2$

***Fig. 6.23 explains another transport peculiarity of $O_2$.*** When the alveolar $O_2$ pressure is low (e.g. due to high altitude, the rate of rise of $O_2$ pressure through the capillary is much slower, resembling CO to some extent because the $O_2$-Hb dissociation curve shows that the rate of association at lower partial pressure is more rapid making the curve steep at this part. Therefore blood takes more time to reach the alveolar $PO_2$. For this reason, during exercise or if there is minimal edema, $O_2$ transport gets more disturbed and becomes more diffusion-limited (as in normal in case of CO). The diffusion of CO and $O_2$ is influenced by the rates of their combination with hemoglobin. If the microanatomy of the air- blood barrier is considered, resistance to diffusion can be divided into two stages from the lumen of alveoli to plasma, crossing the alveolar epithelium, interstitium, capillary endothelium, and then from plasma across RBC membrane to its combining site in hemoglobin in its cytosol (Fig. 6.22).

From Fig. 6.22 it can be seen that resistance from alveolus to plasma may be taken as from membrane. But the resistance from plasma to RBC lies exclusively in the rate of combination of oxygen with hemoglobin. If the union is rapid, $O_2$ is used up within RBC quickly its

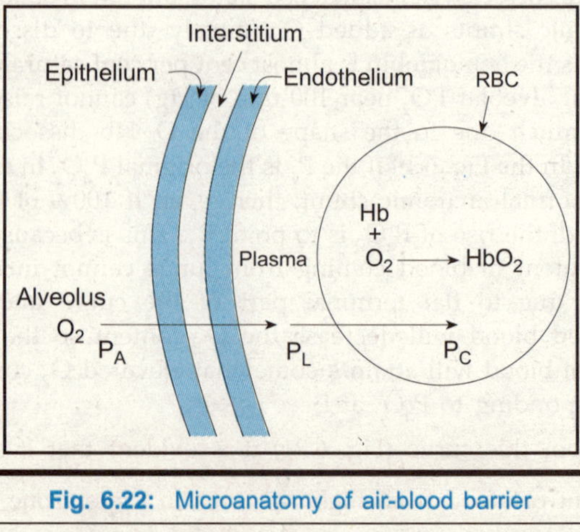


Fig. 6.22: Microanatomy of air-blood barrier

accumulation within RBC and preventing rise in $PO_2$. Thus, $O_2$ transport from plasma to cytosol of RBC will continue uninterrupted. The opposite happens when the rate of combination slows down.

### Measurement of diffusing capacity

***For any gas that diffuses across the pulmonary membrane, the relationship may be expressed as***

$$\dot{V}_{gas} = D_{L\,(gas)} \times (P_A - P_{cap})$$

where $P_A$ is the alveolar partial pressure and $P_{cap}$ partial pressure of the gas dissolved in plasma of pulmonary capillary blood. In case of oxygen, $V_{gas}$ can be measured by spirometry and $P_AO_2$ can be measured by sampling of alveolar air. But average capillary $PO_2$ is difficult to measure, as the exact average time required for equilibration with alveolar gas, and also the blood flow, as the transfer is perfusion limited. But if CO is inhaled in low concentration, the plasma $P_{CO}$ can be taken as zero because CO combines with hemoglobin very quickly leaving little CO in plasma to exert any appreciable pressure. But in heavy smokers the assumption may be erroneous because they contain some CO in their blood. So in case of CO, $D_{L\,CO} = [\dot{V}_{CO}\ (ml/min)]/[P_{A\,CO}\ (mm\ Hg)]$. ***$V_{CO}$ and $P_{A\,CO}$ can be measured by*** (i) **single breath method** and (ii) **steady state method.**

- **In single breath method,** the individual inhales a dilute mixture of CO once. After a 10 sec breath-hold period, $\dot{V}_{CO}$ is measured from inspired and expired air CO concentrations, average $P_{A\,CO}$ from inspired and alveolar $P_{CO}$ values and time.
- **In steady state method,** low concentration CO mixture is inhaled for some time (one-half min or so) for development of a steady state, i.e., constant rate of absorption of CO for a while, during which the $V_{CO}$ at steady state and $P_{A\,CO}$ from alveolar (end-expirate) samples are made out.

$D_{L\,CO}$ at rest is about 25 ml/mm Hg/min. The value for oxygen is somewhat higher , about 30 ml/mm Hg/min. During exercise, the values of $D_{L\,CO}$ and $D_{L\,O2}$ increase 2-3 fold due to increased blood flow and higher pressure gradient in case of $O_2$ because $PO_2$ of mixed venous blood reduces considerably. Their values fall considerably when there is accumulation of fluid or there is thickening of tissues of blood-gas barrier as in interstitial fibrosis (e.g. due to asbestosis etc.) or when there is loss of area and vascularity due to resection of part or all of a lung. A similar situation happens in emphysema also.

### Shunts

In the course of discussion of alveolar-arterial $PO_2$ difference it was seen that part of this difference is due to regional differences in ventilation-perfusion ratios and the rest in health is almost exclusively due to shunting of venous blood to arterial one, bypassing the gas exchange areas of the lungs. **This is called R-L (right to left) shunt.** Bronchial veins drain partially into pulmonary veins and thebesian veins drain left ventricular myocardium to left ventricular cavity. These are physiological shunts. For reasons that have been discussed, this admixture will raise $P_aCO_2$ to insignificant level, but will cause measurable (few mm Hg) fall in arterial $PO_2$ in comparison to alveolar $PO_2$. ***Normally, the magnitude of the shunt is only 1-2% of cardiac output.***

In some pathological conditions, large amount of blood can be shunted. Examples are ***cyanotic congenital heart diseases with ventricular septal defect along with pulmonary hypertension.*** In pulmonary collapse following bronchial obstruction, or in cases of consolidation, ventilation may fall in affected areas but the area may get perfused (though pulmonary vasoconstriction occurs due to hypoxia) causing a *de facto* shunt effect.

The magnitude of bypass in these cases may also be found out with the help of shunt equation. In presence of true anatomical shunt, the content of oxygen in artery cannot be increased substantially by inhaling 100% oxygen because of the flatness of terminal part of the oxygen-dissociation curve. The amount of dissolved $O_2$ (small volume) is increased only, both in non-shunted and shunted blood causing little increase in $PaO_2$. But $O_2$ content and $PaO_2$ considerably increase following 100% $O_2$ in most cases of mismatched ventilation and perfusion. In the shunt equation the blood bypassing gas exchange area is taken as having $O_2$ conc. equal to mixed venous blood. It is an over-simplication, so the equation has inherent limitations.

## ➤ 6.10 Lung volumes and assessment of ventilatory function of the lungs

Measuring the air contained within the lungs and the rate of flow of air out of the lungs provides valuable information regarding ventilatory function of the lungs. The volume of gas contained within the lungs after a maximal inspiration is known as the total lung capacity (TLC) 5,500—6,000 ml. The amount of air that remains within the lungs after a maximal expiration is called the residual volume (RV). The volume of air exhaled when a subject exhales from TLC to RV (i.e., a maximal expiration after a maximal inspiration) is referred to asthe vital capacity (VC), 4,500 ml in males, 3,500 in females when the process of exhalation is slow it is called slow vital capacity (SVC) but when the process is rapid and forceful it is called Forced vital capacity (FVC). Various subdivisions of VC can be calculated from the volume-time recording obtained from a spirometer (an instrument designed to measure lung volumes with/without flow rates). A spirometer cannot measure RV and TLC (so also FRC, see below) because it cannot estimate the volume of air that remains within the lungs. Functional residual capacity (FRC) 2,500 ml refers to the volume of air contained within the lungs after a quiet expiration. At FRC, the

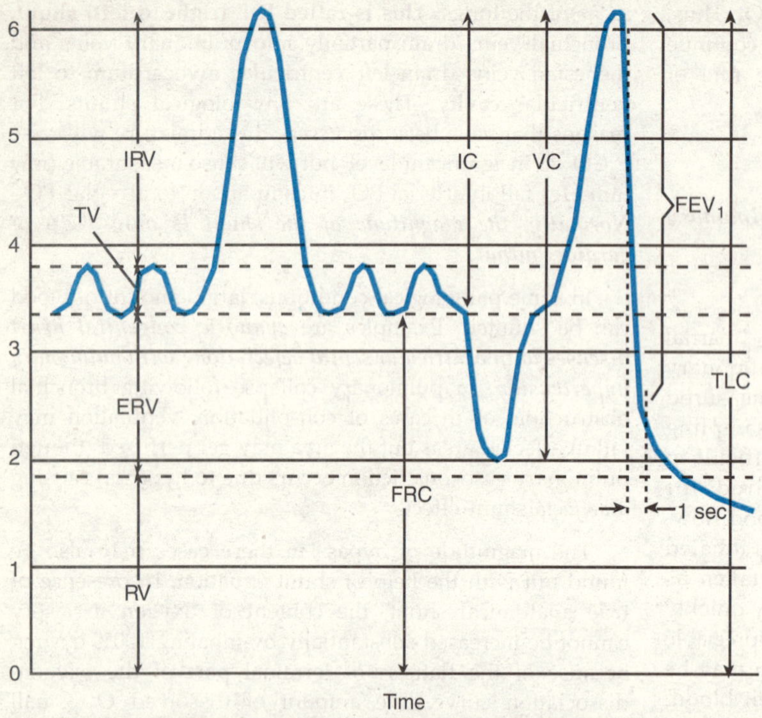


**Fig. 6.23 : Different lung volumes and capacities. See text for abbreviations med.**

tendency of the lungs to collapse towards their hila and the tendency of the chest wall to expand outwardly are exactly balanced. At TLC, the force exerted by the inspiratory muscles to expand the lungs is balanced by the elastic recoil of the lungs. Therefore, TLC is largely determined by the strength of the inspiratory muscles and the stiffness of the lungs.

The various subdivisions of vital capacity (VC) are as follows :

**Inspiratory capacity (IC)** : 3500 ml. the volume of air that can be inhaled from the resting end-expiratory level.

**Inspiratory reserve volume (IRV) :** 3000 ml. The volume of air that can be inhaled from the resting end-inspiratory level.

**Expiratory reserve volume (ERV) :** 1000 ml The volume of air that can be exhaled from the resting end-expiratory level.

**Tidal volume (VT) :** 500 ml. in males; 340 ml in females. The volume of air inhaledor exhaled during normal quiet breathing (Fig. 6.25).

VC and its subdivisions are measuredduring forced expiration from TLC and are interpreted by comparison of the values obtained with those predicted for the individual based on age, sex, height, and ethnicity of the subject. The measured values are expressed as percent of predicted for that individual. It is important to note that correction of the measured values for the atmospheric temperature and pressure are necessary for comparison. In general—considering the variability among normal individuals—values between 80% and 120% of the predicted may be considered as normal. Generally speaking, values are less for females and for those who smoke.

**Timed vital capacity** is an important indicator of ventilatory function. The most common measurement done in clinical practice is FEV1 (forced expiratory volume in 1st second) which is the volume of air exhaled during the first second of forced expiration from TLC (i.e., the FVC maneuver). FEV1 expressed as % of FVC is a better parameter, and is known as FEV1% $\left(\text{i.e. } \frac{FEV_1}{FVC} \times 100\right)$. Normally, FEV1% should be above 80%.

**Expiratory flow** rates measured at mouth level are also useful parameters that indicate ventilatory functional status of the lungs. **Peak expiratory flow rate** (PEFR) is the maximum expiratory flow achieved during the FVC manoeuvre. Forced expiratory flows (FEF) can be measured for various intervals ofthe vital capacity. FEF25-75% (also known as maximal midexpiratory flow rate or MMFR) is the average flow rate during the middle 50% (i.e., from 25% to 75%) of the VC. Its significance islike that of PEFR—both gets reduced in obstructive airway diseases like bronchial asthma.

For **measuring RV, FRC and TLC** either of the following methods may be employed —

- Helium dilution technique (Fig. 6.24).
- Body plethysmography.

**Helium dilution technique :** To determine the FRC, a subject is asked to breathe filled with a known volume of air ($V_1$) containing a **known concentration** ($C_1$) of the **inert gas helium**. As the helium-ocntaining gas is breathed in and out the helium is diluted by the volume of air left in the lungs ($V_2$). A subsequent measurement of the helium concentration ($C_2$) permits this additional volume ($V_2$) to be calculated from the following formula :

$$\textbf{FRC} = \left(\frac{\text{Initial helium concentration}(C_2)}{\text{Final helium concentration }(C_2)} - 1\right)$$

$$\times \text{ volume of spirometer.}$$

The measure the **RV** a similar procedure is used, **but** the subject is asked to **perform a maximal expiration** before breathing from the spirometer containing the helium.

The **difference** in volume between the FEC and RV is the expiratory reserve volume (ERV) while the total lung capacity (TLC) is attained after a **full inspiration**. The volume taken in from the FRC to reach TLC is called the **inspiratory capacity** (IC). The **inspiratory reserve volume** (IRV) is the maximum volume of air that can be inspired

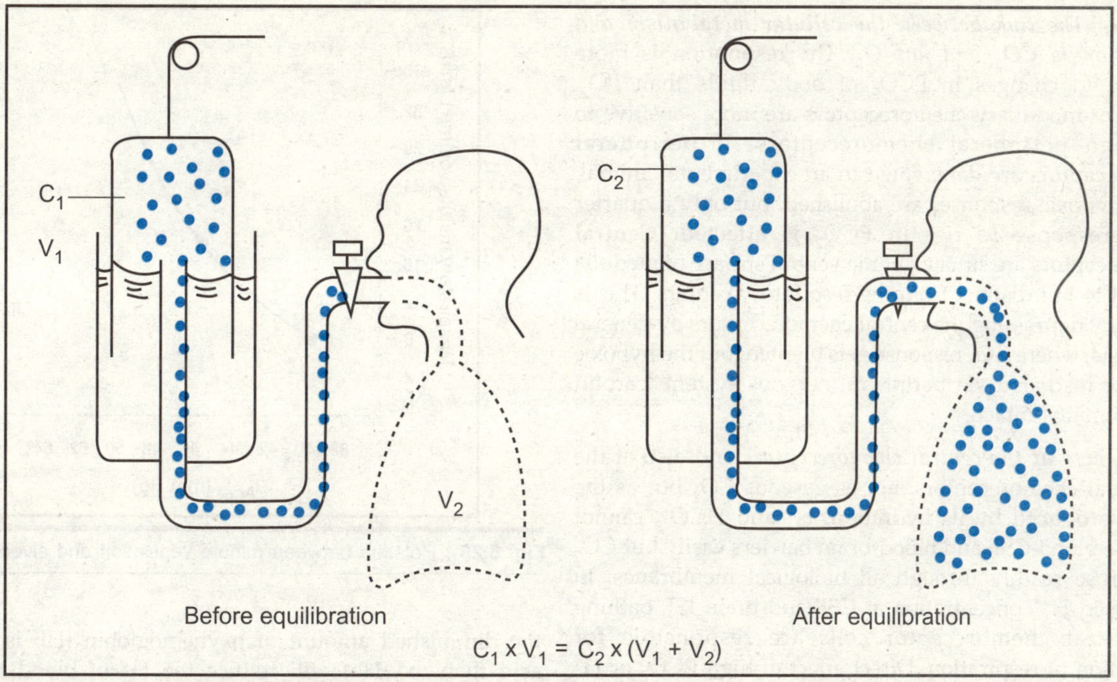


Fig. 6.24

after a normal breath. These quantities are related by the following equations :

FRC = ERV + RV

TLC = FRC + IC

IC = $V_T$ + IRV

where $V_T$ **is the tidal volume**. The **vital capacity** (VC) is the volume of air that can be expired from the total lung volume:

VC = IC + ERV

If either the **FRC** or the **RV** is known, all the other subdivisions of the lung volume (including the total lung volume) can be determined with the aid of a **spirometer**.

Mean values of lung volumes for various ethnic groups are available but they are of little use in clinical practice. In clinical practice, lung function parameters are almost always interpreted by comparing with predicted values.

## Patterns of abnormal ventilatory function

Two major patterns of abnormal ventilatory function are—

- **Obstructive pattern** e.g. bronchial asthma; chronic obstructive pulmonary disease(COPD)
  - chronic bronchitis
  - emphyema
- **restrictive pattern** e.g. sarcoidosis
  - idiopathic pulmonary fibrosis pneumoconiosis
  - neuromuscular diseases causing respiratory muscle weakness (diaphragmatic paralysis, myasthenia gravis etc.)
  - chest wall deformity (obesity, kyphoscoliosis, ankylosing spondylitis)

The distinction between the two major patterns are shown in the table below :

| | *TLC/RV/FRC* | *VC* | *FEV1%* |
|---|---|---|---|
| Obstructive | Normal or ↑ | ↓ | ↓* |
| Restrictive | ↓ | ↓ | Normal or↑ |

* In early phase of obstructive diseases, FEV1% may be normal, and the only abnormality may be a decreased PEFR or MMFR (FEF25-75%).

## 6.11 Ventilatory Response to Alteration in $PCO_2$, $PO_2$ and pH

**External respiration** is precisely controlled so that $O_2$ requirement for respiration of individual cells (internal respiration) is adequate met and $CO_2$ evolved in the process is eliminated, making $PO_2$, $PCO_2$ and pH of body fluids nearly constant.

To monitor and correct the chemicals in blood ($PO_2$, $PCO_2$ and pH) there are chemoreceptors, central and peripheral, which sense and send appropriate signals to respiratory centres in the brain stem which ultimately change the ventilation accordingly.

$CO_2$ : ***The link between the cellular metabolism and respiration is $CO_2$ and not $O_2$.*** The respiration is more sensitive to changes in $PCO_2$ of body fluids than $PO_2$. Central or medullary chemoreceptors are more sensitive to $CO_2$ than peripheral chemoreceptors. If **peripheral chemoreceptors** are denervated in an experimental animal, all the hypoxic responses are abolished, but only a quarter of the response to rise in $PCO_2$ is affected. **Central chemoreceptors** are situated at the ventral surface of medulla adjacent to but distinct from the respiratory centers. This is proved by depressing the central chemoreceptors by general anesthesia, where $CO_2$ response gets blunted, but the hypoxic response mediated via peripheral nervous system (carotid body) remains intact.

***$CO_2$ acts at the central chemoreceptors*** and also at the peripheral chemoreceptors, not as gaseous $CO_2$ but as the $H^+$ ion produced by its hydration. $H^+$ and $HCO_3^-$ cannot cross the blood-CSF and blood-brain barriers easily but $CO_2$ can diffuse readily through all biological membranes. In fact, raised $H^+$ concentration at CSF and brain ISF bathing the central chemoreceptor cells are responsible for stimulation of respiration. Direct effect of high $PCO_2$ or $H^+$ on respiratory centres is inhibition.

During rest, the $P_ACO_2$ is 40 mm of Hg. Whenever there is a rise in $P_ACO_2$, eg. when one rebreathes from a bag, there occurs stimulation of respiration, i.e., rise in rate and depth of breathing. The alveolar ventilation is adjusted so that $P_ACO_2$ returns to normal and the hyperventilating stimulus is over. Similarly, if an individual hyperventilates voluntarily for some time and then stops breathing, his breathing remains suspended for some time due to hypocapnia and then oscillates between apnea and respiration due to interaction between hypoxia and hypocapnia (periodic breathing) ultimately to attain the normal $P_ACO_2$ and tidal respiration.

The same response is also produced if $CO_2$ is produced at a higher rate within the body due to metabolism eg, exercise, thyrotoxicosis, fever etc. (Fig. 6.25).

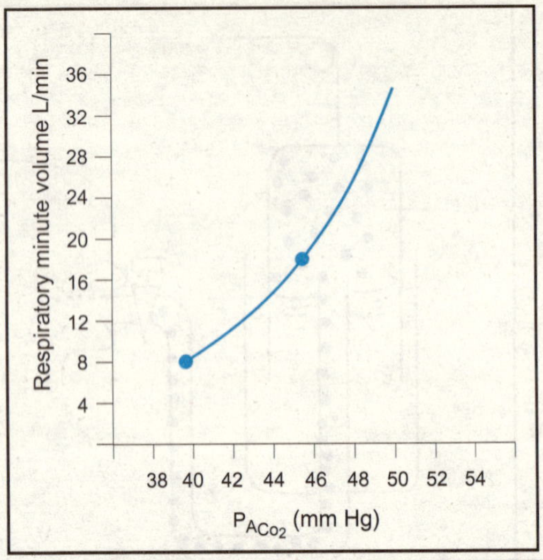


**Fig. 6.25 : Relation between minute ventilation and alveolar $P_{CO2}$**

**Hypercapnia** is accumulation of $CO_2$ within the body. The raised level, if sustained, causes depression of respiration, further hypercapnia, depression of CNS, coma and death.

## Ventilatory response to hypoxia

The respiratory control system is ***much less responsive to hypoxia*** than hypercapnia. From Fig. 6.25 it is apparent that only a few mm increase in $P_ACO_2$ doubles the minute ventilation. But in case of $O_2$ deficit, the $Pa_{O2}$ has to fall below 60 mm Hg (normal 100 mm Hg) to have any appreciable increase in ventilation. It is not that the peripheral chemoreceptor, mostly carotid body, do not send impulses when its perfusing blood has a $PO_2$ below 100 mm of Hg. But the signals are not sufficient to drive the ventilation as any attendant hyperventilation will blow off $CO_2$ to produce hypocapnia which has strong inhibitory effect. Moreover, the diminished amount of oxyhemoglobin (Hb is weaker acid than oxy-Hb) will reduce the $H^+$ of blood to some extent which will inhibit respiration — mainly through peripheral chemorece-ptors. However, when $P_AO_2$ falls below 60 mm of Hg, these inhibitory restraints are overcome and ventilation increases considerably.

***The peripheral chemoreceptors are specially made for detecting the level of partial pressure of $O_2$ of arterial blood and not its total $O_2$ content.*** This is made possible by its enormous blood supply per unit mass, which makes arterio-venous difference of $PO_2$ negligible and, thus, the organs sense the arterial $PO_2$ level. For this reason, during anemia, when the total content of $O_2$ per unit blood volume reduces much, the respiration is not stimulated as the enormous plasma volume bathing the carotid and aortic bodies bear oxygen in dissolved state more than the small requirement of $O_2$ by the body at rest. For the same reason, in polycythemia, where the amount of $O_2$ per unit volume increases, no depression of respiration occurs.

## Interrelation between hypoxic and hypercapnic stimuli

$CO_2$ is the primary stimulus for respiration, not lack of $O_2$. At normal $P_ACO_2$ there takes place differing response to ventilation at variable $P_AO_2$ values, indicating that normal resting $P_ACO_2$ has been driving respiration in presence of variable $P_AO_2$ values. But hypoxic response alone is not sufficient and it requires a minimal accompanying level of $P_ACO_2$ for driving respiration. It is precisely exemplified in cases of shallow water blackout. In the case of a breath-held dive, if an individual hyperventilates before diving, during or immediately after diving, he may become unconscious. The reason is that hyperventilation washes out $CO_2$ to reduce its level sufficiently, so the breaking point is delayed, but $O_2$ consumption during that period is so much that hypoxia is sufficient to depress CNS to the state of unconsciousness. This is because hypoxic stimulus alone is

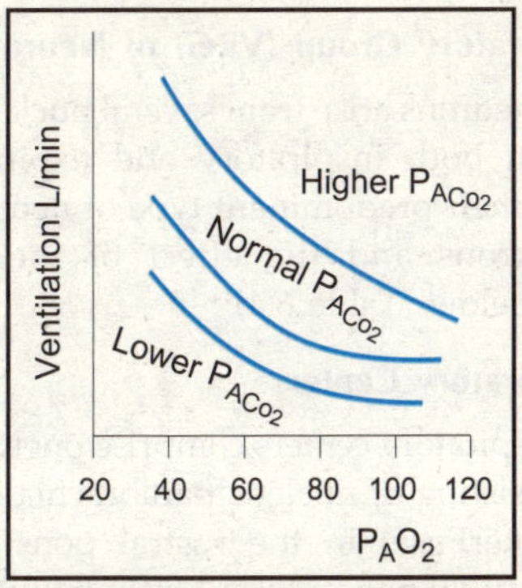


**Fig. 6.26 :** Effect of $P_ACO_2$ level on ventilatory drive due to $O_2$ lack

not adequate till the $PCO_2$ level is sufficient to have a permissive effect. Hypoxia alone is a depressant.

If the inhaled gas mixture is adjusted in such a way that $P_ACO_2$ remains constant but $P_AO_2$ is chan-ged, it is seen that the control system becomes more sensitive to hypoxia in presence of hypercapnia and much less sensitive in presence of associated hypocapnia. In presence of raised $P_ACO_2$, even normal level of $P_AO_2$ can have stimulatory effect (Fig. 6.26).

Lesser sensitivity of control mechanisms to low $PO_2$ is not unexpected. The shape of the oxyhemoglobin dissociation curve entails that hemoglobin is more than 80% saturated even at 60 mm Hg $PO_2$. So the content of oxygen carried by hypoxic blood is sufficient to meet tissue needs. But in case of $CO_2$ even a little accumulation is not tolerated by the system. It is judicious, because $CO_2$ will give rise to $H^+$ on hydration, and small deviation of pH of body fluids may prove very harmful to the system.

### Effect of H+ ion or pH on respiration

$H^+$ ions cannot enter the brain or CSF, but $CO_2$ can diffuse to brain and CSF from blood and, on hydration, liberate $H^+$ ion in the vicinity of central chemoreceptors. Depending upon the buffering power of CSF or brain ISF, $H^+$ will stimulate respiration. The effect of $CO_2$ and $H^+$ is additive. The reason behind the additive effect is that the ultimate stimulating agent is $H^+$ ion which is derived from dissociation of any acid — whether carbonic or non-carbonic. So complex interaction, as seen in case of combinaton of **hypoxia and hypercapnia**— is not possible. At a particular level of ventilation, 1 mmol increase of $H^+$ is associated with 1 mm Hg lowering of $P_{ACO_2}$ value Substantial degree of ventilatory response is abolished if rise in $CO_2$ occurs in the absence of fall in pH of plasma. But $CO_2$ diffuses freely to CSF and CNS where it gets hydrated to give rise to $H^+$ to act locally even if its ($H^+$) rise in extra-neural tissue is prevented by sodibicarb.

In cases of **metabolic or non-respiratory acidosis** there is stimulation of respiration via peripheral chemoreceptors as brain ISF pH changes slowly. In diabetic ketoacidosis, pro-nounced hyperventilation (**'Kussmaul breathing'**) takes place. Similarly, in metabolic alkalosis like vomiting, aspiration of gastric HCl, there occurs depression of respiration to some extent. When acidosis develops due to accumulation of $CO_2$, eg, hypoventilation, it is called **'respiratory acidosis'**, and when body fluid pH rises due to excess removal of $CO_2$, as in high altitude, it is called **respiratory alkalosis.**

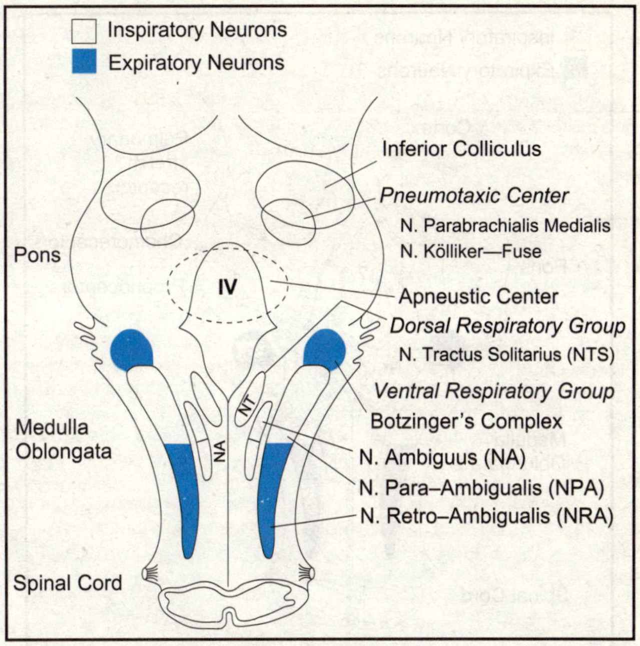


**Fig. 6.27 :** Dorsal view of the brainstein showing the major groups of respiratory related neurons. IV refers to the fourth ventricle.

## 6.12 Control of Ventilation

Proper match between ventilation and $O_2$ consumption (as well as $CO_2$ production) is crucial in maintaining normal blood pH and blood gas tensions. A rhythmic pattern of ventilation with control over its rate and depth serves this purpose. The process is basically involuntary (being controlled by respiratory centers) with some voluntary control.

### Medullary Respiratory Centers

A discrete respiratory center in the medulla has not yet been identified despite thorough search. However, groups of neurons have been identified in the medulla that are related with respiration. They can be divided into **dorsal** and **ventral respiratory groups** (**DRG** and **VRG**), which contain both inspiratory and expiratory neurons (Fig. 6.27).

### Dorsal Respiratory Group (DRG) of Neurons

**DRG** neurons are found in the **nucleus tractus solitarius** (NTS) on both sides and are primarily inspiratory. They

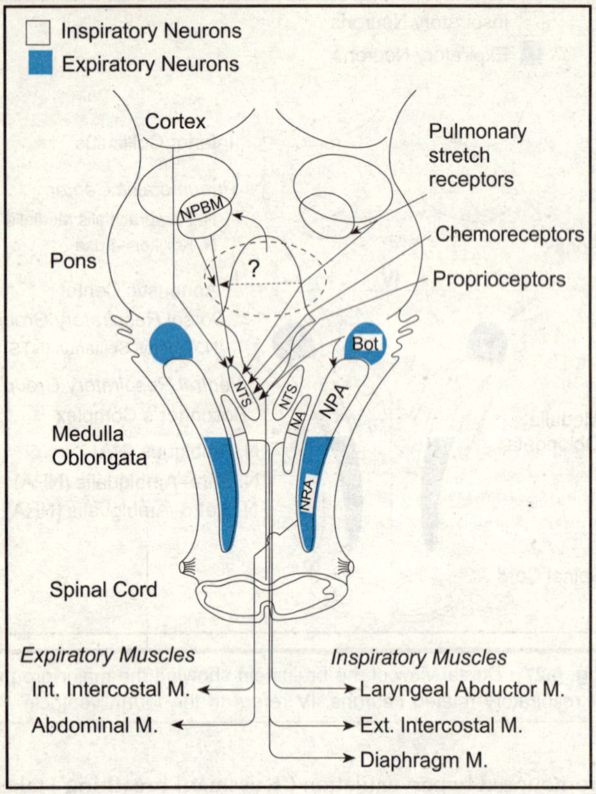


**Fig. 6.28 :** Dorsal view of the brainstein showing facilitory and inhibitoiry inputs to the nucleus tractus solitavius (NTS) and outflow pathways to inspiratory and expiratory muscle groups.

project to the phrenic and external intercostal motor neurons of the opposite side (Fig. 6.28). Rate and depth of inspiration is modulated by these – neurons. Inputs to the DRG neurons come from chemoreceptors (both central and peripheral), pulmonary stretch receptors, somatic pain receptors and mechanoreceptors and cortical and pontine centers. Some expiratory fibers which project to the VRG neurons have been identified in the NTS. On the contrary, very few of the inhibitory VRG neurons project to the NTS.

### Ventral Respiratory Group (VRG) of Neurons

The VRG neurons arise from several nuclei in the medulla which contain both inspiratory and expiratory neurons. These nuclei, their predominant type of neurons, projection of those neurons and the effect of their activity are summarized below (Table 6.4) :

### Pontine Respiratory Centers

Pontine respiratory centers comprise pneumotaxic centers (bilateral, consisting of nucleus parabrachialis medialis and nucleus KollikerFuse) in the rostral pons and apneustic center in the caudal pons. Output from pneumotaxic centers terminates inspiration by stimulating the off-switch neurons. Therefore, it is not surprising that ablation of these nuclei prolongs inspiration. If the vagus nerve which inhibits inspiration by sensing stretch in the pulmonary stretch receptors—is also sectioned (along with ablation of pneumotaxic centers), the result is sustained inspiration with periodic expiration.

### Generation of the Inspiratory Pattern

Inspiration starts and proceeds smoothly to stop abruply at the height of inspiration. The reason for this is smooth and sequential recruitment of diaphragmatic muscle units during inspiration. This in turn is brought about by a smooth increase in phrenic nerve activity that terminates abruptly at the height of inspiration. Phrenic nerve activity is very low during expiration. Complex mutual inhibition and facilitation among several types of respiratory neurons underlies the smoothly increasing (ramp like) discharge pattern of the phrenic motor neurons. The exact neural mechanism of generation of a rhythmic pattern of inspiration and expiration is not yet clear. However, a group of neurons has been identified in an area (**pre-Bottzinger complex**) between the nucleus ambiguus and the lateral reticular nucleus, which may act as pacemaker neurons for generating respiratory rhythm.

### Reflex Control of Ventilation

Ventilation can be modulated by sensory inputs from periphery (like pain, temperature and motion). Additionally, some pulmonary reflexes are also involved in modulating

**Table 6.4**

| Nucleus | Neuron type | Projects to | Effects |
|---|---|---|---|
| Nucleus ambiguus (NA) | Primarily inspiratory neurons | Muscles of larynx, pharynx, and tongue (Major output to abductors of larynx) | Dilatation of airways at the time of inspiration in order to minimize airway resistance. |
| Nucleus retro-ambiguus (NRA) –caudal portion | Expiratory neurons | Motor neurons for contralateral abdominal and internal intercostal muscles | Activated only at high ventilatory rates |
| NRA-rostral portion (Also known as nucleus para-ambiguus, NPA | Inspiratory neurons | Motor neurons to inspiratory muscles | Discharge continuously increases during inspiration |
| Bottzinger's complex (Bot) | Expiratory neurons only | NTS (inspiratory) and phrenic motor neurons | Inhibits both inspiratory NTS and phrenic motor neurons |

central ventilatory drive. Sensory inputs for these reflexes result from unmyelinated C-fiber afferents, naked nerve endings (j-receptors) and myelinated vagal afferents (either from slowly adapting stretch receptors in smooth muscles of the airway, or from rapidly adapting receptors in the epithelium of the airway).

### Hering-Breuer Reflexes

Slowly adapting pulmonary stretch receptors (SARs) located in the smooth muscles of the airways send myelinated afferent nerve fibres through the vagus nerve to the DRG neurons and the pneumotaxic center. Increased lung volume (as occurs towards the height of inspiration) stimulates these receptors to shorten inspiration, and thereby, to limit the tidal volume.

While brief stimulation of SARs inhibits inspiration alone, continued stimulation of these receptors by sustained lung inflation during expiratory phase causes excitation of the central expiratory neurons as well. The classic Hering-Breurer response and the inverse relationship between respiratory frequency and lung volume are illustrated in Fig. 6.29. **Hering-Breuer inflation reflex** does not appear to be important in determining the respiratory frequency in adult humans at rest. However, this reflex may significantly contribute to the regulation of respiratory frequency in adult humans during moderate to strenuous exercise. It may also provide a defence against overexpansion of the lungs in those situations.

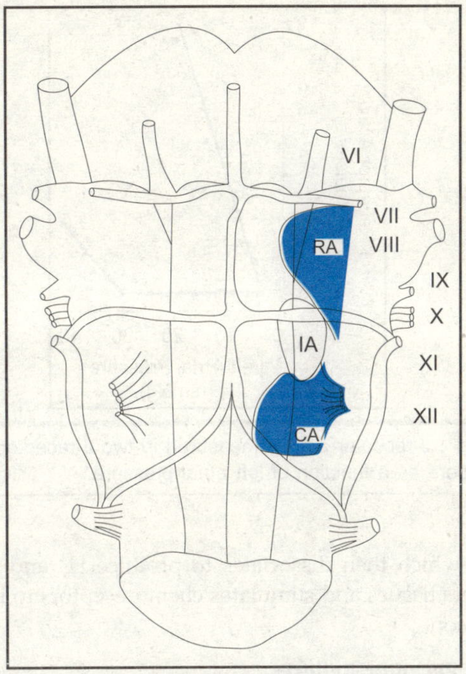


Fig. 6.29 : Central chemoreceptor areas on the ventral surface of the medulla. Rostral (RA) and caudal (CA) area are sensitive to $CO_2$ tension and hydrogen ion, whereas the intermediate area (IA) appears to relay chemoreceptor signals.

### Chemical Control of Respiration

Chemical control of respiration (or ventilation) is achieved by the following factors :

- **Central factors** — $CO_2$ and $H^+$ in CSF
- **Peripheral factors** — Inputs from carotid and aortic body receptors which respond to changes in arterial pH, $PCO_2$ and $PO_2$.

The single most important factor controlling ventilation is the $P_{aCO_2}$ acting on the central chemoreceptors. The $CO_2$ dominated chemical control of respiration maintains a ventilation sufficient for adequate tissue oxygenation, $CO_2$ removal from tissues and maintenance of optimal pH.

### Central Chemoreceptors

These are chemosensitive cells concentrated in two major areas at the ventral surface of the medulla (Fig. 6.30).

The two areas are :

(a) a rostral area (RA, near the roots of CN VI, VII, VIII, IX and X)

(b) a caudal area (CA, near the base of the CN XII).

There is an intermediate area (IA) between the two which most probably integrate the activity of chemoreceptors in RA and CA. Efferents from these receptors pass to the contralateral brainsteam. They have a major projection to the DRG neurons. There is a nucleus called paragigantocellular nucleus adjacent to the chemoreceptor areas. This nucleus appears to mediate chemosensitivity.

The central chemoreceptors are bathed in CSF and they are stimulated by $H^+$ in CSF.

### Mechanism of Central Chemosensitivity

$H^+$ concentration in CSF bathing ventral medulla modulates afferent impulse from central chemoreceptors. CSF $H^+$ is determined by arterial $PCO_2$ and acidosis. Small changes in extracellular pH of ventral medulla cause marked change in tidal volume pH $CO_2$ in blood rapidly equilibrium with CSF. In the CSF $CO_2$ is hydrated to form

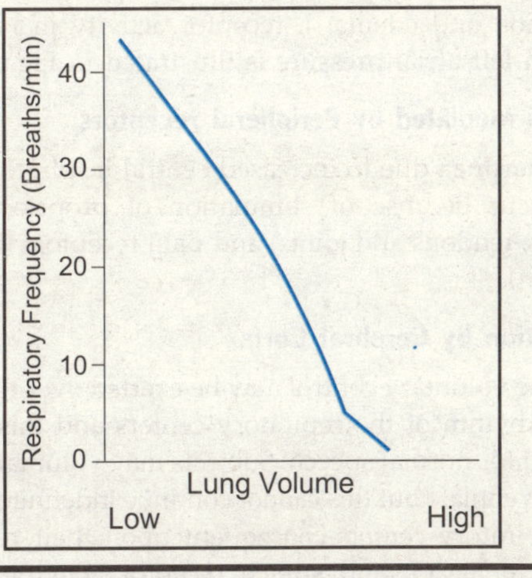


Fig. 6.30 : Respiratory frequency measured from phrenic nerve activity, during static inflation of both lungs in dog.

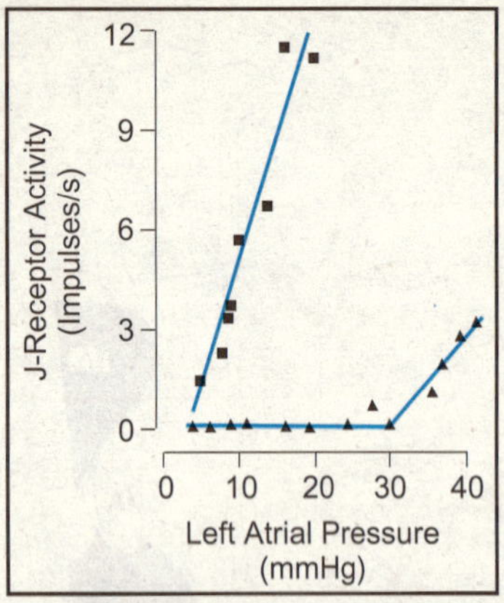


Fig. 6.31 : J-receptor activity measured in two J-receptor afferent nerve fibers as a function of left atrial pressure.

$H_2CO_3$ which then dissociates to produce $H^+$ and $HCO_3^-$. $H^+$ enters tissues and stimulates chemoreceptors to increase ventilation.

## Irritant Receptor Reflexes

These are mediated by rapidly adapting receptors (RARs) located in the tracheal epithelium especially in the carinal region. These RARs are stimulated by mechanical or chemical endogenous irritation of the epithelium. Various pollutants as well as endogenious compounds like histamine and brady kinin can also stimulate the irritant receptors. Responses include coughing, sneezing, tachypnea (increased respiratory rate), bronchoconstriction and increased secretion in the airways.

## J-Receptor Reflexes

**J-receptors** are pulmonary juxtacapillary mechanoreceptors sending afferent impulse through unmyelinated C-fibres. These receptors in the alveolar interstitum sense vascular distension and increases in interstitial fluid volume. Their stimulation causes hyperpnea with or without dyspnea when there is pulmonary vascular congestion and edema. J. receptor activity in response to elevated left atrial pressure is illustrated in Fig. 6.31.

## Reflexes Mediated by Peripheral receptors

**Hyperpnea** due to increased central inspiratory activity may occur because of stimulation of proprioceptors (in muscles, tendons and joints) and pain receptors (in muscles and skin).

## Modulation by Cerebral Cortex

Some voluntary control may be exerted over the intrinsic neural rhythm of the repiratory centers and this is almost essential for normal speech. Subjects may voluntarily hyper- or hypoventilate but this cannot continue indefinitely because the respiratory centers-consequent upon their response to change in $PaCO_2$ and stretch receptor activity-ultimately take over.

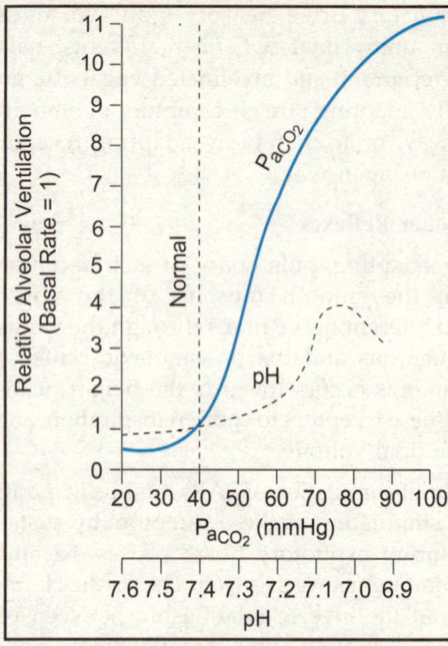


Fig. 6.32 : Stimulation of alveolar ventilation by decreased arterial pH or increased $P_{aCO_2}$.

## Adaptation of Central Chemoreceptors

The ventilatory response to changes in $P_{aCO_2}$ is rapid but it tends to wane with time (hours to days). This is due to passage of $HCO_3^-$ across the blood brain barrier, thereby buffering the $H^+$ of the medullary ECF. Movement of $HCO_3^-$ occurs from plasma to CSF during chronic hypercapnia. $HCO_3$ moves in the opposite direction during chronic hypocapnia.

## Ventilatory Response to $CO_2$ and $H^+$

Changes in $P_{aCO_2}$ increases alveolar ventilation Fig. 6.32. Decrease in arterial pH due to metabolic acidosis also stimulates ventilation but the response is less than that produced by an increase in $P_{aCO_2}$.

## Peripheral Chemoreceptors

Peripheral chemoreceptors are found in the carotid and aortic bodies. Carotid bodies are located at the bifurcation of the common carotid arteries Fig. 6.33; they are small organs, 2 to 3 mm in diameter. Aortic bodies are situated between the ascending aorta and pulmonary artery. Chemoreceptors in these structures are stimulated by both $\downarrow Pao_2$ and $P_{aCO2}\uparrow$. The carotid bodies also respond to decrease in pH in humans. Afferent impulses from carotid bodies are carried to the respiratory centers at the brainstem via a branch of the glossopharyngeal nerve (**Hering's nerve**). Afferent inputs from aortic bodies reach the respiratory centers through the vagus nerve. Carotid bodies receive a blood flow of 2L/min/100g of tissue, which is one of the highest in the body. They utilize a high amount of $O_2$ (8ml/min/100g of tissue) but arteriovenous $O_2$ difference across the carotid bodies is insignificant because of the very

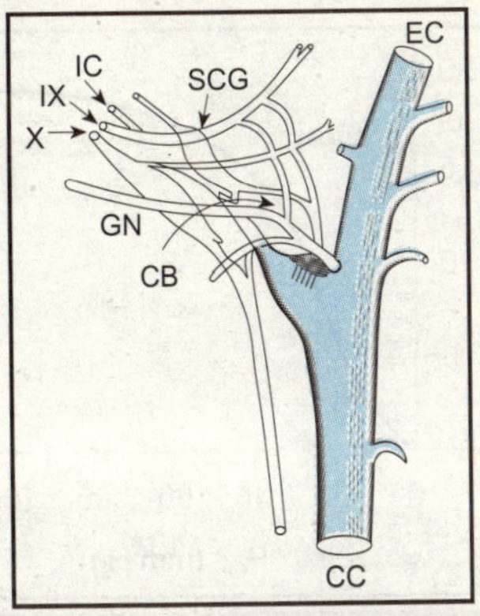


**Fig. 6.33 :** Anatomic location of the carotid body (CB) at the bifurcation of the common carotid artery (CC) into external (EC) and internal carotid arteries (IC). Adjacent structures are the ganglion nodosum (GN); superior cervical ganglion (SCG) and branches of the glossopharyngeal (IX) and vagus (X) nerves.

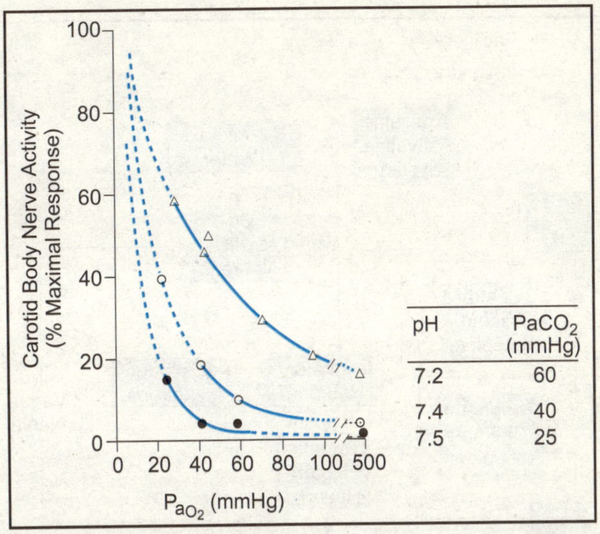


**Fig. 6.34 :** Carotid body nerve activity as a function of $PaO_2$

high blood flow. Therefore, the entire carotid body can sense a $PO_2$ which is almost equal to $P_{aO_2}$. Carotid bodies have a greater response to decreases in $P_{aO_2}$ and a much higher sensitivity to changes in $P_{aCO2}$ than that observed for aortic bodies. **Arteriovenous $O_2$ difference** across aortic bodies is higher and therefore, they respond to changes in either $O_2$ content ($CO_2$) or partial pressure of $O_2$($PO_2$). In conditions in which $CO_2$ is decreased despite a normal $PO_2$ (as occurs in anemia and CO poisoning), aortic bodies (but not carotid bodies) are stimulated.

**Normally, about 20% of the total ventilatory drive** is provided by the carotid bodies. During hypoxia or anesthesia, this can increase upto 40% Fig. 6.34 illustrates carotid body nerve activity in relation to changes in $P_{aO_2}$. Hypercapnia and acidosis increase the firing rate of these nerves to 20% of maximum. **Hypocapnia and alkalosis have an opposite effect.** Hypercapnia and hypoxia often occur concurrently. This results in a greater ventilatory drive than is possible with lowered $P_{aO_2}$ alone.

## Mechanism of Peripheral Chemosensitivity

**Carotid and aortic bodies** have two types of cells in them-type I (glomus) cells and type II (sustentacular) cells. Surrounding these cells are numerous capillaries and sinusoids. **Glomus cells** are rich in mitochondria and catecholamine granules. Synapses are formed on the glomus cells from glossopharyngeal and vagus nerves as well as sympathetic nerves from the stellate ganglion. **Hypoxia** reduces conductance of $O_2$-sensitive $K^+$ channels on type I glomus cells. The resultant decrease in $K^+$ efflux depolarizes the cell to cause $Ca^{2+}$influx primarily through L-type $Ca^{2+}$ channels. This triggers action potentials and neurotransmitter (probably dopamine) release. Consequently, afferent nerve endings are excited.

## Integrated Control of Ventilation

The complex interaction both within and between central and peripheral chemoreceptors integrates the neural and chemical ventilatory stimuli Fig. 6.35 illustrates the effect of changes in $P_{ACO_2}$ on ventilatory response at different levels of $P_{ACO_2}$ in humans. The major components of ventilatory control are illustrated in Fig. 6.36. Reciprocal inhibition of inspiratory and expiratory neurons is an important component of ventilatory control. Phasic inputs from reticular activating system (RAS) to inspiratory neurons have a stimulatory influence on inspiration. The diaphragm-the principal muscle for inspiration-is stimulated through phrenic motor neurons which are under control of

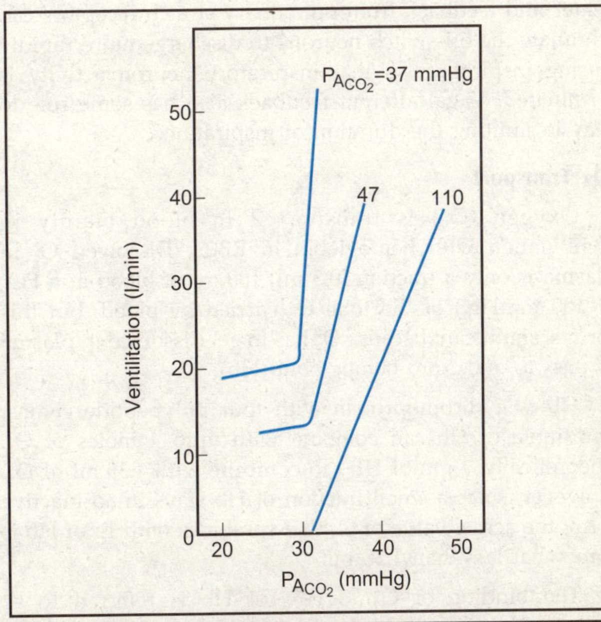


**Fig. 6.35 :** Ventilatory response to changes in $PACO_2$ at various fixed $PAO_2$ vaues.

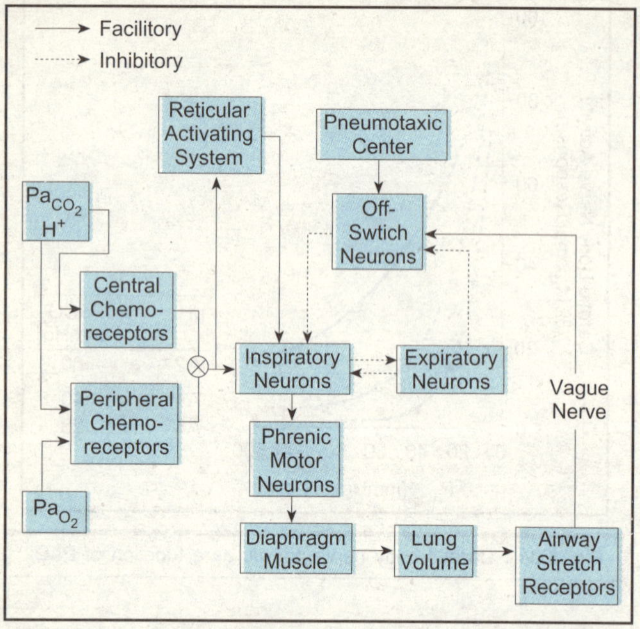


**Fig. 6.36 :** Major components of ventilatory control. Inspiratory neurons are facilitated by the reticular activating system and chemoreceptor output but inhibited by expiratory neurons throughout expiration and off–switch neurons late in inspiration.

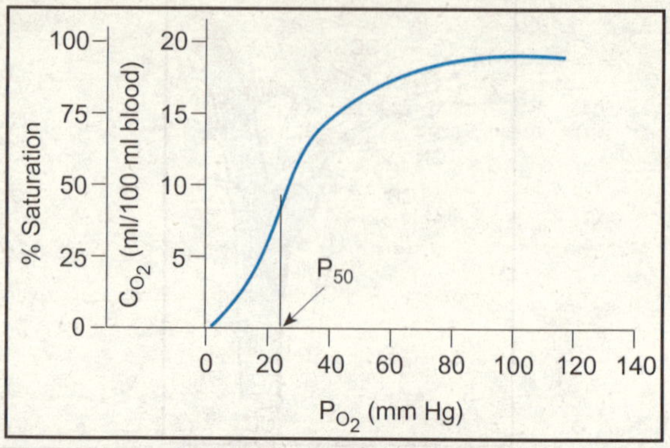


**Fig. 6.37 :** Oxyhemolgobin dissocian curve for hemoglobin. The partial pressure of $O_2$ that results in a 50% saturation of hemoglobin is called $P_{50}$. The normal $P_{50}$ is 26 mm Hg, $CO_2$ represents $O_2$ content and $PO_2$ represents the oxygen partial pressure.

inspiratory neurons. The response of the diaphragm largely determines the tidal volume and is a function of $P_{ACO_2}$, arterial pH and $P_{aO_2}$ stimulation of the chemoreceptors (both central and peripheral). During most part of the inspiratory cycle, the off-switch neurons remain in an inhibited state which decreases with time. The pneumotaxic center and feedback from pulmonary stretch receptors can stimulate the off-switch neurons to discharge more rapidly during inspiration so that inspiratory neuron activity is terminated. Vagal afferent feedback also has some role to play in limiting the duration of inspiration.

## $O_2$ Transport

Oxygen ($O_2$) is transported in blood mainly in combination with hemoglobin in RBCs. Dissolved $O_2$ in plasma is only a fraction (0.3 ml/100 ml of blood at a $PO_2$ of 100 mmHg.) of the total $O_2$ carried by blood, but this form is significant because $O_2$ has to get dissolved in plasma to pass to and from hemoglobin (Hb).

**Hb** is a chromoprotein with four polypeptide chains. One mole of Hb can combine with upto 4 moles of $O_2$. Theoretically, **1 gm of Hb can combine with 1.39 ml of $O_2$**. However, since a small fraction of Hb stays in an inactive form, the actual value of $O_2$ that combines with 1g of Hb is somewhat less than 1.38 ml.

The binding of $O_2$ to $Fe^{2+}$ of Hb is referred to as **'oxygenation'** (instead of oxidation) $Fe^{2+}$ does not change after this combination. Oxygenation of Hb gives rise to oxyhemoglobin ($HbO_2$) which is bright red in color. Deoxygenated Hb. (Hb) is purple in color. Oxidation of Hb results in conversion of $Fe^{2+}$ to $Fe^{3+}$ producing methemoglobin which cannot release its $O_2$ to tissues.

Oxygen content of blood at any particular moment is the volume of $O_2$ combined with Hb plus the volume of $O_2$ in solution. The maximum volume of $O_2$ that can be bound by Hb is known as **$O_2$ capacity of Hb**. The $O_2$ saturation of $HbO_2$ is expressed in terms of percentage of the $O_2$ capacity. In a healthy adult, breathing room air at sea level, the partial pressure of $O_2$ in arterial blood (($PaO_2$) is 100 mmHg and $SaO_2$ is approximately 97.5%; the arterial $O_2$ content ($CaO_2$) being 20ml/100ml of blood. In mixed venous blood of a healthy adult in similar conditions. $PVo_2$, $SVo_2$ and $CVo_2$ are 40 mm Hg, 70% and 15ml/100ml. of blood respectively. This gives an arteriovenous difference in $O_2$ content of (20-15) = 5ml/100ml of blood; this amount of $O_2$ is therefore consumed by the tissue concerned. A blood flow ($\dot{Q}$) of 5000 ml/min will thus ensure an $O_2$ consumption ($VO_2$) of 250 ml. per minute by that tissue. This relationship is expressed by the Fick equation.

$$\dot{V}o_2 = \dot{Q}\left(Ca_{O_2} - Cv_{O_2}\right)$$

### Oxyhemoglobin dissociation curve

The relationship between $O_2$ content and partial pressure of $O_2(PO_2)$ in blood is defined by the oxyhemoglobin dissociation curve (Fig. 6.37). The curve is sigmoid in shape. At high $O_2$ tensions, the curve is flat and thus fluctuations in $O_2$ content can be avoided when alveolar $P_{O_2}$ changes. At lower $O_2$ tensions (especially at $P_{O_2}$ lesser than 70 mmHg.) small changes in $P_{O_2}$ leads to large changes in oxygen content, and this facilitates the release of $O_2$ from Hb in tissues (tissue. $P_{O_2}$ is much lower that that of blood).

The $P_{O_2}$ at which Hb is 50% saturated with $O_2$ is referred to as $P_{50}$. $P_{50}$ is 26 mmHg at physiological conditions (temperature 37°C pH 7.4 and $PCO_2$ 40 mmHg). An increase in $P_{50}$ means Hb is 50% saturated with $O_2$ at a higher $PO_2$, i.e., there is a shift of the oxyhemoglobin dissociation curve to the right; an increase in $P_{50}$ implies decreased affinity of

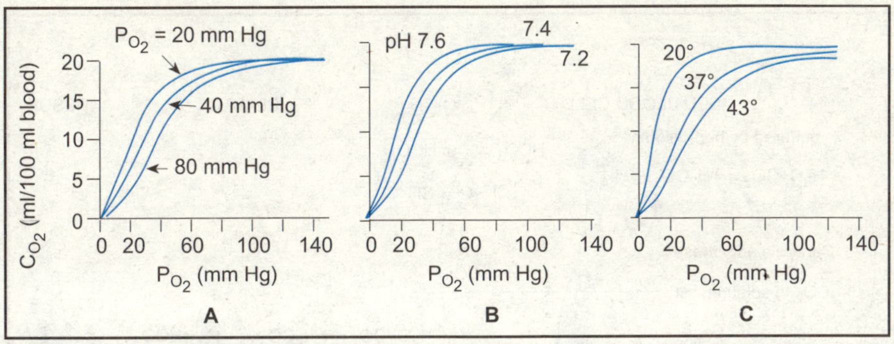


**Fig. 6.38 :** (A) The oxyhemglobin dissociation curve is shifted to the right by an incrase in $PCO_2$ and to the left by a reduction in $PCO_2$ (Bohr effect). (B) The oxy hemoglobin dissociation curve is shifted to the right by a decrease in pH and to the left by an increase in pH. (C) Increasing blood temperature shifts the oxyhemoglobin dissociation curve to the right whereas a reduction in temperature shifts the curve to the left, $CO_2$ refers to $O_2$ content and $PO_2$ is partial pressure of $O_2$.

Hb for $O_2$. A decrease in $P_{50}$ means Hb is 50% saturated with $O_2$ at a lower $PO_2$, i.e., there is a shift of the oxyhemoglobin dissociation curve to the left; a decrease in $P_{50}$ implies increased affinity of Hb for $O_2$.

## Factors affecting the oxyhemoglobin dissociation curve

The oxyhemoglobin dissociation curve shifts to the right if there is increase in partial pressure of carbondioxide ($P_{CO_2}$), or increase in $H^+$ concentration (i.e. decreased pH), or both Fig. 6.38 (A&B). Therefore, when $P_{CO_2}$ is elevated (or pH is decreased). Oxygen content of hemoglobin is less at a given $PO_2$. Release of $O_2$ from hemoglobin (i.e. lowering of $CO_2$ of Hb) at an elevated $P_{CO_2}$ such as that occurs in tissues- is known Bohr effect. $P_{CO_2}$ affects the oxyhemoglobin dissociation independent of the effect of pH. Right shift of the dissociation curve can also be brought about by an increase in blood temperature Fig. 6.38(c). Tissue metabolism causes increase in $P_{CO_2}$, decrease in pH and increase in temperature at tissue level. All of these factors favor unloading of $O_2$ from Hb at a given $P_{O_2}$ due to shift of oxyhemoglobin dissociation curve to the right. However, it is important to remember that the most of the increase in the delivery of $O_2$ to metabolically active tissues is contributed by increases in blood flow and recruitment of capillaries; right shift of the oxyhemoglobin dissociation curve has a small role to play.

RBCs contain **2, 3-diphosphoglycerate (2, 3-DPG), and elevated levels of 2, 3-DPG** cause a decrease in the affinity of Hb for $O_2$. Hence, increased 2, 3-DPG concentration within RBCs is associated with a right shift of the oxyhemoglobin dissociation curve. Increased 2, 3-DPG concentrations are found in RBCs in some conditions associated with impairment of $O_2$ delivery to tissues, e.g., anemia, chronic hypoxemia and thyrotoxicosis; this favors increased unloading of $O_2$ from Hb tissues at a given $P_{O_2}$.

To summarize, factors causing **right shift of the oxyhemoglobin dissociation curve are—**

1. Increase in $P_{CO2}$
2. Increase in $H^+$ concentration (i.e., decrease in pH)
3. Increase in temperature
4. Increase in 2, 3-DPG concentration in RBCs

**A right shift means** increased unloading of $O_2$ from Hb at a given $PO_2$. **Factors causing left shift of the oxyhemoglobin dissociation curve are—**

1. Decrease in **$PCO_2$.**
2. Decrease in **$H^+$** ion concentration (i.e., increase in pH)
3. Decrease in **temperature**
4. Decrease in **2, 3-DPG concentration in RBCs**

**A left shift means decreased unloading of $O_2$ from Hb at a given $P_{O_2}$.**

## Carboxyhemoglobin

Carboxyhemoglobin is formed when carbon monoxide combines with Hb. This form of Hb cannot carry $O_2$ to the tissues. CO has a very high affinity for Hb-240 times greater than oxygen's affinity for Hb. Incomplete combustion of petroleum products produces a lot of CO in the environment. Tobacco smoke is another important source of CO. Normal healthy individuals have a very minute quantity of CO combined with Hb. However, heavy smokers may have as much as 10% of their Hb combined with CO leading to chronic hypoxemia; polycythemia-body's effort to correct hypoxemia is common in these individuals.

## $CO_2$ Transport

**Carbon dioxide ($CO_2$)** is transported in RBCs and plasma in several different forms generated by various reversible chemical combinations (Fig. 6.39). A small amount of $CO_2$ reacts with plasma proteins to form carbamino compounds :

$$R\text{-}NH_2 + CO_2 - R\text{-}NHCOO^- + H+$$

**Some of the $CO_2$ in plasma gets hydrated to form carbonic acid :**

$$H_2O + CO_2 = H_2CO_3 \text{ (Carbonic acid)} = H+ \; HCO_3^-$$

$H_2CO_3$ in turn dissociates into H+ and $HCO_3^-$. The formation of $H_2CO_3$ is much slower than that occuring

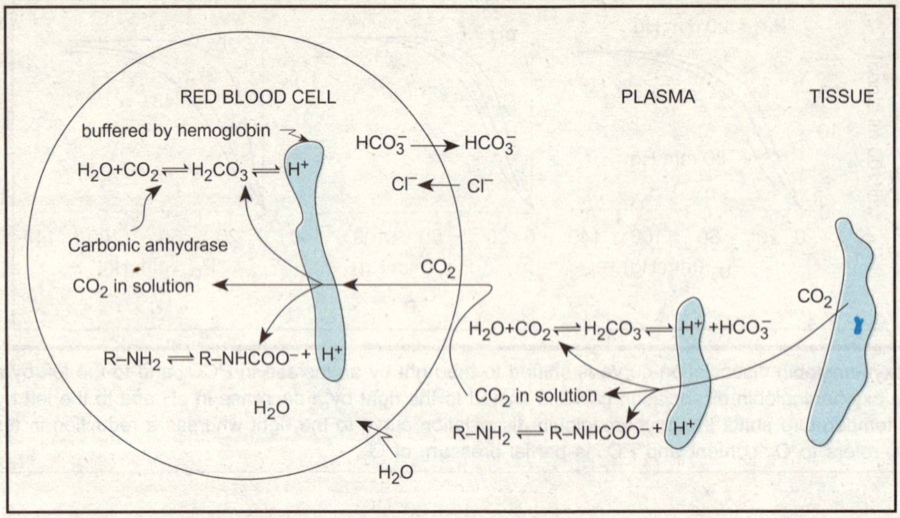


**Fig. 6.39 :** $CO_2$ transport in plasma and in red blood cell. Hydration of $CO_2$ is much faster in red blood cells than in plasma because of the presence of coloured anhydrase within RBC.

within RBCs. This is because the enzyme that enhances the rate of this reaction is not found in plasma. Thus, $CO_2$ in plasma may exist in three different forms; carbamino compounds, $H_2CO_3$ and $HCO_3^-$.

**Carbondioxide** from plasma can freely diffuse through RBC membranes to enter RBCs. In fact, most of the $CO_2$ entering the plasma passes into the RBCs. Some of the $CO_2$ remains in solution within RBCs but a large amount of it combines with Hb to form **carbaminohemoglobin**. $H^+$ is formed in the process and it is buffered by Hb in the RBC. The process is facilitated by the unloading of $O_2$ from Hb and thus, Hb becomes a weaker acid.

**Bicarbonate ($HCO_3^-$)** is the predominant form of $CO_2$ found in RBCs. It is formed by hydration of $CO_2$ forming $H_2CO_3$ with its subsequent dissociation into $H^+$ and $HCO_3^-$. The rate of formation of $H_2CO_3$ is greatly accelerated by the enzyme carbonic anhydrase (CA) present in RBCs. $HCO_3^-$ thus formed comes out of RBCs and enters plasma. Diffusion of $Cl^-$ from plasma to RBCs maintains the electrical neutrality. This phenomenon is known as chloride shift, or **Hamburger shift**. Chloride shift causes the osmotic pressure in RBCs to increase. Water is drawn into RBCs as a consequence of that. The result is an increase in RBC volume in venous blood.

**Plasma $HCO_3^-$** accounts for slightly more than 50% of $CO_2$ in blood while carbamino-hemoglobin accounts for 25%. $CO_2$ dissolved in blood (5%), $CO_2$ combined with carbamino compounds (5%) and $HCO_3^-$ in RBC (15%) accounts for the remaining 25% of $CO_2$ in blood.

## CO2 Dissociation Curve

The $CO_2$ dissociation curve defines the relationship between chemically bound $CO_2$ and $PCO_2$ Fig. 6.42. This curve differs a lot from the **oxyhemoglobin dissociation curve**. Within the physiological range of $PCO_2$ (20 to 55 mmHg), the shape of the $CO_2$ dissociation curve is nearly linear. The $CO_2$ dissociation curve is steeper than the oxyhemoglobin dissociation curve. So, for a given change in $PCO_2$, a lot more $CO_2$ can be transported into blood as compound with $O_2$.

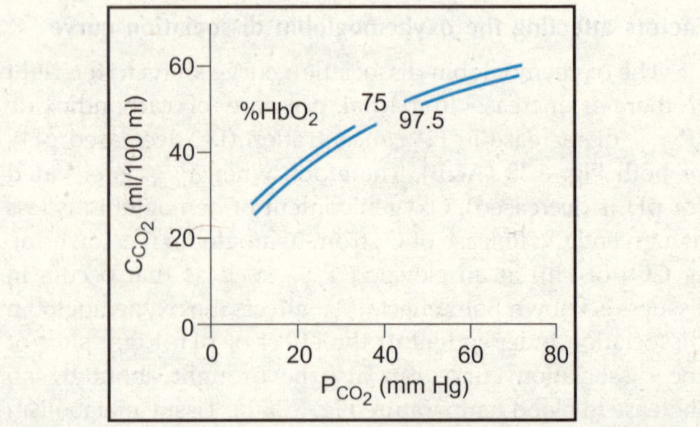


**Fig. 6.40 :** $CO_2$ dissociation curve. The state pf oxygenation of hemoglobin affects the position of the $CO_2$ dissociation curve (Haldane effect). $CCO_2$ represents the $CO_2$ content of the blood and $PCO_2$ represents the partial pressure of $CO_2$.

The position of the **$CO_2$ dissociation curve** is affected by the degree of oxygenation of Hb Fig. 6.41. This is referred to as **Haldane effect. Haldane effect can be explained by**—

1. higher affinity of deoxygenated Hb for $H^+$
2. greater ability of deoxygenated Hb to form carbaminohemoglobin

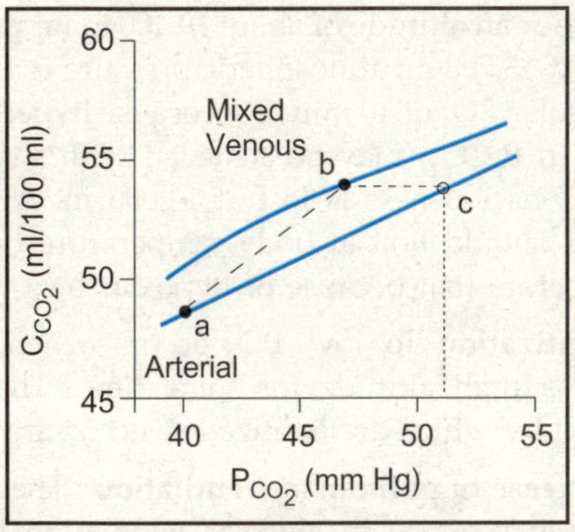


Fig. 6.41 : Haldane effect

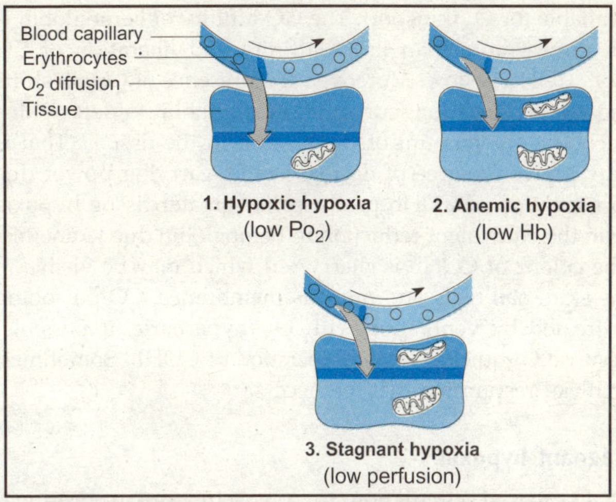


Fig. 6.42 : Defects underlying different types of hypoxia

## 6.13 Respiration in Diseases and Unusual Conditions

### Hypoxia

***Deficiency of oxygen ($O_2$) at tissue level*** is known as hypoxia. Four categories of **hypoxia** have been described :

(i) **Hypoxic hypoxia** — arterial blood $PO_2$ is low,

(ii) **Anemic hypoxia** — blood hemoglobin level is low,

(iii) **Stagnant hypoxia** — blood flow is low,

(iv) **Histotoxic hypoxia** — tissue utilization of $O_2$ is low.

### Effects of hypoxia

In stagnant hypoxia, the effects depend on the tissue involved. In other types, the changes in the central nervous system appear first and are especially important. **Acute hypoxia** produces a clinical picture resembling that of acute alcohol intoxication manifested by impaired judgement, motor incoordination, excitement, disorientation, loss of time sense, dulled pain sensitivity and headache. In **long-standing hypoxia,** there occurs fatigue, drowsiness, apathy, inattentiveness, delayed reaction time and reduced work capacity. Other effects include anorexia, nausea, vomiting and tachycardia. Hypertension may occur in severe cases. In **severe hypoxia,** the vital centres in the brain stem are affected and death is usually due to respiratory failure.

Reduction of $Pa_{O_2}$ causes reduction in resistance of cerebral blood vessels with increase in cerebral blood flow that tends to compensate for the reduced $Pa_{O_2}$. But when the low $Pa_{O_2}$ is accompanied by hyperventilation producing a fall in $Pa_{CO_2}$ that increases cerebrovascular resistance, cerebral blood flow gets reduced and hypoxia worsens.

The metabolic effects include rise in blood lactate level with decrease in bicarbonate giving rise to metabolic acidosis.

The respiratory response to hypoxia is mostly mediated by the carotid and aortic chemoreceptors. Some respiratory sti-mulation also occurs due to the direct effect of oxygen lack on the respiratory centre. The resultant hyperventilation tends to cause respiratory alkalosis due to loss of carbon dioxide ($CO_2$).

**Diminished $PO_2$** in any tissue (except lungs) causes local vasodilation. Diffuse vasodilation, that accompanies gene-ralized hypoxia, results in elevated cardiac output. Hepatic and renal function may be impaired in prolonged and/or severe hypoxia.

**Erythropoietin** secretion from the kidneys is stimulated by hypoxia. This is an important compensatory mechanism in prolonged hypoxia because the resultant increase in the number of circulating RBCs makes more hemoglobin available for carrying more $O_2$.

### Hypoxic hypoxia (Fig. 6.42)

This is found in normal individuals **at high altitude** where the atmospheric $O_2$ is low, as also in a number of respiratory diseases that either causes gas exchange mechanism in the lungs to fail (pulmonary fibrosis, ventilation-perfusion imbalance) or shunts blood from the venous to arterial side of the circulation (right to left shunts) or causes ventilatory failure (fatigue of respiratory muscles, mechanical defects like pneumothorax and bronchial obstruction as in asthma, depression of respiratory center). **Hypoxic hypoxia** ***is the most common type of hypoxia seen in clinical situations.***

### Anemic hypoxia

Oxygen-carrying capacity of blood is reduced with decrease in hemoglobin concentration. Absolute amount of $O_2$ transported per unit volume of blood is reduced but the $P_aO_2$ remains normal. **Anemic hypoxia** ***is usually not severe because of increase*** **in 2, 3-DPG in RBCs**.

**Carbon monoxide (CO) poisoning** produces a condition analogous to anemic hypoxia because the hemoglobin which combines with CO (carboxyhemoglobin, COHb) is not available for $O_2$ transport. The CO-affinity of hemoglobin is 210 times more than its $O_2$-affinity and liberation of CO from COHb is slow. Moreover, the presence of COHb shifts the $O_2$ dissociation curve of hemoglobin to left which decreases the amount of $O_2$ released in the tissues. That is why a given degree of decrease in $O_2$-carrying power due to formation of COHb produces far greater tissue hypoxia than the equivalent reduction in hemoglobin due to anemia. The colour of COHb is cherry red which may be visible in the skin, nail beds and mucous membranes. CO-poisoning is treated by ventilation with $O_2$ (hyperbaric, if possible) because $O_2$ quickens the dissociation of COHb. Sometimes, artificial respiration may be necessary.

### Stagnant hypoxia

Decreased circulation to a specific organ produces localised **stagnant hypoxia**. This may be due to arterial or venous obstruction or may be the result of vasoconstriction (eg, Raynaud's phenomenon). ***Stagnant hypoxia*** is a problem in shock or congestive heart failure. Peripheral circulation is reduced in such patients in an attempt to maintain adequate perfusion to vital organs.

### Histotoxic hypoxia

In histotoxic hypoxia, the tissues are unable to utilize oxygen. This is most commonly seen in **cyanide poisoning.** ***Cyanide inhibits cytochrome oxidase, a respiratory chain enzyme.*** Cyanide poisoning is treated by nitrites or methylene blue which form methemoglobin in blood. Methemoglobin combines with cyanide to form cyanmethemoglobin which is not toxic. Hyperbaric $O_2$ may also be of help in treatment of this condition.

### Effects of decreased atmospheric pressure and acclimatization to high altitude

Barometric pressure diminishes at higher altitudes. Partial pressure of $O_2$ also falls because composition of air remains the same. A number of compensatory mechanisms come into play to counteract the effects of low oxygen pressure on the body in order to increase altitude tolerance. This is known as **acclimatization to high altitude.**

At 3,000 m above sea level (approximately 10,000 ft), alveolar $PO_2$ is about 60 mm Hg and there is increased ventilation due to stimulation of chemoreceptors by hypoxia. At higher altitudes, hyperventilation produces decline in alveolar $PCO_2$. As a result arterial $PCO_2$ falls producing respiratory alkalosis.

**In unacclimatized persons,** ***initial symptoms of hypoxia*** (mental symptoms like irritability) ***appear at an altitude of about 3,700 m. Severe hypoxic symptoms occur at 5,500 m*** and the person ***becomes unconscious usually at 6,100 m*** (approximately 20,000 ft). Supplemental 100% $O_2$ may maintain a normal alveolar $PO_2$ of 100 mm Hg when the atmospheric pressure is 187 mm Hg (assuming an alveolar $PCO_2$ of 40 mm Hg and a vapour pressure of 47 mm Hg), the pressure at an altitude of about 10,400 m (approximately 34,000 ft). At 13,700 m, atmospheric pressure is 100 mm Hg and an alveolar $PO_2$ of 40 mm Hg (because hyperventilation causes fall in $P_aCO_2$) may be achieved with supplemental 100% $O_2$. Consciousness is lost at 14,000 m. At 19,200 m, body fluids should boil at body temperature but persons die much before that because of hypoxia.

**Acclimatization** to low $PO_2$ occurs when a person remains at a high altitude for some time. The principal mechanisms by which acclimatization occur are :

(a) **Increase in pulmonary ventilation** : The immediate effect is a rise in alveolar ventilation by 65% of normal. The rise may be 400% above normal after several days. The respiratory alkalosis that results from initial increase in ventilation tends to oppose the hypoxic stimulation of the respiratory centre by inhibiting it. This inhibition fades away in 2-5 days due to rise in the pH of CSF and brain brought about by active transport of $H^+$ into CSF and, possibly, lactic acidosis in the brain. The increase in ventilation declines over years because of slow desensitization of the respiratory centre to hypoxic stimulation.

(b) **Increase in RBCs and hemoglobin** : **Hypoxia** stimulates **erythropoietin secretion** and **RBC production** increases. Hematocrit rises to about 60 and hemoglobin concentration may rise up to 20 g/dl. There is increase in blood volume by 20-30 per cent as well. RBC count increase in 2-3 days but increase in hemoglobin and blood volume is not apparent until after 2 weeks.

(c) **Decrease in $O_2$ affinity of hemoglobin** : $O_2$-affinity of hemoglobin decreases because of rise in 2, 3-DPG in RBCs. This overrides the opposite effect produced by the respiratory alkalosis. More $O_2$ is thus available to the tissues. Decreased $O_2$ affinity of hemoglobin does not help at very high altitudes because low $O_2$ affinity interferes with $O_2$ uptake in the lungs when $Pa_{O_2}$ is very much reduced.

(d) **Increased diffusion capacity for $O_2$ in the lungs** : This results from :

- increased blood volume in the pulmonary capillaries
- increased lung volume
- increased pulmonary arterial pressure

(e) **Increased cardiac output** : Cardiac output may increase up to 30% above normal almost immediately but comes back to normal as the haematocrit increases.

(f) **Increased capillaries in the tissues** : Increase in number of capillaries in the tissues occurs particularly in animals born and brought up at high altitudes e.g. mountain goats and mountain eagles.

(g) **Cellular changes** : There is increase in number of mitochondria where oxidative reactions take place.

Cellular content of cytochrome oxidase is increased. Myoglobin is also increased. These changes result in more efficient utilization of $O_2$ by tissues.

Natives living at high altitudes have barrel-shaped chest with a proportionately larger chest size compared with the body size which gives a high ratio of ventilatory capacity to mass of the body. The right side of the heart is also larger in those individuals.

When people initially experience the hypoxia of altitude, they often develop an illness known as mountain sickness. The typical symptoms are headache, nausea, giddiness, gastrointestinal disturbances, lassitude and psychological disturbances. Severe dyspnea occurs in response to mild exercise, as the circulation is unable to supply the tissues with adequate amounts of oxygen.

**Sleep apnea**, which is usually with periodic breathing, occurs at altitudes above 4000 meter. The cause of periodic breathing is the hypoxemia due to low $PIO_2$. At sea level, respiration is driven principally by the response of central chemoreceptors to arterial $PCO_2$. At sea level, respiration is driven principally by the response of central chemoreceptors to arterial $PCO_2$. The increase in ventilation that occurs following ascent to high altitude reduces the $PCO_2$ and the ventilatory drive from the central chemoreceptors falls. As a result, breathing is not adequately stimulated by the $PCO_2$ and the ventilation becomes periodic.

**Acute mountain sickness** : Rapid ascent to high altitudes may make some people sick within a few hours to about 2 days after the ascent. Death may ensue if supplemental $O_2$ is not given or if not removed to lower altitude. Edema of brain and lungs are the two frequent events that occur in these people. **Acute cerebral edema** is probably the result of hypoxic vasodilatation of cerebral blood vessels. The cause of acute pulmonary edema is unsettled yet. Pulmonary edema may be quite marked.

**Chronic mountain sickness** : Too long a stay at high altitude may cause this type of sickness occasionally. **The effects that occur are :**

- **RBC count** and hematocrit becomes very **high**
- Severe **pulmonary arterial hypertension**
- Marked enlargement of **the right side of the heart**
- **Fall in peripheral arterial pressure**
- **Congestive cardiac failure.**

Death may occur unless the person is brought to a lower altitude.

## Effects of increased barometric pressure

The ambient pressure increases under the sea. Deep-sea divers and underwater tunnel workers are exposed to high barometric pressures. For every 10 m of depth in sea water, pressure increases by one atmosphere. At these high pressures, one must breathe air or other gases at increased pressure in order to balance the increased pressure on the chest and abdomen.

100% $O_2$ at high pressures produces CNS symptoms of $O_2$ toxicity. This can be prevented by keeping $O_2$ concentration in the inhaled gas mixture to 20% or less.

**Nitrogen narcosis** is a condition due to increased $PN_2$ while breathing compressed air. Euphoria and symptoms resembling alcohol intoxication are commonly found. Nitrogen narcosis can be avoided by breathing a mixture of $O_2$ and helium (He).

Breathing a mixture of $O_2$ and He at high pressure also has its hazards. A condition known as **high-pressure nervous syndrome (HPNS)** develops. The person becomes drowsy and tremors occur. Alpha activity in the EEG is depressed. The cause of HPNS is uncertain but the anaesthetic property of He at high pressure may be a factor.

Rapid ascent from the depth of the sea, breathing compressed air produces **decompression sickness** (the bends, caisson disease). As the ambient pressure becomes less and less with the ascent from the deep, the alveolar $P_{N2}$ falls and $N_2$ diffuses from the tissues into the lungs along its pressure gradient. This is harmless if the ascent is gradual. With rapid ascent, bubbles of $N_2$ form in the tissues and blood. These bubbles are responsible for the symptoms of decompression sickness which include severe pain, paresthesia, itching, paralyses (due to arterial obstruction in the brain), dyspnea and myocardial damage. Prompt recompression followed by gradual decompression in decompression chamber is the treatment.

Gas in the lungs expands rapidly when the ambient pressure falls suddenly. This may lead to rupture of pulmonary veins driving air into the vessels and causing air embolism. This may occur when the pressurized cabin of an aeroplane at high altitude is breached or if a diver breathing compressed gas mixture during a dive holds breath and suddenly comes to the surface.

In breath-hold diving, the body is subjected to a number of environmental changes. Respiration must be suspended, the ambient pressure is increased, the effects of gravity are offset by the buoyancy of the body, the contact with water increases heat loss, and normal somatosensory inputs are impaired.

## Cardiorespiratory changes during exercise

To meet the $O_2$ need of the active tissue and to remove the extra $CO_2$ and heat generated by the active tissue, many cardiovascular and respiratory mechanisms come into play.

**Changes in the cardiovascular system include :**

- increase in muscle blood flow
- increase in cardiac output as a result of increase in both stroke volume and heart rate
- increase in venous return.

**Changes in the respiratory system are :**

- **Increase in pulmonary ventilation and oxygen consum-ption** : Increase in ventilation is abrupt with the onset of exercise. This is followed by more gradual increase after a brief pause. There is increase in both depth and rate of respiration. More $O_2$ enters into the blood in the lungs because of increase in alveolar-capillary $PO_2$ gradient which results from a fall in $PO_2$ (due to tissue consumption) of blood flowing into pulmonary capillaries. Pulmonary blood flow is also increased. Removal of $CO_2$ is also increased. At some point $O_2$ uptake cannot cope with the work load and blood lactate level rises due to anaerobic metabolism in muscles. This results in oxygen debt that is repaid after exercise is over. For this reason respiratory rate after exercise does not reach basal levels for some time (until the $O_2$ debt is repaid). The stimulus for ventilation is the elevated arterial $H^+$ concentration (low pH).

- **Increased oxygen uptake by the tissues** : $O_2$ extraction from each unit of blood is increased by as much as threefold. More $O_2$ is removed from hemoglobin because the capillary bed is dilated and previously closed capillaries open along with a fall in blood $PO_2$ to a range (below 60 mm Hg) where oxygen-hemoglobin dissociation curve is steep. Moreover, accumulation of $CO_2$ and rise in temperature in the active tissues (probably combined with increased red cell 2, 3-DPG) shift the dissociation curve to the right facilitating dissociation of $O_2$ from hemoglobin.

Intense exercise or mental effort produces **fatigue**, a vaguely understood phenomenon. Many disease states also produce fatigue. Acidosis is probably a major factor for fatigue during exercise. The subjective feeling of hardness of exercise correlate with the rate of consumption of oxygen. Exhaustion correlates with depletion of muscle glycogen. Pain during sustained muscle contraction is due to muscle ischaemia and accumulation of *"p factor"* that stimulates pain endings. Accumulation of interstitial fluid in exercising muscle is partly responsible for stiffness of muscle during exertion.

## Dyspnea

Dyspnea is the **symptom of abnormal awareness of breathing.** It may also be defined as an awareness of respiratory efforts. It may occur following exertion, after excitement or after a heavy meal.

The dyspnea may be *inspiratory* or *expiratory or during both the phases of respiration*. The **inspiratory dyspnea** is known as **air hunger** which may occur in pulmonary congestion and pulmonary edema or when there is an obstruction in larger bronchial tubes, trachea or larynx. **Expiratory dyspnea** occurs in obstruction to smaller bronchial tubes and is typically seen in bronchial asthma.

Dyspnea may be complained of if there is **Cheyne-Stokes breathing** (phases of apnea alternating with phases of hyperpnea).

The **causes of dyspnea** are varied but broadly they are classified as *peripheral* and *central*.

The **central causes** are due to stimulation of respiratory centre by hypoxia and acidosis due to any cause — specially uraemia and $CO_2$ excess.

The **peripheral causes** are :

- rigidity of the thoracic cage;
- difficulty of pulmonary expansion from pleural effusion;
- pulmonary fibrosis or emphysema.

**Dyspnea** may arise from psychological disturbances as in hysteria. Psychogenic dyspnea is diagnosed by exclusion of any organic disease.

*Causes of dyspnea :*

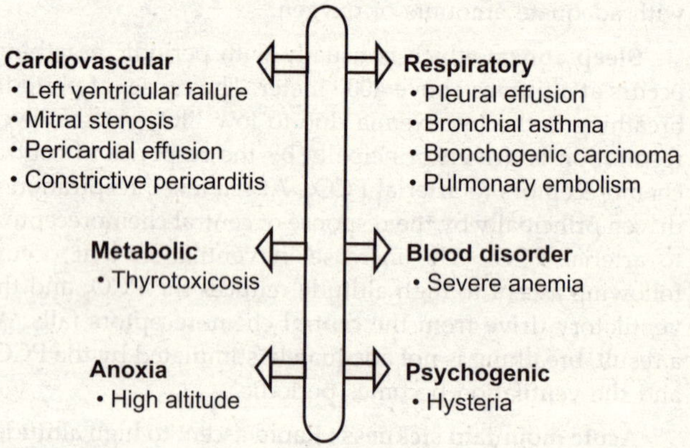


## Asphyxia

In asphyxia, there is prevention of exchange of air between the atmosphere and to the lungs alveoli and there is lack of oxygenation of the tissues.

*Causes of asphyxia—*

(i) **Mechanical**

(ii) **Toxic**

(iii) **Traumatic**

(iv) **Pathological.**

*(i) Mechanical :*

- Constriction around and pressure over the neck eg, hanging; strangulation
- Closure of the external respiratory orifices eg, smothering
- Occlusion of respiratory passage from within eg, gagging
- Restriction of respiratory movements due to compression over the chest eg, traumatic asphyxia.

*(ii) Toxic :*

- Poisons – depressing respiratory centers eg, opium, barbiturates, hydrogen sulphide
- Respiratory tract irritants eg, chlorine gas
- Poisons affecting pick up, carriage and diffusion of oxygen at tissue level eg, cyanides, carbon monoxide

- Lack of oxygen in inhaled air
- Poisons causing paralysis of respiratory muscles eg, cobra venom; curare, muscle relaxants.

***(iii) Traumatic :***

- Injury to both lungs
- Pulmonary embolism.

***(iv) Pathological :***

- Infective conditions
- New growth in respiratory tracts.

### Stages of asphyxia

| | | |
|---|---|---|
| I. | Stage of dyspnea | ↑ $CO_2$ level; cyanosis + |
| II. | Stage of convulsion | Further ↑ $CO_2$ level, Cyanosis ++. |
| III. | Stage of respiratory exhaustion | Further ↑ $CO_2$ level, Cyanosis +++ , BP ↓; Reflexes ↓. |

### Pathogenesis

***Acute asphyxial condition :*** $CO_2$ tension in blood ↑→ capillary dilatation and loss of tonicity of vessel walls → stasis of blood →↓ venous return → further aggravation of ↓$O_2$ level and ↑$CO_2$ level.

### Cyanosis

It is the bluish discoloration of the skin amd mucous membrane due to **excessive amount of reduced hemoglobin in the blood** (*more than 5 gm/100 ml*).

It is observed in the lips, dorsum of tongue, tip of nose, lobules of ear, buccal mucosa, conjunctiva; nail beds.

**Peripheral cyanosis** : It is present generally in presence of normal arterial oxygen saturation. It is due to pronounced oxygen desaturation of venocapillary and capillary blood.

***Mechanism of peripheral cyanosis :***

- Peripheral vasoconstriction
- Low cardiac output.

  It is clinically evident in the ear lobe, tip of the nose, tips of fingers and toes.

***Causes of peripheral cyanosis :***

- acute left ventricular failure
- shock following severe burns or severe haemorrhage
- venous obstruction may lead to local cyanosis.

### Central cyanosis

**Central cyanosis** is due to improper oxygenation of blood in the lungs or it may be due to admixture of venous and arterial blood.

It is *clinically evident* on the *tongue, inner surface of lip* and also in ***sites for peripheral cyanosis.***

### Causes of central cyanosis

**Causes of central cyanosis**

**Cardiac causes**

- Fallot's tetralogy
- Pulmonary arteriovenous communication (Reduced blood by passes the lungs into the systemic circulation)

**Pulmonary causes**

- Corpulmonale
- Pleural effusion
- Respiratory failure
- Bronchial asthma
- Diffuse fibrosis of the lungs

## ➤ 6.14 The Skin

### Structure and function of skin

Skin is the largest organ of the body. It's weight is from 3-4 Kg. and covers an area about 2 sq.m. It is divided into two parts-(1) Epidermis the outer part (2) Dermis the deeper part.

### Epidermis

It is divided into 4 layers from dermis to outside these are

1. **Basal layer :** It consists of undifferentiated proliferating brick shaped single layer of cells. Daughter cells from the basal layer migrate to the outside and begin differentiation. Cell division occurs in this layer.
2. **Stratum spinosum or malpighii :** These cells are polygonal and have junctional bridges with each other, looking like spines. Keratinisation begins in this layer. There are several layers of these cells above the basal layer. The cells are called **keratinocytes** because they contain a fibrous protein called **keratin**. The junctional bridges hold the cells together. The nucleus of these cells are vesicular
3. **Stratum granulosum :** Above the **Malphigian** layer, stratum granulosum consists of 2-6 layers of granular cells which are horizontally oriented and polygonal. They look flattened and contain dark granules containing **keratohyalin**. Degrading enzyme are found in the granular cells which are responsible for the eventual destruction of the nuclei and intracytoplasmic organelles.
4. **Stratum lucidium :** In thick skin as in palms and soles this thin layer is present above stratum granulosum. The cells contain eleidin, which is precursor of keratin.
5. **Stratum corneum :** This is outermost superficial strata. The cells are large, flat, polyhedral and plate like envelops filled with keratin. They do **not contain nuclei**. It contain 15-25 layers in most body surfaces

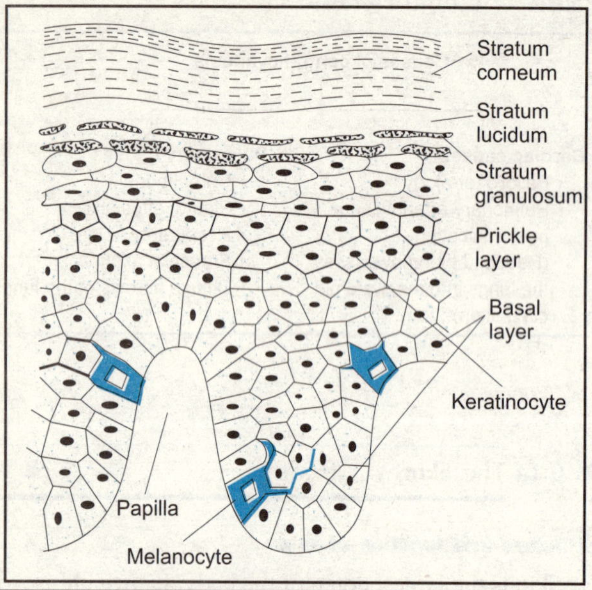


**Fig. 6.43 : Microscopic features of skin**

and about 100 layers on the palms and soles. These cells are held together by a lipid-rich cement in a fashion like bricks and mortar. This tightly packed keratinised envelopes in the stratum corneum provide a semi-impermeable layer that constitutes the most important physical barrier of the skin.

Cells become gradually flattened from basal layer to stratum corneum. In this evolution process the nuclei also change their character and in stratum corneum there are no nuclei. From basal to the outermost keratin layer it takes about 1-2 months time and thereafter the outermost keratin cells are shed regularly in microscopic form.

In addition to basal cells and keratinocytes two other type of specialised cells are present in the epidermis (1) **Melanocytes** and (2) **Langerhans cells**.

(1) **Melanocytes** are dendritic and present in the basal layer at about 10 cells interval. They produce melanin and disperse to prickle cell layer. The melanin protect the skin from ultraviolet radiation.

(2) **Langerhans cells** are also dendritic andare found scattered in the prickle cell layer. They contain tennis racket shaped grounds on electron microscopy and have got immunologic functions and form immunologic barrier of the skin. The epidermis has free nerve terminal but no blood vessels. It gets its nutrition from dermal blood vessels.

## Dermal-epidermal junction

It is called **basement membrane zone** having three distinct layers (1) **Lamina lucida** (2) **Basal lamina** and (3) **anchoring fibrils** on electron microscopy. This zone acts as the 'glue' between epidermis and dermis. Outgrowths of epidermis enter into the dermis and they are called **rete ridges**. Similarly

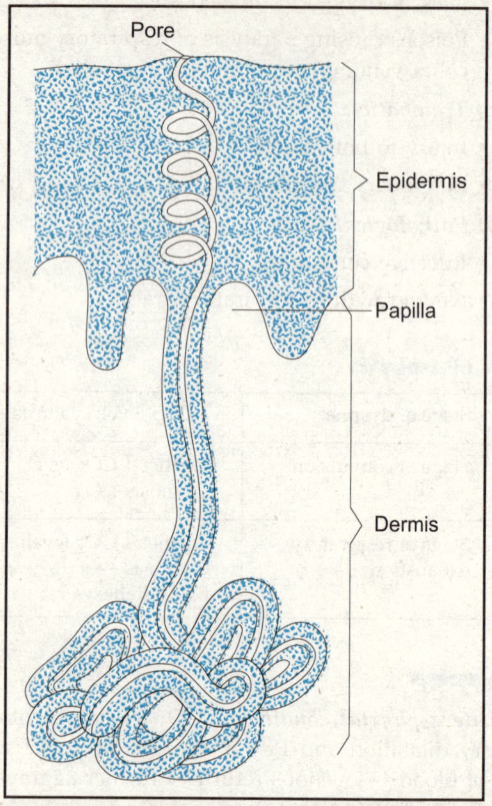


**Fig. 6.44 : Sweat gland**

overgrowths of dermis enter into the epidermis and are called **dermal papillae**. By the help of rete ridges and papillae there form a good anchorage between Epidermis and dermis.

**Dermis :** The dermis is tough and elastic structure which contains blood vessels, nerves, cutaneous appendages and matrix. It is much thicker than epidermis about 1 to 4 mm. The dermal matrix is composed of collagen, elastic and reticulin fibres and ground substance which are synthetised by dermal fibroblasts. Collagen and elastic fibres are fibrous proteins which form a compliant skeletal matrix. The uppermost part (Papillary dermis) contain collagen fibres which are fine and loosely arranged. The lower dermis (reticular dermis) is full of thick and densely packed fibres. The ground substance fill the space between the fibres. It is a material made up of several different mucopolysaccharides often called **proteoglycans**. The ground substance imparts to the dermis a more liquid quality, which helps movement of fluids, molecules and inflammatory substances including cells. Nerves and blood vessels course throughout the whole dermis and also the layer of subcutaneous fat lies below it, cells found in the dermis are (1) **Histiocytes** (2) **Fibroblasts** (3) **Mast cells**.

**Nerves :** The skin is the largest sensory organ. Touch, temperature and pain sensations are detected in the skin by both free nerve terminals and many complicated receptors. The nerve supply of skin is segmental but with considerable overlap between segments.

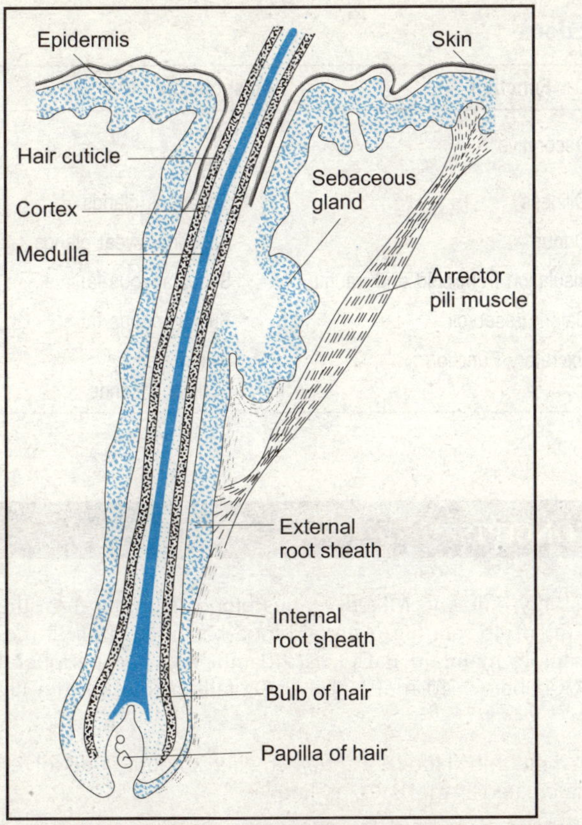


**Fig. 6.45 :** Structure of a hair

**Blood Vessels :** There are plenty of blood vessels, horizontally oriented as two plexuses with plenty of vertical connections. Skin can be an important reservoir of blood. Veins correspond to the arteries. Lymphatic channels are quite sufficient in dermis. The blood vessels of dermis can contract andrelax and can control a quite good amount of regulation of blood. Increased blood flow in the superficial plexus permits heat loss and shunting of blood to the deep plexus conserves heat.

**Skin Appendages :** They are (1) **Eccrine sweat gland** (2) **Apocrine sweat glands** (3) **Hairs with their follicles** (4) **Sebaceous gland and nails**. The details anatomy of these are beyond the scope of this book.

**Subcutaneous fat :** A layer of subcutaneous fat lies between the dermis and underlying fascia. It insulates the body from cold, cushions deep tissues from trauma and serve as a reserve source of food.

## Physiology

Skin performs many functions of which some are essential to life. They are summarised below :

1. It is a firm, elastic and resilient structure and acts as an **effective barrier** against physical, chemical and microbic trauma.
2. It regulates the **body temperature** by means of sweat glands and blood vessels.
3. It **secretes water**, as a means of temperature control. Sweat contains water which when evaporates cools down the skin.
4. Sebum the secretion of sebaceous glands **insulates** and **lubricates the surface of skin** and contain antimicrobial principles and precursor of vitamin D.
5. It contain nerves which **appreciate pain, heat, cold** and **touch**.
6. Skin is a **cosmetic organ**. Healthy skin is attractive.
7. Eye brows diverts sweat to **the lateral sides so that eyes are not** soiled by sweat during hard labour.
8. Nails help to scratch out unwanted materials and to grip minute substances as pin, tablets etc.
9. Chemical constitutents of skin function in many ways :
   (a) Water present in the skin causes elasticity of the stratum corneum.
   (b) Electrolytes as chlorides of sodium, potassium, magnesium and calcium present in skin maintain balance in necessity.
   (c) Carbohydrates as glucose, glycogen and complex glucides may alter microbial flora.
   (d) Glycogen is found in the stratum Malphigii and in the glands of the skin. It takes part in the elaboration of keratin and is found in increased quantity in some inflammatory and neoplastic states.
   (e) The complex glucides and mucopolysaccharides are very important structural constituents of dermis.
   (f) Lipids are found intracellularly as sterols e.g. cholesterol and phospholipids take part in various metabolism. Fatty acids are found in intercellular distribution and has got antimicrobial effect.
   (g) Proteins both globular and fibrous are present in the skin and may act as reserve proteins.
10. Apocrine secretion occurs at axillae, nipple areas and anogenital areas.
11. Melanin pigment of skin and its dispersion contributes to the colour of skin besides protection from the ultraviolet light.
12. Water balance is maintained by skin in many ways :
   (a) Stratum corneum being impermeable water cannot easily pass in or out.
   (b) By evaporation of sweat body is cooled and makes the man thirsty.
   (c) During dehydration, sweat secretion is lowered down.

### Skin Functions

| Function | Responsible structure |
|---|---|
| Barrier | Epidermis |
| Physical | Stratum corneum |
| Light | Melanocytes |
| Immunologic | Langerhans cells. |
| Tough, flexible foundation | Dermis |
| Temperature regulation | Blood vessels<br>Eccrine sweat glands |
| Sensation<br>Grasp | Nerves |

| Function | Responsible structure |
|---|---|
| Decorative | Nails<br>Hair |
| Oiliness | Sebaceus glands |
| Odour | Apocrine sweat glands |
| Insulation from cold and trauma, | Subcutaneous fat |
| Caloric reservoir | Subcutaneous fat |
| Excretory Function : | Sweat gland<br>Sodium Chloride |

## ➤ 6.15 KEY CONCEPTS

1. Gas exchange across the alveolar capillary membrane is very efficient. Mixed venous blood returning from the systemic circulation has a $PvO_2$ of 40 mm Hg and a $PvCO_2$ of 46 mm Hg. Arterial blood has a $PaO_2$ of 95 mm Hg and a $PaCO_2$ of 40 mm Hg. The central chemoreceptors maintain $PaCO_2$ at 40 mm Hg. The peripheral chemoreceptors will increase ventilation (and reduce $PaCO_2$ below 40 mm Hg) if $PaO_2$ falls below 60 mm Hg or if arterial pH is reduced by a metabolic acidosis.

2. Most of the oxygen delivered to the blood is bound to hemoglobin (Hbo2); a much smaller amount is dissolved in the blood. The amount of dissolved oxygen can be calculated if the $PaO_2$ is known.

   Dissolved $O_2$ (mL $O_2$/100 ml)= 0.003. $PaO_2$

3. The amount of O2 combined with hemoglobin can be determined from the oxyhemoglobin saturation curve or saturation of hemoglobin is known, can be calculated.

   $HbO_2$ (mL $O_2$/100 ml) = % Sat. g of Hb. 1.34

4. Hemoglobin is 97% saturated at normal $PaO_2$ (95 mm Hg); 75% saturated at the normal $PVO_2$ (40 mm Hg) and 50% saturated at 27 mm Hg. The $PaO_2$ at which hemoglobin is 50% saturated is called $P_{50}$.

5. The hemoglobin saturation curve shifts to the right when $P_{CO2}$, temperature, $H^+$ concentration or 2, 3 DPG concentration increases. Shifting the curve to the right makes it easier for $O_2$ to dissociate from hemoglobin in the tissues. Interestingly, CO causes Hb saturation curve to shift to the left, making it more difficult for oxygen to dissociate in the tissues.

## ➤ 6.16 DISORDERS/CLINICAL CORRELATIONS

➤ **Bronchial asthma :** Bronchial asthma is a clinical condition characterized by increased sensitivity of the tracheobronchial tree to a number of endogenous or exogenous allergens. This form of hypersensitivity reaction is characterised by ↑ serum IgE, increased eosinophil count, leukocytosis, decreased $FEV_1$ but a normal or subnormal FEV (total).

➤ **Acute respiratory failure of the newborn :** Surfactant and hypoplastic lung syndrome. Acute respiratory failure of the newborn may be caused by any of the three reasons :

- airway obstruction;
- ↓ distensibility of the lungs;
- ↓ central respiratory drive;
- airway may be obstructed by the inspissitated meconium or liquor or secretion;
- ↓ distensibility of the lung is mainly caused by (a) ↓ surfactant, (b) hypoplastic lung (immature, collapsed lung which does not distend);

## ➤ 6.16 DISORDERS/CLINICAL CORRELATIONS

- central respiratory drive may be delayed, sluggish or insufficient or depressed due to anesthetic overdose of anesthesia used.

➤ **Acute respiratory tract infection of the newborn and infants :**

- Contribute significantly to the mortality of the newborn if uncared.
- Increased air hunger interferes with suckling and chances of aspiration during feeding increases.
- Long term malnutrition is more common.

➤ **Pulmonary embolism :** It usually is the result of a systemic venous clot being dislodged and trapped in the lung. It occurs in the setting of prolonged immobilisation or in case of amniotic fluid embolism. Patients present with severe chest pain and shortness of breath. It can be diagnosed definitely by pulmonary artery angiography.

➤ **Pulmonary edema :** It means presence of fluid within the lung. To start with, fluid accumulates in the interstitium of lung parenchyma and then it spills into the alveoli. It can be due to increased hydrostatic pressure in the pulmonary veins (eg, in tight mitral stenosis), due to increased capillary permeability (eg, acute pancreatitis), due to microteas in the pulmonary capillary wall (eg, sudden decompression of massive pleural effusion). Initially the presenting feature is cough but later on the patient begins to have shortness of breath too. Treatment depends on the etiology.

➤ **Acute respiratory distress syndrome (ARDS) :** ARDS is a physiologic and radiologic syndrome with onset of 10-46 hours after severe systemic or pulmonary insult. It is characterized by rapid onset of dyspnea, respiratory distress, tachypnea and fever. It can occur in a variety of conditions. The main clinicopathological feature is formation of non-cardiogenic pulmonary edema. Usually the permeability of lung capillaries is increased leading to pulmonary edema. It is commonly seen in septicemia, acute pancreatitis, massive trauma etc.

➤ **Sleep apnea :** It is characterized by frequent pause in breathing for 10 seconds or more resulting in arterial hypoxemia and $CO_2$ retention. There are two types of sleep apneas : (i) central apnea and (ii) obstructive apnea.

➤ **Respiratory acidosis :** Respiratory acidosis results from hypoventilation due to pulmonary disease in which some alveoli are poorly perfused or substantial amounts of blood are shunted by perfusion of unventilated alveoli.

➤ **Respiratory alkalosis :** Respiratory alkalosis results from hyperventilation which is usually neurogenic in origin produced by a wide variety of causes such as fever, pain, anxiety and hypotension. It may also occur in salicylate poisoning as a result of stimulation of the respiratory centre by salicylate. Respiratory alkalosis is much less common than acidosis but can occur when respiration is stimulated or is no longer subject to feed back control.

## ➤ 6.16 DISORDERS/CLINICAL CORRELATIONS

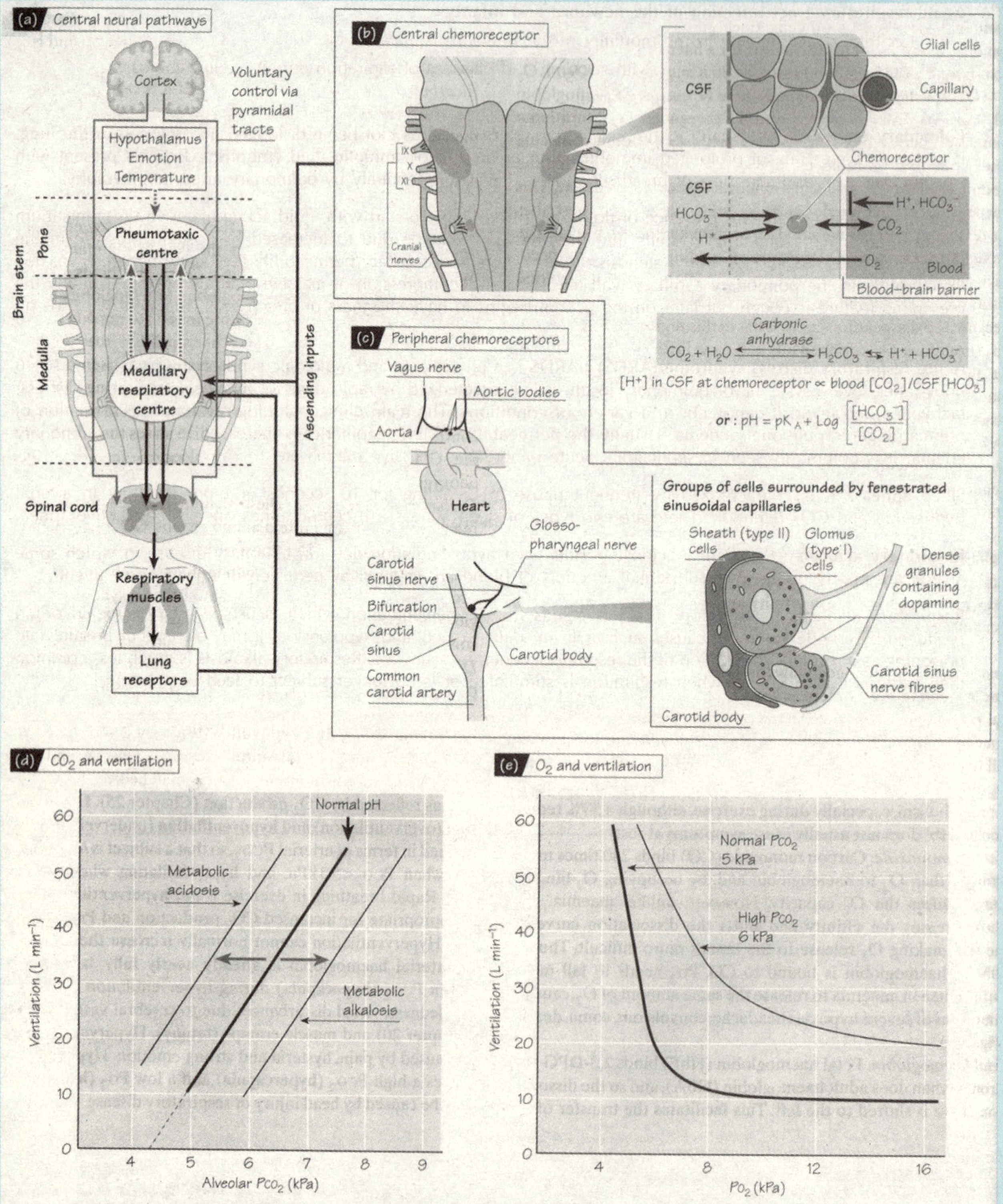


The above figures show the relationship between ventilation, $Pco_2$ and $Po_2$. A metabolic acidosis is caused by a fall in $HCO_3^-$ or increased acid production (e.g. lactic acidosis in severe exercise; diabetic ketoacidosis). Conversely a respiratory acidosis or alkalosis is caused by a change in $CO_2$.

# Cardiovascular Physiology

AGENDA :



7

## ➤ 7.1 CHAPTER OVERVIEW

The heart pumps the blood through the circulation. The cardiac output from the heart must be sufficient to perfuse all the organs and maintain a pressure adequate to perfuse the brain.

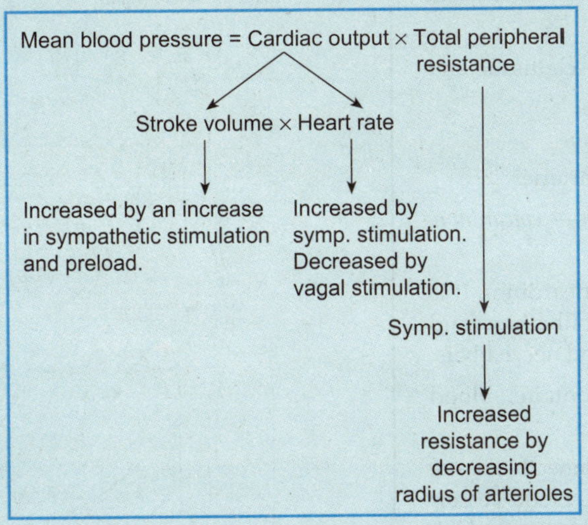


Cardiac output can be measured using Ficks equation $C.O. = \frac{Vo_2 (O_2 \text{ consumption})}{(\text{Arterial } O_2 \text{ content} - \text{Venous } O_2 \text{ content})}$

Resistance can be calculated using the Poisenille equation $R = \frac{8.\eta.L}{\pi.r^4}$ [n = viscosity; L = length; r = radius]

Blood pressure is maintained by the baroreceptor reflex, which responds to a decrease in blood pressure by increasing heart rate, contractility and by decreasing venous compliance.

Blood pressure decreases as blood flows through the circulation. The magnitude of the decrease is proportional to the resistance of each segment of the circulation. The greatest decrease occurs as blood flows through the arterioles.

The velocity of blood through a vessel is proportional to the flow of blood through the vessel and inversely proportional to the area of the vessel. $\left[v = \frac{\dot{Q}}{A}\right]$ Increasing the velocity of blood can change flow from laminar (the fluid moves in a steady, orderly stream) to turbulent. Turbulent flow produces a sound called a **murmur** if it occurs in the heart, or a bruit if it occurs in a blood vessel. Turbulence can be predicted from Reynolds numbers NR $= \frac{P.D.V.}{n}$ [P = density D = diameter V= velocity n = viscosity]

If Reynolds number exceeds 2000-3000, flow is likely to be turbulent.

The quantity of blood flowing into each organ is inversely proportional to the relative resistance of each organ. For example, at rest approximately 20% of the cardiac output flows through the skeletal muscles. During exercise, when the resistance of the skeletal muscle vessels decreases, over 80% of the cardiac output can flow through the skeletal muscles. The organs in the body are in parallel with each other

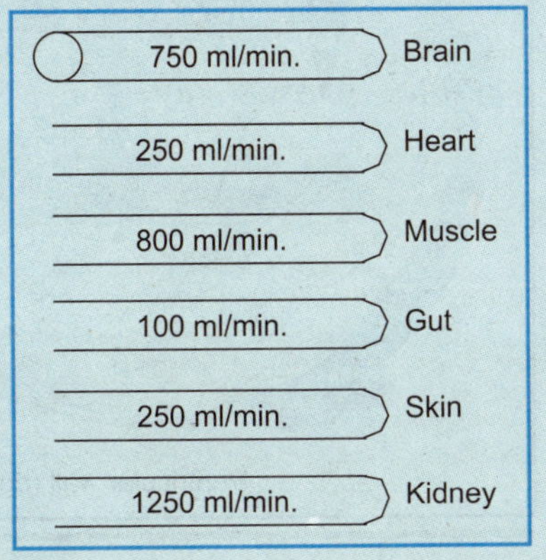


$$\frac{1}{R_T} = \frac{1}{R_1} + \frac{1}{R_2} + \frac{1}{R_3} + \frac{1}{R_4} + \frac{1}{R_5} + \frac{1}{R_6}$$

## 7.2 Gross Anatomy of the Heart and Functions of Cardiovascular System

The **heart** is a hollow muscular pump located within the mediastinum of the thorax. It consists of muscle tissue and four chambers :

- *two atria* — receive blood from veins
- *two ventricles* — pump blood into arteries.

The walls of the heart consist of three layers — *epicardium, myocardium* and *endocardium.*

**Epicardium** : Corresponds to visceral pericardium. It is made of connective tissue covered by epithelium and contains blood capillaries, lymph capillaries and nerve fibers.

**Myocardium** : relatively thick and contains blood capillaries, lymph capillaries and nerve fibers.

**Endocardium** : contains epithelium and connective tissue (elastic and collagenous fibers). It also contains blood vessels and specialised cardiac muscle fibers, known as *Purkinje fibers* (see Figs. 7.1 and 7.2).

Table 7.1
Valves of the heart (see also Fig. 7.3)

| Valve | Location | Function |
|---|---|---|
| **Bicuspid valve (mitral)** | Located in the left atrioventricular orifice | During ventricular contraction, flow of blood is prevented from left ventricle to left atrium |
| **Tricuspid valve** | Located in the right atrioventricular orifice | During ventricular conraction, flow of blood is prevented from right ventricle to right atrium |
| **Pulmonary valve** | Entry to pulmonary artery | During ventricular relaxation, flow of blood is prevented from pulmonary artery into right ventricle |
| **Aortic valve** | Entry to aorta | During ventricular relaxation, flow of blood is prevented from aorta into left ventricle. |

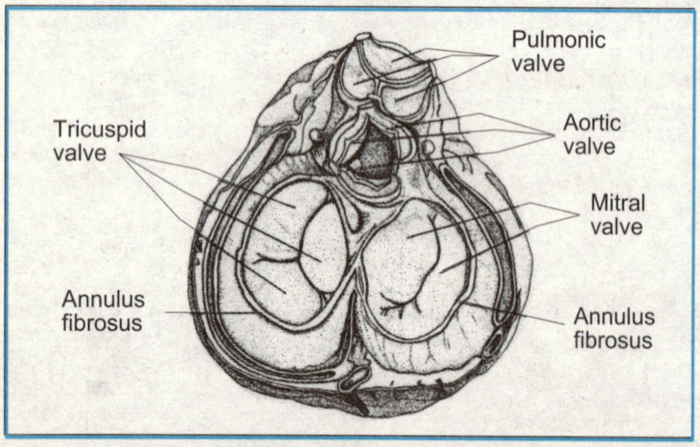


**Fig. 7.1 :** Valves of the heart

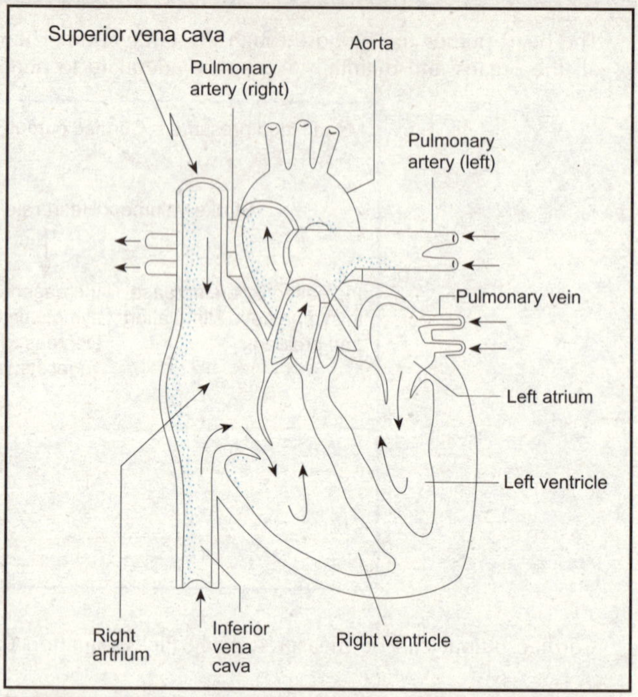


**Fig. 7.2 :** Chambers and vessels of the heart

### Functions of the cardiovascular system

Cardiac muscle has intrinsic capacity for rhythmic excitation. The activation process can spread from cell to cell. Cardiovascular system is a transport system that connects the external environment to the tissues and transports substances essential for metabolism. This system removes $CO_2$ and other by-products of metabolism from

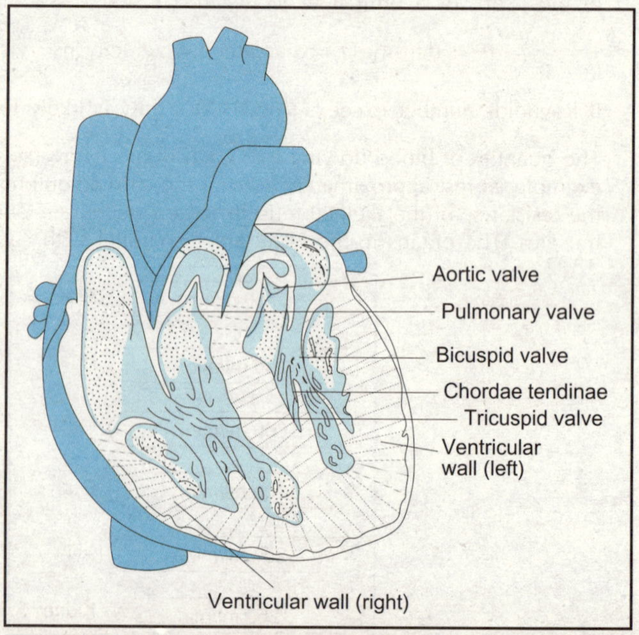


**Fig. 7.3 :** Interior of the heart

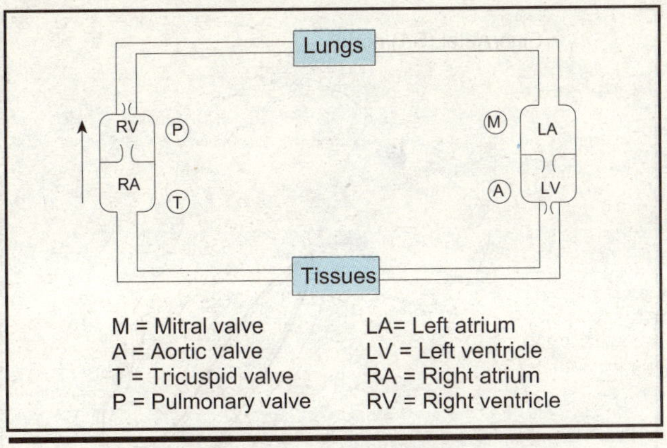


**Fig. 7.4 :** Path of blood through heart

the tissues. Cardiovascular system is crucial in maintaining the homeostasis of the extracellular fluid. Hormones also circulate in it. However, heart itself produces a hormone, *atrial natriuretic peptide*. It is also responsible for heat distribution and maintenance of temperature regulation. Further it also transports the cells and antibodies concerned with body's defence mechanism.

**Flow of blood through the heart (Figs. 7.4 and 7.5.1)**

Superior and inferior venae cavae → right atrium → right ventricle (via the right atrioventricular valve) → pulmonary artery (deoxygenated blood) → lungs (interchange of gases) → pulmonary veins ($O_2$ blood) → left atrium → left ventricle.

The right side of the heart drives blood through the pulmonary circulation.

**Pulmonary circulation** (lesser circulation) is the part of circulation which includes pulmonary artery, lungs and pulmonary veins. **Systemic circulation** (greater circulation) is the part which includes the aorta, other viscera and veins which drain into superior and inferior venae cavae. Blood

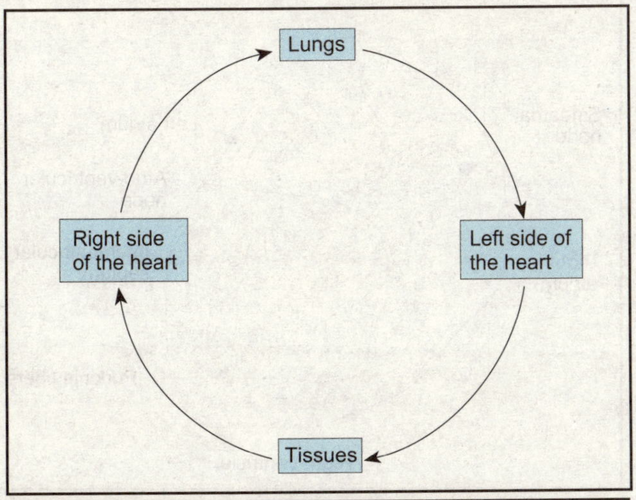


**Fig. 7.5.1 :** Path of blood through the heart

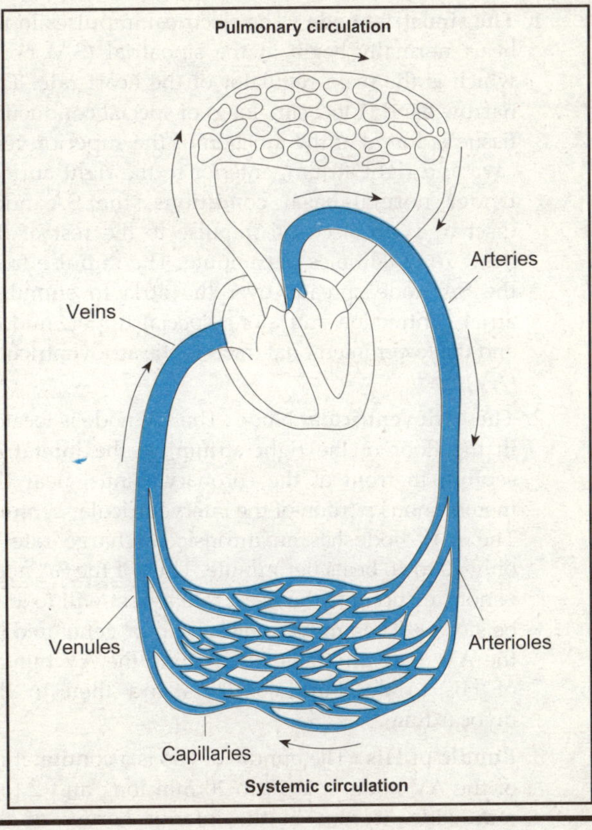


**Fig. 7.5.2**

flow through the systemic circulation depends on contraction of the left ventricle of the heart.

The heart acts as a pump which is responsible for circulation of blood round the body. Left side of the heart pumps blood from the lungs to the tissues but the right side of the heart pumps blood from the tissues to the lungs.

The *right side of the heart* is concerned with *deoxygenated blood* whereas the *left side of the heart* deals with *oxygenated blood*. The vessels which carry blood to the heart are veins whereas the arteries carry blood away from the heart (Fig. 7.5.2).

## Circulation of blood

Main function is to transport nutrients and other materials from one part to another part of the organism. Blood plays a vital role as the intermediary between environment and cells. The heart is responsible for supply of energy for this circulation. Cardiac contraction drives the blood to the tissues via arteries and back to heart via veins.

The conducting system of the heart is made up of atypical cardiac muscle myofibrils that have abundant sarcoplasm, which is very rich in glycogen. This specialized tissue has the capability of rhythmic electrical impulse formation and can conduct impulses much more rapidly than typical cardiac muscle.

1. **The sinoatrial node :** The electrical impulses in the heart normally begin at the sinoatrial (SA) node, which is the main regulator of the heart rate. This narrow band (1 to 2 c.m. long) of special conducting tissue is found at the junction of the superior vena cava and right atrium, anterior to the right auricle. Under normal basal conditions, the SA node discharges an electrical impulse to the rest of the heart 70 to 80 times per minute. The impulse from the SA node spreads over the atria to stimulate atrial contraction and along special upper, middle and the lower internodal tracts to the atrioventricular (AV) node.
2. **The Atrioventricular Node :** The AV node is located in the floor of the right atrium, at the interatrial septum in front of the coronary. Sinus, near the membranous portion of the interventricular septum. The A.V. node has an intrinsic discharge rate of only 40 to 60 beats per minute. Thus, if the SA node is not functioning, the heart rate at rest will tend to be slower. The impulses picked up or generated by the AV node are transmitted along the AV bundle of His to the Purkinje fibers and then to the myocardium.
3. **Bundle of His :** The bundle of His is a continuation of the AV node. It is 10 to 20 mm long and 2 to 4 mm wide. It runs in the inferior border of the membranous portion of the interventricular septum down to the muscular portion of the interventricular septum, where it divides into right and left bundles. The left bundle divides after a short distance into a long, thin anterior branch and a shorter, thicker posterior branch. The right bundle usually continues on to the right ventricle as a single main branch. These three fascicles then subdivide to ramify over their respective ventricles just under the endocardium into terminal branches called **Purkinje's fibers**.
4. **Purkinje's Fibers :** Purkinje'sfibers not only act as the terminal portion of the conduction system, but also can function as a backup intrinsic pacemaker for the heart. However, their discharge rate is only 20 to 40 beats per minute. Thus, they seldom initiate a heart beat except when there is a complete AV block and complete absence of AV nodal impulses.
5. **Accessory Fibers :** Accessory fibers can serve as conduction pathways to bypass the normal AV conduction system. These fibers form the anatomic and physiologic basis for the arrhythmias associated with the pre excitation syndromes.

## Nerve supply of the heart

Apart from the intrinsic impulses generated within the conducting system, the heart is also influenced by ANS, originating in the cardiac center in the medulla oblongata which reach it via ANS. The vagus nerve (X CN) supplies SA and AV nodes and atrial muscle. **Parasympathetic stimulation** reduces the rate at which impulses are produced and force of heart beat. **The sympathetic nervous system** supplies SA and AV nodes and the myocardium of the atrium and the ventricles. Heart rate and force of the heart beat are increased by sympathetic stimulation.

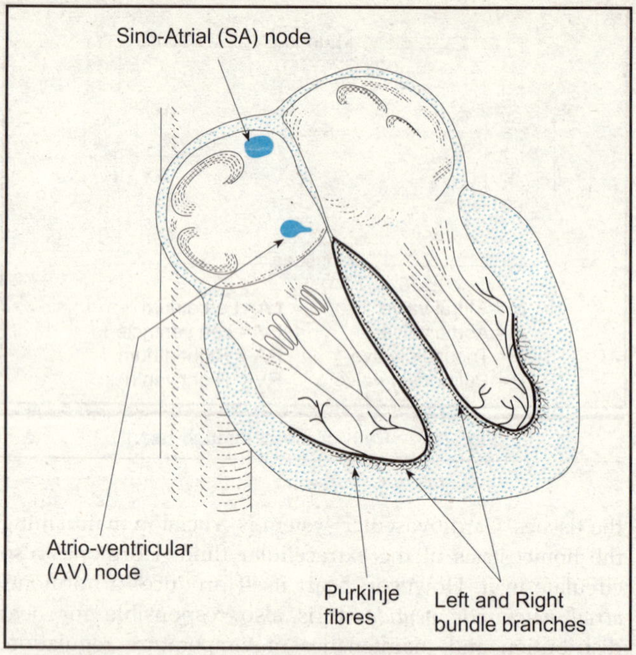


**Fig. 7.6 :** The relationship between the systemic and pulmonary circulations

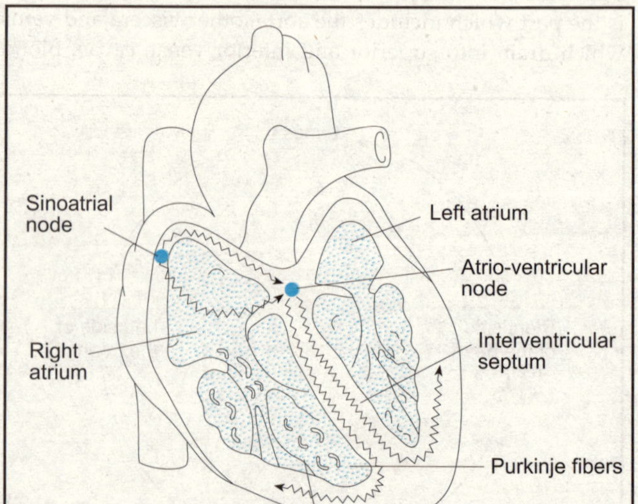


**Fig. 7.7 :** Conducting system in the heart

## 7.3 Cardiac Muscle

Cardiac muscle is also striated like skeletal muscle. But in this case the muscle cells are cylindrical units. The cells branch and interdigitate, one cell abut against another at Z-lines, in wavy intercalated disc, where cell membranes run parallel with strong adhesions between them. Near the disc, adjacent cells unite by low resistance gap junctions through which impulses pass from one cell to another. *So the entire cardiac muscle* behaves as a **functional syncytium** (Fig. 7.8).

The T-tubules (wider than skeletal muscle) are situated at the Z-lines instead of A-I junctions as in skeletal muscle. The molecular motor system is the same actin, myosin, tropomyosin and troponin. Large number of mitochondria is present; cardiac muscle is highly vascular and metabolism is predominantly aerobic (slow oxidative).

### Electrical properties

Cardiac muscle is spontaneously active; neural regulation by parasympathetic and sympathetic nervous system modifies its rate and force of contraction, but is not essential for its contraction. All parts of heart can generate the impulse, but normally, the specialized conducting tissue is responsible for generating and propagating the impulse all throughout the heart. SA node in the right atrium is the normal pacemaker of heart because of its highest rate.

The pacemaker (SA node) contains P cells which have unstable membrane potential. Its *resting membrane potential* is –70 mV, in contrast to *working myocardial cells* (–90 mV). When the resting level is reached, there is progressive depolarization to attain firing level of –55 mV, when there occurs rapid change in membrane potential. This slow depolarization leading to spontaneous generation of action potential is called **prepotential** or **pacemaker potential**. It is due to slow decrease in $K^+$ permeability, and reduced $K^+$ efflux along with leak of $Na^+$ is responsible for early depolarization that is brought up to firing level (Fig. 7.9) by entry of $Ca^{2+}$ by a particular Transient $Ca^{++}$ channel. The spike potential in pacemaker cells is due to entry of $Ca^{2+}$ and to some extent $Na^+$ by special voltage gated $Ca^{2+}$ channels. Repolarization is due to closure of $Ca^{2+}$ channels and exit of $K^+$.

When the working myocardial cells (atrial or ventricular myocytes) is stimulated by impulse reaching them from the pacemaker, the initial part of depolarization is rapid as in skeletal muscle and exceeds zero level (overshoot), ***0 phase***, and the initial small rapid repolarization is ***phase 1***; then a prolonged plateau (200 milliseconds) occurs ***phase 2***; after which there is rapid repolarization ***phase 3***; to return to resting membrane potential ***phase 4***. **The phase 0** is due to rapid increase in $Na^+$ conductance by opening of voltage-gated $Na^+$ channels as occurs in nerve and muscle. ***Phase 1*** is due to closure of $Na^+$ channels and short-lived influx of $Cl^-$. ***Phase 2*** is due to slow but prolonged opening of

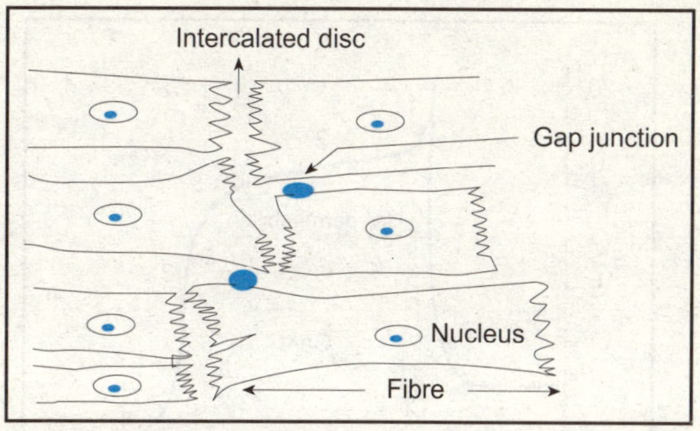


**Fig. 7.8 : Cardiac muscle**

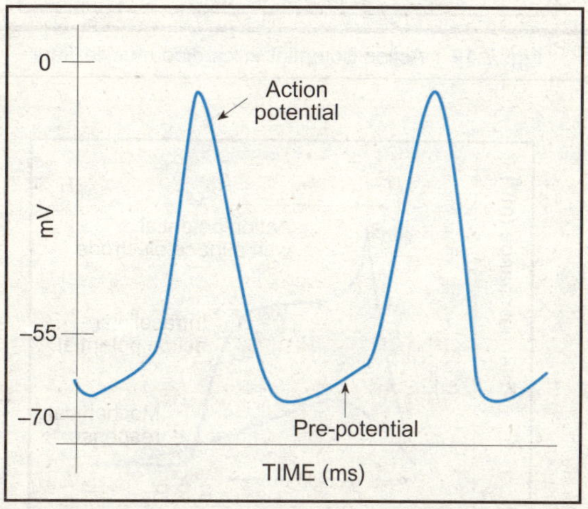


**Fig. 7.9 : Pacemaker potential**

voltage-gated $Ca^{2+}$ channels. ***Phase 3*** corresponds to closure of $Ca^{2+}$ channels and continued opening of $K^+$ channels. The fast $Na^+$ channels have two gates outer gate opens at firing level; the inner gate, initially open, closes quickly, preventing further entry of $Na^+$ ($Na^+$ channel inactivation); outer gate then closes and inner opens after the absolute refractory period. The $Ca^{2+}$ channels are activated at –30 to –40 mV (Fig. 7.10).

The duration of action potential (in ventricles) is dependent on rate of firing. The repolarization time undergoes alteration. At heart rate *of 75/min, action potential duration is 0.25 sec* and *cardiac cycle time is 0.8 sec (systole 0.3 sec); at heart rate of 200/min, action potential duration is 0.15 sec* and *cardiac cycle time is 0.3 sec. of which systole is 0.13 sec.*

### Mechanical (contractile) responses

**Excitation-contraction coupling** mechanism of cardiac muscle is the same as that of skeletal muscle. The contractile response follows immediately after the actin potential and lasts about $1^1/_2$ times more than the action potential. The contraction of muscle is due to sliding of actin filament over myosin filament, after $Ca^{2+}$ binds to troponin C. **In cardiac muscle, $Ca^{2+}$ is derived from two sources**—$Ca^{2+}$ derived during excitation is responsible for further release of $Ca^{2+}$

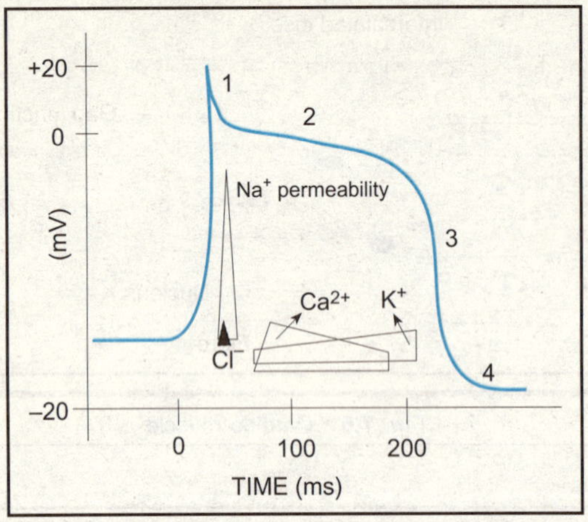


Fig. 7.10 : Action potential in cardiac muscle fiber

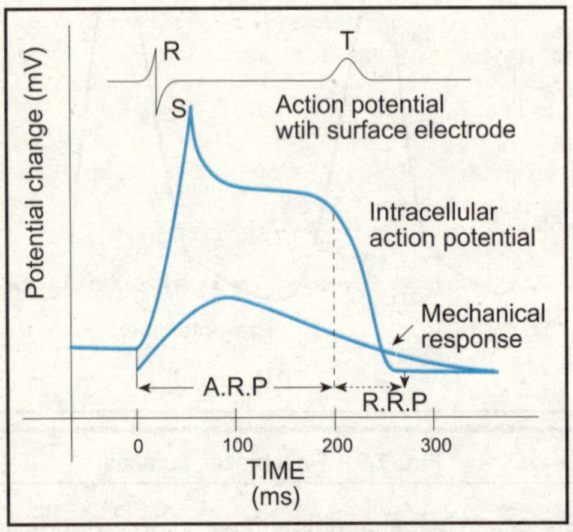


Fig. 7.11 : Electrical and mechanical response of a cardiac muscle fiber on a same time scale. A.R.P = Absolute refractory period; R.R.P. = Relative refractory period.

from sarcoplasmic reticulum. In **skeletal muscle**, depolarization and involvement of dihydropyridine receptor somehow increases $Ca^{2+}$ efflux from endoplasmic reticulum (Fig. 7.11).

The **cardiac muscle is electrically absolutely refractory from the onset of action potential up to –50 mV of phase 3** (sodium channels remain inactivated). From this point to phase 4 is the relative refractory period. So during the refractory period the mechanical response is almost 70% complete. With increase in heart rate, i.e., rate of excitation, the duration of systole and cardiac cycle time also diminish along with the action potential. So tetanization in vivo even in serious tachyarrhythmias is not possible. Even in experimental setting it is not demonstrable. It is protective for cardiac muscle for tetanic contraction would deprive the myocardium of oxygen and have serious consequences.

In the **whole heart, the end of refractoriness concides with the peak of T wave of ECG.** If stimulation falls on the peak of T wave, ventricular fibrillation, not tetanus takes place due to reentry mechansim. Reentry develops because some fibers come out of refractoriness whereas some are in refractory state, creating an ideal situation of multiple cardiac impulses travelling in varied directions producing rapid irregular but ineffective contractions of ventricles and severe reduction of cardiac output.

## The structure of the blood vessels

The blood vessels are classified into four main types : **arteries; arterioles; capillaries** and **veins**. The wall of the larger blood vessels consist of three layers :

(a) **The tunica intima :** Layer of flat endothelial cells overlying a thin layer of connective tissue. The endothelial cells are in direct contact with the blood (Fig. 7.12).

(b) **The tunica media :** Layer of elastic tissue (the internal and external elastic lamina and consists of a circular layer of smooth muscle containing elastin and collagen. The smooth muscle is innervated by sympathetic nerve fibers.

**Function :** Provides the mechanical strength of the blood vessel.

(c) **The tunica adventitia :** Layer of connective tissue.

**Function** : to anchor the blood vessels in place.

The arteries are subdivided into two groups :

(a) The elastic arteries

(b) The muscular arteries

**The elastic arteries :**

- Diameter 1-2 c.m.
- Examples are aorta, pulmonary arteries.
- Walls are very distensible because their tunica media contains a high proportion of elastin.

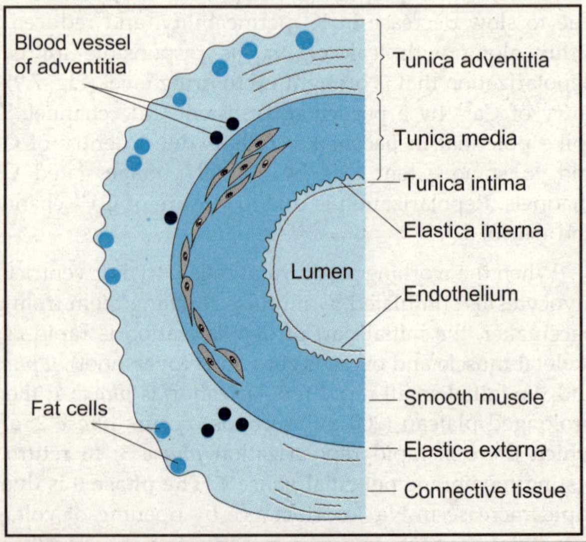


Fig. 7.12 : Principal layers of a muscular artery (the tunica intima, tunica media and tunica adventitia)

**The muscular arteries :**

- Diameter 1 m.m.-1 c.m.
- Tunica media of the muscular arteries contains a higher proportion of smooth muscle than that of elastic arteries
- Function-efficient distribution of blood to the various vascular beds.
- Examples are cerebral; popliteal and brachial arteries.

## 7.4 Hemodynamics

The science of **hemodynamics** is concerned with the study of the physical principles that govern the movement of blood within the cardiovascular system (CVS). The CVS consists of a pump, the heart and a system of tubes, blood vessels that are branched, elastic conduits of various dimensions. Blood circulates in this closed system of vessels in two different circuits in series with each other — **systemic** and **pulmonary circulations**. Blood is a suspension of red and white blood cells and platelets suspended in plasma. So, blood is not a simple fluid. It is, therefore, difficult to describe the pulsatile flow of blood within the vessels in precise mathematical terms. But an understanding of the basic physical principles of fluid mechanics provides considerable insight into the inter-relationships among velocity of blood flow, flow rate, blood pressure, and the dimension of the various components of circulatory system.

### Flow and velocity (Fig. 7.13)

**Velocity** of a fluid is the rate of linear displacement of the individual particles of that fluid. It is expressed as displacement per unit time, i.e., cm/sec. **Flow** refers to the displacement of a volume of fluid per unit time expressed as volume per unit time, i.e., mL/sec. The distribution of forces within a moving fluid is determined by the velocity of the fluid. When a fluid flows through a tube of variable cross-sectional dimensions, **velocity (v) is** directly proportional to the flow ($\dot{Q}$) and inversely proportional to the cross-sectional area (A) of the tube :

$$V = \frac{\dot{Q}}{A}$$

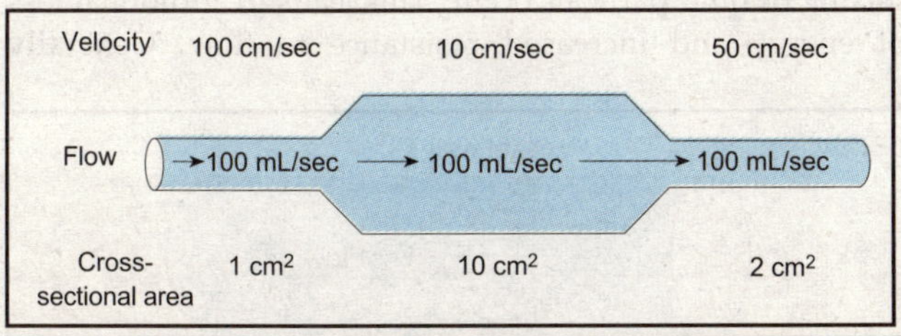


**Fig. 7.13 :** Relationship between velocity and cross-sectional area of a rigid tube at a constant flow

If the fluid is incompressible, neither created nor destroyed within the system, and the tube is rigid, the flow through each cross-section should be identical. Velocity, therefore, is greater in the narrower parts of the tube, and vice versa (Fig. 7.13). This concept applies both to a single large tube as well as to several smaller tubes in parallel. In a system of tubes where the cross-sectional area of several smaller tubes in parallel is more than that of a single large tube in series with them, velocity in the smaller tubes will be lower than velocity in the large tube provided that the flow is constant. ***Thus, velocity of blood in the CVS decreases progressively as it traverses the aorta, its branches and the arterioles.*** Velocity of blood is minimum in the capillaries. Gradual increase in velocity occurs again from the venules to the veins and the venae cavae. While the velocity of blood in different parts of the circulation are related to their cross-sectional area, the flow of blood is dependent upon the pressure gradient, the properties of the fluid, and the dimension of the entire system.

### Pressure-velocity relationships

**Total energy (TE)** in an ideal fluid system having no frictional resistance to flow is the sum of **potential energy (PE)** and **kinetic energy (KE), TE = PE + KE**. In a fluid at rest, distribution of forces is equal in all directions, all the energy is in the form of potential energy which is responsible for hydrostatic pressure. As the fluid moves, the distribution of forces gets altered, the extent of alteration being dependent upon velocity. Some of the potential energy is converted to kinetic energy and the total energy remains the same.

The **pressure** (force per unit area, dyne/cm$^2$) at any point of a moving fluid has two components **end pressure** and **side (or lateral) pressure**. These pressures can be measured with the help of appropriately placed sensors. The sensors facing upstream measure end pressure or total pressure because any fluid particle hitting them stops converting its kinetic energy to potential energy. Other sensors lying tangenital to the axis of flow sense the side (or lateral) pressure. Side pressure is the pressure experienced by the vessel walls. In an ideal system end pressure is the same at every point but side pressure at any point is lower than end pressure. With increase in velocity, the difference between end pressure and side pressure also increases. This difference between end pressure and side pressure can be attributed to the kinetic energy of the fluid in motion and may be called **kinetic or dynamic component ($P_d$)** of the total pressure. $P_d$ may be calculated as :

$$P_d = \frac{1}{2}\rho v^2$$

where ρ = density of the fluid and v = velocity.

In a normal CVS, $P_d$ is very small, but significantly high $P_d$ may be found in conditions like heavy exercise, arteriovenous fistula and regurgitation through cardiac valves where cardiac output is high. It should also be noted that side pressure is responsible for stretching of vessel walls and propulsion of blood through side branches of arteries. ***In aortic stenosis,*** the left ventricular output is ejected at a high velocity through the narrowed aortic orifice. This high velocity of blood is associated with a large kinetic energy and corresponding reduction of side pressure. It may cause reversal of direction of flow in coronary arteries which arise at right-angles from the ascending aorta. This may contribute to the tendency for patients with aortic stenosis to develop precordial chest pain (angina pectoris). The concept that pressure decreases with increase in velocity is the basis of **Bernoulli's principle.**

## Resistance to flow

The particles in a fluid tend to resist each other's movement by mutual interaction. This causes frictional loss of energy and the end pressure drops along the path of flow. The side pressure also drops but the difference between end and side pressures remain the same as it would have been in an ideal system.

**Viscosity** is the flow-determining property of a fluid and refers to the force generated by the particles of the fluid to resist relative motion among them. It depends on the nature of the fluid. **Newton defined *viscosity as the ratio of shear stress to the rate of strain on the fluid.*** Viscosity of blood is the source of frictional loss of energy in the CVS. It is also a determinant of the characteristic of flow of blood.

**Resistance** (R) in fluid mechanics is analogous to electrical resistance. Its relationship with end pressure difference between ***two points (ΔP) and flow (Q) may be described by*** **Darcy's law (analogous to Ohm's law)** :

$$Q = \frac{\Delta P}{R}$$

Using the electrical analogy, the total resistance ($R_T$) for tubes or vessels arranged in series is the sum of resistances in individual tubes :

$$R_T = R_1 + R_2 + \dots\dots\dots\dots + R_n$$

For tubes or vessels arranged in parallel, $R_T$ may be calculated by adding the reciprocals of resistances in individual tubes :

$$\frac{1}{R_T} = \frac{1}{R_1} = \frac{1}{R_2} + \dots\dots\dots\dots + \frac{1}{R_n}$$

**Reciprocal of resistance** is known as **conductance** (C) which is the ease with which fluid can flow through a tube or vessel. From the above relationship, it follows that total conductance ($C_T$) in a parallel circuit is the sum of individual condu-ctances :

$$C_T = \frac{1}{R_T} = \frac{1}{R_1} = \frac{1}{R_2} + \dots + \frac{1}{R_n} = C_1 + C_2 + \dots + C_n$$

**Poiseuille** described the inter-relationship among resistance to flow, viscosity of a fluid and the dimensions of the tube through which the fluid is flowing. The relationship is expressed as :

$$R = \frac{8\eta l}{\pi r^4}$$

where R = resistance to flow, η = viscosity of the fluid, l = length of the tube and r = radius of the tube. Thus, resistance is directly proportional to the viscosity of the fluid and the length of the tube and inversely proportional to the fourth power of the radius of the tube.

Hence, ***for the same pressure gradient (ΔP), flow is directly proportional to the fourth power of the radius of the tube whereas resistance is inversely proportional to the fourth power of the radius.*** That means flow will increase 16-fold if radius is doubled. On the contrary, there will be a 16-fold increase in resistance (with corresponding 16-fold reduction in flow) if radius is halved. These apply to the CVS because, in the CVS, length of a given vessel is more or less constant and viscosity of blood does not vary appreciably in health. Modulations in resistance is, therefore, produced mainly by variations in the radius of blood vessels.

***The arteries, arterioles, capillaries, venules, and veins in the CVS are arranged in series.*** Each type of vessels (except aorta and pulmonary artery) lies parallel with others of the same type. In the CVS, pressure drop is greatest across the arterioles. As the flow is the same all through the vascular system, resistance is greatest in the arterioles which can regulate the radius of their lumen by the thick circular smooth muscle layer present in their walls.

## Flow characteristics laminar and turbulent flow

**Flow of a fluid** in a cylindrical tube may be **laminar** or **turbulent**. In **laminar flow,** the fluid particles move in laminae parallel to each other. Fluid in different laminae move at different velocities. A thin layer of fluid remains motionless in contact with the wall of the tube just wetting it, whereas the central-most lamina moves the fastest. There occurs a gradual increment in velocity in adjacent concentric laminae as one goes from the periphery to the center of the tube. The velocity profile across the tube in laminar flow may be described as a parabolic velocity profile having maximal flow at its center which is twice the mean velocity across the entire cross-section of the tube (Fig. 7.14). Laminar flow is also called **streamline flow.**

**In turbulent flow,** there is no orderly flow pattern and the fluid elements move irregularly. No definite streamlines or laminae as in laminar flow can be found and rapid, radial mixing of fluid particles occur. This leads to additional loss of energy and increased resistance to flow. Generally

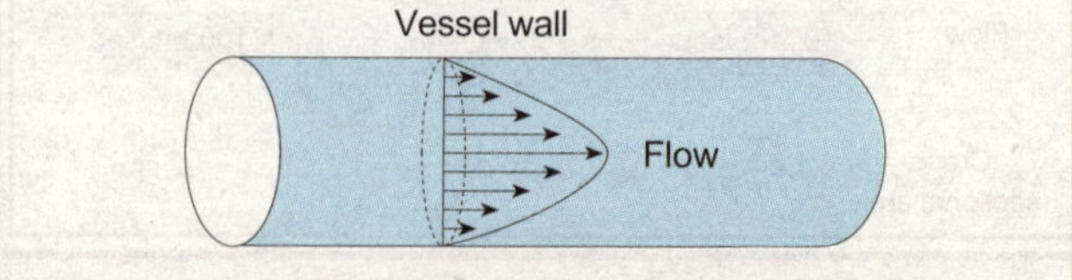


Fig. 7.14 : Parabolic distribution of velocities in streamline flow

speaking, flow is laminar at low velocities and tends to the turbulent as velocity increases. ***Factors that contribute to turbulent flow may be expressed*** by the **Reynolds equation** :

$$Re = \frac{\rho DV}{\eta}$$

where D is the diameter of the tube, ρ is the density, v is the mean velocity and η is the viscosity of the fluid. Re is the **Reynolds number**, a dimensionless number, which may predict whether laminar or turbulent flow will exist in a tube under given conditions. The flow is usually laminar for Re < 2,000 and turbulence is usually found when Re > 3,000. Thus, large tube diameters, high velocities, and low viscosities are the predisposing factors to the development of turbulent flow. Abrupt variations in the dimensions of a tube and irregularities in its wall are other factors contributing to the occurrence of turbulence.

**Turbulence** in a part of the CVS is generally accompanied by vibrations that may be heard as *bruits or murmurs* on auscultation with a stethoscope. One or more of the factors predisposing to turbulent flow as mentioned above are responsible for bruits or murmurs heard clinically. Functional murmurs (i.e., murmurs in the absence of any structural abnormalities) in severe anemia are due to low blood viscosity because of decrease in RBC content and to high blood velocity because of increase in cardiac output associated with anemia.

***Turbulent flow predisposes to the development of blood clots or thrombi.*** This may be a factor for thrombi associated with prosthetic heart valves. It is, therefore, important to design such valves in such a way that turbulent flow does not occur across them, thereby minimizing the changes of thrombosis.

## Capacitance and distensibility

Blood vessels are distensible and resistance depends on perfusion pressure in distensible tubes like blood vessels. **Capacitance (C)** is the measure of distensibility. **Capacitance** is expressed as :

$$C = \frac{V}{P}$$

where V is change in volume in response to change in distending or side pressure (P). Pressure changes within the CVS are generally associated with alterations in the distribution of blood within it. Capacitance differs considerably between veins and arteries (Figs. 7.15 and 7.16.1). The blood volume contained in the veins at a given pressure is much more than that in the arteries. Hence the veins are called the capacitance vessels and act like reservoir of blood in the CVS.

***The distensibility of pulmonary vessels has a beneficial role.*** There is only a slight increase in pulmonary arterial pre-ssure even when the right ventricular output increases considerably. Arterioles are not much distensible and they are the site for most of the peripheral resistance in the CVS.

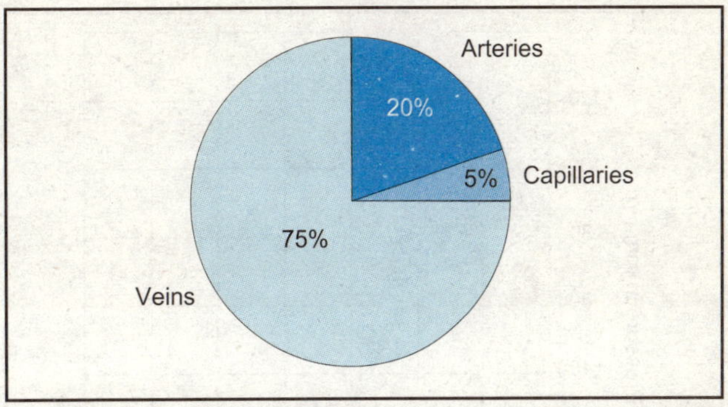


**Fig. 7.15 :** Distribution of blood volume in the systemic circulation

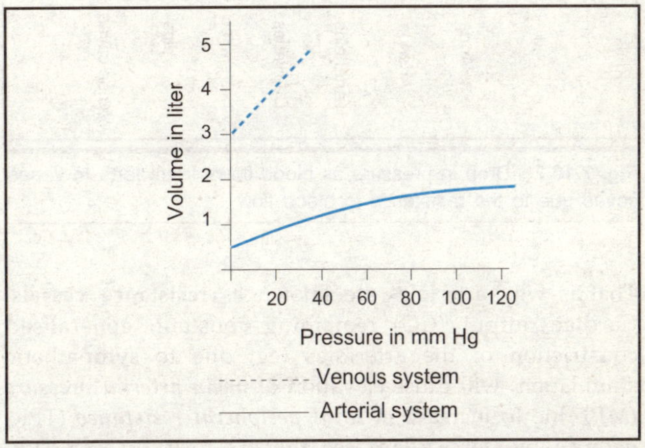


**Fig. 7.16.1 :** Pressure-volume relationships of the arterial and venous systems showing greater capacitance (slopes of the line) of veins

Therefore, blood flow through most of the organs is a linear function of the perfusion pressure. Factors determining the distensibility of a blood vessel includes its radius, wall thickness, amount of connective tissue and muscle in the wall etc.

## Pressure and resistance in the CVS

Though the resistance to blood flow depends both on length and radius of the vessel, it is the radius which is altered for the modulation of blood flow. Resistance is minimal in large arteries because of their large radii. Arteriolar resistance, on the other hand, is quite high because each arteriole has a small radius. This is despite the fact that arterioles are arranged in parallel and that each arteriole is quite short. This highlights the importance of vessel radius as a determinant of resistance. ***Resistance in the capillaries is low because capillaries are numerous and are parallel to each other.*** Veins have large radii and are arranged in parallel. Hence, they offer little resistance to blood flow.

The caliber of a blood vessel is regulated mainly by the contraction and relaxation of the smooth muscles in its wall. Smooth muscle is relatively abundant in the walls of arterioles which are the major site for peripheral resistance.

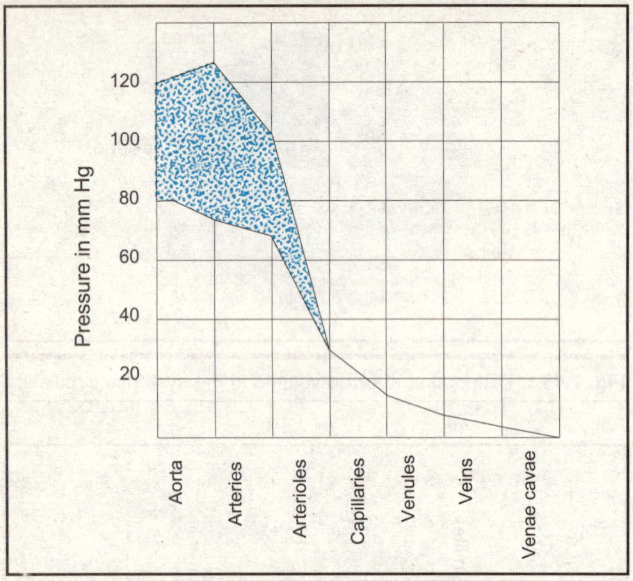


**Fig. 7.16.2 :** Drop in pressure as blood flows from aorta to venae cavae due to the resistance to blood flow

That is why arterioles are known as **resistance vessels**. Cardiac output (CO) remaining constant, generalised constriction of the arterioles (eg, due to sympathetic stimulation) will cause elevation of ***mean arterial pressure (MP)*** due to increase in ***total peripheral resistance*** (TPR) because, by **Darcy's law** (see above) — MP = CO × TPR. Localised arteriolar constriction has negligible effect on TPR and, hence, on MP, but blood flow to the area concerned is diminished. Modulation of vascular resistance plays a key role in the regulation of the CVS.

The **total energy** (expressed as end pressure) for blood flow comes from the heart. This is highest in the aorta. As blood flows from the aorta to the venae cavae through other types of vessels like arterioles, capillaries and venules, energy is lost due to friction (Fig. 7.16.2). The total energy is lowest in the venae cavae. The resistance in each type of vessel is propor-tional to the drop in pressure across it. Larger blood vessels serve as efficient conduits as there is little loss of energy during flow of blood through them. Pressure drops considerbaly in the small arteries and arterioles which are the site for local regulation of blood flow.

The pressure in the arteries and arterioles are pulsatile because flow of blood out of the heart is pulsatile. The peak pressure is the systolic pressure and the minimum pressure is diastolic pressure. The difference between the two is known as **pulse pressure**. The average pressure with respect to time is referred to as mean pressure which, in practice, can be calculated by adding one-third of the pulse pressure to the diastolic pressure. The pressure pulse is propagated along the aorta to the peripheral vessels like blood but at a quicker pace. As it progresses through the arterioles it gets attenuated and at the level of the capillaries and beyond it is almost completely damped.

As the capacitance of arteries changes little from moment to moment, the determinant of arterial pressure is the volume of blood in the arterial system. This volume of blood is dependent upon the balance between the inflow from the heart and outflow through the arterioles. Increase in stroke volume results in increase in both mean pressure and pulse pressure. ***Capacitance of arteries decreases with age because of changes occurring in the arterial wall.*** The effect is an increase in pulse pressure for any given stroke volume. This puts an additional burden on the elderly heart.

## Distending force in the blood vessel wall

The interstitial hydrostatic pressure opposing the distension of a blood vessel by the side pressure exerted on its wall by blood is very low in normal condition. To prevent rupture of the vessel, the distending pressure has to be balanced by the forces within the vessel wall. The tension (T) generated by the transmural pressure ($P_t$) is influenced by the radius (r) and the wall thickness (μ) of the vessel as described by the **law of Laplace :**

$$T = \frac{P_t . r}{\mu}$$

Large tension is generated in the walls of large arteries due to high pressure and large radius. But their thick walls lower the wall tension. While the veins are thin-walled and pressures in them are low, their radii are large. Thus veins can also have substantial wall tension. Pressures in the capillaries are much higher than those in the veins but they have very small radii. Hence, according to the law of Laplace, wall tension is low and capillaries lined by a single layer of endothelial cells rarely, if ever, give way. On the contrary, rupture of thick-walled aorta is not very uncommon.

## Flow volume distribution in vascular system

While flow rate is the same all over the vascular system, the flow velocity differs remarkably because of the difference in total cross-sectional areas of different vessel types. The velocity is highest in the aortic root and lowest in the capillaries. The low velocity of blood in the capillaries allow time for exchange of gases, nutrients and waste products between the tissue cells and blood.

***Out of 5 liter of blood*** contained in the CVS, ***4 liter is in the systemic vessels and 1 liter is in the pulmonary vessels.*** The distribution of blood in different types of vessels in both systemic and pulmonary circulation depends on the side pressures in the vessels and their capacitance. Veins are capacitance vessels and serve the reservoir function. They can change their capacitance as needed by contraction or relaxation of smooth muscles in their walls. **Venous pressure** which is the filling pressure for the heart changes with the change in venous capacitance. ***Modulation of venous capacitance plays an important role in the control of cardiac output*** (CO). CO can be increased by constriction of the veins brought about by stimulation of sympathetic nerves to the veins.

### Viscous drag on the vessel wall

The rapidly flowing blood in large arteries tend to pull the endothelial lining of the arteries along with it. This is known as **viscous drag** which is proportional to the flow rate. In some patients with arterial disease especially hypertension there is patchy degeneration of subendothelial layers causing small areas of endothelium to loose their support. The viscous drag may give rise to dissecting aneurysm by causing tear in the region of unsupported endothelium to allow blood to enter the rift in the vessel lining.

### Rheological properties of blood

Blood is a suspension, principally of RBCs in a relatively homogeneous fluid **the blood plasma**. The viscosity of blood varies according to the hematocrit (ratio of volume of RBCs to that of whole blood). When hematocrit is normal (0.45), blood has a viscosity 2.4 times that of plasma. *Severe anemia reduces blood viscosity due to decrease in hematocrit.* A rise in hematocrit above normal (as occurs in polycythemia) causes an increase in viscosity and, thereby, increase in the resistance to blood flow.

The viscosity of blood diminishes appreciably when it flows through blood vessels with diameters of 0.3 mm or less (eg, arterioles). This phenomenon is called **Fahraeus-Lindqvist** effect after the scientists who described it. In small vessels like arterioles, RBCs tend to accumulate in the faster axial stream and the slower marginal layers mostly contain plasma. It has been shown that this disparity between the relative velocities of the RBCs and plasma produces a fall in hematocrit in these vessels which may be an explanation for the lowering of viscosity in the smaller vessels.

Shear thinning is the reduction in viscosity with increasing shear rate. This can be explained in part by the greater tendency of RBCs to accumulate in the axial stream at higher flow rates. The deformability of RBCs is another factor that allows RBCs of 7.5 μm diameter to pass through vessels with a diameter of 3 μm only. This deformation is more profound at higher hematocrits and at greater rates of flow. Loss of deformability of RBCs as occurs in certain anemias like hereditary spherocytosis makes the phenomenon of shear thinning much less prominent and viscosity may actually increase at greater shear rates.

## 7.5 Mechanism of Production of Heart Sounds, Korotkoff Sound and Murmur

Sound arising from any source must be attended by its vibration. For detection, the frequency should remain in the audible range and amplitude (loudness) must surpass the threshold of hearing. Beating of the heart is associated with production of sounds. **Two sounds** can be detected by unaided ear, better with a clinical stethoscope. **1st heart sound** is dull, prolonged, onomatopoiecally expressed as 'lub' while the **second** is short and sharp, 'dup'. Lub-dup—lub-dup—lub-dup in this way the sounds go on repeating during the life of an individual. Two other sounds **(3rd and 4th heart sounds)** can be detected by stethoscope in some cases in health or disease, but can be recognized regularly by **phonocardiography.** Besides the four heart sounds, musical sounds or murmurs can be detected over the precordium in disease conditions or even during hyperdynamic circulatory states in health.

Whatever way the sounds be named, their generation always requires vibration of some structures, either valves, walls of cardiac chambers or those of vessels. **The 1st heart sound,** 'lub', is synchronous with closure of atrioventricular valves in the beginning of clinical systole. The vibration produced by closure of the valve leaflets along with vibration of ventricular walls and rapid flow of blood that occurs just after the *closure of AV valves through aorta and pulmonary artery* is responsible for the generation of 1st heart sound. The closure of AV valves is of prime importance in the production of 1st heart sound which is evidenced by its diminution of intensity in valve incompetence and its accentuation during tachycardia when, due to shorter diastole, the valve leaflets appose from a distance.

At the onset of ventricular diastole, aortic and pulmonary valves close sharply to produce **2nd heart sound**. Associated vibration of proximal part of vessels may take some part. But the closure of valves is of primary importance as evidenced by softening of 2nd sound in incompetence of semilunar valves and its accentuation when closure occurs forcefully in case of hypertension, systemic or pulmonary. *But in the production of 3rd, 4th heart sounds, murmurs or Korotkoff sounds, vibrations of cardiac chambers or vessel wall occur due to turbulent flow of blood through heart and vessels.*

**Laminar or streamline flow** of blood through a vessel is not associated with sound, but when turbulence occurs, vibration of involved structures reaches the audible range of frequency. Velocity of blood flow determines whether turbulence will develop or not if other factors like lumen diameter, density and viscosity remains unchanged. When the velocity (cm/sec) exceeds a particular level, the *critical velocity* in a vessel, **turbulence occurs**. A number, **Reynolds number (R),** obtained by the formula taking into consideration all probable factors, indicates whether turbulence can develop or not. $R = \rho DV/\eta$, where $\rho$ is density of fluid (g/cm$^3$), D is diameter (cm), V is velocity (cm/sec) and $\eta$ is viscosity (poise). When R exceeds 2,000 there is fair chance of turbulence and generation of sound.

*In cases of stenosed valves* (aortic stenosis, mitral stenosis) the velocity increases tremendously during appropriate phases of cardiac cycle, causing **turbulence** and characteristic **murmurs,** eg, systolic murmur in aortic stenosis and diastolic murmur in mitral stenosis. *In incompetent valves,* the regurgitant blood attains a high velocity through the valve orifice causing **murmurs** in phases of cardiac cycle as expected, eg, *aortic incompetence* causes diastolic murmur and *mitral incompetence* causes systolic murmur.

However, proper timing of murmurs, their characters, radiations, association with ejection clicks or opening snaps depend upon when and where the turbulent flows occur, eg, aortic regurgitant murmur is early diastolic, but murmur of mitral stenosis is **mid-diastolic**. In the production of 3rd and 4th heart sounds, the velocity of blood flow through the AV valve reaches the critical velocity. 3rd heart sound occurs at the rapid filling phase of early ventricular diastole and *4th heart sound takes place at the last rapid filling phase due to atrial systole.* The frequency reaches the audible range, but intensity is too low normally to detect, but can be recognized with stethoscope after exercise (3rd sound) in health due to hyperdynamic circulation or 3rd and 4th sound in heart failure due to rapid rush of blood through AV valves from dilated atria and perturbation of raised volume of blood in dilated ventricle(s).

Not only at the valve sites, but velocity of blood increases at the site of organic or artificial narrowing of lumen diameter also. In indirect recording of blood pressure, a superficial large artery (brachial, femoral) is occluded by inflating a cuff, the pressure developed in it can be measured with a manometer. When the cuff pressure falls below the systolic pressure, a jet of high velocity passes across the narrowed part causing **turbulence** and **production of sound**, which can be detected with a stethoscope just distal to cuff (systolic blood pressure).

Now with gradual release of cuff pressure, more and more part of cardiac cycle time, will allow blood to pass changing the intensity and character of sound. Ultimately, when the cuff pressure is such that flow occurs continuously throughout the cardiac cycle, muffling of the sound occurs. After that, when there is no occlusion of lumen, this sound disappears (diastolic pressure). But in some cases of hyperdynamic circulation (exercise, thyrotoxicosis) **Korotkoff sound** continues till complete deflation of cuff. Muffling is the indicator of diastolic presure in those conditions.

In **atherosclerosis**, vessel lumen may be stenosed by accumulation of lipid substances underneath the endothelium, causing murmur distal to the site of narrowing. Change in viscosity may cause turbulence at valve orifices of heart producing functional murmurs. **In anemia**, fall in viscosity and hyperdynamic circulation raise the Reynold's number, raising the inertial forces (velocity), the numerator and lowering the viscous forces (viscosity), the denominator. **Functional murmur** can be recognized in health during exercise, here there is no change in viscosity but change in velocity is sufficient to bring Reynold's number above the probable level of turbulence.

## Conducting system of the heart

**Ventricular Muscle :** The resting membrne potential of cardiac cells is about –90 mV.

A typical action potential (Fig. 7.16.3) may be divided into 4 phases :

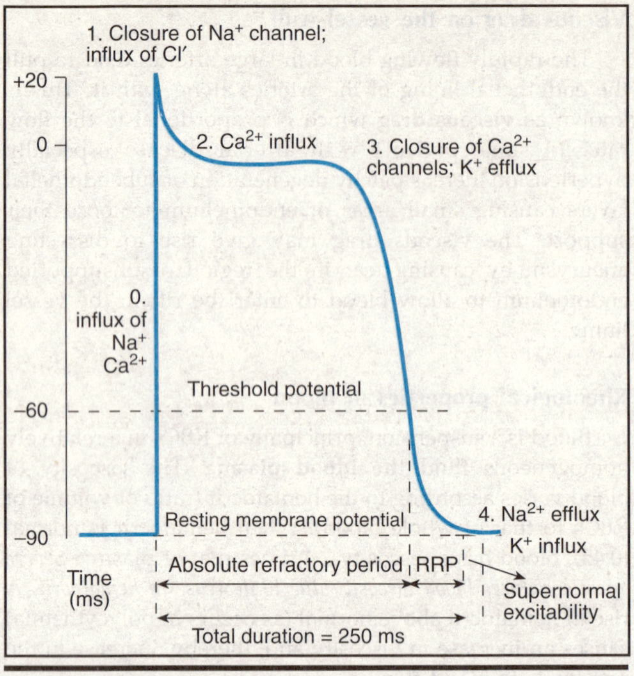


Fig. 7.16.3 : Action potential of a ventricular muscle cell. Phase 0 = depolarization; Phases 1, 2, 3 = repolarization, Phase 4 = return to resting membrane potential. RRP = relative refractory period.

*Phase 0* : **Membrane depolarization.** Rapid increase in permeability to Sodium.

*Phase 1* : **Rapid repolarization** : Rapid decrease in permeability to Sodium, small increase in permeability to potassium.

*Phase 2* : **Slow repolarization :** Plateau effect due to (i) absence of large rapid increase in permeability to $K^+$ (ii) increase in $Ca^{2+}$ permeability.

*Phase 3* : **Rapid repolarization** : gradual increase in Potassium permeability and inactivation of slow inward $Ca^{2+}$ channels.

*Phase 4* : **Resting potential;** High $K^+$ permeability.

**Pace Maker Cells (Fig. 7.16.4) :**

- For example, Sinoatrial node.
- Slow upstroke action potential, mediated by Calcium channels.
- Smaller magnitude of action potential
- No fast Sodium channels.
- Spontaneously depolarizes during diastole (Phase 4 depolarization)

Epinephrine and Norepinephrine make the slope of phase 4 steeper by increasing $Ca^{2+}$ influx, hence heart rate is increased. $Ca^{2+}$ influx also increases force of contraction. Acetylcholine makes slope of phase 4 less steep by increasing $K^+$ efflux, hence heart rate is decreased.

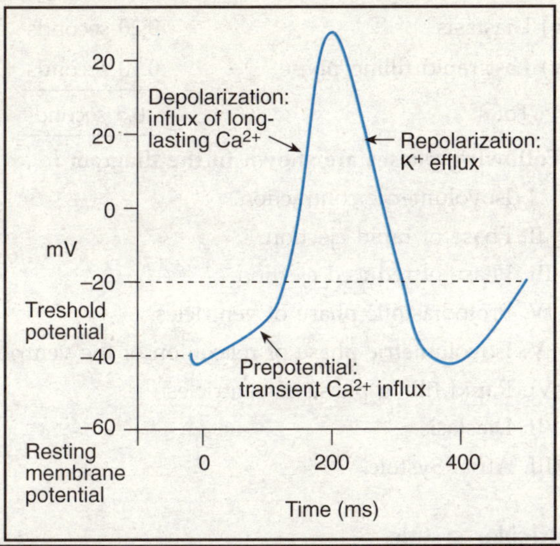


Fig. 7.16.4 : Pacemaker prepotential and action potential. Unlike other action potentials, calcium influx is responsible for depolarization instead of $Na^+$. Note the low and unstable RMP, with spontaneous depolarization (prepotentials).

**Characteristic electrophysiological properties of the cardiac muscle (in contrast to skeletal muscle) are :**

- **Cardiac muscle action potential has a plateau** due to $Ca^{2+}$ influx.
- **Spontaneous depolarization of cardiac nodal cells.**
- **Cardiac myocytes are electrically coupled to each other with the help of gap junctions.**
- **Cardiac muscle contraction depends on extracellular calcium.** This extracellular calcium is responsible for release of calcium from cardiac muscle sarcoplasmic reticulum (Calcium-induced calcium release).

### Actions of Acetylcholine, and Nor epinephrine on cardiac muscle cells

The **A Ch** slows the rate of depolarization during the pacemaker potential of the SA node. As such, the interval between successive action potentials lengthens, slowing the rate at which the pacemaker region drives the heart beat A Ch acts by increasing the Potassium permeability of the muscle fiber membrane, which tends to keep the membrane potential closer to potassium equilibrium potential and they retard the growth of the pace maker potential toward the thresold for triggering an A.P. **Norepinephrine** activates heart rate and increases the strength of contraction. This effect is mediated via increased opening of Calcium channels during depolarization.

As a result of vagal shinulations, cells in in the SA node are hyperpolarized. As a result, the pacemaker potential does not reach threshold to fire the cells. The heart stops beating. After some time, the heart resumes beating and the condition is known as **escape beats**.

Vagal stimulation causes depression of conduction via AV node to the point where conduction fails to reach the ventricle. This condition is known as **heart block**.

## 7.6 Cardiac Cycle

The heart plays a vital role in maintaining a constant circulation of blood throughout the body. The heart is an example of reciprocating pump and its action is having a series of changes termed **cardiac cycle**. The rhythmic activity of the heart produces alternate contraction and relaxation. However, the ventricles result in pulsatile filling of the arterial tree alternating with periods of ventricular filling (see Figs. 7.17&7.18).

The heart contracts and then relaxes during each heart beat. The period of contraction is known as **systole** and that of relaxation is known as **diastole**. The semilunar valves are closed and venous blood flows through the atrium and fills the relaxed heart during diastole. The ventricular pressure is more or less same as venous pressure. During systole, the atrioventricular valves are closed. The contracting heart expels blood via semilunar valves. Left ventricular pressure is more or less same as **aortic pressure**.

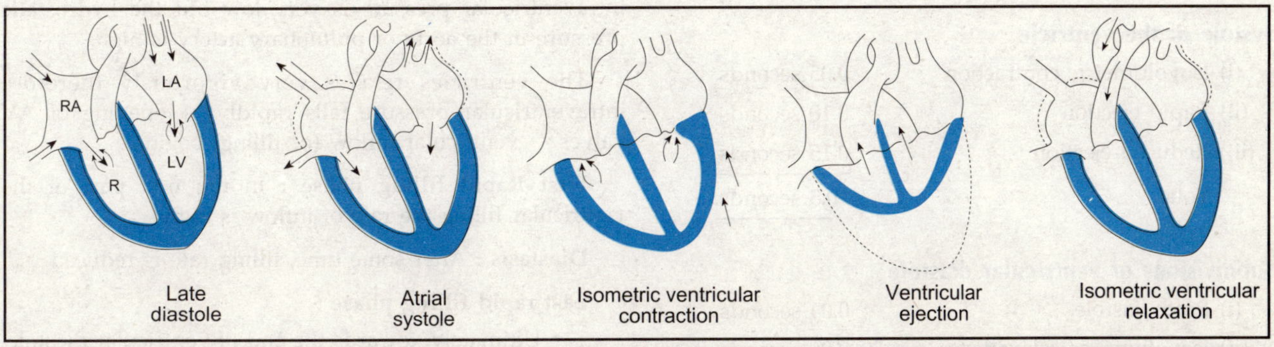


7.17 : Flow of blood in the heart during a single cardiac cycle

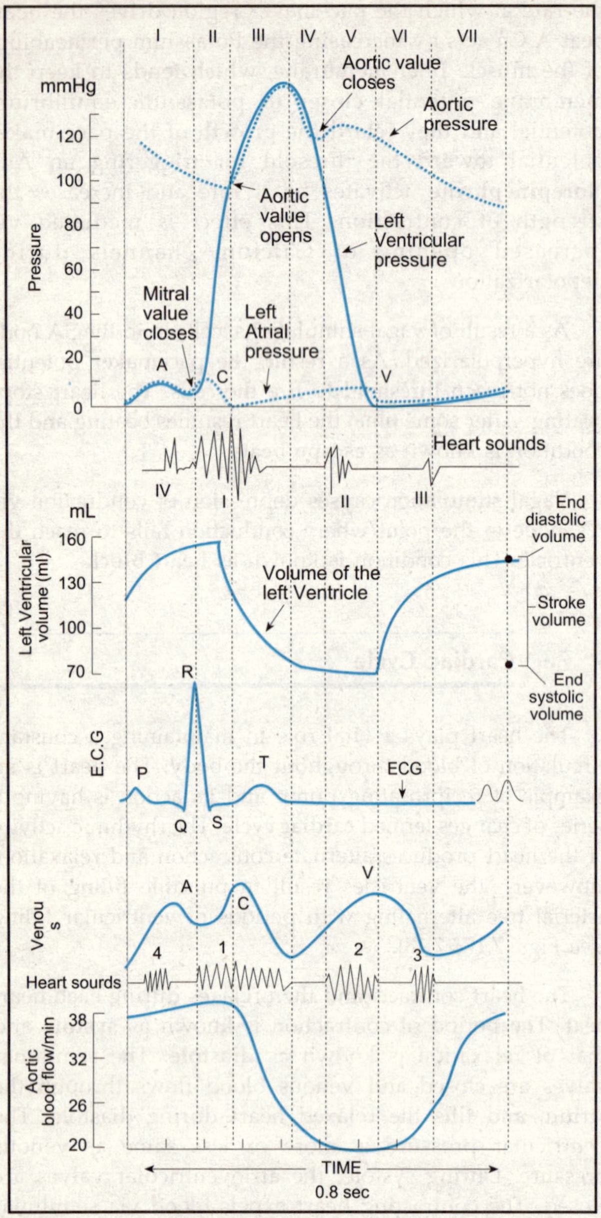


Fig. 7.18 : Mechanical and electrical events during a single cardiac cycle

## Systole of the ventricle

| | |
|---|---|
| (i) Isovolumetric contraction | 0.05 seconds |
| (ii) Rapid ejection | 0.10 seconds |
| (iii) Reduced ejection | 0.15 seconds |
| Total | 0.3 seconds. |

## Subdivisions of ventricular diastole

| | |
|---|---|
| (i) Protodiastole | 0.04 seconds |
| (ii) Isovolumetric relaxation | 0.06 seconds |
| (iii) First rapid filling phase | 0.10 seconds |
| (iv) Diastasis | 0.20 seconds |
| (v) Last rapid filling phase | 0.10 seconds |
| Total | 0.5 seconds |

**Following phases are shown in the diagram :**

I. Isovolumetric contraction.
II. Phase of rapid ejection.
III. Phase of reduced ejection.
IV. Protodiastolic phase of ventricles.
V. Isovolumetric phase of relaxation of the ventricle.
VI. Rapid filling phase of ventricles.
VII. Diastasis.
VIII. Atrial Systole.

## Ventricular systole

Ventricular systole begins after the end of ventricular diastole.

(i) **Isovolumetric phase of contraction :**

- At the beginning of ventricular systole, both Av and semilunar values are closed.
- Ventricles contracts but the blood within it remain confined within the closed ventricle (Isovolumetric phase of contraction)
- The pressure within the ventricle rises very steeply.

(ii) **Rapid ejection phase :**

- The pressure within the ventricle is higher than the hydrostatic pressure within the corresponding artery at the end of isovolumetric phase of ventricular contraction.
- The semilunar valves now open and blood begin to be ejected rapidly (rapid ejection phase)

(iii) **Reduced ejection phase :** Subsequently rate of ejection slows down (Reduced ejection phase).

## Ventricular diastole

After ventricular systole, ventricular diastole begins.

In this phase, semilunar valves close because intraventricular pressure is very low but the hydrostatic pressure in the aorta or pulmonary artery is high.

The ventricles relaxes very vigorously therefore intraventricular pressure falls rapidly → opening of AV valves → ventricular inflow (or filling) begins.

**First Rapid filling phase :** In the first part of the ventricular filling the rate of inflow is high.

**Diastasis :** After some time, filling rate is reduced.

**Last rapid filling phase :**

- Ultimately, towards the end of ventricular diastole, atrial contraction occurs and the filling rate again rises.

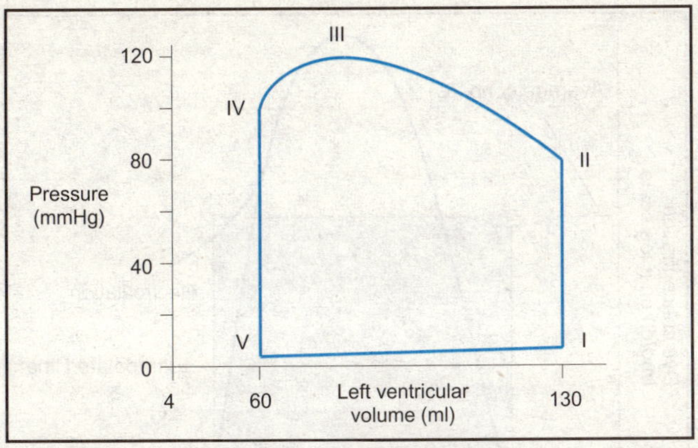


**Fig. 7.19 : Pressure-volume curve**

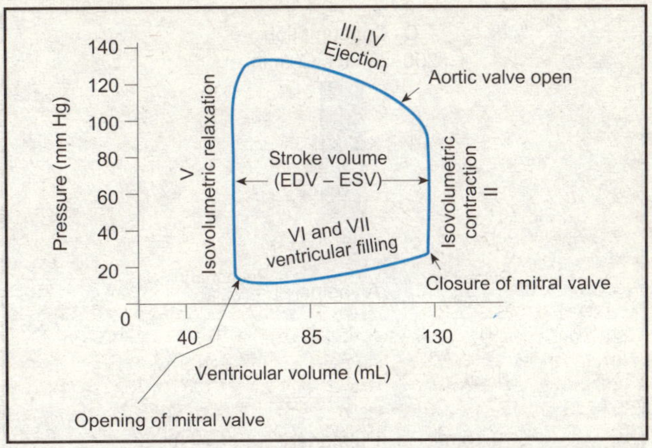


**Fig. 7.20 : Pressure-volume curve**

- The end of the last filling phase marks the end of cardiac cycle and new cycle again starts.

**Atrial changes :**

- **During ventricular systole**, the atrium is receiving blood, either from the venecava or from the pulmonary veins. Atrium is in diastole when the ventricle is in systole.
- **Atrial diastole** continues in the first rapid filling stage as well as in the period of diastasis of the ventricle.
- At the end of atrial diastole, the **atrial systole** occurs.

**The pressure volume curve** (Figs. 7.19, 7.20) ***illustrates the volume and simultaneous pressure in the left ventricle throughout the cardiac cycle.*** **The point I** indicates end diastolic volume (130 ml) and the beginning of isometric contraction which lasts up to point II. Here there is no volume change but abrupt increase in interventricular pressure. **Point II** indicates end of the isometric contraction period, i.e., opening of semilunar valves (aortic valve). Here, there is fall in blood volume due to ventricular ejection that is responsible for some increase in pressure even if there is expulsion of blood because the outflow cannot accommodate all the available blood within that period.

The peak pressure during cardiac cycle is attained **at point III.** From there, up to point IV, there is decrement in pressure in slow ejection period due to changed hemodynamics . **Point IV** indicates the closure of aortic valve and the beginning of isometric relaxation phase. So, there is no change in volume but steep fall of intraventricular pressure up to **point V**. So both points IV and V correspond to end systolic volume (60 ml). The **point V** indicates end of isometric relaxation phase, i.e., opening of mitral valve and beginning of ventricular filling which lasts from point V to point I. Here the pressure change is minimal because the pressure gradient in the atria and ventricle is very low normally during diastole. So the stroke volume is end diastolic volume (point I) – end systolic volume (point V) = 70 ml. So here, ejection fraction = stroke volume/end diastolic volume × 100. Therefore,

$$EF = \frac{70}{130} \times 100 = \frac{700}{13} = 54\%$$

**Stroke volume** ***depends on how much blood enters the ventricle during diastole and how much blood is left in the ventricle following its systole.*** The pressure volume curve can be utilised in changed hemodynamic state like exercise, heart failure, etc. to understand pressure-volume events during cardiac cycle.

## ➤ 7.7 Cardiac Output

The **cardiac output** is a measure of the heart's ability to pump blood.

- Volume of blood expelled from one ventricle of the heart per minute.
- May increase 4-5 times on strenous exertion. Varies with body surface area.
- The cardiac index is the cardiac output per square metre of the body surface and averages about 3.2 l/$m^2$/min.

The amount expelled by each contraction of the ventricles is the **stroke volume**. *Cardiac output is expressed in litres per minute (L/min)* and is calculated by multiplying the stroke volume by the heart rate.

**Cardiac output** = Stroke volume × Heart rate (CO)
(SV) (HR)

At rest, the heart rate is about 70 beats per minute. SV is about 80 ml and CO is about 5.6 litres per minute.

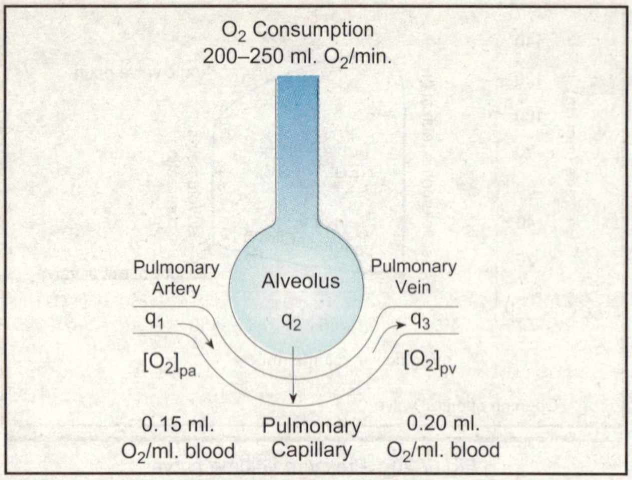


**Fig. 7:21 :** Schematic representation of Fick's method

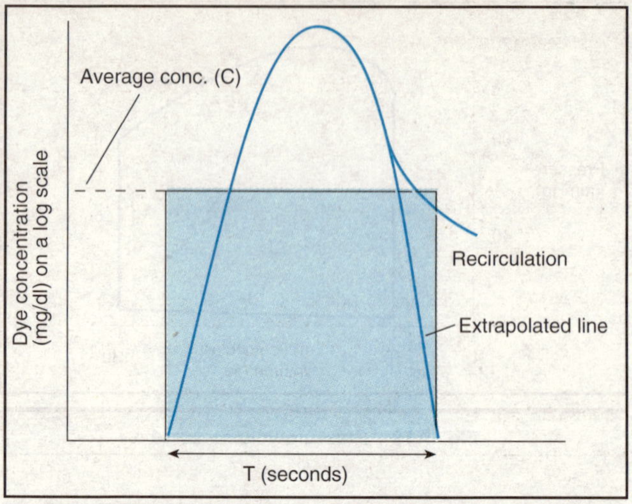


**Fig. 7.22 :** Stewart-Hamilton indicator dilution technique

## Cardiac output

$$= \frac{\text{Mean arterial blood pressure (MABP)} - \text{Mean right atrial blood pressure}}{\text{Total peripheral resistance (TPR)}}$$

$$= \frac{\text{MABP}}{\text{TPR}} \quad \text{(When mean right artrial Pressure is close to zero)}$$

Cardiac output may be expressed also as

$$\text{CO} = \frac{\text{Rate of } O_2 \text{ consumption}}{\text{Arterial } O_2 \text{ content} - \text{Mixed venous } O_2 \text{ content}}$$

Mean arterial pressure = CO × TPR.

## Measurement of cardiac output

Cardiac output can be measured experimentally by placing electromagnetic flow meters or ultrasonic flow probes around the circumference of aorta. One method of measuring cardiac output is **Fick's principle** and another is **indicator dilution technique.**

The cardiac output of the left ventricle is distributed in the systemic circulation in which the organs are connected in parallel (brain, cardiac muscle, gastrointestinal tract, skeletal muscles, kidneys, skin etc.) according to the momentary need. The pulmonary circulation receives the entire cardiac output as it is connected in series to the systemic circulation.

## Measurement of cardiac output by Fick's method (Fig. 7.21)

*The amount of $O_2$ passing in the lungs in the pulmonary arterial blood per minute = pulmonary blood flow × pulmonary arterial $[O_2]$.*

The amount of $O_2$ coming out from the lungs in the pulmonary venous blood = pulmonary blood flow × pulmonary venous $[O_2]$.

$O_2$ absorbed from the alveoli into the pulmonary capillaries must be equal to the difference between the above values.

So, **rate of alveolar $O_2$ absorption** :

Pulmonary blood flow × pulmonary venous $[O_2]$ minus pulmo-nary blood flow × pulmonary arterial $[O_2]$.

As pulmonary blood flow equals cardiac output, it may be written as cardiac output × (pulmonary venous $[O_2]$ – pulmonary arterial $[O_2]$) = Rate of $O_2$ absorption.

***or***

$$\text{CO} = \frac{O_2 \text{ absorption rate}}{\text{Pulmonary venous}[O_2] - \text{Pulmonary arterial}[O_2]}$$

***or,*** it may be written as

$$\text{CO} = \frac{O_2 \text{ absorption rate}}{\text{Systemic arterial}[O_2] - \text{Systemic venous}[O_2]}$$

$$= \frac{250 \text{ ml min}^{-1}}{(190 - 140) \text{ ml L}^{-1}} = 5 \text{ Lmin}^{-1}$$

A vein is cannulated with a long cannula into the right ventricle or may be inserted into pulmonary artery to obtain a sample of mixed venous blood. The $O_2$ content is analyzed. 100 ml venous blood contains 14 ml oxygen.

**Another method is the Stewart-Hamilton indicator dilution technique (Fig. 7.22).**

A more popular method for measuring cardiac output is thermodilution method using cold saline.

Indicator (radioactive isotope or dye like indocyanine green) is injected into the venous circulation in the right ventricle. Then it quickly mixes with cardiac contents. The concentration of the mixture is determined by continuous sampling from an artery in the arm for one complete circulation. The **mean concentration of the indicator** and time for a complete circulation through the heart are found out from the time-concentration plot.

$$\text{Now, } O_X \text{ (C.O.)} = \frac{\text{Amount of indicator injected}}{\text{Mean concentration of indicator} \times \text{Time for one complete circulation}}$$

## Factors which are responsible for cardiac output (Figs. 7.25, 7.26, 7.27)

1. **Heart rate** : It is regulated mainly by autonomic nervous system. Heart receives both **sympathetic** ($T_1$-$L_2$) and **parasympathetic** supply but sympathetic supplies the whole heart such as atrial muscles, SAN, AVN, His-Purkinje system and CMC of ventricles. The parasympathetic supplies only the atria including SAN and AVN but does not supply ventricles including His-Purkinje system. As such, it has no direct effect on ventricles.

**Stimulation of the sympathetic nerves increases the heart rate :** The sympathetic preganglionic nerves that supply the heart originate in spinal segments T1 to T6 (mainly T1-T3). They synapse in the ganglia of the thoracic sympathetic chain from where they project to the heart via long postganglionic fibers. The varicosities of the post ganglionic fibers secrete nor epinephrine, and the effect of stimulating these nerves is to increase the rate at which the heart beats.

**Sympathetic stimulation** causes (a) +ve **chronotropic** action (heart rate ↑) (b) +ve **inotropic action** (contractility of myocardium ↑), (c) +ve **bathmotropic** (excitability ↑) action and (d) +ve **dromotropic** (conductivity ↑) action.

Heart rate increases due to sympathetic action on SAN — intrinsic rhythm of SAN is excited and there is rise in heart rate.

**Vagal nerve fibers** synapse with post ganglionic parasympathetic neurons in the heart itself an short post ganglionic fibers synapse mainly on the cells of the sinoatrial and atrioventricular nodes. They release acetylcholine from their terminals which acts to slow the heart rate (an effect known as bradycardia). Vagal stimulation also reduces the rate of conduction of the cardiac impulse from the atria to the ventricles by decreasing the excitability of the AV bundle fibers.

In general, cardiac output increases as heart rate increases. However at a very high heart rate, (> 150 per minute) stroke volume begins to decrease causing a fall in cardiac output.

Factors controlling heart rate include modulation in sympathetic and parasympathetic nerve activities and baroreceptor mediated reflexes (see "Cardiovascular regulation" section 7.8 for details).

A normal adult at rest usually has a heart rate between 60 and 100 beats per minute. A heart rate above 100 beats per minute (B.P.M.) is known as **Tachycardia** while a heart rate below 60 B.P.M. is called **Bradycardia**.

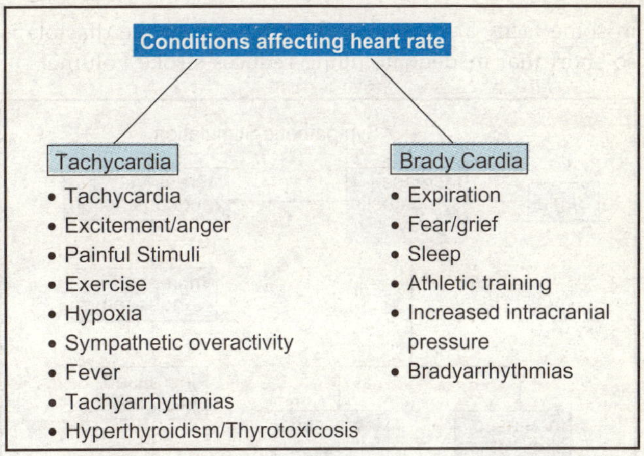


Generally, increase in the heart rate accompanies increase in blood pressure and vice versa. However in some conditions, there may be exceptions, for example in increased intracranial pressure hypertension is accompanied by bradycardia.

**Contractility** rises due to the effect of sympathetic stimulation resulting in rise of cAMP in cardiomyocyte → opening of $Ca^{2+}$ channel. As such, contractility rises. The entry of $Ca^{2+}$ ions within the cells, due to sympathetic stimulation, causes changes in the cardiac AP particularly in the slow response AP.

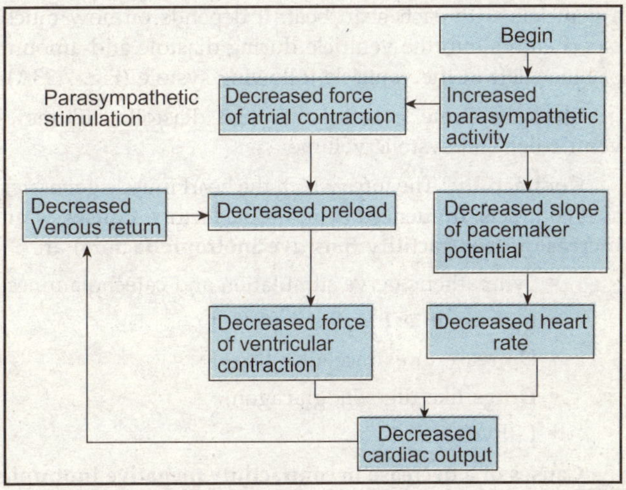


**How does vagal stimulation decrease the heart rate?** The acetylcholine released by the nerve terminals of the vagal nerves increases the permeability of the nodal cells to potassium. This has **two effects : it decreases the slope of the pace maker potential and hyperpolarizes the membrane potential.**

**Cardiac output = Stroke volume × heart rate**. Therefore, if the stroke volume remains the same or elevated, tachycardia is responsible for raised cardiac output e.g. during exercise. But if heart rate increases tremendously as in some tachy-arrhythmias like atrial flutter the diastole is so short that inadequate filling reduces stroke volume.

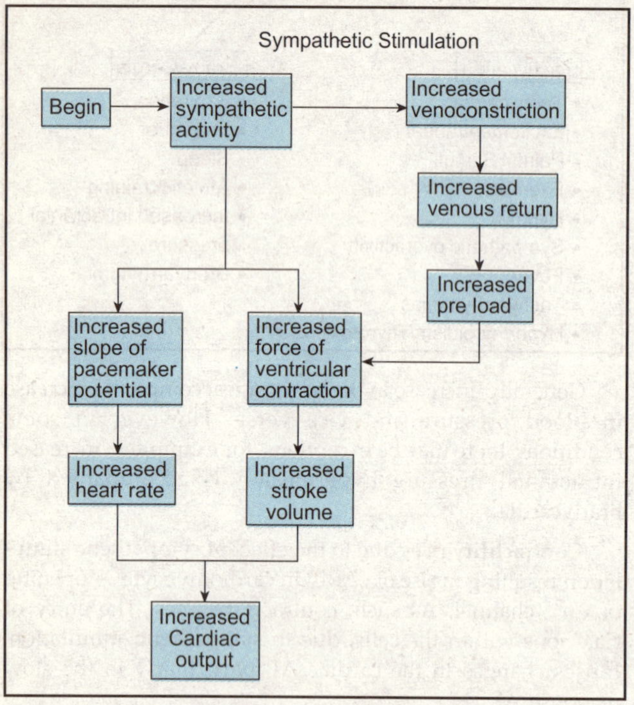


2. **Stroke volume** : It is the amount of blood ejected by a ventricle with each heart beat. It depends on how much blood enters into the ventricle during diastole and amount of blood left in the ventricle following systole (Fig. 7.23A).

**Stroke volume** = ventricular end diastolic volume – ventricular end systolic volume.

**Contractility :** The force which the heart muscle generates as it contracts. Influenced by inotropic factors. **Causes of an increase in contractility (positive inotropic factors)** are :

- Sympathetic nerve stimulation and catecholamines.
- Increase in extracellular [Ca2+]
- Decrease in extracellular [Na+]
- Drugs like digoxin; glucagon,
- L-thyroxine

**Causes of a decrease in contractility (negative inotropic factors) are :**

- Drugs like β-blockers; antiarrhythmic drugs.
- Heart failure
- Hypoxia; Hypercapnia, and acidosis.

3. **Preload** : Ventricular end diastolic volume indicates how much heart is stretched prior to contraction. It increases with increase in venous return (Fig. 7.23B).

The relationship between the preload (left ventricular end diastolic volume) and stroke volume is described by the **Frank-Starling law**, which states that the force developed in a muscle fiber depends on the degree to which the fiber is stretched.

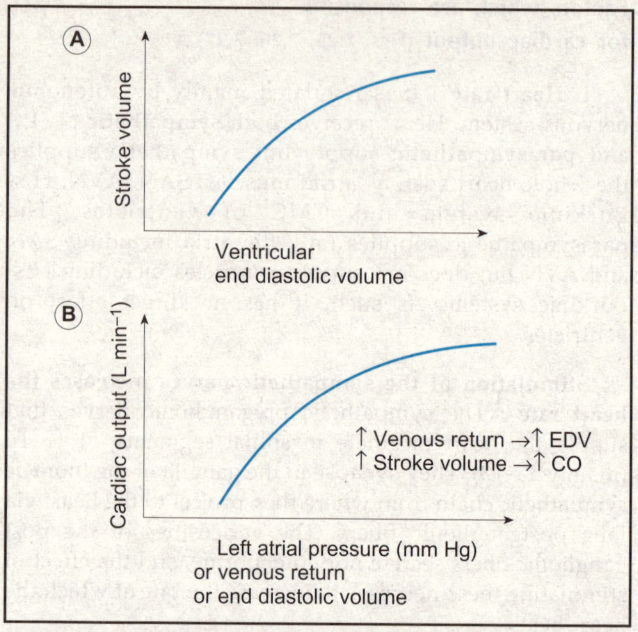


**Fig. 7.23 :** Relationship between contractility and length of muscle fibers

4. **Afterload** : For ejection of blood, heart has to generate pressure to overcome the pressure of vessels for opening of semilunar valves – simply, diastolic pressures in aorta and pulmonary trunk. It is a function of total peripheral resistance. Stroke volume is inversely related to afterload at constant preload and contractility. Stroke volume is increased with decreased peripheral resistance. Afterload increases with increased blood pressure.

**Preload** = ventricular EDV

**Afterload** = peripheral resistance (diastolic pressure)

Venous dilators such as nitroglycerine decrease preload and vasodilators (eg, hydralazine) decrease afterload. SV is increased when there is increased preload or decreased after load. Preload is increased due to exercise, extra blood and excitement. Preload is responsible for pumping of the heart.

5. **Contractility** : ***It is the force the heart is capable of developing as it contracts.***

6. **Ejection fraction (EF)** : It is an index of ventricular function and is equal to stroke volume divided by ventricular end diastolic volume.

The EF for each ventricle can be readily calculated from the ESV and EDV by the following formula :

$$\text{Ejection fraction} = \frac{\text{End diastolic volume(EDV)} - \text{End systolic volume(ESV)}}{\text{End diastolic volume(EDV)}}$$

$$= \frac{\text{Stroke volume}}{\text{EDV}}$$

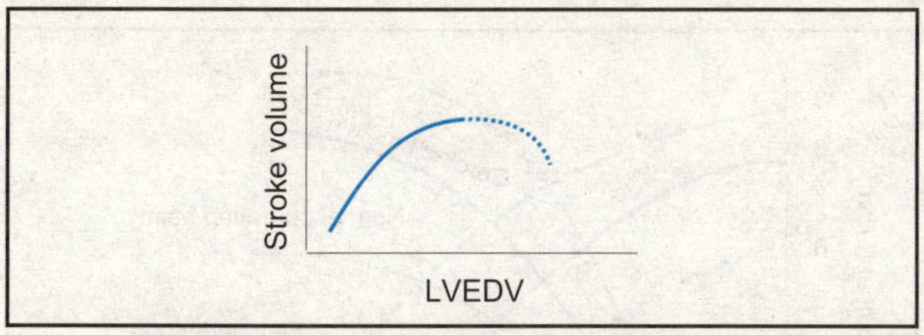


Fig. 7.24 : Ventricular fun-ction curve

Ejection fraction is approximately 60-70%. It gives a good estimate of ventricular function.

## Starling's law of the heart (Figs. 7.24 and 7.25)

**Starling's law of the heart** determines that the work done by ventricle is a function of end diastolic fiber length. Otto Frank first established similar effects in the heart of a frog approximately about 20 years earlier. It is commonly called **Frank Starling law**–the relationship between contractility and length of muscle fibers. The strength of contraction of a heart muscle fiber varies with its length. ***The intrinsic mechanism involved in the control of the cardiac output is usually referred to*** as ***Starling's law of the heart*** or the Frank-Starling mechanism. There is an increase in the force of contraction because the resting length of the cardiac muscle fibers is also increased — resulting in increase in stroke volume.

Tension in cardiac muscle rises progressively as the whole heart is stretched. Intraventricular pressure rises as the intraventricular volume (index of fiber length) is increased due to venous return. This intraventricular volume or diastolic volume is the index of fiber length.

***Starling's law*** : Energy of contraction is a function of the length of the muscle fibers. But this law has its limitations up to a certain length of muscle fibers. The ventricular function curve explains **Starling's law**. Here stroke volume is plotted against left ventricular end diastolic volume (LVEDV).

**Stroke volume** is increased with preload up to the point of optimal initial sarcomere length. This is the time when actin and myosin filaments are present to form the maximum number of force generating sites. Contractile force decreases when muscle fibers are stretched beyond their physiological limits. At this point cross-bridges between the actin and myosin filaments cannot form.

LVEDV increases with increased venous return (blood volume returning to the heart per unit time). **Venous return is increased by sympathetic venoconstriction, exercise and overtransfusion and is decreased by venodilation, hemorrhage and diuretics.**

**What factors determine the end-diastolic volume of the ventricle?**

End diastolic volume and the degree of stretch of the ventricles is an important determinant of the cardiac output

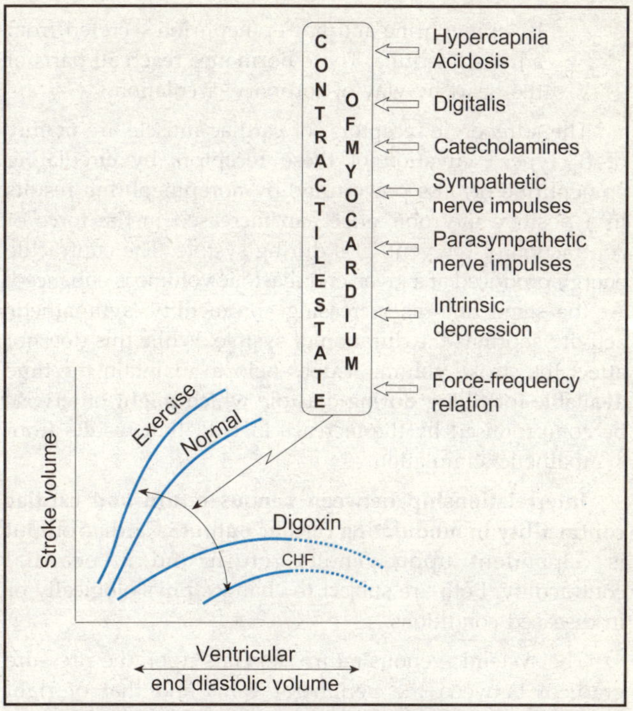


Fig. 7.25 : Work done by ventricle is a function of end diastolic fiber length

and the work performed by the heart. The pressure outside the heart is the intrathoracic pressure. This is altered by breathing. During inspiration, contraction of the diaphragm increases the volume of the chest and decreases the volume of the abdominal cavity. This results in a fall in the pressure within the thorax and a rise in the pressure within the abdominal cavity. This pressure difference favors the flow of blood from the abdominal to the thoracic veins and entrances the filling of the right ventricle.

The pressure inside the right ventricle at the end of diastole is more or less equal to the pressure in the superior and inferior rena caval as they enter the heart.—**Central venous pressure**. Since ventricular filling is largely determined by the central venous pressure, it follows from the Frank-Starling relationship that the central venous pressure is an important determinant of cardiac output.

Extrinsic regulation of the stroke volume the modulation of myocardeal contractility by the sympathetic nervous system:

Both sympathetic and parasympathetic nerve fibers innervate the sinoatrial and atrioventricular nodes. In contrast, the ventricles receive a rich innervation of sympathetic fibers but have little or no parasympathetic innervation. **Increased sympathetic activity increases the heart rate and the inotropic state of myocardium, both in the atria and in the ventricles. This is achieved in two ways :**

- Via sympathetic nerves which are widely distributed throughout the heart.

- By epinephrine and nor epinephrine secreted from adrenal medulla. These hormones reach all parts of the heart by way of coronary circulation.

The adrenergic receptors of cardiac muscle are mainly of $\beta_1$ type. Activation of these receptors by circulating epinephrine or, less powerfully, by norepinephrine results in a positive inotropic effect, an increased in the force of contraction of the ventricles during systole. The contractile energy produced at a given end diastolic volume is enhanced. At the same time as increasing contractility, sympathetic activity shortens the duration of systole. While this doesnot affect the stroke volume it does help to maintain the time available for filling during diastole which might otherwise be compromised by the increase in H.R. that results from sympathetic stimulation.

**Interrelationship between venous return and cardiac contractility in modulating cardiac output** : Cardiac output is dependent upon venous return and myocardial contractility. Both are subject to changes physiologically or in diseased conditions.

The systemic venous return depends upon the pressure gradient between the peripheral veins and that of right atrium (central venous pressure). When the atrial pressure becomes ***less positive to negative direction,*** venous return increases. The relationship can be easily understood by the venous return curve, in which the abscissa is the CVP and ordinate is the CO.

On the other hand, if we consider only the atria and ventricles, the more the pressure in atria, the more is the ventricular filling and the more is the cardiac output. This relationship can be documented by cardiac function curve in which abscissa and ordinate represent the same parameters as the venous return curve.

In the Figure (Fig. 7.26) critical closing pressure is +7 mm of Hg which indicates that if CVP is raised experimentally to 7 mm of Hg, venous return will decrease to zero. It is also the same pressure if the heart is stopped and pressure throughout the circulatory system is allowed to attain an equilibrium value, because in that hypothetical state, venous return is zero, same also is the cardiac output.

Now the point of intersection is the normal operating point, CVP average 2 mm Hg and cardiac output 5-6 litres per minute. Now, with sympathetic stimulation due to the inotropic effect on heart, CO increases at a particular CVP, so that the curve is shifted to the left (dashed line of curve).

In this curve the ***point A indicates initial change in cardiac output*** but, with better pumping activity of heart, there is drainage of venous blood reducing the CVP and the equilibrium point shifts finally to point B with diminished CVP and moderately elevated CO in comparison to point N.

When there is increment in blood volume or there is depletion of blood volume, the venous return curve remains parallel to control venous return curve and CO decreases correspondingly, at least initially.

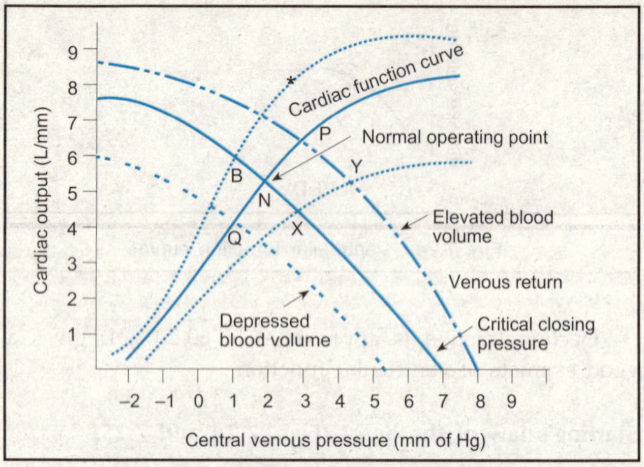


Fig. 7.26 : Interrelationship between venous return and cardiac contractility in modulating cardiac output. *Point N*—Normal operating point corresponding CVP and C.O. *Point B* — indicates C.O. with sympathetic stimulation. *Point X* — indicates C.O. with sympathetic inhibin. *Point P* — indicates C.O. with elevated blood volume. *Point Q* — indicates C.O. with depressed blood volume.

***Cardiac contractility then changes due to multiple reflex mechanisms.*** So the initial points P and Q will shift with change in the cardiac function curves (not shown). During heart failure, in most cases, blood volume is elevated to start with and there is diminished contractility so that the equilibrium is shifted towards right and down from normal equilibrium point (X).

Now, with accumulation of fluids in the vascular system (backward failure), the blood volume increases. So the final point of equilibrium in compensated heart failure is moderate rise in CVP and some fall of cardiac output (Point Y). In this way, changes in hemodynamics which affect CVP and cardiac output in different physiological conditions can be understood by the illustration of the curve.

## ➤ 7.8 Cardiovascular Regulation

**Cardiovascular system** has evolved for supply and removal of substances to and from every part of the body, during rest and also at various stressful states. Increased blood flow thorugh exercising muscles, secreting glands and sweating skin are examples of needful changes.

The increased requirement of blood flow may be limited to a particular part (eg, if only a joint is moved or as in GI epithelium during absorption), the circulation through rest of the body being kept unchanged. The requirement is almost generalised (throughout the body) in running, swimming etc. but even then there is a differential distribution; working muscles get more supply in exchange of non-active/less active muscles and viscera.

Now, for the purpose of these adaptations, appropriate changes occur in every possible parameter, eg, change in the lumen diameter to decrease vascular resistance, changes in cardiac output by influencing cardiac contractility, heart rate and venous return, and also in blood volume. To bring about the required changes, not only CVS but respiratory, endocrine, excretory and nervous systems (in fact all the systems) operate together to produce the desired effect.

***The regulation is mediated by cardiovascular reflexes, local and general responses to chemical mediators.*** Besides these involuntary adjustments, humans and even animals, utilize external physical forces eg, gravity, to assist in the recovery process. Thus cardiovascular regulation is an integration of multiple regulatory functions. However, to have an understanding of the control system, it can be discussed under *two headings* – **regulation at local/organ level** and regulation at **general systemic level.**

## Regulation at local/organ level

Here the blood flow is changed by altering the lumen diameter. Vasoconstriction and vasodilatation are terms applied in relation to small arteries and arterioles. It can be elaborated under separate headings.

(a) **Autoregulation** : Vascular beds in general, but especially those of some organs like kidney, brain, heart, liver etc., have developed a mechanism by which they maintain a constant flow (volume/time) in the face of moderate change in perfusion pressure. Flow in an organ = average perfusion pressure/average resistance. Now if there occurs increase in perfusion pressure (blood pressure), initially there may occur some enhanced flow, but subsequently it falls to previous level.

With fall in perfusion pressure, reverse changes take place. This is due to change in the caliber of the resistance vessels in appropriate direction, so that the flow remains unaltered. These theories, either single or in combination, have been set up to explain underlying mechanisms of autoregulation. These theories are (i) **myogenic,** (ii) **metabolic** and (iii) **tissue pressure**.

(i) **Myogenic theory** suggests that the blood vessel musculature responds to stretch, increasing and decreasing its contractile force in response to dilation and constriction of its lumen.

(ii) **Metabolic theory** points to the rate of removal of vasodilator metabolites accumulating constantly in a tissue. When the blood flow becomes low after fall in perfusion pressure in a vascular bed, the metabolites accumulate in the intestitium to relax the resistance vessel and increases the flow.

(iii) **Tissue pressure theory** tries to impress that accumulated interstitial fluid formed due to elevated capillary hydrostatic pressure consequent upon raised perfusion pressure will press upon thin walled capillaries and venules to decrease their lumen and blood flow. Opposite occurs with fall in perfusion pressure.

(b) **Vasoactive chemical mediators** : Metabolic theory of autoregulation suspects role of chemicals in changing blood flow. In fact, in exercising muscles and secreting glands there appear substances that do change the diameter of resistance vessels. Some may act as vasoconstrictors, others act as vasodilators. Vasoconstrictors of definite importance in local regulation are serotonin and prostaglandin (thromboxane) liberated from platelets as well as endothelins (peptides) liberated from endothelial cells. They may act by opening ligand-gated $Ca^{2+}$ channels in smooth muscle cells. However, vasoconstriction is sometimes secondary to physical processes eg, cold or trauma can constrict vessels directly. In severe cold, vasoconstriction may be severe enough to cause ischemic necrosis (frost-bite).

Vasodilators are derived from various sources in exercising skeletal muscles, for example, decreased $O_2$ tension, increased $CO_2$ tension, increased $K^+$ in interstitial fluid, fall in pH, accumulation of lactate, and rise in temperature. They all act in unison to dilate the resistance vessels. In cardiac muscles, besides these factors, adenosine is also a recognized vasodilator.

Endothelium liberates *EDRF* (endothelium derived relaxation factor) which is *nitric oxide (NO)*, in response to some mediators to cause vasodilatation and also to modify **vasoconstrictive effects** of others. ***Acetylcholine, bradykinin,*** and ***vasoactive intestinal peptide liberate*** NO, while adenosine, **ANP** and histamine have **vasodilator activity** by different mechanisms. ***ADH, angiotensin II, noradrenalin and serotonin are potent*** **vasoconstrictors**, but they also liberate EDRF, which play some braking effect. Acetylcholine is a stirpped off vasodilator physiologically, but, if the endothelium is, they act directly on vascular smooth muscle (similar to GI smooth muscle) to constrict them.

Endothelial cells also secrete potent vasoconstrictors called **endothelins** which are polypeptides with characteristic disulphide bonds. They are local vasoactive agents and their circulating level is very low. ***Endothelins (1, 2 and 3) are liberated in response to stretching of the vessels, and also by thrombin and adrenaline.*** Endothelins increase production of vasoactive prostaglandins (thromboxane and prostacyclin) by activating phospholipase.

Endothelins are secreted from various organs where they perform important biological functions besides vasoconstri-ction. As for example, they have positive inotropic and chronotropic effects on heart, decrease GFR at kidneys, increase ANP, renin secretion and broncho-constriction to name a few.

## Regulation at general/systemic level

**Regulation at systemic level** is effected by the participation of chemical mediators and neural impulses that discharge from CNS via some reflexes are primarily responsible.

Chemical mediators originate from numerous sources that have generalized effect on resistance vessels, venules and also heart chambers. Some of them have already been mentioned in connection to local regulation.

***The important ones acting as vasoconstrictor are (a) epine-phrine; (b) norepinephrine; (c) dopamine; (d) angiotensin II and (e) vasopressin.*** Epinephrine, norepinephrine and dopamine are secreted from adrenal medulla in response to sympathetic stimulation. Their levels vary according to the stimuli concerned. Norepinephrine is also secreted from postganglionic sympathetic neurons. The three catecholamines have positive chronotropic and inotropic effects on heart.

**Norepinephrine** is a generalized ***vasoconstrictor causing sustained vasoconstriction and prolonged rise in mean blood pressure*** in anesthetized experimental animals. Though norepinephrine is primarily a cardiac accelerator, baroreceptor reflexes induce bradycardia and fall in cardiac output. But epinephrine, that is secreted at a higher rate than norepine-phrine in response to same stimuli, causes transient rise in blood pressure in experimental situations due to vasoconstriction in sites other than skeletal muscles and liver.

With ***epinephrine, there is moderate rise in systolic BP*** due to stimulation of heart, some decline in diastolic pressure, but mean pressure shows little change. There is net fall in peripheral resistance (an effect opposite to that of norepinephrine), rise in heart rate and rise in cardiac output. ***Dopamine is a generalized vasoconstrictor*** except in renal and mesenteric vessels. It raises systolic pressure in experimental setting, but its physiological role in pressure homeostasis is unknown. In cases of fall in BP, norepinephrine and dopamine are more effective than epinephrine. Their effects vary depending on the types of receptors.

**Vasopressin or ADH** is released in response to substantial fall in BP besides its relation to tonicity of body fluids. In a normotensive individual, injected ADH increases peripheral resistance by vasoconstriction everywhere, but fall in heart rate and lack of inotropic effect results in fall in cardiac output, so the ultimate effect on pressure is insignificant. But in hypotensive states, it does raise blood pressure by vasoconstriction and water reabsorption (repletion of blood volume). ADH also induces thirst. Role of ADH in blood pressure regulation is thus secondary.

**Angiotensin II,** an eight amino acid peptide, is a potent vasoconstrictor. It is formed from angiotensinogen, an $\alpha_2$ globulin of plasma protein. Renin, a proteolytic enzyme/hormone, of MW 40,000 (340 amino acids) is liberated from juxtaglomerular cells in response to renal ischaemia. It splits decapeptide angiotensin I from angiotensinogen. This circulating compound (A I) is converted to octapeptide (A II) angiotensin II, by a dipeptidylcarboxypeptidase called **angiotensin converting enzyme (ACE)** present in endothelial cells of the blood vessels, mostly within lung capillaries.

Angiotensin II raises both **systolic and diastolic blood pressures** by **generalized vasoconstriction**. At the same time, it **stimulates adrenal cortex to liberate aldosterone** which reabsorbs sodium from kidney and elsewhere, simultaneously retaining water by osmotic attraction. Ang II also **stimulates thirst**, increases secretion of ACTH and ADH from pituitary, facilitates norepinephrine release from postganglionic sympathetic neurons and decreases GFR by stimulating glomerular mesangial cells. Angiotensin II has a half life of 1-2 minutes. It is degraded by enzymes grouped under the heading angiotensinase. Removal of aspartate residue at N-terminal end of Ang II gives rise to formation of A III (des-Asp A II), which has moderate pressor activity, but minimal aldosterone liberating activity.

In a particular situation, eg, after an episode of hemorrhage, it is not possible to assess the degree of involvement of individual humoral vasoconstrictors to restore the pressure, though epinephrine, nor-epinephrine and A-II are mostly responsible. Their actions are supplemented by neural activity, mediated by various reflexes.

**Vasodilators of physiological importance are** (a) ***kinins***, (b) ***atrial natriuretic peptide (ANP)***. Kinins are peptides formed in tissues, lysyl bradykinin, a decapeptide, and bradykinin (a nonapeptide) in circulation from kininogens by enzymes called **kallikreins** derived from pre-kallikreins. **Pre-kallikrein** activators are fragments of activated clotting factor XII (Hageman or surface factor). Tissue kallikreins are involved in the formation of lysylbradykinin in glands and viscera like sweat glands, salivary glands, pancreas, GI epithelium etc. where vasodilation increases blood flow during secretion.

**Kinins once formed are destroyed by** (i) kininase I (carboxy-peptidase), (ii) kininase II (dicarboxypeptidase), that is same as angiotensin converting enzyme (ACE) forming Ang.II from Ang.II. Thus, formation of a vasoconstrictor is attended by destruction of a vasodilator (Fig. 7.27).

The term ***kinin*** is derived from ***Greek 'kinesis', meaning movement***. Kinins have numerous actions : (a) contraction of visceral smooth muscle, (b) relaxation of vascular smooth muscle via NO (EDRF) causing hypotension, (c) increase in blood flow at tissue level by relaxing resistance vessels, (d) increases in capillary permeability and also (e) induction of pain sensation. They resemble histamine closely in physiologic effects.

| | |
|---|---|
| Arg-Pro-Pro-Gly-Phe-Ser-Pro-Phe-Arg | Bradykinin |
| Lys-Arg-Pro-Pro-Gly-Phe-Ser-Pro-Phe-Arg | Lysylbradykinin |

**Atrial natriuretic peptide (ANP)** : A peptide of 28 amino acid, having a ring formed by disulphide linkage (species specific) is secreted from atrial muscle cells in response to hypervolemia. It ***increases excretion of sodium and water***. It is also involved ***in the control of blood volume.*** It also relaxes ***vascular smooth muscle and decreases blood pressure***.

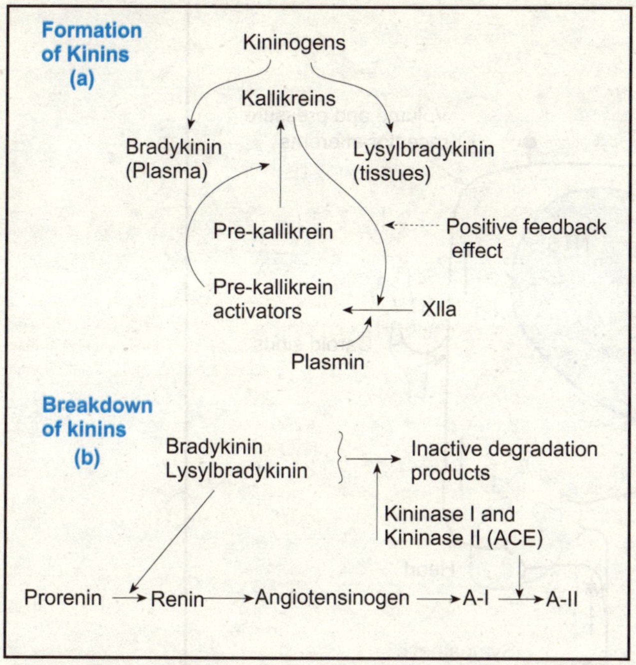


**Fig. 7.27** : Formation of kinins and (b) Breakdown of kinins

***ANP lowers blood volume, cardiac output and blood pressure by the following mechanisms*** :

(i) Antagonizing the pressor actions of vasoconstrictors like angiotensin II etc. by decreasing the sensitivity of smooth muscle of vessels to them.

(ii) Reducing aldosterone stimulating effect of angiotensin II.

(iii) Reducing secretion of ADH and renin.

(iv) Causing increased excretion of $Na^+$ along with water via the kidneys, probably by acting directly over renal tubules and also by increasing GFR by relaxing glomerular mesangial cells (increase surface area of filtration bed).

ANP level changes (increases) not only in abnormal condition like hypervolemia, induced by intravenous saline but physiologically with change of posture and immersion in water. When an individual is immersed up to neck, there is raised central venous pressure (water pressure counteracts gravity) and atrial pressure; there is increased ANP secretion from stretched atrial muscle. This is also associated with decrease in (baroreceptor mediated) renin and aldosterone secretion; all favouring natriuresis. Even change from supine to erect position causes expected change in ANP secretion. Normal ANP level is around 5 picomol/litre of plasma; during immersion, it gets more than double.

## $Na^+$-$K^+$-ATPase inhibition

Endogenous steroid compounds with similar molecular effect of digitalis glycoside ($Na^+$-$K^+$-ATPase inhibition) inhibit $Na^+$ reabsorption in renal tubules by blocking sodium pump, resulting in natriuresis and diuresis diminishing plasma volume, reducing cardiac output and blood pressure. The putative compound is thought to be secreted from the adrenal gland. $Na^+$-$K^+$-ATPase inhibition should cause vasoconstriction by increasing intracellular $Ca^{2+}$, but here the natriuretic effect overrides vasoconstrictive property and induces hypotension.

**Table 7.2**
**List of vasoactive elements**

| Constrictors | Dilators |
|---|---|
| Postganglionic noradrenergic fibres | Sympathetic and parasympathetic cholinergic fibres |
| Norepinephrine | Epinephrine at skeletal muscle and liver |
| Epinephrine (except at skeletal muscle and liver) | ANP |
| Angiotensin II | Kinins |
| Arginine vasopressin | Histamine |
| Serotonin | Calcitonin gene related peptide |
| Cold | (CGRP $\alpha$) |
| Endothelins | VIP |
| Neuropeptide-Y | NO |
| Circulating $Na^+$-$K^+$-ATPase inhibitor | Substance P<br>$O_2$ lack<br>$CO_2$ excess<br>Increased $H^+$ ion concentration $\uparrow K^+$, lactate, adenosine, increased local temperature |

## Neural regulation (Figs. 7.28)

Blood vessels bear receptors for compounds brought to them humorally. They are also innervated by autonomic division (mostly sympathetic) of nervous system. Postganglionic neurons secrete norepinephrine which is a generalised vasoconstrictor. There exists continuous stimulation to produce tonic contraction, which undergoes modulation in response to reflexes which have their central connections at brain stem level. In some organs, both sympathetic and parasympathetic innervations are observed eg, heart, lungs, kidney, uterus (both parenchyma and vasculature). In skeletal muscles there is also a supply of sympathetic cholinergic fibers, where the neurotransmitter is acetylcholine. The cholinergic fibers are vasodilators, but they have no tonic activity.

Cholinergic fibers liberate as co-transmitter, a vasodilator, VIP and noradrenergic fibers secrete a co-transmitter, neuropeptide-Y of vasoconstrictive function. **Substance P,** a

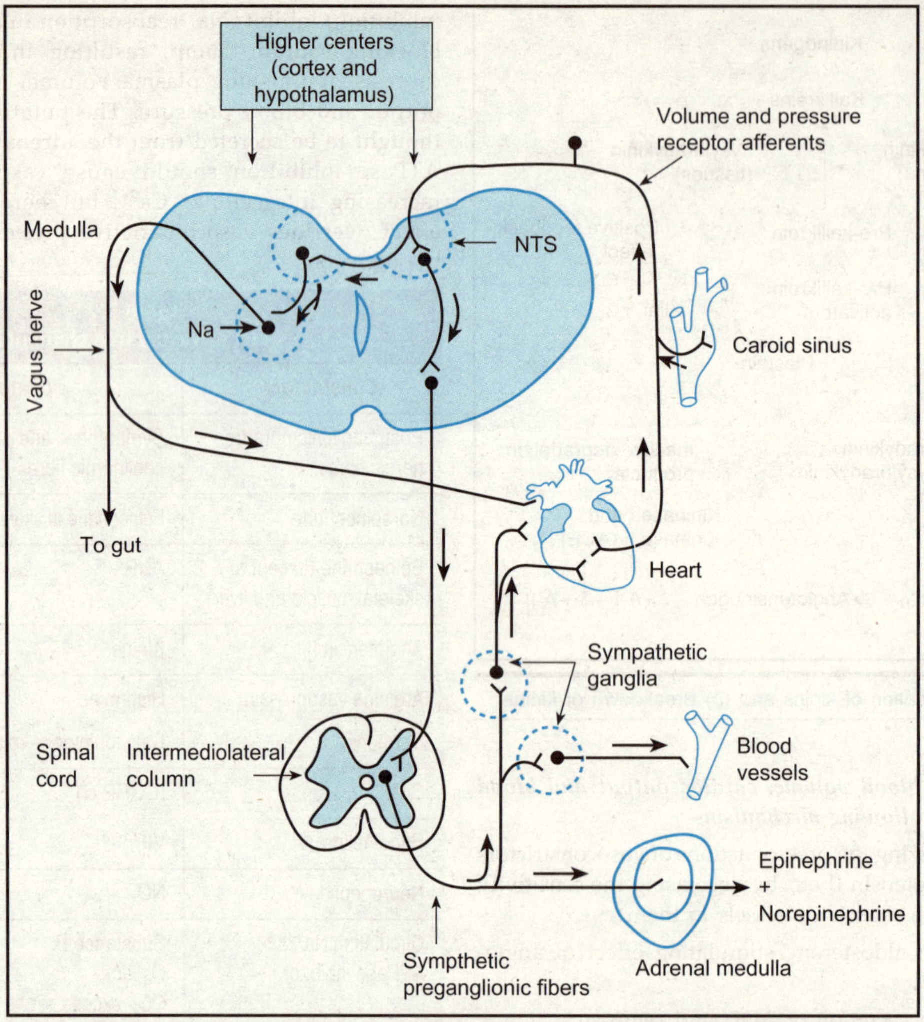


Fig. 7.28 : Cardiac reflexes. Effect of parasympathetic nerves and events taking place in the heart

neurotransmitter of nociceptors causing vasodilation of nearby vessels by antidromic conduction via a branch is responsible for axon reflex. It also increases capillary permeability.

## Baroreceptors (Fig. 7.29)

Afferents of neural circuits of cardiovascular reflexes arise from pressure/volume receptors situated at different sites of the circulatory system. ***They are stretch receptors situated at the (adventitia) walls of heart and blood vessels.*** They can be grouped as (a) **high-pressure baroreceptors** located at ***carotid sinus and aortic arch*** and ***also in the wall of left ventricle.*** (b) **low-pressure baroreceptors** situated at ***right and left atria, and pulmonary veins.***

**The cardiac baroreceptor reflex :** Stretch receptor neurons innervate the arterial walls of the aorta and specialized regions of the carotid arteries, the carotid sinuses. These stretch receptors are activated by stretch of the artery wall produced by the pulse pressure. These neurons then make excitatory connections with neurons in the nucleus of the solitary tract in the medulla. The solitary tract neurons project via additional inter neurons to the parasympathetic preganglionic neurons of the heart, located in the nucleus of the vagus nerve (Nucleus Ambiguus) andto reticulospinal neurons that send axons to the spinal cord. The reticulospinal neurons (VMC) (RVLM) projecting to the sympathetic centres in the spinal cords are tonically active (1/sec.). NTS projects to these VMC neurons via inhibitory neurons (CVLM). So, stimulation of the NTS results in inhibition of the VMC. Increased activity of the stretch receptors excites the parasympathetic preganglionic neurons, which then excite the parasympathetic neurons of the heart and increase the release of acetylcholine. The reticulospinal neurons excite neurons in the spinal cord which then regulate sympathetic preganglionic neurons involved in control of the heart.

## Carotid sinus and aortic arch baroreceptors (Fig. 7.30)

The **carotid sinus** is a small dilatation at the ***beginning of internal carotid artery***. Over its adventitia, the receptors

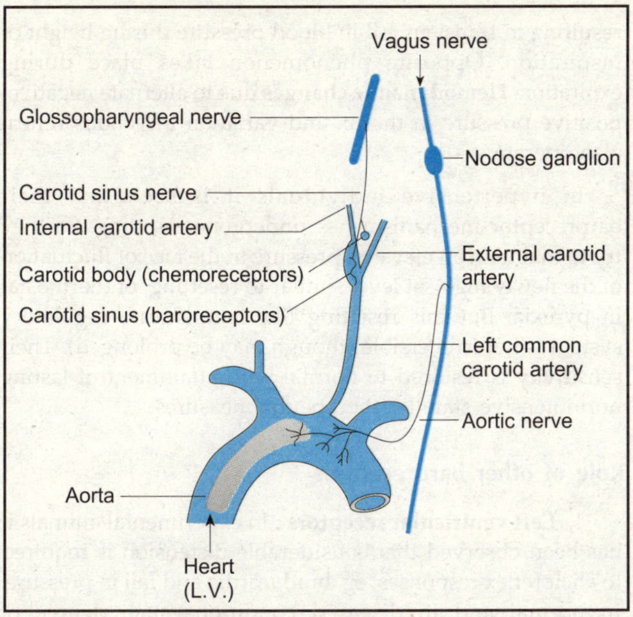


**Fig. 7.29 : Position and nerve supply of the aortic and carotid baroreceptors.**

are unmyelinated plexus of terminations of thinly myelinated axons of sinus branch of glossopharyngeal nerve (IX). The arch of aorta is similarly provided with afferents that travel with vagus nerve (X).

Large arteries of thorax and neck also have similar receptors. The baroreceptors of the systemic arteries respond to blood pressure increment with stretching of their walls. They initiate the process of restoring the pressure to previous level similar to buffers resisting change in pH of the media. They are also called **buffer nerves**.

Before going into the function of baroreceptors, **the role of cardiac innervation** is to be considered. Heart is supplied by both parasympathetic (vagus) and sympathetic divisions of autonomic nervous system. **Vagus supplies** mainly the ***atria and junctional tissues,*** but the ***distribution of sympathetic is extensive***. Their actions are opposite to each other. Heart experiences a tonic vagal discharge, because cholinergic blocking drugs increase heart rate even if the sympathetic activity remains same.

Sympathetic nerves send tonic discharges, and selective sympathetic inhibition reduces the heart rate exhibiting the tonic inhibitory effect of vagus. In human subjects, if the heart is denervated, the rate is around 100/min, while in heart with intact innervation it is 72/min at rest. Sympathetic is overall cardiac stimulator and parasympathetic is an all-round depressor. Heart is affected along with blood vessels in baroreceptor reflexes through the mediation of vasomotor centre of medulla.

**Vasomotor centre (VMC)** is a collection of neurons in the ventrolateral medulla that influences the contraction of smooth muscles of blood vessels and the myocardium. The

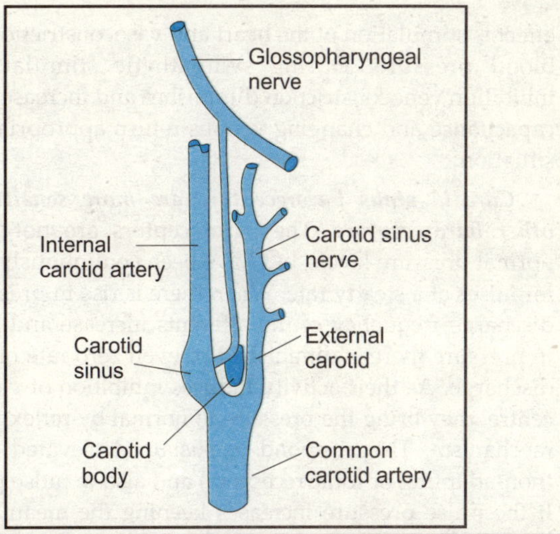


**Fig. 7.30 : Relative position of the carotid body and carotid sinus**

afferents from carotid sinus and other baroreceptors end bilaterally in the nucleus of the tractus solitarius (NTS) of medulla. From these nuclei interneurons arise which connect to neurons of ipsilateral side. These neurons include cells of $C_1$ area stimulating sympathetic centres of spinal cord and also vagal centres (dorsal motor nucleus, nucleus of tractus solitarius and nucleus ambiguous). From the $C_1$ area, descending fibers travel to intermediolateral horn of spinal cord.

Intermediolateral horn cells of spinal cord from $T_1$-$L_2$ are the preganglionic neurons of the sympathetic nervous system. These cells receive stimulatory impulses from neurons of $C_1$ area of VMC, they also get inhibitory impulses from separate neurons of medulla. Both the stimulatory and the inhibitory neurons receive fibers from nucleus of tractus solitarius, vagal nuclei, fibers from cerebral cortex and hypothalamus. ***The stimulatory and inhibitory descending fibers of VMC are affected by afferents from lungs and other viscera and from reticular formation that is influenced by numerous stimuli, including pain. The excitatory neurons are stimulated directly by hypercapnia and hypoxia.***

### Function of buffer nerves

When the carotid sinus and aortic arch receptors are stimulated by elevated transmural pressure, the afferents along glossopharyngeal and vagus nerves end bilaterally in the nuclei of tractus solitarius. From there second order neurons arise which cause inhibition of $C_1$ neurons that give rise to stimulatory descending fibers ipsilaterally, thus inhibiting tonic sympathetic discharge.

On the other hand, vagal fibers supplying heart get stimulated by separate neural connections. The effect produced is diminished rate and force of contraction of heart leading to fall in blood pressure. When there occurs fall in blood pressure, the afferent impulses in buffer nerves get fewer, the preganglionic sympathetic neurons receive less inhibition and vagal centres get less stimulation. The effect is stimulation of the heart and vasoconstriction raising blood pressure. During sympathetic stimulation and inhibition venoconstriction diminishes and increases venous capacitance and changing venous return appropriate to the situation.

***Carotid sinus baroreceptors are more sensitive than other baroreceptors.*** The baroreceptors are not silent at normal pressure levels, but have been continuously sending impulses at a steady rate. When there is rise in pressure, the discharge frequency of the afferents increase and with fall in pressure there is diminished or even zero rate of afferent discharge. As their activity induces inhibition of vasomotor centre, they bring the pressure to normal by reflex feedback mechanism. They respond to sustained elevated pressure (non-adapting or tonic receptors) and also to pulse pressure. If the pulse pressure increases keeping the mean pressure unaltered, impulse frequency increases. As the pressure is fluctuating in systole and diastole of a cardiac cycle, their discharge frequency increases and decreases with the phases of cardiac cycle.

In experimental animals, with isolated carotid sinus, on recording impulse frequency in afferent nerve, it has been observed that, if the pressure falls abysmally low, the receptors get silent, but in the normal range of pressure, they respond almost linearly. Now, if the pressure becomes too high, there is a limit up to which the discharge frequency can increase, further increase in pressure fails to stimulate them any more.

Thus, in an experimental setting, after hemorrhage, there occurs severe hypotension; the baroreceptors get functionless. Even then, the section of afferent nerve (carotid sinus n.) causes further fall of pressure indicating the passage of some stimulatory impulse through them. This is from carotid and other chemoreceptors which respond to stagnant hypoxia during profound hypotensive state and stimulate vasomotor centre to cause vasoconstriction trying to elevate the pressure.

***The chemoreceptors are primarily involved in regulation of respiration.*** **Peripheral chemoreceptors** respond to hypoxic, stagnant and histotoxic forms but not to anemic forms of hypoxia and also to hypercapnia and acidosis. The result is hyperventilation (central chemoreceptors respond to $CO_2$ tension) which is associated with stimulation of vasomotor centres. Chemoreceptors also send separate stimuli that lead ultimately to vasoconstriction reflexly via vasomotor areas.

During normal respiration and voluntary hyperventilation, the pulse rate increases during inspiration and decreases during expiration. Part of this response is due to afferents arising from stretch receptors in lungs which travel via vagus nerve and inhibit the nuclei of the same nerve causing tachycardia. Irradiation of stimuli from respiratory centres and also from descending fibers from brain to involve VMC are also operative. The same afferents from lungs, during inspiration, inhibit VMC to cause vasodilatation. Effect of vasodilatation overrides that of tachycardia, resulting in transient fall in blood pressure during height of inspiration. Opposite phenomenon takes place during expiration. **Hemodynamic changes** due to alternate negative-positive pressure in thorax and variation in venous return also operate.

In hypertensive individuals it is seen that their baroreceptor mechanism has undergone resetting. So they try to maintain an elevated pressure in the face of fluctuation of the newly high set level similar to resetting of thermostat in pyrexia. But this resetting like temperature regulatory system is not irreversible (though may be prolonged). Their sensitivity is restored to normal with attainment of lasting normotensive state by therapeutic measures.

## Role of other baroreceptors

1. **Left ventricular receptors** : In experimental animals it has been observed that considerable distension is required to elicit reflex responses, eg, bradycardia and fall in pressure. In normal and in diseased conditions such degree of dilatation is not possible, yet it is thought that they are partially responsible for resting vagal tone.

Of the baroreceptors or separate receptors, whatever they may be, it has been observed that vagal afferents from the heart can be stimulated injecting serotonin, veratridine, phenyldiguanide etc. in left coronary artery to produce reflex tachypnea, bradycardia and hypotension the **Bezold-Jarish reflex** or **coronary chemoreflex**. The same chemoreflex is suspected to cause sustained hypotension in cases of myocardial infarction, where chemical mediators liberated from dead tissue may stimulate the receptors which send impulses via C fibers along vagus nerve.

2. **Pulmonary vascular receptors** : Vagal afferents derived from C fibers are involved in reflex tachypnea, bradycardia and hypotension ( pulmonary chemoreflex) when chemicals like serotonin, veratridine etc. are injected into pulmonary arteries. The latency of response indicates the location of the receptors near pulmonary capillaries.

## Atrial baroreceptors

**Atrial wall** is provided with two types of receptors **A-type discharges** during systole and **B-type** during rapid filling phase of diastole. **B-type receptors** respond when venous return increases and are inhibited when venous return is obstructed by positive pressure breathing. The effect is vasodilatation, fall of blood pressure and increased heart rate. These are due to a reflex through vagal afferents and not by mechanical interference. Atrial baroreceptors thus sense and control the central venous pressure.

Rapid intravenous infusion of saline in anaesthetized animal with normal heart rate increases the rate via reflexes through the atrial baroreceptors (**Bainbridge reflex**). This reflex response is different from that of baroreceptors elsewhere which cause bradycardia. But, if the initial heart rate is high saline infusion fails to accelerate it further – the signifi-cance of which is difficult to explain. The physiological role of this reflex is obscure.

### Some physiological events related to vasomotion

1. **Relation with endocrine system** : Baroreceptors mediate appropriate reflex adjustments in relation to secretion of hormones. With depletion of blood volume, baroreceptors of atria and other low pressure areas increases secretion of ADH from posterior pituitary to conserve water. Associated sympathetic stimulation releases renin from J-G apparatus to generate Ang II which is a vasoconstrictor and mineralocorticoid inducer conserving salt and water. Volume depletion also reduces blood pressure. Carotid sinus and other high pressure receptors send impulses that reinforce the above compensa-tory processes.

2. **Emotional fainting—sympathetic vasodilator system** : Apart from its vasoconstrictor system, sympathetic system also carries vasodilator fibers that are cholinergic. ***The anatomy of this vasodilator system is cerebral cortex*** → hypo-thalamus → mid-brain → preganglionic cholinergic neurons of intermediolateral horn cells of spinal cord → sympathetic preganglionic fibers (cholinergic) → postganglionic fibers which are also cholinergic, supplying blood vessels of skeletal muscle. This vasodilator system is activated during emotions like fear, apprehension and rage. It may override concomitant vasoconstrictive effect to produce profound transient fall in blood pressure, cerebral ischaemia and fainting. Stimulation of adrenal medulla at the same time liberates epinephrine which induces vasodilation of skeletal muscles and liver via non-innervated β-receptors of blood vessels, producing additional vasodilatation.

This vasodilatation is independent of requirement of oxygen supply and excess flow largely by-passes the nutritive capillaries via throughfare channels. Their functional significance is poorly understood.

### Cushing reflex

Vasomotor area is responsive both to indirect and direct effects of hypoxia and hypercapnia. Direct effect of hyper-capnia is more prominent. Direct effect on VMC is exposed in cases of raised intracranial pressure due to any reason. Raised intracranial pressure reduces blood supply to vasomotor areas causing local hypoxia and hypercapnia which stimulate the VMC directly. The resulting vasoconstriction raises blood pressure which, by means of carotid and other baroreceptors, reduces heart rate but fails to counter the potent vasomotor discharge due to direct involvement of VMC. This rise of blood pressure in response to raised intracranial tension (**Cushing reflex**) increases blood flow to brain, but it is associated with bradycardia.

$CO_2$ diffuses easily through all biological barriers. But the effect of elevated arterial $P_{CO_2}$ produces no Cushing type response because raised $Pa_{CO_2}$ will affect VMC by both direct and indirect (via chemoreceptors) ways but, at the same time, it will relax peripheral vessels directly. So the central vasoconstrictive effect is counteracted by peripheral vasodilator action.

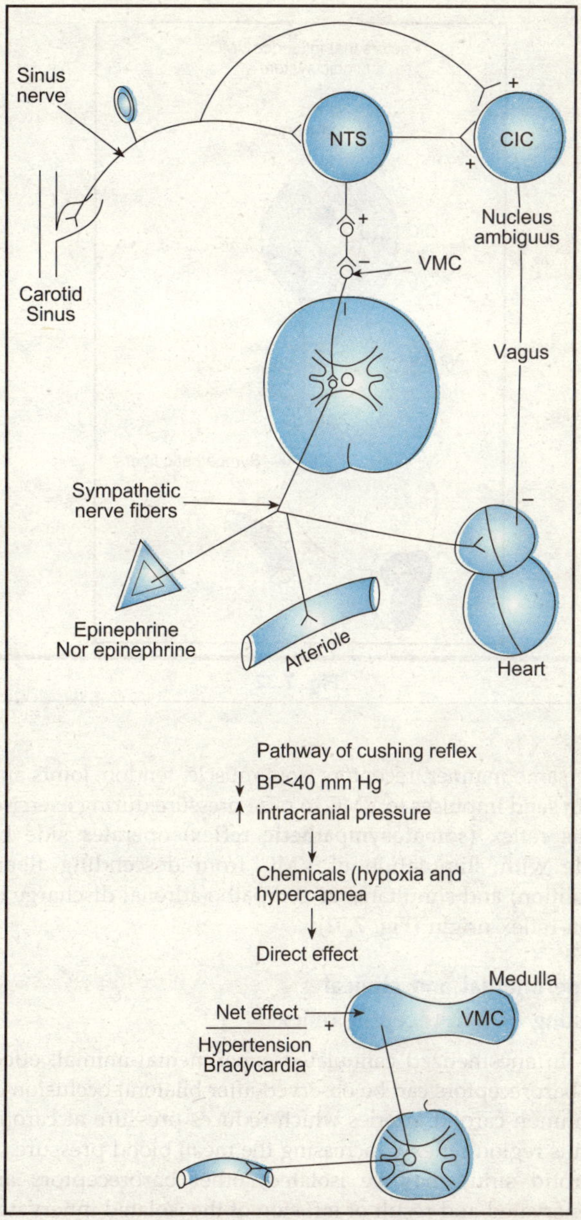


Fig. 7.31

Hyperventilation produces hypocapnia which is associated with cutaneous and cerebral vasoconstriction directly, but VMC is less active to send constrictive neural signal. So the blood pressure fails to rise appreciably (Fig. 7.31).

### Role of nociceptors

Pain pathways have diffuse terminations and, at the level of brain-stem, afferents converge ultimately to $C_1$ area of VMC to send pressor signals elevating blood pressure. In

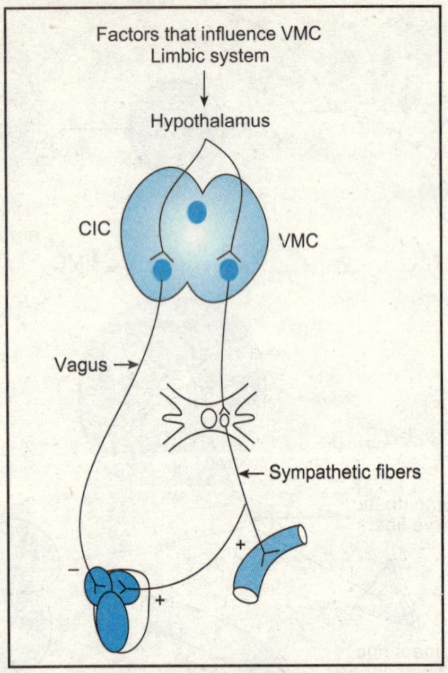


Fig. 7.32

the same manner, receptors from muscle, tendon, joints and skin send impulses to VMC to raise pressure during exercise. This reflex (**somatosympathetic reflex**) operates side by side with stimulation of VMC from descending fibers (volition) and simultaneous sympatho-adrenal discharge of non-reflex origin (Fig. 7.32).

### Experimental and clinical testing of baroreceptor reflex

In anesthetized cannulated experimental animal, effect of baroreceptors can be observed after bilateral occlusion of common carotid arteries which reduces pressure at carotid sinus region reflexly increasing the mean blood pressure. A carotid sinus may be isolated, other baroreceptors are denervated and result of infusion of the isolated innervated sinus can be observed and electrical activity of the afferent can also be recorded.

Clinically, heart rate and blood pressure variations with change in posture from supine to standing position can be noted. The change in heart rate due to infusion of some vasopressor drug (phenylephrine) can also be observed. The function of the baroreceptors can also be tested by Valsalva (forced expiration with closed glottis) maneuver. At the beginning of straining (a) there occurs small increase in arterial pressure as rising intrathoracic pressure will press large arteries; (b) when the breath is held, there occurs fall in blood pressure due to diminution of venous return and cardiac output. Due to fall in mean and pulse pressure by means of baroreceptor reflex mechanism, pulse rate increases; (c) when the effort is over, the intrathoracic pressure falls abruptly and venous return increases rapidly to bring the output to normal or more. But, as the peripheral vasoconstriction is yet to pass away, blood pressure rises transiently reducing the heart rate by the baroreceptor reflex. This ultimately brings back the pressure to normal. The heart rate and pressure changes associated with Valsalva maneuver is diminished but not abolished in sympathetomized individuals because parasympathetic (vagus) component of the reflex remains functional. But in cases of autonomic insufficiency, the heart rate changes are absent due to extensive involvement of both the divisions of ANS.

### Parasympathetic vasodilator fibers

**Craniosacral parasympathetic fibers** supply blood vessels along with structural elements of salivary glands, tongue, cerebral vessels, bladder, rectum and external genitalia. These fibers are not tonically active, but causes vasodilatation of the organs concerned during activity. ***They synapse with postganglionic cholinergic neurons*** that ultimately supply the vessels concerned. Their activity brings about vasodilation and increased local blood flow but it is inadequate to influence the circulation in general. Cholinergic blocking drugs like atropine can inhibit their action partially; probably the kinin system (lysylbradykinin) becomes operative simultaneously.

### Factors affecting VMC

- ***Direct stimulation*** hypoxia, hypercapnia
- ***Vasoconstrictive neural inputs*** chemoreceptors, nociceptors, skin, muscle sense organs, cerebral cortex through hypothalamus.
- ***Vasodilating neural inputs*** baroreceptors, lungs, cerebral cortex through hypothalamus.

## ➤ 7.9 Control of Arterial Blood Pressure

Arterial blood pressure is the product of cardiac output (CO) and peripheral resistance (PR) BP = CO × PR.

Therefore anything that affects CO or PR will have some effect on B.P. PR is regulated through changes in arteriolar caliber (Diameter of the arteriole). On the other hand, cardiac output depends on the status of cardiac function (like heart rate and contractility) and changes in venous return to the heart (which results from changes in blood volume)

Mechanisms that regulate B.P. may act rapidly or over a long period of time (table shows in page).

### Neural control

Neural mechanisms acting through the vasomotor center (VMC) in the medulla are largely responsible for the short term control of blood pressure. VMC activates sympathetic nerves and increased sympathetic activities can increase blood pressure by —

(i) Increasing heart rate and cardiac contractility. (i.e. increase in CO)

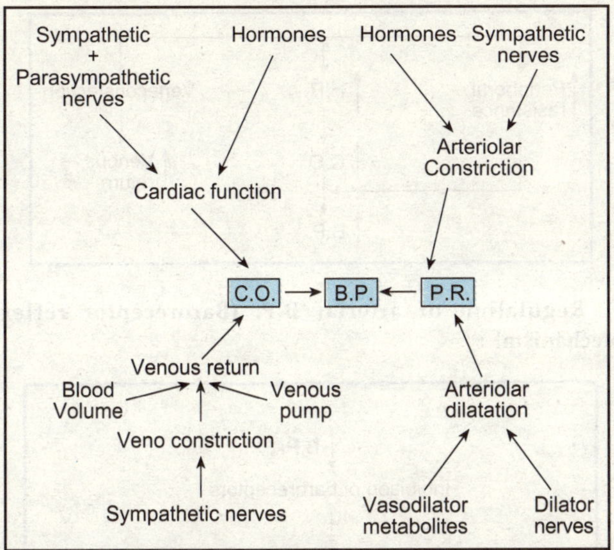


**Table shows the key control that affect arterial B.P.**

(ii) Arteriolar vasoconstriction (i.e. increase in PR)

(iii) Venoconstriction (i.e. increase in venous return raising CO).

## The Cardiac baroreceptor reflex

The Cardio inhibitory center reduces B.P. by activating parasympathetic nerves which cause slowing of the heart decreasing CO.

Increased B.P. causes stimulation of the arterial baroreceptors. This reduces sympathetic outflow to the cardiovascular system (thereby reducing CO and PR) and increases parasympathetic outflow to the heart (thereby reducing CO). The net effect is reduction of BP. Just the opposite events occur when there is fall in B.P.

Increased blood volume results in increase in B.P. due to increased venous return raising CO.

When blood pressure rises, the increased pressure is sensed by stretch receptor neurons whose nerve endings are located in the walls of the carotid artery in a specialized region called the **carotid sinus**. Additional stretch receptors innervate the walls of the aorta, the main artery leaving the heart. When B.P. rises, the walls of the blood vessels expand, increasing the rate of action potentials in the stretch receptor neurons. Increased activity in these neurons reflexly decreases the sympathetic input to the heart and increases the cardiac parasympathetic input. This process decreases heart rate and cardiac output, which then lowers blood pressure. Conversely, if blood pressure drops below normal, the arterial walls will be less stretched and activity in the stretch-sensitive neuron declines. Inhibition of cardiac sympathetic preganglionic neurons in the spinal cord is reduced, as is the excitation supplied to the parasympathetic preganglionic neurons in the nucleus of the vagus nerve. Activity thus increases in the sympathetic innervation of the heart and decreases in the parasympathetic innervation, raising both heart rate and cardiac output. In this manner, the reflex maintains the arterial B.P. at a particular level, adjusting heart rate and cardiac output to produce reflex changes in blood pressure.

Sympathetic fibres also activates low pressure cardiopulmonary baroreceptors in the walls of great veins atria and the pulmonary artery. Less sympathetic stimulation results in fall of B.P. due to

- Reduction in sympathetic activity (reducing peripheral resistance)
- Release of ADH (vasopressin) causing vasoconstriction and stimulation of water reabsorption from the kidneys.

Tissue hypoxia activates peripheral chemoreceptors which stimulate vasoconstrictor sympathetic nerves raising B.P.

When B.P. is extremely low, cerebral blood flow remarkably decreases, leading to accumulation of $CO_2$ and $H^+$ in brain tissues.

$CO_2$ and $H^+$ are potent stimuli to the VMC and they greatly increas the sympathetic outflow to the cardiovascular system. The result is restoration of normal B.P.

**Cushing reflex :** Rise in intracranial pressure compresses arteries in the brain, leading to cerebral ischemia, which stimulates sympathetic nervous activity raising B.P. Rise in B.P. above the intracranial pressure helps restore cerebral blood flow. This is known as **Cushing reflex**. Remarkable feature of the Cushing reflex is a simultaneous fall in HR which is a result of stimulation of the cardio inhibitory center consequent upon increase in B.P. (detected by arteriolar baroreceptors). Cushing reflex (hypertension accompanied by bradycardia) is a classical sign found in raised intracranial pressure.

## Hormonal Control

This is another mechanism for short term control of B.P. However some hormones may take hours to days for full effect.

- Catecholamines : They tend to increase B.P. by increasing HR, cardiac contractility and PR.
- ADH : Increases blood volume.

**Renin angiotensin aldosterone system :** A low B.P. is associated with decrease in renal blood flow causing the juxtraglomerular apparatus of the kidneys to secrete Renin. Renin converts angiotensinogen to angiotensin I which inturn is converted to angiotension II by *angiotensin converting enzyme*. Angiotensin II is a potent vasoconstrictor. It also stimulates the release of aldosterone (from the adrenal cortex), which promotes renal reabsorption of Sodium and water (thereby increasing blood volume) Both vasoconstriction and increasing blood volume are responsible for rise in B.P.

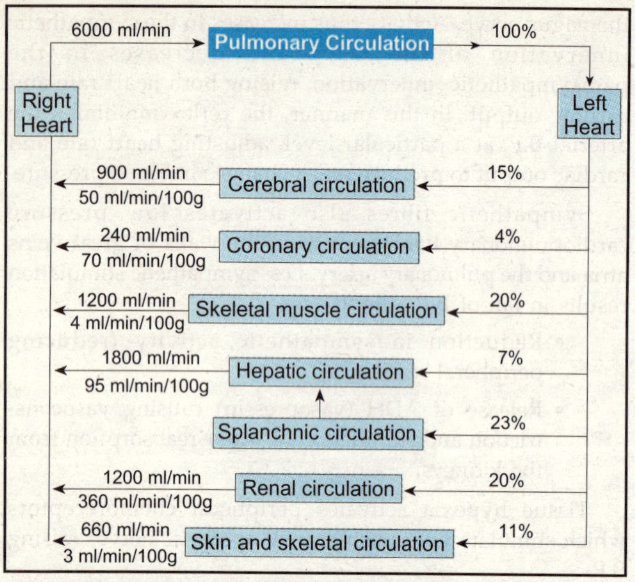


**Fig. 7.33 : Blood flow through different parts of the body**

## Long term Control

The long term regulation of B.P. has not yet been precisely understood but long term regulation of blood volume appears to be an important factor. Several hormonally controlled renal mechanisms may also be involved.

- Changes in B.P. may lead to changes in renal blood flow and GFR.
- ADH facilitates renal reabsorption of water when blood volume is decreased.
- Aldosterone tends to retain Sodium and water when there is fall in B.P.
- Atrial natriuretic peptide (ANP) causes Sodium and water excretion by the Kidneys.

Most persons with hypertension (high blood pressure) have a high peripheral resistance but the factors responsible are unknown in most of the cases.

The cardio inhibitory center reduces B.P. by activating parasympathetic nerves which causes slowing of the heart decreasing CO.

Increased B.P. causes stimulation of the arterial baroreceptors. This reduces sympathetic outflow to the cardiovascular system (thereby reducing CO and PR) and increases parasympathetic outflow to the heart (thereby reducing CO). The net effect is reduction of B.P.) Just the opposite events occur when there is fall in B.P.

Increased blood volume results in increase in B.P. due to increased venous return raising CO.

**Hormonal control of blood volume provides long term regulation of blood pressure :**

Change of posture from supine to an upright position → Decreased venous return → Decreased stroke volume → Baroreceptor activity → ↑Sympathetic tone.

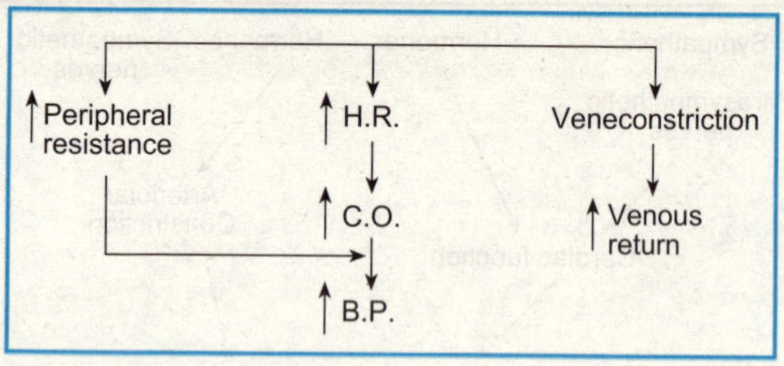


**Regulation of arterial B.P. (Baroreceptor reflex mechanism) :**

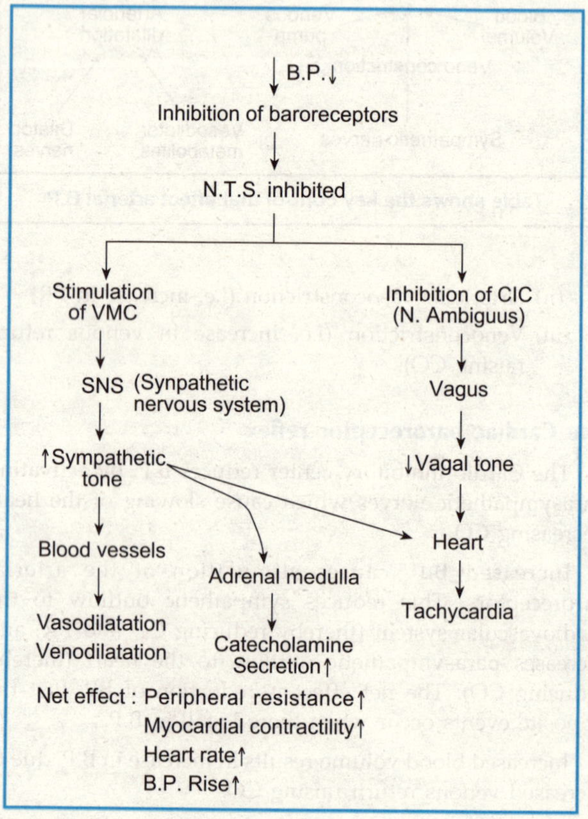


## 7.10 Regulation of Regional Blood Flow (Fig. 7.33)

Each tissue controls its own local blood flow according to its metabolic needs. In general, blood flow is directly proportional to the metabolism in an organ. It has been shown experimentally that the blood flow to a particular tissue is regulated in such a manner as to meet its requirements exactly. This ensures a minimum workload on the heart to provide the optimum metabolic requirements to the tissues. Control of blood flow at the local level satisfies the widely varying needs of different tissues for perfusion.

### Blood flow control mechanisms

*Control of local blood flow can be achieved in two phases :*

1. *Acute control*
   - Occurs within seconds to minutes
   - Mediated by rapid changes in diameter of the arterioles, metarterioles, and precapillary sphincters in the local area.
2. *Long term control*
   - Occurs over a period of days, weeks, or sometimes, months
   - In addition to changes in the caliber of the microvasculature, numbers of blood vessels are also altered in the local area
   - Provides a far better control of flow.

## Acute control

Acute control of local blood flow comes into play with changes in the rate of tissue metabolism or the availability of oxygen. Two different theories have been put forward to explain the regulation of local blood flow **the vasodilator theory** and **the oxygen demand theory**.

***Vasodilator theory*** : This theory proposes that a vasodilator substance is formed at a greater rate whenever there is increase in the metabolic rate of the tissue or decrease in the availability of oxygen or some other nutrients to the tissue. The vasodilator substance diffuses in the adjacent area to cause dilatation of the arterioles, metarterioles, and precapillary sphincters and a consequent increase in local blood flow. The oxygen deficiency is thought to be the main stimulus for the release of the vasodilator. ***Various vasodilators have been suggested which include adenosine, carbon dioxide ($CO_2$), lactic acid, adenosine phosphate compounds, histamine, potassium ions ($K^+$), and hydrogen ions ($H^+$).***

Adenosine, an end product of ATP degradation, appears to be the most important local vasodilator. It causes relaxation of vascular smooth muscles by acting on $A_2$-adenosine receptors. Upon restoration of blood flow, production of the vasodilator substance is diminished and that which was released is degraded or washed away. It is worth noting that no single vasodilator has yet been identified that alone can explain the increase in blood flow. Probably the combined effects of all the vasodilators are responsible.

**Oxygen demand theory** : This may also be called **"nutrient demand theory"** ***because other nutrients (besides oxygen) are probably involved as well.*** Adequate supply of oxygen and other nutrients are required to maintain the contraction of vascular smooth muscles. When their concentrations fall, vascular smooth muscles relax causing dilatation of microvasculature of the tissue and, thereby, the local blood flow is increased.

Though both the vasodilator theory and the oxygen demand theory can explain regulation of local blood flow depending on the metabolic need individually, a combination of both appears to be operative in reality.

Two special instances of metabolic control of local blood flow are **active** and **reactive hyperemia** :

*Active hyperemia* : The rate of blood flow through any tissue increases when it becomes highly active. The increased tissue metabolism causes deficiency of oxygen and other nutrients and there is release of vasodilator substances as well. This results in dilatation of local blood vessels causing increase in local blood flow called **active hyperemia**.

*Reactive hyperemia* : This is another manifestation of the metabolic regulation of local blood flow. When the blood supply to a tissue is unblocked after a short period of vascular occlusion, the tissue blood flow increases several times over normal. Here, the lack of flow during vascular occlusion brings in all the factors causing vasodilation. On removal of the occlusion, extra blood flows to the area giving rise to **reactive hyperemia**. The phase of reactive hyperemia continues for sufficient enough time to repay the tissue oxygen deficit accrued during the period of vascular occlusion.

## Autoregulation of blood flow

An acute increase in arterial pressure in any tissue of the body causes an immediate rise in blood flow which returns toward the normal level within a short period of time. This is known as **autoregulation**.

There are **two views** about the *mechanism of autoregulation* the **metabolic theory** and the **myogenic theory**.

With increase in arterial pressure, extra blood flow to the tissue supplies excess of oxygen and other nutrients which cause the blood vessels to constrict more than normal. Thus, flow returns almost to normal in spite of the increased pressure. This is the basis of the **metabolic theory**.

The **myogenic theory** proposes a different mechanism independent of tissue metabolism. It has been observed that smooth muscles in the wall of small blood vessels contract in response to sudden stretch. Stretching of the small blood vessels due to high arterial pressure causes these vessels to constrict. Local blood flow is thus returned nearly back to normal.

## Role of nitric oxide

Nitric oxide (NO), also known as ***endothelial-derived relaxation factor (EDRF)***, is synthesized in endothelial cells from L-arginine by the action of the enzyme **NO synthase**. NO probably diffuses to the smooth muscles in the blood vessels like arterioles causing them to dilate. This mechanism can dilate the larger arteries as well. The stimuli for release of NO from endothelial cells are multiple and include shear-stress on the endothelial cells, acetyl choline, bradykinin and ATP among others.

NO produces secondary increase in the dimensions of the larger blood vessels supplying a tissue in which local blood flow has been increased by dilatation of its microvasculature. This maintains the effectiveness of local blood flow control. The stimulus for increased NO production in such case appears to be the shear-stress on the endothelial cells due to rapid flow of blood.

### Long term control

Long term regulation of local blood flow occurs over a period of hours, days and weeks. This develops in addition to the acute regulation and provides more complete regulation.

Long term control is brought about by a change in the degree of vascularity of tissues in response to changes in arterial pressure or metabolic activity of the tissues. Apart from changes in size of vessels, the number of vessels are also altered.

Oxygen is important in long term control also. Lack of oxygen causes increase in tissue vascularity. ***This is why tissue vascularity is more in the animals living at high altitudes where atmospheric oxygen is low.*** Administration of oxygen to premature babies lead to cessation of vascular growth in retina but when oxygen therapy is discontinued there is overgrowth of new vessels some of which may grow into the eye's vitreous humor leading to a condition known as **retrolental fibroplasia.**

### Growth of new vessels

Growth of new blood vessels is called **angiogenesis.** Angiogenic factors are factors that cause angiogenesis. These factors may be released from ischemic tissues, rapidly growing tissues or tissues with very high metabolic rates. Deficiency of oxygen or other nutrients or both in the tissue is probably responsible for the formation of the angiogenic factors.

Most of the **angiogenic factors** are small peptides. Endothelial cell growth factor, fibroblast growth factor, and angiogenin are a few of them.

### Development of collateral circulation

New vascular channels develop around a blockage in a blood vessel and partial blood supply to the part is restored. The development of collaterals follows the principles of local blood flow regulation — both **acute** and **chronic**. Initial rapid dilatation of collateral vessels is followed by growth and enlargement of the vessels over a longer period of time.

### Humoral regulation of the circulation

Regulation of the circulation by substances in the body fluids (eg, hormones and ions) is also important in maintaining homeostasis. Some of these substances are synthesized locally and have a local effect only while others are formed in special glands and are circulated through blood stream to have a generalized effect. These substances regulate the circulation by dilating or constricting the blood vessels. Some of the important regulatory substances are :

***Vasoconstrictor agents***

- Norepinephrine
- Epinephrine
- Angiotensin
- Vasopressin
- Endothelin

***Vasodilator agents***

- Bradykinin
- Serotonin (also has some vasoconstrictor property)
- Histamine
- Prostaglandins (some of them have vasoconstrictor property)

***Ions and other chemicals*** — their effects are summarised in Table 7.3.

**Table 7.3**
**Effects of ions and chemicals on vascular dimension**

| *Vasodilation* | *Vasoconstriction* |
|---|---|
| ↑ $K^+$ | ↑ $Ca^{++}$ |
| ↑ $Mg^{++}$ | ↓ Osmolality |
| ↑ $Na^+$ | ↓ $H^+$ |
| ↑ Osmolality | |
| ↑ Acetate | |
| ↑ Citrate | |
| ↑ $CO_2$ | |

## 7.11 Cerebral Circulation (Fig. 7.34)

Under resting conditions, ***blood flow through the brain*** tissue of the ***adult is about 50 mL/min/100 gm*** and about 900 mL/min for the entire brain. This accounts for about 15% of cardiac output. ***The human brain consumes oxygen at a rate of about 3.5 mL/min/100 gm of brain tissue.*** The overall oxidative metabolism of the brain gray matter is four to six times as great as the white matter. Accordingly, the rate of blood flow to gray matter is also four to six times as great. The brain, especially the gray matter, is extraordinarily sensitive to hypoxia. ***Consciousness is lost within 5 to 10 seconds if blood flow to the brain is totally ceased.*** Therefore, the primary function of the cerebral circulation is to ensure a continuous and optimum supply of oxygen to the brain.

### Measurement of cerebral blood flow

**Cerebral blood flow (CBF)** may be measured by applying the Fick principle which states that the blood flow to any organ can be measured by detecting the amount of a given substance ($Q_x$) removed from the blood stream by the organ per unit of time and dividing that by the

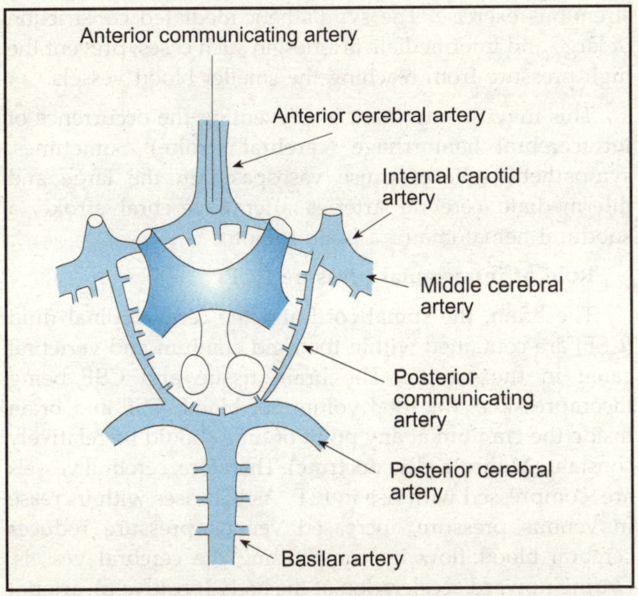


**Fig. 7.34 :** Anatomy of cerebral circulation

arteriovenous difference of the concentration of that substance across the organ concerned ($[A_x] - [V_x]$) :

$$CBF = \frac{Q_X}{[A_X]-[V_X]}$$

The substance used for clinical determination of CBF is inhaled nitrous oxide ($N_2O$) and the method is known as **Kety method.** Kety method is based on the fact that $N_2O$ (in subanesthetic concentration) equilibrates within about 10 minutes with brain substance, then concentration of $N_2O$ in cerebral venous effluent is equal to that of brain. So, if the cerebral venous $N_2O$ concentration after equilibration as also time required for it and several simultaneous arterial and cerebral venous $N_2O$ concentrations are known, the equation of CBF can be utilised for its estimation by taking

(a) $Q_x$ = Final concentration of $N_2O$ in cerebral venous blood as equal to $N_2O$ uptake per unit brain tissue (ml/100g).

(b) $[A_x] - [V_x]$ or $[A_{N_2O}] - [V_{N_2O}]$ can be calculated from the plot relating arterial and cerebral venous $N_2O$ concen-tration in respect of time for equilibration, the average value can be determined by the surface area between traces and then dividing it equally by the length of time plot (abscissa) to have the value in ml/100 ml for the sake of expressing the value in ml/100g for the time of equilibration, which is ultimately converted to ml/min/100g.

***The Kety method gives an average value for the perfused areas of the brain only.***

## Measurement of regional blood flow in brain and effect of cerebral activity on flow

Nowadays, it is possible to measure and monitor regional blood flow in brain in living humans. A tracer like $^{133}Xe$ or $^{123}I$-labeled iodoamphetamine ($^{123}I$-IMP) is used. Its arrival and clearance are monitored by scintillation counters placed externally. The output is processed in a computer and is displayed in colour the colour corresponding to the location of each counter being proportional to the flow it detects. Computerized tomographic reconstruction of the output provides better resolution and the technique is known as **SPECT (single photon emission computed tomography)**.

*Regional blood flow* in brain can also be measured by **positron emission tomography (PET)**. This technique of imaging, detects concentraton of 2-deoxyglucose labelled with a short-half life positron emitter like $^{18}F$, $^{11}O$ or $^{15}O$ in any part of the brain and the output is reconstructed in a computer. The tight coupling of blood flow to brain metabolism is the basis of detecting brain blood flow using local uptake of 2-deoxy-glucose.

Another imaging technique to monitor regional blood flow in brain is functional **magnetic resonance imaging (MRI)** which may be better than PET.

A characteristic feature of cerebral function is that the blood flow to a region of the brain fluctuates with fluctuation in activity; greater the activity, greater the blood flow. For example, voluntary clenching of the left hand causes increase in flow in the hand area of the right motor cortex as well as in the corresponding sensory areas in the postcentral gyrus.

***Imaging techniques like SPECT and PET have been used to study different neurological disorders.*** During seizures, epileptic foci have been found to be hyperemic. Bilateral reduction in blood flow to the caudate nucleus is an early change in **Huntington's disease** and this holds promise to detect asymptomatic individuals at risk of this disease. When depressed, patients with bipolar affective disorder (manic depression) have generalized decrease in cortical blood flow. Schizophrenics tend to have decreased blood flow to the frontal lobes, temporal lobes and basal ganglia of their brains. The earliest change in ***Alzheimer's disease*** is decreased blood flow and metabolism in the superior parietal cortex which then spread to the temporal cortex followed by the frontal cortex.

## Regulation of cerebral circulation (Figs. 7.35 and 7.36)

The total cerebral blood flow is generally kept constant under different conditions. ***The factors that affect the total cerebral blood flow are the arterial and venous pressures at brain level, the intracranial pressure (ICP), the blood viscosity, and the diameter of the cerebral arterioles.***

### Metabolic control of flow

An increase in arterial $CO_2$ concentration results in an increase in the cerebral blood flow. $CO_2$ combines with water to form carbonic acid which dissociates into $H^+$ and $HCO^-_3$ ions. The $H^+$ ions are responsible for the vasodilatation. Other substances like lactic acid, pyruvic

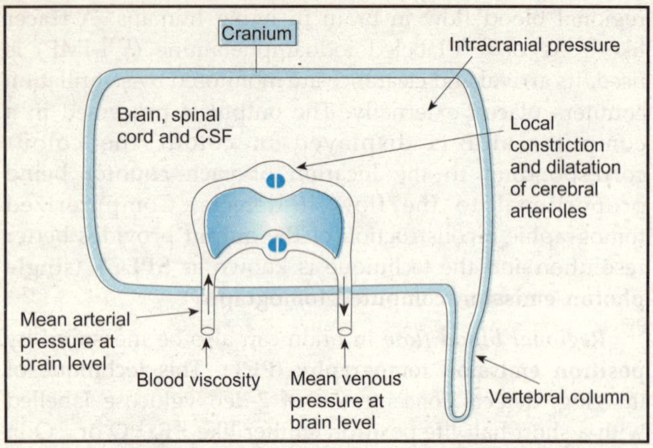


**Fig. 7.35 : Regulation of cerebral circulation**

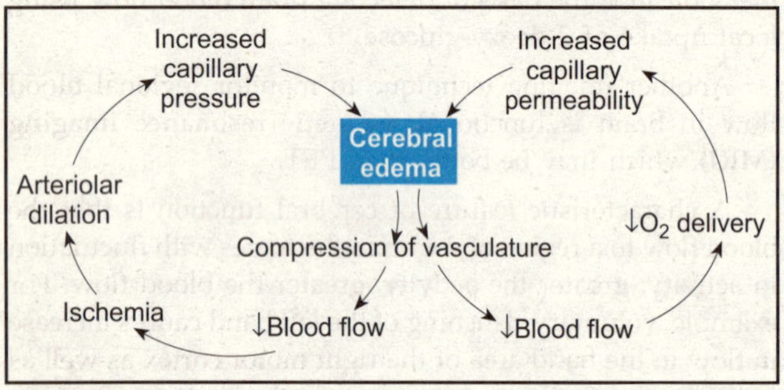


**Fig. 7.36 : Cerebral oedema**

acid etc. that increases the acidity of the brain tissue, i.e., increases $H^+$ ion concentration, also cause vasodilatation.

Increase in blood flow with increase in $H^+$ ion concentration carries away $CO_2$ and other acidic substances from the tissue. Thus a constant pH is maintained which is essential for optimal function of the neurons. Low pH depresses neuronal activity.

Oxygen deficiency also causes cerebral vasodilatation when the cerebal tissue $P_{O_2}$ falls below 30 mm Hg and cerebral blood flow begins to rise. This mechanism also protects against depression of neuronal activity due to low $P_{O_2}$ .

*Autoregulation* : The autoregulatory mechanism keeps cerebral blood flow reasonably constant between the arterial pressure limits of ***60 and 140 mm Hg.*** In hypertensives, this range shifts to higher pressure levels of up to ***180-200 mm Hg.***

**Neural control**

***The role of the postganglionic sympathetic and parasympathetic nerves on cerebral blood flow is debatable.*** The vasoconstriction produced by sympathetic stimulation and the vasodilation produced by parasympathetic stimulation are both weak and appears to be insignificant. However, under some circumstances, cerebral arteries may be constricted markedly by cerebral sympathetic stimulation. This happens when the cerebral arterial pressure rises significantly during excessive circulatory activity like strenuous exercise. The sympathetic-mediated constriction of large and intermediate arteries, in such cases, prevent the high pressure from reaching the smaller blood vessels.

This may be important in preventing the occurrence of intracerebral hemorrhage (**cerebral stroke**). Sometimes, sympathetic reflexes cause vasospasm in the large and intermediate cerebral arteries after a cerebral stroke, a subdural hematoma or a brain tumour.

**Role of intracranial pressure (ICP)**

The brain, the spinal cord and the cerebrospinal fluid (CSF) are contained within the rigid cranium and vertebral canal in the adult . The brain tissue and CSF being incompressible, the total volume of blood, CSF and brain inside the cranium at any point of time should be relatively constant (**Monro-Kellie doctrine**). Therefore, cerebral vessels are compressed with rise in ICP. As ICP rises with increase in venous pressure, increased venous pressure reduces cerebral blood flow by compressing the cerebral vessels. During upward acceleration of the body (positive g), arterial pressure at the head level decreases because blood moves toward the feet. This is accompanied by fall in venous pressure and ICP as well. Therefore, pressure on cerebral vasculature decreases and cerebral blood flow is maintained towards normal. Just the opposite happens during downward acceleration (negative g). Similar mechanism operates while straining during defecation or delivery.

Rise in ICP produces reflex rise in blood pressure with bradycardia and slowing of respiration. This is known as **Cushing reflex**. The elevated ICP causes cerebral ischemia by reducing blood flow. Systemic blood pressure rises due to stimulation of vasomotor area by the ischemia. Vagal stimulation leads to bradycardia and slowing of respiration. The Cushing reflex is important for maintaining the cerebral blood flow in the face of rising ICP.

**Cerebral "stroke"**

Blockage of arterial blood supply to a part of the brain causes a disturbance in brain function commonly referred to as **"stroke"**. Stroke may be thrombotic, embolic or hemorrhagic.

In thrombotic stroke, a blood clot develops at the site of arteriosclerotic plaque in a cerebral artery and the clot eventually blocks the arterial blood supply.

**In embolic stroke**, a dislodged thrombus from a distant site (eg, the heart or a proximal artery) occludes the arterial blood supply.

**In hemorrhagic stroke**, hemorrhage from a ruptured cere-bral artery usually because of high blood pressure is responsible for the disturbance in brain function.

The neurological deficits arising out of a stroke depends on the area of the brain affected. Blockage of one of the middle cerebral arteries is one of the most common types of stroke.

**Cerebral edema**

**Cerebral edema** usually results from either great increase in capillary pressure or damage to the capillary wall. The cause may be :

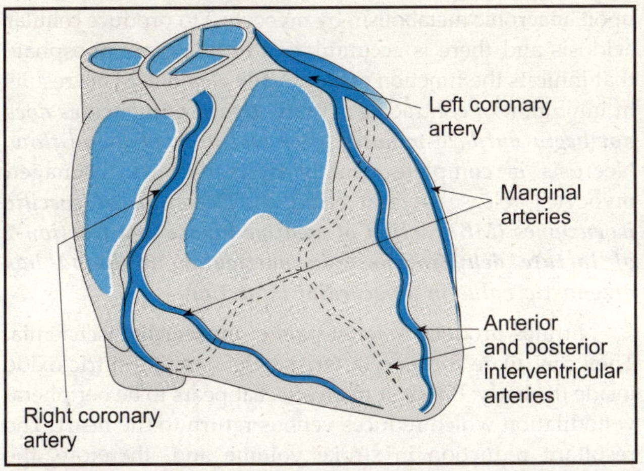


**Fig. 7.37 : The organization of the coronary blood supply. Origin of the coronary arteries at the base of the aorta.**

(i) ***Brain concussion*** : Most common, fluid leaks from traumatized capillaries into the brain tissues.

(ii) ***Sudden increase in cerebral artery pressure*** : Pressure so high that autoregulatory mechanism fails.

Measures to control cerebral edema include :

(i) ***Intravenous infusion of concentrated osmotic substance like 20% mannitol.*** This draws fluid from brain tissue by osmosis.

(ii) ***Ventricular puncture*** removes fluid quickly from the lateral ventricles.

## 7.12 Coronary Circulation (Fig. 7.37)

**Blood flow to the heart is *about 70 ml/min/100 gm (240 ml/min for the whole heart)*** at rest which constitutes about 4% of the cardiac output. Five to six-fold rise in flow may occur during maximal cardiac work. Blood flow to left ventricle (80 ml/min/100 gm) is twice the flow to right ventricle. Atrial blood flow is about one-fourth of the ventricular blood flow. ***Oxygen consumption by the myocardium is very high*** 8 ml/min/100 gm at rest, increasing up to about five-fold during maximal cardiac work. To meet this requirement, 70-80% of $O_2$ is extracted from the coronary blood compared to the whole body average of 25% at rest.

***Phasic changes in coronary blood flow. Effects of myocardial compression and intramyocardial pressure***

Average blood flow through the capillaries of left ventricle falls during systole due to compression of myocardium around the intramuscular vessels. The cardiac muscles relax during diastole and blood flow increases. These phasic changes in blood flow to left ventricular capillaries is depicted in Fig. 7.38.

Similar phasic changes in blood flow occurs also in right

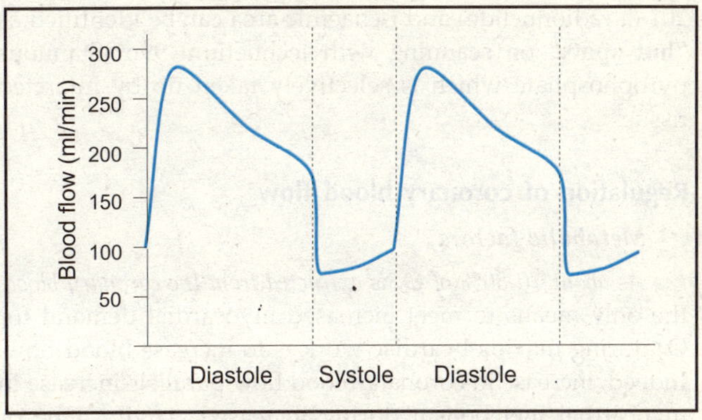


**Fig. 7.38 : Flow through left ventricular myocardium**

ventricle but changes in blood flow is not so marked because the force of contraction of the right ventricle is much less.

***Blood flow in the arteries to the subendocardial parts of the left ventricle occurs only during diastole.*** This is because of the fact that the left ventricular pressure during systole is slightly higher than that in the aorta. However, the epicardial parts of the left ventricle receives some flow of blood throughout the cardiac cycle as the effect of intraventricular pressure is sufficiently dampened in these parts. At higher heart rates, diastole is shortened and, therefore, left ventricular flow is reduced during diastole.

Blood flow to right ventricle and atria is not appreciably reduced during systole. The reason for this is that the differences between pressure in right ventricle or atria and aorta are greater during systole than diastole (Table 7.4).

Subendocardial parts of the left ventricle are vulnerable to ischaemic damage and is a common site of myocardial infarction. In aortic stenosis, pressure in the left ventricle is much higher than that in aorta because the ventricle has to force blood against a narrow aortic orifice. This leads to severe compression of coronary vessels during systole producing symptoms of myocardial ischaemia.

**Table 7.4**
**Pressure differentials between ventricles and aorta during systole and diastole**

| | Pressure (mm Hg) | | | Pressure differential (mm Hg) between aorta and ventricles | |
|---|---|---|---|---|---|
| | Right ventricle | Left ventricle | Aorta | Right ventricle | Left ventricle |
| Systole | 25 | 121 | 120 | 95 | –1 |
| Diastole | 0 | 0 | 80 | 80 | 80 |

### Measurement of coronary blood flow

Coronary blood flow can be measured by **Kety method** using $N_2O$. Myocardial perfusion scan is done using thallium

201 (a radionuclide) and ischaemic area can be identified as **"hot spots"** on scanning with technetium 99m Stannous pyrophosphate which is selectively taken up by infarcted tissue.

## Regulation of coronary blood flow

*Metabolic factors*

*As about 70-80% of $O_2$ is extracted from the coronary blood,* the only means to meet increased myocardial demand for $O_2$ during maximal cardiac work is to increase blood flow. Indeed, increase in coronary blood flow parallels increase in myocardial metabolism during increased activity. One or more of the vasodilator metabolites are responsible for coronary vasodilatation that brings about increase in blood flow. Adenosine has received great attention in recent times. However, oxygen deficiency, increased local concentrations of $H^+$, $CO_2$, $K^+$, lactate, prostaglandins, bradykinin and adenine nucleotides also have some role. The reactive hyperemia seen in the heart is believed to be due to release of adenosine.

*Neural factors*

***Both α-adrenergic (mediating vasoconstriction) and β-adrenergic receptors are present in the coronary arterioles.*** Noradrenergic activity in the heart causes increase in heart rate and force of contraction of the heart via β-adrenergic receptors. Release of vasodilator metabolites due to increased cardiac activity causes dilation of coronary arterioles which overrides the direct α-adrenergic receptor-mediated vasoconstriction.

Direct effect of acetyl choline on coronary arterioles is vasodilation. However, concomitant slowing of the heart rate reduces cardiac metabolism and $O_2$ demand. Thus, metabolic factors come into play which tend to dominate over the direct effects of acetylcholine on vascular tone. The net effect of vagal stimulation is, therefore, a reduction in blood flow.

Reflex noradrenergic overactivity during fall in systemic blood pressure increases coronary blood flow secondary to metabolic changes in the cardiac muscle and thereby preserves the circulation of the heart.

## Coronary artery disease

Interruption of coronary blood flow results in myocardial ischemia producing **angina pectoris** (precordial chest pain). Death of myocardial tissue (myocardial infarction) may occur if the ischaemia is severe and prolonged. Myocardial infarction is a common cause of death, particularly in developed countries. A ***thrombus*** over an atherosclerotic plaque in a coronary artery is usually the cause of **myocardial infarction.** High serum cholesterol level is a recognized risk factor for atherosclerosis. Circulating levels of lipoprotein(a) interferes with fibrinolysis and homocysteine have also been positively correlated with atherosclerosis.

Within 30 seconds of interruption of blood flow to a part of the myocardium, enough lactic acid builds up (consequent upon anaerobic metabolism by myocytes) to produce cellular acidosis and there is accumulation of inorganic phosphate that inhibits the function of contractile elements. This results in inhibition of contractile activity. ***Death of myocytes does not begin until 20 minutes after cessation of blood flow.*** Necrosis is complete usually by 3-6 hours. Damaged myocytes release several enzymes. ***Detection of specific isoenzymes (MB fraction of creatine kinase and fraction-1 of lactate dehydrogenase in particular) in blood has diagnostic value in myocardial infarction.***

Nitrates produce relief of pain of myocardial ischaemia. They can dilate coronary arteries by generating nitric oxide inside the body. But their main effect appears to be peripheral venodilation which reduces venous return to the heart. The resultant reduction in stroke volume and, therefore, the myocardial $O_2$ demand, helps reduce the ischaemia.

***Streptokinase*** is a protein obtained from hemolytic streptococci and tissue-type plasminogen activator (t-PA) is a naturally occurring protease that can be produced by recombinant DNA technology. Both convert plasminogen to plasmin which has fibrinolytic activity. Intracoronary infusion of these agents within the first few hours of onset of myocardial infarction may lyse the clot responsible for the attack and may reduce the extent of myocardial damage.

## ➤ 7.13 Pulmonary Circulation (Fig. 7.39)

The pulmonary vessels accommodate a blood flow which is almost equal to the flow in all other organs of the body. The pulmonary vasculature is distensible and pressures in these vessels are low. ***The mean pulmonary arterial pressure is about 15 mm Hg*** (systolic pressure 20-24 mm Hg and diastolic 5-9 mm Hg). With a diastolic left atrial pressure of about 0-5 mm Hg, the pressure gradient across the pulmonary system is about 12 mm Hg. This is much less than the gradient in systemic circulation which is about 90 mm Hg (Fig. 7.36) The fall of pressure from the pulmonary artery to the capillaries is small whereas pressure drop in veins is relatively large. The blood volume in the pulmonary vessels at any instant is about 1,000 ml. Less than 100 ml of this is contained in the capillaries. A red blood cell takes about 0.75 second to pass through the pulmonary capillaries at rest. This comes down to 0.3 second or less during exercise.

There is an inwardly directed pressure gradient in the pulmonary capillaries because ***pulmonary capillary pressure is about 10 mm Hg while oncotic pressure is 25 mm Hg.*** Therefore, no fluid accumulates in the lung alveoli under normal circumstances. In left ventricular failure, pulmonary capillary pressure may rise above 25 mm Hg causing reversal of the gradient leading to pulmonary edema.

To be more precise, the forces behind filtration across pulmonary capillaries also include interstitial hydrostatic pressure that is equal to intrapleural pressure i.e, **Net ultrafiltration pressure** = Capillary hydrostatic pressure –

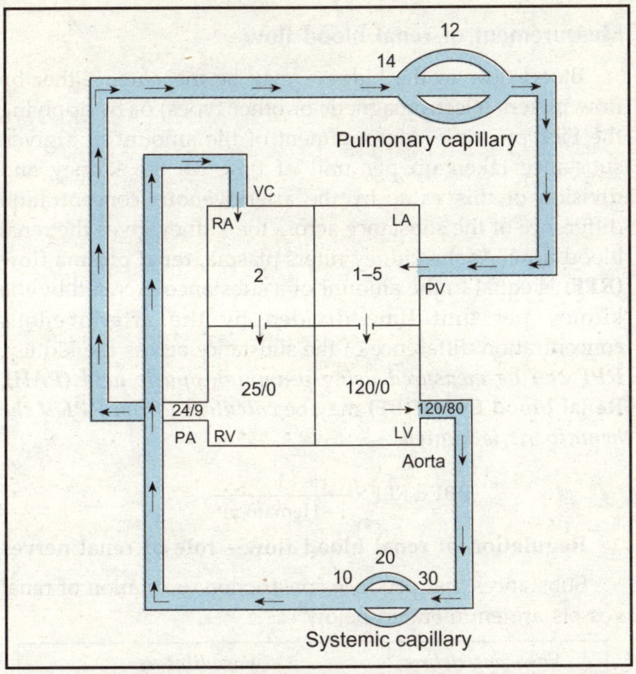


**Fig. 7.39 :** Schematic diagram showing pressures in different parts of systemic and pulmonary circulation. All pressures are in mm Hg. RA = Right atrium. LA = Left atrium. PA = Pulmonary artery. VC = Venae cavae. PV = Pulmonary veins. RV = Right ventricle. LV = Left ventricle.

intra-pleural pressure – colloid osmotic pressure of plasma. So, with more negative intrapleural pressure as in forced inspiration or depletion of surfactant, the filtration pressure rises to increase transudation of fluid into the interstititum to be carried by lymphatics.

**Effect of gravity on pulmonary blood flow and ventilation perfusion ratios** *(Fig. 7.40).*

In the upright position, pulmonary blood flow increases in a linear fash-ion from the apices to the bases of the lungs because of the effect of gravity (Fig. 7.40). Pulmonary ventila-tion also increases similarly from the apices to the bases of the lungs. However, the ventilation/perfusion ratio is higher in apices than in the bases of the lungs. The ventilation/perfusion ratio ($\dot{V}_A/\dot{Q}$) for the whole lung at rest is about 0.7. High alveolar $P_{O2}$ resulting from high $\dot{V}_A/\dot{Q}$ at the lung apices provides favorable environment for growth of *Mycobacterium tuberculosis* and, hence, tuberculosis commonly involves the lung apices.

As the pulmonary capillaries are compressed by the alveolar pressure, blood flow through them depends on alveolar pressure as well. This gives rise to **three possible conditions :**

(i) ***No blood flow when local capillary pressure*** is less than alveolar pressure both during systole and diastole.

(ii) ***Intermittent blood flow*** when local capillary pressure exceeds alveolar pressure during systole only.

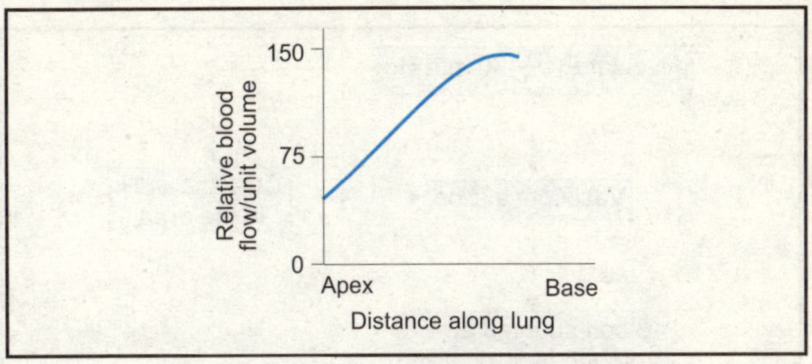


**Fig. 7.40 :** Pulmonary blood flow from apices to bases in the upright position

(iii) ***Continuous blood flow*** when local capillary pressure exceeds alveolar pressure both during systole and diastole.

Under normal conditions, intermittent flow is found in the lung apices and continuous flow is found in the other areas below. The condition of "no flow" is found in disease states only. During exercise, blood flow increases in all parts of the lungs, the increase in flow in apices being higher than that in the bases. Flow is continuous in the pulmonary capillaries all over the lungs because pulmonary vascular pressures become considerably higher during exercise.

## Reservoir function of the pulmonary vasculature

The pulmonary veins function as an important blood reservoir because of their distensibility. ***Pulmonary blood volume increases by about 400 ml on lying down.*** This causes lowering of vital capacity and gives rise to orthopnea (shortness of breath on lying down) in heart failure.

## Regulation of pulmonary circulation

***Pulmonary blood flow is almost equal to cardiac output.*** Factors controlling cardiac output control pulmonary blood flow as well. Blood is distributed to the segments of lung that are best aerated by the mechanism as follows :

It is to be noted here that lack of $O_2$ and low pH cause vasodilation in other parts of the body. Systemic hypoxia causes pulmonary arteriolar constriction leading to increase in pulmonary arterial pressure.

When blood flow to a part of the lung is reduced, alveolar $P_{CO_2}$ decreases in that area which leads to local broncho-constriction. Thus ventilation is shifted away from the poorly perfused area (Fig. 7.41).

Pulmonary vessels are extensively innervated by autonomic nerves but their role in controlling pulmonary blood flow is unsettled. ***Sympathetic stimulation causes a slight increase in pulmonary vascular resistance and vagal (parasympathetic) stimulation causes marginal decrease in resistance.*** However, sympathetic venoconstriction may displace blood from the lungs to other areas to combat low blood pressure.

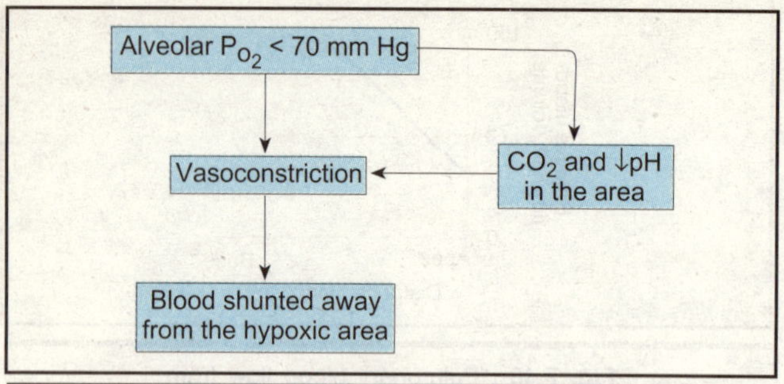


**Fig. 7.41 : Systemic hypoxia also causes pulmonary arteriolar constriction**

Embolic blockage of branches of the pulmonary artery provokes reflex vasoconstriction (mediated by sympathetic nerves) leading to a rise in pulmonary arterial pressure. Tachypnea (rapid, shallow breathing) also occurs.

## 7.14 Renal Circulation

The adult kidneys receive ***about 1,200 ml of blood per minute (360 mL/min/100 g of kidney tissue) which is about 20% of the cardiac output.*** In addition to the supply of nutrients to the kidneys and removal of waste products from them, this extremely high blood flow is necessary to supply enough plasma for filtration in the glomerulus.

**Renal blood flow** is ***determined by the renal artery pressure, renal vein pressure and total renal vascular resistance :***

$$\text{Renal blood flow} = \frac{\text{Renal artery pressure} - \text{Real vein pressure}}{\text{Total renal vascular resistance}}$$

The major sites for renal vascular resistance are interlobular arteries, afferent arterioles and efferent arterioles. Resistance in these vessels is regulated by sympathetic discharge, circulating hormones, and various local factors. ***Renal blood flow is kept fairly constant over an arterial pressure range between 80-170 mm Hg by autoregulatory mechanisms.***

### Regional blood flow

Blood flow through **renal cortex** is ***about 500 ml/min/100 g.*** **Medullary blood** flow is much less than cortical blood flow ***250 ml/min/100 g*** in the ***outer medulla and 60 ml/min/100 g in inner medulla.*** As most of the active reabsorption and secretion of constituents take place in the renal cortex, rate of $O_2$ consumption per unit renal tissue is more in cortex. But as cortical blood flow rate is very high, the $O_2$ extraction (i.e. A-V $O_2$ concentration difference) is low as in superficial and deep part of medulla. A-V $O_2$ difference is one-fourth in case of renal circulation in comparison to that of whole body. The medulla is more vulnerable to hypoxia. Low medullary blood flow helps to maintain the osmotic gradient in the medulla.

### Measurement of renal blood flow

Blood flow in the kidneys may be measured either by flow meters (electromagnetic or other types) or by applying the Fick principle. Measurement of the amount of a given substance taken up per unit of time by the kidney and division of this value by the arteriovenous concentration difference of the substance across the kidney gives the renal blood flow. As the kidney filters plasma, **renal plasma flow (RPF)** is equal to the amount of a substance excreted by the kidney per unit time divided by the arteriovenous concentration difference of the substance across the kidney. ***RPF can be measured using p-aminohippuric acid (PAH).*** **Renal blood flow (RBF)** may be ***calculated from RPF if the hematocrit is known*** :

$$\text{RBF} = \text{RBF} \times \frac{1}{1 - \text{Hematocrit}}$$

**Regulation of renal blood flow – role of renal nerves**

Substances that produce constriction or dilation of renal vessels are enumerated below :

| *Vasoconstrictors* | *Vasodilators* |
|---|---|
| Norepinephrine | Dopamine |
| Epinephrine | Acetylcholine |
| Endothelin | Nitric oxide |
| Angiotensin II | Prostaglandins ($PGE_2$ and $PGI_2$) |
| | Bradykinin |

***Norepinephrine and epinephrine*** have greatest effect on the interlobular arteries and the afferent arterioles. ***Dopamine*** causes natriuresis as well. Effect of angiotensin II is particularly on the efferent arterioles. ***Prostaglandins*** tend to increase blood flow in renal cortex but they decrease blood flow in medulla. A high protein diet increases renal blood flow by unknown mechanism.

Renal vasoconstriction may be produced by stimulation of sympathetic nerves supplying the kidney by the vasomotor area of the medulla oblongata, parts of the brain stem and cerebral cortex. Some tonic discharge is always there at rest. Decreased baroreceptor discharge during systemic hypotension produces renal vasoconstriction as a part of generalized vasoconstrictor response.

The **effects of sympathetic noradrenergic stimulation are:**

(i) ***Vasoconstriction causing decrease in renal blood flow*** and glomerular filtration rate (GFR). This is mediated by $\alpha_1$-adrenergic receptors. Postsynaptic $\alpha_2$-receptors may also have some role.

(ii) ***Increased renin secretion*** by juxta-glomerular cells mediated by $\beta_1$-adrenergic receptors.

(iii) ***Increased*** $Na^+$ reabsorption possibly by direct action of norepinephrine on renal tubular cells.

### Autoregulation of renal blood flow

Renal blood flow is maintained at a relatively constant level over an arterial pressure range ***between 80-170 mm Hg.***

Both metabolic and myogenic factors appear to be involved. Involvement of nitric oxide has also been suggested. Angiotensin II formed in circumstances associated with decreased arterial pressure or volume depletion preferentially constricts efferent arterioles. This helps in autoregulation and maintains GFR. Renal failure may develop in patients with low renal perfusion receiving angiotensin-converting enzyme inhibitor because of loss of this mechanism.

## ➤ 7.15 Skeletal Muscle Circulation

**Blood flow in resting skeletal muscle** varies according to the fiber type. Skeletal muscle consisting of mixed fiber types (tonic and phasic) has a ***blood flow of 2-4 ml/min/100 g and its basal $O_2$ consumption is low (about 0.3 ml/min/100 g).*** However, blood flow in muscles may increase more than 20 to 30-fold during exercise.

Rich innervation of skeletal muscle arterioles by sympathetic vasoconstrictor fibers maintains a resting arteriolar tone due to tonic discharge from those fibers. Further sympathetic stimulation leads to reduction in blood flow due to increased arteriolar resistance.

During exercise, vascular resistance falls in skeletal muscle. This is because of the metabolic vasodilation that overrides vasconstrictor sympathetic discharge. Fall in tissue $P_{O_2}$, rise in tissue $P_{CO_2}$ and accumulation of $K^+$ and other vasodilator metabolites all play role in the metabolic vasodilation in exercising skeletal muscle. Rising temperature in active muscle dilates the vessels further. There is a 10-100-fold increase in the number of open capillaries. Oxygen extraction from blood may reach up to 90% (as against 25-30% at rest).

***Compression of intramuscular arteries during contraction of skeletal muscle causes significant reduction in blood flow.*** If the contraction is rhythmic (Fig. 7.42) increased blood flow during relaxed state is sufficient to maintain the $O_2$ demand. During strong, sustained contraction, muscle becomes hypoxic and there is accumulation of metabolites like lactate causing ischemic pain which acts as a warning that the muscle needs to be relaxed. On relaxation, $O_2$ debt is repaid by increased blood flow.

$K^+$ is important for arteriolar dilation in exercising muscle, particularly during the initial part of exercise. Individuals with low $K^+$ are at a greater risk to develop exertional **rhabdomyolysis** (disintegration of muscle during exertion).

## ➤ 7.16 Splanchnic Circulation (Fig. 7.43)

Circulation through the vasculature of the gastrointestinal tract, liver, spleen and pancreas is known as splanchnic circulation (Fig. 7.43). The **splanchnic circulation** serves two principal functions (1) transportation of absorbed nutrients to the liver and systemic circulation and (2) mobilization of blood to the systemic circulation during stress.

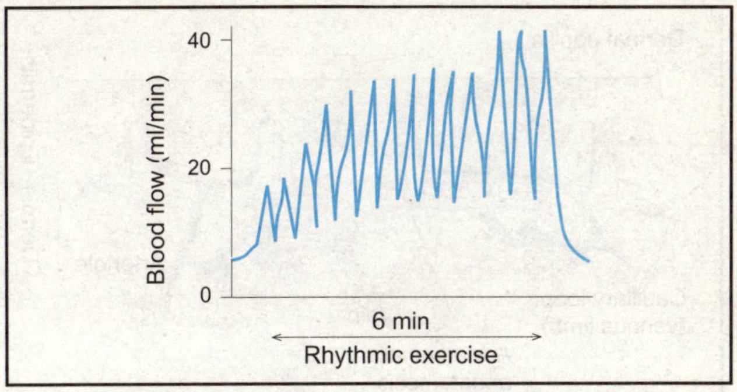


Fig. 7.42 : Blood flow through skeletal muscle during rhythmic contraction

The important features of the splanchnic circulation are :

### Active hyperemia produced by food ingestion

Following a meal, all the digestive organs become metabolically active. Blood flow to the small intestine gets doubled after a meal and persists up to 3 hours. This post-prandial hyperemia is mediated by several factors including those which are unique to a particular region. Metabolic factors, gastrointestinal hormones, and neuropeptides may have role in increasing blood flow after a meal.

**Sensitivity of splanchnic arterioles to extrinsic control mechanisms :**

Blood from splanchnic vessels are diverted to other parts of the body during periods of stress. Thus splanchnic vessels contribute significantly towards whole body homeostasis. This is due to considerable innervation of splanchnic vessels by sympathetic constrictor nerve fibers and their exquisite responsiveness to circulating vasoconstrictors like vasopressin and angiotensin II. The remarkable reduction in splanchnic blood flow that occurs

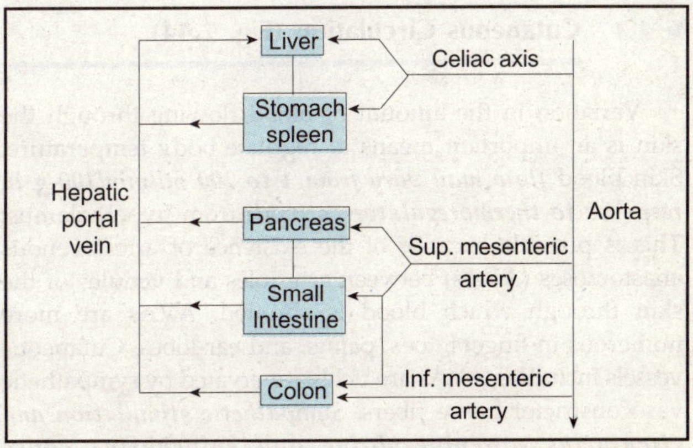


Fig. 7.43 : Splanchnic circulation

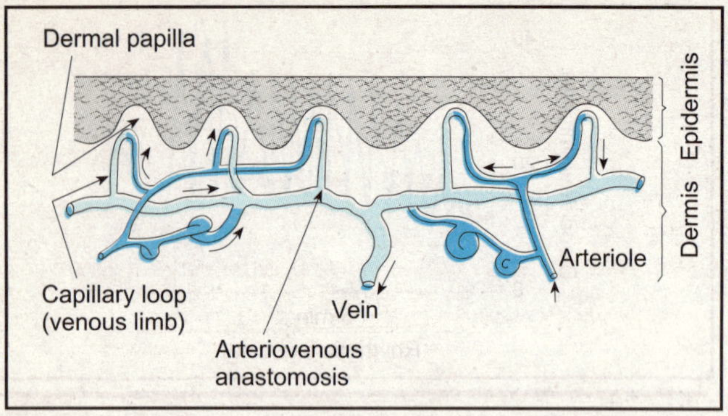


Fig. 7.44 : Cutaneous circulation

after severe hemorrhage is probably due to vasoconstriction produced by the combined effects of norepinephrine, vasopressin and angiotensin II.

**Reciprocal control of blood flow between the liver and other splanchnic organs :**

There is a reciprocal relationship between the hepatic arterial and portal venous blood flow. Under normal conditions, 75% of liver blood flow is contributed by the $O_2$-poor blood from the portal vein and the remainder comes from hepatic artery. When portal venous flow increases, arterioles originating from the hepatic artery constrict. This prevents sudden rise in flow and pressure in the sinusoids downstream.

The abdominal viscera including liver receive about 30% of cardiac output. Most of the blood supplied by branches of celiac and superior mesenteric arteries are returned by portal circulation to liver.

***In congestive cardiac failure,*** there is increase in systemic venous pressure leading to passive dilation of portal venous radicles. The resultant venous congestion increase the amount of blood in the liver and there is hepatic enlargement.

## 7.17 Cutaneous Circulation (Fig. 7.44)

Variation in the amount of blood flowing through the skin is an important means to regulate body temperature. Skin blood ***flow may vary from 1 to 200 ml/min/100 g in response to thermoregulatory stimuli*** from hypothalamus. This is possible because of the existence of arteriovenous anastomoses (AVAs) between arterioles and venules of the skin through which blood is shunted. AVAs are more numerous in fingers, toes, palms, and ear-lobes. Cutaneous vessels including AVAs are richly innervated by sympathetic vasoconstrictor nerve fibers. ***Sympathetic stimulation and circulating norepine-phrine and epinephrine cause vasoconstriction in cutaneous vessels.***

With lowering of body core temperature, thermoregulatory areas of hypothalamus induce an increased sympathetic discharge to the cutaneous vessels, especially the AVAs leading to their constriction. This reduces skin blood flow and dissipation of heat from the body is diminished which tends to keep the body temperature towards normal. Increase in body temperature has the opposite effects.

Vasodilator nerve fibers to skin vessels have not been found. Vasodilation is probably brought about by decrease in vasoconstrictor tone, bradykinin secreted by local sweat glands, and vasodilator metabolites. Production of bradykinin by sweat glands is due to heat-induced parasympathetic stimulation.

The characteristic pale, cold skin of hypovolemic shock is a manifestation of cutaneous vasoconstriction that shunts blood to other organs to maintain vital functions. These patients should not be warmed to the point where their body temperature rises.

### White reaction

Light stroke on skin with a pointed object causes pallor along the stroke line. This is known as **white reaction** which appears in ***about 15 seconds***. This is due to draining of blood out of the capillaries and venules subsequent to contraction of precapillary sphincters by the mechanical stimulus.

### Triple response

More firm stroke on skin with a pointed object elicits a three stage reaction known as **triple response.**

**Red reaction** appears in 10 seconds. There is reddening of the site. The redness is due to dilatation of capillaries in response to pressure.

**Wheal** is the local swelling that develops in a few minutes due to edema consequent upon increased permeability of the local capillaries and postcapillary venules.

**Flare** is the progression of initial redness to the surrounding area producing a diffuse, motted appearance. ***This is due to arteriolar dilation.***

Triple response is a normal reaction to injury and is present even after total sympathectomy. Evidences suggest that this response is due to an axon reflex. **An axon reflex** is a reflex where stimulation of the sensory nerve ending generates an impulse that is transmitted antidromically along other branches of the same nerve to produce physiologic effect (Fig. 7.45). The **wheal** probably has both **histaminergic** (histamine released from mast cells, acting on $H_1$-receptors) and **peptidergic** (substance P and CGRP released from sensory neurons) components.

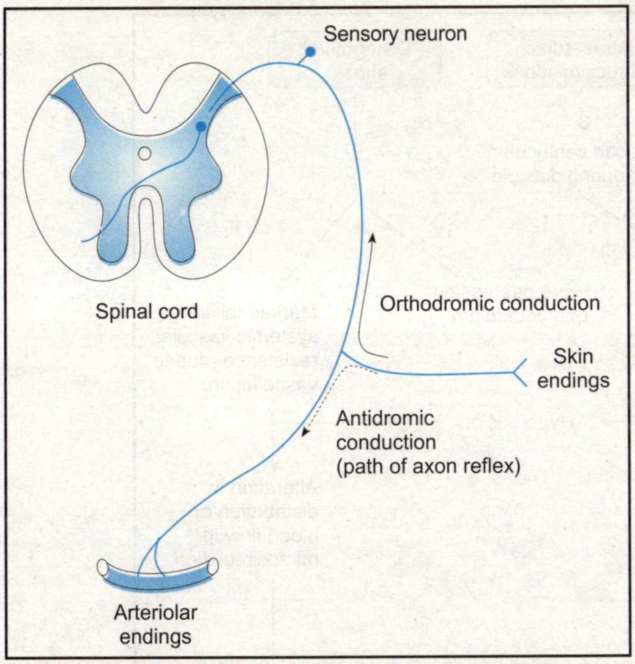


**Fig. 7.45 :** Hypothetical pathway involved in axon reflex

## ➤ 7.18 Cardiovascular Homeostasis in Health and Disease

## SHOCK

**Shock** may be defined as profound and widespread inadequacy of tissue perfusion which leads first to reversible and then, if prolonged, to irreversible cellular injury, associated with a relatively or absolutely inadequate cardiac output.

Shock may be classified as

- Hypovolemic or oligemic shock;
- Cardiogenic shock;
- Extracardiac obstructive shock;
- Distributive shock.

### Hypovolemic shock

***Causes*** : (i) hemorrhage; (ii) fluid depletion (eg, vomiting, diarrhea); (iii) burns; (iv) trauma; (v) surgery.

This is probably the most frequently encountered shock in clinical practice and also the best studied. Loss of intravascular fluid leads to inadequate ventricular filling (decreased preload) reflected by decreased left and right ventricular end-diastolic volumes and pressures. This leads to an inadequate cardiac output causing shock.

### Cardiogenic shock

***Causes*** : (i) myocardial infarction; (ii) arrhythmias; (iii) congestive heart failure.

Severe depression of cardiac performance is the key factor in causing this type of shock. Myocardial infarction involving 40% or more of the left ventricular myocardium is the commonest cause.

### Extracardiac obstructive shock

***Causes*** : (i) pericardial tamponade (cardiac tamponade); (ii) constrictive pericarditis; (iii) pulmonary embolism; (iv) tension pneumothorax.

The principal abnormality here is the impaired ventricular filling during diastole (due to external pressure on heart) which limits the stroke volume and cardiac output.

### Distributive shock

***Causes*** : (i) septic shock; (ii) anaphylaxis; (iii) neurogenic shock.

A profound decrease in peripheral vascular resistance is the major abnormality. The capacity of the circulation is increased by marked vasodilation and, therefore, there is relative inadequacy of cardiac output. In septic shock, bacterial toxins (eg, endotoxin of gram-negative bacteria) cause vasodilation. In anaphylaxis, large quantities of histamine released as a result of antigen-antibody reaction causes vasodilation. Vasodilation in neurogenic shock is the result of sudden autonomic activity as in strong emotion. Shock may be more severe in febrile patients because the cutaneous blood vessels are dilated by fever as well.

Inadequate tissue perfusion leads to anaerobic glycolysis in tissues in all forms of shock. This gives rise to lactic acidosis which causes myocardial depression (↓ contractility) and decrease in peripheral vascular responsiveness to catecholamines.

### Refractory shock

Compensatory mechanisms try to reverse the changes occurring in shock. In some patients, circulation is restored to normal. In some cases, circulatory changes progress in spite of compensatory responses and treatment. This is called **refractory shock**. The factors contributing to refractoriness of shock are :

- spasm of the precapillary sphincters and venules particularly in the splanchnic area reducing capillary perfusion;
- release of free radicals (especially $O_2$) from granulocytes in the capillaries;
- depression of the vasomotor and cardiac areas of the brain due to profound cerebral ischemia;
- myocardial depression.

***The chain of events that occurs in various types of shock is summarized in Fig. 7.46.***

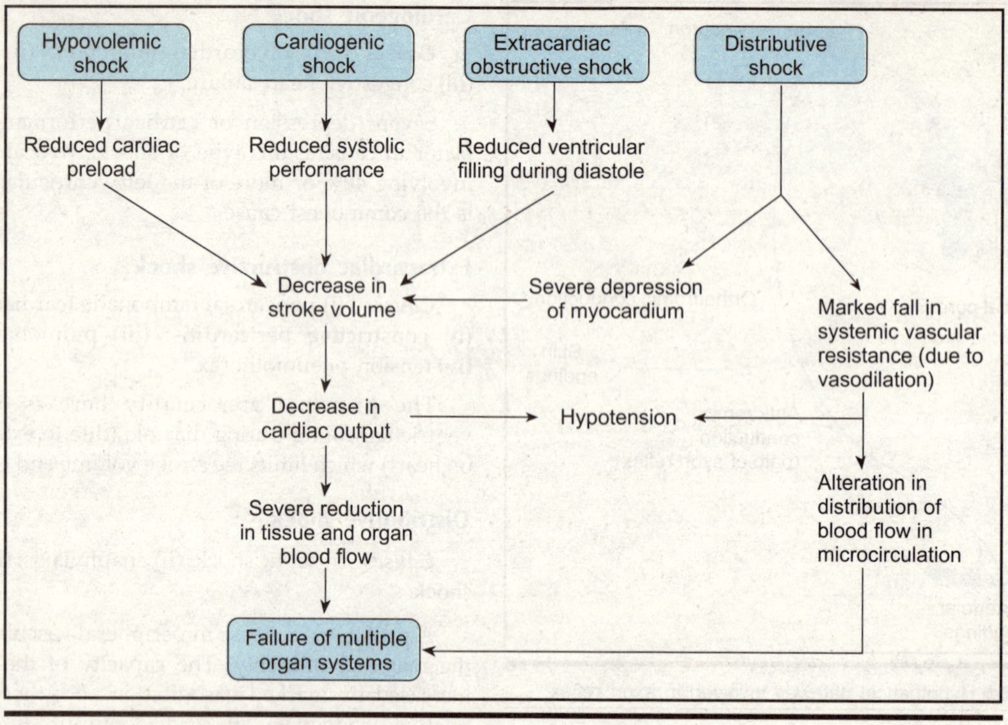


**Fig. 7.46 :** Chain of events that occurs in shock

The final event in shock is cell death. Once large numbers of cells in vital organs die, shock becomes irreversible and death ensues despite correction of the underlying cause.

## Compensatory reactions in hypovolemic shock

Some of the compensatory reactions develop rapidly. Others come into operation only in the long term.

### Short-term reactions

*Vasoconstriction* : This is generalized and involves all the vessels except those in brain and heart. Vasoconstriction is most marked in skin, kidneys and viscera. The intense cutaneous and splanchnic vasoconstriction shifts blood from these organs to maintain perfusion in vital organs like brain and heart. ***Glomerular filtration rate (GFR) is decreased in the kidneys*** but filtration fraction is increased because kidneys try to maintain GFR in the face of reduced renal plasma flow (afferent arteriolar constriction is less than that of efferent arterioles). Consequently, urine formation is markedly decreased. More sodium is retained by the kidneys. ***Azotemia or uremia results from retention of nitrogenous products of metabolism that circulate in blood.*** Acute renal failure may develop if hypotension is prolonged.

*Tachycardia* : Like vasoconstriction, tachycardia also occurs reflexly mediated by arterial baroreceptors.

*Increased adrenal medullary secretion of norepinephrine and epinephrine* : Circulating catecholamines are increased as a result of increased adrenal medullary secretion as well as increased sympathetic discharge. This does not have much vasoconstricting effect but some stimulation of reticular formation occurs which may explain the restlessness and apprehension found in many patients. When cerebral ischemia and acidosis predominate, patients become quiet and apathetic. Increased motor activity during restlessness causes increased pumping of blood from skeletal muscles.

*Tachypnea* : The loss of RBCs and reduced blood flow cause anemic and stagnant hypoxia which stimulates the chemo-receptors in carotid and aortic bodies. Chemoreceptor stimulation occurs due to acidosis as well. The result is respiratory stimulation and vasoconstriction. **Tachypnea** occurring due to respiratory stimulation leads to increased thoracic pumping of venous blood.

*Increased secretion of renin* " Increase in plasma renin activity leads to increase in circulating angiotensin II levels. Angiotensin II acts on the subfornical organ to stimulate thirst. Intake of fluid helps to restore the ECF volume. **Angiotensin II** also helps in maintaining blood pressure. **Aldosterone**, the secretion of which is increased by angiotensin II, causes sodium and water retention and, thus, helps to restore blood volume.

*Increased secretion of vasopressin* : Vasopressin probably plays an important role in maintaining blood pressure. It also causes sodium and water retention.

*Increased secretion of glucocorticoids*

*Increased movement of fluid into capillaries* : Capillary pressure drops because of decrease in blood volume. This leads to movement of fluid from interstitium into the capillaries along most of their length which helps to maintain the intravascular volume.

### Long-term reactions

***Increased synthesis of plasma proteins*** : Apart from entry of preformed albumin from extravascular stores into the blood, increased hepatic synthesis of plasma proteins over 3-4 days tends to compensate for the loss of plasma proteins.

***Increased erythropoietin secretion*** : This leads to increased RBC formation (erythropoiesis) in the bone marrow and the lost RBCs are replaced in 4-8 weeks.

### Clinical manifestation

Some of the clinical manifestations are same for all types of shock. This is characterized by hypotension. The patient's usual blood pressure must be considered while interpreting the extent of hypotension. Other common features include tachycardia, oliguria, clouded sensorium and cool, clammy extremities indicating reduced skin blood flow. Extremities are not cold in distributive shock.

Other clinical features are specific to the particular type of shock.

### Treatment of shock

Generally speaking, the goals of treatment are

- to maintain blood flow to vital organs like kidney, CNS, lungs and liver,
- to maintain a mean arterial pressure above 60 mm Hg in order to maintain adequate tissue perfusion in vital organs;
- to correct metabolic acidosis.

Specific therapies are directed at the underlying process. In hypovolemic shock, correction of intravascular volume with blood, plasma or plasma expanders and stopping volume loss is the mainstay of therapy. Cardiogenic shock requires treatment for myocardial ischaemia. Removal of obstruction (eg, by pericardiocentesis in cardiac tamponade) is the goal of therapy in extracardiac obstructive shock.

## HEART FAILURE (vide Fig. 7.47)

Compromise in the ability of the heart to propel blood through the circulation is known as **heart failure**. A decrease in cardiac contractility causes rise in venous pressure and decrease in cardiac output. The decrease in cardiac output produces the characteristic symptoms of limited capacity for physical activity and fatigue. A rise in venous pressure is the most prominent clinical feature of the failing heart. The heart may fail in a number of ways which include loss of muscle mass (myocardial infarction), failure secondary to increased workload, myopathy and infection. ***The most common diseases producing heart failure are hypertension and coronary artery diseases.***

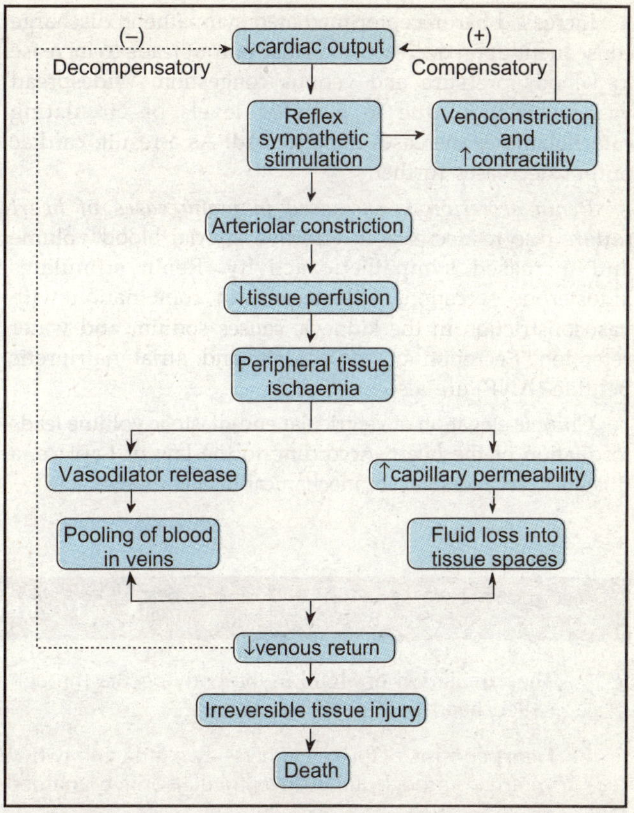


**Fig. 7.47 :** Events occurring in the failing heart

When the heart cannot maintain a cardiac output adequate for normal tissue perfusion, it is known as **"forward failure"**. **"Backward failure"** refers to the venous congestion due to the failure of the heart to pump out all the blood returned by the veins. Either side of the heart may fail independently. Venous congestion occurs on the side of the heart that is failing. Pulmonary venous congestion leading to pulmonary edema is a feature of **left-sided heart failure**.

**In right heart failure**, there is systemic venous congestion leading to edema in the dependent parts of the body. In some cases like myopathy, both sides of the heart may fail together (biventricular failure). In patients with thyrotoxicosis, beriberi or a large arteriovenous fistula, cardiac output is actually elevated but the elevated output is not adequate to maintain tissue perfusion. Hence, the heart failure seen in those patients may be referred to as **"high-output failure"**.

Reduced myocardial contractility initially affects exercise tolerance manifested clinically by exertional dyspnea (shortness of breath) and fatigue. When the heart failure is progressive, resting cardiac output is also decreased. Dyspnea then occurs even at rest. In advanced cases, dyspnea is precipitated by lying down and relieved by sitting up (orthopnea). The decrease in myocardial contractility may be due to decreased myosin ATPase activity in cardiac muscles.

Increased baroreceptor-mediated sympathetic discharge consequent upon decrease in cardiac output leads to increase in venous pressure and venous congestion. Widespread vasoconstriction due to elevated levels of circulating catecholamines increases the afterload. As a result, cardiac output decreases further.

*Renin secretion is increased in many cases of heart failure* due to decrease in effective arterial blood volume and increased sympathetic activity. Renin stimulates aldosterone secretion. **Aldosterone,** in combination with vasoconstriction in the kidneys, causes sodium and water retention. Secretion of vasopressin and atrial natriuretic peptide (ANP) are also increased.

Chronic elevation of ventricular end-diastolic volume leads to dilation of the heart. According to the law of Laplace, a dilated heart faces severe mechanical disadvantage.

**Treatment of heart failure** is aimed at :

- improvement of cardiac contractility
- decreasing the cardiac load
- relief of symptoms.

*Myocardial contractility may be improved by digoxin and related cardiac glycosides as well as newer inotropic agents like amrinone.* Arterial vasodilators can be used to reduce the afterload while venodilators reduce the preload. Sodium retention can be corrected by the use of diuretics. ACE inhibitors (captopril, enalapril, etc.) reduces angiotensin II levels in plasma and, thereby, reduces afterload. Angiotensin receptor blockers (eg, losartan) have a similar effect. ACE inhibitors occupy an important place in the treatment of heart failure nowadays.

## ➤ 7.19 KEY CONCEPTS

1. **The circulation of blood** in the body occurs through the cardiovascular system consisting of the muscular pump called heart and blood vessels.

2. **Heart** consists of four chambers—two atria and two ventricles, each atrium communicating with the corresponding ventricle through the atrioventricular orifice guarded by atrioventricular valves.

3. **The conducting system** of the heart is made up of atypical cardiac myofibrils that have abundant sarcoplasm. The electrical impulses in the heart normally begin at the sinoatrial (SA) node. The atrioventricular (AV) node is situated in the floor of the right atrium at the inter atrial septum close to the membranous portion of the interventricular septum. The bundle of His is a continuation of the AV node. Purkinje's fibers not only act as the terminal portion of the conducting system, but also can function as a back-up intrinsic pacemaker of the heart.

4. During each beat, mechanical events of the heart takes place in a cyclic order called the **cardiac cycle**. In each cardiac cycle, both the atria and the ventricles go through a filling — relaxation period and an ejection contraction period. The **first heart sound** due to closure of AV valves at the begining of the systole and the **second heart sound** due to closure of aortic and pulmonary valves at the end of systole are audible by the stethoscope.

   **Abnormal sounds** produced by turbulent blood flow during the cardiac cycle are called **murmurs**. These may be pathological or may also occur normally during health.

   Cardiac output is increased and venous pressure is decreased during increased cardiac contractility. Both cardiac output and venous pressure are increased in increase of blood volume. On the other hand, both cardiac output and venous pressure are reduced on increase in venous tone.

   Anxiety, exercise and pregnancy increase the stroke volume. Pulse pressure depends on the stroke volume. The stroke volume decreases during heart failure.

5. Both intrinsic and extrinsic mechanisms influence the **stroke volume** of the heart. Sympathetic nervoussytem and adrenalin arethe main external influences on the stroke volume. The intrinsic factors that influence stroke volume are the contractility of the heart, the filling pressure, the arterial pressure and the ventricular diastolic compliance.

6. **Ejection fraction** : End-systolic volume (ESV), end-diastolic volume (EDV) and ejection fraction (EF) can be determined now, using special right ventricular catheters, angiography or echocardiography calculation can be done by the following formula $EF = \frac{EDV - ESV}{EDV} = \frac{SV}{EDV}$. The normal EF for the left ventricle is 60% to 70%. The normal EF for right ventricle is about 50% to 60%. In sepsis, although cardiac output may be high, EF is generally lower than normal.

   Normal ejection fraction is about 60 to 80% and it gives a good estimate of ventricular function.

## ➤ 7.20 DISORDERS/CLINICAL CORRELATIONS

➤ **ELECTROCARDIOGRAPH :** This is a sensitive instrument which records and amplifies the differences in electrical potentials between any two points on the surface of the body.

The basis of this equipment is the string galvanometer. This consists of a quartz fiber coated with a conducting material which is suspended between the poles of a strong magnet. Electric currents derived from the heart, flow through the fiber and powerful magnetic field causes it to move. A light source and the lens system magnify these movements about a thousand times and they are recorded on a specially treated paper with a heated stylus so that, a permanent record is available at once. For recording there must be two points of contact with the body to lead the electrical activity of the heart to the galvanometer. These connections are termed as electrocardiographic leads.

➤ **Lead Systems :** The ECG may be recorded using one active or exploring electrode and another indifferent electrode at zero potential (unipolar recording) or the recording may be between two active electrodes (bipolar recording).

➤ **Unipolar leads (V leads ) :** Nine standard locations for the exploring electrode (leads) are used for routine clinical electrocardiography. The six unipolar chest leads (precordial leads) are designated as $v_1$ to $v_6$.

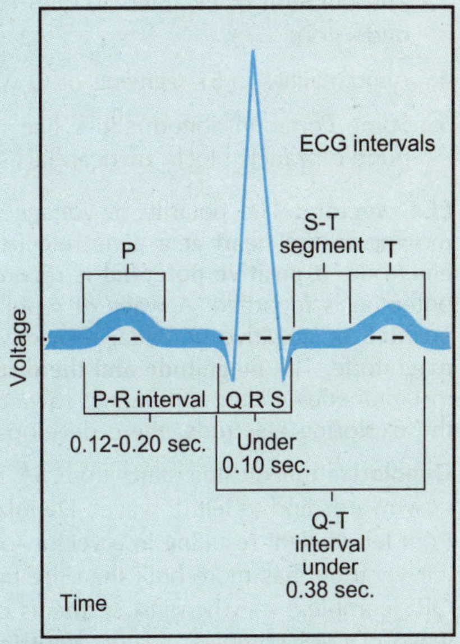


$V_1$ : 4th intercostal space, at the right border of sternum.

$V_2$ : 4th intercostal space, at the left border of sternum.

$V_3$ : midway between $v_2$ and $v_4$.

$V_4$ : 5th intercostal space, midclavicular line on the left side.

$V_5$ : 5th intercostal space, anterior axillary line on the left side.

$V_6$ : 5th intercostal space, midaxillary line on the left side.

The three unipolar limb leads are VR (right arm), VL (left arm) and VF (left foot). The augmented leads designated by the letter 'a' are generally used (aVR, aVL and aVF). The augmented limb leads are recordings between one limb and the other 2 limbs. This increases the size of the potentials by 50% without any change in configuration.

➤ **Bipolar Leads :** These are the standard limb leads I, II and III.

I : between left armand right arm.

II : between right arm and left foot.

III : between left foot and left arm.

➤ **Electrocardiographic paper :** This is a special type of graph paper on which a permanent record can be obtained by a heated stylus. It shows horizontal and vertical lines at 1 mm intervals. A thick line is present at every 5 mm. The amplitude is measured along the vertical axis. Time is measured along the horizontal axis. When the paper is moved at a speed of 25 mm/sec., then 1 mm = 0.04 sec. and 5 mm = 0.2 sec.

➤ **Recording Conventions :**

**Standardization (calibration) of the instrument :** A potential difference of 1 mV should give a deflection of 1 c.m. (10 mm). Hence vertically each small square represents 0.1 mV horizontally the duration of the waves is measured. The usualy speed of recording is 25 mm/sec., though a faster speed of 40 mm/sec. is also available in most of the instruments. At the usual speed of recording (25 mm/sec.) each small square represents a time duration of 0.04 second.

By convention, upward recording is taken as the +ve wave and a downward recording as the –ve wave. The upward recording indicates the activity spreading towards the electrode and the downward one indicates the activity moving away from the electrode.

➤ **Procedure for Recording :** The subject is asked to lie in bed after making certain that he has nothing metallic on him. Electrodes are then applied to the limbs and the chest. The limb leads are applied to the two wrists and the left leg just above the ankle joint. The jelly is first applied on the above mentioned areas and then metal plates are placed and secured in position with the straps. The appropriately marked lead is then connected to the actual plate. The right foot of the subject is connected to the ground.

The precordial leads are applied on the chest at the different sites and according to their position are marked from $V_1$ to $V_6$.

While recording, the lead selector can be moved and each lead brought in circuit as and when required.

## ➤ 7.20 DISORDERS/CLINICAL CORRELATIONS

The twelve lead ECG shows the three standard limb leads (I, II and III), the three augmented limb leads (aVR, aVL and aVF) and the six chest leads ($V_1$ to $V_6$)

➤ **Interpretation :**

1. Heart rate and rhythm should be observed in the ECG. In each cycle if all the waves are present or not should be noted.
2. The ECG of a normal subject shows the P, Q, R, S and T waves. There is a small isoelectric period between P and Q and between S and T. The configuration of waves has to be interpreted keeping the sequence of activation of the heart as well as the position of heart relative to the electrodes in mind.

   P wave is due to atrial depolarization.

   QRS complex is due to ventricular depolarization and T wave due to ventricular repolarization.
3. The duration of PR interval, QRS complex and QT interval should be noted and their significance should be understood.
4. Abnormalities in ST segments or Q waves should be noted.
5. Some common abnormalities like heart block (first degree, second degree and complete) and right and left bundle branch block, myocardial ischaemia and infarction should be studied.

➤ **ECG vector :** The polarity of voltage change depends on the direction in which wave of potential change is moving in the heart at a given electrode. When the wave of depolarization is travelling towards the positive electrode, a **positive potential** is recorded and when the wave is travelling away from the electrode a negative potential is recorded. A wave of repolarization travelling towards or away from the positive electorde causes a **positive** or negative potential respectively. **Vector** is the resultant of all the dipoles having both direction and magnitude. The **magnitude and the direction** of the resultant dipole changes from moment to moment. When the instantaneous vector approaches towards an exploring electrode the ECG records the wave; when it records from the exploring electrode, there develops negative wave.

➤ **Depolarization** of atria starts from SA node → then atrial muscle to AV node → **net result is** a vector directed downwards and to left (P wave). **Depolarization of ventricle** commences in interventricular septum → depolarizes from left to right resulting in a vector → proceeds downwards and to the right (first wave of QRS complex). As the left ventricle has more bulk than the right, mean direction of vector is downwards and to the left (2nd wave of QRS complex) → when last segments of myocardium is activated vector directed upwards and to the right (third wave of QRS complex) results. **Ventricular repolarization** spreads from outer to the inner surface of ventricular myocardium, it produces vector in the same direction, i.e., downwards and to the left (T wave).

The connections which are made with the body surface to convey the electrical activity to the galvanometer are known as **electrographic leads**. The leads in common use are as follows :

(a) Standard limb leads (Bipolar limb leads).

(b) Unipolar or V leads (Unipolar limb leads/Unipolar chest leads).

➤ **Bipolar limb leads or Standard limb leads :** ECG interpretation is facilitated by imagining that the standard leads look at the electrical activity of the heart from following view points in a coronal plane—

The greater positive deflection (R wave due to left ventricular depolarization) is thus normally seen in lead II and this is the **cardiac axis**. Right or left axis deviation is detected by examining R in standard leads.

In **standard limb** leads two electrodes are placed on different points of body surface and the resultant potential differences existing between them are recorded. It is worthwhile to remember Einthoven's law to avoid mislabelling the leads which states that a complex in lead II is equal to the sum of the corresponding complexes in lead I and lead III :

**Lead I** → RA (–ve) + LA (+ve);

**Lead II** → RA (–ve) + LF (+ve);

**Lead III** → LA (–ve) + LF (+ve).

➤ **Einthoven Triangle :** It is an imaginary triangle joining right shoulder, left shoulder and middle of the left inguinal region. It is an equilateral triangle with heart at the center.

➤ **Einthoven law :** The algebraic summations of the voltage fluctuation in lead I and that of lead III together equals the voltage fluctuations in lead III.

## ➤ 7.20 DISORDERS/CLINICAL CORRELATIONS

**Einthoven** considered the three points — the right and left shoulder and the midpoint of the left inguinal region. When joined together, they constitute an equilateral triangle and the heart occupies the middle of such a triangle.

In a volume conductor like human body, two electrodes can be placed on any two of the three above-mentioned points and the electrodes may be attached with ECG machine. In such condition, two electrodes will constitute a standard lead and the ECG machine will record the difference of potential between these two points.

**Einthoven's** assertions were not fully correct. Thus the triangle formed was not exactly an equilateral triangle nor the heart occupies exactly the middle of the triangle. As a result, some current does flow through the central terminal. The **central terminal** is formed by joining apices of Einthoven's triangle and in ideal situation the sum of potentials at any instant should be zero with current source at center. Therefore, to make the central terminal truly at zero potential, **Wilson** introduced a very high resistance in the central terminal and this is now called **Wilson's central terminal**, which can be considered as indifferent terminal with zero potential. It is connected to –ve terminal of galvanometer.

➤ **Bipolar Recording :** ECG is recorded using two active electrodes. The deflection recorded here at any moment represents the algebraic sum of potentials of two constituent leads.

**Bipolar leads** or **classical (standard) limb leads** of Einthoven are :

(1) **Lead I :** records the difference in potential between RA and LA (LA → positive).

(2) **Lead II :** records the difference in potential between RA and LF (LF → positive).

(3) **Lead III :** records the difference in potential between LA and LF (LF → positive).

Thus,

Lead I, records ($V_L - V_R$) — main QRS deflection is same as in aVL.

Lead II, records ($V_F - V_R$) — main QRS deflection is same as in $aV_F$.

Lead III, records ($V_F - V_L$) — main QRS deflection is same as in $aV_F$.

At any given instant, the sum of the potentials in lead I and lead III equals the potentials in lead II.

Lead II = lead I + lead III.

$V_F - V_R = (V_L - V_R) + (V_F - V_2) = V_F - V_R$.

➤ **Interpretations of ECG findings :** Ventricular or Heart rate.

(1) **Rate** : The number of smallest squares from one R wave to next R wave (or from one S to next P to P) is counted. The total time for 10 beats is measured from ECG and divided to give an average beat to beat interval. It is then used to calculate an average heart rate eg. distance from first P wave to 11th P wave (10 × P–P intervals) = 208 mm. Average = 20.8 mm = 0.83 second. Standard ECG chart speed = 25 mm $S^{-1}$. Heart rate = 60 ÷ 0.83 = 72 beats $min^{-1}$, or, 1,500 is divided by the number to give the heart rate per minute. The paper moves at a speed of 1,500 mm per minute.

[**Calculation** :

Let, the number of small divisions be d.

Then d × 0.04 seconds is the time for 1 beat.

In one second, the no. of beats = 1/d × 0.04.

∴ In 60 seconds, the number of beats

= 60/d × 0.04

= 60 × 100/4d

= 1,500/d].

If the heart is beating irregularly then ECG in a lead is taken for a longer period, say 20 sec, and the number of atrial and ventricular complexes scattered during that period is counted and expressed per minute.

(2) **Ventricular rhythm :** Count the number of mm squares between two consecutive R-R waves in different leads; see whether it is similar or not.

(3) Determine the atrial rate and rhythm by finding the distance between two consecutive P-P waves.

(4) Analysis of duration and amplitude of P wave; PR interval; PR segment; QRS complex; Q wave, Q-T interval; ST segment; U-wave; S-T interval and T-wave.

## ➤ 7.20 DISORDERS/CLINICAL CORRELATIONS

### Axis of Heart :

**Axis of the heart** : The direction of the vector at any instant at any particular plane is the electrical axis of the heart at that instant.

**Mean electrical axis** : It is the direction and magnitude of electrical activity at a particular plane (frontal or horizontal) taking place during a cycle of depolarization — a summated rather than an instantaneous vector.

**Normal electrical axis of the heart** lies in the range *of –30 to +110 (in degrees).* If the axis is beyond –30°, it is called **left axis deviation,** e.g., in *left ventricular hypertrophy, deep expiration and left bundle branch block.* If the axis is beyond +110°, it is known as **right axis deviation,** e.g., *right ventricular hypertrophy, deep inspiration and in right bundle branch block.* **Axis determination can be done by noting the amplitude of R wave in the standard limb leads.** If the R wave is tallest in lead II, the electrical axis is parallel to lead II. If the R wave is tallest in lead III, axis is parallel to lead III (shows left axis deviation). If the R wave is tallest in lead I axis is parallel to lead I which shows right axis deviation.

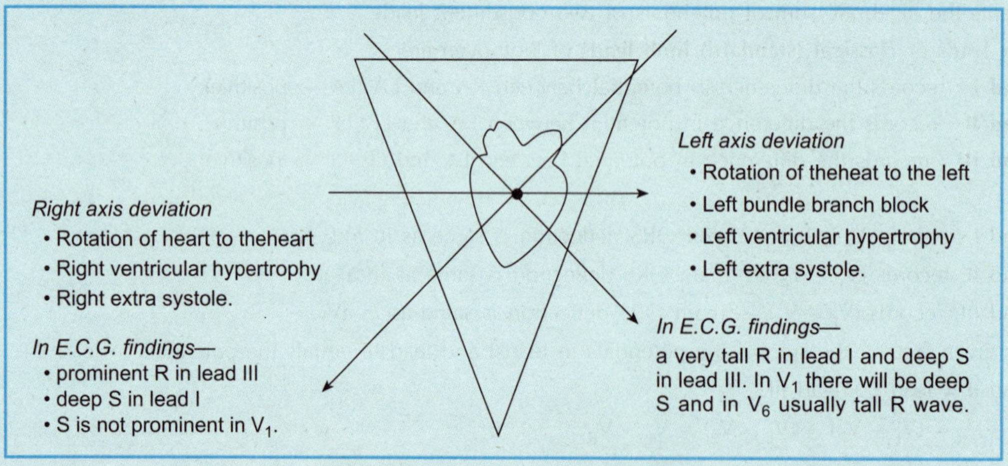


Axis deviation and clinical significance

Theoretically, the coordinates of two or more leads can be drawn and according to the direction of the axes of the leads (–ve → +ve) the net QRS voltage (R–S) negative or positive are plotted appro-priately; then perpendicular drawn from the points on respective leads will meet at the point which when connected with the origin gives the direction of mean axis (frontal or horizontal).

The chest leads that give equal amplitude R and S waves (usually $V_3$ or $V_4$) overlies the anterior edge of the interventricular septum and is called **transition point**.

**Clinically the axis deviations are assessed** by finding the amplitude of the R wave in the bipolar limb leads eg.

- If the **R wave** is tallest in lead II, it indicates the **axis is normal**.
- If **R wave is tallest in lead I**, it indicates a left axis deviation.

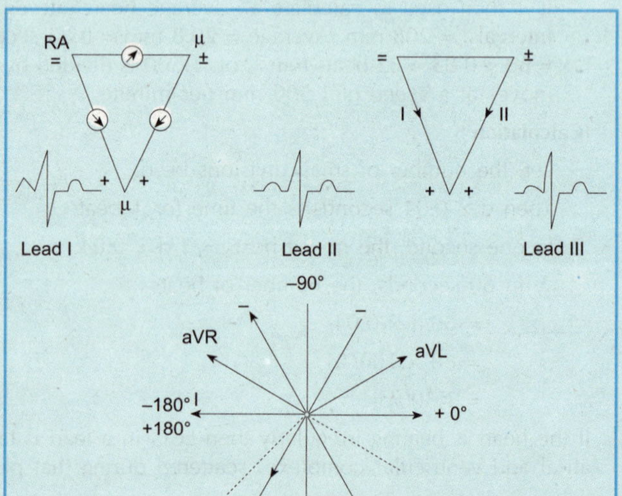


Standard limb leads with axis

## ➤ 7.20 DISORDERS/CLINICAL CORRELATIONS

- If the **R wave is tallest in lead III**, it indicates as **right axis deviation** (height of R wave more than 15 mm, usually indicates an abnormal axis deviation).

➤ **Abnormal ventricular conditions that cause axis deviation :** The electrical axis of the ventricles averages approximately 60°, it can swing to the right or left in the normal heart by approximately 20°. In addition, there are a number of conditions that can cause axis deviation beyond these normal limits. The **mean electrical axis** of the heart tends to shift to the left when the diaphragm rises during expiration and when a person lies down. Angulation of the heart to the right can occur during inspiration when standing. When the muscle of one ventricle hypertrophies, the axis tends to deviate toward the hypertrophied ventricle.

When the left bundle branch is blocked, cardiac depolarization spreads through the right ventricle two to three times as rapidly as through the left ventricle. Thus the right ventricle becomes electronegative while the left ventricle remains electropositive during most of the depolarization process. Consequently a very strong positive vector projects from the right ventricle towards the left ventricle producing intense left axis deviation. When the right bundle branch is blocked, the left ventricle depolarizes far more rapidly than the right ventricle so that intense right axis deviation occurs.

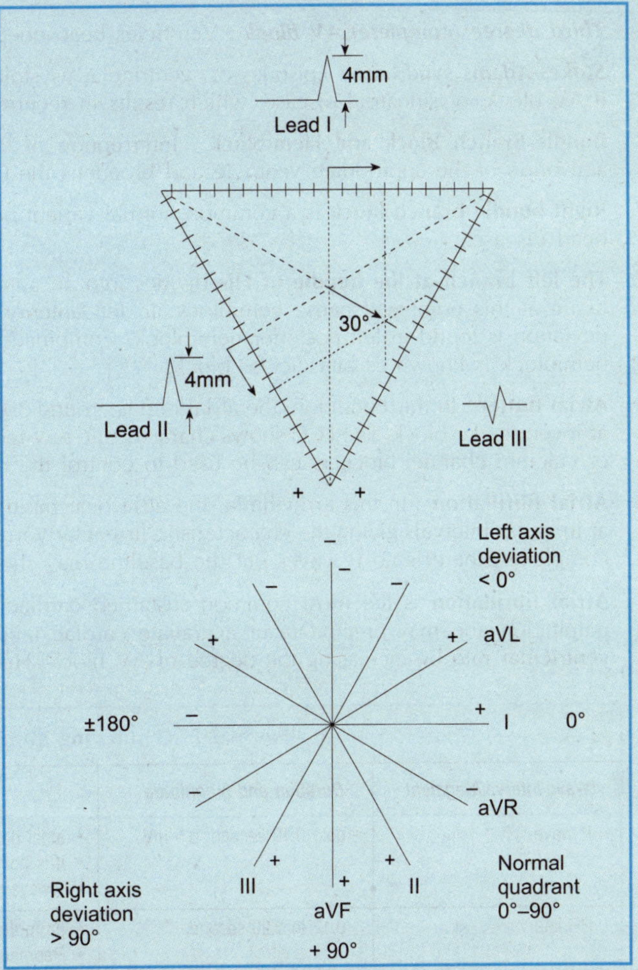


**Top :** Explains the determination of mean electrical axis by plotting the deflection of any two leads vectorially. **Bottom :** Showing the orientation and polarities of all six limb leads.

➤ **Myocardial infarction :**

Occlusion of a coronary artery leads to ischaemic necrosis of myocardium — this is known as **myocardial infarction**. Pain is the cardinal symptom of myocardial infarction. The ECG is usually a sensitive and specific way of confirming the diagnosis. The earliest ECG change is usually ST elevation; later on there is diminution in the size at the R wave, and in transmural (full thickness) infarction a Q wave begins to develop.

➤ **Atrioventricular and Bundle-Branch block** : Atrioventricular conduction is influenced by autonomic activity; AV block can, therefore, be intermittent and may only be evident when the conducting tissue is stressed by a rapid atrial rate.

(a) ***First degree AV block*** : All atrial impulses reach the ventricles but are slowed, producing a long PR interval.

(b) ***Second degree AV block*** : Not all atrial impulses reach the ventricles. There are more P waves than QRS complexes.

***Mobitz Type-I second degree AV block*** : There is progressive lengthening of successive PR intervals culminating in a dropped beat. The cycle then repeats itself. This is known as **Wenekebach phenomenon** and is usually due to impaired conduction proximal to the bundle of His. This phenomenon may be physiological and is sometimes observed at rest or during sleep in athletic young adults with high vagal tone.

***Mobitz Type-II second degree AV block*** : In this condition, the PR intervals of the conducted impulses remain constant but some P waves are not conducted. This is usually caused by disease below the bundle of His and is more serious than Mobitz Type-I.

## ➤ 7.20 DISORDERS/CLINICAL CORRELATIONS

***Third degree (complete) AV block*** : Ventricles beat independent of and usually at a slower rate than the atria.

***Stokes-Adams syndrome*** : Episodes of ventricular asystole may complicate complete heart block, Mobitz Type-II AV block, or sinoatrial disease, which results in recurrent syncopes ('Adams-Stokes' attacks).

➤ **Bundle-Branch Block and Hemiblock** : Interruption of the right and left branch of the bundle of His delays activation of the appropriate ventricle and broadens the QRS complex (0.12 second or more).

**Right bundle branch block** is a common normal variant but left bundle branch block usually signifies underlying heart disease.

**The left branch at the bundle of His** divides into an anterior and posterior fascicle. Damage of the conducting tissue at this point will cause hemiblock. In left anterior hemiblock, there is left axis deviation and right axis deviation is found in left posterior hemiblock. Combination of right bundle branch and left anterior or posterior hemiblock is known as bifascicular block.

➤ **Atrial flutter** : In this condition, the atrial rate is around 300/min. It is associated with 2 : 1, 3 : 1, 4 : 1 or variable atrioventricular block. The ECG shows characteristic saw-toothed flutter waves. Digoxin, β-adrenoceptor antagonists or calcium channel blockers can be used to control the rapid ventricular rate.

➤ **Atrial fibrillation** : In this arrhythmia, the atria beat rapidly, chaotically and ineffectively; the ventricles respond at irregular intervals giving the characteristic 'irregularly irregular' pulse. The ECG shows normal but irregular QRS complexes; there is no P waves but the baseline may show irregular fibrillation (f) waves.

**Atrial fibrillation** is the most common sustained cardiac arrhythmia. The onset of atrial fibrillation can cause palpitation and may precipitate or aggravate cardiac failure. Digoxin or $Ca^{2+}$-channel blocker will reduce the ventricular rate by increasing the degree of AV block. Here, heart rate is usually between 350-600/min.

**Normal ECG showing durations and significance**

| *Wave/Interval/Segment* | *Duration and magnitude* | *Significance* |
|---|---|---|
| P wave | upto 0.10 second; 0.5 mV | • atrial depolarization<br>• It is normally positive in all ECG leads except AVR.<br>• Always inverted in AVR. |
| PR interval | 0.12 to 0.20 second | • From the beginning of the P wave to the beginning of the QRS complex<br>• Represents conduction of the electrical impulse from the SA node to A.V. node. It represents atrial depolarization and conduction to A.V. node. |
| PR segment | 0.12 to 0.16 second | • The PR segment is the isoelectric portion between the P wave and QRS complex.<br>• A prolonged PR interval indicates a first degree heart block. |
| QRS complex (Ventricular Complex) | 0.08 to 0.12 second; 1-5 – 2 mV | • Represents ventricular depolarization.<br>• Small initial downward deflection after PR segment. |
| Q wave | < 0.04 second | • Represents invasion of the interventricular septum by excitation process. |
| Q.T interval | 0.40 to 0.43 second | • Beginning of the Q wave to the end of the T wave represents the refractory period of the heart.<br>• It represents ventricular depolarisation and ventricular repolarisation. |
| ST segment | 0.04 to 0.08 second | • Following QRS complex there is a long iso electric period which extends from the end of the 'S' wave to the beginning of the 'T' wave, called **ST segment**. |
| U wave (rarely seen) | 0.08 second | • Not seen in normal ECG. It is prominent in leads $V_1$ and $V_2$.<br>Slow repolarisation of the papillary muscles. |
| ST interval | 0.32 second | • The end of the 'S' wave to end of the T wave the normal duration is 0.32 second.<br>• It represents ventricular repolarisation. |
| T-wave | 0.27 sec; 0.5 mV | • Ventricular repolarization. |

# Renal Physiology

AGENDA :



8

## ➤ 8.1 CHAPTER OVERVIEW

The Kidney is responsible for maintaining the constancy and volume of extracellular fluid. The functional unit of kidney is the glomerulus and its associated **nephron**. Each day, 160 to 180L of fluid are filtered into the approximately one million nephrons in the human kidney.

The kidneys consist of an outer cortex (containing the glomeruti and proximal and distal convoluted tubules) and an inner medulla (containing the loops of Henle and the collecting ducts and tubules). There are two types of nephrons. Outer **cortical nephrons** constitute 85% of the total and lie almost completely within the cortex. The remaining 15% are **juxtamedullary/salt-saving nephrons**), with long loops of Henle extending into the medulla. The nephron consists of a glomerulus, proximal convoluted tubule, loop of Henle, distal convoluted tubule and collecting tubule and ducts. The **juxtaglomerular apparatus** is located at the junction of the distal convoluted tubule and the afferent and efferent arterioles. It consists of a macula densa (special cells of the distal tubule), extraglomerular mesangial cells and granular cells containing renin.

The **juxtaglomerular apparatus** can be stimulated by the sympathetic nervous system, decreased renal perfusion, hyperkalemia or decreased Sodium in the distal tubule to release renin. **Renin** converts angiotensinogen into angiotensin I, which is then converted to angiotensin II by ACE. Angiotensin II is a powerful vasoconstrictor that increases the release of aldosterone from the adrenal cortex.

**Renal blood flow** averages 1000 to 1250 ml/min. This results in an average renal plasma flow (RPF) of 625 ml/min and an average glomerular filtration rate (GFR) of 125 ml/min. The ratio of GFR/RPF is called the **filtration fraction** and averages 0.2. When cardiac output or blood pressure falls, renal vascular resistance increases disproportionately, causing an even greater decrease in renal blood flow. Stimulation of sympathetic nervous system results in renal arterial and arteriolar constriction thereby decreasing RPF. Efferent arteriolar vasoconstriction, however, generally prevents a corresponding decrease in G.F.R. Glucose, aminoacids, phosphate and sulfate are examples of thresold substances. They are entirely reabsorbed by the tubules, unless they are present in greater than normal amounts in the plasma. Over 99% of the filtered sodium is removed by the tubules and returned to the blood.

## ➤ 8.2 Introduction

### Urinary system

**The urinary system** consists of (a) **two kidneys** responsible for formation of urine; (b) **two ureters** responsible for transport of urine to urinary bladder from kidney; (c) *one* **urinary bladder** temporary store-house of urine and (d) *one* **urethra** by which urine is transported to exterior. It plays an important role in maintaining water and electrolytic concentrations within the body. Urine generally contains urea, uric acid and excess ions.

### Kidney

The kidneys are a pair of retroperitoneal organs, the hila of which are located at an anatomical level of $L_1$. The kidneys are highly vascularised, receiving ***approximately 20-25% of the cardiac output*** via the renal arteries which are derived directly from the abdominal aorta.

Each kidney is a reddish-brown, bean-shaped structure (12 cm long, 6 cm wide and 3 cm thick in adults and weights 150 gm). It is embedded in a tough, fibrous capsule. It is located on the posterior abdominal wall, one on each side of the vertebral column, just posterior to peritoneum and below the diaphragm. It lies at the level ***of 12th thoracic vertebra to 3rd lumbar vertebra***.

The waste products of kidney include urea from protein, uric acid from nucleic acid, creatinine from muscle creatinine and also the end-products of hemoglobin.

### Kidney structure (Fig. 8.1)

Each kidney consists of a medulla and surrounding cortex and, under normal circumstances, the cortex receives 80% of renal blood flow. At perfusion pressures between 80-180 mm Hg the kidney maintains blood flow via local vasodilatation and constriction of afferent and efferent blood vessels. This mechanism is termed as **autoregulation**.

The lateral border of each kidney is convex and its medial side is deeply concave. There is a depression leading to a hollow chamber termed as **renal sinus**. Hilum is the portion through which blood vessels, nerves, lymphatics, renal pelvis and ureter pass. The renal pelvis is located inside the renal sinus. The pelvis is subdivided into two or three tubes known as **major calyces** and, again, they are subdivided into eight to fourteen **minor calyces.**

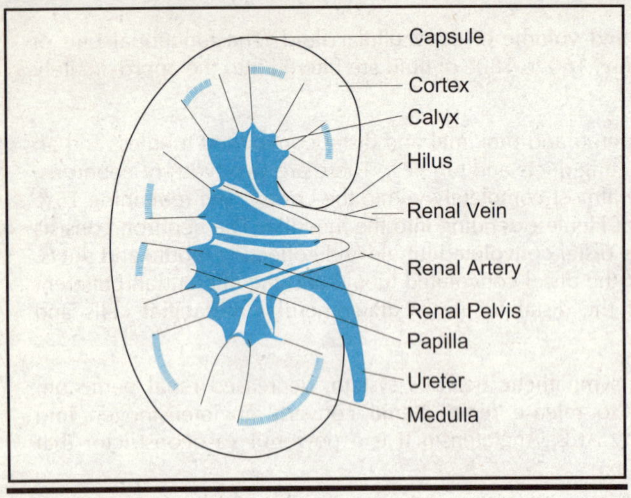


**Fig. 8.1 : Structure of Kidney**

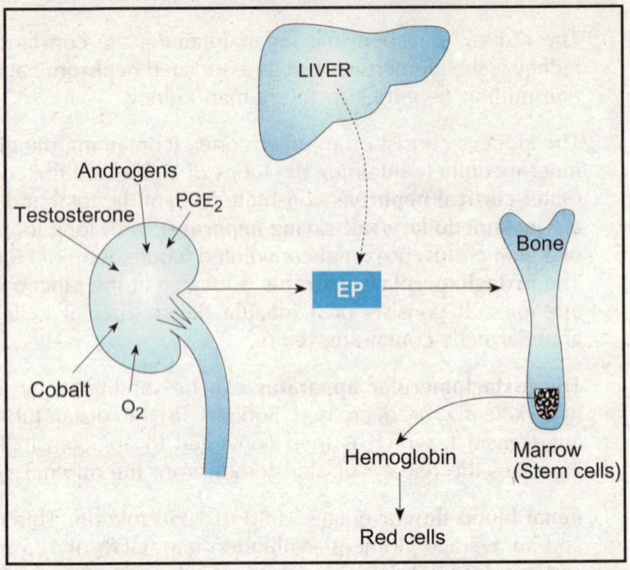


**Fig. 8.2 : Erythropoietin production**

**Kidney**

↓ ↓

***Renal medulla***

Conical masses of tissue known as renal pyramids whose bases are directed towards the convex surface of the kidney.

***Renal cortex***

Looks granular and forms a shell surrounding medulla. This granular appearance of cortex is due to the arrangement of nephrons.

## 8.3 Functions of the Kidney

1. **Homeostatic function** : Constancy of internal environment of body is maintained by regulating the volume and composition of ECF via the conservation and excretion of water and solutes.

2. **Endocrine function :**

(a) ***Renin*** : It plays an important role in the renin angiotensin system to regulate blood pressure.

(b) ***Erythropoietin/renal erythropoietic factor*** : Erythropoietin is an interesting hormone. It is an example of a growth factor or Cytokine. It is a 34-KDa glycoprotein-and is secreted by peritubular interstitial cells in the kidney. The synthesis and release of Erythropoietin is increased by a low hematocrit or a fall in blood oxygen carriage. It acts on erythroid progenitor cells in the bone marrow as a colony-stimulating factor and RBC production will be increased.

(c) ***1, 25-dihydroxycholecalciferol*** –

Cholecalciferol (dietary vitamin $D_3$)

↓ *25 hydroxylase in liver*

25-hydroxycholecalciferol

↓ *1-α hydroxylase in kidney*

1, 25-dihydroxy vitamin $D_3$ calcitriol. (It is the biologically most active form of vitamin D)

(d) Prostaglandin $I_2$; $E_2$.

(e) Bradykinin.

3. **Gluconeogenesis** : The kidney has an important function to synthesize and secrete glucose produced from non-carbohydrate sources when there is prolonged starvation and chronic respiratory acidosis.

4. It controls electrolytic balance and maintains blood pH.

5. It removes metabolic waste products from the blood and it is excreted in the urine.

6. It also removes toxic products from the blood and excretes them in the urine.

7. Kidneys help to regulate red blood cell production, blood pressure, calcium ion absorption and volume, composition and pH of blood.

In short, **endocrine functions of kidney are :**

- Endothelial cells of peritubular capillaries secrete erythropoietin in response to hypoxia.
- Juxta-glomerular cells secrete renin in response to ↓ renal arterial pressure → renal nerve discharge.
- Conversion of 25-OH vitamin D to 1, 25 (OH) vit D by 1α hydroxylase which is activated by PTH.

**In short, physiological functions of kidney are :**

- Removal of nitrogenous waste products.
- Regulation of ion status including sodium, potassium and calcium.
- Regulation of water balance.
- Regulation of acid-base status.
- Hormone synthesis : endocrine and paracrine.

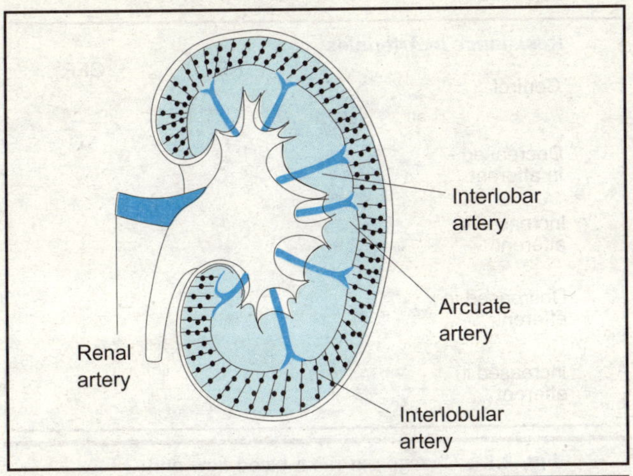


Fig. 8.3 : Blood vessels of kidney

## 8.4 Blood Vessels of Kidney and Renal Blood Flow

**Blood vessels of kidney (Fig. 8.3)**

Renal artery – branch arising from aorta
↓ subdivides
Interlobular artery
↓
Afferent arterioles
↓
Glomerular capillaries
↓
Efferent arteriole
↓
Peritubular capillaries

The efferent arterioles of cortical glomeruli subdivide into a network of microvessels which surround mainly proximal convoluted tubule and distal convoluted tubule in the cortex. A special type of peritubular capillaries, known *as* **vasa recta** is produced from efferent arterioles of JMnephroxy. Hair-pin loops are formed along the side of the loops of Henle. The vasa recta and peritubular capillaries in the cortex form an anastomosing network with capillaries from the adjacent efferent arterioles.

### Innervation of renal vessels (Fig. 8.4)

Renal vessels have rich sympathetic nonadrenergic innervation. The sympathetic discharge is very low at rest but it may increase markedly during states of cardiovascular stress. Hemorrhage leads to renal vasoconstriction.

### Renal blood flow (Fig. 8.5 and 8.6)

Both kidneys are supplied by ***renal arteries*** which are the branches of ***abdominal aorta*** → after having long course and branches, renal artery terminates in venous plexus.

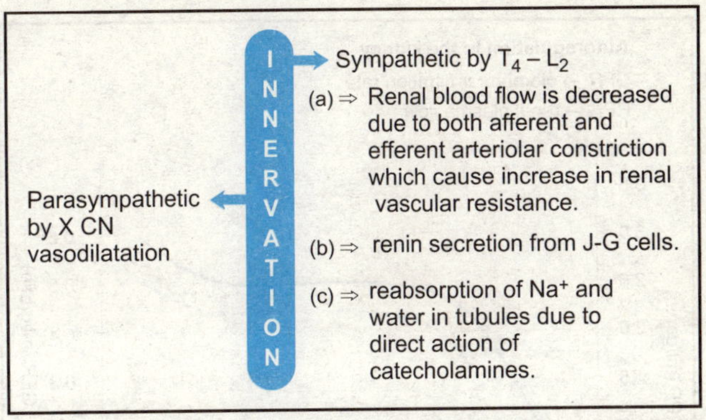


Fig. 8.4 : Innervation of renal vessels

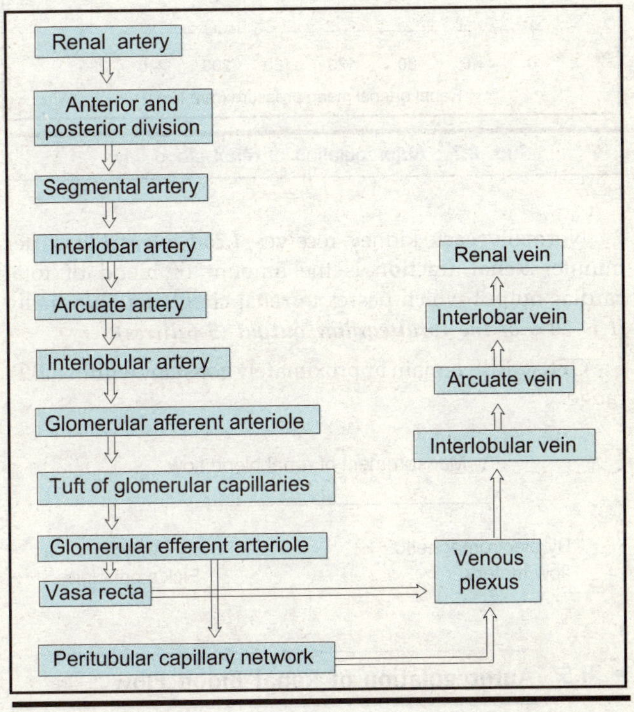


Fig. 8.5 : Pathway of blood via the blood vessels of the kidney and nephron

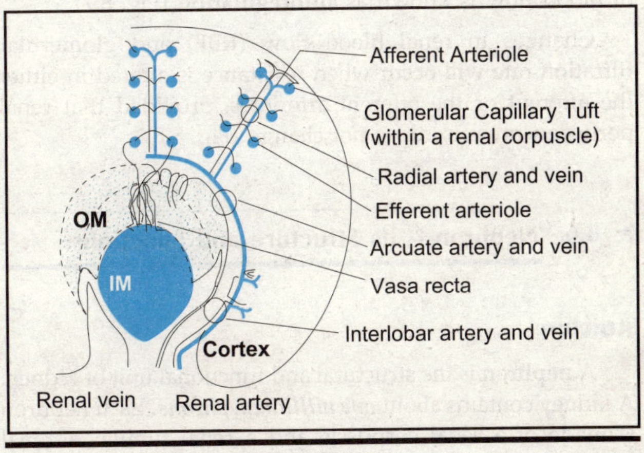


Fig. 8.6 : Renal blood flow

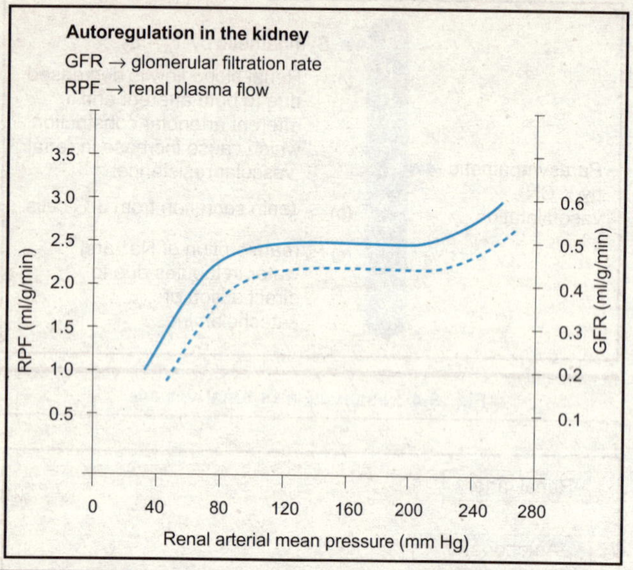


**Fig. 8.7 : Autoregulation of renal blood flow**

Normally each kidney receives ***1,250 ml of blood*** per minute. **Renal fraction** is the amount of blood of total cardiac output which passes to renal circulation. Normally ***it is 20% of the total cardiac output (5-6 litres).***

GFR & RBF remain approximately constant within a B.P. range.

Measurement of renal blood flow

- By electromagnetic flow meters
- By applying Fick's principle

## 8.5 Autoregulation of Renal Blood Flow

The kidney can maintain its blood flow normal under any condition within physiological limits. This mechanism of blood flow is known as **autoregulation** (Fig. 8.7).

Changes in renal blood flow (RBF) and glomerular filtration rate will occur when resistance is altered in either the afferent or the efferent arterioles, provided that renal perfusion pressure does not change (Fig. 8.8).

## 8.6 Nephron— its Structure and Functions

### Structure

A **nephron** is the structural and functional unit of kidney. A kidney contains about ***one million nephrons***. Each nephron is made of a renal corpuscle and a renal tubule. A renal corpuscle is composed of cluster of blood capillaries

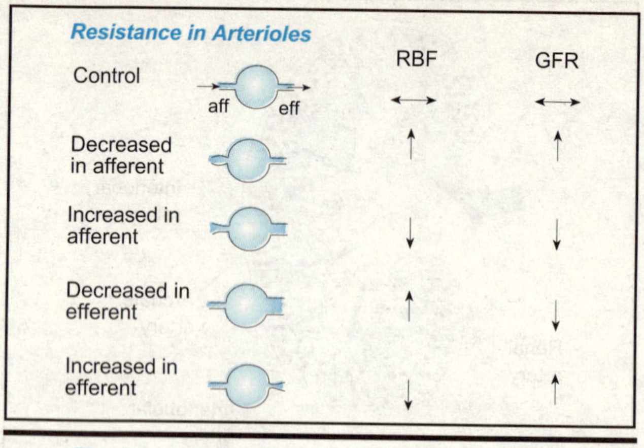


**Fig. 8.8 : Changes in renal blood flow and G.F.R.**

(glomerular) termed as *glomerulus* and a surrounding sac-like structure called **Bowman's capsule** —

**Corpuscle** = Glomerulus plus glomerular capsule

**The parts of the renal tubules are** : (Figs. 8.9 and 8.10)

- Proximal convoluted tubule
- Ascending and descending limbs of loop of Henle
- Distal convoluted tubule
- Collecting duct

The collecting duct empties into the minor calyx of renal pelvis.

### Nephron (basic functional unit of kidney)

(a) ***Bowman's capsule*** :

- Dilated end of nephron
- Visceral and parietal layer
- Bowman's space

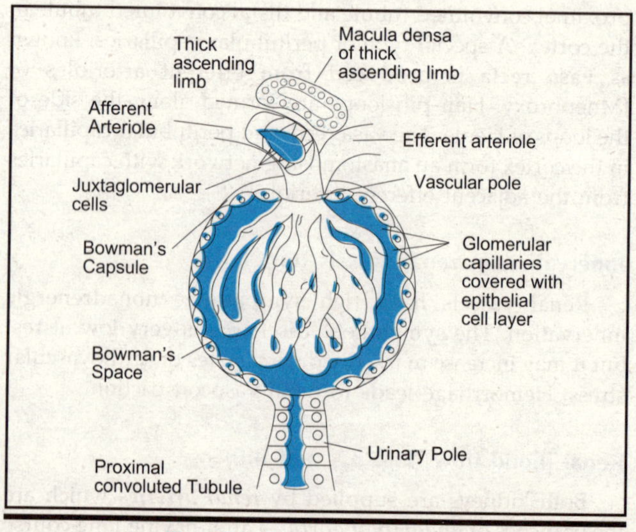


**Fig. 8.9 : Structure of nephron**

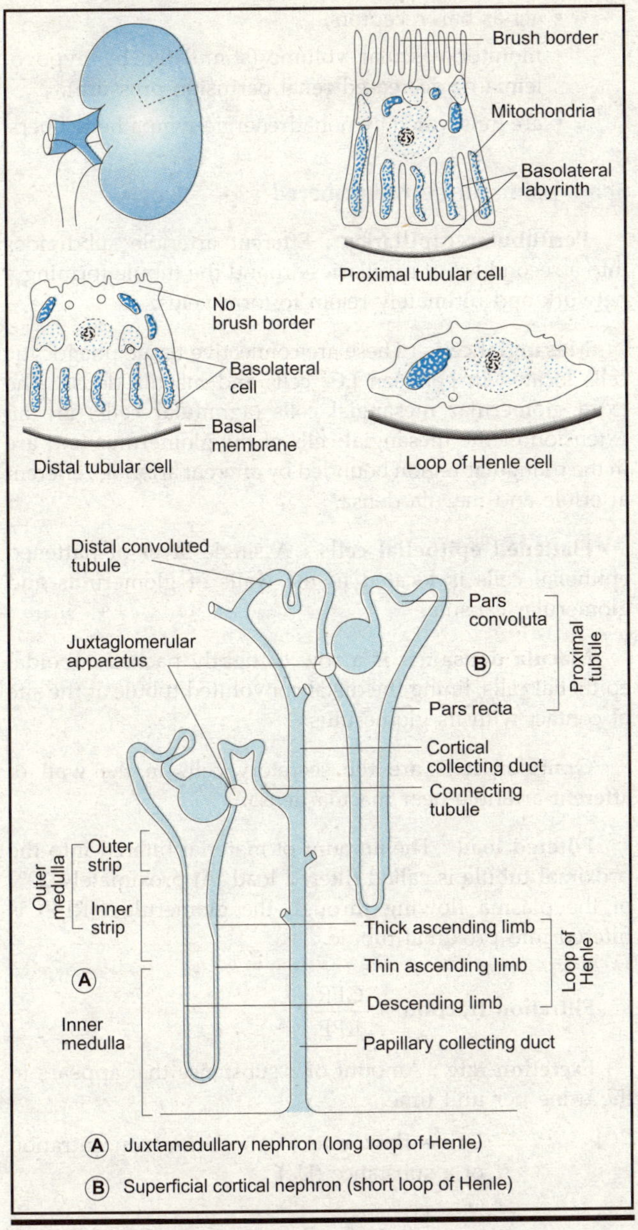


**Fig. 8.10 : Histological structure of nephron**

(b) ***Glomerulus*** – *(200 µm in diameter)*

- Tuft of capillaries
- Capillaries supplied by afferent arteriole and drained by efferent arteriole
- Glomerular membrane

(c) ***Proximal convoluted tubule (PCT)***

(i) continuous with Bowman's capsule
(ii) 15 mm long and 55 µm in diameter
(iii) tubular cells :

- rich in mitochondria
- responsible for active transport of 80% $Na^+$ filtered into peritubular capillary blood

(iv) Parts :

- pars convoluta – convoluted portion of PCT
- pars recta – straight portion of PCT

(d) ***Loop of Henle***

(i) descending limb arises in continuation with terminal part of PCT
(ii) continued as thin segment (2-14 µm)
(iii) thin segment – thick ascending limb (12 µm) contains mitochondria

(e) ***Distal convoluted tubule (DCT)***

(i) Ascending limb of loop of Henle is continuous with DCT
(ii) This tubule comes very close to its own glomerulus and establishes a close proximity to the afferent and efferent arterioles of the glomerulus. At this site the cells of DCT get modified to become columnar and closely crowded together → this part is **macula densa**.
(iii) **Juxtaglomerular apparatus** – macula densa + adjacent juxtaglomerular part of afferent arteriolar wall + mesangial cells.

(f) ***Collecting tubules (CT)*** : DCTs join to form collecting tubules. CT passes through renal cortex and medulla to empty into pelvis.

The whole kidney is enveloped by a thin but tough fibrous membrane called *renal capsule*. It limits the swelling if the kidney becomes edematous, this increases interstitial pressure which decreases GFR and precipitates anuria.

***Arrangement of nephron in the kidney :*** All the glomeruli, all the DCT and all but the terminal part of PCT lie in the renal cortex while CT lies in renal medulla.

| *Cortical nephrons* | *Juxtamedullary nephrons* |
|---|---|
| 85% of nephrons in the kidney | 15% of nephrons in the kidney |
| Smaller size glomeruli in renal cortex | Large size glomeruli at junction of cortex and medulla |
| Descending limb of loop of Henle contains a thin segment whereas ascending limb contains a thick segment | Both descending & ascending limbs of loop of Henle contain thin segment |
| Rate of filtration – low | High – responsible for concentration of urine (counter-current system) |
| They are most numerous and have corpsucles near the surface of the kidney | They have corpuscles near the medulla |

**Functions of the components**

| *Part* | *Function* |
|---|---|
| **Glomerulus** | Water and dissolved substances are filtered from the plasma. |
| **Glomerular capsule** | Glomerular filtrate is received. |

| *Part* | *Function* |
|---|---|
| **PCT** | (1) Glucose, creatinine, amino acid, lactic, citric, uric and ascorbic acids, phosphate, sulphate, potassium, calcium, sodium ions are reabsorbed by active transport. (2) 70% water is reabsorbed without ADH by osmosis. (3) Chloride ions are reabsorbed by electrochemical attraction. (4) Penicillin, histamine, creatinine and hydrogen ions are actively secreted. |
| **Descending limb of loop of Henle** | Water is reabsorbed by osmosis. |
| **Ascending limb of loop of Henle** | Sodium, potassium and chloride ions are reabsorbed by active transport. |
| **DCT** | (1) Sodium ions are reabsorbed by active transport. (2) Water is reabsorbed in presence of ADH. (3) Hydrogen ions are actively secreted. |
| **Collecting duct** | (1) Potassium ion is secreted actively and by electrochemical action. (2) Water is reabsorbed by osmosis (ADH). |

**Table 8.11**
**Hormones acting on the kidney**

| | *Stimulus for secretion* | *Action on kidneys* |
|---|---|---|
| **Vasopressin (ADH)** | ↓ Blood volume<br>↑ Plasma osmolarity | • ↑ $H_2O$ permeability of cells in collecting ducts |
| **Aldosterone** | ↓ Blood volume<br>↑ Plasma [$K^+$] | • ↑ $Na^+$ reabsorption<br>• ↑ $K^+$ secretion<br>• ↑ $H^+$ secretion<br>(DCT & CT) |
| **Angiotensin II** | ↓ Blood volume | • Contraction of mesanglial cells<br>• ↓ GFR<br>• ↑ $Na^+$ and $HCO^-_3$ reabsorption in PCT |
| **Atrial natriuretic peptide (ANP)** | ↑ Atrial pressure | • ↓ $Na^+$ reabsorption<br>• ↑ GFR |
| **PTH** | ↓ Plasma [$Ca^{2+}$] | • ↑ $Ca^{2+}$ reabsorption<br>• ↓ $PO^{4-}$ reabsorption<br>• ↑ 1, 25 $(OH)_2$ vitamin D production |

## Juxtaglomerular apparatus

**Juxtaglomerular apparatus** lies at the junction between distal convoluted tubule and the afferent and efferent arterioles. **Juxtaglomerular apparatus** = macula densa plus juxta-glomerular cells. The tunica media of the afferent arterioles of the kidney contain modified smooth muscle cells containing prominent granules. The granules consist of a proteolytic enzyme called **renin**. These cells are called **juxta-glomerular cells** and :

- act as baroreceptors;
- monitor vascular volume (stimulated by hypovolemia or decreased renal perfusion pressure);
- are innervated by nonadrenergic sympathetic fibers.

## Some points to be remembered

**Peritubular capillaries** : Efferent arteriole subdivides into a second set of capillaries around the tubule forming a network and ultimately rejoin to form veins

**Mesangial cells** : These are connective tissue phagocytic cells located in between J.G. cells and macula densa. The extra glomerular mesangial cells (agranular cells) are an extension of the mesangial cells of the glomerulus and are in the triangular region bounded by afferent arteriole, efferent arteriole and macula densa.

**Flattened epithelial cells** : A single layer of flattened epithelial cells is located in the walls of glomerulus and glomerular capsule.

**Macula densa** : It is a row of tightly packed cuboidal epithelial cells, lining the distal convoluted tubule at the site of contact with its glomerulus.

**Granular cells** are the secretory cells in the wall of afferent arteriole near macula densa.

**Filtered load** : The amount of material filtered into the proximal tubule is called filtered load. Approximately 20% of the plasma flowing through the glomerulus (RPF) is filtered into proximal tubule.

$$\textbf{Filtration fraction} = \frac{GFR}{RPF}.$$

**Excretion rate** : Amount of a substance that appears in the urine per unit time

$$= \text{Urine flow rate } (\dot{V}) \times \text{Urine concentration of a substance } (U_X)$$

$$= \dot{V} \times U_X$$

$$= \text{ml/min} \times \text{mg/ml}$$

$$= \text{mg/min.}$$

## Renal tubular transport maximum ($T_m$)

It is the maximal amount of a given solute that can be transported per minute by renal tubules. Highest attainable rate of reabsorption is called the **maximum tubular reabsorptive capacity** and is designated **$T_r$ or $T_m$**. Substances that are reabsorbed by an active carrier method, eg, $HPO^{2-}_4$ (phosphate ion) sulphate ($SO^{2-}_4$), glucose, amino acid, albumin, acetoacetate, β-hydroxybutyrate. Highest attainable rate of secretion is called the **maximum tubular secretory capacity** and termed $T_s$ or $T_m$ eg, penicillin, loop diuretics, salicyate, para amino hippuric acid (PAH)

**RENIN SECRETION**

***Local macula densa cell events***

The macula cells are important to detect the sodium content of tubular fluid and relay to juxtaglomerular complex. ↓sodium load → stimulation of renin release.

***Baroreceptor mediated events***

Renin secretion is regulated by renal perfusion pressure that is stretched by baroreceptors located in J–G cells or associated endothelial cells. A fall in perfusion pressure stimulates renin secretion.

***Sympathetic nervous system mediated events***

J–G cells are innervated by sympathetic neurons. Renin secretion is increased by increased low intensity β sympathetic stimulation. The remaining secretion is stimulated by high intensity of sympathetic activity.

**Fig. 8.11 : Renin secretion**

## 8.7 Renin and Angiotensin System

The **renin and angiotensin system** ***is the*** key regulator of aldosterone release. The mRNA for renin has been found in a number of tissues including brain, adrenal gland, uterus and placenta. It is believed that kidney is the physiologically most important site of renin synthesis. In kidney, renin is synthesized and stored as a preprohormone in the cells of the juxta-glomerular complex. Renin release is stimulated by a number of factors which are influenced by changes in sodium load and plasma volume and include reduced sodium intake, decreased arterial pressure, a fall in extracellular fluid volume, stress and trauma. These effectors influence renin release by following three basic mechanisms (Fig. 8.11) :

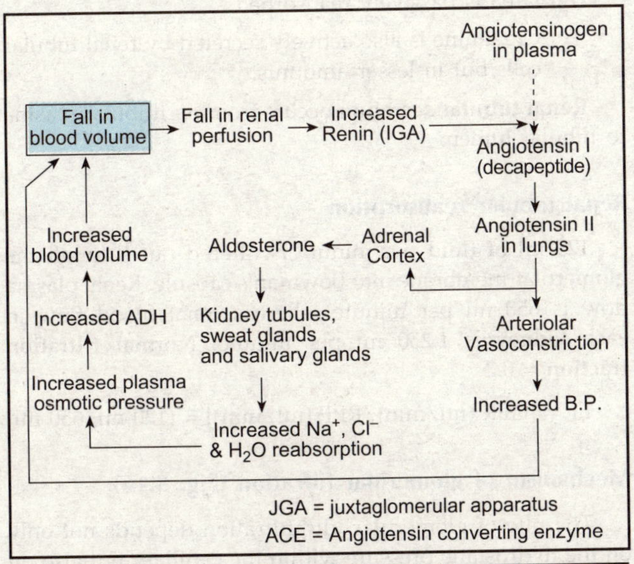


**Fig. 8.12 : Production of angiotensin II**

| | | |
|---|---|---|
| Proximal tubule | • Angiotensin II<br>• Glucocorticoids | NaCl $H_2O$<br>NaCl $H_2O$ |
| Thick ascending limb | • Aldosterone<br>• Vasopressin | NaCl<br>NaCl |
| Distal convoluted tubule and collecting duct | • Aldosterone<br>• Atrial Natriuretic Peptide<br>• Prostaglandins<br>• Bradykinin<br>• Vasopressin | NaCl<br>↓ NaCl ↓ $H_2O$<br>↓ NaCl ↓ $H_2O$<br>↓ NaCl<br>NaCl $H_2O$ |

**Fig. 8.13 : Hormones that control NaCl and water reabsorption**

### Renin

**Renin** is synthesized and secreted by modified smooth muscle cells in the walls of arterioles when decrease in ECF volume is sensed by the kidney or decreased perfusion pressure is detected by baroreceptors in the afferent arterioles It results in increased renin synthesis and release. Renin causes circulating angiotensinogen to be cleaved resulting in angiotensin I. Angiotensin I → angiotensin II, the most potent vasoconstrictor. The enzyme catalyzing this reaction is known as **converting enzyme** located primarily in the lung vasculature.

Table showing the pathway how renal sympathetic nerve is activated by hemorrhage and production of angiotensin II (Fig. 8.12).

Table showing the hormones which control NaCl and water reabsorption (Fig. 8.13).

Table showing aldosterone cascade (Fig. 8.14).

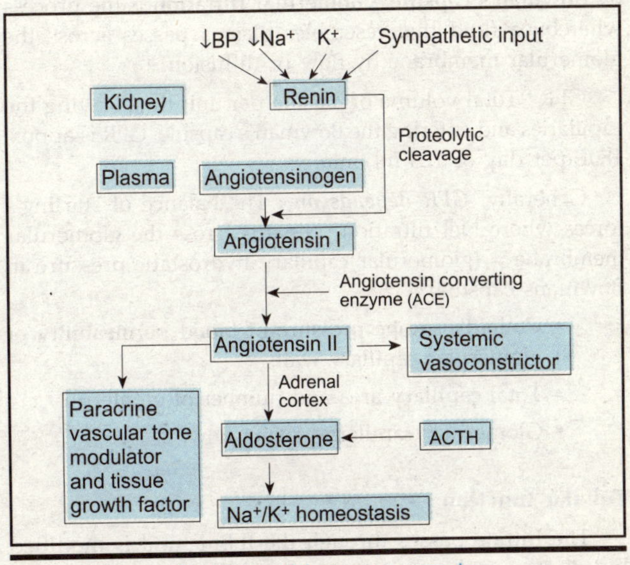


**Fig. 8.14 : Aldosterone cascade**

### Action of angiotensin II

- ↑**SBP** and ↑**DBP** by arteriolar constriction.
- **Stimulates zona glomerulosa** of adrenal cortex to increase aldosterone secretion resulting in increased sodium reabsorption by the kidneys.
- **Release of norepinephrine**.
- Contraction of mesangial cells with a resultant decrease in GFR.
- Stimulates supraoptic and paraventricular nuclei located in hypothalamus to release **ADH**.
- **Inhibition of ANP** produced from atria of the heart.
- **Increases BP** and thirst by a central mechanism.
- Constricts **both afferent and efferent arterioles** but also increases level of prostaglandins. Prostaglandin decreases the relative amount of afferent arteriolar constriction and, thereby, acts to maintain the GFR despite high level of circulating angiotensin II.

**Regulation of renin secretion**

| **Stimulation of J-G cells** *by* | **Inhibition of J-G cells** *by* |
|---|---|
| • ↑Sympathetic activity | • ↑Afferent arteriolar pressure |
| • ↑Catecholamines | • Angiotensin II |
| • Prostaglandin | • Vasopressin (ADH) |

## ➤ 8.8 Formation of Urine

### Glomerular functions

**The glomerulus** is a network of capillaries surrounded by **Bowman's capsule. Glomerular filtration** is the process whereby a fluid that resembles plasma passes across the glomerular membrane by flow or diffusion.

GFR : Total volume of plasma per unit time leaving the capillaries and entering the Bowman's capsule. GFR is appox. 180L per day or 120 ml/min.

Generally, ***GFR depends on :*** The balance of starling's forces where Net filtration pressure across the glomerular membrane = (glomerular capillary hydrostatic pressure in Bowmans capsule)

- Colloid osmotic pressure of blood permeability of glomerular capillary wall.
- Total capillary area and number of glomeruli.
- Glomerular capillary plasma flow.

### Tubular function

The filtrate passes through the tubule and is modified by selective reabsorption and tubular secretion. Generally,

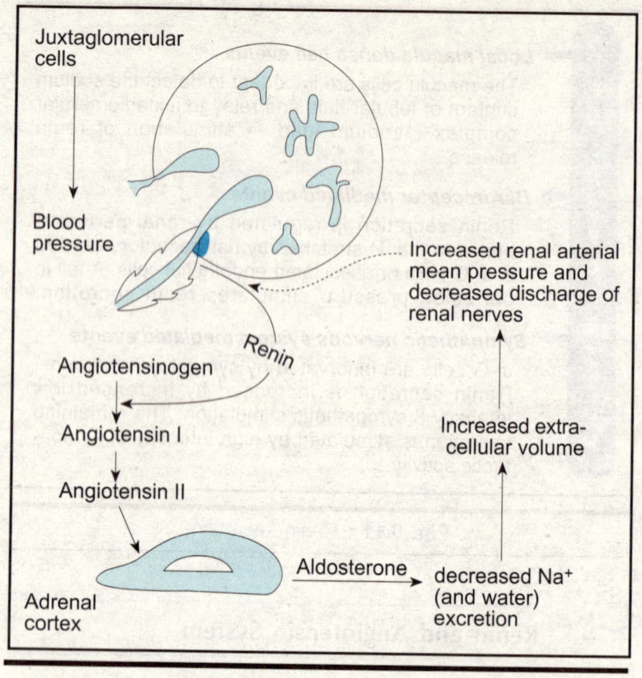


**Fig. 8.15 : Mechanism of renin-angiotensin system**

180 litres of water are filtered normally in 24 hours through the glomeruli of kidney. ***Urinary output is 1-1.5 litres per day.***

***The dissolved substances are selectively reabsorbed by the tubular cells*** :

(i) Glucose, amino acids, sodium and calcium are actively reabsorbed.

(ii) Phosphates and sulphates are less reabsorbed.

(iii) Potassium and uric acid are both reabsorbed and secreted.

(iv) Urea is passively reabsorbed.

(v) Creatinine is also actively secreted by renal tubular cells but in lesser amounts.

**Renal tubular secretion** occurs from peritubular plasma to tubular lumen.

### Renal tubular reabsorption

125 ml of fluid per minute is filtered out through the glomerular membrane into Bowman's capsule. Renal plasma flow is 650 ml per minute whereas renal blood flow in each kidney is 1,250 ml per minute. **Normal filtration fraction** = 0.2

FF = [GFR (ml/min)/RPF (ml/min)] = (120 ml/650 ml)

### Mechanism of glomerular filtration (Fig. 8.16)

The rate of glomerular ultrafiltration depends not only on the hydrostatic pressure within the capillary but also on the total capillary surface area available for filtration.

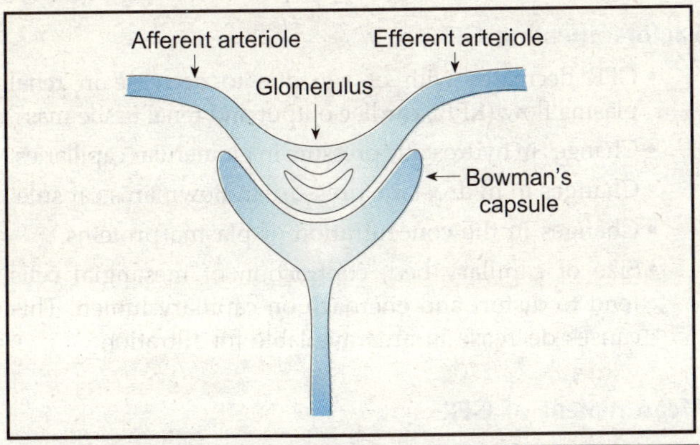


Forces favouring filtration = Hydrostatic pressure ($P_{GC}$) of glomerular capillaries + oncotic pressure of Bowman's space ($\Pi_B$).
Forces opposing filtration = Hydrostatic pressure of Bowman's space ($P_B$) + Oncotic pressure of glomerulus ($\Pi_{GC}$).
Net filtration pressure = $(P_{GC} - P_B) - (\Pi_{GC} - \Pi_B)$.

**Fig. 8.16 : Mechanism of glomerular filtration**

**Glomerular capillary blood pressure** is about 55 mm Hg. This pressure is opposed by osmotic pressure of blood (30 mm Hg) and by *filtrate hydrostatic pressure* (15 mm Hg) in the glomerular capsule.

Net filtration pressure is, therefore, 55 – (30 + 15) = 10 mm Hg.

## Simple filtration

Filtration takes place through the semipermeable walls of the glomerulus and glomerular capsule. Water and a large number of small molecules pass through it. Some of them are reabsorbed later. Blood cells, plasma proteins and other large molecules are not filtered through and remain in the capi-llaries.

Filtration is assisted by the difference between the blood pressure in the glomerulus and the pressure of filtrate in the glomerular capsule. Because diameter of the efferent arteriole is less than that of the afferent arteriole, a capillary hydrostatic pressure about 55 mm Hg builds up in the glomerulus. ***This pressure is opposed by the oncotic pressure of the blood, about 30 mm Hg and by filtrate hydrostatic pressure of about 15 mm Hg in the glomerular capsule. The net filtration pressure*** is 55 – (30 + 15) = 10 mm Hg. About 125 ml/min, i.e., 180 litres, of dilute filtrate are formed each day by the two kidneys. Of these 1 to 1.5 litres are excreted as urine. The difference in volume and concentration is due to selective reabsorption of some constituents of filtrate and secretion by tubular cells of others.

## Autoregulation of filtration

Hydrostatic pressure in the glomeruli remains fairly constant because constriction or dilatation of the afferent arterioles maintain pressure which compensates for changes in systemic blood pressure. When the blood pressure falls to below 80 mm Hg, eg, in severe shock, autoregulation fails and hydrostatic pressure decreases, impairing the function of the nephrons.

## Selective reabsorption

**Selective reabsorption** is the process by which the compo-sition and volume of the glomerular filtrate are altered during its passage through the convoluted tubule, the medullary loop and collecting tubule.

The fundamental job of this process is to reabsorb those filtrate constituents needed by the body to maintain fluid and electrolytic balance and blood alkalinity. Active transport is carried out at carrier sites in the epithelial membrane which use chemical energy to transport substances against their concentration gradient.

Some constituents of glomerular filtrate do not normally appear in urine because they are completely reabsorbed unless they are present in blood in excessive quantities. The kidney's maximum capacity for reabsorption of a substance is the **transport maximum** or **renal threshold** eg, normal blood glucose level is 2.5-5.3 mmol/L (80-120 mg/100 ml). If the level rises above the renal threshold (180 mg/100 ml) glucose appears in the urine because all the carrier sites are occupied and the mechanism for active transfer out of tubules is overloaded. Other substances reabsorbed by active transport include amino acids, sodium, calcium, potassium, phosphate and chloride ions (Fig. 8.17).

Reabsorption is regulated by the following hormones :

- Parathormone (reabsorption of $Ca^{2+}$ and phosphate)
- ADH
- Aldosterone

## Secretion (Fig. 8.18)

Filtration occurs as the blood flows through the glomerulus. Substances not required and foreign materials or drugs may not be cleared from the blood by filtration because of the short time it remains in the glomerulus. Such

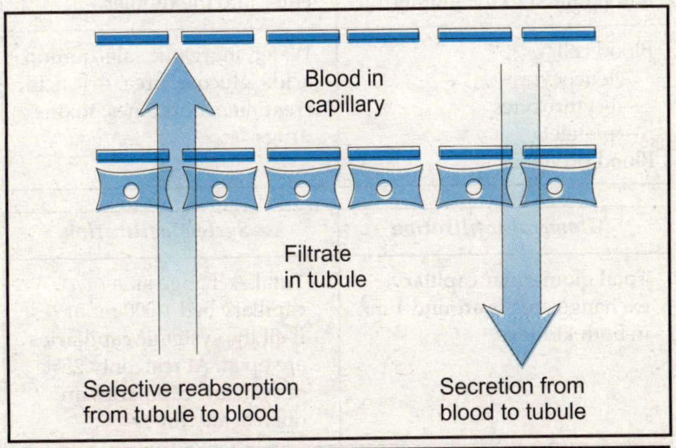


**Fig. 8.17 : Selective reabsorption**

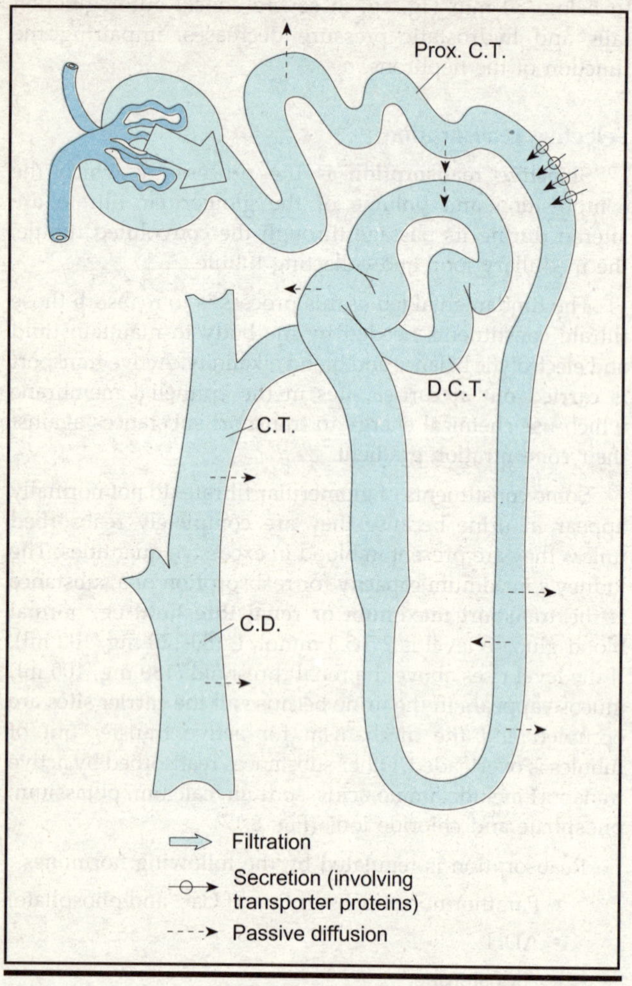


Fig. 8.18 : Elimination of waste materials by filtration and secretion

substances are cleared by secretion into convoluted tubules and excreted from the body in the urine.

| Glomerular filtration | |
|---|---|
| Large molecules not filtered and retained in the glomerulus | Small molecules filtered and enter into the tubules |
| Blood cells<br>– leucocytes<br>– erythrocytes<br>– platelets<br>Blood proteins | Water, inorganic salts, amino acids, glucose, urea, uric acid, creatinine, hormones, toxins, drugs. |

| *Glomerular filtration* | *Systemic filtration* |
|---|---|
| Total glomerular capillary exchange area is around 1 $m^2$ in both kidneys. | Total exchange area of capillary bed 1,000 $m^2$ at rest if all the systemic capillaries are open. At rest, only 25% of systemic capillaries are open at any time. |
| Fluid filtered from glomerular capillaries is 180 L/day. | Fluid filtered from systemic capillaries approx. 20 L/day. |

## Factors affecting GFR

- GFR decreases with of age due to decrease in renal plasma flow (RPF), cardiac output and renal tissue mass.
- Changes in hydrostatic pressure in glomerular capillaries.
- Changes in hydrostatic pressure in Bowman's capsule.
- Changes in the concentration of plasma proteins.
- Size of capillary bed; contraction of mesangial cells tend to distort and encroach on capillary lumen. This causes decrease in area available for filtration.

## Measurement of GFR

It can be measured by the relationship GFR = $U\dot{V}/P$ for any substance which is freely filtered and not reabsorbed or secreted :

$$GFR = \frac{U\dot{V}}{P}$$

$U\dot{V}$ = Amount per minute in urine

P×GFR = Amount entering Bowman's space per minute from plasma

GFR = Amount filtered per minute across glomerulus.

Amount in Bowman's space in case of freely filtered solute = amount in plasma which is filtered per minute at the glomerulus.

$$= GFR \times P = U\dot{V} \text{ or } GFR = U\dot{V}/P$$

## Net Filtration pressure

It is the net pressure that forces substances out of the glomerulus.

**Filtration pressure** = force favoring filtration (A) – force opposing filtration (B).

A = Glomerular capillary hydrostatic pressure

B = Capsular hydrostatic pressure and glomerular osmotic pressure.

Filtration is due to hydrostatic pressure inside the glomerular capillaries. The composition of the filtrate is similar to that of the tissue fluid.

## Filtration rate

It varies with the filtration pressure. Filtration pressure depends on the diameters of afferent and efferent arterioles. The rate of filtration through glomerulus varies with the blood flow.

## Regulation of filtration rate

- When activity of sympathetic nerve is increased, the GFR will be decreased.
- Juxtaglomerular cells release renin when there is reduction in tubular fluid NaCl concentration.
- There is maintenance of a constant blood flow by the autoregulation mechanism of an organ or tissue under particular conditions when arterial blood pressure is changing.

### Filtration fraction (FF)

It is the fraction of the plasma passing through kidneys which is filtered at the glomerulus, i.e., ratio of GFR to renal plasma flow (RPF) :

$$FF = \frac{GFR\ (ml/min)}{RPF\ (ml/min)}$$

$$= \frac{125\ ml/min}{700\ ml/min} = 0.16$$

Normally, 700 ml of plasma flows through the kidney per minute. Out of this 1/5th is filtered and rest 4/5th pass into peritubular capillaries.

## 8.9 Hormonal Influences on Water and Ion Transport in Nephron

### Aldosterone

Aldosterone acts on the distal tubule : Aldosterone increases $Na^+$ reabsorption and $K^+$ secretion by the principal cells of the cortical and medullary collecting ducts. Aldosterone acts on the cell nucleus increasing $Na^+$ conductance of the apical membrane (which by allowing more $Na^+$ to enter the cell, increases Na+ reabsorption), the number of $Na^+$ $K^+$ –ATPase pump sites (which, by increasing intracellular $K^+$ concentration, increases $K^+$ secretion) and the concentration of mitochondrial enzymes.

**Aldosterone** secretion is controlled by the renin angiotensin system. Renin is released from the juxtaglomerular cells (JG cells) in response to (i) decreased perfusion pressure within the afferent arteriole (ii) Sympathetic stimulation of the JG cells, and (iii) decreased Cl– concentration in fluid bathing the macula densa. Renin catalyzes the conversion of angiotensinogen to angiotensin I. Angiotensin I is converted to angiotensin II (AII) by angiotensin-converting enzyme (ACE) located within the lung. AngII stimulates aldosterone secretion from the adrenal cortex. Extracellular $K^+$ is controlled by aldosterone. Increases in extracellular $K^+$ stimulate the secretion of aldosterone, causing $K^+$ secretion and increase $Na^+$ transport into tubular cells.

ANP release in controlled directly by stretch receptors within the right atrium. It decreases $Na^+$ reabsorption by the renal epithelial cells of the medullary collecting ducts.

### ADH

(a) **By increasing water permeability** of the apical part of the cells due to the action of cyclic AMP inserting more pores into the membrane.

(b) **When ADH is absent** the distal nephron becomes impermeable to water and so the urine becomes hypotonic. The maximum excretion of water is then around 15% of GFR. Thus 15% of filtered water is under hormonal regulation (**facultative reabsorption**) whereas the other 85% is always reabsorbed (**obligatory reabsorption**).

(c) **The extracellular osmolarity** is controlled by ADH. Increases in osmolarity stimulate the release of ADH from posterior pituitary gland. ADH returns osmolarity toward normal by decreasing the amount of water excreted by the kidney. When osmolarity is decreased, ADH release is decreased and osmolarity is returned toward normal by increased water excretion.

ADH also is secreted in response to low blood pressure. Under these conditions, reabsorption of water by the kidneys can make the extracellular fluid hypotonic.

Antidiuretic hormone (ADH) regulates the absorption of water from the collecting ducts :

The absorption of ions by the ascending limb of the loop of Henle results in the tubular fluid becoming hypo osmotic as it approaches the distal tubule. The tubular epithelium is still relatively impermeable to water. ADH regulates water permeability in the last third of the distal tubule and in the collecting ducts. The hormone is secreted in response to increased plasma osmolality or to a reduction in blood pressure. Its secretion is regulated by sensors known as **osmoreceptors** which are located in the hypothalamus close to the supraoptic and paraventricular nuclei which produce the hormone and transport it to the posterior pituitary.

**ADH controls the insertion of water channels into the apical membrane of the P-cells of the collecting ducts.**

**ADH** circulating in the blood binds to receptors on the basolateral surface of the P-cells of the collecting ducts. These receptors are coupled to adenylyl cyclase and the resulting increase in CAMP activates a protein kinase. The protein kinase then initiates the fusion of vesicles containing water channels (AQUAPORIN) with the apical membrane. The water channels are taken back into the cells to await recycling. The permeability of the apical membrane of the P-cells to water is regulated by the insertion and removal of specific water channels. The water that enters the cell across the apical membrane passes freely into the lateral intercellular space.

### Measurement

The measurement of clearance involves a comparison of the rate of urinary excretion (urine volume x urinary concentration) with the plasma concentration.

Various substances can be used for measuring the GFR by determining its clearance.

If the substance is neither excreted nor reabsorbed, i.e. all of the plasma filtered has been cleared of the substance e.g.inulin, then clearance = GFR

$$\textbf{Clearance} = \frac{\text{Amount excreted/min}}{\text{Plasma concentration of substance (x)}}$$

$$\textbf{GFR} = \frac{UxV}{Px}$$

Ux = Urine concentration (mmol/L)

V = Volume of urine (ml/min.)

Px = Plasma concentration (m mol/L)

GFR = ml/min.

The term **clearance** was first used by Van Slyke to denote the volume of plasma that was 'cleared' or emptied of urea per minute.

**Plasma clearance of a substance** may be calculated as UV/p, where U is the concentration of the substance in the urine (usually in mg/dl), V is the volume (ml) of urine excreted per minute and P is the concentration of the substance in the plasma (usually in mg/dl).

**Clearance formula** produces a number that describes the rate at which the kidney removes a substance from the plasma. Clearance refers to the volume of plasma that will providethe quantity of the substance excreted in the urine in 1 minute. The clearances that are most frequently measured include creatinine, inulin, urea and para-amino hippurate (PAH).

## Inulin clearance test

A known amount of inulin is given into the blood at a constant rate. Inulin passes freely through glomerular membranes → concentration in the glomerular filtrate equals that in the plasma. Inulin is not reabsorbed or secreted → the rate at which it is excreted in the urine can be used for the calculation of the glomerular filtration rate.

Creatinine is filtered but is not reabsorbed or secreted by the kidneys. **Creatinine clearance test** is the method in which patient's plasma and urine creatinine concentrations can be used to estimate GFR. Blood always maintains a constant level of creatinine. A single measurement of plasma creatinine level is an approximate index of kidney function. **Another plasma clearance test** is done with **para amino hippuric acid (PAH)**. It filters freely through the glomerular membrane. All PAH passing through the kidney appear in the urine because PAH remaining in peritubular capillary plasma after filtration is secreted into PCT. As such, the rate of PAH clearance can be used to calculate the effective renal plasma flow.

It is appropriate to mention here that creatinine undergoes net secretion to some extent. Hence, its clearance should exceed GFR, but its plasma concentration is over-estimated due to non-specific chromogens, so its clearance becomes almost equal to insulin clearance or GFR.

## Renal plasma flow (RPF)

RPF is generally measured by taking **para-amino hippuric acid (PAH).** It is determined by the amount of PAH in the urine per unit time divided by the difference in its concentration in renal arterial or venous blood.

**RPF = 650 ml/min.** Approximately 125 ml/min. of the 650 ml/min. is filtered at the glomerulus as ultrafiltrate, 65% is reabsorbed in the proximal tubule, 14%, in the loop of Henle, 15% in the distal tubules and 6% in the collecting ducts.

## Measurement of renal plasma flow

It is estimated by measuring the clearance of a substance which is completely removed from the plasma in a single passage through the kidneys, i.e., its concentration is reduced to zero before the plasma reaches the renal venous system. This requires active secretion.

**Rate of delivery in arterial blood** = Rate of urinary excretion

**Rate of delivery** = Renal plasma flow × Plasma concentration (P)

**Rate of excretion** = Urine concentration (U) × Urine volume ($\dot{V}$)

From this equation

$$\text{Renal plasma flow} \times P = U \times \dot{V}$$

$$\therefore \text{Renal plasma flow} = (U \times \dot{V})/P$$

It seems necessary to mention that no substance can be eliminated completely during a single passage through the renal circulation because renal arterial blood supplies non-filtering areas like capsule, pelvis, etc. along with nephrons. So, the part perfusing nephrons (**effective renal plasma flow**, ERPF) has its venous effluent free from PAH or similar compounds.

So the formula of renal clearance of a substance like PAH is better called **ERPF** rather than RPF.

$$\text{So ERPF} = \frac{U_{PAH} \times \dot{V}}{P_{PAH}}.$$

Now its extraction ratio is about 0.9, ie.

$$\frac{\text{ERPF} \times P_{PAH}}{\text{RPF} \times P_{PAH}} = 0.9$$

So RPF = $\frac{\text{ERPF}}{0.9}$, so if ERPF is 630 ml/min then **RPF** becomes 700 ml/min.

## ➤ 8.10 Proximal Tubule, Loop of Henle & Distal Tubule Function

The **proximal tubule** is responsible for reabsorbing most of the material filtered from the glomerulus.

| Material | % Reabsorbed | Mechanism |
|---|---|---|
| $Na^+$ | 90-99 | $Na^+/H^+$ exchange, Na nutrient cotransport; diffusion |
| $K^+$, urea, $Cl^-$ | 60-70 | Diffusion & solvent drag |
| Glucose, Aminoacid | 100 | Na nutrient cotransport |
| Phosphate | 90 | Na Nutrient cotransport |
| Bicarbonate | 85 | Indirectly via $Na^+/H^+$ exchanger |

**The loop of Henle :**

- Produces a dilute filtrate.
- Reabsorbs approximately 25% of the salt and 15% of the water filtered from the glomerulus. The filtrate flowing from the loop of Henle to the distal convoluted tubule has a $Na^+$ concentration of approximately 100 meq/L.

**The distal nephron :** Regulates salt and water balance. $Na^+$ balance is regulated by aldosterone and atrial natriuretic peptide (ANP). Water balance is regulated by ADH (Arginine vasopressin). $K^+$ balance is regulated by aldosterone.

## Aldosterone

Aldosterone increases $Na^+$ reabsorption and $K^+$ secretion by the Principal cells of the cortical and medullary collecting ducts. Aldosterone acts on the cell nucleus, increasing $Na^+$ conductance of the apical membrane/which by allowing more $Na^+$ to enter the cell, increases $Na^+$ reabsorption); the number of $Na^+$ $K^+$ ATPase pump sites (which, by increasing intracellular $K^+$ concentration, increases $K^+$ secretion) and the concentration of mitochondrial enzymes.

**ANP : Stretch receptors** are present within **right atrium. ANP decreases $Na^+$ reabsorption** by the renal epithelial cells of medullary collecting ducts.

**ADH :** ADH is synthesized in the supraoptic nuclei ($5/6^{th}$ of ADH) about 1/6th of ADH is synthesized in paraventricular nuclei. Both of these nuclei have axonal extensions to the post pituitary. Once ADH is synthesized, it is transported down the axons or the neurons that terminate in the posterior pituitary.

**ADH increases water reabsorption by the principal cells of the cortical and medullary collecting ducts**. ADH upregulates the number of water channels on the apical membrane of the epithelial cells by a cyclic — AMP — dependent process.

**Regulation of ADH Secretion :**

| Increase ADH secretion | Decrease ADH secretion |
|---|---|
| ↑Plasma osmolarity | ↓Plasma osmolarity |
| ↓Blood volume | ↑Blood volume |
| ↓Blood pressure | ↑Blood pressure. |
| Nausea | Drugs |
| Hypoxia | Alcohol |
| Drugs | Clonidine |
| Nicotine | Haloperidol |
| Cyclophosphamide. | |

## Osmoreceptor-ADH Feed back system

When osmolarity (plasma Sodium concentration) increases above normal → ↑extra cellular fluid osmolarity stimulates osmoreceptor cells in the anterior hypothalamus, near the supraoptic nuclei → sends signal to post pituitary gland → action potentials conducted to the post pituitary stimulate release of ADH → transported in the blood to the kidney → increases water permeability of the late distal tubules, cortical collecting tubules, and medullary collecting ducts via $V_2$ receptors → Increased water permeability in the distal nephron segments causes increased water reabsorption and excretion of a small volume of concentrated urine Fig. TBW. The opposite sequence of events occurs when the ECF becomes too dilute (hypo-osmotic).

Cardiovascular reflex stimulation of ADH release occurs due to decreased arterial pressure, decreased blood volume or both.

ADH release is also regulated by cardiovascular reflexes, the arterial baroreceptor reflex and the cardiopulmonary reflexes. Afferent stimuli carried by vagus and glossopharyngeal nerves synapse with the nuclei of tractus solitarius and projections from these nuclei control ADH synthesis and secretion.

When there is a fall in BP (during hemorrhage), increased a ADH secretion through these reflex pathways causes increased fluid reabsorption by the kidneys, restores B.P. & blood volume towards normal levels.

## Renal transport of Sodium

99% of filtered sodium load is reabsorbed (60% in proximal tubule by $Na^+/H^+$ exchanger 25% in thick ascending limb by $Na^+/Cl^-/2K^+$ cotransport and 10% in distal tubule collecting duct via an epithelial $Na^+$ channel which is electrically coupled to a $K^+$ channel.)

**Sodium Balance is regulated by**

- Glomerular filtration rate.
- Aldosterone via the renin-angiotensin system
- ? Atrial natriuretic peptide.
- Angiotensin 11.

**Renal transport of other solutes :**

Potassium secretion—

- 7% of filtered potassium load is excreted. Almost all potassium is actively reabsorbed in the proximal tubule.
- Passive secretion of potassium occurs in the distal tubule in exchange for sodium, promoted by aldosterone. Hydrogen and potassium ions complete for this exchange.

**Chloride transport :** $Cl^-$ moves passively in association with $Na^+$ except in the ascending limb of the loop of Henle where it is actively transported.

**Sugar and aminoacids —**

- Completely reabsorbed in proximal tubule via active, carrier mediated mechanism sodium dependent.

- Glucose reabsorption is saturable i.e. when blood glucose reaches 10 mmol/l, glycosuria occurs.

**Urea :** 87% filtered urea is reabsorbed; 50% is passively reabsorbed in the proximal tubule. Only onefifth of the remaining urea entering the collecting duct leaves in the urine; the remainder is returned to the blood stream.

Water is reabsorbed passively along osmotic gradients set up by active transport of solutes, mainly $Na^+$, $Cl^-$ and urea. 80% of filtered water is reabsorbed isosomotically in the proximal tubule. 10-15% is reabsorbed in the loop of Henle, distal tubule and partly in the collecting ducts, in presence of ADH.

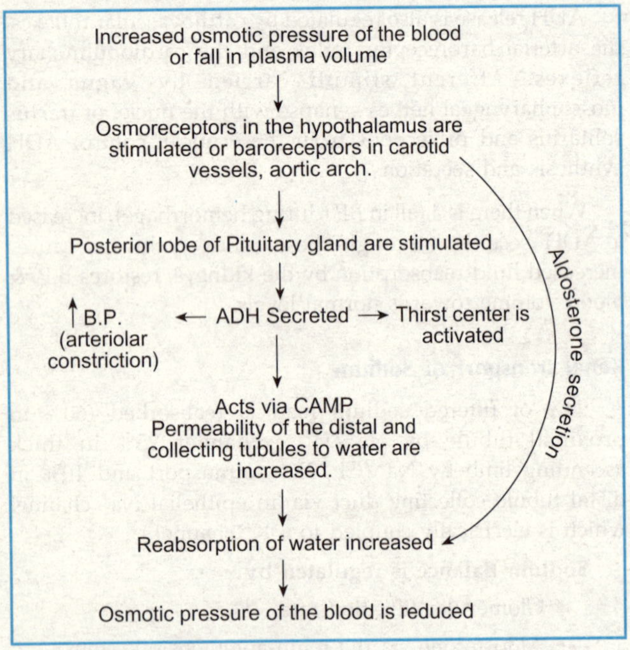


Causes of ADH excess :

- Syndrome of inappropriate ADH secretion (SI ADH).
- Increased pituitary ADH.
- Increased sensitivity to ADH e.g. chlorpropamide.
- Ectopic source of ADH e.g. Bronchogenic carcinoma.

**Causes of ADH deficiency :**

- Cranial diabetes insipidus.
- Nephrogenic diabetes insipidus.

## DCT and collecting ducts

There are two important mechanisms which play a role in $Na^+$ and water reabsorption in these regions.

***Sodium reabsorption*** : Most of the remaining $Na^+$ load is actively reabsorbed from the distal convoluted tubule and collecting ducts so that less than 1% of the filtered $Na^+$ is excreted in the urine. Important fraction of this reabsorption depends on stimulation by the hormone ***aldosterone,*** allowing $Na^+$ excretion to be regulated so as to maintain a normal extracellular fluid volume.

**Glomerulo-tubular balance** : In connection with $Na^+$, and also with water reabsorption, a term **glomerulo-tubular balance** is frequently coined. ***This signifies that within a physiological range of GFR, a fixed fraction of filtrate load of $Na^+$ is reabsorbed by the whole kidney (but specially applicable to PCT), so that, with fall of GFR, urinary sodium diminishes but can never be absent completely.*** To be more particular, say in a particular individual, 99% of filtrate load of sodium is reabsorbed, then with $P_{Na}$ of 150 mmol/L and GFR 180L/day.

$T_{Na}$(reabsorbed)

$$= \text{filtrate load} \times \frac{99}{100} = 180 \times 150 \times \frac{99}{100} \text{mmol / day}$$

So $U_{Na} \times V = 180 \times 150 \times \frac{1}{100}$ mmol/day = 270 mmol/day.

Now if GFR becomes 182 L/day, then excreted amount ($U_{Na} \times V$) becomes $182 \times 150 \times \frac{1}{100}$ mmol/day.

So additional excretion is $(182–180) \times 150 \times \frac{1}{100}$ mmol/day.

$$= 2 \times 150 \times \frac{1}{100} \text{ mmol/day}$$

$$= 3 \text{ mmol/day}$$

If a constant amount happens to be reabsorbed, then excess excretion becomes = $2 \times 150$ mmol/day = 300 mmol/day.

***In this way glomerulo-tubular balance reduces sodium loss.*** Onthe contrary, if GFR reduces to 178 L/day and if the reabsorbed amount is kept fixed at $180 \times 150 \times \frac{99}{100}$ mmol/day, the excreted amount would have been $(178 \times 150 - 180 \times 150 \times \frac{99}{100})$ mmol/day = –30 mmol/day, ie, all sodium gets reabsorbed, causing a pathological condition of sodium retention. But this does not occur due to the remaining 1% of filtrate load, ie $178 \times 150 \times \frac{1}{100}$ mmol/day is eliminated; it is only lower by 3 mmol/day of normal excretion of 270 mmol/day.

**The physiological factors behind this phenomenon are—**

(a) **Cellular** : epithelial cells of the nephron adjust reabsorption in proportion to load offered to them.

(b) **Physical** : change of GFR causes change in same direction of oncotic pressure of peritubular fluid, affecting its reabsorptive capacity.

When GFR is raised, RPF being unaltered by autoregulation, then oncotic pressure of peritubular capillaries increase due to excess loss of fluid in filtrate. The peritubular capillaries have reabsorptive force = $(\Pi_{cap} - \Pi_{interstitium})$ –

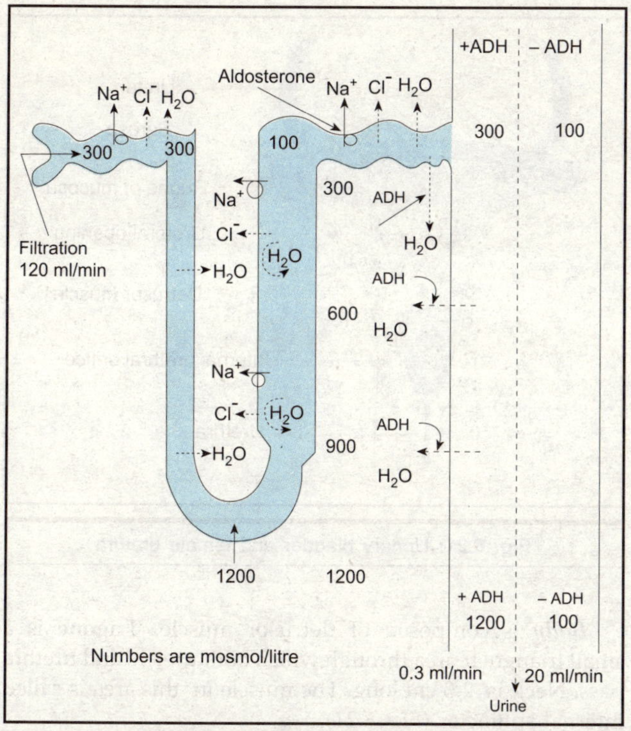


**Fig. 8.19 : Sodium and water reabsorption in the nephron**

$P_{cap} - P_{interstitium}$) where Πcap is capillary oncotic pressure, $P_{cap}$ is the hydrostatic pressure of capillary.

$= \Pi_{cap} - P_{cap} + P_{interstitium} - \Pi_{interstitium}$ ($\Pi_{interstitium}$ is negligible, $\Pi_{cap}$ is also low).

$= \Pi_{cap} - P_{cap} + \Pi_{interstitium}$, is positive and, so, effective.

So if $P_{cap}$ rises, the reabsorbtive force also increases. This heightened reabsorptive force help to take up more sodium and water.

**'Tubuloglomerular feedback'** is a term that sounds close to glomerulo-tubular balance, but it is a different proposition. ***It refers to the ability of the distal nephron to control its fluid input, so that its capacity of reabsorption is neither undermined nor overflooded.*** This is required to maintain homeostasis as DN (distal nephron) is responsible for finer regulation of $Na^+$, $K^+$, $H^+$ elimination.

Whenever there is increase in flow rate in the ascending limb of loop of Henle or $Na^+$ reabsorption rate at macula densa increases then there is decrease in GFR. **Macula densa cells *liberate prostaglandins or somehow triggers renin-angiotensin system to constrict afferent arteriole to reduce GFR.***

Whenever there is fall in GFR leading to low flow rate in ascending limb of Henle's loop. Which results in diminished $Na^+$ load to macula densa, vasodilation of afferent arteriole takes place to increase GFR. The sensor is macula densa.

## 8.11 Regulation of Blood pH

The kidneys regulate the amount of $HCO^-_3$ reabsorbed from the glomerular filtrate and also generate $HCO^-_3$ to replace that lost in buffering strong acids formed in the body. Both reabsorption of filtered $HCO^-_3$ and generation of new $HCO^-_3$ are accomplished by one process – **the secretion of $H^+$ *by tubular epithelial cells.***

### Secretion of $H^+$

**Secretion of $H^+$** takes place in ***epithelial cells of proximal convoluted tubules*** and ***collecting tubules*** and begins when $CO_2$ diffuses from peritubular blood or tubular fluid into epithelial cells or is produced from metabolic reactions within epithelial cells. Here, with CA, $CO_2$ combines with $H_2O \rightarrow H_2CO_3$. The $H_2CO_3$ then dissociates into $H^+$ and $HCO^-_3$ ions and $H^+$ is secreted into the tubular fluid.

**In PCT** secretion of $H^+$ is primarily coupled to passive movement of $Na^+$ ions from tubular fluid into epithelial cells a mechanism known as ***$Na^+$, $H^+$ counter-transport***.

**In collecting tubules** : $H^+$ secretion is primarily an active process. An important feature of $H^+$ secretion is that $HCO^-_3$ formed during the dissociation of $H_2CO_3$ can diffuse from the epithelial cells into peritubular blood. For every $H^+$ secreted, one $HCO^-_3$ is returned to blood.

***In order to understand the relationship between $H^+$ secretion and $HCO^-_3$ reabsorption, we will have to follow the* fate of $H^+$ ions.**

Most of the $H^+$ ions secreted into tubular fluid react with $HCO^-_3$ to form $H_2CO_3$ which, in turn, dissociates into $CO_2$ and $H_2O$. The $CO_2$ diffuses into epithelial cells to generate additional $H^+$ for secretion or it diffuses through the epithelial cells into peritubular blood for eventual elimination by the lungs.

In proximal tubular fluid, the dissociation of $H_2CO_3$ into $CO_2$ and $H_2O$ is catalyzed by CA. Each time a secreted $H^+$ ion reacts with $HCO^-_3$ in proximal tubular fluid, an $HCO^-_3$ is lost from the fluid.

However, the secretion of $H^+$ also results in the addition of an $HCO^-_3$ into peritubular blood. Thus when $H^+$ reacts with $HCO^-_3$ in tubular fluid, the net result of $H^+$ secretion is reabsorption of $HCO^-_3$. The basic mechanism whereby the kidneys reabsorb filtered $HCO^-_3$ is based on reaction of secreted $H^+$ with $HCO^-_3$ in tubular fluid (Fig. 8.20a).

**$NH_3$ (ammonia)** in certain concentrations is a poisonous waste product derived from the deamination of amino acids. The liver converts much of the ammonia to a less toxic compound called **urea**. Urea and ammonia both become part of the tubular fluid and are subsequently expelled from the body. Any ammonia produced by the deamination of amino acids in the tubule is secreted into the tubular fluid. When $NH_3$ forms in the distal and collecting tubular epithelial cells it diffuses out of the cells into tubular fluid and combines with $H^+$ for ammonium ion ($NH^+_4$). $NH^+_4$ is

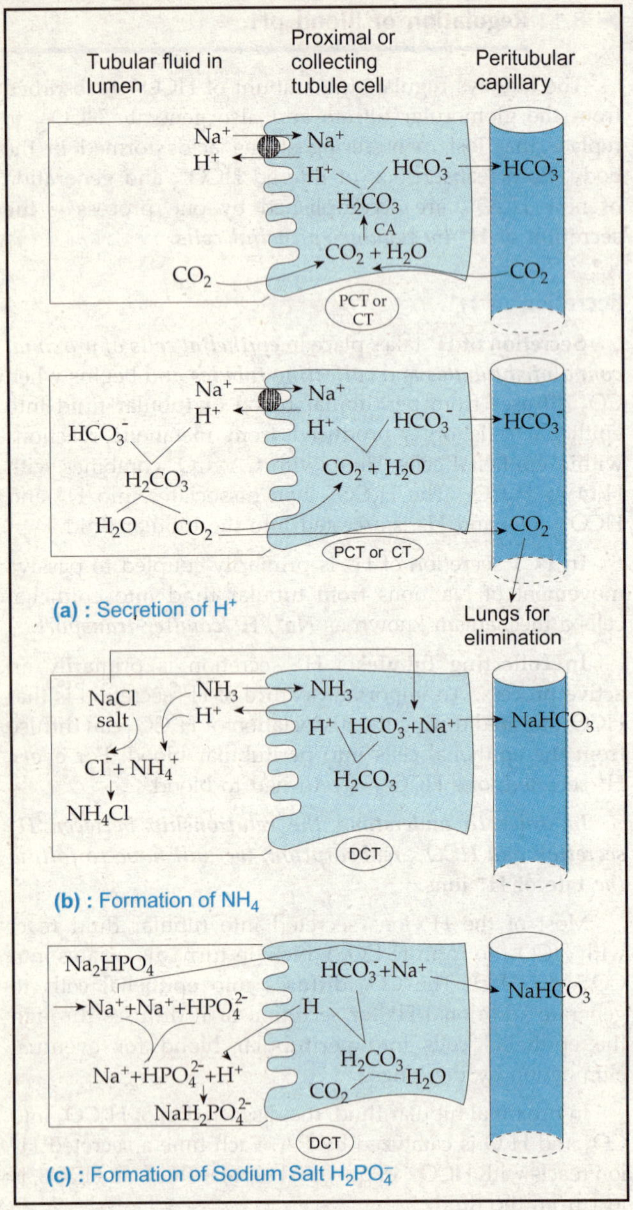


Fig. 8.20 : Regulation of [H+] of blood

then excreted from the body in combination with chloride ($Cl^-$) ions as $NH_4Cl$ (Fig. 8.20b).

**The phosphate buffer system is the second important** buffer for secreted $H^+$ ions. The $H^+$ ions can react with sodium salt of monohydrogen phosphate ($HPO^{2-}{}_4$) ions in tubular fluid ($Na_2HPO_4$) to form sodium salt of dihydrogen phosphate ($H_2PO^-{}_4$) ions which are then excreted from the body ($NaH_2PO^{2-}{}_4$) (Fig. 8.20c).

## URINARY BLADDER

**Urinary bladder is** composed of (i) **body**, (ii) **trigone** and (iii) **neck.**

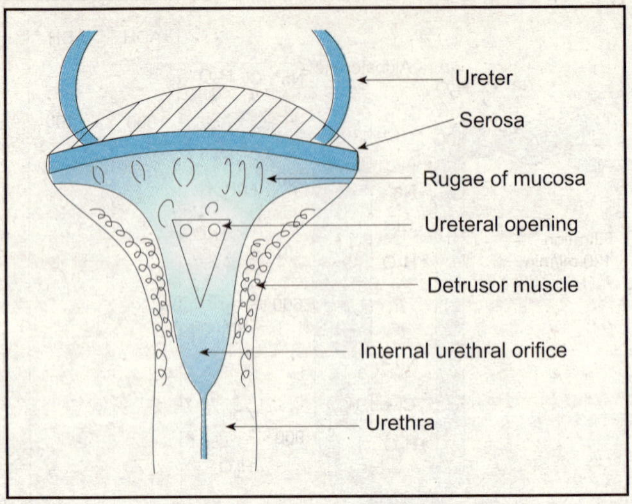


Fig. 8.21: Urinary bladder and female urethra

*Body* is composed of detrusor muscle. **Trigone** is a small triangular area through which both ureters and urethra pass. **Neck** is 2-3 cm long. The muscle in this area is called internal sphincter (Fig. 8.21).

It is a reservoir for urine. It is a hollow muscular organ situated in the pelvic cavity posterior to symphysis pubis. It is directly anterior to rectum in case of male but in female it is anterior to vagina. Its size and position vary, depending on the amount of urine it contains. When distended, bladder rises into the abdominal cavity (Fig. 8.22).

Bladder is a balloon-like chamber with walls of smooth muscle. The smooth muscle at the neck of the bladder is sometimes called **internal urethral sphincter**. The three orifices in the bladder wall form a **triangle** or **trigone**. The upper two orifices on the posterior wall are the openings of the ureters. The lower orifice is the point of origin of the urethra. Where the urethra originates there is a thickening of the smooth muscle layer which acts as a sphincter and controls the passage of urine from the bladder into urethra.

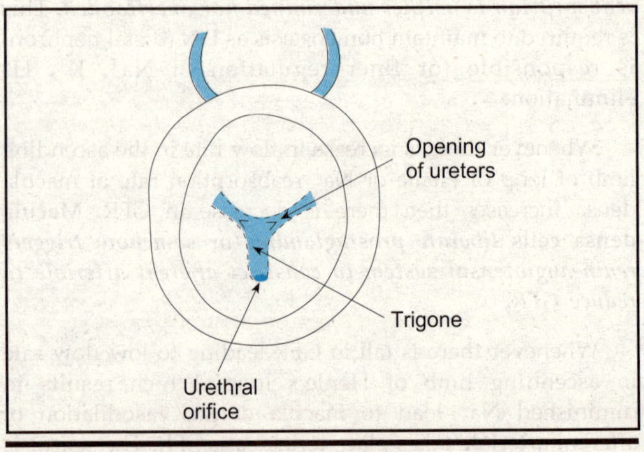


Fig. 8.22 : Internal structure of bladder

**Neuroanatomic consideration of bladder**

- Efferent innervation Or Motor innervation } Sympathetic ($T_{12}$, $L_1$ and $L_2$) segments of spinal cord
- Parasympathetic ($S_{2,3,4}$) via pelvic splanchnic nerves
- Somatic via pudendal nerve ($S_{2,3,4}$)

**Fig. 8.23** : Neuroanatomy of bladder

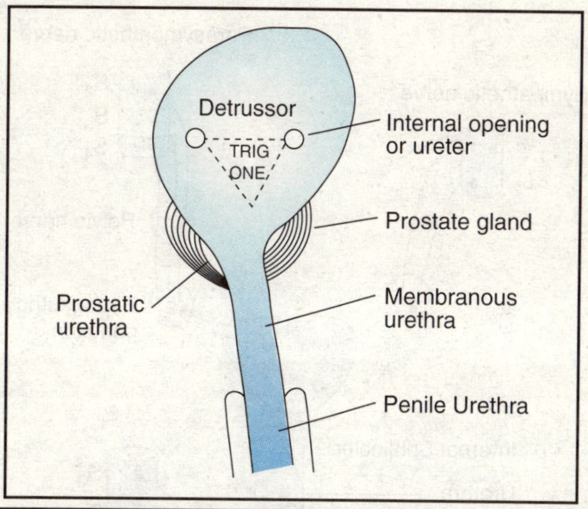


**Fig. 8.24** : Parts of bladder and urethra

This internal sphincter, like the muscle layer, is under autonomic nerve control.

***Histological structure :***

(i) ***Mucosal layer*** innermost coat. Mucus membrane contains transitional epithelium.

(ii) ***Submucosa*** middle layer. A layer of connective tissue, between mucosa and muscular coat.

(iii) ***Outer layer*** muscular coat is composed of detrusor, inner longitudinal, middle circular and outer longitudinal muscles. Close to opening to the urethra, the circular fibers form an internal sphincter. The external sphincter is located just below the internal sphincter (see Fig. 8.21).

## Characteristics of urine

Urine flow through the ureters to the bladder occurs continuously, propelled by contraction of ureteral wall smooth muscle. The urine is stored in the bladder and intermittently ejected during urination (**micturition**).

***Characteristics of normal urine :*** A normal adult excretes ***1 to 2 liters of urine per day***. The amount of urine excreted depends on the fluid intake as well as water loss through the skin and GI tract. ***The colour of urine*** is normally ***straw or amber***. A darker urine indicates that it is more concentrated. Normal urine, is clear; not turbid. The ***specific gravity*** of urine lies between ***1.010 and 1.025***; a lower value indicates a dilute urine and vice versa. Average urine pH ***is 6*** but it may vary from ***4.6 to 8.0***; diet having the greatest effect on it. The normal urine consists of water (95%); various salts (5%) and waste products. The important nitrogenous wastes that are excreted in urine include urea (from amino acid metabolism); creatinine (from muscle metabolism) and uric acid (from nuclei acid metabolism).

## Abnormal urinary constituents

***Glucose*** is excreted in the urine (glycosuria) when the plasma glucose level crosses the renal threshold for glucose e.g. in diabetes mellitus. The presence of protein in urine is known as **proteinuria** which is found when the glomerular permea-bility increases e.g. in glomerulonephritis. **Hematuria** means presence of blood in urine and may occur when the glomeruli are too permeable or there is bleeding somwhere inside the urinary tract. Though traces of ketones are normally found in urine, higher levels of ketones in urine (ketonuria) indicate increased fat and protein breakdown for energy as may occur in uncontrolled diabetes mellitus, starvation, and a high protein diet. The presence of bacteria in urine (bacteriuria) suggests the possibility of urinary tract infection (UTI) but it should be remembered that bacteria present normally near the urethral meatus may contaminate urine. The presence of large number of pus cells (pyuria), which are modified $WBC_s$, is a good indicator of UTI. A large number of bacteria and/or pus cells in the urine may give it a turbid appearance.

## ➤ 8.12 Micturition

Micturition is a process by which urine is voided from the urinary bladder. It is a reflex process. The functional anatomy and nerve supply of urinary bladder are essential for the process of micturition (Fig. 8.24).

**Nerve supply to urinary Bladder and Sphincters :** Urinary bladder and the internal sphincter are supplied by both sympathetic and parasympathetic divisions of autonomic nervous system whereas the external sphincter is supplied by the somatic nerve.

**Sympathetic nerve supply :** Preganglionic fibers of sympathetic nerve arise from first two lumbar segments (L1 and L2) of spinal cord. After coming out of spinal cord, the fibers pass through lateral sympathetic chain without any synapse in the sympathetic ganglia.

**Functions of Sympathetic nerve :** The stimulation of sympathetic nerve causes relaxation of detrusor muscle and constriction of the internal sphincter. So, it causes filling of urinary bladder and the sympathetic nerve is called **Nerve of filling**.

**Parasympathetic nerve supply :** The preganglionic parasympathetic fibers arise from second, third and fourth sacral segments of spinal cord. All the fibers unite to form

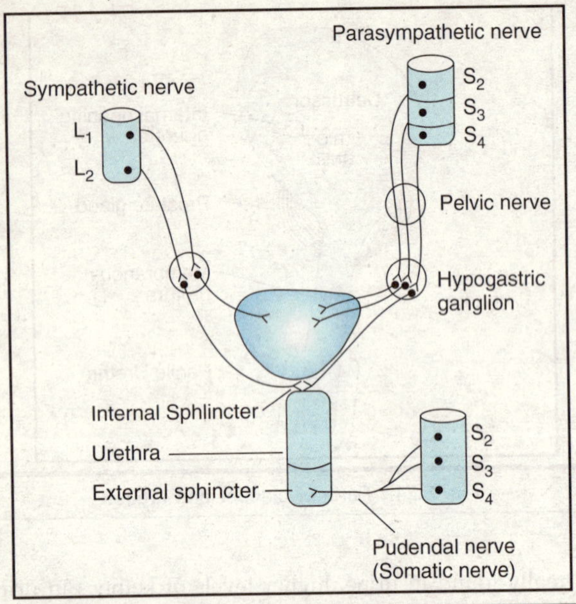


**Fig. 8.25 : Nerve supply to urinary bladder and urethra**

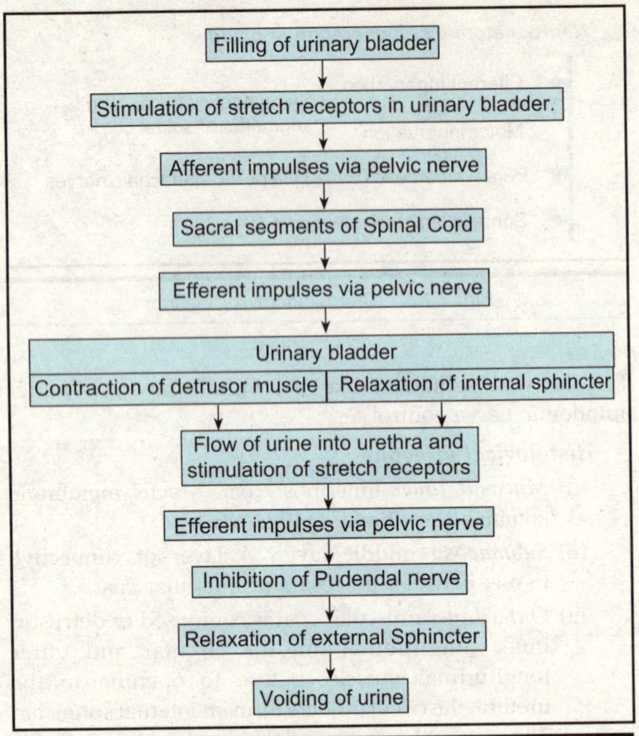


**Fig. 8.26**

the pelvic nerve—**nervi erigentes**. The fibers of pelvic nerve end in hypogastric ganglion. From here, the postganglionic fibers arise and supply the detrusor muscle and internal sphincter.

**Function of Parasympathetic nerve :** The stimulation of pelvic nerve causes contraction of detrusor muscle and relaxation of the internal sphincter leading to emptying of urinary bladder. So the **parasympathetic nerve** is called **nerve of emptying** or **nerve of micturition**.

The pelvic nerve has sensory fibers also. The sensory fibers carry impulses from stretch receptors present on the wall of the urinary bladder and urethra to C.N.S.

**Somatic Nerve Supply :** The external sphincter is supplied by the somatic nerve namely pudendal nerve. It maintains the tonic contraction of the skeletal muscle fibers forming external sphincter so that the external sphinter is contracted, always. During micturition, this nerve is inhibited. Thus the pudendal nerve is responsible for voluntary control of micturition (Fig. 8.25).

**Functions of nerve supplying urinary bladder and sphincters :**

| Nerve | On detrusor muscle | On internal sphincter | On external sphincter |
|---|---|---|---|
| Sympathetic nerve | Relaxation | Contraction | Not supplied |
| Parasympathetic nerve | Contraction | Relaxation | Not supplied |
| Somatic nerve | Not supplied | Not supplied | Contraction |

## Micturition reflex

Micturition reflex starts due to the stretching of the wall of the bladder when about 300-400 ml of urine is collected. The wall of the urinary bladder has stretch receptors. The stretch receptors are present in the urethra also.

The stretch receptors are stimulated when bladder is filled with urine and the pressure increases. Sensory impulses reach the sacral segments of the spinal cord through the pelvic (parasympathetic) nerve. From the spinal cord, the efferent (motor) impulses travel through motor fibers of the pelvic nerve towards bladder and internal sphincter. The motor impulses cause contraction of detrusor muscle and relaxation of internal sphincter so that, urine enters the urethra from the bladder.

When urine enters urethra → receptors in urethra are stimulated and send afferent impulses to spinal cord via pelvic nerve fibers. These impulses inhibit pudendal nerve. So the external sphinter also relaxes and micturition occurs.

When micturition reflex begins → initial contraction of bladder activates the receptors to cause further increase in sensory impulses from the bladder and urethra → further increase in reflex contraction of bladder. The cycle is repeated again and again until the force of contraction of bladder reaches the maximum and urine is voided out completely (Fig. 8.26).

## Disorders of micturition

From the study of micturition reflex it can be assumed that lesions may involve multiple sites of neural circuit to affect urination.

1. **Spinal cord injury above sacral level** : During the spinal shock stage the micturition reflex is depressed. The bladder wall is flaccid and urine accumulates to overfill it. Then the passive stretch becomes sufficient to overcome the sphincters to force some volume to leak till the pressure falls to a value so that normal sphincteric tone blocks the passage of urine again.

### Overflow incontinence

When the spinal shock stage is over, the reflex returns but there will be no volitional control. After some interval the involuntary reflex is responsible for contraction of detrusor to force out adequate amount of urine similar to newborn children **(automatic bladder).** But for the reflex to be able to empty the bladder it requires that its wall be protected from injury due to over-distension in the spinal shock days by voiding it with catheter. Patient gains some control by stroking skin at inner side of thigh or perineal region.

In some cases, specially with infection, the bladder wall becomes hypertrophied, capacity becomes less and the reflex becomes exaggerated, increasing the frequency of micturition **spastic neurogenic bladder.**

2. **Tabes dorsalis**, a manifestation of late syphilis, is associated with afferent nerve lesion of sacral segment. As no feeling of distension reaches the brain, the voluntary control becomes weak and the reflex also becomes abolished. Chronic inability of voiding leads to excessive accumulation of urine causing thinning of the bladder wall and increase in its capacity. The urine dribbles because of over-distension and incontinence (overflow incontinence). The condition is **atonic bladder**, but the voluntary control persists.

3. The **bladder may be *dissociated functionally from the spinal cord*** by tumours involving cauda equina or destruction of sacral cord. The isolated bladder initially remains flaccid and accomodates excess urine; the response of the smooth muscle (detrusor) to stretch is responsible for incomplete evacuation of bladder. Within few days, the bladder wall becomes hypertrophied with diminution of capacity. The subject has neither sensation or volitional influence over micturition.

4. ***Normally, impulses from higher centres contract the external sphincter.*** During voluntary micturition this stimulus is withdrawn to relax the sphincter. The inhibitory and facilitatory effects on micturition come from different areas of brain and travel through different fibers. So lesions at higher centers, brainstem and spinal cord may damage in such a way that facilitation of micturition predominates, such that small filling of bladder is adequate to initiate (voluntary) micturition (non-inhibited neurogenic bladder). On the other hand, when the inhibition of urination predominates, then sufficient bladder distention is required to elicit voluntary micturition. So frequency of micturition becomes less.

## ➤ 8.13 Countercurrent Multiplier Kuhn's Hypothesis

*Countercurrent* : Refers to the flow in opposite direction in the adjacent limbs of a U-shaped loop such as that of Henle.

*Multiplier* : Countercurrent flow is causal in the formation of concentration gradients along the axis of the adjacent limbs, so that from the beginning of the limb of loop of Henle (descending limb) to the point of turning, the osmolality is multiplied many times. Similar changes in osmolality take place in renal interstitial fluid also.

### Countercurrent mechanism

Concentration of urine is necessary for excretion of excess solutes through it, which is achieved by a process called **countercurrent mechanism**. This concentrating mechanism depends on a special arrangement of loop of Henle and vasa recta in the renal pyramid for the production and maintenance of a gradient of increasing osmolality extending from corticomedullary junction to the tip of the papilla.

### Interstitium of kidney

Kidney is demarcated into two parts; *cortex (superficial part) and medulla (deeper part)*. The space located in between the nephrons, glomeruli and blood vessels is termed **interstitium. $Na^+$ concentration of the interstitial fluid** is low (at par with plasma) at the cortex. As such, the osmolality of the fluid is low but, at the deeper part of the medulla, [$Na^+$] of the medullary interstitial fluid is progressively high and consequently, the osmolality of the fluid is very high.

### Medullary gradient

The continuous increase in osmolality from the cortex to the medulla is called **medullary gradient**. Velocity of blood circulating in the vasa recta is very slow. Slow removal of solutes maintains an optimum medullary gradient for the concentration of urine. When there is increased velocity of blood in the vasa recta, the medullary gradient will subsequently be reduced. Ultimately, there will be production of dilute urine.

### Vasa recta

It consists of a descending portion and an ascending portion which are parallel to each other. The solutes remain concentrated within the medulla due to the arrangement of the ascending and descending portions of the vasa recta which makes blood flow in opposite direction in two limbs of the vasa recta. This again is a countercurrent flow (see Figs. 8.27 and 8.28).

***Blood entering the vasa recta has a solute concentration of about 300 milliosmole per litre.*** When the blood flows down the descending portion into the medulla where the interstitial fluid becomes more and more concentrated, NaCl

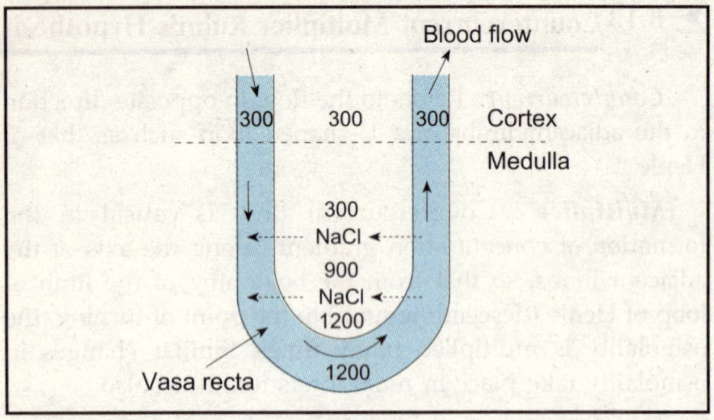


**Fig. 8.27 :** Countercurrent exchange in the vasa recta refers to the passive diffusion of $Na^+$ and $Cl^-$ from the ascending to descending blood capillary loop.

and urea diffuse into the blood and water into interstitium. Vasa recta are capillaries permeable passively to small molecules across its lining.

As the blood becomes more concentrated, it flows into the ascending portion of the vasa recta where the interstitial fluid becomes less and less concentrated. As a result, urea and NaCl diffuse from the blood into the interstitial fluid and water seeps in so, the blood leaving the vasa recta has a concentration only slightly higher than the blood entering it. The essential features of the countercurrent flow through the vasa recta is that high medullary concentration of the solutes are maintained since blood passing through the vasa recta removes very little solutes.

**Site of development (medullary gradient)** : Though this mechanism acts both in the cortical and juxtamedullary nephrons, it is more pronounced in the juxtamedullary nephrons having long loop of Henle and similar V-shaped long delicate vasa recta.

**Thin descending limb** : Initially, isotonic to cortical peritubular fluid i.e., about 300 mosmoles/litre. This nephron is permeable to water and impermeable to $Na^+$ ions. Osmolality rises from superficial to deep.

**Tubular fluid in thin ascending limb tubule** is impermeable to water but permeable to $Na^+$ ions. In the thin ascending limb of Loop of Henle, $Na^+$ passively comes out to the interstitium, gradually diminishing the osmolality.

**Tubular fluid in thick ascending limb** : Water is not reabsorbed and electrolytes alone are reabsorbed making it hypotonic.

The medullary interstitium has a progressively increasing osmolality ***increasing from 300 milliosmole/litre in the cortex to as high as 1,300 milliosmole/litre at the tip***. The descending limb of the loop of Henle is freely permeable to water but not the solutes or ions. While, the ascending limb is permeable to ions and impermeable to water. Tubular epithelium of the collecting ducts become highly permeable to water by the action of ADH ***which acts through $V_2$ receptors*** and cAMP mediated pathway to insert proteins (water channel) called **aquaporins** into the luminal membrane of the collecting ducts.

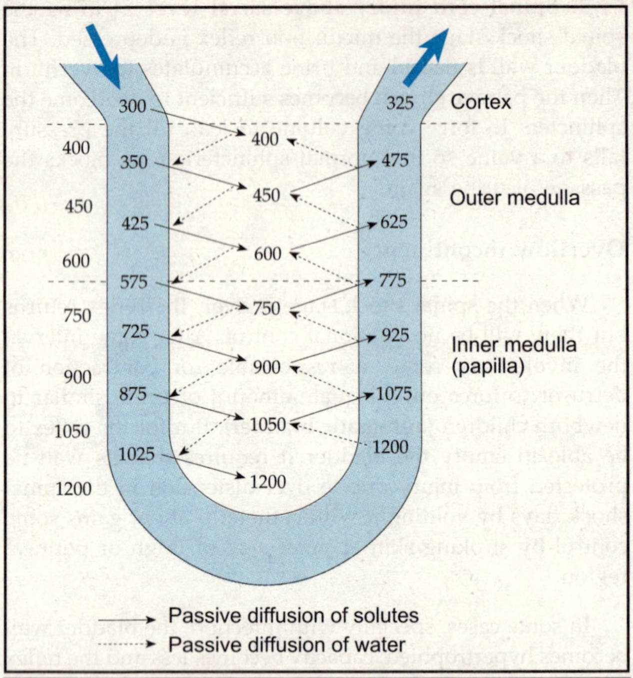


**Fig. 8.28 :** Showing countercurrent exchange system in the vasa recta including passive transport of solutes and passive movement of water

## The process proper

The glomerular filtrate, after passing through the proximal convoluted tubule, enters the descending limb of loop of Henle as isotonic fluid. ***As the fluid descends through the descending limb surrounded by interstitium with progressively increasing osmolality, water gradually flows out along the osmotic gradient (as descending limb of loop of Henle is permeable to water and not to ions) so that at the tip of the loop of Henle the tubular fluid is highly hypertonic (Fig. 8.29).***

Now, during its ascent through the ascending limb, this hypertonic tubular fluid gradually diminishes in osmolality as in the surrounding interstitium. This is due to $Na^+$ and $Cl^-$ moving out into the interstitium and so the fluid passing into the collecting duct is hypotonic (or isotonic for cortical nephrons). When need for greater concentration of urine arises, ADH is released. ADH acting on the collecting duct (according to some authors also on distal convoluted tubules) makes it permeable to water and thereby water flows from the collecting duct into the interstitium by osmosis. This makes urine more concentrated.

## Factors responsible for maintenance of medullary gradient

(1)Active transport of solutes (mainly $Na^+$, also co-transport of $K^+$, $Cl^-$, etc) from the thick portion of the ascending

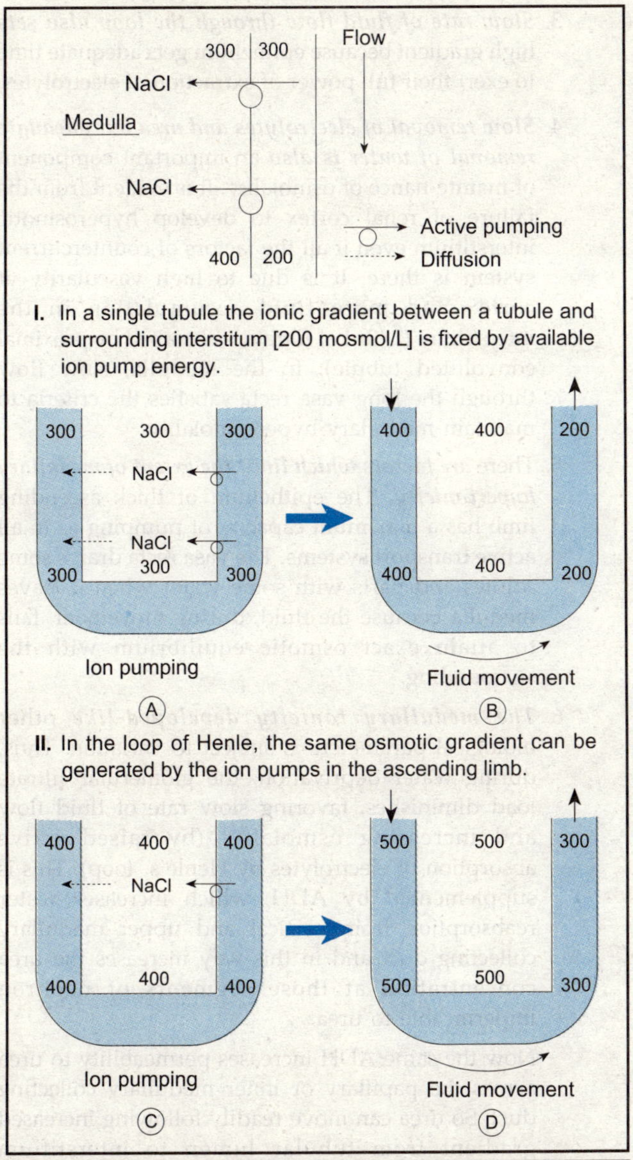


**Fig. 8.29 :** Principles of the countercurrent multiplier mechanism

limb of loop of Henle to the interstitium is the primary cause. Besides the thin ascending limb being permeable to ions, the passive diffusion of ions through it acts as an **additional countercurrent multiplier** (Fig. 8.30).

(2)Diffusion of urea from inner portion of collecting duct into the interstitium plays an important role in maintaining the hyperosmolarity of interstitium. Only the proximal tubule and collecting duct epithelium being permeable to urea the tubular fluid reaching the collecting duct has high concentration of urea. This diffusion of urea is facilitated by vasopressin, in the absence of which urea may move from interstitium to the tubular fluid as no-absorption of water makes the concentration of urea in lumen less than the interstitium.

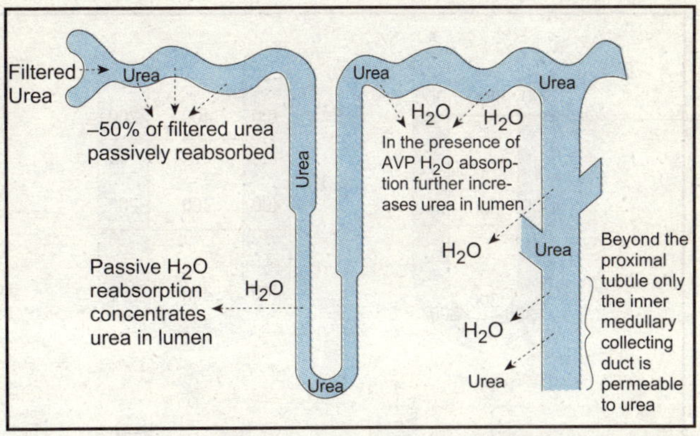


**Fig. 8.30 :** Factors responsible for maintaining of medullary gradient

(3)The active transport of ions from the collecting duct into the interstitium also helps in maintaining the gradient to a small extent.

(4)The vascular system (**vasa recta**) of the renal medulla deserves special mention in this regard which acts as **countercurrent exchanger**. Solutes and ions move in and water comes out as blood travels through the descending limb of vasa recta. On the other hand, when blood moves up through the ascending limb of the vasa recta the ions move out and water gets into the blood. Thus, only a little amount of solutes are carried away by the blood thereby main-taining the hyperosmolarity of the medulla.

Besides, the scanty blood flow of the medulla also assists in maintenance of the hyperosmolarlity. The vasa recta also increases the osmolarity of the interstitium by carrying away the water entering the medulla from the collecting ducts and descending limb of Henle's loop.

**Countercurrent system** of operation is not peculiar to renal physiology but similar mode of adaptation is seen in blood vessels draining from periphery in many species of animal kingdom, where warm arterial blood gives up heat to closely placed venous channels which drain centrally conserved heat. Same type of arrangement is seen in testes where the closely placed arterial and venous vessels exchange heat and male sex hormone to keep the temperature of testis below core temperature and maintain hormonal milieu around germinal epithelium optimum.

The generation of osmotic gradient in medullary interstitium and luminal fluid of Henle's loop becomes apparent when it is thought to develop through some hypothetical stages in cortial nephron (Fig. 8.31).

**Stage I :** *Prior to onset of countercurrent multiplier* process, osmolality is same everywhere.

**Stage II :** *Due to active absorption of $Na^+$ and $Cl^-$*, osmolality is less in luminal fluid than that of interstitium and the fluid in the descending limb of Henle's loop equilibrates quickly with interstitial fluid.

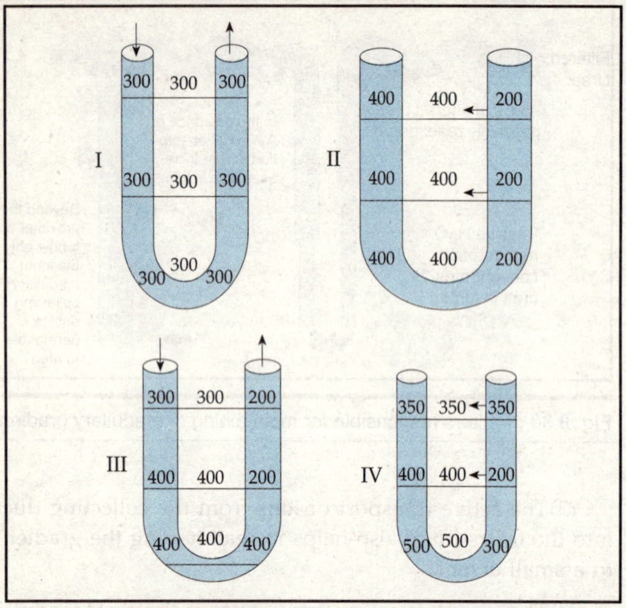


Fig. 8.31 : The generation of osmotic gradient in medullary interstitium

**Stage III** : ***Movement of additional fluid from proximal convoluted tubule*** having osmolality 300 mosmol/litre pushes the fluid in the descending limb to ascending limb to have osmolality distribution as in the figure.

**Stage IV** : ***Pumping by thick ascending limb of Henle's loop makes*** the difference of tonicity (200 mosmol/litre) between it and other compartments. Thus it becomes clear how the osmolality of interstitium and descending limb of loop of Henle goes on increasing as traced to hair pin end and at the same time how the fluid in the ascending limb gets more and more hypotonic as it approaches the cortex (distal tubule) (Fig. 8.32).

From the discussion above it can be **summarised** that :

1. ***The pumping activity of ascending limb of Henle's loop*** is essential in the generation of osmotic gradient. If this pumping activity is suppressed by loop diuretics like frusemide, the gradient disappears and concentrating capacity is lost temporarily.
2. ***More the length of Henle's loop,*** more will be the gra-dient. The desert rats have thick medulla so that loops of Henle have increased length and their juxtaglomerular nephrons are more numerous. Capacity to concentrate peritubular fluid is different in different species. In human beings, it is 1,200 mosmol/litre, in dogs it is almost double and in desert rats it is about 4 times than that of human being. Whereas, in aquatic beavers, the medulla is thin and kidney's concentrating capacity is low.
3. ***Slow rate of fluid flow through the loop also sets*** high gradient because epithelium gets adequate time to exert their full power of extraction of electrolytes.
4. ***Slow removal of electrolytes and urea but adequate removal of water is also*** an important component of mainte-nance of osmolality. It is evident from the failure of renal cortex to develop hyperosmotic interstitium even if all the factors of countercurrent system is there. It is due to high vascularity at cortex and more fluid accumulation in the interstitium (2/3rd of filtrate is absorbed by proximal convoluted tubule). In the medulla, slow flow through the long vasa recta satisfies the criteria to maintain medullary hyperosmolality.
5. There ***are factors which limit the extent of medullary hypertonicity.*** The epithelium of thick ascending limb has a maximum capacity of pumping as in all active transport systems. The vasa recta drains some solutes and parts with some water when it leaves medulla because the fluid, during movement, fails to attain exact osmotic equilibrium with the surrounding.
6. ***The medullary tonicity developed-like*** other biological parameters is subject to variation. Thus, during water deprivation, the glomerular filtrate load diminishes, favoring slow rate of fluid flow and increasing osmolality (by raised active absorption of electrolytes by Henle's loop). This is supplemented by ADH, which increases water reabsorption from cortical and upper medullary collecting duct and in this way increases the urea concentration at those segments of nephron impermeable to urea.

   Now the same ADH increases permeability to urea across the papillary or inner medullary collecting duct. So urea can move readily following increased gradient from tubular lumen to interstitium contributing more to osmolality than in normal hydrated state. Medullary tonicity increases further due to these reasons, so that water conservation is facilitated.

   Urea is an example of a substance transported passively by renal tubules. When the urine volume increases, more urea (more than 50% of filtrate load) is eliminated, but when urine gets concentrated, more of the filtrate load (80% or more) gets reabsorbed.

   On the contrary, when there is water diuresis in the absence of ADH there is low urea concentration in collecting duct and its permeability is also reduced, so its contribution to medullary osmolality is less. The medullary interstitium loses some of its tonicity.
7. ***Urea arrives at the tubular fluid*** via glomerular filtrate. So the filtrate load of urea depends upon its plasma concentration which depends upon amino

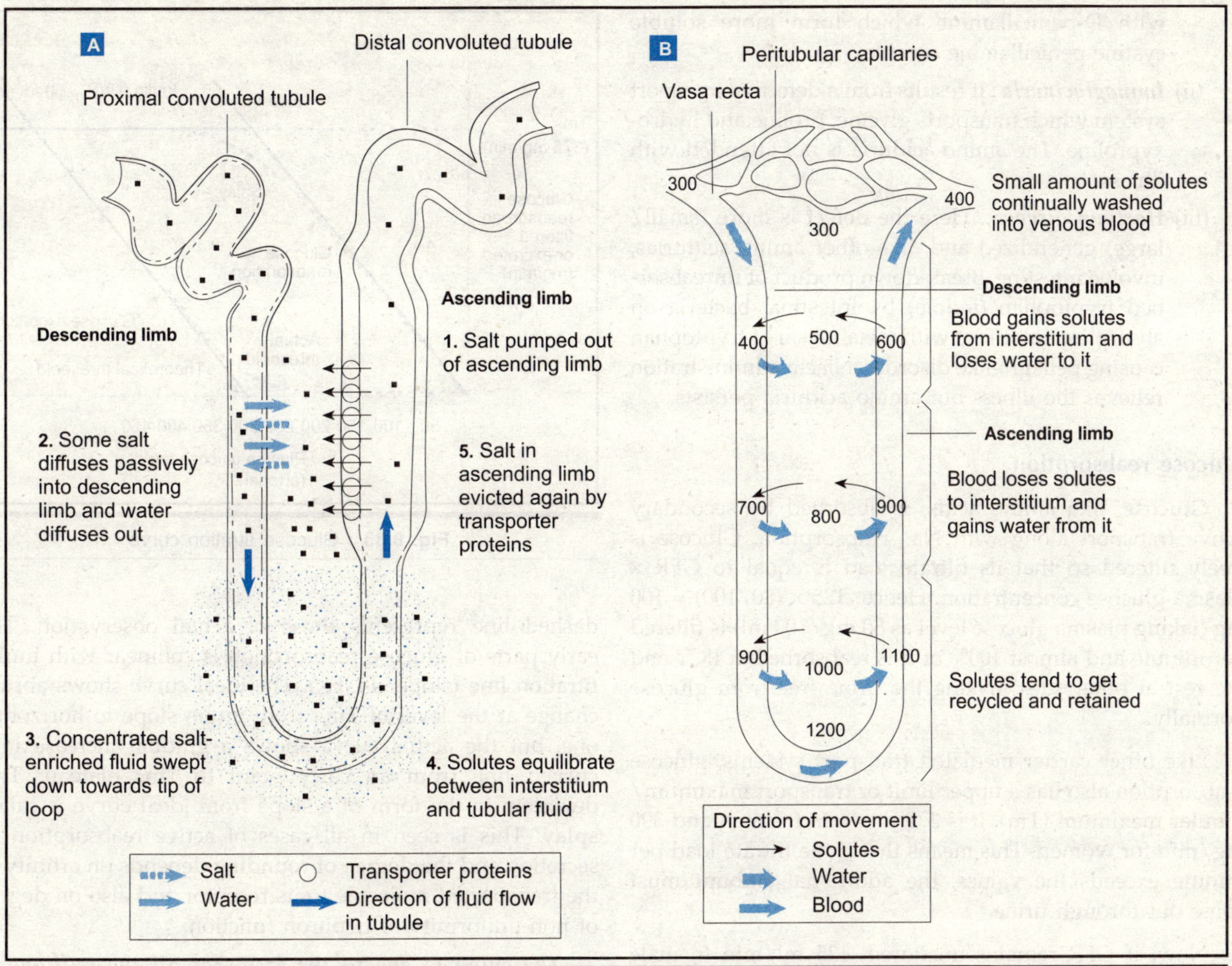


**Fig. 8.32 :** Medullary hypertonicity

acid catabolism secondary to protein intake. So high protein diet increases plasma urea and its accumulation in renal peritubular fluid makes the medullary fluid more hypertonic. Concentrating power of kidneys increases. Opposite phenomenon takes place with protein deficient diet.

## ➤ 8.14 Renal Tubular Transport : Reabsorption and Secretion of Organic Compounds

As glomerular filtrate flows along the nephron, the organic compounds in the filtrate are handled differently by the tubular epithelial cells mostly at proximal convoluted tubules. They undergo (a) ***complete reabsorption***; (b) ***incomplete reabsorption***; (c) ***non-reabsorption*** and (d) ***secretion with or without reabsorption***.

The transport system utilizes the processes similar to inorganic constituents eg, diffusion, facilitated diffusion, active transport, secondary active transport and endocytosis.

### Reabsorption

***Complete reabsorption :*** Amino acids, proteins, peptides, glucose, ascorbic acid are examples of compounds that undergo complete reabsorption.

Peptides (hormones) and proteins (mainly albumin) that appear in the filtrate are taken up by the epithelial cells (of PCT) by pinocytosis. They are digested intracellularly by lysosomal enzymes to amino acids to be carried away by blood from cells by diffusion. Amino acids in the filtrate are absorbed by secondary active transport along with primary reabsorption of $Na^+$ at PCT. There appears to be separate carrier proteins or systems for neutral amino acids, dicarboxylic acids, dibasic acids, imino acids and glycine. **Amino acidurias** are conditions when there is excretion of amino acids in the urine. They develop due to mutation in the transport system of amino acids in selective or generalised patterns. Examples are :

(i) ***Cystinuria*** : There is defect in the transport of dibasic amino acids (cystine, lysine and ornithine). Cystine crystals form stones in urine. They can be eliminated by alkalinizing the urine and treating with D-penicillamine which form more soluble cystine-penicillamine complex.

(ii) ***Iminoglycinuria*** : It results from a defective transport system which transports glycine, proline and hydroxyproline. The amino aciduria is not attended with illness.

(iii) ***Hartnup disease*** : Here the defect is more (small/large) generalized and, like other amino acidurias, involve intestine. Break-down product of unreabsorbed tryptophan (indole) by intestinal bacteria on absorption interferes with metabolism of tryptophan causing pellagra-like disorder. Niacin administration relieves the illness but amino aciduria persists.

## Glucose reabsorption

**Glucose**, like amino acids, is absorbed by secondary active transport along with $Na^+$ reabsorption. Glucose is freely filtered so that its filtrate load is equal to GFR × plasma glucose concentration. Hence 125 × (80/100) = 100 mg (taking plasma glucose level as 80 mg/100 ml) is filtered per minute and almost 100% of it is reabsorbed at PCT and the rest at other sites making the urine free from glucose normally.

Like other carrier mediated transport systems, glucose reabsorption also has a upper limit or transport maximum/tubular maximum (Tm). It is 375 mg/min for men and 300 mg/min for women. This means that if the filtrate load per minute exceeds the values, the additional amount must come out through urine.

Now, if GFR remains unaltered, 125 ml/min in male then from the $Tm_G$ value, it corresponds to plasma (renal arterial) glucose concentration of (375 mg/min)/(125 ml/min), i.e., 3 mg/ml or 300 mg/dl. It may appear that below the plasma glucose concentration of 300 mg/dl there should be no glucose in urine because the filtrate load is below $Tm_G$. But the observed value of plasma glucose below which the urine is free of glucose (renal threshold) is much lower than 300 mg/dl (theoretical renal threshold), it amounts to 200 mg/dl of renal arterial plasma, matching to 180 mg/dl of systemic venous plasma. ***To summarize the renal reabsorption of glucose, the following comments can be made*** :

- **up to renal threshold** complete reabsorption;
- **renal threshold to theoretical threshold** increasing reabsorption and excretion;
- **beyond theoretical threshold** reabsorption is fixed at $Tm_G$ and excretion of remainder of filtrate load.

The relation between plasma glucose and glucose that is reabsorbed, excreted and filtered can be displayed in a graphical way called **glucose titration curve**. ***The curve explains the renal handling of glucose in an ideal or theoretical condition and in actual state (Fig. 8.33).***

Uninterrupted lines of the glucose titration curve show glucose reabsorption and excretion in ideal situation and

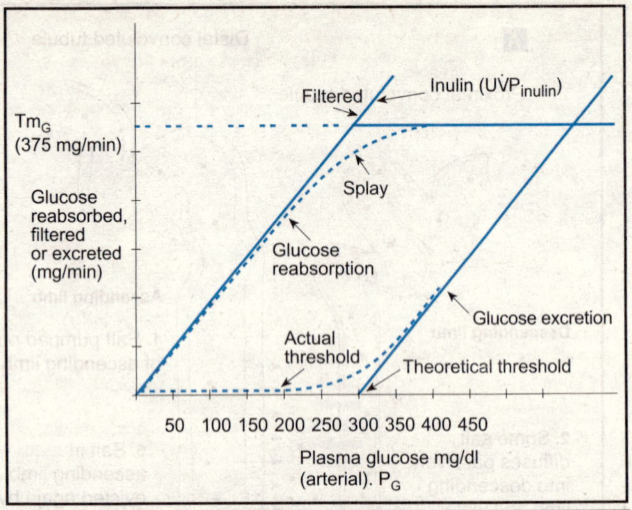


**Fig. 8.33 : Glucose titration curve**

dashed line represents those of actual observation. The early parts of glucose reabsorption is collinear with inulin titration line (slope is GFR). The ideal curve shows abrupt change at the level of $Tm_G$ from inulin slope to horizontal one, but the actual curve shows a gradual increase in a curved line from an early point to $Tm_G$ plateau. This deviation in the form of a slope from ideal curve is called **splay**. This is seen in all cases of active reabsorption or secretion and the degree of rounding depends on affinity of the transported molecule to its receptor and also on degree of non-uniformity of nephron function.

***The splay is due to the fact that all the millions of nephrons are not uniform in function.*** The $Tm_G$s of nephrons differ, in some filtration rate is above average, in some the transport mechansim may be below average. So it is possible that with increase in plasma glucose concentration the filtrate load in some nephrons is not completely reabsorbed. On the other hand, the filtrate load up to or beyond theoretical threshold is readily reabsorbed.

The excreted value is the sum of excretions from individual nephrons. The sum of non-uniform functions of renal tubules thus explain splay in active transport mechanism. Even if the nephrons had been homogenous in function, there would also have been rounding (splay) to some extent because, for glucose, carrier-binding is reversible, leaving some free glucose to be eliminated in the urine.

In the same figure (Fig. 8.35) the excretion curves of glucose shows the same splay pattern and, ultimately, it parallels the inulin titration curve. In case of any compound (x) that is handled by kidney, its reabsorption and/or secretion (transport) can be summarized by the formula

$$U_x \times \dot{V} = GFR \times P_x \pm T_x,$$

where $U_x$ is the urinary concentration of the compound (x), $\dot{V}$ = urine formed per unit time, $P_x$ is plasma concentration and $T_x$ is net amount of x transferred per unit time.

Now in case of inulin/mannitol there is no transport of the compound either by reabsorption or secretion. So they are examples of organic compounds which do not undergo absorption. So, with inulin, $U_{inulin} \times \dot{V} = GFR \times P_{inulin}$. So inulin clearance ($C_{in}$) = $(U_{inulin} \times \dot{V})/P_{inulin}$ = GFR, the slope of inulin titration curve.

In case of glucose up to actual renal threshold, $U_G \times \dot{V} = 0$. Hence $T_G = GFR \times P_G$, so [$T_G$ (reabsorbed glucose per unit time)]/$P_G$ = GFR, so its slope equals to that of inulin titration curve and filtration curve at any $P_G$. Thus, early part of actual titration curve of glucose corresponds to inulin titration curve. In the excretion curve (in case of ideal one), up to theoretical renal threshold the urinary excretion is zero as expected but, after that, if we consider two values of plasma glucose as $P_a$ and $P_b$ mg/dl (a > b), then, for two cases

$$U_a.\ \dot{V} = GFR \times P_a + Tm_G$$

$$\text{and } U_b.\ \dot{V} = GFR \times P_b + Tm_G,$$

$$\text{so } U_a.\ \dot{V} - U_b.\ \dot{V} = GFR\ (P_a - P_b).$$

So the trace will be a straight line with slope $(U_{a.}\dot{V} - U_{b.}\dot{V})/P_a - P_b$ = GFR, i.e., parallel to inulin titration curve.

Glucose is not the only substance reabsorbed having a transport maximum (Tm). **Tm-limited reabsorption** is also seen in other compounds transported only actively, eg, creatinine, sulfate, amino acids, acetoacetic acid, lactic acid, ascorbic acid, phosphate, hemoglobin, etc. $Na^+$, $Cl^-$ though transported mainly actively, also enjoys passive transport partly. So they have no transport maximum, because the part of their passive absorption depends upon luminal concen-tration, i.e., rate of urine formation and the time available for equilibration of the physical process of diffusion. Their absorption is thus concentration gradient-time dependent. Regarding organic compounds, urea is the most important compound that is excreted; its reabsorption is purely passive either by simple or (in some sites) facilitated diffusion.

It also displays concentration gradient-time mediated reabsorption. The amount of urea that is reabsorbed in parts of nephron beyond PCT depends upon its concentration gradient in respect of peritubular fluid. So if urine flow rate is increased by water diuresis it is seen that its clearance increases with urine flow rate, and above 2 ml/min it approaches 2/3rd of inulin (Fig. 8.34). Inulin clearance is plotted in the same figure to show its non-dependence on urine flow rate and its equality to GFR.

## Tubular secretion of organic compounds

**Proximal convoluted tubule** is primarily the site for ***secretion of organic compounds present in peritubular capillaries.*** They at first undergo filtration at glomerulus and then undergo secretion by the proximal convoluted tubules. Now the secretion is unidirectional in case of active secretion of organic compounds in ionic (acids and bases)

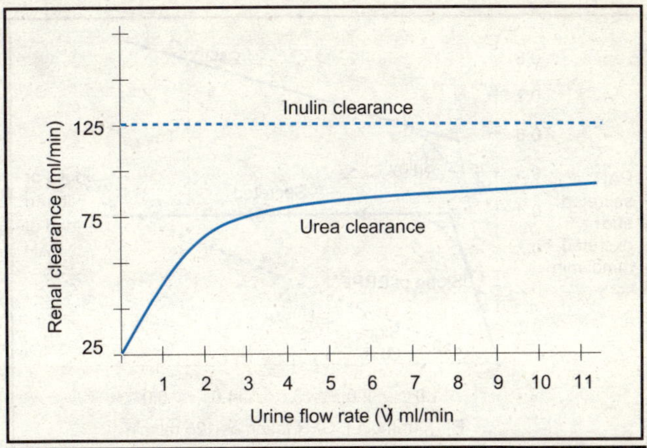


**Fig. 8.34 :** Relation between urea clearance and urine flow rate

forms. But in cases of non-ionic compounds or weak organic acids and bases the secretion is bidirectional and mostly passive depending upon chemical gradient across epithelium and reaction of luminal fluid. ***The following is a short list of organic acids and bases secreted by proximal convoluted tubules, secretion is mostly active and unidirectional but some enjoy bidirectional transport.***

| | |
|---|---|
| *Organic acids* | *Endogenous* : Bile acids, 5-hydroxy indole acetic acid, oxalic acid, uric acid.<br>*Exogenous* : Chlorthiazide, ethacrynic acid, frusemide, PAH, penicillin, salicylate. |
| *Organic bases* | *Endogenous* : Creatinine, dopamine, epinephrine, norepinephrine, serotonin, thiamin.<br>*Exogenous* : Atropine, cimetidine, morphine, neostigmine, quinine, trimethoprim. |

## Renal handling of PAH

Paraaminohippuric acid is a compound, whose handling by the kidney will help to understand the behaviour of actively secreted substances. PAH is freely filtered by the glomeruli. Then, then from the peritubular capillaries, it is actively secreted as an anion by the epithelium of PCT. The epithelial cells concentrate PAH diffusing out of peritubular capillaries actively and from the epithelial cells, PAH diffuses into the lumen by facilitated diffusion. When the PAH concentration in plasma is very low, all the PAH present in peritubular capillaries can be secreted actively to tubular lumen, so that, by a single trip, the blood perfusing nephrons become free of PAH. In that case, the urinary PAH per unit time becomes equal to PAH in renal perfusion for unit time,

i.e., $U_{PAH} \times \dot{V}$ = ERPF (effective renal plasma flow) $\times P_{PAH}$.

So the clearance of PAH, $(U_{PAH} \times \dot{V})/P_{PAH}$ is equal to ERPF. But when the plasma level goes on increasing the amount transported reaches a maximum limit to saturate the active transport system. In symbols, $U_{PAH} \times \dot{V} = GFR \times P_{PAH} + T_{PAH}$, where $T_{PAH}$ is PAH secreted actively by

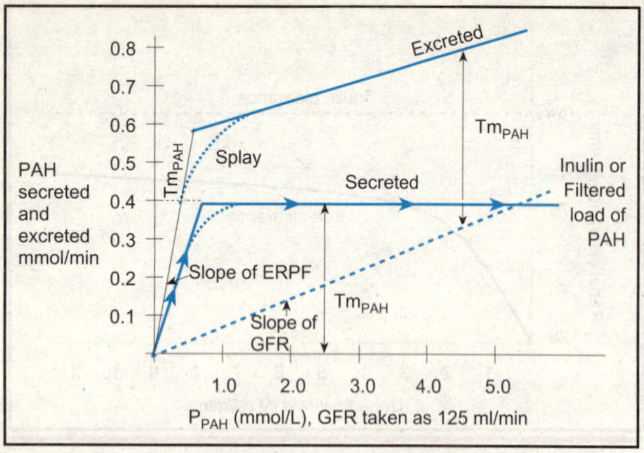


**Fig. 8.35 :** PAH titration curve

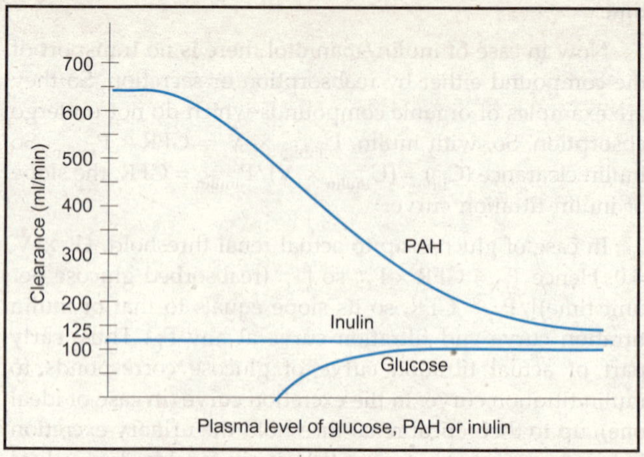


**Fig. 8.36 :** Plasma level of glucose, PAH or inulin

PCT, now up to the point of saturation of transport system

$$U_{PAH} \times \dot{V} = GFR \times P_{PAH} + T_{PAH} = ERPF \times P_{PAH}, \quad ...(1)$$

because the venous effluent becomes PAH free. But, beyond the saturation on transport maximum at any plasma level

$$U_{PAH} \times \dot{V} = GFR \times P_{PAH} + Tm_{PAH}. \quad ...(2)$$

Now if PAH titration curve (Fig. 8.35) is drawn in pursuance of glucose titration curve proximal to $P_{PAH}$ value corresponding to $Tm_{PAH}$, the trace will have a slope of ERPF (Eq. 1). But after that the slope will be equal to that of filtered load on GFR, as evident from Eq. 2, and explained already in glucose titration curve (Fig. 8.33).

From fig. 8.36 it is evident that splay pattern of actual curve in comparison to ideal curve is evident by rounding at excreted and secreted traces at the site of turning. ***When the $P_{PAH}$ is very low, the slope of excreted trace is ERPF, but the slope of the filtered load is always GFR, i.e., the line of inulin titration curve traced simultaneously.*** $Tm_{PAH}$ is nearly 0.4 mmol/min, which corresponds to a plasma concentration of PAH near 1 mmol/L. Now, if plasma PAH level is 4 mmol/L the amount of PAH excreted per minute

$= GFR \times P_{PAH} + Tm\ P_{PAH}$

$= 125$ ml/min $\times$ 0.004 mmol/ml + 0.4 mmol/min

$= 0.5$ mmol/min + 0.4 mmol/min

$= 0.9$ mmol/min.

Comparison between clearances of inulin, PAH and glucose can be considered if their clearance values are plotted against different plasma levels. The curves demonstrate the dynamics of their transports by both systems (Fig. 8.36).

Inulin is not handled by epithelial cells, so its clearance is GFR and independent of plasma value, because $U_{inulin} \times \dot{V} = GFR \times P_{inulin} \pm 0$, i.e., no transport at all. But in case of glucose after renal threshold (actual), glycosuria increases in magnitude and clearance from zero level approaches the inulin clearance but never reaches it. Symbolically, at plasma level above theoretical threshold, $U_G \times \dot{V} = GFR \times P_G - Tm_G$. Now, clearance of glucose $C_G = (U_G \times \dot{V})/P_G = GFR - Tm_G/P_G$, so with progressively higher level of $P_G$, $Tm_G/P_G$ will decrease and $C_G$ will approach but never reach GFR, i.e., inulin clearance. In case of PAH, when $P_{PAH}$ corresponding to Tm PAH is exceeded the excreted amount in symbols is $U_{PAH} \times \dot{V} = GFR \times P_{PAH}$ + Tm PAH. So clearance at that state, $C_{PAH} = (U_{PAH} \times \dot{V})/P_{PAH} = GFR + Tm\ PAH/P_{PAH}$.

Now, with further increase in $P_{PAH}$, $Tm_{PAH}/P_{PAH}$ will go on declining, bringing the $C_{PAH}$ value lower to approach GFR, but will never reach it as $Tm_{PAH}/P_{PAH}$ can never be zero. From these discussions, it is apparent that in case of compounds where there is net reabsorption their clearances are always less than inulin. On the other hand, for those with net secretion, clearances are more than that of inulin.

It deserves mention in the transport of organic acids and bases by active transport that in both groups of substances there are competitions as if a common system is involved. Probenecid, which interferes with acid secreting mechanism, hinders the secretion of penicillin and keeps its level higher for prolonged period for proper antimicrobial effect. But it is not clear whether a single cell can secrete both organic acids and bases or there are separate cells for their secretion.

## Transport of compounds with bidirectional transport

As mentioned earlier, bidirectional transport takes place in case of weak organic acids and bases and also in non-ionic constituents. *The transport occurs mainly by the process of diffusion*, but in some cases, associated active transport may take place. Organic acids and bases which are in dissociated forms at pH of body fluid are actively secreted by PCT epithelium. But weak organic acids and bases remain mostly undissociated at that pH. As they (undissociated forms) are lipid soluble, they diffuse into the

**Table 8.2**

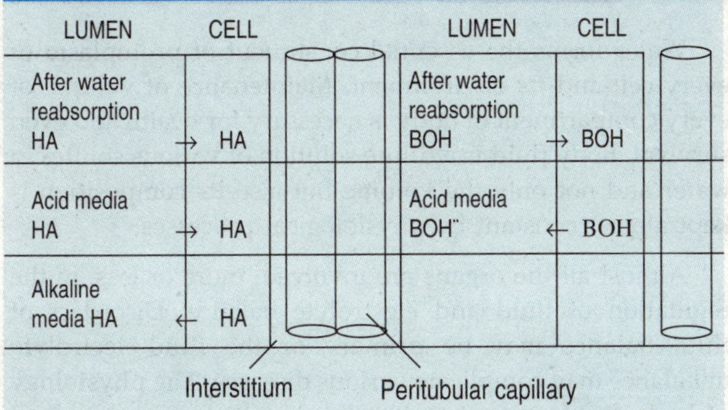


HA and BOH are undissociated forms of acids and bases, respectively

epithelial cells from peritubular fluid and into the lumen along concentration gradient. ***Their bidirectional transport is an example of non-ionic diffusion.*** The transport of weak organic acid and base are discussed separately.

### Weak organic acid

When an endogenous or exogenous (drug) weak organic acid is carried by blood to kidney, it is filtered at glomerulus and the undissociated form enters the epithelial cells from peritubular capillaries by the process of diffusion. The filtered acid undergoes concentration due to absorption of water. Now, if the concentration of its undissociated form increases to value more than the epithelial cell peritubular fluid, then it undergoes reabsorption by diffusion following the concentration gradient. But if its luminal concentration remains below that of cell-ISF then secretion occurs. Thus bidirectional transport is possible. Now, from the symbolic dissociation of a weak acid $HA \rightleftharpoons H^+ + A^-$, the reaction will go from right to left in an acid media depending upon pK of the acid concerned. Thus, if the luminal fluid is made acidic, the undissociated form of the acid predominates and there occurs reabsorption by diffusion. But the alkaline media will favour dissociation, lower the undissociated form and transport in the reverse direction (secretion).

In case of weak organic base, the filtered and concentrated base will tend to get reabsorbed if the luminal fluid is alkaline, discouraging dissociation (acidic media favour dissociation and subsequent secretion of non-ionic forms). So, to flush out, toxins or drugs that are weak organic acids, urine is to be alkalinized, but, to get rid of weak bases, urine needs acidification (Table 8.2).

### Tubular transport of uric acid

Uric acid is the metabolic end product of purine bases (adenine and guanine). Serum concentration of uric acid ranges from 0.18 to 0.42 m.mol/litre which corresponds to 3-7 mg/dl (mmol/L value can be obtained by multiplying mg/dl concentration by 0.06 approximately). *The filtrate load per day is 180 L (GFR) × 0.30 mmol/litre, i.e., approximately 50 mmol/day.* But the amount excreted ($U_{uric} \times \dot{V}$) per day is 5 mmol/day, i.e., 10% of the filtrate load or fractional excre-tion is 10%. Now if the fractional excretion of uric acid falls to 5%, the serum concentration rises so that daily elimination remains same but high serum concentration may cause gouty attacks.

$$FE_{uric} \text{ (Fractional excretion)} = \frac{U_{urea} \times \dot{V}}{GFR \times P_{urea}}$$

So, if $FE_{uric}$ is halved keeping $U_{uric} \times \dot{V}$ unaltered and GFR remaining constant then $P_{uric}$ must get doubled. So with 10% $FE_{uric}$ with urinary output of 5.4 mmol/day, the plasma level is 0.30 mmol/litre, where GFR is 180 L/day. With 5% $FE_{uric}$ with same urinary output, $P_{uric}$ shoots up to 0.60 mmol/litre which may cause illness. The example cited above explains the plasma level and other aspects of any excreted solute that has no other route to be eliminated. Uric acid displays bidirectional transport. Of 50 mmol/day filtered daily about 49 mmol/day gets reabsorbed. The remaining 1 mmol plus secreted 4 mmol/day totalling 5 mmol, is excreted per day. Both the reabsorption and secretion are active processes. Probenecid can inhibit reabsorption of uric acid, while pyra-zinoic acid inhibits its secretion.

When the plasma uric acid level exceeds 7 mg/dl in men and 6 mg/dl in women, the condition is called **hyperuricemia**. Hyperuricaemia is responsible for deposition of urate in different tissues of the body including joints and may precipitate inflammatory gouty arthritis. Uric acid crystals may precipitate in acid urine to form **urate stones**. **Gout (hyperuricemia)** may be of primary and secondary variety. **Primary gout** (common in middle aged males) is due, in most cases, to poorly defined ***disorders causing either increased uric acid production, decreased excretion or by a combination of them.***

Only in a minority, definite enzyme disorders have been explored. They are (a) increased activity of 5-phosphoribosyl-1-pyrophosphate synthetase (PRPP synthetase), (b) partial deficiency of hypoxanthine guanine phosphoribosyl transferase (HGPRT), affecting purine salvage pathway and increasing PRPP and purine synthesis and, ultimately, urate formation (Lesch-Nyhan syndrome), (c) Glycogen storage, Von Gierke's disease causing deficiency of glucose-6-phosphatase → ↑glucose-6-phosphate → ↑HMP shunt pathway → ↑ribose-1-phosphate → ↑PRPP → ↑purine synthesis and ultimately uric acid formation. (d) Increased activity of glutathione reductase → ↑$NADP^+$ → ↑HMP shunt pathway → rest as in (c).

Secondary gout is a manifestation of other disorders involving purine metabolism. Examples are malignant disorders, leukemia, other myeloproliferative disorders, specially when they are treated by chemotherapeutic drugs, because rapid cell destruction increases purine metabolism to increase uric acid formation and its plasma concentration to precipitate gouty attacks. Hyperuricemia may develop also in chronic renal failure and hyperthyroidism.

### Renal metabolism and oxygen consumption

The kidneys are highly active and essential organs for survival. Their principal function is filtration of plasma, removal of harmful or redundant substances and reuptake of useful constituents. The process of filtration is essentially a passive process, the force being generated by heart, but the reabsorptive process is mostly energy-dependent primary and secondary active transports.

**Minute filtrate volume** is 125 ml and the perfusion is about 1250 ml/min. For this reason, whatever the magnitude of extraction, the arterio-venous oxygen difference is low, in comparison to other active tissues like heart and brain. Of the minute oxygen consumption of 250 ml, the approximate contribution by kidney, heart and brain are 20, 30 and 50 ml, respectively, while their perfusion per minute is 1,250 ml, 250 ml, and 750 ml, respectively. So the A-V difference becomes $(20/1,250) \times 1,000$, i.e., 16 ml/litre; $(30/250) \times 1,000 = 120$ ml/litre and $(50/750) \times 1,000 = 200/3 = 67$ ml/litre respectively.

Of the oxygen consumption, the cortex is the site for major consumption as the active reabsorption and secretion take place mostly by PCT and DCT at cortex. The cortex is also highly vascular (receives 90% of renal blood flow). As $Na^+$ is the principal cation of the filtrate, its absorption claims major part of oxygen consumption as expected.

In most organs, change in blood flow is normally secondary to changed metabolic activity, but if the metabolic functions remain unaltered, changed blood flow will change arterio-venous oxygen difference in the expected direction. But, in the kidney, primary change in renal blood flow is not attended by changes in arterio-venous difference. This is due to the fact that increased blood flow will increase filtration, reabsorption and secretion. This will increase metabolic activities of the kidney and additional consumption of oxygen, making the A-V difference of $O_2$ unchanged. The kidney utilises all sorts of fuel, free fatty acids, glucose, glycerol, ketone bodies, glutamine and amino acids. This is required for continuous supply of energy and ATP generation by oxidative phos-phorylation in mitochondria at cortex, but in medulla which has reduced blood flow, glycolysis is a major path for ATP generation. In the cortex, FFA is the most important fuel.

Glucose is available to kidney tissues both from blood and also from production de novo by neoglucogenesis. Though in terms of per unit tissue mass, kidney is more efficient than liver in neoglucogenesis, yet the glucose produced by kidney is meant only for local use and not for distribution elsewhere as in hepatic gluconeogenesis. The gluconeogenesis operates actively during hypoglycemic state and acidosis. Epinephrine and glucagon have stimulating effect on neoglucogenesis. Kidneys, unlike liver, can both produce and utilize ketone bodies.

## ➤ 8.15 Physiology of Body Fluids

Water forms the essential constituent of protoplasm of every cell and its environment. Maintenance of volume of every compartment of body is necessary for health and even survival. Body fluid is a dilute solution of various solutes in water and not only the volume but also its composition is kept almost constant by physiological processes.

Almost all the organs are involved, more or less, in the regulation of fluid and electrolyte balance. Disorders of fluid balance may be primary or the fluid-electrolyte imbalance may complicate various diseases. **The physiology of body fluids** is intricately related to that of its dissolved substances, principally electrolytes, comparable to an object and its shadow. Water forms about 60% of body weight on average. The percentage depends upon fat content. Fat is water-poor substance. This is the main reason for differences in the content of water at different ages and between sexes.

**The composition of an adult individual on average (in % of body weight).** Water–60%, Proteins–17%, Minerals–7%, Carbohydrate–1% and Fat–15%. **Water** is thought to be distributed in ***different compartments***. (a) **Intracellular fluid,** (b) **Extracellular fluid,** which can be subdivided to (a) **interstitial fluid,** (b) **plasma,** (c) **dense connective tissue** like carti-lage etc. (d) **bones** (e) **transcellular fluid.**

**Interstitial fluid** is the fluid in between cells except dense connective tissue and bones. **Transcellular fluid** is that portion of extracellular fluid which is kept separated by epithelial layer eg, gut, biliary tract, urinary tract, CSF, pleural fluid, perito-neal fluid etc.

But, clinically, when ECF volume is measured, the markers do not readily enter into bones, dense connective tissues and transcellular fluids. So the ECF volume measured exclude them, but includes plasma and interstitial fluid only. So clinically simplified distribution is used. **Total body water (TBW)** can be divided into two compartments **ICF** 40% of body weight and **ECF** 20% of body weight, of which interstitial fluid comprises 15% and plasma 5% of body weight. Blood contains both the compartments, its volume is approximately 8% of body weight.

### Measurement of body fluid compartments

The basis of measurement of a body fluid compartment is to inject a compound into it and to determine the volume of distribution of the marker after equilibration. The marker must not affect the fluid volume distribution, it must be non-toxic and preferably non-degradable or, if split, its change in concentration should be measured. It should be sampled easily and measured readily :

$$\text{Volume of the compartment} = \frac{\text{Material injected removed by urine}}{\text{Concentration of the substance after equilibrium}}$$

### Extracellular fluid volume

The measurement requires a marker that remains extracellular but moves freely out of vascular system. No ideal compound is available that distributes rapidly and evenly to all ECF components. Most of the marker penetrate poorly to bones, dense connective tissues, and transcellular spaces. But there remains variation among the substances regarding their capacity to penetrate, some even may enter partially to ICF. The markers are radioactive ions like $Na^+$, $Cl^-$, $Br^-$, $SO_4^=$, $S_2O_3^=$ containing salts, and nonmetabolizable sugars like inulin, mannitol, raffinose, sucrose. Saccharides remain exclusively in the ECF compartment, but their spread is slower than sodium salts, but $Na^+$ may enter to some extent in ICF. So the volume of distribution is unique to each substance and ECF value obtained by them vary in an individual. For this reason they are called **sucrose space, inulin space, bromine space** etc. Most accurate is that measured with inulin tagged with radioactive 14c. ECF volume is 1/3rd of TBW or 20% of body weight. Thus, a 60 kg individual has an ECF volume of 12 L (approximately).

The principal mechanisms responsible for restoring the effective circulating volume (ECV) following loss of isotonic fluid (Fig. 8.37).

The principal mechanisms responsible for restoring the ECV after its expansion by the intake of salt and water (Fig. 8.38).

### Total body water

Here the marker chosen enters freely across all boundaries including cell membranes. Isotopes of water, deuterium oxide ($D_2O$) or **tritium oxide** (HTO) are ideal candidates. In their absence antipyrine can be used but it is less pervasive than $D_2O$ or HTO. ***Total body water** comprises approximately 60% of body weight. So total body water (TBW) of a 60 kg individual is 36 L approximately. In both ECF and TBW measurements, plasma can be drawn as representative sample.*

### ICF volume

ICF volume cannot be measured directly as it is impossible to have a substance that remains confined to ICF after administration. ICF volume is calculated by subtracting ECF volume from that of TBW, i.e., ICF = TBW – ECF. In a 60 kg individual, ICF volume is 36 L – 12 L = 24 L approximately.

### Interstitial fluid volume (ISF volume)

ISF and plasma are in direct communication. So ISF volume is determined indirectly by subtracting plasma volume from ECF volume, i.e., ISF = ECF – plasma volume. In a 60 kg individual ISF volume = 12L – 3L = 9L approximately.

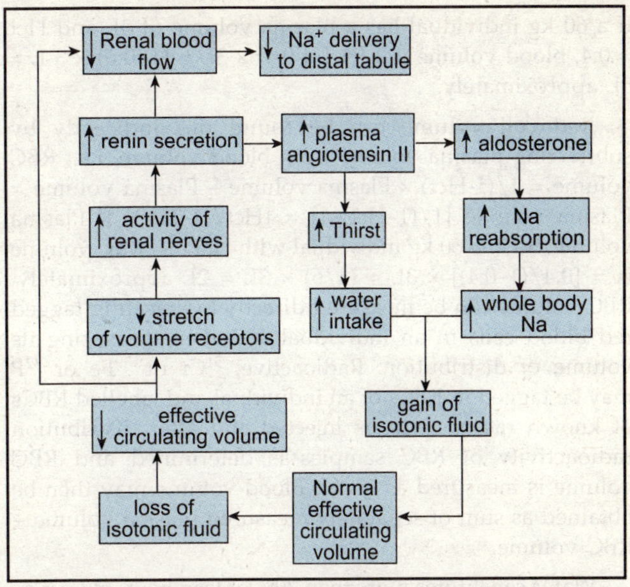


**Fig. 8.37 :** The principal mechanisms responsible for restoring the effective circulating volume (ECV) following loss of isotonic fluid.

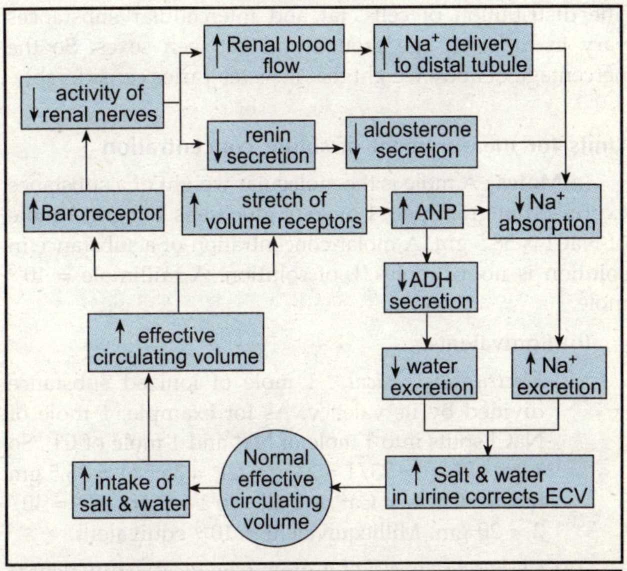


**Fig. 8.38 :** The principal mechanisms responsible for restoring the ECV after its expansion by the intake of salt and water.

### Plasma volume, red cell volume and blood volume

Plasma volume can be measured by tagging plasma proteins with dyes like Evans blue (T-1824) or radioactive iodine. As plasma proteins remain mostly intravascular the volume of distribution of above markers gives the plasma volume. Plasma volume is approximately 5% of the body weight of an individual. So an individual of 60 kg body weight has a plasma volume of 3L. If hematocrit (in decimal fraction) of an individual is known, then blood volume of that individual is 1/(1–Hct) × plasma volume.

If a 60 kg individual has a plasma volume of 3L and Hct = 0.4, blood volume is 1/(1 [–] 0.4) × 3L = (1/0.6) × 3 L = 5L approximately.

Red cell volume can be found out indirectly by subtracting plasma volume from blood volume, i.e., RBC volume = 1/(1-Hct) × Plasma volume – Plasma volume = Plasma volume [1/(1–Hct)–1] = [Hct/(1–Hct)] × Plasma volume. So in a 60 kg individual with Hct 0.4, RBC volume is = [0.4/(1–0.4)] × 3L = (4/6) × 3L = 2L approximately. RBC volume can be measured directly by injecting tagged red blood cells in an individual and then measuring its volume of distribution. Radioactive, $^{51}Cr$ or $^{59}Fe$ or $^{32}P$ may be tagged to RBCs of an individual and labelled RBCs of known radioactivity is injected and after distribution radioactivity of RBC samples is determined and RBC volume is measured as usual. Blood volume may then be obtained as sum of separately measured plasma volume + RBC volume.

Water constitutes more than 70% of lean body mass, i.e., (body weight – fat). Fat is poor in water so increase in adipose tissue reduces the percentage of water accordingly. Living cells contain between 70-85% of its mass as water. The distribution of cells, fat and intercellular substances vary in different age groups and between sexes. So the percentage of body weight that is water varies considerably.

## Units for measurement of solute concentration

(a) **Moles** : A mole is the molecular weight of a substance expressed in grams, eg, 1 mole of glucose is 180 gm, 1 mole of NaCl is 58.5 gm. A molar concentration of a substance in solution is no. of moles/L of solution. A millimole = $10^{-3}$ mole.

(b) **Equivalents** :

(i) *Electrical equivalent* : 1 mole of ionized substance divided by its valency. As for example, 1 mole of NaCl splits into 1 mole of $Na^+$ and 1 mole of $Cl^-$. So 1 eq. of $Na^+$ = 23/1 = 23 gm, $Cl^-$ = 35.5/1 = 35.5 gm but for $CaCl_2 = Ca^{2+} + 2\,Cl^-$, so 1 eq. of $Ca^{++}$ = 40/2 = 20 gm. Milliequivalent = $10^{-3}$ equivalent.

(ii) *Chemical equivalent* : A gram (chemical) equivalent is weight of a substance in grams that is equivalent to 8.00 gm of oxygen. It is not necessarily equal to electrical equivalent. A non-electrolyte has chemical equivalent but no electrical equivalent.

In case of compounds formed of elements of fixed equivalent weight, the equivalent weight of the compound is sum of its components. As for example CaO, calcium has gram equivalent of 20 gm and that of oxygen is 8. So the equivalent weight of CaO is 28 gm, whereas its mole is 40 + 16 = 56 gm. In case of $Na_2SO_4$, equivalent weight of Na is 23 and that of $SO_4$ is 48. So its equivalent weight = 23 + 48 = 71, but its mole = 2 × 23 + 96 = 46 + 96 = 142. In case of compounds with elements of variable valence, the equivalent weight of an element will vary, eg, $FeCl_3$ and $FeCl_2$ has equivalent weights of Fe = 55.85/3 = 18.62 and 55.85/2 = 27.93, respectively. So their equivalent weights are (18.62 + 35.5) and (27.93 + 35.5), respectively. A normal solution of an acid or alkali contains its gram equivalent per litre, eg, in HCl it is 1 + 35.5 gm/L or 36.5 gm/L or in $H_2SO_4$ it is 1 + 48 or 49 gm/L. Osmolality of body fluids is dependent mainly on major electrolytes in different compartments. In ECF, it is dependent on $Na^+$ and its associated anions and in ICF it is due to $K^+$ and its accompanying anions. The role of other solutes are small.

In case of distribution of $Na^+$ in TBW it is important that all the $Na^+$ (total 58 meq/kg) is not exchangeable, only 70% is exchangeable ($Na_E$). In case of $K^+$, 90% of 45 meq/kg of body weight is exchangeable ($K_E$). The non-exchangeable forms of $Na^+$ and $K^+$ remain in bound form in bones and other tissues. The exchangeable fractions are measured by volume of distribution of radioactive sodium ($^{24}Na$) and potassium ($^{42}K$) within total pool.

***Total body osmolality is due to distribution of ($Na_E$ + its univalent anions) + ($K_E$ + its univalent anions) in the midst of TBW***. So total body osmolality = $(2\,Na_E + 2\,K_E)$/TBW taking the case of an individual of 60 kg, TBW = 36 kg,

$$Na_E + K_E = \frac{70}{100} \times 58 \times 60 + \frac{90}{100} \times 45$$

$$= 2{,}436 + 2{,}430 = 4{,}866 \text{ meq.}$$

So total body osmolality

$$= \frac{4{,}866 \times 2}{36} \text{ meq/kg or 270 mmol/kg or 270 mosmol/kg}$$

as $Na^+$ and $K^+$ are univalent ions.

From the knowledge of osmolality and dimensions of body fluid compartments, changes of volume and osmolality of fluid compartments due to gain or loss of fluids and electrolytes can be estimated. ***Example*** : In a 60 kg individual there was diarrheal loss of 1,200 mosmoles of electrolytes (original osmolality of body fluids 300 mosmol/L). Let us see how it affects different compartments. Before loss, total osmotically active particles amount to = $TBW \times 300$ mosmols = $36 \times 300$ mosmoles. After loss it declines to = $36 \times 300 - 1200 = 32 \times 300$ mosmoles. Assuming no loss of fluid volume occurs the new osmolality = (32 × 300)/36 mosmoles/L. As loss occurs from ECF volume exclusively, then osmotically active particles in ECF after diarrhea is = 12 × 300 – 1200 = 8 × 300 mosmoles. So ECF volume will now be = $(8 \times 300)/[(32 \times 300)/36] = (8 \times 300 \times 36)/(32 \times 300) = 9$ L. ICF volume will be 36 – 9 = 27 L. There occurs substantial reduction of ECF volume, leading to fall in vascular volume and in cardiac output and blood pressure. On the other hand, ICF volume increases, body fluids get hypotonic.

## Regulation of volume and osmolality of body fluids

The volume and osmolality of body fluids of an individual remain more or less constant. It is possible due to equal amount of intake of water and electrolytes as are lost from the body (**the concept of balance**). In growing infants and children and in pregnant women and in individuals regaining body weight after disease, there occurs a positive balance of fluid and solutes. But it is a slow process. For short time consideration, the concept of balance is applicable in all cases. Loss or gain of water and solutes occurs from ECF but as all fluid compartments are in communication, ICF will be influenced correspondingly. So regulation of volume and osmolality is the same as the processes by which the balance of water and its major osmotically active particle $Na^+$ are maintained.

### Water balance

***The gain of water in the body takes place from three sources***: (a) **drinks** 1-2 L; (b) **water content of food** 1 L; (c) **water generated during oxidation of** foodstuff, eg, 1 mole of glucose ($C_6H_{12}O_6$) when oxidised gives rise to 6 mole of water, i.e., 180 gm of glucose gives 108 gm of water.

***Loss of water takes place by four ways*** (a) ***urine volume*** per day 1-2 L; (b) ***insensible losses***, i.e., loss due to transpiration or diffusion of water molecules through epithelium of skin and lungs, normally equal in both sites, but depend on environmental temperature, humidity and rate of ventilation – 1 L/day. (c) ***Sweating***, the active secretion by sweat gland, varies from negligible amount in extreme cold to even 10 L/day during hot, humid environment and physical exercise – 200 ml/L on average. (d) ***Fecal loss*** – 100-200 ml/day, but in diarrheal diseases, it may exceed 5 L/day. Physiologically, urine volume is the important variable route of water loss. Water loss in insensible perspiration, sweating, feces along with urinary loss required to eliminate wastes altogether forms the volume of obligatory loss which is 0.5-0.6 L/day.

### Control of water balance (Fig. 8.39)

Balance of water between input and output is done by regulating the volume ingested as drinks and by controlling the urine output. The volume ingested is determined by thirst and urinary output via ADH from posterior pituitary. In both these regulating mechanisms, plasma osmolality and plasma volume are the prime mediators.

### Role of osmolality

***The normal plasma osmolality is approximately 280 mosmol/L,*** whenever there is increase in osmolality due to loss of water (eg, sweating in summer) the osmoreceptors of anterior hypothalamus stimulate thirst. Appropriate amount of water is taken so that the osmolality reaches the normal value. The sensitivity of thirst mechanism to change in osmolality is high, only 1% change is sufficient to arouse the sensation.

### Role of plasma volume

Whenever there is fall in blood volume, there originates a signal from volume receptors (low pressure baroreceptors in atria, pulmonary vessels and high pressure baroreceptors in aorta, carotid sinus) to increase ADH secretion. The threshold of change of ADH secretion by change in volume (≥ 10%) is much higher than a change in osmolality, but the response is strange. In fact, even in the face of hypoosmolality, reduction of plasma volume increases rather than decreases ADH secretion, an appropriate response for survival (volume overrides tonicity). Diminished volume also increases angiotensin II formation. Angiotensin II stimulates thirst and increases $Na^+$ reabsorption by kidneys via increased aldosterone secretion and, at the same time, prevents loss of water by increased ADH secretion (Fig. 8.40).

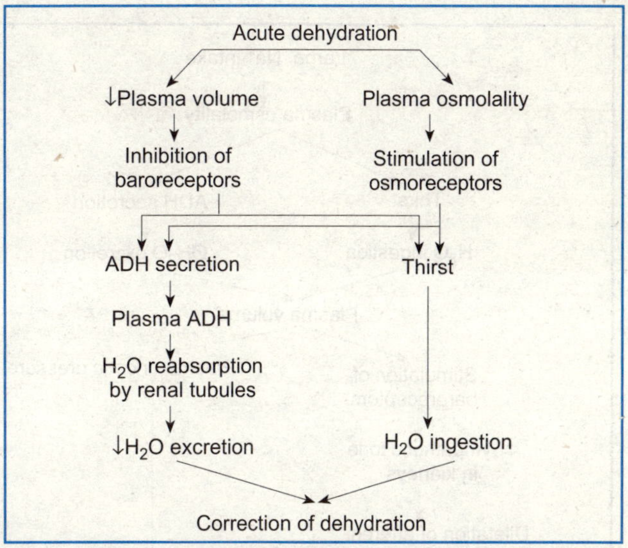


**Fig. 8.39 :** Control of water balance

### Sodium balance

Sodium and its accompanying anions form the major osmotically active particles in ECF and regulation of ECF

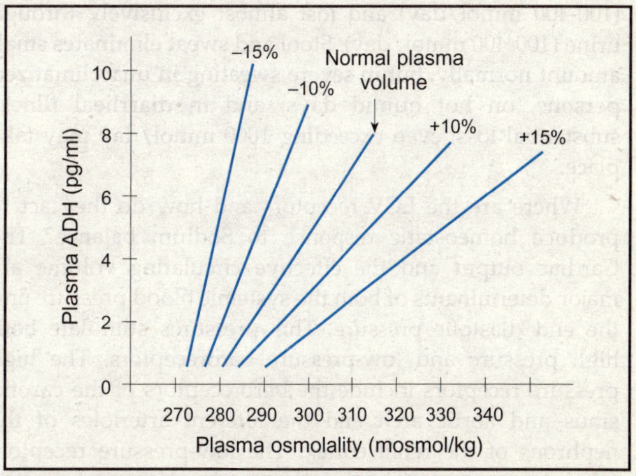


**Fig. 8.40 :** Relationship of plasma osmolality and ADH at different plasma volumes

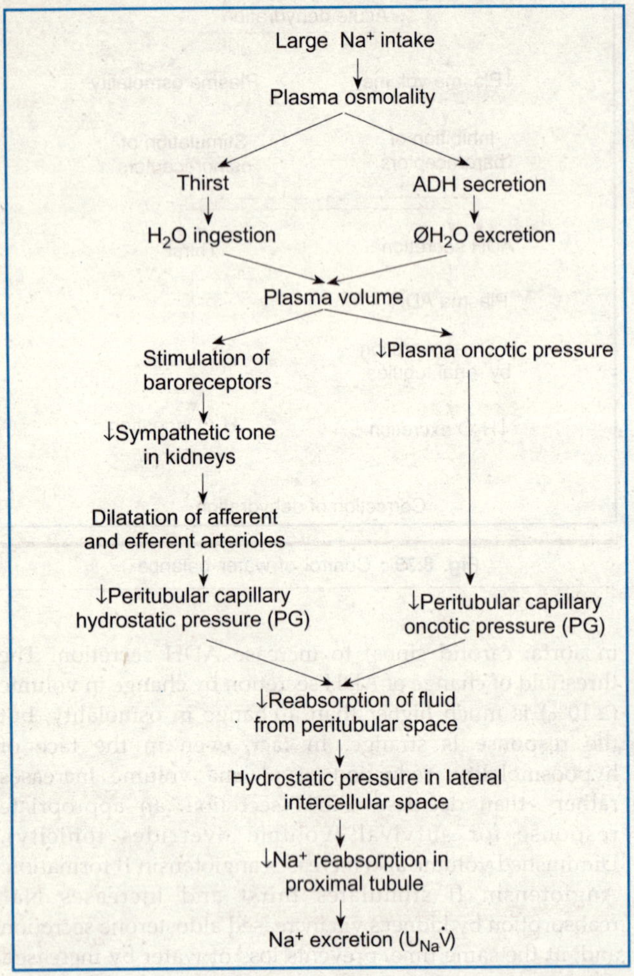


**Fig. 8.41 :** Role of physical forces as component of third factor effect in maintaining $Na^+$ balance

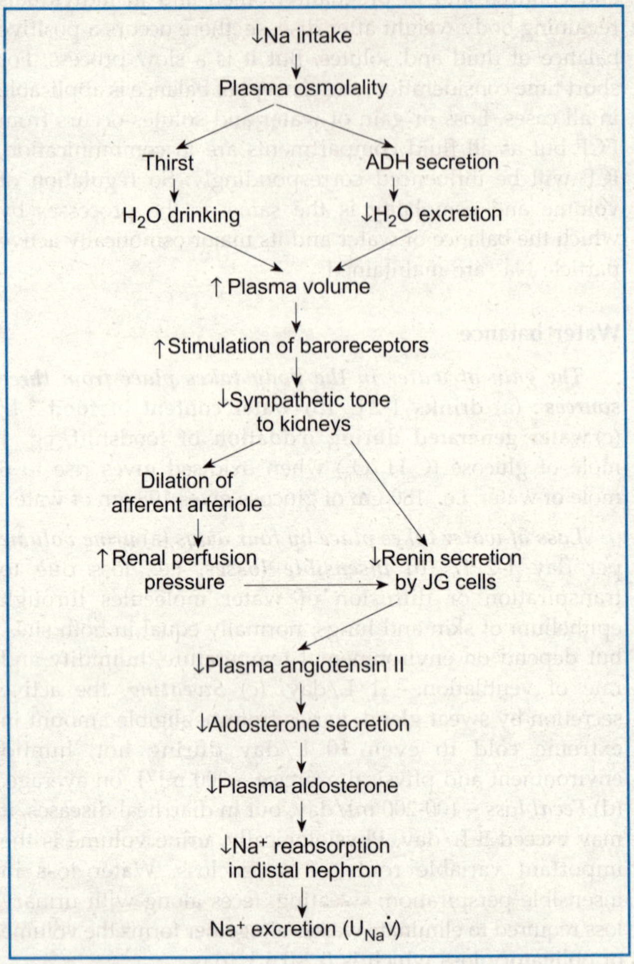


**Fig. 8.42 :** Role of aldosterone in $Na^+$ balance

volume implies keeping the gain and loss of this element equal. Sodium chloride is taken in with food and drinks (100-400 mmol/day) and lost almost exclusively through urine (100-400 mmol/day). Stool and sweat eliminates small amount normally, but in severe sweating in unacclimatized persons, on hot humid days, and in diarrheal illness substantial loss, even exceeding 1000 mmol/day may take place.

Where are the ECV receptors and how do they act to produce homeostatic response to Sodium balance? The Cardiac output and the effective circulating volume are major determinants of both the systemic blood pressure and the end diastolic pressure. This pressures stimulate both high pressure and low-pressure baroreceptors. The high pressure receptors include the baroreceptors of the carotid sinus and aortic arch and the afferent arterioles of the nephrons of the renal cortex. The low-pressure receptors (also known as volume receptors) are found in the pulmonary circulation and cardiac atria. In addition, the muscle cells of the atria secrete a hormone, atrial natriuretic peptide or ANP and the ventricular myocytes BNP. In response to increased end-diastolic pressure. Increased plasmalevels of ANP and BNP act on the renal tubules to promote sodium excretion.

## Regulation of sodium balance

Normally the balance is maintained by adjusting losses through urine to match the input. **Three important regulatory mechanisms exist.** (1) **change in GFR**; (2) **aldosterone secre-tion**; (3) **third factor effect** (Figs. 8.41, 8.42, 8.43).

***Change in GFR*** : Increase in sodium intake causes corresponding changes in blood/plasma volume and increases GFR and filtrate load of sodium and its excretion is increased. But the loss by this mechanism is low, because renal tubules adapt to fluctuations of filtrate load, so that the fraction of the filtrate load reabsorbed remains constant (**glomerulo-tubular balance**). Moreover, the increase in GFR itself is retarded to some extent by autoregulation of renal blood flow and by tubulo-glomerular feedback that control

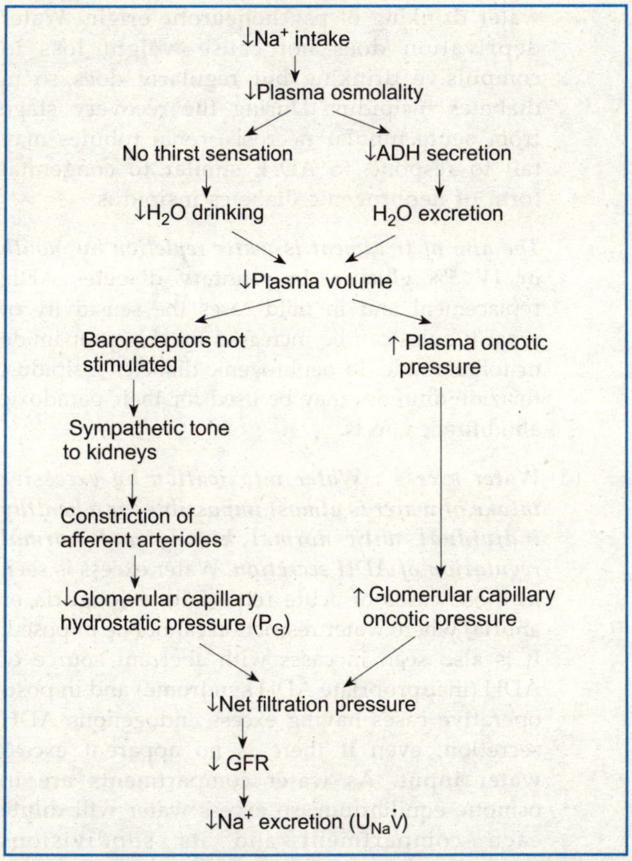


**Fig. 8.43 :** Pathway by which GFR could restore $Na^+$ balance following diminished sodium intake

glomerular filtration in response to flow in distal nephron. Atrial natriuretic peptide increases GFR in raised plasma volume and enhances sodium excretion (Fig. 8.42).

*Aldosterone secretion* : Second and more important mediator of sodium regulation is **aldosterone**. **Aldosterone secretion is stimulated by four factors** (i) ***increased plasma angiotensin II; (ii) decreased plasma sodium concentration*** ($P_{Na}$); (iii) ***increased plasma potassium concentration ($P_K$)***, (iv) ***ACTH***.

In the regulation of sodium balance, angiotensin II is the principal variable for controlling aldosterone secretion. $P_{Na}$ is a poor regulator. Moreover there is not much change of $P_{Na}$ with change in sodium intake, as water turnover is changed correspondingly by thirst and ADH mechanism. Angiotensin II formation is secondary to renin secretion from kidney. Major factors regulating renin secretion are renal perfusion pressure and renal sympathetic activity (Fig. 8.43).

*Third factor effect* : Even if GFR and aldosterone levels remain unchanged, increased sodium input is attended by increased urinary loss, and decreased input by reduced urinary loss. The processes responsible for this phenomenon is grouped together as **'third factor effect'**. It ***includes the role of atrial natriuretic peptide (ANP) and changed state of physical forces controlling reabsorption***. Keeping GFR and aldosterone level constant, small increments of sodium can be handled equally well by proximal and distal nephron. But when there is a large input of sodium, proximal tubules are principal sites for its regulation as 2/3rd of filtrate load is reabsorbed at this site. ANP increases GFR, but, as a member of third factor, it inhibits $Na^+$ reabsorption from renal tubules, reduces the aldosterone secreting capacity of angiotensin II, and even decreases its formation by lowering renin secretion. **ANP** also inhibits vasopressin secretion. **Prostaglandins** directly or indirectly via renin-angiotensin system can control $Na^+$ reabsorption.

## Disturbances of water and salt balance

Multiple disorders affect salt and water balance. The input and output of salt and water occurs to and from ECF compartment, and the ICF volume changes take place secondary to osmotic equilibrium with ECF. **ECF is *composed of interstitial fluid (ISF) and plasma and ISF/plasma volume ratio may change keeping ECF volume unchanged.*** As for example in hypoproteinemia the oncotic pressure in plasma is low. So plasma volume diminishes and ISF volume rises even if the ECF volume remains same. The clinical features depend on the magnitude of changes in volume of vascular, interstitial and intracellular compartments.

In clinical practice, though 'pure' conditions affecting either water or salt is seldom encountered, for ease of understanding the **pathophysiology**, four 'pure' disturbances are considered (a) **sodium depletion**; (b) **sodium excess**; (c) **water depletion**; (d) **water excess**.

(a) ***Sodium depletion*** : Excessive loss of sodium containing fluid from GI tract during vomiting and diarrhea and loss through urine due to salt losing kidney diseases and suprarenal failure are causes of sodium depletion.

Sodium is a major constituent of extracellular fluid. ***So reduction of sodium content diminishes extracellular volume while raising the ICF volume in 'pure' sodium depletion.*** The symptoms and signs arise due to fall in ECF and plasma volume like postural hypotension, reduction in renal blood flow and GFR causing retention of urea; decreased skin turgor, shrunken tongue or soft eyeballs.

Except in cases of renal or suprarenal diseases the urinary sodium output is drastically reduced and urinary loss more than 50 mmol/day excludes sodium depletion as a cause of hypovolemia and postural hypotension. In salt depletion, there is raised hematocrit and plasma protein concentration due to loss of plasma volume.

***The aim of treatment is to replete the salt and ECF volume by infusion of isotonic saline,*** taking care that adequate but no over-correction occurs which may cause pulmonary edema and raised central venous pressure. Pulmonary edema causes fine inspiratory crepitations at lung bases.

(b) *Sodium excess* : As long as the kidney function remains normal it is difficult to produce a sodium excess syndrome in a healthy individual. The **sodium excess** is seen in cases of heart **failure, liver failure** and **protein depletion**. In these, loss of vascular volume and perfusion pressure causes retention of sodium by lowering filtrate load and enhanced reabsorption in kidneys by renin-angiotensin-aldosterone mechanisms. Excessive administration of sodium salts and saline in cases of impaired kidney function may also result in salt excess state.

***The elevated ECF volume, due to water retention along with salt, is responsible for breathlessness due to pulmonary congestion or edema, gain in weight and even peripheral edema.*** For peripheral edema to develop retention of more than 6 litres of isotonic saline in an adult is required.

There occurs expansion of ECF and plasma volume, but hematocrit and plasma protein concentration remains within normal range. Urinary excretion of sodium is low, because it is the primary cause of most cases of salt overload. ***Treatment is by salt restriction and diuretics.*** But if the kidneys are diseased, excess salt can be removed by dialysis.

(c) *Water depletion* : Water deprivation may occur in an individual who may not take water, either in abnormal environmental circumstances (desolation) or may be unconscious or too weak to call for water. Water depletion also occurs in diabetes insipidus.

As water compartments of the body are in osmotic equilibrium, all the compartments and their subdivisions proportionately share the depletion in volume. Predominant symptom is thirst. There occurs raised osmolality of plasma; hemoconcen-tration is characterized by raised sodium concentration, hematocrit and plasma protein concentration. Urinary osmolality rises in all cases except diabetes insipidus. Diabetes insipidus is to be distinguished from compulsive water drinking of psychoneurotic origin. Water deprivation does not cause weight loss in compulsive drinking but regularly does so in diabetes insipidus. During the recovery stage from acute tubular necrosis, renal tubules may fail to respond to ADH, similar to congenital form of nephrogenic diabetes insipidus.

***The aim of treatment is water repletion by mouth or IV 5% glucose.*** In pituitary diabetes ADH replacement and in mild cases the sensitivity of renal tubules can be increased by chlorpropamide or tolbutamide. In nephrogenic diabetes insipidus, thiazide diuretics may be used for their paradoxic antidiuretic effects.

(d) *Water excess* : ***Water intoxication by excessive intake of water is almost impossible for a healthy individual with normal kidney and normal regulation of ADH secretion.*** Water excess is seen in those cases of acute renal failure (oliguria or anuria) where water restriction cannot be imposed. It is also seen in cases with aberrant source of ADH (inappropriate ADH syndrome) and in post-operative cases having excess endogenous ADH secretion, even if there is no apparent excess water input. As water compartments are in osmotic equilibrium, so excess water will dilute each compartment and its subdivisions proportionately.

There will be hemodilution due to raised plasma volume, sodium concentration will be very low, hematocrit and plasma protein concentrations will also decline. Symptoms occur due to cellular overhydration in central nervous system. There may be headache, confusion, epileptic fits and coma according to the degree of overhydration. The treatment consists of restriction of water intake and administration of drugs depressing the sensitivity of renal tubules to ADH like demeclocycline. In some cases it may require removal of water by peritoneal dialysis against hypertonic saline.

**Table 8.3**
**Disorders of salt and water balance**

| *Disorders* | *Principal clinical features* | *Plasma osmolality* | *GFR* | *Plasma volume* | *Interstitial volume* | *Intracellular volume* |
|---|---|---|---|---|---|---|
| **Water depletion** | Thirst | Hyperosmolar | Decreased | Decreased | Decreased | Decreased |
| **Water excess** | Headache, convulsion, coma | Hypoosmolar | Increased | Increased | Increased | Increased |
| **Sodium depletion** | Postural hypotension | Normal or minimally hypoosmolar | Decreased | Reduced | Reduced | Increased |
| **Sodium excess** | Oedema, systemic and pulmonary | Normal or minimally hyperosmolar | Increased | Increased | Increased | Reduced |

| **Conditions affecting thirst and ADH release** | |
|---|---|
| ***Positive stimuli*** | ***Inhibitors*** |
| • ↑ Plasma osmolality<br>• ↓ Plasma volume<br>• Angiotensin II<br>• β-adrenergic agents<br>• Cholinergic drugs<br>• Barbiturate<br>• Morphine (ADH)<br>• Nicotine (ADH)<br>• Pain, emotion, stress (ADH) | • ↓ Plasma osmolality<br>• ↑ Plasma volume<br>• Ethanol (ADH)<br>• α-adrenergic agents<br>• Diphenylhydantoin (ADH) |

## ➤ 8.16 Acid-base Physiology

**Introduction :** ***During the course of metabolism*** all the living cells of the body generate compounds which raise the ***hydrogen ion concentration of body fluids.*** **As for example,** $CO_2$ produced due to internal respiration reacts with water to give rise to carbonic acid which dissociates into bicarbonate anion and $H^+$ ion; besides lactic acid and other acids are also formed by the cells. In spite of continuous production hydrogen ion; concentration of body fluids (both ECF and ICF) is maintained remarkably constant, close to pH 7.40. So there occurs a system that operates alongside these $H^+$ generating processes and effectively counter its rise to bring the **pH to normal range.**

The **normal range** is narrow, **pH 6.9-8.0,** beyond which life is not possible. ***Change in pH is responsible for change in protein configuration and optimum functioning of enzymes depends on maintenance of normal pH. So a large deviation form normal will affect the functioning of all organs,*** specially the central nervous system. Cells add $H^+$ ion at first to ICF. $CO_2$, though produced in cells, diffuse readily to ECF. Though $H^+$ ion diffuses with difficulty across membrane the pH difference between ECF and ICF is not much. The $H^+$ ion is at first mopped to some extent by buffers in ICF and ECF. But **two organs** have been working continuously to eliminate acid and restore the buffers lost in the process of buffering. They are the **lungs** and **kidneys.** ***GI system*** and ***skin*** have a minor contribution also.

### $H^+$ ion concentration in body fluids

***pH is the negative logarithm of $H^+$ ion concentration in moles/L,*** i.e., pH = – log [$H^+$], eg, at 25°C pH of water = 7.0, so its $H^+$ ion concentration is $10^{-7}$ moles/L. **Body fluids are** dilute solutions and $H^+$ concentration is conveniently expressed as nanomoles/L. Now pH = – log [$H^+$], so [$H^+$] = $10^{-pH}$ moles/L = $10^{-pH} \times 10^9$ nmoles/L = $10^{9-pH}$ nmoles/L.

So log [$H^+$] nmol/L = log $10^{9-pH}$ = 9 – pH.

∴ [$H^+$] in nmol/L = antilog (9 – pH).

So when pH = 7.0 then [$H^+$] nmol/L = antilog (9 – 7) = anti log 2 = 100. Similarly, at pH 7.4 it can be shown that [$H^+$] in nmol/L = 40 nmol/L. pH of some fluid compartments (transcellular fluids) differ considerably from ECF. They may be strongly acidic, as in the stomach contents at the height of secretion (pH is near 1.0). On the other hand, the **pancreatic secretion** has a pH of 8.0. The **pH of urine** is largely variable, it ranges from weakly **alkaline** pH 8.0 to acidic **up to pH 4.5**, depending on the metabolic state.

Arterial or venous plasma is sampled for measuring $H^+$ concentration of ECF and body fluids in general. ***Arterial plasma pH is a measure of acid-base status of body fluids.*** It is convenient that within the narrow range of body fluid pH, from pH 7.40 to 7.50, the $H^+$ in nanomoles varies in reverse order of the numbers after decimal, eg, of pH 7.40 it is 40 nmol/L (approx) at 7.50 it is 30 nmol/L and at pH 7.30 it is 50 nmol/L (approx), it is also applicable in case of values in between them.

### Buffer system

**Important Buffer Systems in the body :** Buffering according to body compartments :

| **Compartments and major buffers** | **% of total body buffering** |
|---|---|
| **Plasma**<br>Bicarbonate<br>Inorganic phosphate<br>Plasma proteins | 13 |
| **Erythrocytes**<br>Hemoglobin<br>Bicarbonate<br>Inorganic and organic phosphate | 6 |
| **ICF (excluding erythrocytes)**<br>Bicarbonate<br>Tissue protein, organic phosphate in skeletal muscle | 51 |
| **Kidneys**<br>Bicarbonate<br>Inorganic phosphate<br>Ammonium | 30 |

**The buffers** are compounds, whose presence in solution (watery) resist change of its hydrogen ion concentration when acids and bases are added. **Acids** are substances that in watery solution can donate proton or $H^+$. **Bases** are substances that accept protons, HCl dissociates into $H^+$ and $Cl^-$ in watery solution, so it can be defined as an acid, whereas $Cl^-$ is a proton acceptor or a conjugate base of the acid.

**Buffers** in the body fluids are weak acids. Weak acids unlike strong acids, dissociates incompletely even in dilute solutions. **A weak acid**, HA, dissociates partially into $H^+$ and $A^-$, so the watery solution of it contains three components, undissociated or protonated HA, $H^+$ and $A^-$.

Now, from the law of mass action, at a particular temperature, their concentrations at equilibrium is related by the formula—

$$K_a = \frac{[H^+] \times [A^-]}{[HA]}$$

where $K_a$ is the apparent dissociation constant. So, $1/[H^+] = 1/Ka \times [A^-]/[HA]$. Taking logarithms on both sides $\log [1/H^+] = \log [1/K_a] \times [A^-/HA]$, i.e., $\log [H^+] = -\log [K_a] + \log [A^-]/[HA]$ or $pH = pK_a + \log [A^-]/[HA]$.

***This is the Henderson-Hasselbalch equation for determination of pH of a buffer solution.*** In the equation if the ratio of $[A^+]/[HA]$ is equal to 1, then $pH = pK_a$ (true dissociation constant is applicable in that state when the inter ionic forces are negligible). **Now to understand *the role of buffers it is assumed that a buffer has a $pK_a$ = 7.0 (equal to pH of $H_2O$) and its pH is adjusted to 7.0.*** So the $[A^-]/[HA] = 1$, now two condi-tions are possible (A) where each $[A^-]$ and [HA] is 20 mmol/L, another (B) both are 2 mmol/L. When 1 mmol of HCl is added to 1 litre water (non-buffered) the $[H^+]$ concen-tration rises from $10^{-7}$ mol/L to $10^{-3}$ mol/L, i.e., pH falls from 7.0 to 3.0.

But **when 1 mmol HCl is added to 1 litre of buffer A,** then, new $A^-$ concentration will become 19 mmol and HA becomes 21 m.mol, so $pH = pK_a + \log [A^-]/[HA] = 7.0 + \log (19/21) = 7.0 + \log 19 - \log 21 = 7.0 + 1.2788 - 1.3222 = 7.0 - .0434 = 6.96$, pH shifts from 7.0-6.96 only. But in buffer B, $[A^-]$ becomes 1 mmol/L and HA becomes 3 mmol/L, $pH = 7.0 + \log (1/3) = 7.0 - \log 3 = 7.0 - .47771 = 6.5$. pH shifts further than A, but this shifting is still less than that observed in unbuffered water.

$HA \rightleftharpoons H^+ + A^-$ ...(1) when HCl is added it completely dissociates to $HCl \rightarrow H^+ + Cl^-$. So in equation (1) the reaction would shift to left diminishing $A^-$ and increasing HA correspondingly. ***A buffer system operates most effectively when the pH of the system is equal to $pK_a$ and also on the absolute concentration of the buffer.***

The diagram shows that the slope of thick line is minimum at the point P which corresponds to $pK_a$ (7.0) in this instant. Where the dashed line (water) indicates its deviation of pH at any addition of base and acid it is much more than the buffer (Fig. 8.44).

**Buffer system of body fluids** : In different compartments of *body fluids the buffering substances are different* —

(i) **in ICF,** principal buffers are proteins and organic phosphates, besides bicarbonate and inorganic phosphate;

(ii) **in interstitial fluid**, bicarbonate is the main buffer, besides inorganic phosphate;

(iii) **blood** consists of both intracellular and extracellular compartments.

But the buffers in blood work in unison and can be consi-dered together as an ECF buffer system. **The principal buffers** are **hemoglobin, plasma proteins**, and **bicarbonate**

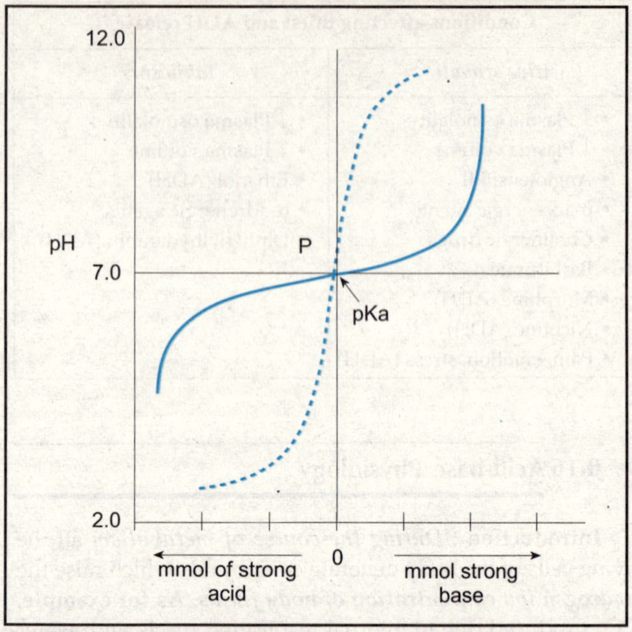


**Fig. 8.44 :** That the slope of thick line is minimum at point P corresponding to pKa (7.0) where the dashed line ($H_2O$) indicate its large deviation of pH at any addition of base and acid much more than the buffer

**buffers**. Quantitatively blood buffer anions, bicarbonate, hemoglobin and plasma proteins together normally amount to **48 mEq/L** (approx). But buffers elsewhere (mostly skeletal muscles and bones) have five times more buffering capacity than blood.

***Regarding bicarbonate buffer content***

(i) ***Plasma and interstitial fluid,*** i.e., ECF has $HCO^-_3$ concentration of 24 mEq/L (approx);

(ii) ***Intracellular fluid (muscle)*** has $HCO^-_3$ content of 12 mEq/L;

(iii) As ***ECF volume*** (20% of body weight) is half of the ICF volume (40% of body weight), their bicarbonate stores are approximately equal.

***Two (ECF + ICF) together contain about 50% of total bicarbonate store of body.*** The remaining 50% is present in the inorganic matrix of bones. Bones contain a huge store of carbonate and bicarbonate salts of calcium, magnesium, and sodium in mineralized intercellular substance. ***The content of carbonate and bicarbonate are approximately in the ratio of 3 : 1.***

Turnover of bone fluid and its mineral contents are slow. But bones definitely take part in buffering $H^+$ ion, and in cases of chronic metabolic acidosis, they are seen to lose minerals and weight.

## Protein and hemoglobin buffers

The proteins are amphoteric molecules. At isoelectric pH they are neutral, in ***more acidic media*** they behave ***as***

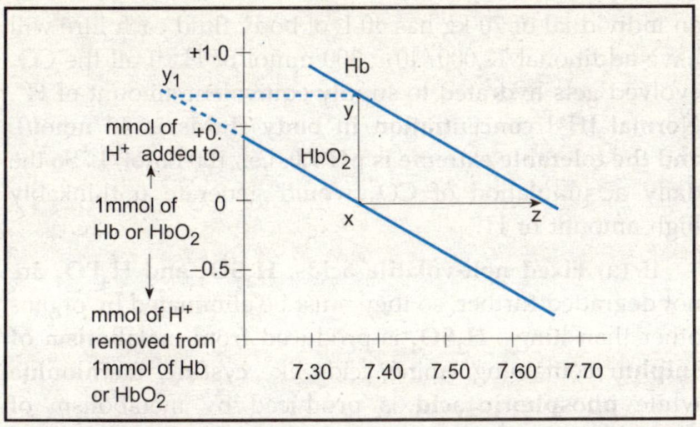


**Fig. 8.45 :** The titration curve of hemoglobin and oxyhemoglobin shows the role how the change in pH in venous blood is resisted by changed buffering capacity

***acids***, in more ***alkaline media*** they behave ***as base***. The ionizable groups present in N-terminal $NH_2$, C-terminal COOH, and also COOH groups of dicarboxylic acids like aspartic acid, glutamic acid and free $NH_2$ groups of diamino acids like lysine, and imidazole moiety of histidine act as buffers.

***The pK of ionizable groups are different in different proteins.*** It has been observed that imidazole group of histidine and N-terminal amino groups have pK nearer the normal pH, and as proteins are present in high concentration within cells and plasma they are important buffers.

**Hemoglobin** is an important buffer of blood. It is about six times effective as buffer than albumin though their molecular weights are almost equal as its concentration is four times more than that of albumin. ***For 1 litre of whole blood hemoglobin amounts to 150 gm and albumin averages to*** 7/100 gm/ml of plasma × 500 ml (hematocrit 0.5) = 35 gm. Besides, hemoglobin containing 38 histidine moieties, about twice as albumin. More surprising is that the buffering capacity of hemoglobin varies with its oxygenation.

***Oxyhemoglobin is a stronger acid and weak buffer than deoxyhemoglobin which is a weaker acid and a stronger buffer.*** As $CO_2$ is evolved and oxygen is lost in tissues, deoxy-hemoglobin formed is better able to buffer $H^+$ and, at the same time, indirectly helps in the carriage of $CO_2$ and significantly reduces the tendency of venous plasma pH to fall. ***The pH of venous plasma is 7.38, little less than arterial plasma of 7.40.*** The titration curve of hemoglobin and oxyhemoglobin shows the role how the change in pH in venous blood is resisted by changed buffering capacity (Fig. 8.45).

From this titration curve, it is evident that if, at the point X, the normal arterial point, 0.7 mmol of $H^+$ is added to 1 mmol of $HbO_2$, $HbO_2$ changes to Hb and effectively buffers it so that pH remains unchanged, otherwise pH will fall to much lower (foot of ordinate from $Y_1$).

On the other hand, if the venous blood (point Y) loses 0.7 m.mol of $H^+$ in the form of $CO_2$ simultaneous oxygenation of Hb maintains the pH to 7.4, otherwise it would have shifted to pH near 7.70, point Z. This pH would also be detrimental. Now if R (respiratory exchange ratio) 0.7 for oxygen liberated from 1 mole of $HbO_2$ (subunit of Hb) generates 0.7 mol of $CO_2$ which corresponds to 0.7 mol of $H^+$ and one mole of $HbO_2$ converted to 1 mole of Hb. So if R is 0.7 all the $H^+$ added due to addition of $CO_2$ at tissues will be mopped by the corresponding deoxyhemoglobin formed from $HbO_2$, i.e., perfect buffering is possible. But in reality R is 0.85 (average). So the **pH falls** to some extent in **venous blood**.

## Phosphate buffers

**Phosphate buffer** system is second in importance to bicarbonate buffer system in plasma and ECF. The weak dibasic acid $H_2PO^-_4$ dissociates into $HPO_4^=$ and $H^+$, i.e., $NaH_2PO_4 \rightleftharpoons H^+ + NaHPO_4^-$. pK value of this system is 6.8. This is, to some extent, further from normal arterial plasma pH 7.4, yet phosphate buffer is important intracellularly because of its high concentration. Phosphate is also important in the lumen of uriniferous tubules, because it gets concentrated in distal nephron due to relatively more absorption of water proximally and the luminal pH is low.

## Bicarbonate buffer

**Bicarbonate buffer system** is an important buffer system, because its components are readily measured and assessment of acid base status of the system and guidelines of therapy in disorder are obtained from its study :

$$H_2CO_3 \rightleftharpoons H^+ + HCO_3^-$$

$$pH = pK_a + \log \frac{[HCO_3^-]}{[H_2CO_3]} \quad ...(1)$$

is the Henderson-Hasselbach equation for this system. $pK_a$ = 3.7, however $[H_2CO_3]$ is low and cannot be measured directly, but $H_2CO_3$ remains in equilibrium with dissolved $CO_2$ ($H_2O + CO_2 \rightleftharpoons H_2CO_3$) by replacing $CO_2$ for $HCO^-_3$ equation (1),

$$pH = 6.1 + \log \frac{[HCO_3^-]}{[CO_2]} \quad ...(2)$$

Now molar concentration of dissolved $CO_2$ is proportional to partial pressure of $P_{CO_2}$, $[CO_2] = S \times [P_{CO_2}]$, S = Solubility constant = m.mol of $CO_2$/L/mm Hg = 0.0301 × $[P_{CO_2}]$ then

$$pH = 6.1 + \log \frac{[HCO_3^-]}{0.0301 \times P_{CO2}} \quad ...(3)$$

This is the clinically relevant equation as pH and $P_{CO_2}$ can be measured by sensitive electrodes and $[HCO^-_3]$ can be derived indirectly.

The changes in the bicarbonate buffer system follow change in pH, but pH change also affects components of other buffer systems correspondingly, eg,

$$pH = 6.1 + \log\frac{[HCO_3^-]}{CO_2}$$

$$= 6.8 + \log\frac{[HPO_4^=]}{H_2PO_4}$$

$$= pK_{Prot} + \log\frac{[Prot]}{[H_{Prot}]}$$

This interrelation of different buffer systems of the body is called **isohydric principle**. Though the pK of bicarbonate system is not very close to 7.40, and its concentration is not very high, yet it is an important buffer, because its components are continuously being regulated by two systems. Lungs are eliminating $CO_2$, which is volatile and lowers the denominator of the Henderson-Hasselbalch equation of bicarbonate system and kidneys can conserve or eliminate $[HCO^-_3]$ as required. For this reason the equation of bicarbonate system is expressed as

$$pH = pK + \log\frac{Kidney}{Lungs}$$

If the normal values are put to this equation taking at first

$$pH = 7.40 = 6.1 + \log\frac{[HCO_3^-]}{[CO_2]}$$

then $\frac{[HCO_3^-]}{[CO_2]}$ = antilog 1.3 = 20

So, $[HCO^-_3] = 20 \times [CO_2]$

$= 20 \times 0.03 \times PCO_2$

$= 20 \times 0.03 \times 40$

= 24 m.mol/L.

## Details of factors affecting $H^+$ concentration in body fluids

As mentioned in the beginning, metabolism is the physiological cause of generation of $H^+$, but drugs and even foods may influence the pH of body fluids. **The acidic metabolites** can be divided into (1) volatile acid, $CO_2$ and (2) nonvolatile acids, which can be subdivided into (a) fixed or non-degradable like sulphuric and phosphoric acids and (b) degradable like lactic, pyruvic, acetic and β-hydroxy butyric acids.

I. **Volatile acid, $CO_2$** : By means of spirometry it has been measured that about 200 ml of $CO_2$ is produced per minute by a resting adult. So the volume per day is 200 × (1,440/1,000) L at 37°C = 288 L.

Assuming pressure to be the same

at 273°K, 1 mol gas occupies 22.4 L

so at 300°K, 1 mol gas occupies (22.4 × 300)/273 L

= 24.61 L.

Hence, mass of $CO_2$ produced/day = 288/24.61 moles = 11.70 moles, i.e., 12 moles or 12,000 mmoles/day. Now if an individual of 70 kg has 40 L of body fluid each litre will have additional 12,000/40 = 300 mmol of $H^+$ if all the $CO_2$ evolved gets hydrated to supply equivalent amount of $H^+$. **Normal [$H^+$] concentration in body fluids is 40 nmol/L and the tolerable extreme is pH 7.0**, i.e., 100 nmol/L. So the daily accumulation of $CO_2$ would generate unthinkably high amount of $H^+$.

II. (a) **Fixed non-volatile acids, $H_2SO_4$ and $H_3PO_4$** are not degraded further, so they must be eliminated by organs other than lungs. **$H_2SO_4$** is produced from **metabolism of sulphur** containing amino acids like **cystine, methionine** while **phosphoric acid** is produced by metabolism of phosphorus containing compounds like **nucleotides, phospholipids, phosphoproteins.**

These acids are responsible for generation of 50-100 m.mol of $H^+$ per day, and high protein diet increases their formation further. If those acids are continuously being produced without elimination of $H^+$ and restoration of buffers, then their accumulation will have changes predictable from the following calculation. If an individual of 70 kg with 40 L of body fluid generate 80 mmol of $H^+$/day, each litre will have 2 m.mol/L. Now normal [$H^+$] concentration is 40 nmol/L, so the new value is $2 \times 10^{-3}/40 \times 10^{-9} = 5 \times 10^4$ times normal value. So the elimination of these acids and restitution of the lost buffers are essential for survival.

(b) **Nonvolatile but degradable or organic acids** are pyruvic, lactic ,acetoacetic and β-OH butyric acids. These acids are produced by break-down of carbohydrates and fats. Normally they are degraded in the body, but in anoxic conditions like hypovolemic shock lactic acid from anaerobic metabolism may accumulate and in **diabetes mellitus**, due to lack of insulin, keto acids, acetoacetic and β-OH butyric acids can be produced in excess from lipids. With restoration of circulation, lactic acid gets eliminated and with supply of insulin and glucose, keto acids are also dispensed with. But whenever there occurs excess formation of $H^+$, buffers and organs like lungs and kidneys try to bring the pH back to normal level.

**Buffers** in different compartments play **diverse roles** in respect of buffering. Bicarbonate buffer is not effective in countering $H^+$ ion produced by carbonic acid. So in **respiratory acidosis**, where $CO_2$ accumulation occurs, $CO_2$ evolving primarily from cells reacts with intracellular non-bicarbonate buffers, the extracellular buffering is negligible as non-bicarbonate buffers are of low concentration here. Similarly, **loss of excess $CO_2$** due to hyperventilation reduces the intracellular concentration of $CO_2$ and fall in $H^+$ is counteracted primarily by dissociation of abundant non-bicarbonic acids intracellularly.

III. **Metabolic (non-carbonic) acids** are counteracted by both non-bicarbonate and bicarbonate buffers. As acids are produced within cells, which are rich in protein and phosphate buffers besides bicarbonate (and as ICF compartment is larger than ECF compartment) **80% of buffering takes place intracellularly. The remaining 20%**

**is due to involvement of bicarbonate and phosphate buffers of ECF**. Metabolic alkalosis, on the other hand, is due to loss of acid containing fluid from stomach, excess loss of $H^+$ through urine and ingestion of antacids by GI system, i.e., loss occurs primarily from ECF. So the ECF buffers are responsible for handling $^2/3$rd of base load and the remaining $^1/3$rd is due to buffering capacity of ICF buffers.

## Respiratory regulation of pH

**Internal respiration** is responsible for production of $CO_2$ by oxidation of carbohydrates, lipids and carbon skeletons of amino acids. $CO_2$ is removed by external respiration, so that the $[HCO^-_3]/[CO_2]$ ratio of Henderson-Hasselbalch equation of bicarbonate buffer system remains constant. Ventilation can be changed according to the need of the system. Whenever there is a rise in $P_{CO_2}$ due to increased metabolism there is increase in ventilation. ***Medullary and peripheral chemo-receptors mediate this change.*** Alveolar ventilation is inversely proportional to $P_{CO_2} \cdot \dot{V}_{CO_2} = \dot{V}_A \times CA_{CO_2}$. Now $CA_{CO_2} = K{\cdot}PA_{CO_2} = K{\cdot}Pa_{CO_2}$, so $\dot{V}_{CO_2} = \dot{V}_A \times K \times Pa_{CO_2}$ where K is a constant.

$$PaCO_2 = \frac{\dot{V}CO_2}{K \cdot \dot{V}_A} \text{ if } \dot{V}_{CO_2} \text{ remains constant then } PaCO_2 \propto \frac{1}{\dot{V}_A}$$

Similarly when there is fall in $Pa_{CO_2}$ due to hyperventilation. Ventilation will decline subsequently and accumulation of $CO_2$ will restore the $Pa_{CO_2}$ and pH to normal.

Respiration is also linked to production of non-carbonic acids in metabolic acidosis. Peripheral chemoreceptors then send signals to increase ventilation. The blowing off of $CO_2$ reduces the denominator of $[HCO^-_3]/[CO_2]$ and tries to bring pH back to normal by matching decline of $[HCO^-_3]$. Similarly, in metabolic alkalosis, there is depression of respiration.

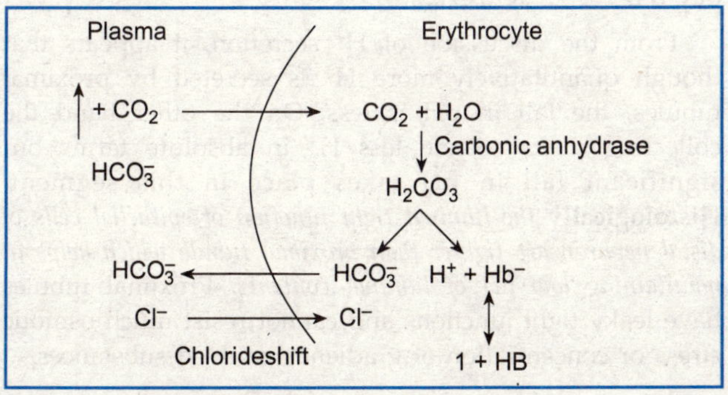


## Renal regulation of pH

**The kidneys** are the organs by means of which the nonvolatile acids are eliminated. ***50-100 mmol/day of $H^+$ ion*** is eliminated and the ***lost bicarbonate anion is recovered***, eg, $H_2SO_4 + 2NaHCO_3 = Na_2SO_4 + 2H_2O + 2CO_2$. $NaHCO_3$ is generated by the renal tubules by eliminating $H^+$ and taking up $Na^+$; bicarbonate is formed within cells.

In addition to generation of lost bicarbonate, bicarbonate load per day, i.e., GFR × plasma bicarbonate concentration is also recovered by the process of reabsorption. ***When GFR is 180 L/day and bicarbonate concentration is 24 mmol/L, the filtrate load is 180 × 24 mmol/day = 4320 mmol/day. Almost all of the filtrate load of $HCO^-_3$ is reabsorbed normally. Loss of $NaHCO_3$ in urine is equivalent to gain of corresponding amount of acid within the system.***

***$H^+$ is*** always secreted actively from ***the renal tubular epithelial cells*** into the lumen, and there lies in the lumen buffers obtained either from filtration or prepared by renal tubules to mop up $H^+$ secreted, so that pH does not fall much. If pH falls below 4.5, further $H^+$ secretion stops. This is the limiting pH. Bicarbonate, phosphate and ammonia constitute urinary buffers. The proximal convoluted tubules and distal nephrons are the sites of $H^+$ ion secretion.

The proximal convoluted tubular epithelial cells contain carbonic anhydrase in the cytosol and also in the microvillus or brush border. Within the cytosol, carbonic anhydrase is responsible for formation of $H_2CO_3$ from $CO_2$ derived either from cellular metabolism or by diffusion from blood or lumen.

**$H_2CO_3$** dissociates into $H^+$ and $HCO^-_3$. $H^+$ ion is secreted by antiport mechanism in exchange of $Na^+$ into the lumen, an example of secondary active transport, as $Na^+$ concentration gradient is maintained by $Na^+$-pump of the epithelial cells to ISF side. $H^+$ ion then unites with $HCO^-_3$ in the lumen left out by $Na^+$, to from $H_2CO_3$ which is quickly broken-down to $H_2O$ and $CO_2$ by brush border carbonic anhydrase. $CO_2$ formed diffuses into the cells, either to be rehydrated or carried away by blood. In this way, $NaHCO_3$ is reabsorbed by the proximal convoluted tubule. The $HCO^-_3$ reabsorbed is not the same molecule as filtered, but derived by hydration of $CO_2$ within the cell. However, there is net reabsorption of $HCO^-_3$ filtered.

**Luminal pH** does not change by this process, as $H^+$ is taken up by $HCO^-_3$ in lumen and converted to $CO_2$ and $H_2O$. In the proximal tubule this is the principal mechanism of secretion of $H^+$. At the end of proximal tubule pH falls to near 6.8. From this it is evident that when the secreted $H^+$ is buffered by luminal bicarbonate, there is only reabsorption and no generation of new $HCO^-_3$ and luminal pH will remain unchanged. But fall of pH from 7.4-6.9 or so indicates that other buffers work here also, resulting in generation of new $HCO^-_3$ and, at the same time, fall of pH to some extent. Those are ammonia and phosphate buffers (Fig. 8.46).

**In the distal nephron**, mainly collecting tubules/ducts contain principal cells or P cells which absorb water and I cells or intercalated cells which secrete acid similar to oxyntic cells of stomach. These cells contain carbonic anhydrase and tubulovesicular structure which bear **$H^+$-ATPase** and when increased $H^+$ secretion is required the tubulovesicles merge with luminal membrane. These cells are devoid of microvillus border, but elsewhere there is anion exchanger (band 3) similar to RBC membrane exchanging $Cl^-$ for $HCO^-_3$, for transporting the later to interstitial space.

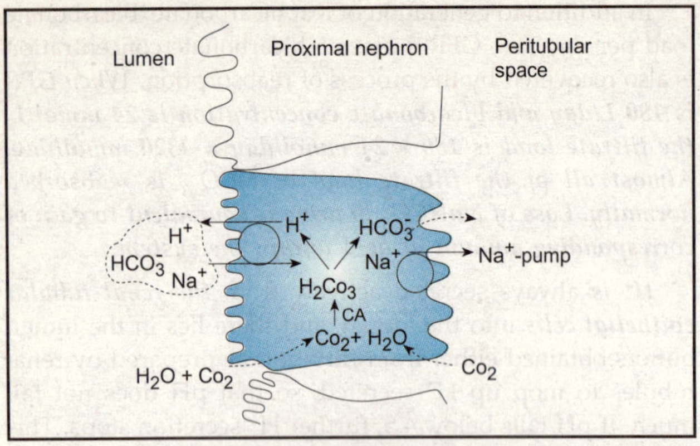


**Fig. 8.46 : Principal mechanism of secretion of $H^+$**

In contrast to proximal tubule, distal nephron cells secrete hydrogen ion by primary active transport into lumen by $H^+$-ATPase. Normally, most or all of the $HCO^-_3$ filtered is reabsorbed in proximal convoluted tubule. In the distal nephron, $H^+$ secreted has to unite with phsophate and ammonia buffers.

## Role of phosphate buffer

***The pK value of the phosphate buffer system is 6.8,*** nearer the luminal pH, but its concentration in plasma is lowl. Moreover 75-85% of filtered phosphate is actively absorbed by proximal convoluted tubules. However, in the **distal nephron**, its concentration rises to some extent and it acts as an effective buffer. $H^+$ is produced in the cytosol in the same way as in the proximal convoluted tubule and on secretion it reacts with basic phosphate to form acid phosphate

$$Na_2HPO_4 + H^+ \rightarrow NaH_2PO_4 + Na^+$$

The $Na^+$ is actively absorbed by epithelial cells along with $HCO^-_3$ formed inside the cell due to hydration of $CO_2$. This $HCO^-_3$ is a new bicarbonate and is a replenishment of the lost $HCO^-_3$ by buffering noncarbonic acids. $\mathbf{NaH_2PO_4}$ is the acid phosphate and it is the compound responsible for titratable acidity when urine is titrated with strong base like NaOH to normal pH 7.40. **Phosphate buffer** system is effective, but its total amount cannot be increased as it is derived only from filtration, even in face of acidosis. *Normally 12-40 mmol/day of $H^+$ can be eliminated as acid phosphate.*

## Ammonia buffer

**Henderson-Hasselbalch equation of $NH_3$ buffer system** is pH = pK + log $[NH_3]/[NH^+_4]$, pK is 8.3. $NH_3$ is produced by epithelial cells of proximal tubules and distal nephron by the action of the mitochondrial enzyme glutaminase upon glutamine. Glutamine $\xrightarrow{\text{Glutaminase}}$ glutamic acid + $NH_3$. 60% of ammonia is derived by this reaction. Remaining 40% is derived by other ways like glutamic acid $\xrightarrow{\text{Glutamic dehydrogenase}}$ α-ketoglutaric acid + $NH_3$ and also by transamination of amino acids like glycine, alanine with transfer of amino group to a-ketoglutaric acid to form glutamic acid which can be acted upon by glutamic dehydrogenase.

$NH_3$ is a lipid-soluble gas and diffuses readily across membranes and, due to its high pK, it combines with $H^+$ available within lumen with high affinity to form $NH^+_4$, and it is eliminated as compounds like $NH_4$ Cl. $NH_4^+$ formed in the lumen cannot diffuse back to cells as it is a polar nonlipid soluble molecule. So the concentration gradient of $NH_3$ is maintained and further transport can take place. It is an example of 'nonionic diffusion' and 'diffusion trapping'.

***Normally 30-70 mmol per day of $H^+$ is eliminated as ammonium salts.*** But ammonia system is superior to other buffer systems in that its synthesis is subject to adaptation and when there is acidosis, ***there is increased production of $NH_3$ either from increased glutaminase activity*** and/or increased mitochondrial transport of glutamine. In this way, in diabetic acidosis, even more than 500 m mol of $H^+$ per day can be eliminated as ammonium salts. *Due to its high pK value (8.3), when acidic urine is titrated to 7.40 by strong base like NaOH, $NH^+_4$ will part with negligible $H^+$ to take part in neutralization process, because at pH 7.4 $[NH_3]/[NH^+_4]$ ratio will be near 1 : 100.*

On the other hand, uric acid (pK 5.75), creatinine (pKa 4.97) β-OH butyric acid and acetoacetic acids (pK 4.8 each), all are weak acids with some buffering activity, contribute normally to a small extent to titratable acidity. *But in diabetic acidosis they may contribute significantly.* When **ammonia buffer system operates,** there is also generation of new bicarbonate as $H^+$ secreted reacts with $NH_3$ and not $HCO^-_3$. ***So by the operation of phosphate and ammonia buffer system there is replenishment of 50-100 mmol of bicarbonate lost per day during titration of non-carbonic acids*** like sulphuric acid and phosphoric acid, lactic acid etc. **Net acid secretion** is the sum of titrable acidity (phosphate and others) + $NH^+_4$ + unreabsorbed bicarbonate eliminated per day (Fig. 8.47.1 & 8.47.2).

From the discussion of $H^+$ secretion, it appears that though quantitatively more $H^+$ is secreted by proximal tubules, the fall in pH is less. On the other hand the collecting ducts secrete less $H^+$ in absolute terms but significant fall in pH takes place in this segment. **Histologically** *the luminal tight junction of epithelial cells of distal nephron are tighter than proximal tubule which helps in maintaining low pH of luminal contents.* Proximal tubules have leaky tight junctions and cannot resist much osmotic stress or concentration of gradient dissolved substances.

## Factors affecting $H^+$ secretion

The factors affecting **the rate of $H^+$ secretion** by ***renal tubules*** in general are (a) intracellular pH, (b) carbonic anhydrase activity and (c) amount of functioning kidney tissue.

(a) **Intracellular pH** : Increase in the intracellular $H^+$ ion concentrations, enhances its secretion to lumen

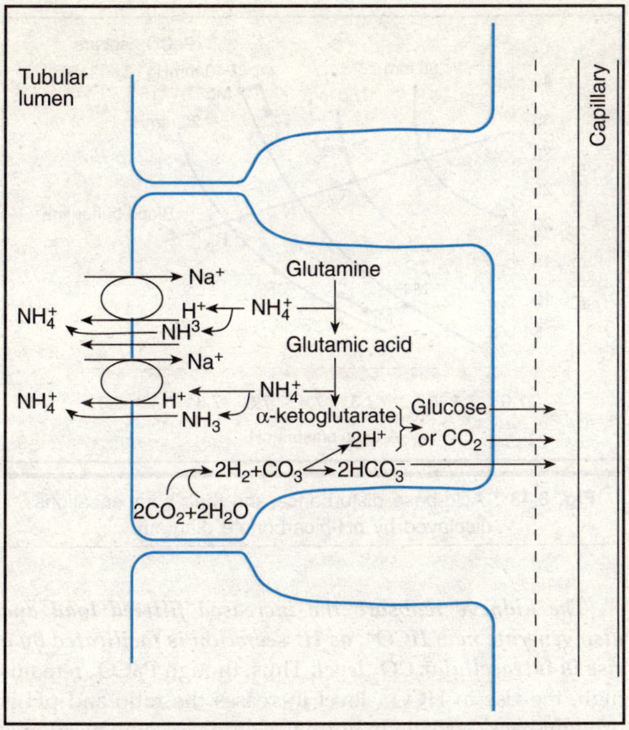


Fig. 8.47.1 : $NH_4^+$ production and secretion by tubular cells and consequent procedure of $HCO_3^-$ for the plasma.

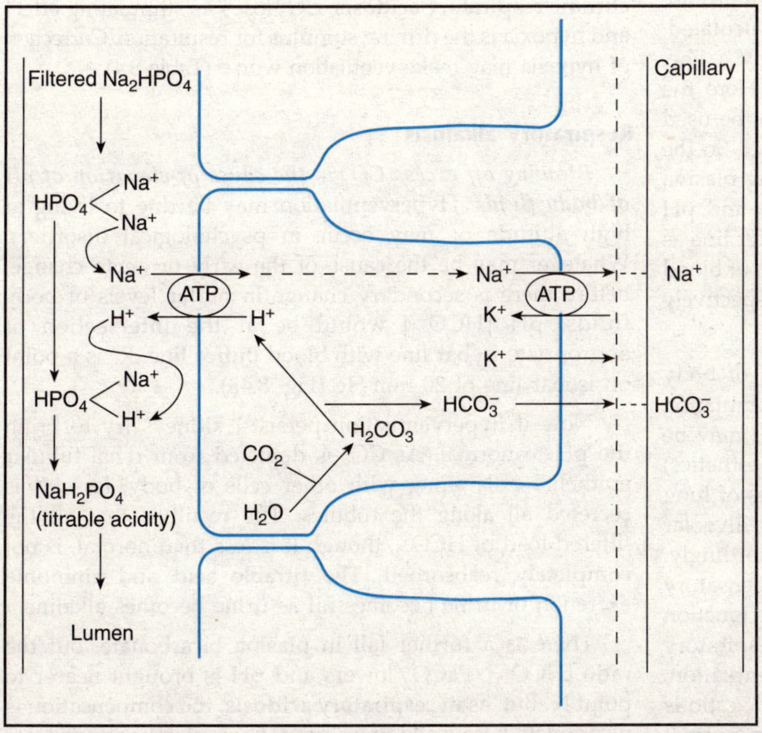


Fig. 8.47.2 : Formation of titrable acidity and $NH^+_4$ in distal nephron

of the tubules. Increased $H^+$ concentration may be due to rise in $CO_2$ level in cells as in **respiratory acidosis** or due to rise of non-carbonic acid concentration as in **diabetic ketoacidosis**. Rise in $PaCO_2$ is the primary factor as increased ventilation due to metabolic acidosis lowers cellular $CO_2$ level and $H^+$ secretion. But as acidosis continues in spite of hyperventilation, adaptive changes like increased $NH_3$ formation occurs along with increased $H^+$ secretion. In **hypokalaemia**, intracellular $H^+$ concentration rises because in this state $K^+$ enters from ICF to ECF and its place is taken by $H^+$ ion from ECF and subsequently it is secreted.

(b) **Carbonic anhydrase activity** is reduced by drugs like acetazolamide. $H^+$ secretion is inhibited in the distal nephron, $K^+$ is secreted in excess in exchange of $Na^+$ the load of which increases because a part of $Na^+$ reabsorption in proximal tubule occurs in replacement of $H^+$ secreted. So $K^+$ depletion occurs.

(c) In **renal diseases** there is **decrease of functioning renal tissue**. As $H^+$ is secreted actively, its secretion is affected when there is much destruction of renal parenchyma.

In addition to the above general factors, there are some regional differences regarding $H^+$ secretion, in proximal tubule as $H^+$ is secreted by antiport in exchange of $Na^+$, any factor increas-ing $Na^+$ reabsorption (eg, diminished plasma volume) increases $H^+$ secretion and any factor decreasing $Na^+$ reabsorption (raised plasma volume) inhibits $H^+$ secretion.

Moreover as (because of leaky tight junctions) pH of proximal renal tubule does not fall below 6.9, plasma bicarbo-nate level or filtrate load of bicarbonate also affects $H^+$ secretion. Bicarbonate buffer prevents fall in pH of luminal fluid. So, if bicarbonate load is low, $H^+$ secretion can be continued till the pH falls to 6.9 reducing its elimination.

***In the collecting tubules, $H^+$ secretion is indirectly coupled to $Na^+$ reabsorption.*** So any factor that increases the rate of $Na^+$ reabsorption in distal nephron (collecting tubule/duct) increases $H^+$ and also $K^+$ secretion and subsequent excretion. When $Na^+$ is reabsorbed at a heightened rate at this part of nephron, the luminal negativity increases as anions fall behind $Na^+$ entry. This luminal negativity is responsible for enhanced secretion of $H^+$ and $K^+$. Aldosterone increases $Na^+$ reabsorption in distal nephron.

Most diuretics cause alkalosis as follow : Increased flow in distal and collecting tubules. This in turn leads to increased renal reabsorption of $Na^+$ in these parts, which is coupled to increased $H^+$ secretion. This leads to **alkalosis.** However carbonic anhydrase blockers inhibit $H^+$ secretion and $HCO^-_3$ reabsorption. This leads to **acidosis**.

## Preliminaries to acid-base disturbances

The **normal pH of arterial plasma is 7.4**. The pH of other fluid compartments are close to it. When there is fall of arterial plasma pH below 7.38 it is called **acidosis**, and when it exceeds 7.42 it is called **alkalosis**. ***Acidosis and alkalosis may be due to respiratory or non-respiratory origin. Henderson-Hasselbalch equation of bicarbonate buffer system helps to understand the types of deviation***

$$pH = 6.1 + \log\frac{[HCO_3^-]}{[CO_2]} = 6.1 + \log\frac{[HCO_3^-]}{0.03 \times PaCO_2}$$

In ***respiratory acidosis,*** there is accumulation of $CO_2$ and $PaCO_2$ rises causing fall in pH.

In ***respiratory alkalosis,*** there is elimination of excess $CO_2$ and $PaCO_2$ falls raising pH.

In ***metabolic acidosis,*** there is fall in $HCO^-_3$ concentration due to buffering of non-carbonic acid, and fall in pH takes place.

In ***metabolic alkalosis,*** there is rise in $HCO^-_3$ resulting in increase in pH.

***The states of acid-base disturbance and their compensations*** is displayed by **pH-bicarbonate diagram**. In this graphical representation, pH is plotted over the abscissa and arterial plasma bicarbonate concentration along the ordinate. The points are plotted to draw $PaCO_2$ isobars. At a particular $PaCO_2$ level, different bicarbonate concentration values are put in the above equation and pH values are calculated; after which the pH, $[HCO^-_3]$ points are joined by a line. Another line called blood buffer line is drawn. Here the $Pa_{CO2}$ values are changed, but the equation cannot be used for pH measurement as $[HCO^-_3]$ varies with $Pa_{CO2}$. So the pH is to be measured experimentally by subjecting plasma to equilibrate with gas mixtures of known $PCO_2$ and pH $[HCO^-_3]$ couples are plotted. It is called blood buffer line as its slope and position will depend on concentration of blood non-bicarbonate buffers and bicarbonate buffers, respectively (Fig. 8.48).

**Respiratory acidosis** is a state of fall in pH of body fluids due to increase in $PaCO_2$ resulting from accumulation of $CO_2$ within the body out of hypoventilation. It may be due to drugs (like morphine, barbiturate or anesthetics) depressing the respiratory centres or from diseases of lung or chest wall. As $PaCO_2$ is inversely proportional to alveolar ventilation, hypoventilation increases $PaCO_2$ accordingly. In the pH-bicarbonate diagram, before any compensatory steps are taken, the pH will fall on isobar line at its junction with blood buffer line. $R_a$ is the point of acute respiratory acidosis. In absence of any improvement of ventilation, kidneys try to restore the pH. The $[HCO^-_3]/PaCO_2$ ratio is decreased but the value of $[HCO^-_3]$ is more than normal due to rise in $H_2CO_3$, and its dissociation.

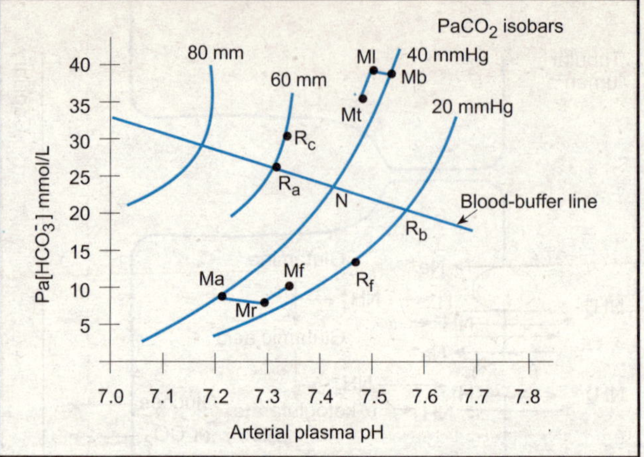


**Fig. 8.48 :** Acid-base disturbance and their compensations displayed by pH-bicarbonate diagram

***The kidneys reabsorb the increased filtered load and also generate new $HCO^-_3$ as $H^+$ secretion is facilitated by a rise in intracellular $CO_2$ level.*** Thus, though $PaCO_2$ remains high, the rise in $HCO^-_3$ level increases the ratio and pH is brought back partially to normal. Complete compensation is not possible as kidneys cannot keep pace with continuously evolving $CO_2$ throughout the body. *The point (pH) of chronic respiratory acidosis will be on isobar line, in the diagram it is on $R_c$ (Fig. 8.48).*

***Treatment of respiratory acidosis is to improve ventilation.*** Inadvertent $O_2$ therapy may cause harm because, **in chronic respiratory acidosis**, $CO_2$ loses its stimulating effect and hypoxia is the driving stimulus for respiration. Correction of hypoxia may make ventilation worse (Table 8.4).

## Respiratory alkalosis

***Blowing off excess $CO_2$ is the cause of elevation of pH of body fluids.*** Hyperventilation may be due to living at high altitude or may occur in psychological disorders. Whatever may be the cause of the early or acute change, before there is secondary change in buffer levels of body fluids, pH $[HCO^-_3]$ would be at the intersection of appropriate isobar line with blood buffer line. $R_b$ is a point on isobar line of 20 mm Hg (Fig. 8.48).

Now if hyperventilation persists, kidneys try to bring the pH to normal. As $CO_2$ is depleted from renal tubular epithelial cells along with other cells of body, less $H^+$ is secreted all along the tubules. The result is that all the filtered load of $HCO^-_3$, though it is less than normal, is not completely reabsorbed. The titrable acid and ammonia excretion of urine becomes nil as urine becomes alkaline.

There is a further fall in plasma bicarbonate, but the ratio $[HCO^-_3]/PaCO_2$ lowers and pH is brought nearer to point N. But, as in **respiratory acidosis**, the compensation is incomplete because kidneys cannot completely compensate the generalised abnormality, ***in chronic cases pH will follow***

**Table 8.4**

**Acid-base disorders result from failure of the respiratory system and kidneys to maintain $PCO_2$ and $HCO^-_3$ at their normal levels.**

| Disturbance | Examples | Compensation | Blood-gas profile |
|---|---|---|---|
| **Respiratory acidosis** | • Depresion of the respiratory Centers<br>• Respiratory muscle fatigue | Kidney produces new $HCO_3$ | $PaCO_2\uparrow$ (Cause)<br>$pH\downarrow$ (result)<br>$HCO^-_3\uparrow$ (compensation) |
| **Respiratory alkalosis** | • Hypoxemia anxiety | Kidney excretes $HCO^-_3$ | $PaCO_2\downarrow$ (cause)<br>$pH\uparrow$ (result)<br>$HCO^-_3\uparrow$ (compensation) |
| **Metabolic acidosis** | • Excessive fixed acid production, as in diabetes<br>• Failure of kidney to excrete $H^+$ as in renal tubular acidosis | Hyperventilation | $HCO_3\downarrow$ (cause)<br>$pH\downarrow$ (result)<br>$PaCO_2\downarrow$ (compensation) |
| **Metabolic alkalosis** | • Loss of acid as in excessive vomiting.<br>• Movement of $H^+$ into cells, as in hypokalemia | Hypoventilation | $HCO_3\uparrow$ (Cause)<br>$pH\uparrow$ (result)<br>$PaCO_2\uparrow$ (Compensation) |

***the isobar line of 20 mm Hg below the blood buffer line to point $R_f$.*** The aim of treatment is to remove the cause of hyperventilation. Of course individuals living at high altitude get acclimatized to rarefied atmosphere in course of time and ventilation is somewhat reduced.

## Metabolic acidosis

**Metabolic acidosis** is associated with reduction of bicarbonate concentration and fall of $[HCO^-_3]/PaCO_2$ ratio. Most of the cases are due to disorders in the metabolic state as in diabetic ketoacidosis or lactic acidosis as a result of hypovolemic shock. It may also be due to loss of bicarbonate containing alkaline fluid from the body as in diarrhea or failure of diseased kidneys to dispose off $H^+$ adequately.

In **every case of metabolic acidosis,** compensatory changes start at once, but for ease of understanding, the acute state is thought to follow the isobar line of normal $PaCO_2$ of 40 mm Hg to a point of $M_a$, both bicarbonate and pH below normal. Now respiratory compensation occurs early. There is hyperventilation in response to acidotic stimuli to peripheral chemoreceptors.

The hyperventilation blows off excess $CO_2$ to reduce the $PaCO_2$ value, further reducing the initially lowered (primary change) bicarbonate level, but raising the ratio of bicarbonate/$PaCO_2$ nearer to normal, so that pH is brought near 7.4. The pH due to respiratory compensation (it is also the only compe-nsation available to renal acidosis) will be on point $M_r$. Due to hyperventilation, $CO_2$ is eliminated at an increased rate and the $PaCO_2$ will fall.

The renal tubular cell will have low $H^+$ secretion due to low a intracellular $P_{CO2}$. But the lower than normal secretion is adequate to recover the much reduced filtered load owing to primary fall in bicarbonate and also to generate new bicarbonate by utilizing the titrable buffers and ammonia buffer system. Ammonia synthesis increases further by the process of adaptation. ***The ultimate result of renal compensation is to raise $[HCO^-_3]$ to some extent and raising the pH even nearer to normal.*** This final pH after respiratory and renal compensation will be on $M_f$ on the isobar line passing through $M_r$. The final compensation will approach normal point, N, but fail to reach it. The respiratory compensation will cease as a fall in $P_{CO_2}$ is sensed by the chemoreceptors. Moreover, the fall in cellular $P_{CO_2}$ due to hyperventilation will brake $H^+$ secretion by kidneys to some extent.

## Anion gap

In the evaluation of metabolic acidosis, **anion gap**, is taken into consideration when the electrolytes of plasma are measured and expressed in electrical equivalents; the number of cations altogether should equal the number of all anions, i.e., $Na^+ + K^+ + Ca^{2+} + Mg^{2+}$ + other cations etc = $Cl^- + HCO^-_3 + SO^=_4 + PO^{\equiv}_4$ + other anions. But only $Na^+$, $K^+$ and $Cl^-$ and $HCO^-_3$ are routinely measured; normally $Na^+$ and $K^+$ expressed in equivalents (or mmoles/L as they are univalent) their sum exceeds that of $Cl^-$ and $HCO^-_3$ in equivalents or mmoles/L as they are univalent). Eg, normal $Na^+$ conc. = 145 mmol/L, $K^+$ conc. = 5 mmol/L, total 150 mmol/L, whereas $Cl^-$ conc. = 110 mmol/L, $HCO^-_3$ = 25 mmol/L combined, 135 mmol/L, so the anion gap here is 150-135 = 15 mmol/L.

Now it is understandable, that if $Ca^{2+}$, $Mg^{2+}$ or cations other than $Na^+$ and $K^+$ are increased, they will be matched by anions including $Cl^-$ and $HCO^-_3$, whose concentration also rise. So $Na^+ + K^+$ remains same but $Cl^- + HCO^-_3$ rises, and anion gap will fall. But if $Cl^-$ and $HCO^-_3$ remain normal and protein anions, anions of organic acids like lactic, acetoacetic acids etc. increase, they will be accompanied by cations including $Na^+$ and $K^+$, but some bicarbonate anion will be lost due to reaction of the acids with sodium bicarbonate. So the anion gap widens.

In most cases of **metabolic acidosis** like diabetic ketosis, lactic acidosis etc, **anion gap increases**. But where the acidosis is due to loss of bicarbonate as in diarrhea or in renal disease or ingestion of acidifying drugs like $NH_4Cl$, there is loss of bicarbonate, with equal gain of chloride and the sum of $Cl^-$ and $HCO^-_3$ remains unaltered and the gap remains same. For example, on buffering (1) $HA + NaHCO_3 \rightleftharpoons Na^+ + H_2O + CO_2$. Na is measured, but not $A^-$ but in (2) $HCl + NaHCO_3 = NaCl + H_2O + CO_2$, both $Cl^-$, $Na^+$ are measured. In (2) there is one for one exchange of $Cl^-$ against $HCO^-_3$ but in (1) $HCO^-$ is exchanged for $A^-$ which remained unmeasured. So $Na^+$ remains same, but $HCO^-_3$ falls ultimately raising the anion gap. ***The normal range of anion gap is 10-20 meq/L.***

## Metabolic alkalosis

The primary abnormality leads to raised plasma bicarbonate level, i.e., rise in pH secondary to raised $[HCO^-_3]/PaCO_2$ ratio. In most cases, **metabolic alkalosis** occurs secondary to loss of acidic fluids as in vomiting, naso-gastric suction or due to diuresis by most diuretics. It may be due to increased $HCO^-_3$ intake in the form of $NaHCO_3$ as antacid.

***In metabolic alkalosis, compensatory changes take place right from its onset.*** So the uncompensated acute state is considered for theoretical reasons in which pH change occurs along the $PaCO_2$ isobar of 40 mm Hg.

***Respiratory compensation occurs early, due to fall in $H^+$ concentration peripheral chemoreceptors signal*** negatively with decline in ventilation causing accumulation of $CO_2$ and raised $PaCO_2$ value. But the compensation is limited in comparison to metabolic acidosis, because peripheral chemoreceptors are more sensitive to fall rather than rise in pH of fluids bathing.

Moreover, slightly raised $PaCO_2$ due to initial hypoventilation will cut off the stimulus of alkalosis. The pH shift will be to $M_l$, compensation made by lungs and it is also the final compensation where *the alkalosis is due to renal involvement*, i.e., by diuretics. After initial compensation, by lungs, renal compensation takes place in cases where kidneys are not primarily involved.

But the renal response is complex here and biased by renal handling of volume depletion and respiratory compensation. Rise in $PaCO_2$ by respiratory depression will accelerate $H^+$ secretion, but at the same time there is enhanced filtered load of bicarbonate. The raised $H^+$ secretion is inadequate to reabsorb completely, the increased filtered load and no new bicarbonate is generated in cases where there is no fluid volume depletion. So alkaline urine will be excreted, lowering the bicarbonate level and also pH. The point will lie on isobar passing through $M_l$ to terminal value $M_f$ approaching normal point N.

***In most cases of metabolic alkalosis there is associated fluid loss,*** eg, in diuresis. When there is fall in plasma volume there is increase in $Na^+$ reabsorption in the proximal convoluted tubule, and along with increased $Na^+$ reabsorption, there is accelerated excretion of $H^+$ in exchange. In distal nephron $Na^+$ reabsorption is increased due to raised aldosterone secretion. Luminal negativity increases and $H^+$ excretion rises along with $K^+$. Whenever there is excretion of $H^+$, there takes place reabsorption of $HCO^-_3$, or generation of new $HCO^-_3$. So the bicarbonate level in metabolic alkalosis with fluid depletion tends to rise maintaining the raised pH instead of reducing it. For renal compensation to have appropriate effect, the loss of fluid is to be made up therapeutically. So the mainstay of treatment of metabolic alkalosis is fluid volume repletion, removal of causal factor and if necessary, admini-stration of acidifying drugs like $NH_4Cl$.

**Table 8.5 : Acid-base disturbances**

| Acid-Base abnormality | Primary disturbance | Effect | | Base excess | Compensatory response |
|---|---|---|---|---|---|
| | | pH | $PO_2$ | | |
| Respiratory acidosis | $\uparrow PCO_2$ | ↓ | ↓ | | $\uparrow [HCO_3^-]$ |
| Metabolic acidosis | $\downarrow [HCO_3^-]$ | ↓ | N or ↑ | –ve | $\downarrow PCO_2$ |
| Respiratory alkalosis | $\downarrow PCO_2$ | ↑ | N or ↑ | | $\downarrow [HCO_3^-]$ |
| Metabolic alkalosis | $\uparrow [HCO_3^-]$ | ↑ | N or ↑ | +ve | $\uparrow PCO_2$ |

## Clinical evaluation of acid-base disorders

To appraise the severity of disorders of acid-base balance, it is required to measure the pH of arterial plasma, and also plasma bicarbonate concentration. pH of arterial plasma samples can be recorded reliably with pH sensitive electrodes and $PaCO_2$ from plasma samples by (secluded from air) $CO_2$ sensitive electrode and bicarbonate concentration can be derived from the **Henderson-Hasselbalch equation of the bicarbonate buffer system.** Sampling of arterial blood is difficult. So free flowing venous blood sample can be taken for the estimation of pH, $P_{CO2}$ and $HCO^-_3$ concentration. But in venous samples $P_{CO2}$ will be higher, pH will be lower and $HCO^-_3$ will be higher than corresponding values of arterial samples. So interpretation of the data should require these considerations.

## Siggard-Anderson curve nomogram (Fig. 8.49)

***The nomogram is helpful for plotting data of pH, $P_{CO_2}$ in cases of acid-base disorders.*** This helps to have insight of the magnitude of abnormality and indicates line of therapy.

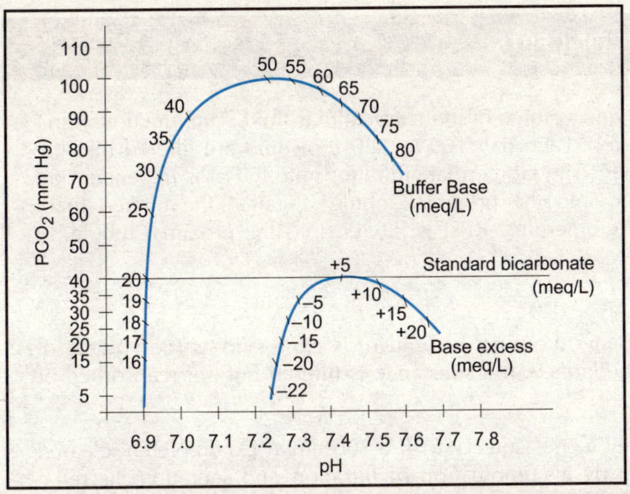


**Fig. 8.49 :** Siggard-Anderson curve nomogram

The abscissa indicates the pH values of arterial plasma and the ordinate the $P_{CO_2}$ value (in log scale). The straight line parallel to abscissa is the standard bicarbonate line from $P_{CO2}$ 40 mm Hg. Any point above this line indicates **hypoventilation** and any point below hyperventilation. If a straight line is drawn parallel to ordinate from pH 7.4, any point left to it indicates acidosis and any on the right shows alkalosis.

In actual practice, arterial blood samples are collected and pH of its plasma is measured. Now the same blood is equilibrated with two known gas mixtures containing $CO_2$ and pH values in each case is measured. Two points of pH and $P_{CO_2}$ obtained are then plotted in the nomogram and connected by a straight line. **The Henderson-Hasselbalch equation is**

$$pH = pK + \log\frac{[HCO_3^-]}{[PaCO_2 \times S]} = pK + \log[HCO_3^-] - \log PaCO_2 - \log s,$$

The **objective of treatment** is to correct the acid-base abnormality to a sufficient extent to ward off the harmful effects and partial correction is adequate for most cases. Same guidelines are also applicable for correction of fluid and ele-ctrolyte disorders.

The danger of rapid correction is exemplified by considering the case of metabolic acidosis. In **metabolic acidosis,** there is respiratory compensation and $P_{CO_2}$ is low everywhere in body fluids. Spinal fluid equilibrates with plasma bicarbonate slowly. Now, if **rapid correction** is attempted by $NaHCO_3$ administration, the pH of body fluid elsewhere including plasma rises, the peripheral chemoreceptors become silent and ventilation falls towards normal. The $P_{CO_2}$ rises everywhere including CSF as $CO_2$ diffuses to every compartment quickly but bicarbonate introduced lags behind $CO_2$ in entering CSF. The CSF pH falls further and depression of CNS occurs.

## ➤ 8.17 KEY CONCEPTS

1. The kidney is responsible for maintaining the constancy and volume of the extracellular fluid. The functional unit of the kidney is the glomerulus and its associated nephron. Each day 160 to 180 L of fluid are filtered into the approximately one million nephrons in the human kidney. The glomerular filtration rate (GFR) is dependent on the Starling forces. The amount of a substance filtered into the proximal tubule is called the filtered load. Approximately 20% of the plasma flowing through the glomerulus (RPF) is filtered into the proximal tubule.

   $$\text{Filtration fraction} = \frac{\text{GFR}}{\text{RPF}}$$

   The relative amount of a substance excreted by the kidney (the renal clearance) is expressed as the volume of plasma that is completely cleared of the substance by the kidney. If a substance is filtered but not reabsorbed or secreted, its renal clearance will be equal to the GFR.

   The **clearances of creatinine** or **inulin** are used clinically to measure GFR. If a substance is completely cleared from the plasma during its passage through the kidney by a combination of filtration and secretion, its renal clearance will be equal to the RPF. The clearance of PAH is used clinically to measure RPF.

2. The proximal tubule is responsible for reabsorbing most of the material filtered from the glomerulus.

| Substance | % Reabsorbed | Mechanism |
|---|---|---|
| Na+ | 60-70 | Na/H exchange<br>Na Nutrient cotransport; Diffusion |
| $K^+$, urea; $Cl^-$ | 60-70 | Diffusion. |
| Glucose; amino acids | 100 | Na-Nutrient cotransport |
| Phosphate | 90 | Na-nutrient cotransport |
| Bicarbonate | 85 | Indirectly via $Na^+/H$ exchange |

3. The **loop of Henle** is responsible for producing a dilute filtrate. It reabsorbs approximately 25% of the salt and 15% of the water filtered from the glomerulus.

4. The **distal nephron** is responsible for regulating salt and water balance. Na+ balance is modulated by aldosterone and atrial natriuretic peptide (ANP). Water balance is regulated by ADH (Arginine vasopressin, AVP). K+ balance is regulated by aldosterone.

5. The **extracellular osmolarity** is controlled by ADH and extracellular volume is controlled by the salt content of the extracellular fluid. Salt content is controlled by aldosterone and ANP. Extracellular volume is monitoredby low pressure baroreceptors within the thoracic venous vessels and the atria and by pressure receptors within the afferent arteriole.

6. 15,000 m mol of volatile acid ($CO_2$) and 50 to 100 m eq of fixed acid (Hydrochloric acid, lactic acid, phosphoric acid, sulphuric acid etc.) are produced by metabolism each day. The pH of the extracellular fluid is maintained by buffering the acid as it is formed and excreting the acid overtime. $CO_2$ is rapidly excreted by the lungs. The kidneys require 24 hrs. to excrete the fixed acids.

   $$CO_2 + H_2O \overset{CA}{\longleftrightarrow} H_2CO_3 \longleftrightarrow H^+ + HCO_3^-$$

   When $CO_2$ is added to water, it forms H+ and $HCO_3^-$. The pH of plasma is calculated with the Henderson-Hasselbach equation.

   $$pH = 6.1 + \log \frac{HCO_3^-}{0.03 \cdot PCO_2}$$

   The H+ concentration of plasma is calculated with the Henderson equation.

   $$H^+ = 24 \cdot \frac{PCO_2}{HCO_3^-}$$

   Plasma $PCO_2$ is normally maintained at 40 mm Hg by the central chemoreceptors. Increases in $PCO_2$ cause an increase in ventilation, decreases in $PCO_2$ cause a decrease in ventilation. The respiratory system rapidly eliminates all the $CO_2$ produced by metabolism.

   $$H^+ \longleftrightarrow + HCO_3^- \longleftrightarrow H_2CO_3 \longleftrightarrow CO_2 + H_2O$$

## ➤ 8.17 KEY CONCEPTS

Plasma $HCO_3^-$ concentration is normally maintained at 24 meq/L by the kidneys. $HCO_3^-$ is an important buffer for fixed acids produced by metabolism.

The $HCO_3^-$ lost during the buffering process is replaced by the distal nephron as the fixed acid ($H^+$ + anion) is excreted. The replaced $HCO_3^-$ is called new bicarbonate. The H+ secreted into the urine is buffered by titratable acids (mostly phosphate) and ammonia.

7. The **kidneys** are important endocrine organs. They produce and secrete renin, kinins, 1, 25-dihydroxy vitamin $D_3$, prostaglandin and erythropoietin. **Renin** maintains BP and sodium and potassium balance by activating the *renin – angiotensin – aldosterone system.* **Prostaglandins** and **kinins** are vasoactive and are responsible for regulation and modulation of renal blood flow. **Erythropoietin** enhances red blood cell formation by the bone marrow. 1, 25-dihydroxy vitamin $D_3$ is responsible for reabsorption of $Ca^{2+}$ by gastrointestinal tract and for its deposition in the bone.

8. **Fall of blood pressure** or fall in ECF volume may lead to ischemia of kidney. As a result the juxtaglomerular cells of the kidney produce renin which leads to activation of angiotensinogen into angiotensinogen II. **Angiotensinogen II has several functions** such as :
   - It increases the systemic blood pressure as well as reabsorption of water and electrolytes in the PCT;
   - acts on the adrenal cortex to stimulate production of aldosterone which, in turn, increases $Na^+$ reabsorption and $K^+$ secretion in the collecting duct.

9. **Transport mechanisms** in the membrane facing the tubular lumen help in entry of $Na^+$ down its electrochemical gradient. Active secretion of hydrogen ions occurs not only in PCT but also in DCT and CD. Excretion of metabolic by-products, drugs and toxins also occur in the proximal tubule, being helped by the secretory mechanisms.

10. The **descending limb of loop of Henle** is highly permeable to water and not to solutes, while the ascending limb has almost no permeability for water. Similarly, the proximal part of the distal tubule is not permeable to water but permeable to solutes. As a result, NaCl is reabsorbed from the tubular fluid while passing through the above resulting in dilution of urine.

11. The movement of $Na^+$ across the luminal membrane in the distal tubule occurs through several mechanisms (NaCl cotransport, $Na^+/H^+$ and $Cl^-/HCO_3^-$ antiport, $Na^+$ channel). **Aldosterone** acts on the CD and distal tubular epithelium and stimulates $Na^+$ reabsorption and $K^+$ secretion by the distal tubule and collecting duct.

12. The **kidneys** act in coordination with the **respiratory system** to maintain the acid-base balance. The precise role of kidneys in the above is as follows :
    - they allow excretion of bases like $HCO_3^-$, $SO^{2-}$, $HPO^{2-}$;
    - they produce and collect $HCO_3^-$ ;
    - they excrete $H^+$.

13. All the body fluids have important buffering action. The ICF has slow action but can buffer about 55% of an acid load while the ECF acts fast (within about half an hour) but buffers only about 45% of the acid load.

14. The **normal capacity of bladder** is 300-400 ml. Larger volumes stimulate the desire to micturate. Afferent fibers travel via parasympathetic nerves to the spinal micturition centre ($S_{2,3,4}$). The concentration of the bladder is initiated by parasympathetic efferents. The spinal "micturition center" is normally inhibited by higher motor centers when micturition begins. As such, the bladder empties completely.

15. **Diuretics :** A diurectic is a substance that increases the rate of urine volume output—increased water output in most cases, occurs secondary to inhibition of tubular sodium reabsorption which osmotically cause reduction in water reabsorption. Renal tubular reabsorption of other solutes like $K^+$, $Cl^-$, $Mg^{2+}$, $Ca^{2+}$ is influenced secondarily by sodium reabsorption. Thus, many diuretics increase renal output of these solutes as well.

    **Indications :** Excessive ECF volume especially associated with edema and hypertension.

## ➤ 8.17 KEY CONCEPTS

**Common Diuretics**

| Class | Mode of action | Example | Site |
|---|---|---|---|
| **Osmotic diuretics** | Increased osmolarity of tubular fluid $\xrightarrow{\ominus}$ water and solute reabsorption | Mannitol, Sucrose | **Proximal tubules** |
| **Loop diuretics** | Inhibit Na-K-Cl Cotransport | Frusemide | **Thick ascending loop of Henle** |
| Thiazide diureties | Inhibit Na-Cl cotransport | Chlorothiazide | **Early distal tubules** |
| **Aldosterone inhibitors (competitive)** | Decreases Na+ reabsorption and K+ secretion | Spironolactone | **Collecting tubules** |
| **Sodium channel blockers** | Block entry of Na+ via Na+ channels | Amiloride | **Collecting tubules** |
| **Carbonic anhydrase inhibitors** | Inhibit H+ secretion, $HCO_3^-$ reabsorption and therefore Na+ reabsorption decreases | Acetazolamide | **Proximal tubules** |

## ➤ 8.18 DISORDERS/CLINICAL CORRELATIONS

- **Edema** : Edema is an abnormal accumulation of extracellular fluid within the interstitial spaces. A variety of factors can cause edema including decrease in the plasma protein concentration, obstruction in lymphatic vessels, increased venous pressure and increased capillary permeability. Localised edema follows injury and inflammation of a body part. Systemic oedema is the result of an imbalance between the movement of water out of and into capillaries, that is, between filtration and osmosis. Edema is a symptom rather than a disease. Treatment is done by correcting the specific cause. The volume of tissue fluid may be diminished by a low salt diet and diuretics.

- **Acid base imbalances** : Chemical and physiological buffer systems maintain the hydrogen ion concentration of the body fluids within very narrow pH ranges. Abnormal conditions may disturb the acid base balance, pH of arterial blood is normally 7.35-7.45. A value below 7.35 produces acidosis. A pH above 7.45 produces alkalosis.

  Acidosis results from an accumulation of acids or a loss of bases both of which cause abnormal increase in the hydrogen ion concentrations of body fluids. Conversely, alkalosis results from a loss of acids or an accumulation of bases accompanied by a decrease in hydrogen ion concentration. The two major types of acidosis are respiratory acidosis and metabolic acidosis. Similarly, two major types of alkalosis are respiratory alkalosis and metabolic alkalosis.

  Excessive loss of carbon dioxide and consequent loss of carbonic acid causes respiratory alkalosis. Metabolic alkalosis is due to excessive loss of hydrogen ions or gain of bases.

- **Incontinence and Retention :**

  ***Incontinence*** is inability to hold urine. It can be overflow incontinence or stress incontinence. It can also be due to a vesico-vaginal fistula.

  ***Retention*** means collection of urine in the bladder, either due to obstruction to the urinary outflow or due to paralysis of bladder musculature.

- **Hyponatremia and Hypernatremia :**

  ***Hyponatremia*** means fall in serum concentration of sodium. It can be due to reduced intake of sodium, excessive vomiting or due to excessive diuresis. Patients present with altered sensorium. It is treated with hypertonic saline or oral sodium if the degree of hyponatremia is not severe.

  ***Hypernatremia*** means increased serum concentration of sodium. It is usually due to intake of hypertonic oral rehydration solution in dehydrated children.

## ➤ 8.18 DISORDERS/CLINICAL CORRELATIONS

➤ **Hypokalemia and Hyperkalemia :**

***Hypokalemia*** means reduced concentration of serum potassium. It is usually the result of overzealous diuretic therapy without proper potassium supplementation. It has characteristic ECG manifestations. Treatment is oral or IV potassium supplementation.

***Hyperkalemia*** means increased concentration of serum potassium. It is usually associated with acute or chronic renal failure and acidosis. It can be caused by transfusion of stored blood or in any condition where there is cell destruction and associated release of intracellular $K^+$. It is treated by intravenous $Ca^{2+}$ gluconate, insulin and glucose infusion or by dialysis.

➤ **Urinary tract calculi (Kidney stones)** : Stones in the urinary tract may be found in the kidney, ureter or urinary bladder. They can present with loin pain radiating to groin, hematuria, dysuria or acute retention depending on the location of the stone in the urinary tract. Most of these stones are composed of calcium, uric acid, cystine or struvite (magnesium ammonium phosphate). All are radio-opaque except the uric acid stones which are radiolucent. So most of kidney stones are visible by routine abdominal radiography. Stones composed of uric acid appear as radiolucent filling defects. These stones are treated by removal either surgically or by lithotripsy.

➤ **Glomerular diseases :**

***Glomerulonephritis*** **:** It means inflammation of the glomeruli. It is a bilateral affliction of the kidneys. It is usually secondary to streptococcal infection elsewhere in the body eg, skin lesions. It presents with ↓ volume of urine, hematuria, proteinuria, water retention, generalised edema and occasionally, hypertension. There are various types of glomerulonephritis. Some of these, eg. minimal lesion glomerulonephritis, are benign, respond very well to corticosteroids. Other types, eg. mesangio-proliferative GN, recurs in spite of treatment and ultimately leads to chronic glomerulonephritis. These conditions are treated by salt restriction, corticosteroids, immuno-suppressive therapy etc.

➤ **Renal failure** may be defined as the inability of the kidneys to exrete the by-products of cellular metabolism in adequate quantities. Consequently urea and other nitrogeneous substances accumulate in the blood; oliguria may or may not be present; other manifestations of renal failure incude disturbances of acid base and electrolyte and water balance.

➤ **Anuria** : It means no passage of urine for 24 hours. Oliguria can lead to anuria if it is severe.

➤ **Uremia** : It refers to a constellation of signs and symptoms associated with chronic renal failure of any etiology.

The **clinical features** of uremia depend on the magnitude of decrease in functioning renal mass and the rapidity with which renal function is lost. When the GFR is reduced to 35-50% of normal, overall renal function is sufficient to keep the patient symptom-free although renal reserve is diminished. At this level, biosynthetic excretory and other regulatory functions of kidney are well-maintained; when the GFR is between 20-35% of normal azotemia occurs.

➤ **Oliguria :** It is often the first clinical sign of acute impairment of renal function. It is defined as urine output less than that required to excrete the products of metabolism. A urine volume of less than 400 ml/day in an average size adult male is usually considered to be oliguria. It may be defined as urine output of less than $0.25\ ml.kg^{-1}.h^{-1}$ or $240\ ml.m^{-2}.d^{-1}$.

➤ **Diuresis :** Abnormal increase in urine flow is called **diuresis**. Coffee, tea and alcoholic beverages are diuretics. Certain substances can inhibit sodium ion reabsorption →↓ plasma sodium ion concentration →↓ ADH concentration → inhibition of facultative water reabsorption, mainly at the level of the collecting tubule.

Some chemicals inhibit sodium ion reabsorption and, thus, inhibit osmotic water reabsorption. These chemicals are known as **diuretics**. Thus urinary flow is increased resulting in diuresis.

Diuresis and antidiuresis can be expressed as volume of urine excreted per unit time ($\dot{V}$).

Diuresis = $\uparrow \dot{V}$ due to reduced osmotic water reabsorption and solute reabsorption.

Antidiuresis = $\downarrow \dot{V}$ due to water deprivation and reduced circulating blood volume.

## ➤ 8.18 DISORDERS/CLINICAL CORRELATIONS

➤ **Dysfunction of bladder :**

- ***Lack of normal inhibition :*** It is asssociated with frequency with small volumes of urine and generally occurs in auxiety, cold weather.
- ***Atonic bladder :*** When the bladder is distended, with overflow of urine but there is no desire to micturate eg. diabetes mellitus.
- ***Automatic bladder :*** Bladder empties partially when volume of about 250 ml is reached but the patient has no desire to micturate.
- ***Autonomous bladder :*** It occurs with LMN cord lesion at $S_{2,3,4}$ level. There is large residual urine volume but bladder contraction is weak and uncoordinated with no desire to micturate.

**(a) Relationship between $PCO_2$, $HCO_3^-$ and pH, and the Henderson–Hasselbalch equation**

$$CO_2 + H_2O \Leftrightarrow H_2CO_3 \Leftrightarrow HCO_3^- + H^+$$

$$K = \frac{[HCO_3^-] \times [H^+]}{[H_2CO_3]} \quad \text{(From Law of Mass Action)}$$

$$\log K = \log [H^+] + \log \frac{[HCO_3^-]}{[H_2CO_3]}$$

K = dissociation constant;
$K_A$ = corrected for $CO_2$
Solubility (s) =
0.0039 ($PCO_2$ in kPA)
0.3 (mmHg)

$$-\log [H^+] = -\log K + \log \frac{[HCO_3^-]}{[H_2CO_3]}$$

$$pH = pK + \log \frac{[HCO_3^-]}{[H_2CO_3]}$$

But: $[H_2CO_3] \propto [CO_2]$ ($K_A$ = 6.1)
and: $[CO_2] = PCO_2 \times s$ (solubility)

$$pH = 6.1 + \log \frac{[HCO_3^-]}{PCO_2 \times s}$$

**(b) Davenport diagram: relationship between $PCO_2$, $HCO_3^-$ and pH**

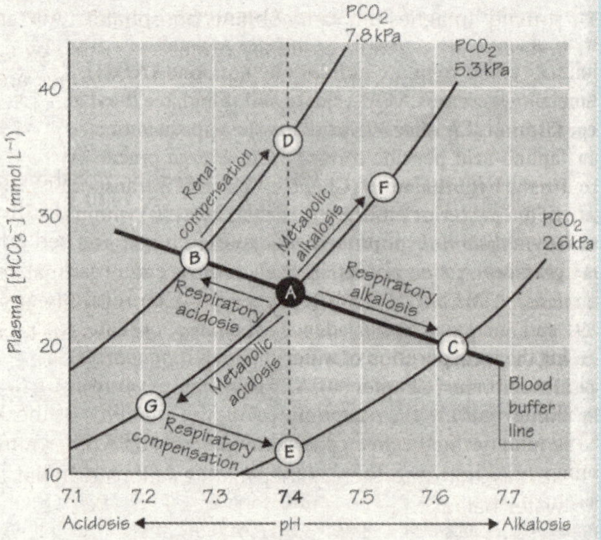

# Endocrine Physiology

AGENDA :



9

## ➤ 9.1 CHAPTER OVERVIEW

**Endocrine system,** along with the nervous system, acts as an important homeostatic control mechanism. The mediators of the functions of the endocrine system are **hormones** which are carried in circulation to distant cells where they act. Hormones act through receptors that are either ***intracellular*** (in case of **steroid hormones**) or on ***the cell membrane*** (in case of **peptide hormones**). Hypothalamus plays a key role in regulating several aspects of the endocrine system.

**The pituitary gland** is the master endocrine gland that secretes a number of trophic hormones which stimulate release of hormones from other endocrine glands. The **anterior pituitary hormones are *TSH, ACTH, FSH, LH, GH*** and ***prolactin*. Secretion of those hormones** are under control of ***hypothalamic releasing/inhibiting factors like TRH, CRH, GnRH, GHRH and PIH***. The posterior pituitary secretes vasopressin or **ADH** (important for osmoregulation) and **oxytocin** (concerned with milk ejection reflex and contraction of uterus during labor).

The **thyroid hormones** ($T_3$ and $T_4$) are derivatives of the amino acid tyrosine and maintain the optimal metabolic activity of the body. Glucocorticoids, mineralocorticoids and sex steroids are secreted by different parts of the adrenal cortex. Glucocorticoids have important actions on metabolic activity and are important during periods of stress. **Mineralocorticoids** are involved mainly with fluid and electrolyte balance. **Sex steroids** play an important role as regards secondary sexual characteristic and sexual function. **Catecholamines** are released from the adrenal medulla and they, in conjunction with the autonomic nervous system, hold a key position in the homeostatic regulation of different systems including the CVS (Cardiovascular system).

The **endocrine pancreas** (islets of Langerhans) secretes insulin, glucagon and somatostatin. Insulin is the principal hormone that regulates glucose metabolism.

**Parathormone** (PTH), secreted by the parathyroid glands, regulates blood calcium and phosphate levels. **Calcitonin,** a hormone secreted by the parafollicular cells of the thyroid gland, and calcitriol (the active form of vitamin D) are also important regulators of blood calcium level.

Deficiency or excess of an individual hormone or a group of hormones have remarkable physiological consequences leading to well-defined disease states or syndromes. Features analogous to hormone deficiency or excess states may occur due to abnormalities in the receptor/post-receptor level as well.

## ➤ 9.2 Introduction

The **endocrine system** consists of glands which have no direct anatomical links and are commonly termed as **ductless glands** because the hormones they secrete pass directly into the blood. The **endocrine** or **'ductless'** glands secrete chemical substances (hormones) directly into the blood stream. The hormones then travel to other organs where they bring about their effects influencing the function, growth and nutrition of these organs (Fig. 9.1).

The endocrine glands are **pituitary gland, parathyroid glands, thyroid gland, adrenal glands, islets of Langerhans of pancreas, pineal gland, thymus gland, ovaries** and **testes.**

Many endocrine glands are stimulated by hormones secreted by the pituitary gland known as **'trophic'** hormones (the glands that are affected are known as **'target'** organs). These target glands then secrete their hormones into the blood stream and their concentration is, in turn, measured by the hypothalamus, which regulates the output of 'trophic' hormones. This is known as **'negative feedback'**.

A diagram (Fig. 9.1a) shows the mechanism of 'negative feedback'.

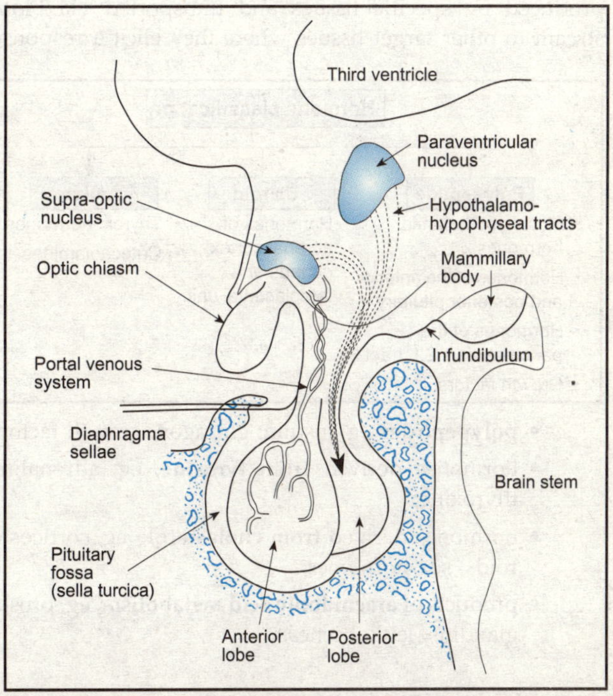


Fig. 9.1 : Endocrine system

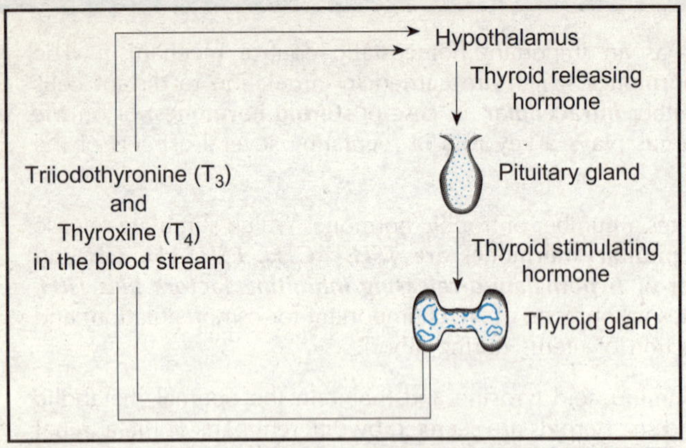


**Fig. 9.1a : Mechanism of negative feedback**

Raised levels of $T_3$ and $T_4$ in the blood stream lead to reduced amounts of thyroid releasing hormone production. Reduced levels of $T_3$ and $T_4$ in the blood stream lead to increased production of thyroid releasing hormone.

Some non-endocrine organs secrete hormone by isolated cells without forming any organized gland e.g. gastrointestinal tract, kidney, heart, secreting gastrin, renin, ANP, (atrial natriuretic peptide) respectively.

**The hypothalamus** controls both autonomic nervous activity and several aspects of endocrine function. It is located close to the third ventricle in the forebrain. It is linked up by the hypophyseal stalk to the pituitary gland.

**Hormones** may be defined as molecules which are produced by specific tissues and transported via blood stream to other target tissues where they elicit a response.

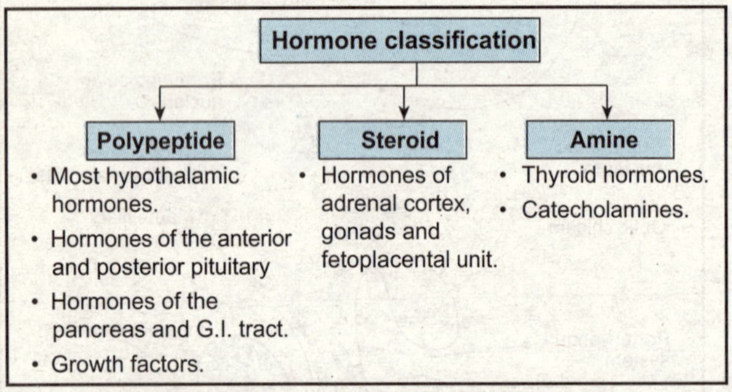


- **polypeptides** eg, insulin; glucagon; growth factors;
- hormones derived **from tyrosine,** eg, adrenaline; thyroxine;
- hormones derived **from cholesterol,** eg, corticosteroids, sex hormones;
- products of **arachidonic acid metabolism,** eg, prostaglandins, leukotrienes.

### General features of hormones

Hormones carry information to cells. They are normally part of regulatory systems. The hormone concentration in the plasma can vary widely, eg, insulin, catecholamines, ADH and aldosterone. Again, hormone concentration may vary little. Thyroxine is a good example.

The **functions** of hormones are multiple and complex :

(i) development of physical, sexual and mental characteristics are promoted;

(ii) promotion of adjustment of performance levels;

(iii) to maintain homeostatic function.

**Hormone functions :**

(i) hormones can act **directly on the target organs** e.g., sex hormones;

(ii) they can regulate the synthesis and release of effector hormones, eg, thyrotropic hormones.

### Transport in blood

**Hormones** are carried in the plasma. The hormone may be **free** in the plasma or **bound** to binding proteins. Generally, the steroid, thyroid and a few polypeptide hormones circulate in plasma largely **bound** to **plasma proteins** :

On the other hand, most of the peptide hormones, catecholamines, prostaglandins are carried in the plasma in free form.

## ➤ 9.3 Mechanisms of Hormone Action

**Steroid** — Cholesterol, Aldosterone, Progesterone, Testosterone.

**Protein** — (from peptides) → TSH; FSH, LH, prolactin oxytocin; Insulin; glucagon.

**Derivatives of amino acid** — tyrosine — T3 T4. Epinephrine, Nor epinephrine, Dopamine.

### Introduction

Any hormone that causes changes in the target cells does not act directly on **cellular structure**. First hormone combines with receptors present in the target cells to form receptor-hormone complex, which may be on the cell membrane, cytoplasm, or nucleus.

Cell membrane —Catecholamines
Pituitary gland
Parathyroid gland

Cytoplasm — Steroid hormones

Nucleus — Thyroid hormones

### Mechanism of Hormone action

1. Altering the permeability of cell membrane: Neurotransmitters in a synapse or Neuromuscular junction act by changing the permeability of post synaptic membrane.

Ach reaches post synaptic membrane **receptor** → open $Na^+$ gated channel → $Na^+$ enters neuromuscular junction from ECF → $Na^+$ alter RMP → E.P.P. developed.

2. By activating the intracellular enzyme (protein hormones and catecholamine) :

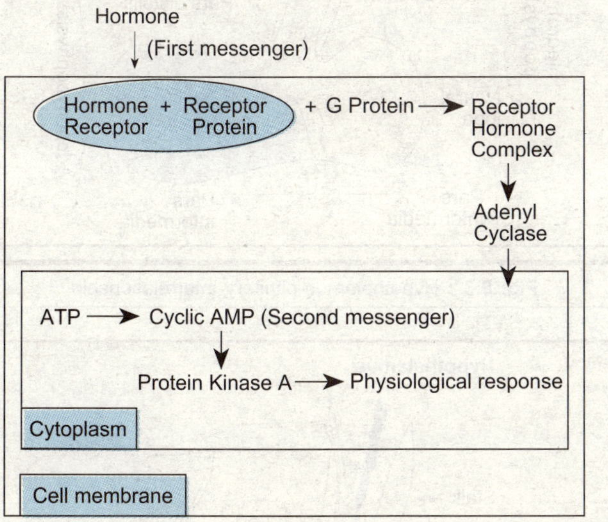


First messenger (Hormone) → Receptor hormone complex → Second messenger (cyclic AMP) → Effect of the hormone inside the cell.

**Formation of cyclic AMP :**

I. Receptor protein + another protein (G Protein) → Receptor Hormone complex → This complex activates enzyme Adenyl cyclase (cell membrane) → protrudes in cytoplasm → converts to ATP → cyclic AMP (second messenger)

II. **$Ca^{2+}$ ions and Calmodulin or TroponinC** : By increasing Calcium ion which acts as (second messenger) which binds with TroponinC → Skeletal muscle contraction or with calmodulin → Smooth muscle contraction.

III. By IP3 (Inositol triphosphate)

IV. DAG — Diacylglycerol

V. cGMP Cyclic guanosine monophosphate

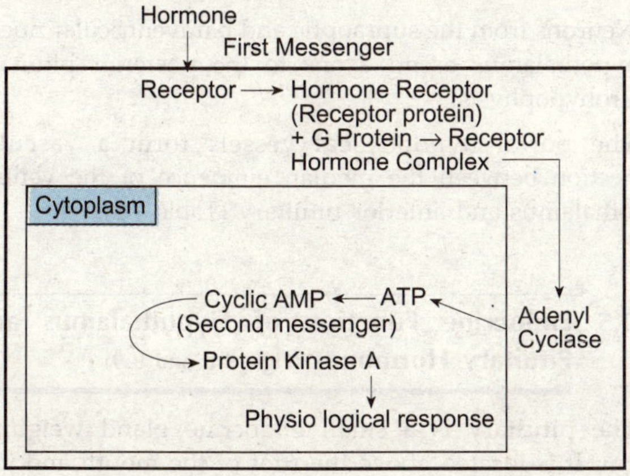


3. **By acting on Genes** (Thyroid and Steroid hormones) : The hormone enters the interior of the cell and binds with receptor in cytoplasm (Steroid hormone) or in nucleus (thyroid hormone) forming receptor hormone complex. This complex is transported towards DNA.

The binding of receptor-hormone complex to DNA increases transcription of mRNA. The mRNA moves out of nucleus and reaches ribosomes and activates them.

The ribosomes produce large quantities of proteins, which cause the physiological responses in the target cells.

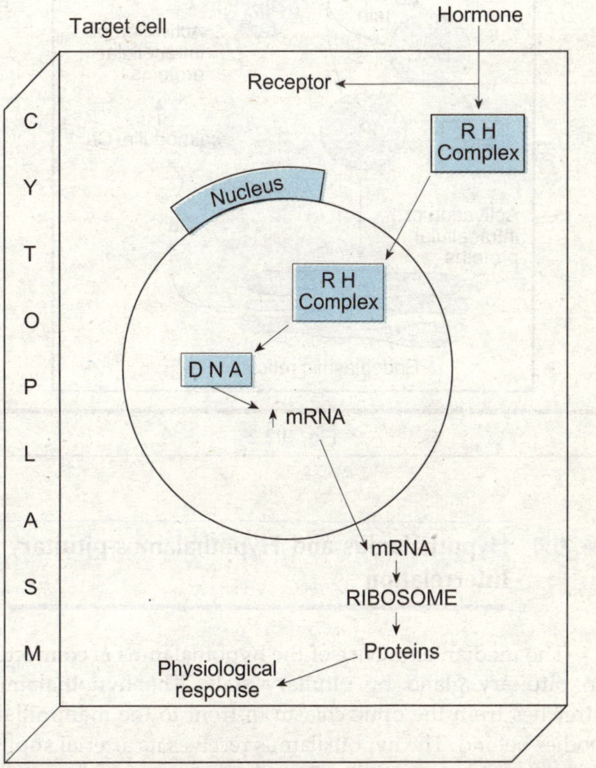


**Fig. 9.2.1**

**IP3 :** It is formed from phosphatidyl inositol diphosphate (PIP2). Some hormone-receptor complexes activate the enzyme phospholipase which converts PIP2 into IP3 (Fig. 9.2.2).

**IP3 :** Proteinkinase C → physiological response

**DAG :** Produced from PIP2. It acts on protein kinase C → response.

**cGMP :** It acts on protein kinase — A

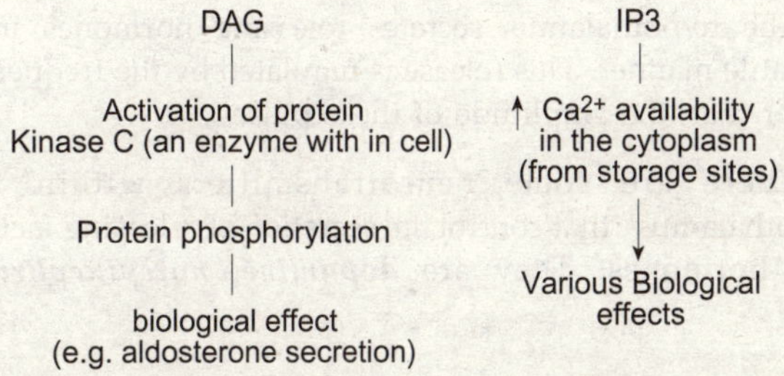

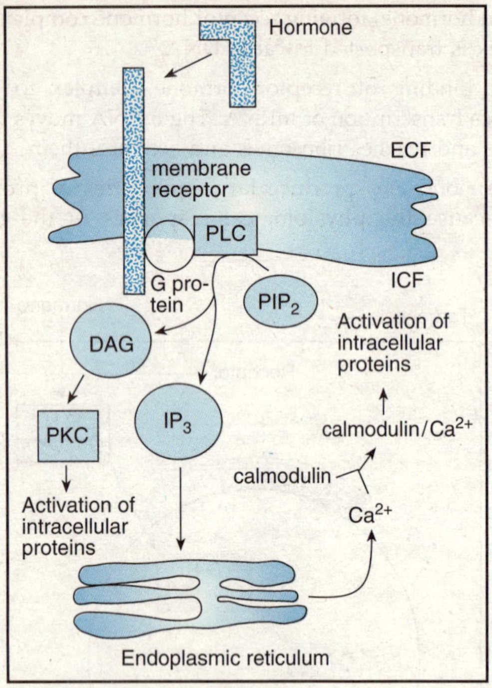


Fig. 9.2.2

## ➤ 9.4 Hypothalamus and Hypothalamus-pituitary Interrelation

The median eminence of the hypothalamus is connected to pituitary gland by pituitary stalk. The hypothalamus stretches from the optic chiasm in front to the mammillary bodies behind. The hypothalamus receives its arterial supply from the circle of Willis. The supraoptic nucleus and the paraventricular nucleus synthesise posterior pituitary hormones.

The activity of central nervous system is converted into a chemical signal and the hypothalamus (together with adrenal medulla and pineal gland) is referred to as a 'neuro-endocrine transducer'.

### Hormones and factors of the hypothalamus

The median eminence of the hypothalamus synthesizes hypothalamic releasing and inhibiting hormones (Figs. 9.3 and 9.4).

The hypothalamus secretes releasing hormones in a pulsatile manner. This release is regulated by the frequency rather than the amplitude of these pulses.

There are some neurotransmitters within the hypothalamus that control the secretion of releasing factors and hormones. They are ***dopamine, norepinephrine,***

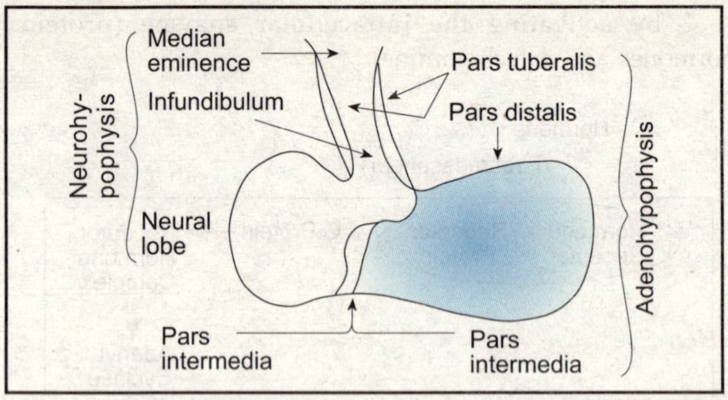


Fig. 9.3 : Hypothalamus-pituitary interrelationship

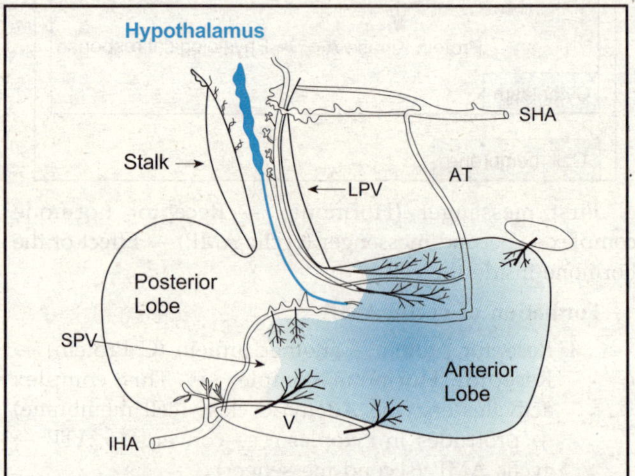


Fig. 9.4 : Vascular supply of pituitary gland

***calcitonin; γ-amino-butyric acid, serotonin, substance P*** and ***endorphins.***

### Hypothalamic Regulatory Hormones

Neurons from the supraoptic and paraventricular nuclei of hypothalamus asend axons to the posterior pituitary (Neurohypophysis).

The portal hypophyseal vessels form a vascular connection between the median eminence of the ventral hypothalamus and anterior pituitary (Table 9.2).

## ➤ 9.5 Endocrine Function of Hypothalamus and Pituitary Hormones (Figs. 9.8 and 9.9)

The **pituitary** is a small endocrine gland weighing 0.5 gm. It is located above the roof of the mouth and just below the hypothalamus. ***It synthesis :***

**Mechanisms of Hormone Action (Summary)**

**On cell membrane**

**Via cyclic adenosine 3′5′ monophosphate (cAMP)** as a **'second messenger'** polypeptide hormones (ACTH, ADH, TSH, LH, PTH and glucagon), many biogenic amines and some prostaglandins. The first messenger is the hormone that binds to the membrane receptor and leads to activation of the membrane bound enzyme adenyl cyclase which converts Adenosine triphosphate to cyclic AMP (cAMP). cAMP exerts biologic activity via the phosphorylation of cAMP dependent protein kinases which can lead to the activation or the inactivation of other proteins.

**By controlof membrane permeability** (not via cyclic AMP) e.g. insulin-induced increased entry of glucose into cells. Other peptide hormones that may change membrane permeability include GH, ACTH, ADH and PTH.

**In Cytosol**

**Via a hormone-receptor complex,** e.g. mainly steroid hormones, T3, T4 and Somatomedin. Binding of free hormone to specific cytosol receptor proteins in target cells. The hormone-receptor complex then migrates to the nucleus, where the usual effect is to produce an increase in mRNA synthesis.

**Table 9.1**
**Peptide, steroid and amino acid derivative hormones**

| | | Hormones | Source | Production | Plasma form | Receptor |
|---|---|---|---|---|---|---|
| **Polypeptide** | | Most hypothalamic hormones, Hormones of the anterior and posterior pituitary, Hormones of the pancreas and G.I. Tract, Growth factors. | Hypothalamus, pituitary gland, pancreas, parathyroid | rER | Unbound | Cell membrane |
| **Steroids** | | Glucocorticoids, mineralo-corticoids, androgen, vit. D, estrogen, progesterone | Adrenal cortex, ovaries, testes, placenta | sER | Protein bound | Cytoplasm |
| **Amino acid derivative** | Steroid-like function | Thyroxine ($T_4$) Triiodothyronine ($T_3$) | Thyroid gland, nerves | Cytoplasm | Protein bound | Nucleus |
| | Peptide-like function | Epinephrine, norepinephrine, dopamine | Adrenal medulla | Cytoplasm | Unbound | Cell membrane |

**Table 9.2**

| Hypothalamic hormone | Pituitary hormone released | Functions |
|---|---|---|
| **Releasing Hormones** | | |
| Thyrotrophin releasing hormone (TRH) | TSH and Prolactin | Stimulates thyroid gland to produce thyroxine. |
| Growth hormone releasing hormone (GHRH) | GH; Insulin; glucagon, gastrin release | Stimulates linear growth in epiphyseal cartilages |
| Prolactin-releasing hormone (PRH) | Prolactin | Stimulates Lactogenesis. |
| Corticotrophin releasing hormone (CRH) | ACTH | Stimulates adrenal gland to produce corticosteroids and sex hormones. |
| Gonadotrophin releasing hormone (Luteinizing hormone) | LH and FSH | Stimulates ovarian follicles and production of estrogen and progesterone. |
| **Inhibitory Hormones** | | |
| Prolactin-inhibiting factor or dopamine (PIF) | Suppresses release of prolactin; Luteotrophin | Reduces lactogenesis |
| Growth hormone inhibiting hormone (GHIH) or somatostatin. | GH, TSH, FSH | Reduces linear growth in epiphyseal cartilages. |

**It synthesises :**

| *Hormones* | *Target* | *Physiological functions* |
|---|---|---|
| *Glycoprotein family :* | | |
| **TSH** | Thyroid gland | ↑ Synthesis and secretion of thyroid hormones |
| **FSH** | Ovary | ↑ growth of follicles; ↑ estrogen |
| | Testis | ↑ maturation of sperm ↑ (Sertoli cells) |
| **LH** | Ovary | ↑ Formation of corpus luteum |
| | Testis | Leydig cells for ↑ Testosterone |
| *Growth hormone/Prolactin family :* | | |
| **GH** | Tissues | ↑ Growth; ↑Protein synthesis; ↑ Glucose utilisation |
| **Prolactin** | Mammary gland | ↑ Milk formation; ↑ Growth of breast |
| *Proopiomelanocortin family :* | | |
| **ACTH** | Adrenal cortex | ↑ Adrenal cortical hormones |
| **β Lipoprotein** | ? | ? |
| **β Endorphin** | ? | ? |

The instructions from the central nervous system and blood-borne factors from target organs regulate the anterior pituitary gland and hypothalamus. **The anterior pituitary gland** secretes **six main hormones** which act directly on tissue target cells or on other endocrine cells and also have effects on reproduction, metabolism and development.

Prolactin causes development of breast and is responsible for milk production after childbirth. FSH and LH act directly on the development of the germ cells and cause the gonads to act as endocrine organs. ***The following are the other newly discovered peptides :***

***Melanocyte stimulating hormone*** is produced from the pars intermedia. Function is not clear. There are two types of MSH in animals — **α-MSH** and **β-MSH**. The structure of α-MSH is closely related to residues 1-13 of ACTH as is evident in hypoadrenalism. There is increased synthesis of melanin and hyperpigmentation if there is excess production of MSH or ACTH. MSH secretion is controlled by releasing or inhibiting hypothalamic neurohormones. The melanocyte stimulating hormone (MSH) contains 13 and 22 amino acids. In mammals, MSH is responsible for skin pigmentation.

## 9.6 Physiology of Anterior Pituitary

The anterior pituitary develops from **Rathke's pouch** which is an upward evagination of the ectoderm of the

**Table 9.3 : Peptides and their functions**

| ***Gastrin*** | ***Gastric acid secretion is increased*** |
|---|---|
| **CCK** | Gall bladder contraction, pancreatic enzyme secretion |
| **Secretin** | Pancreatic bicarbonate secretion is increased. |
| **Gastric inhibitory peptide (GIP)** | Insulin release is stimulated, gastric acid inhibition |
| Motilin | Motility is increased |
| **Vasoactive intestinal peptide (VIP)** | Muscle is relaxed, vasodilatation |
| **Somatostatin** | Oppose the release of peptide |
| **Substance P** | Contraction of muscle, vasodilation |
| **Bombesin** | Peptides are released |
| **Neurotensin** | Trophic agent, vasodilatation |

pharyngeal roof. **Pars tuberalis** is formed from the proliferation of cells of the upper part. The posterior part forms the **pars intermedia**. The **anterior lobe** is derived from the primitive gut and the posterior lobe (neural lobe) is derived from the brain stem. The pituitary is located in a depression in the sphenoid, the *sella turcica*. The hypothalamus is located immediately above the pituitary gland (Fig. 9.1).

The pituitary gland is described as the **"master gland"** as its hormones control the growth and activity of thyroid, adrenals and gonads.

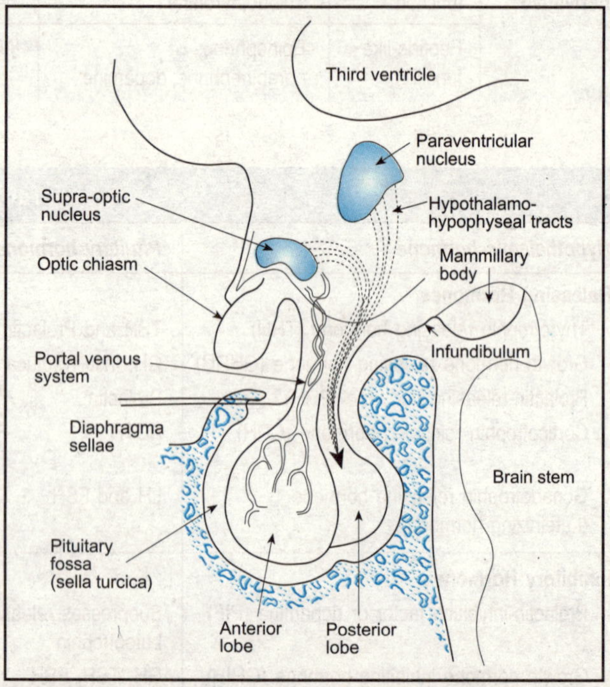


**Fig. 9.5 : Endocrine system**

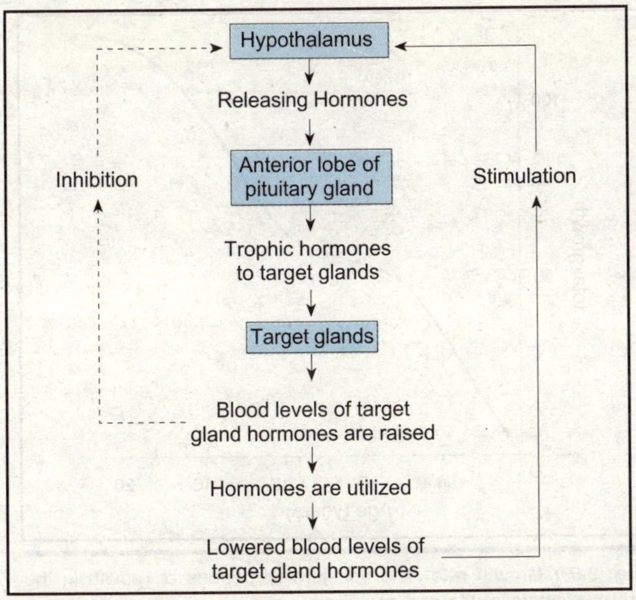


**Fig. 9.6 : Endocrine function of hypothalamus**

The pituitary gland is connected to the hypothalamus by a thin stalk known as **infundibulum.**

Histologically, the **anterior** lobe consists of large polygonal cells arranged in cords and covered with sinusoidal capillary system. The **posterior** lobe consists of two major portions : the *infundibulum* or *stalk* and the *infundibular processor* or *neural lobe.* The posterior lobe is richly supplied with nonmyelinated nerve fibers that contain electron dense secretory granules.

The anterior lobe is connected to the brainstem by the hypothalamo-hypophyseal portal system.

**Anterior pituitary gland histology :**

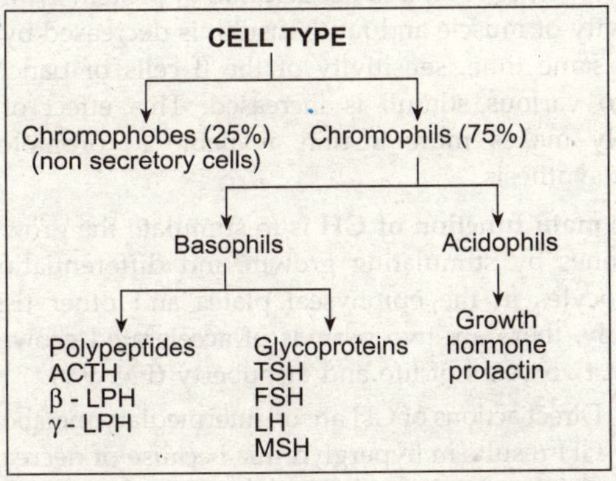


**Adrenocorticotropic hormone** : Adrenocorticotropic hormone (ACTH) is produced in response to corticotropin releasing hormone (CRH) from the hypothalamus. Endogenous opiate β-endorphin and precursor of melanocyte stimulating hormone are also synthesized along with ACTH. ACTH stimulates the flow of blood to the adrenal cortex. Concentrations of cholesterol and steroids, particularly cortisol are increased in the adrenal gland.

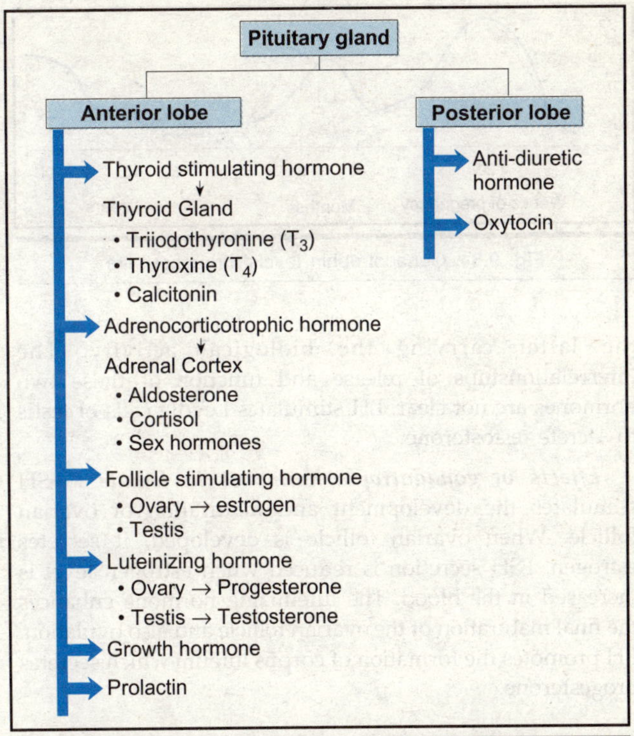


**Fig. 9.7 : Pituitary gland and its hormones**

***Thyroid stimulating hormone (TSH) or thyrotropin*** is secreted in response to thyrotropin releasing hormone from the hypothalamus. Growth and activity of the thyroid gland are stimulated by this hormone and, subsequently, $T_3$ (tri-iodothyronine) and $T_4$ (tetraiodothyronine/thyroxine) are secreted. It is a glycoprotein having two polypeptide chains α and β.

**Prolactin** : It is a protein with a molecular weight of 24,000. Chemically, it is similar to growth hormone.

*Control of secretion :* It is inhibited by hypothalamic factors. Dopamine is the main prolactin inhibitory factor. Serotonin and TRH stimulate prolactin release. Estrogen enhances prolactin synthesis.

***Function of prolactin*** : High levels of prolactin inhibit pulsatile GnRH secretion and estrogen secretion by the ovary.

***Gonadotropic hormones*** : These are released in response to luteinizing hormone releasing hormone (LHRH). This is also known as **gonadotropin releasing hormone (GnRH)** and is released from the hypothalamus.The gonadotropins have molecular weight of 28,000. They are metabolized in the liver and kidneys and a significant fraction is excreted in urine. LH has a half life of around 20 min and FSH twice this.

***Effects of gonadotropic hormones (FSH and LH)* in male** : FSH stimulates the epithelial tissue of the seminiferous tubules in the testis resulting in spermatozoa production. Both FSH and LH are glycoproteins with an α and β-chain,

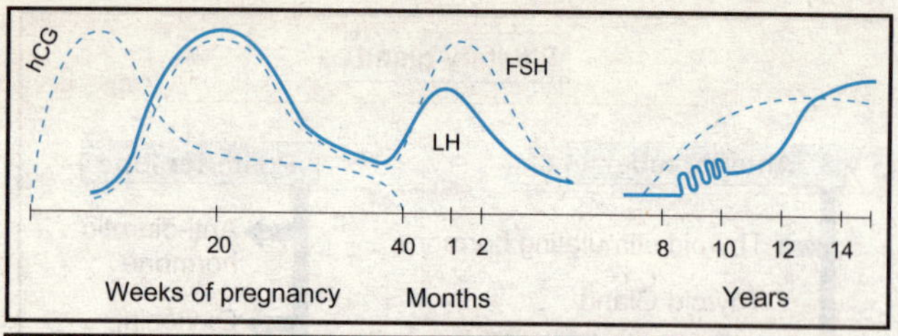


Fig. 9.8 : Gonadotrophin levels throughout life

the latter carrying the biological activity. The interrelationships of release and function of these two hormones are not clear. LH stimulates Leydig cells of testis to secrete testosterone.

***Effects of gonadotropic hormones in female*** : FSH stimulates the development and maturation of ovarian follicle. When ovarian follicle is developed, it secretes estrogen. FSH secretion is reduced when estrogen level is increased in the blood. The luteinizing hormone enhances the final maturation of the ovarian follicle and also ovulation. LH promotes the formation of corpus luteum which secretes progesterone.

## Growth Hormone (GH)

**Effects on skeletal growth :** Growth hormone promotes skeletal growth by stimulating cellular proliferation in the epiphyseal plates causing columns of chondrocytes to elongate and epiphyseal plates to widen. It may also help in remodeling of bones.

These effects are mediated by insulin like growth factors (**IGF–I** and **IGF-II**), previously called **somatomedins** (somatotropin mediators). The availability of GH, in general, is reflected by the plasma concentration of IGF-I. It is more or less clear that IGF-I accounts for almost all the growth-promoting actions of GH including stimulation of cell division in cartilage and other tissues.

**IGF-I** and **IGF-II** are very similar in structure to proinsulin. They are small unbranched peptides having molecular weights of about 7,500. The IGF-I receptors are also similar to insulin receptors. When stimulated, these receptors catalyze phosphorylation of some of its own tyrosine residues as well as those of some other proteins. Most of the circulating IGF-I is secreted by the liver and is protein bound; the most important binding protein is IGF BP-3 whose synthesis is regulated by GH. Both IGF-I and its binding proteins are produced locally in target cells for IGF as well.

**Direct effects of IGF-1 :**

- Stimulates an increase in organ size and function.
- Has dramatic effects on the chondrocytes in bone.
- Increases transcription, protein synthesis, chondroitin sulfate incorporation and cell size number, all of which lead to an increase in linear growth.

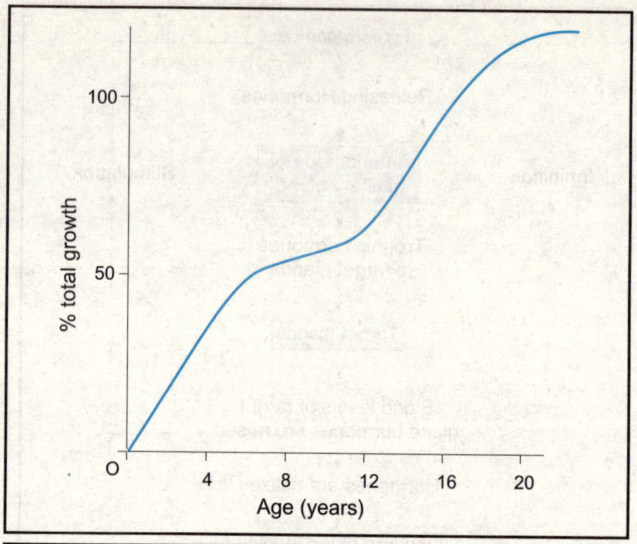


Fig. 9.9 : Growth rate. The accelerated periods of growth in the first two years of life and at puberty

**Effects on body composition :** GH increases body protein stores, particularly in muscles, with relative decrease in fat (by lowering the amount of intracellular triacylglycerols). However, differentiation of preadipocytes into fat cells in young children appears to be GH dependent. Growth of most of the internal organs proportionate to the body is regulated by GH. GH appears to have little role in the growth of thyroid, gonads or reproductive organs.

**Effects on energy metabolism :** Metabolic effects of GH are independent of IGF-I. GH causes decrease in the rate of glucose uptake in tissues (especially muscle and adipose tissue), preservation of glycogen stores in muscle, breakdown of stored triacylglycerol in adipose tissue (increasing plasma concentration of FFA) and acceleration of protein synthesis. Sensitivity of muscle and fat to insulin is decreased by GH. At the same time, sensitivity of the β cells of pancreatic islets to various stimuli is increased. This effect of GH probably makes more insulin available to promote net protein synthesis.

The **main function of GH** is to stimulate the growth of long bones by stimulating growth and differentiation of chondrocytes in the epiphyseal plates and other tissues. Generally, there are two periods of accelerated growth; in the first two years of life and at puberty (Fig. 9.9).

- Direct actions of GH are on intermediary metabolism. GH results in hyperglycemia because of decrease in glucose uptake and increase in glucose production.
- **Adipose tissue** : glucose uptake is decreased and increased lipolysis leading to a decrease in adiposity.
- **Muscle :** Decrease in glucose uptake and increase in aminoacid uptake and protein synthesis leading to an increase in lean body mass.
- **Liver :** Increase in gluconeogenesis and increase in IGP - 1 release

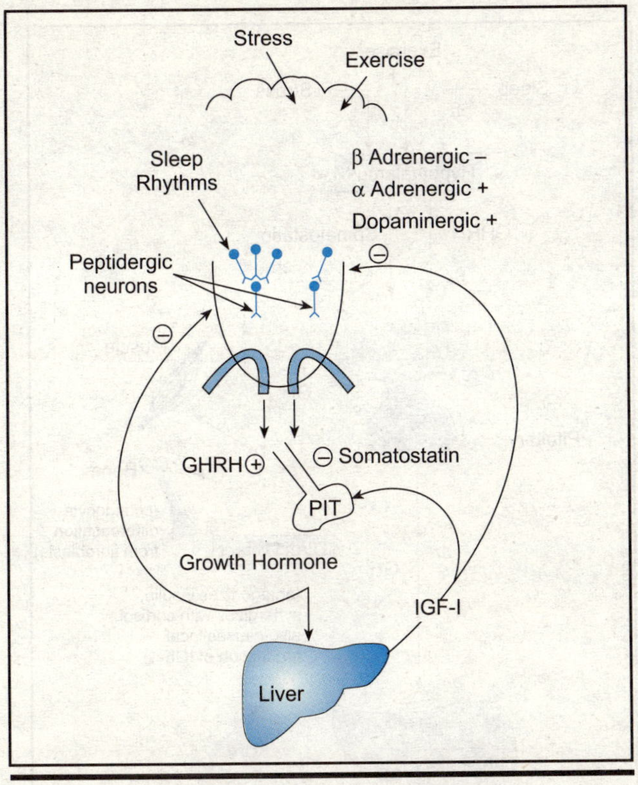


**Fig. 9.10 : Control of GH secretion**

- **Metabolic effects of growth hormone :** (Protein synthesis is in increased, stimulation of lipolysis; Intestinal absorption of calcium is increased, renal absorption of phosphate is increased; positive nitrogen balance and insulin antagonism.

### Disorders involving GH

**GH deficiency :**

- Childhood hypopituitarism, isolated GH deficiency lead to short stature (dwarfism)
- Childhood hypogonadism

**GH excess :**

- Childhood — gigantism
- Postpubertal — acromegaly.

### Hormonal control of GH secretion (Fig. 9.10)

**Posterior pituitary gland** and ADH & Oxytocin.

Oxytocin and vasopresin are synthetized in separate neurons whose cell bodies are located in the S.O.N. & PVN of the hypothalamus. They are formed as preprohormone molecules and packaged in secretory vesicles in the golgiapparatus.

Two classes of receptors linked to separate transduction system : $V_1$ receptors signal vascular muscle contraction by means of phospho inositol pathway whereas V2 receptors use the cAMP system to produce antidiuretic effect in renal tubules.

**Table 9.4**
**Abnormalities of pituitary function**

| *Deficient secretion* | *Excess secretion* |
|---|---|
| • Lack of ACTH — corticosteroid deficiency | • Elevated ACTH — corticosteroid excess |
| • Lack of TSH–thyroid deficiency | • Elevated prolactin — reproductive function is impaired |
| • Lack of FSH/LH–sexual function is disturbed | • Elevated hGH — abnormal growth |
| • Lack of hGH (childhood)–dwarfism | • Elevated ADH–fluid retention and low plasma osmolality |
| • Lack of ADH–diabetes insipidus | |

### ADH

- It **increases water reabsorption** from distal convoluted tubule and collecting duct in the kidney.
- It **increases permeability of membrane** of DCT & C.D. acting through cyclic AMP.
- **In large amounts, it causes constriction of the arteries** in all parts of the body vasoconstriction →↑B.P.

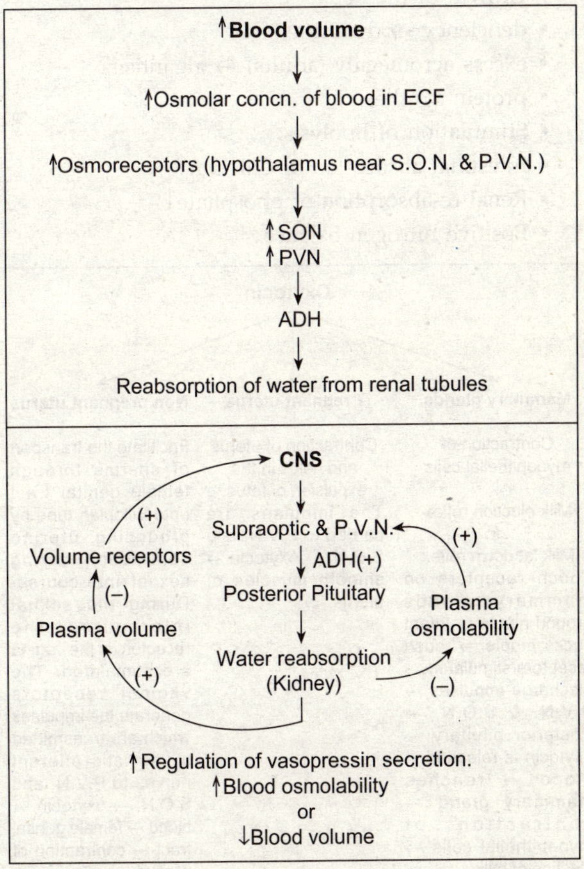

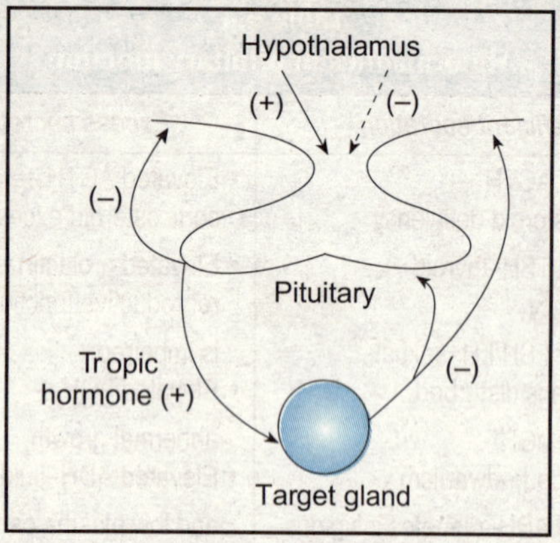


**Fig. 9.11 : Summary of regulation of anterior pituitary hormone secretion**

**Oxytocin :**

- Mainly by P.V.N. (Para ventricular n.)
- Small quantity by S.O.N. (Supra optic n.)
- Oxytocin appears to act through a single receptor that signals through the phosphoinositol pathway.

1. **Growth hormone :**
- Growth of all the tissues of the body.
- Size and No. of cells increased by mitotic division.
- Growth of the body.
- deficiency → dwafism.
- excess acromegaly (adults) → gigantism.
- protein synthesis↑
- Stimulation of lipolysis.
- Intestinal absorption of Calcium↑
- Renal re-absorption of phosphate↑
- Positive nitrogen balance.

**Oxytocin**

**Mammary glands** ↓ Contraction of myoepithelial cells ↓ Milk ejection reflex or Milk let down reflex. Touch receptors on mammary glands around nipple → infant sucks nipple → touch receptors stimulated → discharge impulses → P.V.N. & S.O.N. → Posterior pituitary → oxytocin is released in blood → reaches mammary gland → contraction of myoepithelial cells → ejection of milk.

**Pregnant uterus** ↓ Contraction of uterus and helps in the expulsion of fetus. The impulses are carried to P.V.N. and S.O.N. → oxytocin → smooth muscles of uterus.

**Non pregnant uterus** ↓ Facilitate the transport of sperms through female genital tract upto fallopian tube by producing uterine contraction during sexual intercourse. During the sexual intercourse the receptors in the vagina are stimulated. The vaginal receptors generate the impulses which are transmitted by somatic afferent nerves to P.V.N. and S.O.N. → oxytocin → blood → female genital tract → contraction of uterus → Fallopan tube.

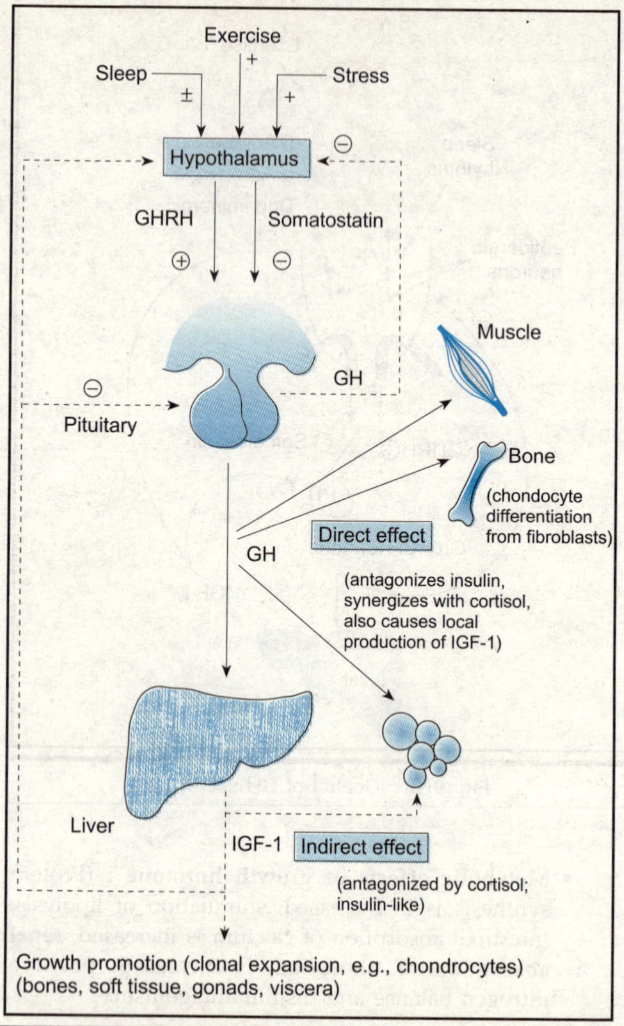


**Fig. 9.12 : Main actions of growth hormone and factors that regulate its secretion.**

**Somatomedin**

Insulin like growth factor I (IGF I)

Insulin like growth factor II.

IGF-I acts on bones & causes growth and other effects on bones.

**Regulation of growth hormone (Fig. 9.12)**

Growth hormone releasing hormone from hypothalamus causes release of growth hormone from ant. pit. Growth hormone acts on various tissues. It also activates the liver cells to secrete somatomedin C(IGF—I). IGF—I, in turn suppresses the release of growth hormone from anterior pituitary. IGF—I causes release of somatostatin (GHIH) from hypothalamus. GHIH inhibits release of growth hormone from pituitary whenever the blood level of growth hormone is decreased, GHRH is secreted from the hypothalamus. This inturn causes secretion of growth hormone from the pituitary.

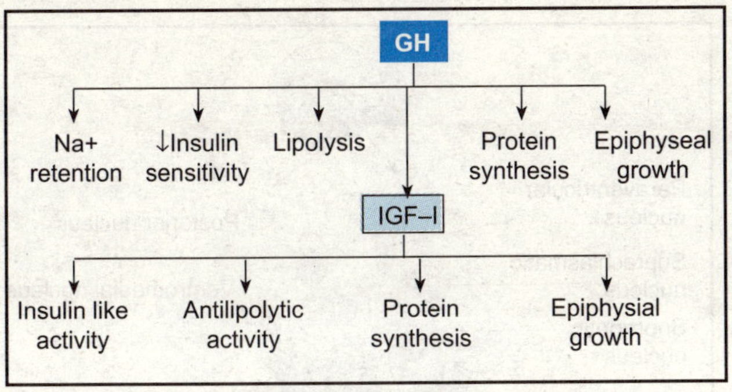


**1. Functions of Insulin; IGF-1 and IGF-II :**

| | Insulin | IGF—I | IGF—II |
|---|---|---|---|
| Other name | | SomatomedinC | Multiplication; Stimulating activity. |
| Source | β cell | Liver and other tissues | Diverse tissues |
| Major role | Control of metabolism | Skeleton and cartilage growth | Growth during fetal development |

**2. TSH—Function :**

- ↑No. of thyroid cells (cuboidal) → (columnar cells) → development of thyroid follicles.
- ↑iodine pump activity of iodine trapping in the cells.
- ↑thyroglobulin secretion into the follicles.

**Mode of action :** Via cyclic AMP.

**3. Adrenocorticotropic Hormone :**

- It maintains structural integrity and vascularization of Zona faciculate and Zona reticularis of adrenal cortex.
- It converts cholesterol into pregnenenolone. Thus ACTH is responsible for synthesis of glucocorticoids.
- Cause release of glucocorticoids.
- mobilizes fat from tissues.

Cortisol by a negative feed back effects inhibits ACTH production by acting an anterior pituitary and hypothalamus.

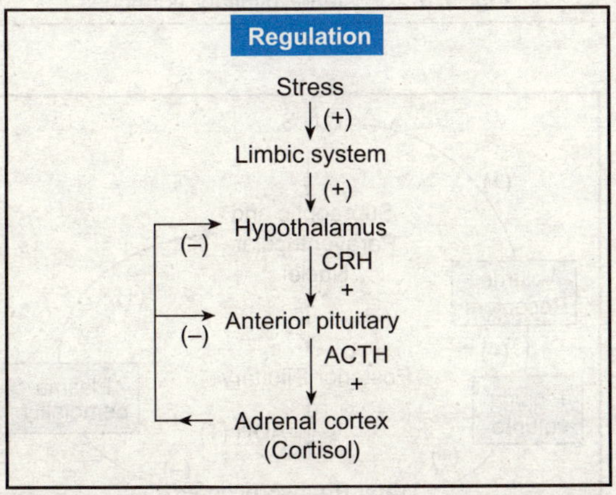


Fig. 9.13 : Cortisol by a negative feed back effects inhibit ACTH production by acting on anterior pituitary and hypothalamus.

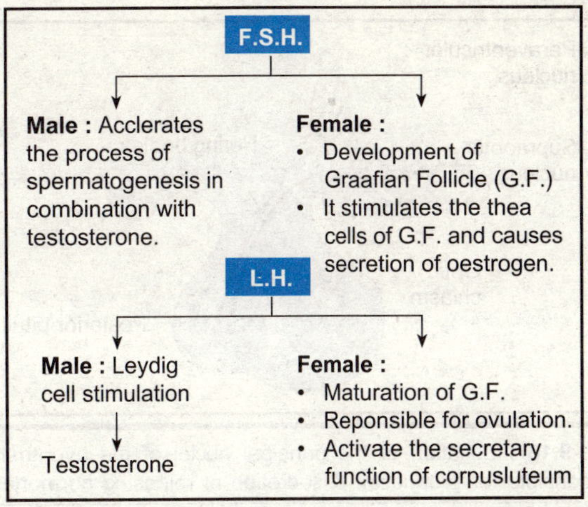


Fig. 9.14

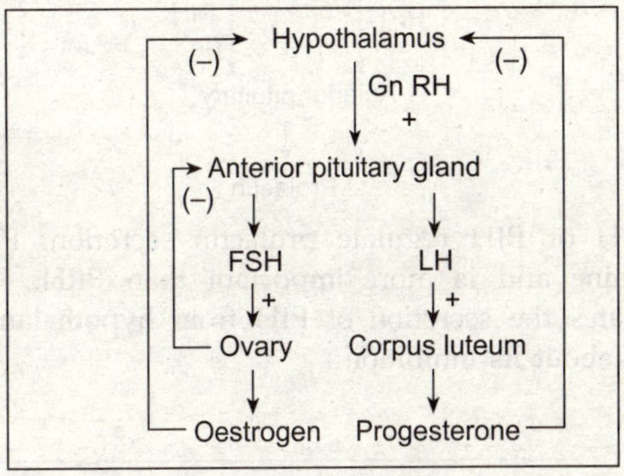


Fig. 9.14(a) : Regulation of FSH and LH in female.

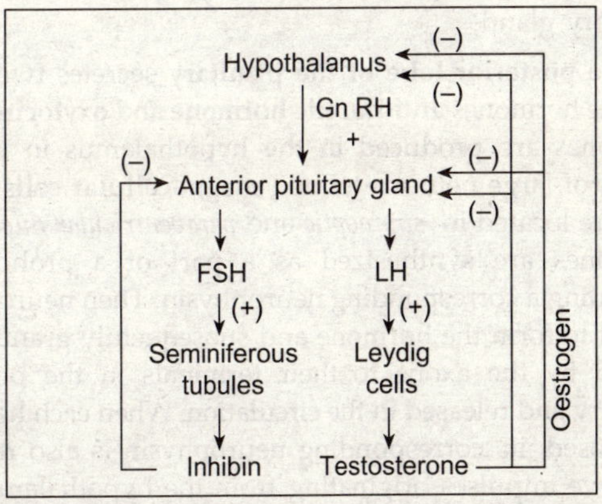


Fig. 9.15 : Regulation of FSH and LH in male.

**5. Prolactin :** Prolactin is necessary for the final preparation. of mammary glands for production and secretion of milk. Prolactin acts directly on the epithelial cells of the mammary glands and causes localized alveolar hyperplasia.

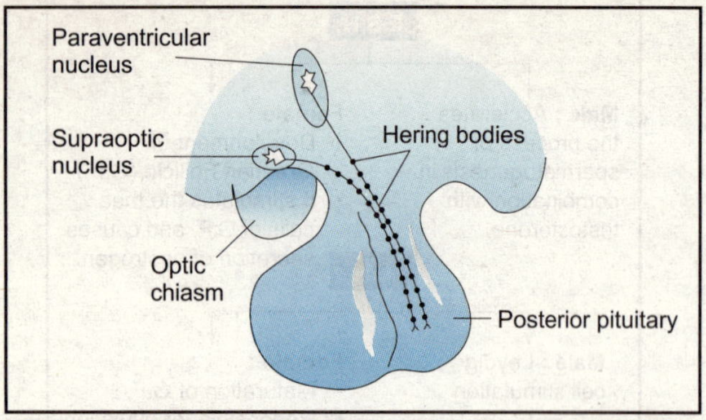


**Fig. 9.16 :** Location of the principal nuclei of the hypothalamus responsible for production & secretion of releasing hormones.

Regulation of prolactin production :

Hypothalamus
PRH (+) ↓ PIH (–) ↓
Anterior pituitary
↓
Prolactin

PRH or PIH regulate prolactin secretion. PIH is a dopamine and is more important than PRH. Prolactin stimulates the secretion of PIH from hypothalamus and brings about its inhibition.

## ➤ 9.7 Physiology of Posterior Pituitary (Fig. 9.18, 9.19 & 9.22)

The **posterior pituitary** (neurohypophysis) is a neurosecretory gland.

The **posterior lobe of the pituitary** secretes two nonapeptide hormones **antidiuretic hormone** and **oxytocin.** These hormones are produced in the hypothalamus in the cell bodies of large neurons termed **magnocellular cells**. These cells are located in *supraoptic* and *paraventricular nuclei*. The hormones are synthesized as a part of a prohormone containing a corresponding neurophysin. Then neurophysin is split to form the hormone and subsequently granules are carried by the axons to their terminals in the posterior pituitary and released in the circulation. When each hormone is released, its corresponding neurophysin is also released by nerve impulses originating from the hypothalamus.

### Arginine-vasopressin (antidiuretic hormone)

The human antidiuretic hormone is the nona-peptide arginine vasopressin (Cys-Tyr-Phe-Glu-Asp-Cys-Pro-Arg-Gly-$NH_2$).

Arginine Vasopressin (other name for ADH) is produced in the supraoptic cell bodies of the paraventricular nuclei and of the hypothalamus and is translocated to the posterior

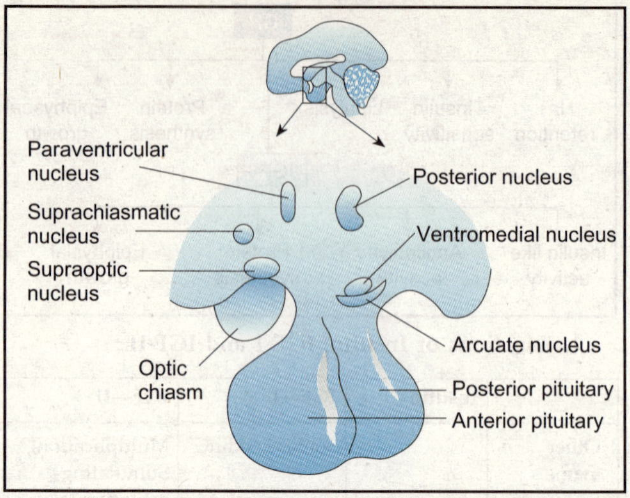


**Fig. 9.17 :** The relationship between the supraoptic and paraventricular nuclei and the posterior pituitary gland. The neurosecretory fibers originate in these nuclei and terminate in the posterior pituitary gland itself.

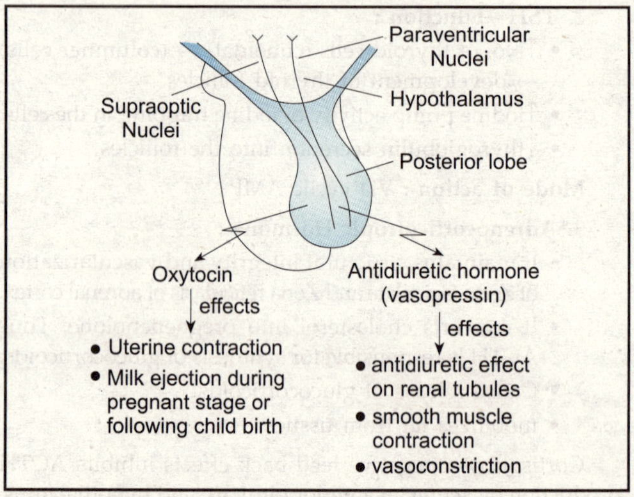


**Fig. 9.18 :** Posterior pituitary hormones

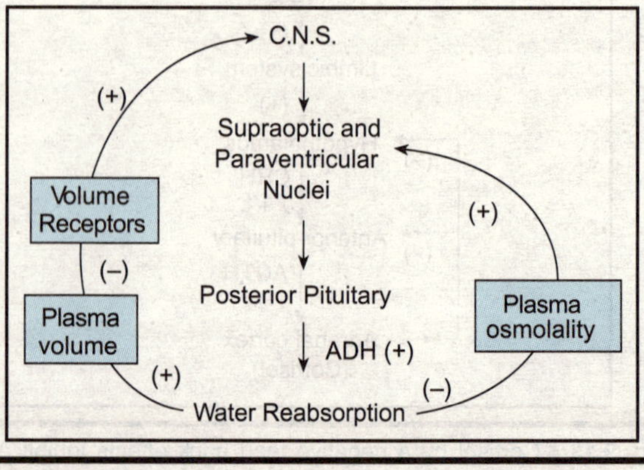


**Fig. 9.19 :** Summary of vasopressin secretion

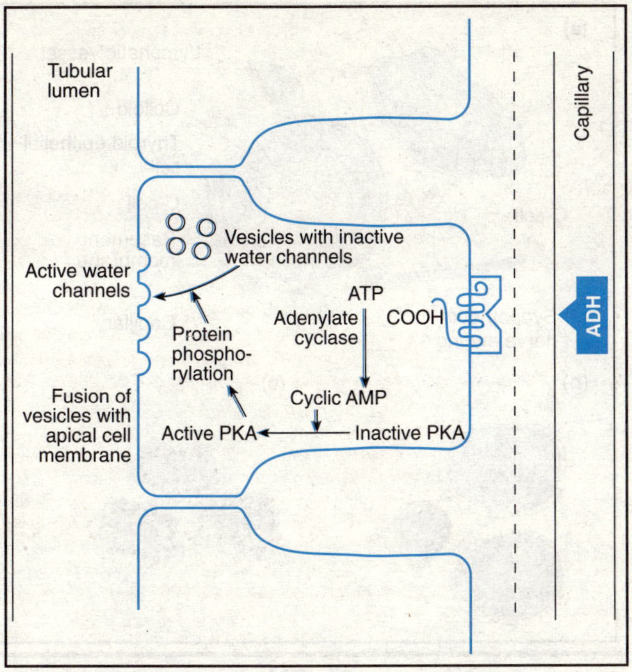


Fig. 9.20 : The cellular of ADH in the collecting tubular (principal cells) leading to the incorporation of water channels in the apical cell membrane and hence an increase in water permeability. PKA = protein kinase A.

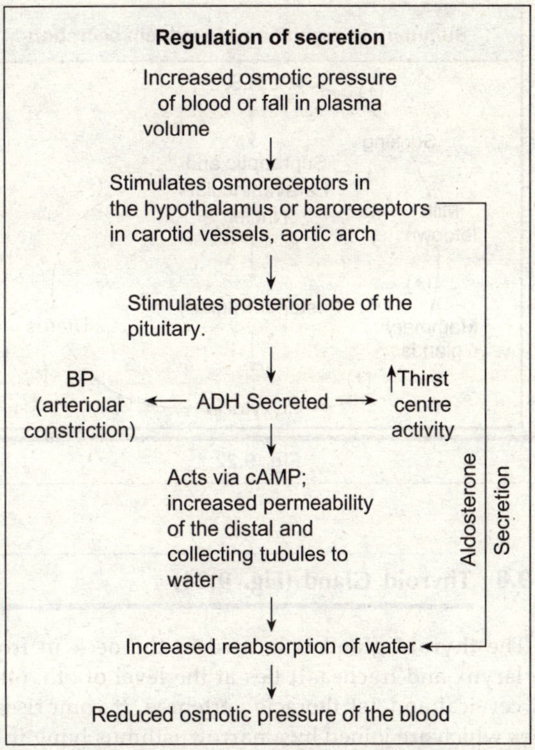


Fig. 9.21

pituitary gland for storage and release. The regulation of ADH release is normally under the control of osmolality of the immediate extracellular fluid environment near the osmoreceptors near the supraoptic and paraventricular nuclei of the hypothalamus.

The ability of ADH to increase water permeability in the collecting tubule and duct involves the binding of ADH to receptors on the surfaces of epithelial cells, the activation of adenylate cyclase, and the generation of cyclic AMP, which in turn leads to the insertion of protein-containing aggregates into the luminal membrane. These aggregates apparently function as channels for water movement (Fig. 9.21).

ADH is essential for the reabsorption of water from the distal tubule and collecting ducts. If there is an absence of ADH, as may occur with hypothalamic or posterior pituitary disease or with intracranial trauma, the cells of the distal tubule and the collecting tubules are rendered impermeable to water. These portions of the tubules are then unable to reabsorb water, and large volumes of dilute urine is excreted, even if the patient needs to conserve water. This condition is called **diabetes insipidus**. If adequate ADH is produced, but the kidney becomes unresponsive to the ADH, the patient is said to have **nephrogenic diabetes insipidus**.

**Antidiuretic hormone receptors** : Arginine vasopressin (**AVP**) binds to specific receptors (**$V_2$ receptors**) on the collecting duct cells, (basolateral membrane) causing activation of adenylyl cyclase and conversion of ATP to cyclic AMP. This initiates a chain of intracellular events that culminate in the insertion of water channels in the apical membrane of the cell, rendering it permeable to water.

**Main physiological action :** It increases the permeability of the renal collecting tubules to water and thus promotes water reabsorption and the excretion of a hypertonic urine. It also causes arteriolar constriction.

**Table : 9.5**
**Oxytocin**

- ***Stimulation of the uterus***
- Stimulation of the myoepithelial cells of the breast resulting in milk ejection
- Oxytocin is released in pulses during labour as a result of a neural reflex arising from the cervix and lower genital tract ***(Ferguson's reflex)***.
- Oxytocin is also released ***from fetal pituitary during labour***.
- ***During suckling***, oxytocin is released.
- Oxytocin is also released ***during orgasm*** in the male.

## Oxytocin (Fig. 9.23)

It is a ring-like nonapeptide similar in structure to ADH but differs in two amino acid residues. The metabolism and synthesis of oxytocin are similar to ADH.

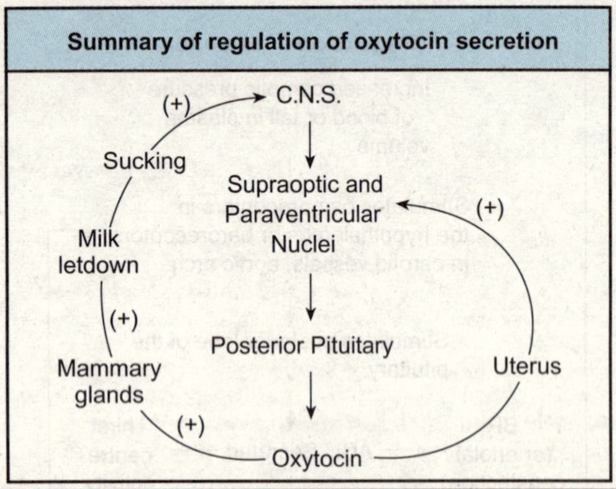


Fig. 9.22

## ➤ 9.8 Thyroid Gland (Fig. 9.24)

The **thyroid gland** is located in the neck in front of the larynx and trachea. It lies at the level of 5th, 6th and 7th cervical and 1st thoracic vertebrae. It comprises two lobes which are joined by a narrow isthmus lying in front of the trachea. The gland is bright red due to presence of a rich blood supply. Histologically, there are numerous spherical follicles. The outer layer of follicles are lined with cuboidal epithelium. A proteinaceous colloid fills the follicles.

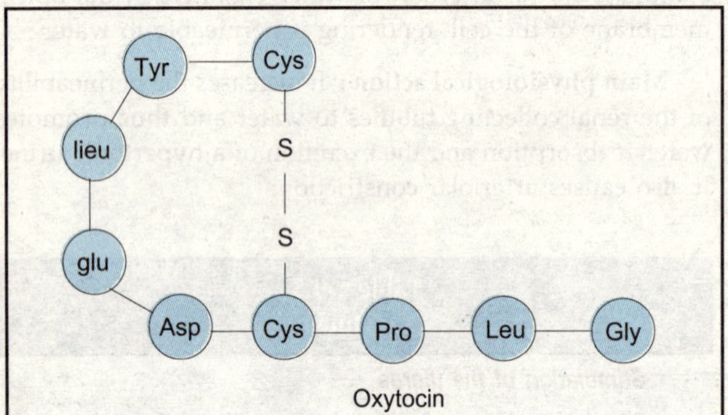


Fig. 9.23 : *Top* — Structure of oxytocin. *Bottom* —Structure of ADH

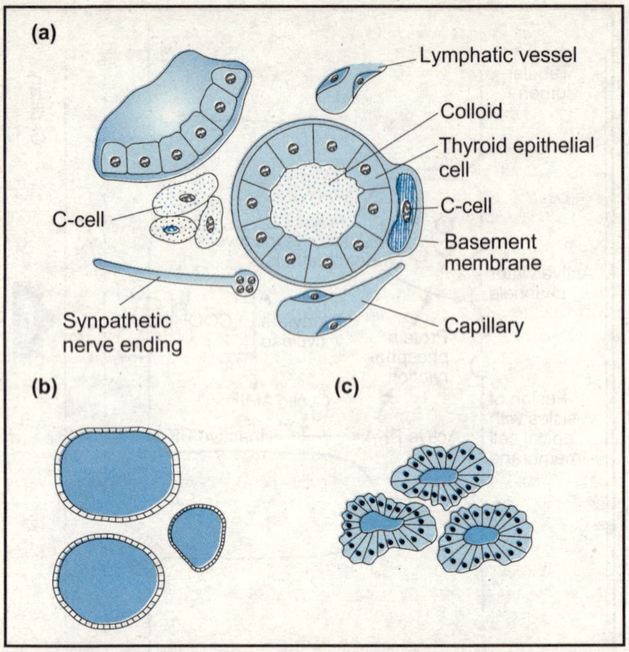


Fig. 9.24

These follicles are responsible for synthesis, storage and release of thyroid hormones (Fig. 9.25). The thyroid gland secretes two iodine containing hormones, **thyroxine ($T_4$)** and **triiodothyronine ($T_3$)** and the **peptide calcitonin**.

Each follicle is composed of a single layer of epithelial cells surrounding a cavity. The thyroid hormones are stored as integral components of the storage protein, **thyroglobulin**.

Thyroid hormones are iodinated derivatives of tyrosine – $T_4$ and $T_3$. Although $T_3$ is secreted by the thyroid gland, a large proportion of it (70-80 per cent) is produced by the peripheral deiodination of $T_4$.

In order to make $T_4$ and $T_3$, it is essential for the thyroid gland to have an adequate supply of iodine. Dietary iodide absorbed from the gut into the blood stream is actively trapped by the follicular cells of the thyroid which can

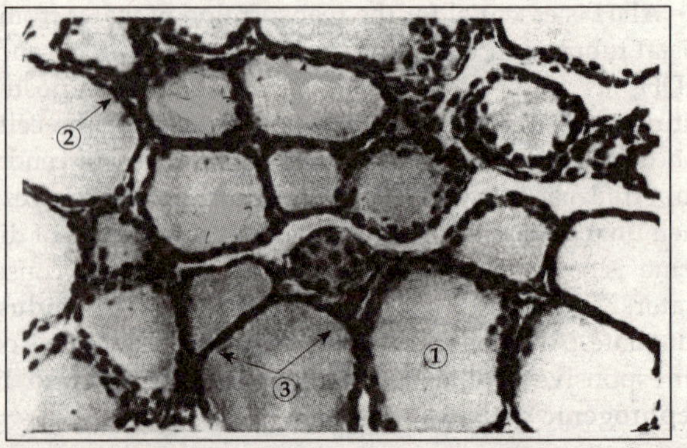


Fig. 9.25 : Structure of thyroid gland
(1) Thyroglobulin (TGB) • (2) Epithelium of follicle • (3) Thyroid follicle

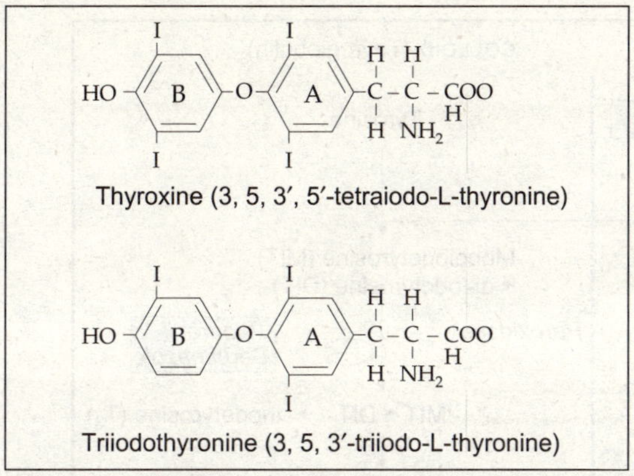


**Fig. 9.26 : Thyroid hormones**

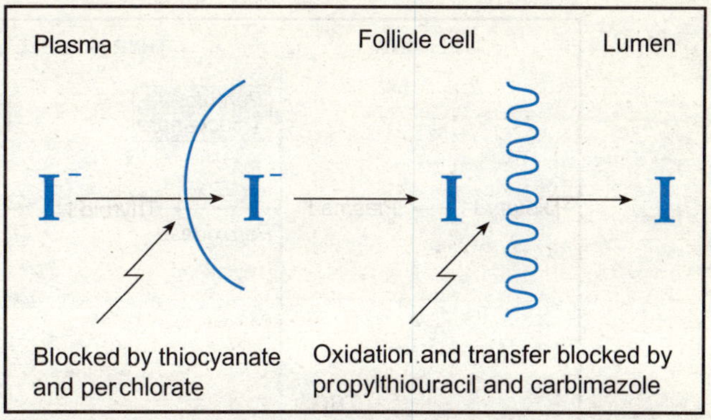


**Fig. 9.28 : Iodide is cleaved from the plasma and transferred to the luminal surface of the thyroid cell**

concentrate it 20 times more than in the perfusing blood. Between 100 and 200 mg of iodide are taken up by the thyroid each day.

The thyroid gland also secretes the ***peptide hormone,*** **calcitonin** (Fig. 9.26). Structurally, $T_4$ contains four iodine atoms whereas $T_3$ has three. $T_4$ concentration in the plasma is 50 times that of $T_3$. In the tissues $T_4$ is converted to $T_3$ or to reverse $T_3$ (3, 3", 5" tri-iodothyronine) by deiodination. $T_3$ is active in target cells.

Regulation of secretion of thyroxine and tri-iodothyronine is given in (Fig. 9.27).

**Thyroid hormone** is secreted in two forms :

1. **Thyroxine ($T_4$) :** 98% of active thyroid hormone. Mainly protein bound 75% to thyroxine-binding globulin (TBG), 15% to thyroxine-binding prealbumin (TBPA) and 10% to albumin. 0.05% exists as free hormone which is the physiologically active form.

2. **Tri-iodothyronine ($T_3$) :** 0.5% exists as the free hormone. Five times as potent as $T_4$ with a shorter half-life and less strongly bound. $T_3$ is the active hormone at tissues level. Approximately 1/3rd of $T_4$ is converted to $T_3$ in tissues.

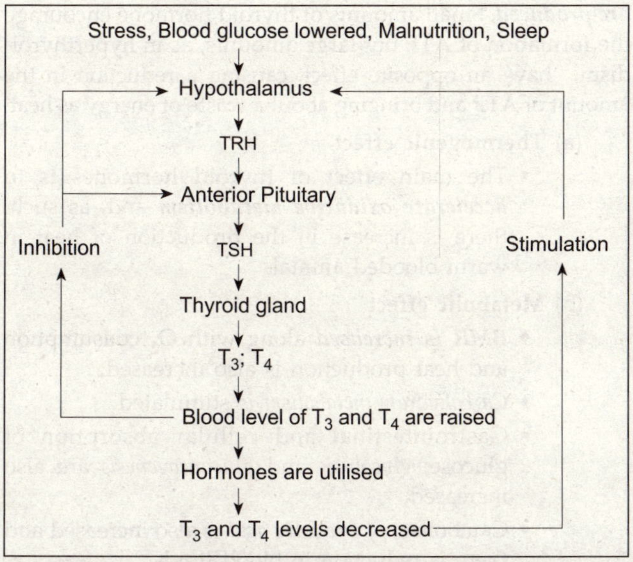


**Fig. 9.27 : Secretion of thyroxine and tri-iodothyronine**

**Metabolism (Figs. 9.28 and 9.29)**

**The events :**

(1) **Iodine trapping** (Fig. 9.28) : Iodine is absorbed and circulates in the blood as inorganic iodide. About 150 µg per day is required. Iodide is cleared by the thyroid. The thyroid serum iodide ratio is about 25 : 1, rising to 250 : 1 in iodine deficiency. The iodine **"pumps"** are blocked by perchlorate and thiocyanate.

(2) **Oxidation of iodide** in the microvilli by a membrane bound peroxidase releases free iodine at the cell colloid surface. It is blocked by propylthiouracil and carbimazole.

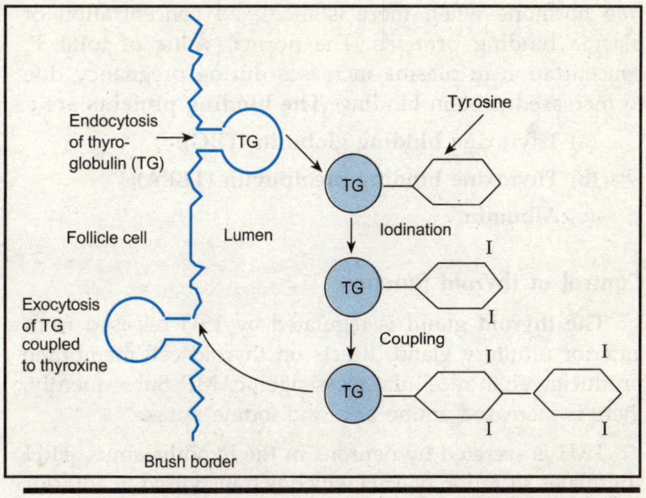


**Fig. 9.29 : Iodination of tyrosine takes place on the thyroglobulin molecule in the lumen**

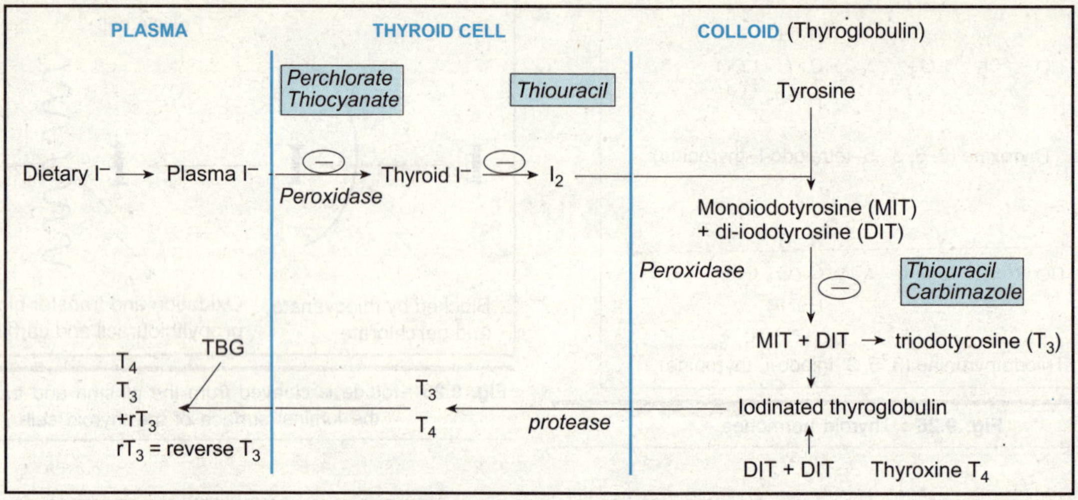


Fig. 9.30 : Synthesis of thyroid hormones.

(3) **Synthesis of thyroglobulin** (Figs.9.29 and 9.30).

(4) Tyrosine molecules are attached **by peptide linkages** to the thyroglobulin molecules in the lumen. Iodine attaches to the tyrosyl groups.

(5) **Coupling of iodotyrosines** then occurs to form T3 and T4. These remain attached to thyroglobulin which constitutes the storage depot.

(6) **Ingestion of colloid** by pinocytosis is followed by proteolysis in lysosomes to release $T_4$ and $T_3$.

### Protein transport of thyroid hormones

The thyroid hormones are present in the blood bound with plasma protein **thyroid-binding globulin (TBG)**. The free (unbound) hormone is biologically active. It can diffuse out of the capillaries into body cells. $T_3$ and $T_4$ concentrations are increased without affecting the levels of free hormone when there is increased concentration of plasma binding proteins. The normal value of total $T_4$ concentration in plasma increases during pregnancy due to increased protein binding. **The binding proteins** are :

(a) **Thyroxine binding globulin (TBG);**

(b) **Thyroxine binding prealbumin (TBPA);**

(c) **Albumin.**

### Control of thyroid function

**The thyroid gland** is regulated by TSH released from anterior pituitary gland. It acts on thyroid cell membrane producing an intracellular messenger, cAMP. Subsequently, there is increased amino acid and iodine uptake.

TRH is secreted by neurons in the hypothalamus. TRH stimulates secretion of TSH which is transported to anterior pituitary in hypophyseal portal vessels. TRH action is due to rise of cytosolic $Ca^{2+}$ which is triggered by second messenger inositol triphosphate. TSH secretion is also controlled by feed- back inhibition by $T_3$ and $T_4$ on the anterior pituitary where they may reduce the number of cell receptors for TRH.

The amount of TSH stimulation of the thyroid depends upon how much of it is synthesized and released from the pituitary gland. This is controlled largely by the negative feedback of thyroid hormones on the pituitary, though the sensitivity of this feedback mechanism is modulated by a hypothalamic hormone called **thyrotropin releasing hormone (TRH).**

### Action of thyroid hormones

Thyroid hormones are important physiologically because of their major role in ***energy production. The hormones are bound to mitochondria where the high energy bonds of ATP are produced.*** Small amounts of thyroid hormone encourage the formation of ATP but large amounts, as in hyperthyroidism, have an opposite effect, causing a reduction in the amount of ATP and bringing about a waste of energy as heat.

(a) **Thermogenic effect**

- The main effect of thyroid hormones is to ***accelerate oxidative metabolism*** and, as such, there is increase in the production of heat in warm blooded animals.

(b) **Metabolic effect**

- ***BMR is increased*** along with $O_2$ consumption and heat production is also increased.
- *Carbohydrate metabolism is* stimulated.
- Gastrointestinal and cellular absorption of glucose; *glycolysis* and *gluconeogenesis* are also increased.
- Catabolism *of free fatty acid* is also increased and there is reduction in blood lipids.
- Stimulates *protein synthesis.*

(c) **Effect on growth and development**
- *Skeletal growth* in childhood is stimulated
- *Normal brain development* in early postnatal period
- They have a permissive *role on GH action*

(d) **Neurological effects**
- Essential for *normal myelination of nerves;*
- *Development of nervous system* in childhood
- *Restlessness and hyperexcitability*

(e) **Systemic effects**
- Due to increased metabolic demand of tissues, it has got direct *stimulatory action on heart rate.* As a result, heart rate and force of contraction are increased
- *Cardiac output and pulse pressure* are increased
- *Gastrointestinal motility* is increased
- *Alertness*
- Thyroid hormones are required for development of *foetus, erythropoiesis* and *synthesis of vitamin A.*

- **Causes of increased serum thyroid-binding globulin :**

Pregnancy
Estrogen therapy
Oral contraceptive pill
Drugs like phenothiazines, clofibrate
Myxedema

- **Causes of decreased serum thyroxine binding globulin :**

Hypoproteinemia
Acromegaly
Thyrotoxicosis
Androgens and anabolic steroids

- **Causes of reduced TBG binding :**

Renal failure
Drug displacement by e.g. salicylates, phenytoin; phenylbutazone.

*Insufficiency of hormone* : **Hypothyroidism** may be due to disease of the pituitary or of the thyroid gland and may be due to severe deficiency of iodine in the diet. When severe hypothyroidism is present in an adult, it is called **myxedema.** When hypothyroidism is present in infants, the condition is called **cretinism.** Cold intolerance, slow mentation, husky voice, weight gain and decreased reflexes are the features of myxedema. Cretinism is characterized by growth retardation as well as mental retardation.

**Deficiency of thyroid hormones** leads to anovulation associated with increased LH levels.

*Excess of hormone* : Hyperthyroidism (thyrotoxicosis) is due to excessive production of thyroid hormones. It is manifested by a high metabolic rate, tachycardia, restlessness, weight loss and increased sensitivity to heat.

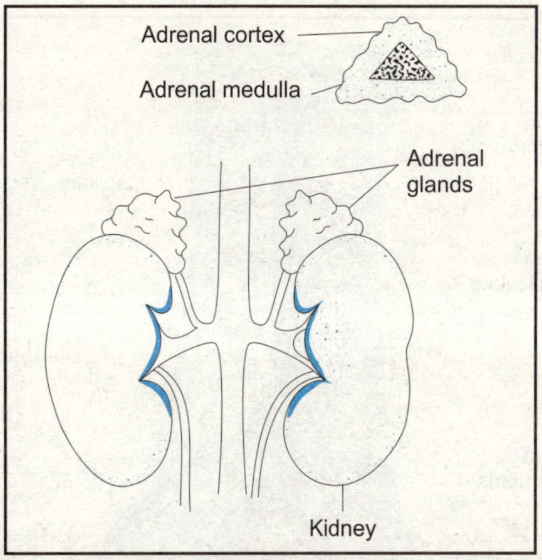


Fig. 9.31 : Adrenal gland

**Hypothyroid features**

Mental and physical sluggishness, sensitivity to cold, decreased BMR, retarded growth, raised blood cholesterol level, decreased cardiac output and low glucose uptake.

**Hyperthyroid features**

The patient is active but restless mentally and physically and is sensitive to heat. BMR is increased; blood cholesterol level is lowered. Cardiac output is increased. There is high glucose uptake.

**Goiter** is an enlargement of thyroid gland due to excessive amounts of TSH or thyroid stimulating immunoglobulin.

**Iodine deficiency goiter** is due to inadequate amount of dietary iodine to maintain synthesis of thyroid hormones.

**Grave's disease** is the most common cause of hyperthyroi-dism. In this disease, thyroid stimulating immunoglobulins stimulate the TSH receptors on thyroid cells.

## 9.9 Adrenal Gland

There are two **adrenal glands** located on each side of the upper pole of each kidney. The adrenal gland is composed of two parts, inner one is medulla which is derived embryologically from neural tissue. Surrounding the medulla are the cells of the **cortex.** The **adrenal medulla** secretes catecholamines (**epinephrine, norepinephrine** and **dopamine**). The adrenal cortex secretes steroid hormones (Fig. 9.31).

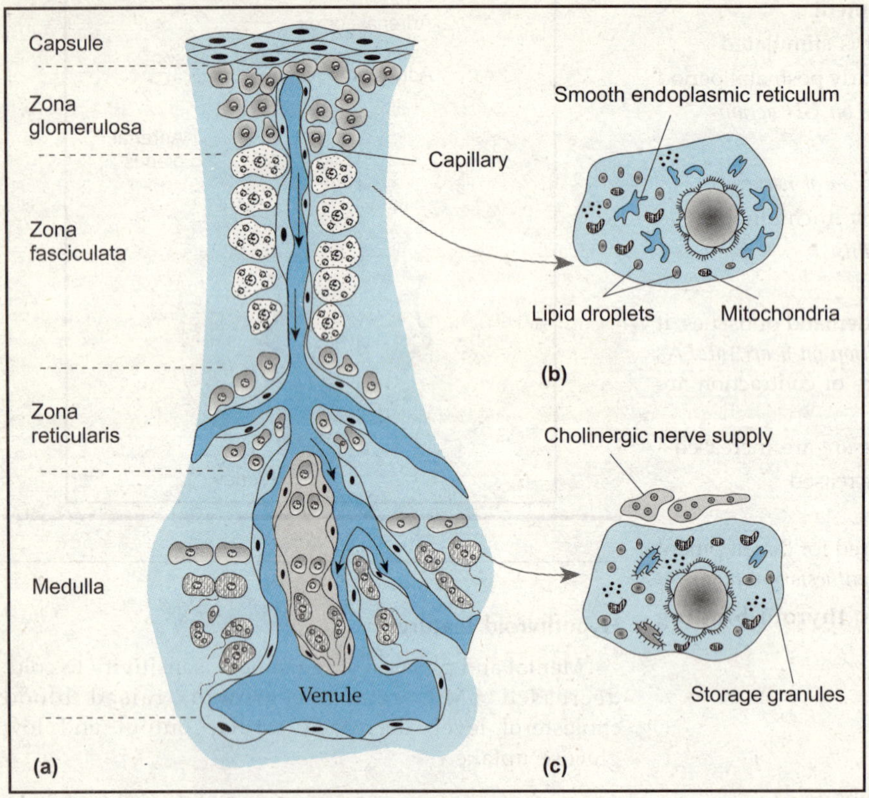


Fig. 9.32 : Section through the cortex and medulla of the adrenal gland.

## Adrenal medulla (Fig. 9.32)

The **adrenal medulla** arises from ***neural crest cells*** and comprises 10% of the gland. The synthetic pathway of its products, the catecholamines, is shown in Fig. 9.32 (overleaf). The inner core of adrenal gland is **adrenal medulla**. The chromaffin cells of adrenal medulla secretes **epinephrine**, **norepinephrine** and **dopamine**. Their actions are diverse. They stimulate heart rate and contractility. There is inhibition of gut motility, stimulation of glycogenolysis. One type of chromaffin cells produces adrenalin (epinephrine) and the other cell type secretes noradrenalin (norepinephrine). ***80% of catecholamines are produced by the medulla***. Some chromaffin cells are located outside the medulla and lie adjacent to the chain of sympathetic ganglia. The ***medulla secretes about 75% epinephrine*** and ***20% norepinephrine***. Apart from catecholamines, the adrenal medulla contains dynorphins, neurotensin, enkephalin, somatostatin and substance P. The function of these adrenal peptides are not clear.

Norepinephrine is converted to epinephrine by the enzyme, ***phenylethanolamine N-methyltransferase (PNMT)***. The catecholamines bind with ATP and protein and are stored in chromaffin granules. These granules are released by acetylcholine from preganglionic fibers. The cell membranes' permeability to calcium is increased by acetylcholine. Dopamine, dopamine beta-hydroxylase, ATP and other proteins are also released. The half life of catecholamines in the circulation is two minutes.

### Control of secretion

The ***secretion of medullary hormones*** into the blood stream is regulated by ***nerves and hormones.*** Chromaffin cells are innervated by sympathetic nerves. These sympathetic nerves release neurotransmitter acetyl choline which stimulates the cells to secrete hormones by exocytosis. The secretion of catecholamines is initiated by sympathetic nervous system. It occurs in response to pain, excitement, hypoglycemia, cold and hemorrhage and is controlled by hypothalamus. The sympathetic nerve suply to adrenal medulla has only preganglionic fibers. No postganglionic fibers are present. Norepinephrine and epinephrine are released into the blood as hormones in response to preganglionic nerve activity.

### Cellular action of the adrenal catecholamines

**Adrenal catecholamines** bind to α and β adrenoceptors on the target cell membrane. Norepinephrine action is more pronounced than epinephrine at α receptors and epinephrine is more potent agonist at β-receptors. Intracellular concentration of second messengers (eg, cAMP may rise or fall) are regulated by the activation of these receptors.

***The action of catecholamines are regulated by alpha and beta adrenergic receptors***. They are further subdivided into ***alpha-1, alpha-2, beta-1 and beta-2 receptors***. The effect of these circulating catecholamines on these receptors are same as the effect of catecholamines released from noradrenergic terminations of post-ganglionic axons of sympathetic nervous system.

**Catecholamines** : Biologically active amines are dopamine, norepinephrine (20%) and epinephrine (80%) which are collectively known as **catecholamines**. Bound to ATP and protein and stored as membrane bound granules, called chromaffin granules. Norepinephrine and epinephrine are also produced in the adrenal medulla.

**Synthesis and metabolism of Catecholamines :**

- The plasma half-life of the catecholamines is 1-3 minutes.
- Sympathetic nerve endings take up the catecholamines from the circulation, which leads to non enzymatic inactivation by intraneuronal storage and to enzymatic inactivation in the synaptic cleft

- These transmitters are destroyed by the enzymes, monoamine oxidase (MAO) and catechol-O-methyl transferase (COMT)

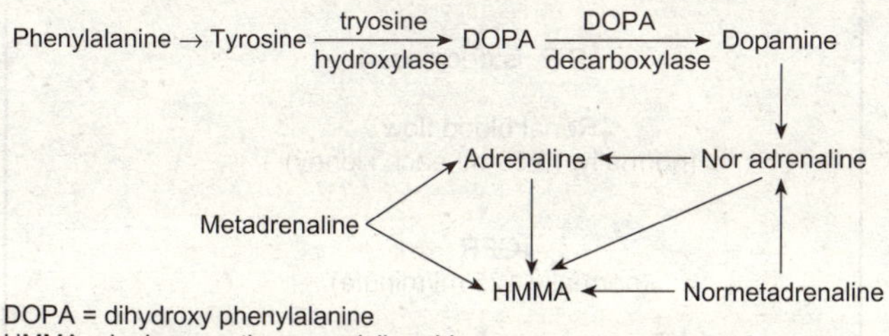


DOPA = dihydroxy phenylalanine
HMMA = hydroxy methoxymandelic acid

**The actions of epinephrine are :**

- Total peripheral resistance is decreased
- Heart rate is increased.
- Cardiac output is increased.
- No change in mean blood pressure.
- Vasoconstriction in skin and viscera.
- Vasodilation in the skeletal muscle.
- Basal metabolic rate is increased.
- Glycogenolysis (liver and muscle) is stimulated.
- Increased gluconeogenosis.
- Increased lipolysis (fat cells).

**Norepinephrine**

- Total peripheral resistance is increased.
- Mean blood pressure is increased.
- Heart rate and cardiac output are decreased.

### Abnormalities of adrenal medullary function

Tumour in the adrenal medulla is known as **pheochromocytoma** which leads to oversecretion of catecholamines by chromaffin cells. Hypertension may be present due to norepinephrine secretion in excess or there may be hyperglycemia due to epinephrine secretion in excess. High metabolic rate is also present in patients with pheochromocytoma. A patient with pheochromocytoma is treated by surgical removal of the tumour which is usually unilateral and benign.

**Table 9.6**
**Difference between epinephrine and norepinephrine**

| | *Epinephrine* | *Norepinephrine* |
|---|---|---|
| **Receptor predominance** | $\beta > \alpha$ | $\alpha > \beta$ |
| **Total peripheral resistance** | ↓ | ↑ |
| **Cardiac output** | ↑ | ↓ |
| **Heart rate** | ↑ | ↓ |
| **Blood pressure** | ↑ | ↑ |

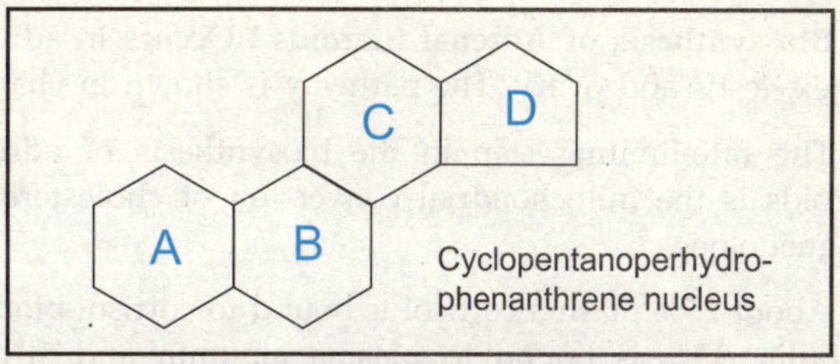


**Fig. 9.33 : Structure of steroid hormones**

**Table 9.7**
**Catecholamines behave like steroid and other hormones (peptide group)**

| | *Peptide* | *Steroid* |
|---|---|---|
| **Mode of action** | There is interaction with the receptors of the cell membrane | Nucleus is affected and new protein synthesis occurs |
| **Form of circulation** | Water-soluble; free in circulation | Sparingly water soluble; circulate with binding proteins |

### Adrenal cortex

The **adrenal cortex** consists of three zones ***zona glomerulosa, zona fasciculata*** and ***zona reticularis*** (outer to inner) according to their histological appearance. The middle zone is the widest of all, comprising about 75% of the cortex.

### Secretion of steroid hormones

| | |
|---|---|
| Site of production : | Hormone |
| **Zona glomerulosa :** | Mineralocorticoids<br>— Aldosterone<br>— Deoxycorticosterone<br>— Corticosterone<br>(also a glucocorticoid) |
| **Zona fasciculata :** | Glucocorticoids (cortisol)<br>Androgens (dehydroepian drosterone)<br>Androstenedione; testosterone |
| **Zona reticularis :** | estrogens (estradiol)<br>Progestogens |

### Structure of Steroid Hormones

Basic structure for all steroid hormones is the cyclopentano perhydrophenanthrene nucleus.

Estrogen : $C_{18}$ steroids.
Androgens : $C_{19}$ steroids.
Glucocorticoids
Mineralocorticoids
Progestogens $C_{21}$ steroids.

**Bio synthesis of Adrenal Steroids :** Occurs in adrenal cortex, testis and ovary. The pathway is shown in chart.

The rate-limiting step in the biosynthesis of adrenal steroids is the mitochondrial conversion of cholesterol to pregnenolone

About 75% plasma cortisol is bound to cortisol-binding globulin; 15% is bound to plasma albumin and 10% is unbound.

### Intracellular actions of adrenal steroids (Fig. 9.34)

Adrenal steroids can pass easily through the plasma membrane of target cells and bind with intracellular receptors. Then the receptor-hormone complexes reach the nucleus. Modification of DNA transcription occurs here and, subsequently, there is increased production of enzymes.

### Mineralocorticoids

**Aldosterone :** $C_{21}$ mineralcorticoid hormone secreted by the zona glomerulosa of the adrenal cortex.

**Normal plasma range** = 0.9 – 3 m mol/L (on salt restricted diet) and 0.1 – 0.4 m mol/L (on high salt diet)

**Aldosterone** is the ***main mineralocorticoid hormone***. The principal function of **aldosterone** is to increase renal reab-sorption of sodium and chloride in DCT and CD in exchange of $K^+$ and $H^+$ ions (secretion of $K^+$ and $H^+$) leading to retention of $Na^+$ and increase in ECF volume. Hypertension, mild hypokalemia and alkalosis develop. *Aldosterone acts at the DNA level. Specific mRNA synthesis*

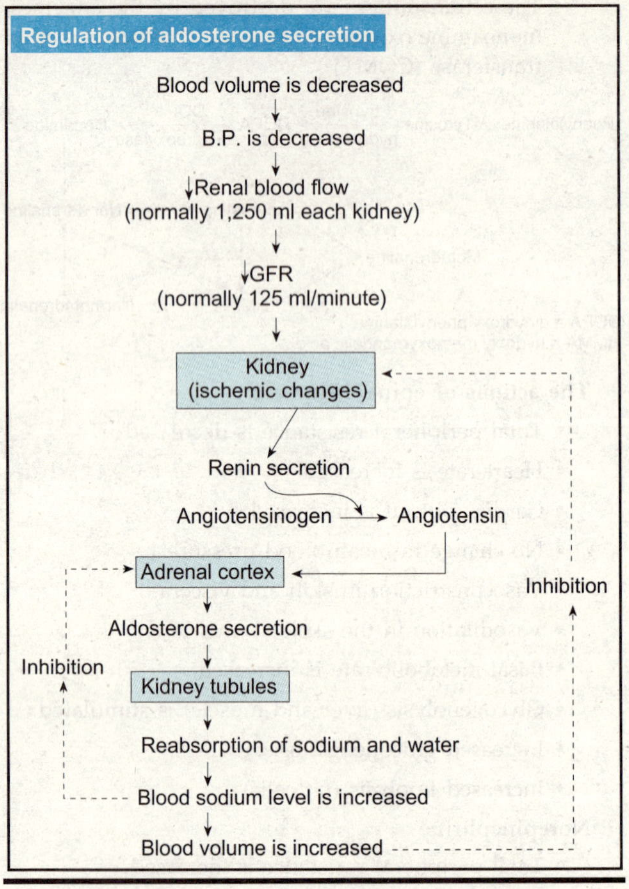


Fig. 9.34 : Regulation of aldosterone secretion

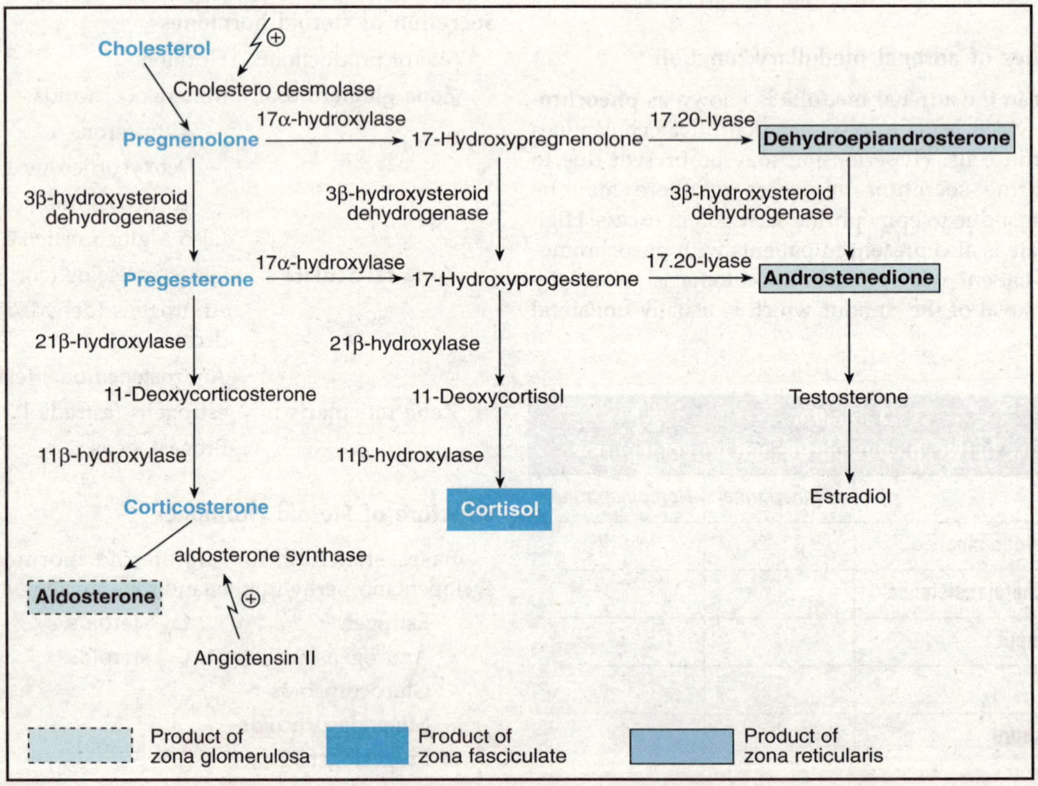

***is also increased but exact function is not clear.*** Aldosterone exerts its action by binding to cell cytosolic receptors and moving into the nucleus where it stimulates protein synthesis and luminal membrane sodium permeability.

## Regulation of aldosterone secretion

The ***key regulator*** of aldosterone secretion is **angiotensin II** which is produced by **renin-angiotensin system**. When plasma $K^+$ concentration is increased, there is more release and secretion of aldosterone by the adrenal cortex (from zona glomerulosa). Adrenocorticotropic hormone plays an important role in stimulating aldosterone secretion.

**Renin** is a peptide hormone which is produced from juxta-glomerular cells (JG) which are present in renal afferent arterioles.

**Angiotensinogen** is produced by the liver. Renin releases angiotensin I which is converted to angiotensin II (octapeptide) by angiotensin converting enzyme present in endothelial cells. Angiotensin II stimulates adrenal cortex to release aldosterone. Cholesterol is converted to pregnenolone by ACTH, angiotensin II and potassium.

**Actions of angiotensin II :**

- Potent arterial and venous vasoconstrictor.
- Increases synthesis and release of aldosterone and ADH centrally
- Increases thirst by a central mechanism.
- Increases level of prostaglandins.

**Angiotensin**—converting enzyme-(located on chromosome 17)

- Key enzyme in the renin-angiotensin and KalliKrein-Kinin systems by activating angiotensin I to angiotensin II.

**Causes of increased aldosterone secretion :**

- High potassium and low sodium intake
- Hemorrhage
- Anxiety
- Following surgery
- Primary hyper aldosteronism (Conn's syndrome)
- Secondary hyper aldosteronism
- Renal artery stenosis

**Causes of decreased aldosterone secretion :**

- Dietary sodium intake (if increased).
- Intravenous saline infusion.
- Adrenalectomy.

**Causes of decreased renin release :**

- Angiotensin II, ADH; hypernatremia; hyperkalemia; β Blockers; Angiotensin — converting enzyme inhibitors (ACEI) prevent conversion of angiotensin I to II.

***The secretion of renin is stimulated by :***

- Reduced ECF volume
- Reduced renal blood flow
- Reduced GFR
- Decreased systemic blood pressure
- Decreased renal arterial pressure
- Increased renal sympathetic nerve discharge.

## Reabsorption of $Na^+$

The function of mineralocorticoids is to stimulate active reabsorption of $Na^+$ from DCT leading to osmotic reabsorption of water. The overall effect is that the extracellular fluid and plasma volume are expanded due to increase in the total $Na^+$ content of the extracellular space.

## Secretion of $K^+$

Mineralocorticoids stimulate active secretion of $K^+$ from plasma into distal convoluted tubule (DCT).

## Secretion of $H^+$

Mineralocorticoids stimulate secretion of $H^+$ into DCT. This effect is less pronounced.

## Glucocorticoids

1. Cortisol and corticosterone (secreted at 1/10th amount of cortisol).

2. Bound to corticosteroid binding globulin (CBG) or transcortin; 10% free in plasma, which is the biologically active fraction.

## Action of glucocorticoids

(a) *Metabolic function*

- Breakdown of protein
- Glucose is synthesized from amino acids
- Mobilization of fat stores
- Protein catabolism is increased
- Increased lipolysis
- Plasma lipids and ketone bodies are increased.

(b) ***Cortisol enhances*** *rapid supply of glucose to the body tissues.*

(c) ***Glucocorticoids*** *are responsible for* ***maintenance of normal*** *myocardial contractility and vascular resistance.*

(d) ***Glucocorticoids decrease*** *the permeability of vascular endothelium and, as such, they can maintain blood volume.*

(e) ***Stress*** : How the body adapts to stress is not clear but release of cortisol increases during stress.

(f) ***Immune response*** : In large doses, glucocorticoids suppress the immune response.

(g) ***Anti-inflammatory property*** : Glucocorticoids are used in the treatment of rheumatoid arthritis and allied diseases.

(h) ***Synthesis of surfactant*** : They are also used to enhance the synthesis of surfactant production.

(i) ***Hepatic and gastrointestinal enzymes*** *are induced.*

(j) ***Circulating neutrophils, platelets and red blood cells are*** *increased and circulating eosinophils, lymphocytes and monocytes are decreased. Size of the lymph nodes and thymus are reduced.*

(k) ***Excretion of free water*** *is increased.*

(l) ***Central nervous system disorders*** *such as change in personality may occur on corticosteroid administration.*

(m) ***Glucocorticoids inhibit the conversion*** *of membrane phospholipids to arachidonic acid which helps to reduce mediators of inflammation* eg, leukotrienes, prostacyclin and prostaglandin.

(n) Increased secretion of hydrochloric acid and pepsin.

(o) Some mineralocorticoid action.

| Summary of peripheral actions of glucocorticoids | | |
|---|---|---|
| 1. ***Pituitary/ hypothalamus*** | : | Inhibition of CRH and ACTH secretion. |
| 2. ***Kidney*** | : | ↑ $Na^+$ reabsorption; ↑ GFR |
| 3. ***Nervous system*** | : | Depression in deficiency; euphoria in excess. |
| 4. ***Liver*** | : | ↑ Gluconeogenesis from amino acids. |
| 5. ***Placenta*** | : | ↑ Estrogen production ↓ Progesterone production |
| 6. ***Lungs*** | : | ↑ Surfactant production during fetal development |
| 7. ***Muscle*** | : | ↑ Protein catabolism ↓ protein synthesis |
| 8. ***Bone*** | : | ↑ Resorption ↓ Formation |

## Deficient secretion

(a) ***Hypoadrenalism or Addison's disease :*** It is primarily due to reduction in adrenal gland function. It may also be secondary due to defect of anterior pituitary gland.

It is a condition of generalized adrenocortical hormone deficiency. It may be due to atrophy of the gland or its destruction by tuberculosis. Both cortex and medulla are affected.

***Primary hypoadrenalism*** : It is caused by failure of adrenal cortex following tumour invasion or surgery, infection, or due to autoantibodies. Corticoid level is decreased and ACTH is increased. This is a disorder of the adrenal gland.

***Secondary hypoadrenalism*** : It is due to decreased stimulation of the gland by ACTH following a disorder of the hypothalamic and pituitary axis. Both corticoid and ACTH levels are decreased causing secondary hypoadrenalism and hypothalamic-pituitary disease or may be due to hypothalamic-pituitary inhibition.

(b) ***Aldosterone deficiency :***

- $Na^+$ and water loss are increased in urine
- Plasma $[K^+]$ is increased (hyperkalemia)
- $H^+$ is retained by the kidney leading to metabolic acidosis

(c) ***Glucocorticoid deficiency :***

- Weight loss and appetite loss
- Reduced resistance to infection and trauma.

## Excess secretion

(a) ***Primary hyperaldosteronism (Conn's syndrome)*** : when there is excessive production of aldosterone, due to a tumour of zona glomerulosa of the adrenal cortex, it is known as Conn's disease or primary aldosteronism. It is manifested by weakness of the muscle and loss of potassium in the urine.

**Main effects are :**

- There will be retention of water and renal $Na^+$ resulting in increased blood volume and hypertension.
- Renal $K^+$ loss resulting in reduction of plasma $[K^+]$ (hypokalemia) which is responsible for muscle weakness.
- Metabolic alkalosis develops due to renal loss of $H^+$.

The effect of chronic mineralocorticoid excess results in increased ECF volume. When the ECF expansion has reached a particular point, there is decreased sodium retention in spite of continued stimulation of aldosterone secretion. This condition is known as **aldosterone escape phenomenon**. There is no such escape present in potassium excretion.

In short, in ***case of primary hyperaldosteronism*** the cause may be adrenal tumour or adrenal hyperplasia. It is found in early middle life and is associated with marked hypertension due to salt and water retention which occurs under the influence of aldosterone.

(b) ***Secondary hyperaldosteronism*** may be due to congestive heart failure, cirrhosis with ascites and nephrosis. When there is increased glucocorticoid activity, **Cushing's syndrome** develops. It may be due to excess secretion of ACTH, prolonged treatment with glucocorticoids and glucocorticoid secreting tumor in the adrenal cortex. It is manifested by increase in blood glucose, protein breakdown and weight gain. Hypertension may be present due to mineralocorticoid effects of cortisol.

*Adrenal androgens* are produced from the zona reticularis of the adrenal cortex which is stimulated by ACTH.

*Adrenogenital syndrome* is a biochemical defect which results in increased secretion of androgen from the adrenal glands.

There is excessive androgen secretion in adrenogenital syndrome. Masculinization in the female and precocious puberty in the male may develop.

## 9.10 The Pancreas

The **pancreas** is both an *exocrine* and *endocrine gland.* The endocrine cells of the pancreas are localized in the islets of Langerhans. The digestive enzymes are synthesized and released by the exocrine pancreas. However, the endocrine part plays an important role in controlling plasma glucose concentration. The pancreas consists of acini and ducts which are responsible for secretion of enzymes into the duodenum. Small groups of specialised cells are present for endocrine secretion which form the islets of ***Langerhans. B (β) cells of islets of Langerhans produce* insulin** and **glucagon** is ***produced by A (α) cells of islets of Langerhans.*** Another hormone from the pancreas. Somatostatin (identical to GHRH secreted by hypothalamus) is synthesized from D (*δ*) cells of islets of Langerhans of pancreas. **Gastrin** is secreted from D (*δ*) cells. **Pancreatic polypeptide** is another product of the islets of Langerhans but its role is unclear (Fig. 9.35).

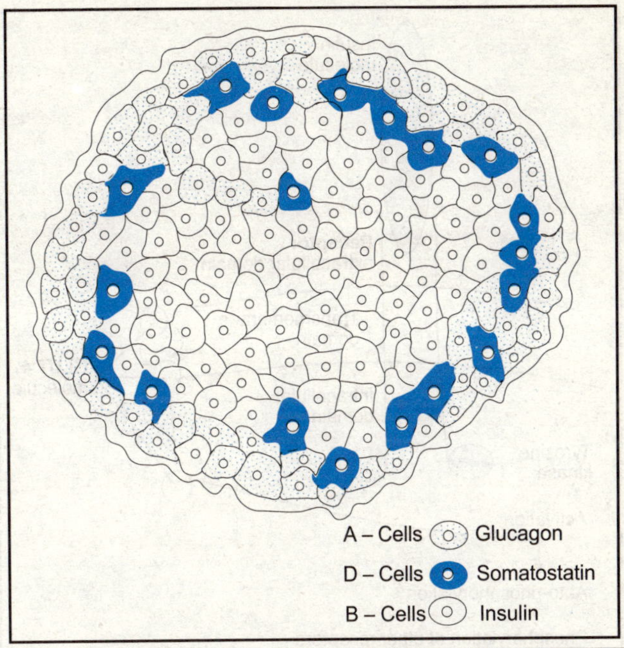


**Fig. 9.35 : Different types of cells in a typical delite**

The islet cells :

Islet cells :
- 25% α → Glucagon
- 70% β → Insulin
- 5% δ → Somatostatin
- F → Pancreatic polypeptide

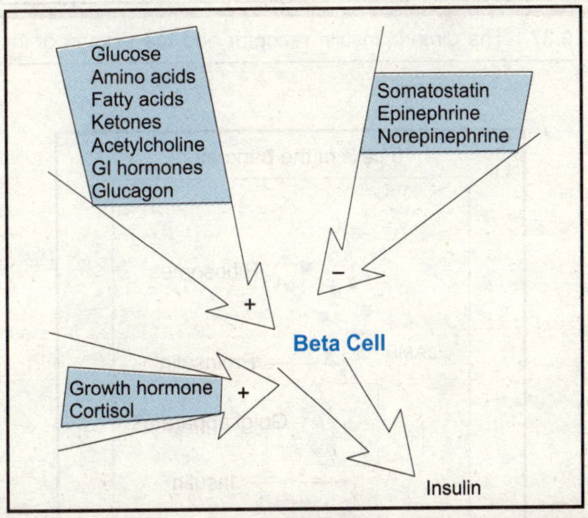


**Fig. 9.36 : Different types of influences on insulin secretion**

### Insulin

**Insulin** is a polypeptide hormone. It is produced by the β-cells of islets of Langerhans. Insulin consists of 51 amino acids arranged in two polypeptide chains A and B which are attached each other by two disulfide bridges. The A chain is composed of 21 amino acid residues and the B chain is composed of 30 residues. Insulin produced by the β-cells of the islets of Langerhans of the pancreas is in close relation with the pancreatic α-cells (which release glucagon). The insulin and glucagon are regulated so that hepatic glucose production is kept equal to the use of glucose by peripheral tissues.

Insulin is produced from a larger single polypeptide, (preproinsulin). Preproinsulin splits off soon after synthesis and is converted to proinsulin. Then there is cleavage of the connecting peptides, insulin is formed with two peptide chains. Insulin is stored in the cytosol in granules. Insulin is released into the circulation by exocytosis when there is an increase in blood glucose (Fig. 9.36.1).

### Mechanism of insulin action (Fig. 9.37)

Insulin binds with specific high affinity receptors in the cell membrane of most tissues including liver, muscle and adipose tissue. The receptor consists of two α subunits which bind the hormone and two β subunits which contain tyrosine specific protein kinases. The **insulin receptor** is a protein kinase which phosphorylates tyrosine residues on the receptor itself (autophosphorylation) and other proteins. Ultimate biological effect of insulin is clear. When insulin binds with receptors, there is a reduction of intracellular cAMP level (Figs. 9.38 and 9.39).

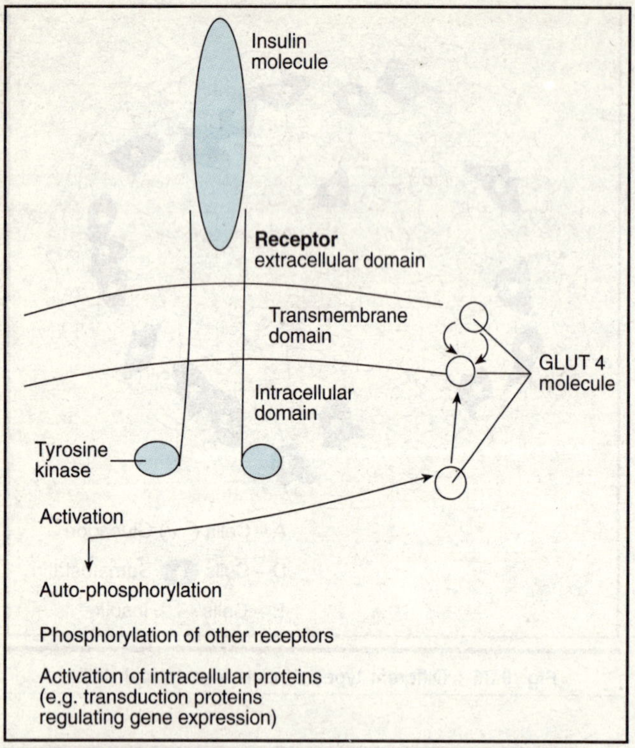


**Fig. 9.37 : The dimeric insulin receptor and the actions of insulin.**

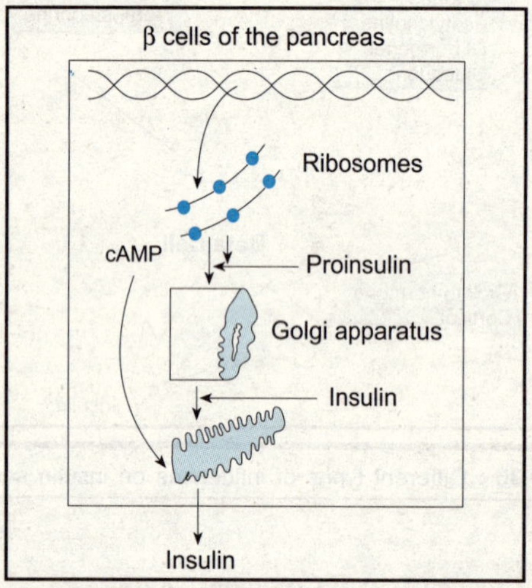


**Fig. 9.38 : Cellular action of insulin**

## Regulation of insulin secretion

The key stimulator of insulin secretion is a rise in blood glucose. *Amino acids* (such as arginine) are potent stimulators for release of insulin. *Intestinal protein* plays an important role to regulate insulin secretion. ***Sympathetic stimulation, catecholamine and somatostatin are the strong inhibitors of insulin release*** (Fig.9.40).

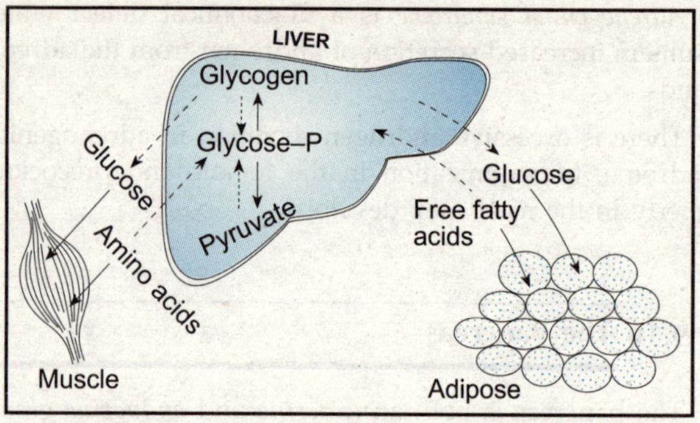


**Fig. 9.39 : Main metabolic effects of insulin**

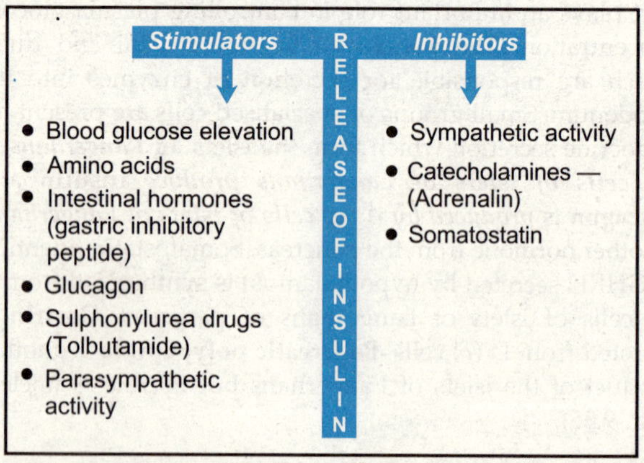


**Fig. 9.40 : Regulation of insulin secretion**

## Actions of Insulin

### Muscle :

- Increased glucose uptake
- Increased glycogen synthesis
- Increased aminoacid uptake
- Increased protein synthesis.
- Decreased protein catabolism
- $K^+$ uptake increased.

### Adipose tissue :

- Glucose entry increased.
- Fatty acid synthesis and lipid storage increased.
- Inhibition of lipolysis.
- Activation of lipoprotein lipase and hormone-sensitive lipase
- $K^+$ uptake increased
- Increased triglyceride formation.

### Liver :

- Increased glucose uptake
- Increased glycogen synthesis
- Inhibition of gluconeogenesis

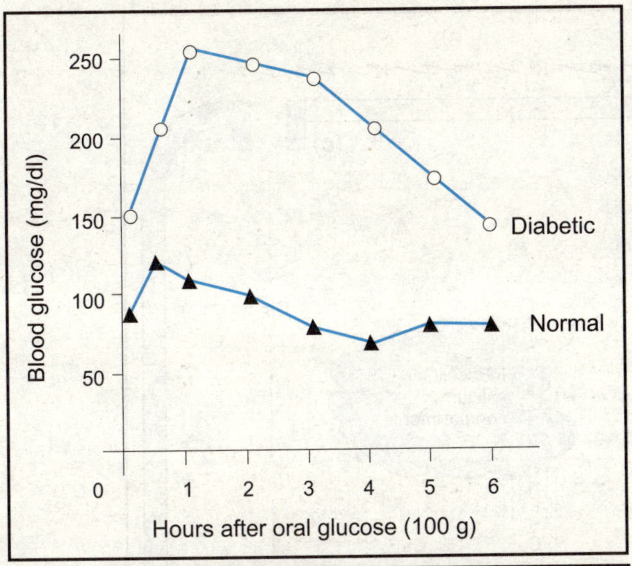


**Fig. 9.41** : Glucose tolerance tests in normal man and diabetic subjects

- Increasedlipogenesis
- Inhibition of Ketogenesis
- Protein synthesis increased

There is a transient rise in plasma amino acid level following ingestion of protein → induces immediate secretion of insulin. Among all amino acids, elevated plasma arginine is a potent stimulus for insulin secretion.

Secretin, gastric inhibitory peptide and other gastro-intestinal hormones stimulate insulin secretion. These hormones are released following ingestion of food (Fig. 9.42).

## Abnormalities of endocrine functions of the pancreas

Inadequate insulin secretion leads to several metabolic derange-ments causing a clinical syndrome called **diabetes mellitus**.

## The Regulation of Plasma Glucose

Glucose is an essential metabolic substrate, particularly for the CNS. Plasma glucose is closely regulated between 4 and 8 m mol/$L^{-1}$ by a number of hormones. These include insulin, glucagon, glucocorticoids, catecholamines, GH and thyroid hormones. All except insulin are hyperglycemic in their actions.

Factors involved in the regulation of insulin secretion by the β cells of the pancreatic islets and the principal actions of insulin (Fig. 9.43).

Plasma glucose is determined by the balance between intestinal absorption, storage and synthesis by the liver and uptake by other tissues. Glucose may be stored in the form of glycogen and synthesized from non carbolydrate precursors (gluconeogenesis). The latter takes place chiefly in the liver.

Insulin is synthesized by the β cells of the pancreatic islets. It is secreted chiefly in response to a rise in plasma glucose and aminoacids. It stimulates the uptake and utilization of glucose by cells (particularly liver) adipose tissue and skeletal muscle, thereby causing a fall in plasma glucose. It stimulates both glycogen and protein synthesis. A lack of insulin or of insulin receptors gives rise to diabetes mellitus in which there is hyperglycemia leading to polyuria, excessive thirst and weight loss.

Glucagon is the most potent hyperglycemic hormone. It is secreted by the α cells of the pancreatic islets and acts to promote the release of glucose into the blood. In effect it acts in antagonism to insulin to provide short term regulation of plasma glucose. Hypoglycemia is principal stimulus for the secretion of glucagon which then stimulates glycogenolysis, lipolysis and gluconeogenesis.

During more prolonged periods of fasting, other hyperglycemic hormones such as cortisol, catecholamines, GH and thyroid hormones play a more significant role.

In the absorptive phase of metabolism, plasma glucose is high, insulin levels are high and the hyperglycemic hormones are inhibited.

**Hormonal regulation** of plasma glucose concentration. During the absorptive state, insulin promotes the uptake of glucose by the liver and by muscle and adipose tissue. In the post-absorptive state, glucose levels are maintained by glycogenolysis in the liver (which is stimulated by glucagon and epinephrine) and by gluconeogenesis which is regulated by cortisol and glucagon lipolysis makes fattyacids available for oxidation and this process is promoted by growth hormone, glucagon and epinephrine (Fig. 9.44 & Fig. 9.45).

**Diabetes mellitus** is a condition that occurs when inadequate uptake of glucose by the cells of the body causes high levels of glucose in the blood (hyperglycemia). Diabetes mellitus may be caused by a failure of the pancreas to produce sufficient insulin or, rarely, to insulin resistance due to a lack of normally functioning insulin receptors.

The classical symptoms of diabetes mellitus are the passage of an increased volume of urine (polyuria); intense thirsts, (polydipsia) and, in many cases, weight loss. The characteristic metabolic changes occurring in uncontrolled diabetes include a rise in blood glucose, an increase in glycogen breakdown, an increase in the rate of gluconeogenesis, increased fatty acid oxidation, and increased production of Ketones which can lead to Ketoacidosis. Glucose appears in the urine (glycosuria) as a result of excessive plasma glucose levels which lead to saturation of the renal glucose carriers. Glycosuria induces an osmotic diuresis by reducing the amount of water reabsorbed in the distal part of the nephron. This loss of water induces thirst. Weight loss is due to an increased rate of breakdown of fats and protein.

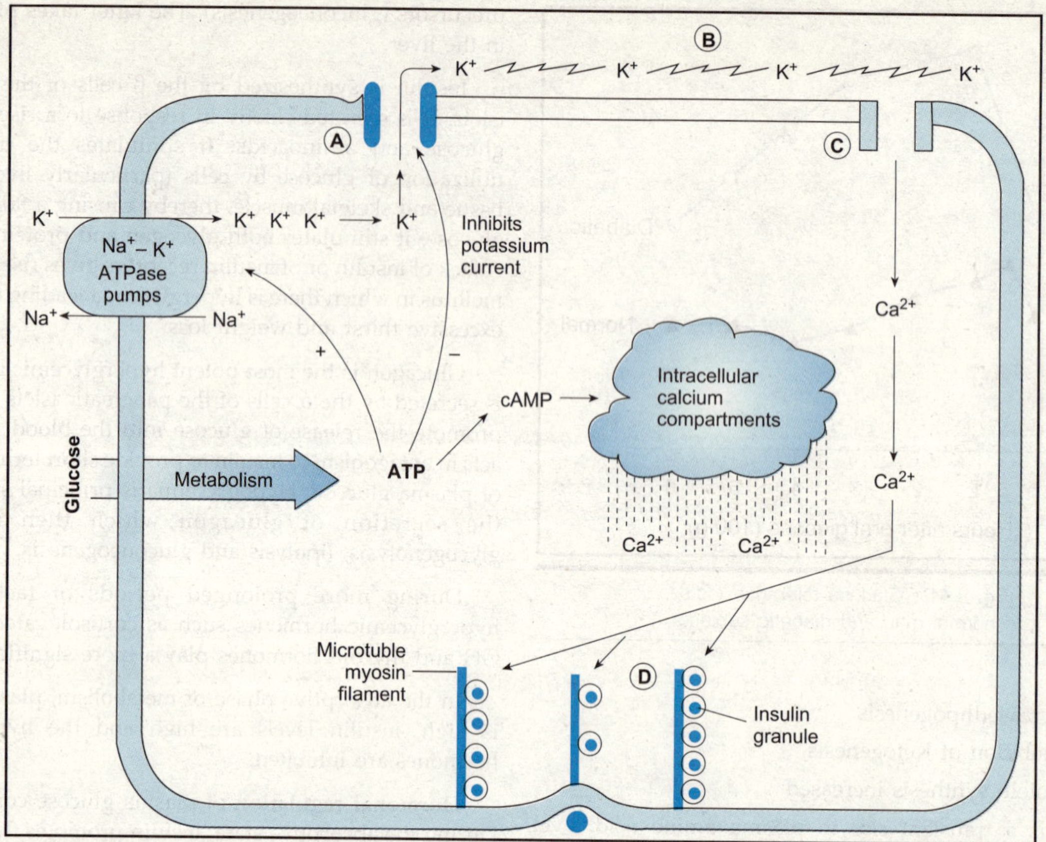


Fig. 9.42 : Schematic diagram of glucose-stimulated insulin release from B cell. Potassium ($K^+$) efflux **(A)** polarizes the B cell membrane and prevents $Ca^{2+}$ entry by clossing a voltage-dependent $Ca^{2+}$ channel **(B)**. When glucose is taken up by B cells, the metabolism of glucose is thought to inhibit $K^+$ efflux, thus depolarizing the cell and allowing $Ca^{2+}$ entry **(C)**. $Ca^{2+}$ stimulates the secretion of insulin-containing vesicles **(D)**.

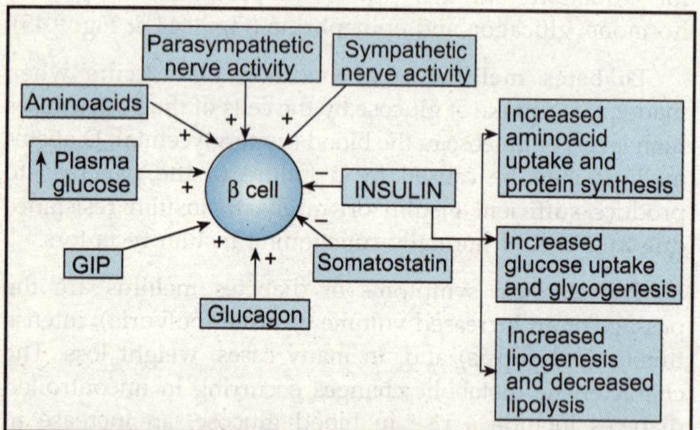


Fig. 9.43 : Factors controlling the secretion of insulin and the principal actions of insulin.

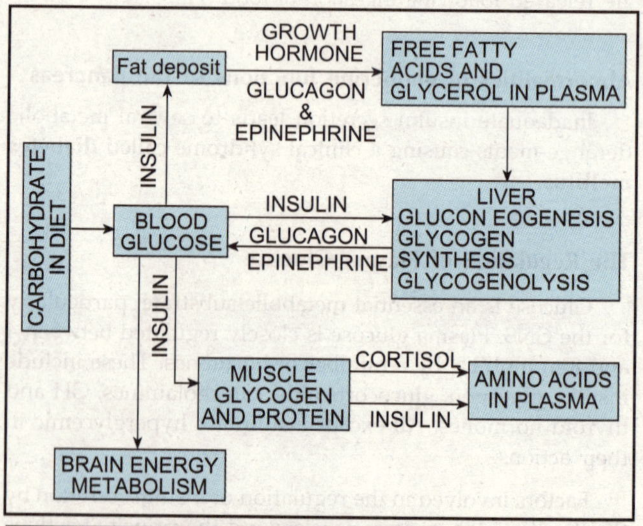


Fig. 9.44

## ➤ 9.11 Glucagon

**Glucagon** is a polypeptide with a molecular weight of 3,500. It is produced by the **A (α) cells of the islets of Langerhans** of the pancreas. It contains 29 amino acid residues. Human preproglucagon contains 179 amino acids and is located in A cells and also in the L cells of the lower

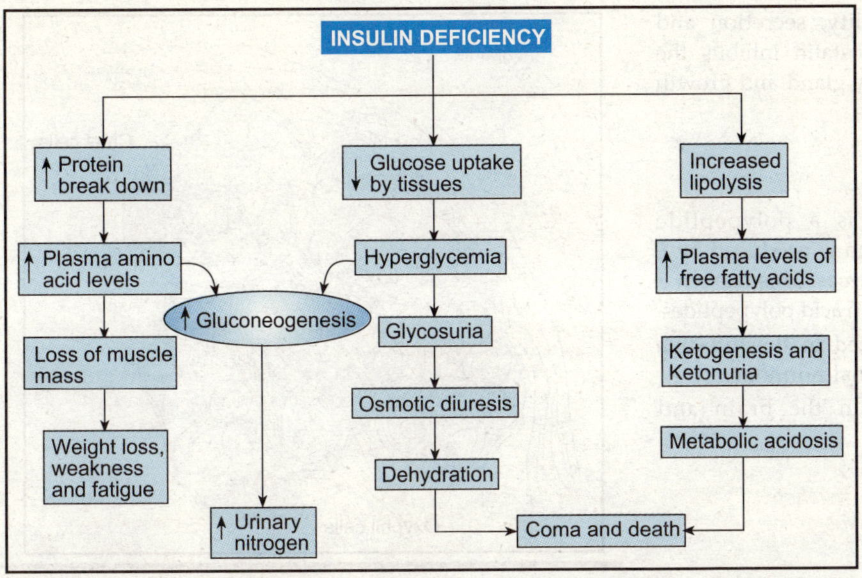


Fig. 9.45

gastrointestinal tract, and also in the brain. Like insulin it is stored in granules and released by exocytosis. It increases blood glucose levels. **Glucagon *stimulates glycogenolysis and gluconeogenesis in the liver via cAMP*.** Glucagon secretion is also ***stimulated by amino acids.*** Fall in the blood glucose level due to elevation of insulin is prevented by the action of glucagon.

β-cells of the pancreas release GABA. GABA acts on the A cells to inhibit glucagon secretion ***via activation of $GABA_A$*** receptors. The $GABA_A$ receptors are $Cl^-$ channels. A cells are hyperpolarized by $Cl^-$ influx (Figs. 9.46 and 9.47).

**Actions :**

(i) Glycogenolytic, gluconeogenic, lipolytic, ketogenic.

(ii) Stimulates secretion of GH, insulin and somatostatin.

(iii) Reduces intestinal motility and gastric acid secretion.

The **secretion of glucagon** is stimulated ***by low blood glucose concentration,*** amino acids derived from dietary protein and low levels of epinephrine. Increased blood glucose level markedly inhibits glucagon secretion.

***Regulation of secretion*** : Glucagon secretion is increased by hypoglycaemia and decreased by rise of plasma glucose.

***Regulation of glucagon release from pancreatic α-cells :*** The α-cells respond to a variety of stimuli that signal actual or potential hypoglycaemia. Glucagon secretion is increased by Amino acids, epinephrine and low blood glucose. Glucagon secretion is decreased by elevated blood sugar and by insulin (Fig. 9.48).

**Agents that affect glucagon secretion**

*Stimulators*

- Amino acids (alanine, serine, glycine, cysteine, and threonine)
- Cortisol
- Gastrin
- CCK
- Infections
- β adrenergic receptors
- Acetyl choline

*Inhibitors*

- Somatostatin
- Glucose
- Secretin
- Insulin
- Ketones
- α adrenergic receptors
- GABA

Fig. 9.46 : Agents affecting glucagon secretion

## Somatostatin

It is a **peptide hormone** produced by δ-cells in the pancreas when there is increased amount of plasma glucose, amino acids (arginine) and fatty acids. Somatostatin is released from gastrointestinal tract into the peripheral blood. ***It inhibits the release of both insulin and glucagon.*** Somatostatin slows

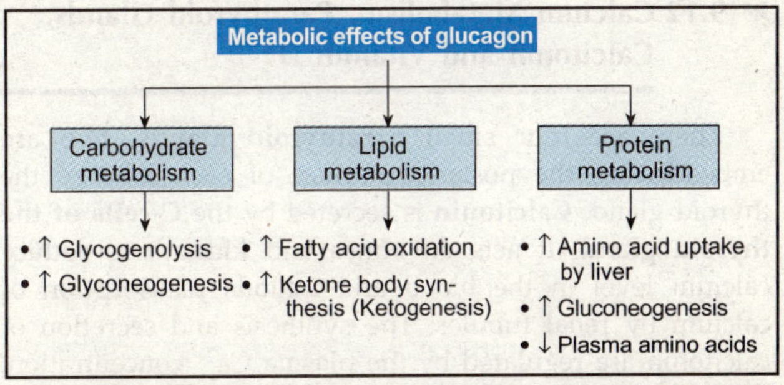


Fig. 9.47 : Metabolic effects of glucagon

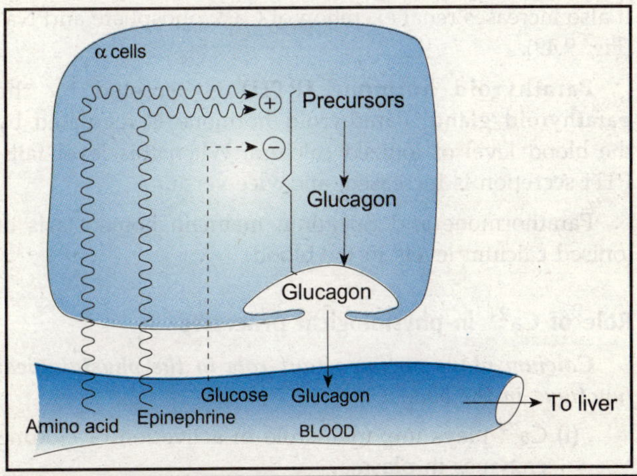


Fig. 9.48 : Regulation of glucagon release from pancreatic α-cells

down gastrointestinal function. Motility, secretion and absorption are also decreased. Somatostatin inhibits the release of thyrotropin from the pituitary gland and growth hormone release.

### Pancreatic polypeptide

Human pancreatic polypeptide is a polypeptide containing 36 amino acid residues which is produced ***by F cells of islets of Langerhans in the pancreas.*** This has got a close relationship with two other 36 amino acid polypeptides.

- Polypeptide YY which is located in the intestine probably acts as a gastrointestinal hormone.
- Neuropeptide Y is located in the brain and autonomic nervous system.

**Secretion is increased by**

- Protein meal
- Fasting conditions
- Acute hypoglycemia
- Exercise

**Secretion is decreased by**

- Somatostatin
- Intravenous glucose

## ➤ 9.12 Calcium Metabolism, Parathyroid Glands, Calcitonin and Vitamin D

There are four small **parathyroid glands,** two are embedded in the posterior surface of each lobe of the thyroid gland. **Calcitonin** is secreted by the **C-cells of the thyroid gland**. It acts on bones and kidneys to reduce calcium level in the blood and inhibits reabsorption of calcium by renal tubules. The synthesis and secretion of calcitonin are regulated by the plasma $Ca^{2+}$ concentration, cyclic AMP, epinephrine, glucagon, gastrin and cholecytokinin. Calcitonin can directly inhibit bone reabsorption by altering osteoclastic and osteocytic activity. It also increases renal excretion of $Ca^{2+}$, phosphate and $Na^{+}$ (Fig. 9.49).

**Parathyroid hormone (PTH)** is secreted by the **parathyroid gland**. Parathyroid hormone is regulated by the blood level of ionized calcium. When this level falls, PTH secretion is increased, and vice versa.

Parathormone and calcitonin maintain homeostasis of ionised calcium levels in the blood.

### Role of $Ca^{2+}$ in physiological processes

***Calcium plays an important role in the physiological functions in the body :***

(i) $Ca^{2+}$ plays important role in activation of clotting enzymes in plasma.

(ii) $Ca^{2+}$ controls membrane excitation and $Ca^{2+}$ influx occurs during excitation of nerve and muscle.

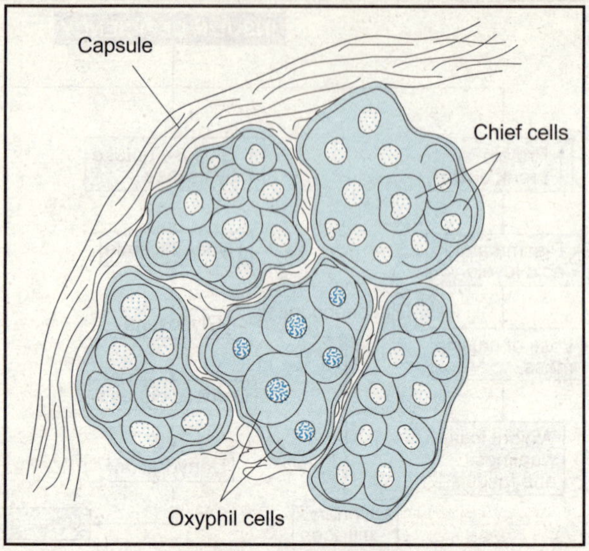


Fig. 9.49 : Small chief cells and large oxyphil cells of parathyroid gland

(iii) It maintains normal permeability of the cell membrane.

(iv) Release of neurotransmitters, many hormones and exocrine secretions are mediated by the action of $Ca^{2+}$.

(v) $Ca^{2+}$ is necessary for formation of bone and teeth.

(vi) $Ca^{2+}$ is essential for muscle contraction.

(vii) $Ca^{2+}$ is necessary for the production of milk.

(viii) Lack of $Ca^{2+}$ in vascular smooth muscles reduces vasospasm and causes fall of B.P.

(ix) $Ca^{2+}$ acts as 2nd messenger in the molecular action of many hormones and is necessary for the release of many NTs (eg. NA) from their respective neurons.

### Calcium in the body (Fig. 9.50)

1-2 kg of calcium is present in adult human body. About 98% of the total amount is contained in the skeleton and rest is present in plasma and cells. ***Normally, total plasma calcium concentration is 10 mg/dl.*** 50% of this is protein-bound (particularly albumin) and rest are free ions. Ionic plasma calcium plays an important physiologic role and maintains neuromuscular and other cellular functions. Vitamin D metabolite, calcitriol, regulates intestinal absorption of calcium. ***Reabsorption and excretion of calcium in kidney is regulated by parathormone (PTH)*** and *calcitonin*. The reabsorption and deposition of calcium in the bone is mediated via PTH and calcitonin.

The normal *daily intake* of calcium in adults *is 0.5-1 gm.* Calcium balance is regulated on an intake which exceeds 0.5 gm (Fig. 9.51).

Calcium absorption from the intestine is stimulated by vitamin D. The mode of action of vitamin D is not clear.

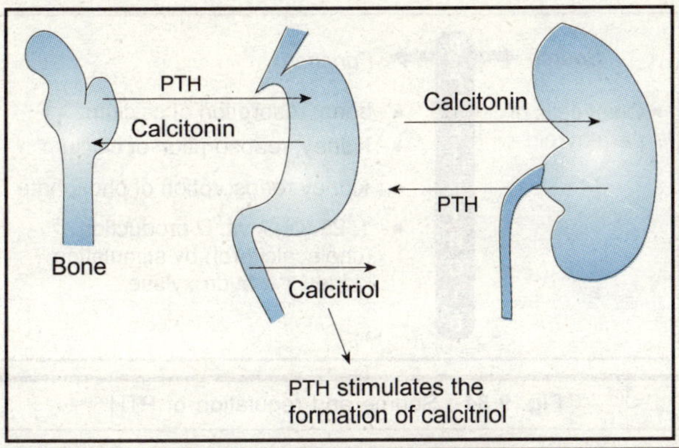


**Fig. 9.50 : Calcium in the body**

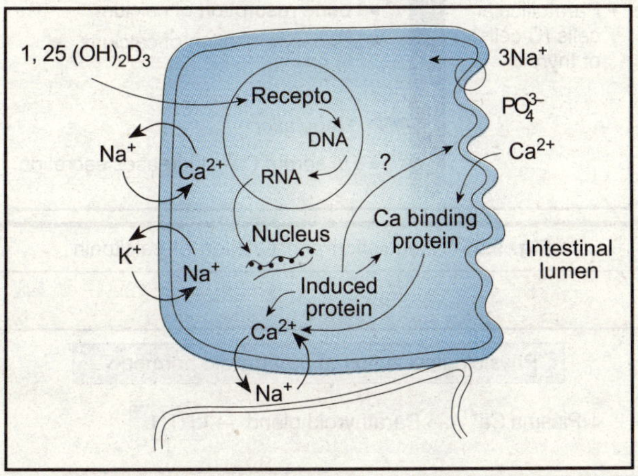


**Fig. 9.51 : Effects of 1,25 $(OH)_2$ $D_3$ on intestinal transport of calcium**

**Deficient absorption of calcium occurs** :

- When there is deficiency of calcium in the diet.
- When there is dietary deficiency of vitamin D.
- When there is disturbances of fat absorption, there is deficient absorption of vitamin D.
- Excessive precipitation of calcium in the intestine.

**Overview of $Ca^{2+}$ regulation :**

- Regulation of three tissues (bone, intestine and kidney).
- Three hormones (PTH, calcitonin and activated vitamin $D_3$).
- Regulates three cells (osteoblasts, osteocytes and osteoclasts).

**Parathyroid glands (Fig. 9.52)**

Each parathyroid gland is small, yellowish in colour and covered with a thin capsule of connective tissue. Each gland is composed of secretory cells which are supplied by capillaries.

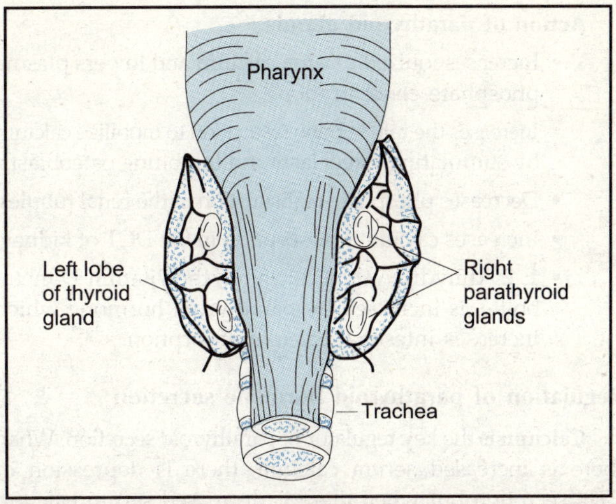


**Fig. 9.52 : Parathyroid glands**

**Parathyroid hormone**

PTH is secreted by the parathyroids in response to a drop in the blood $Ca^{2+}$ level. It increases production of $1,25(OH)_2D$ by the kidney, increases $Ca^{2+}$ resorption from bone and decreases $Ca^{2+}$ excretion in urine. It thus tends to elevate blood $Ca^{2+}$ levels. High serum $Ca^{2+}$ levels blocks production of PTH. $1,25(OH)_2D$ increases $Ca^{2+}$ absorption from gut. Dietary deficiency of it D causes rickets in which there is defective bone formation.

**PTH is the second major hormone influencing calcium balance and bone.** Its action is mediated by intracellular cyclic adenosine monophosphate (cAMP). Any fall in ionized calcium is countered by secretion of PTH. The fall in calcium is controlled by the direct effects of PTH on bone and kidney and its indirect stimulation of calcium absorption from the gut mediated by 1, 25 OH vit. D.

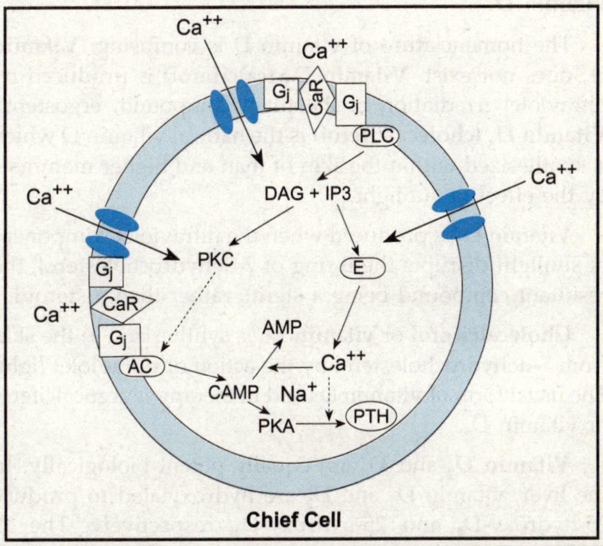


**Fig. 9.53 : Regulation of PTH secretion by $Ca^{2+}$**

**Action of parathyroid glands :**

- Increases ionized plasma calcium and lowers plasma phosphate concentration.
- Increases the rate of bone resorption to mobilize calcium by stimulating osteoclasts and inhibiting osteoblasts.
- Decreases phosphate reabsorption in the renal tubules.
- Increases calcium reabsorption in the DCT of kidney.
- 1, 25 dihydroxycholecalciferol, the vitamin D metabolite, is increased by parathyroid hormone which increases intestinal calcium absorption.

### Regulation of parathyroid hormone secretion

**Calcium** is the key regulator of parathyroid secretion. When there is increased serum calcium, there is depression of PTH secretion but when there is decreased serum calcium level, PTH secretion is elevated (see Figs. 9.54, 9.55 and 9.56).

**Calcitonin : Calcitonin** is produced by **parafollicular (C cells)** of the thyroid. It is also called **thyrocalcitonin**. It is secreted in response to an elevated serum $Ca^{2+}$ level and inhibits bone resorption.

Calcitonin has a 32 amino acid structure and is produced from a precursor molecule of 135 amino acids.

- Calcitonin inhibits osteoblastic activity.
- It diminishes the osteolytic activity of osteocytes and osteoclasts (inhibitory effect on ostesclast activity?).
- It helps to increase alkaline phosphatase synthesis from osteoblasts.
- It inhibits gastric motility and HCl secretion in the stomach.
- It stimulates intestinal secretion.
- It enhances the urinary excretion of phosphate, $Ca^{2+}$ and $Na^{+}$.

### Vitamin D

The nomenclature of vitamin D is confusing. **Vitamin $D_1$** does not exist. **Vitamin $D_2$ (calciferol)** is produced by ultraviolet irradiation of the plant compound, ergosterol. **Vitamin $D_3$ (cholecalciferol)** is the natural vitamin D which is synthesized within the skin of man and higher mammals by the effect of sunlight.

Vitamin $D_3$ is produced when the ultraviolet component of sunlight disrupts the B ring of 7-dehydrocholesterol, the resultant compound being a sterol, rather than a steroid.

**Cholecalciferol** or **vitamin $D_3$** is synthesized in the skin from 7-dehydrocholesterol by the action of ultraviolet light. The usual form of vitamin D used in therapy is ergocalciferol or vitamin $D_2$.

**Vitamin $D_2$** and **$D_3$** are equally potent biologically. In the liver, vitamin $D_2$ and $D_3$ are hydroxylated to produce 25-hydroxy-$D_2$ and 25-hydroxy-$D_3$, respectively. The 25 hydroxy $D_3$ is the abundant vitamin D in the circulation. It is again hydroxylated in the kidneys to 1, **25 dihydroxy-$D_3$**

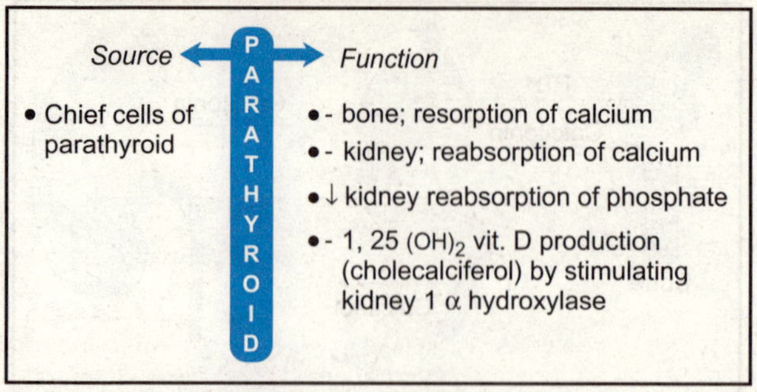


**Fig. 9.54 : Source and regulation of PTH**

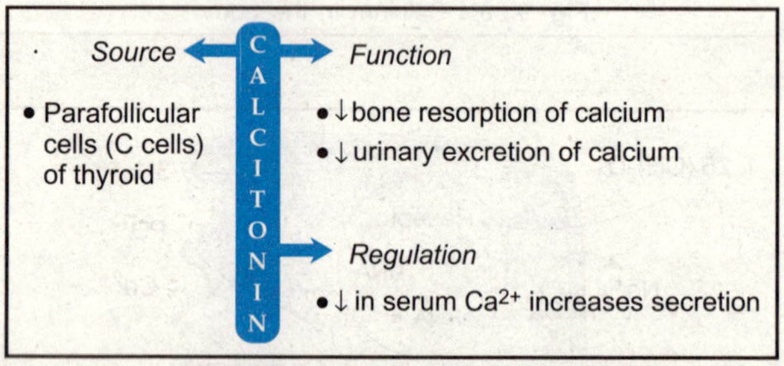


**Fig. 9.55 : Regulation and function of calcitonin**

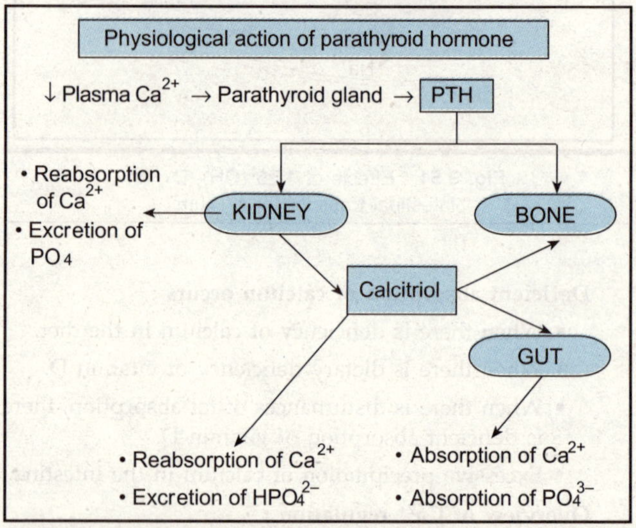


**Fig. 9.56 : Physiological action of parathyroid hormone**

**(calcitriol)** the active form of vitamin D. The main function of 1, 25 dihydroxy-$D_3$ is to increase absorption of dietary calcium and phosphate in the gastrointestinal tract.

### Regulation (Fig. 9.57)

The synthesis of 1, 25-dihydroxy-$D_3$ in the kidney is regulated by PTH, serum phsophate and its own level. When serum phosphate or 1, 25-dihydroxy $D_3$ is high or PTH is low, the kidney hydroxylates it in another position, producing the inactive 24, 25-dihydroxy $D_3$.

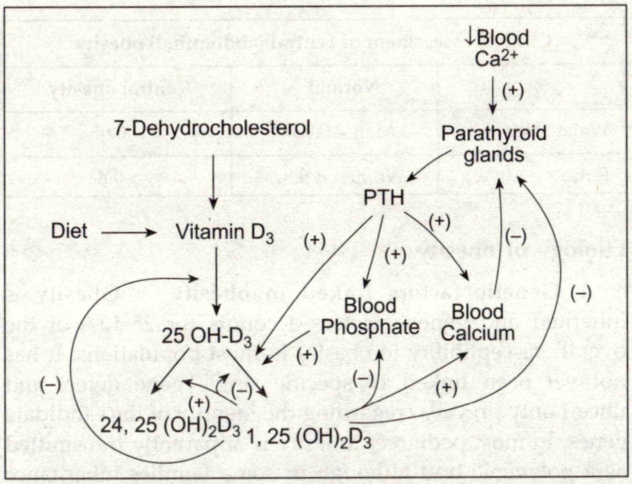


Fig. 9.57 : Regulation of 1 α, 25-dihydroxy-cholecalciferol synthesis

**Main effects :**

- Intestinal mucosa.
- Bone
- Kidney

**Intestinal mucosa** : It synthesizes the $Ca^{2+}$ binding protein and facilitates $Ca^{2+}$ absorption.

**Bone :** Alkaline phosphatase, stimulated by Calcitriol, helps in the deposition of phosphate on bone.

**Kidney** helps in the absorption of both $Ca^{2+}$ and $PO_4^{-3}$.

### Deficiency of hormone

Vitamin D deficiency results either due to inadequate exposure to sunlight or due to fat malabsorption. Bones are not adequately calcified and results in osteomalacia in adults. **Vitamin D deficiency** causes **rickets** in *children* where bone fails to mineralize, epiphyses fail to fuse and there may be fractures.

Physiologic actions of 1, 25 $(OH)_2$ $D_3$ increase calcium and phosphate concentrations in extracellular fluid. These effects are exerted on intestine, bone and kidney. In short, 1, 25 $(OH)_2$ $D_3$ is concerned with regulation of intracellular calcium concentrations, enzyme induction, and cell growth and differentiation.

**Hypervitaminosis D** : The main effect of the overdosage with vitamin D is excessive absorption of calcium and is possibly due to the excessive absorption of phosphate (Fig. 9.58).

### Bone

Bone may be considered as a pool of calcium and phosphate. The diagram (Fig. 9.59) shows an idealized bone and the general process of calcium transport.

### Hormonal regulation of calcium, phosphate and bone

The function of bone, kidney and gut in calcium and phosphate homeostasis are regulated by hormones chiefly PTH and vitamin D. Thyroid and adrenal hormones as well as glucagon, growth hormone and sex steroids also have an influence. The place of calcitonin in this system has not been fully characterized.

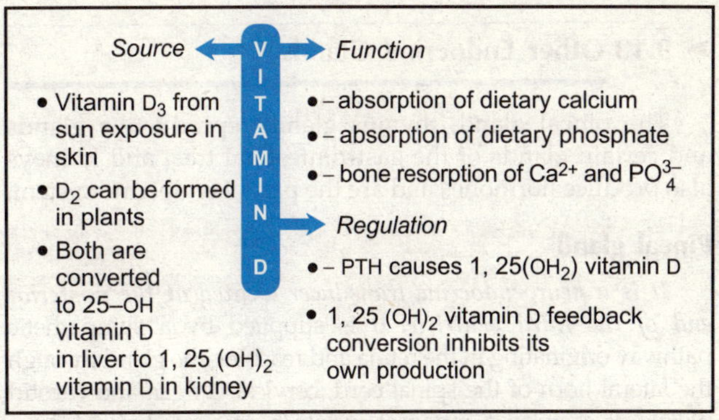


Fig. 9.58 : Source and functions of vitamin D

Bone $Ca^{2+}$ is present in the form of hydroxyapatite crystals. The empirical chemical formula is $Ca_{10}$ $(PO_4)_6$ $(OH)_2$ or $[(Ca_3\ PO_4)_2]_3$.

Bone is composed of bone cells, protein matrix and mineral. The matrix comprises about half of the bone volume and bone cells only about 3 percent.

After epiphyseal closure, the cellular activity of bone represents a dynamic balance between resorption and resynthesis. Osteoblasts are rich in alkaline phosphatase. Its level rises in the blood when their activity increases as in conditions of rapid bone turnover.

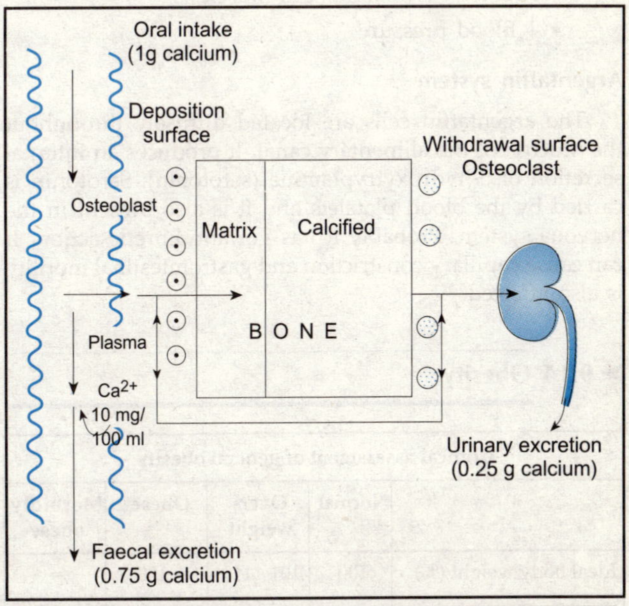


Fig. 9.59 : General process of calcium transport

## ➤ 9.13 Other Endocrine Glands

The pineal gland, thymus gland, reproductive glands and certain glands of the gastrointestinal tract and kidneys also produce hormones and are the part of endocrine system.

### Pineal gland

***It is a neuroendocrine transducer located at the posterior end of the third ventricle.*** It is supplied by a sympathetic pathway originating in the retina and reaching the gland through the lateral horn of the spinal cord, cervical ganglia and carotid plexus. It secretes a range of indole hormones derived from serotonin during darkness, one of which is melatonin.

### Thymus gland

The thymus gland is located in the mediastinum posterior to the sternum and between the lungs. It is large in young children and diminishes in size with age. This gland secretes hormones called **thymosins** which affect production of certain white blood cells (T lymphocytes).

**The reproductive organs** secrete estrogen and progesterone from ovaries and produce estrogen, progesterone and two gonadotropins from placenta and testosterone from testes. (This is discussed in Reproductive Physiology chapter).

### Atrial natriuretic peptide (ANP)

It is a 28-amino acid peptide produced mainly by the cardiac atria where it is synthesized; responds to stretch.

Natriuretic hormone antagonises the sodium-potassium dependent ATPase pump and reduces sodium reabsorption.

**Function :**

- ↑ excretion of $Na^+$ and water
- Controls blood volume
- Relaxes vascular smooth muscle
- ↓ Blood pressure

### Argentaffin system

The argentaffin cells are located diffusely throughout the mucosa of the alimentary canal. It produces an internal secretion of 5-hydroxytryptamine (serotonin). Serotonin is carried by the blood platelets and it is also present in the nervous system. Probably it has got antidiuretic action. It can cause capillary constriction and gastrointestinal motility is also affected.

## ➤ 9.14 Obesity

**Clinical assessment of general obesity**

| | Normal | Over-weight | Obese | Morbidly obese |
|---|---|---|---|---|
| Ideal body weight (%) | 100 | 101 - 119 | > 120 | – |
| Body mass index (BMI) (Kg/mt$^2$) | 18.5-25 | >25 - <30 (Grade 1) | >30 - <40 (Grade 2) | >40 (Grade 3) |

**Clinical assessment of central (abdominal) obesity**

| | Normal | Central obesity |
|---|---|---|
| Waist : Hip | Men < 0.95 | > 0.95 |
| Ratio | Women < 0.8 | > 0.8 |

### Etiology of obesity

**I. Genetic factors linked to obesity** : **Obesity** is inherited and genetic factors accounts for 25-40% of the overall susceptibility to obesity in most populations. It has not yet been linked to specific single gene defect and uncertainty prevails/regarding the identity of the candidate genes. In most pedigrees, obesity is apparently transmitted as a polygenic trait although in some families inheritance appear to be consistent with a single autosomal gene. So far about 20 candidate genes on 12 different chromosomes have been implicated but not beyond doubt. Some of these are discussed below :

(a) **Putative obesity genes encoding metabolic enzymes that could lead to insulin resistance** : Due to inherited insulin insensivity in the skeletal muscles peripheral uptake of glucose and its utilisation through either glycolysis (oxidative disposal) or glycogen formation is impaired. The liver may also be insulin resistant (specially in Type 2 diabetes) and so insulin fails to suppress gluconeogenesis and hepatic glucose production. Insulin insensivity of skeletal muscle would cause failure of glucose entry into the insulin resistant muscles and diversion of this glucose to relatively insulin sensitive adipose tissue resulting in increased triglyceride synthesis. Insulin insensitivity of liver would cause conversion of amino acids derived from dietary proteins into glucose due to unrestrained hepatic gluconeogenesis and subsequently from glucose to triglycerides. Dietary fat, even though meagre, tends to be channeled into body fat stores.

Thus this pattern of genetically conditioned resistance to insulin action in skeletal muscles and liver favour accumulation of fats and consequent obesity when food is readily available. A number of putative genes have been investigated as candidate genes for insulin resistance. These are ***insulin receptor gene, insulin receptor substrate 1 (IRS-1), the rad gene, glucose transporters, hexokinase II, glycogen synthase, protein phosphatase 1 etc.***

(b) **Thrifty gene hypothesis** : This hypothesis proposes that mechanisms for efficient storage of energy, leading to storage of fat and weight gain evolved to successfully counter periods of energy deprivation. This **'thrifty'** adaptation was designed for periods of caloric deprivation. However, during periods of caloric excess this 'thrifty' process which favours energy storage led to excess body fat and obesity.

Thus, humans are better adapted to counter dietary energy deficit than its excess. Thus ready availability of food calories is predisposed individuals genetically conditioned for deficit of food calories leads to to excess energy storage and obesity.

**II. Neuroendocrine factors :**

(a) **Leptin** is a hormone secreted from adipose tissue. It is a 16 KDa protein expressed in white adipose tissue and secreted into the circulation. Putative leptin receptors have been proposed in the hypothalamus and other sites. Leptin has been linked to satiety, hypophagia and increased energy expenditure via the hypothalamus. Weight loss causes reduction of leptin levels which promotes hyperphagia and weight gain. It has been proposed that low intracerebral levels of leptin seen in obesity could promote hyperphagia and weight gain. Abnormalities of leptin receptors could have a role in reducing efficacy of leptin and weight gain.

(b) **$\beta_3$-adrenoceptors** are found in brown adipose tissue, particularly visceral fat, where it probably regulates lipolysis and energy expenditure. Theoretically, mutation of these receptors could lead to reduced energy expenditure, insensitivity to insulin and contribute to development of obesity.

(c) **Tumor necrosis factor-alpha (TNF-$\alpha$)** is expressed by white adipose tissue and increased levels of this substance found in obesity could be contributory to the obesity by inducing insulin resistance in skeletal muscles.

**III. Environmental factors linked to obesity :** Altered eating behavior leading to excess energy intake :

(i) Hunger and greed specially for sweets (hedonistic factors)

(ii) Macronutrient selection mediated via paraventricular nucleus

- alpha adrenergic stimuli and neuropeptide Y stimulate carbohydrate intake (while serotonin inhibits the same);
- galanins stimulate fat intake (however, this is poorly regulated);

(iii) Eating to alleviate boredom or depression

- frequent intake of snacks.

### Etiologic factors linked to central (abdominal) obesity

(a)Genetic factors : as described before

(b) Environmental factors : central deposition of fat may be favored by

(i) overeating;

(ii) reduced physical activity;

(iii) smoking (perhaps);

(iv) excess alcohol consumption;

(v) psychosocial stress : increased cortisol secretion.

**Associations of central obesity** hyperinsulinemia, insulin resistance, Type 2 diabetes, dyslipidemia, hypertension, coronary artery disease.

### Obesity associated with other diseases

(a) ***Endocrine and related disorders :***

(i) Cushing's syndrome;

(ii) Insulinemia;

(iii) Turner's syndrome;

(iv) Male hypogonadism.

(b) ***Genetic syndromes associated with obesity*** :

(i) Prader-Willi syndrome;

(ii) Laurence-Moon-Biedl syndrome;

(iii) Alström syndrome;

(iv) Cohen syndrome;

(v) Carpenter syndrome.

## ➤ 9.15 KEY CONCEPTS

1. **Hormones are chemical messengers** secreted by specific cells and transported to target cells through blood in low concentration where they bind with their specific receptor to produce its specific cellular response. Protein and peptide hormones after their synthesis are stored in membrane bound vesicles from where they are secreted by exocytosis. Steroid hormones are cholesterol derivatives. Degradation of hormones takes place in the liver, kidney and in the target tissues. The levels of different hormones in the blood varies under different conditions (Fig. 9.61).

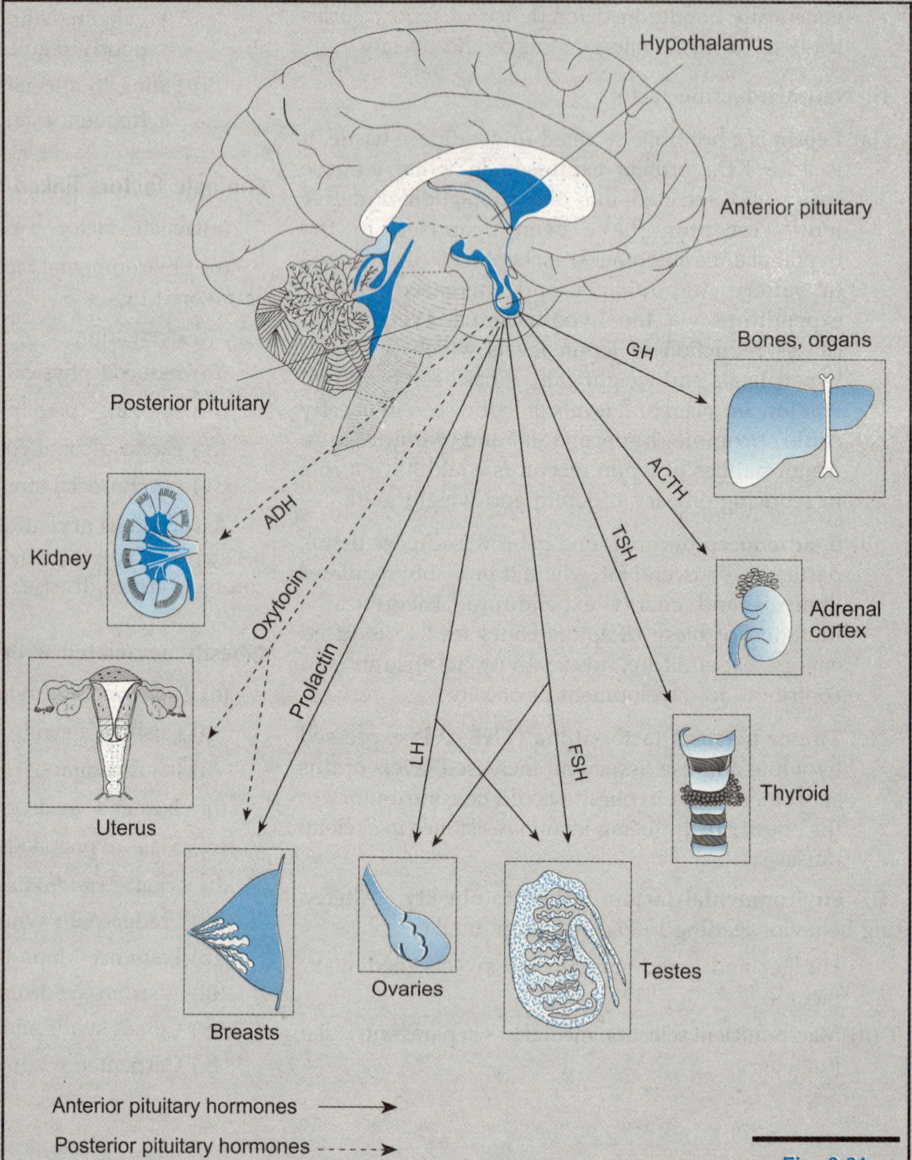


Fig. 9.61

**Pituitary hormones**

**Pituitary gland**

**Anterior lobe**

- Derived from primitive gut
- Blood supply via a system of capillary beds
- Secretes six protein hormones : TSH; FSH; LH; ACTH; GH; PRL
- Secretion is regulated by hypothalamic neurons

**Neural lobe (posterior lobe)**

- Derived from brain stem.
- Blood supply directly through superior and inferior hypophyseal arteries.
- Secretes two peptide hormones : Oxytocin and Vasopressin (these are synthesized in the cells bodies of neurons in the hypothalamus.)
- Secretion is controlled by neuroendocrine reflexes.

## ➤ 9.15 KEY CONCEPTS

2. **The thyroid hormones** $T_3$ and $T_4$ are amino acid derivatives (tyrosine derivatives) and are essential for optimal metabolic activity of the body. These are also essential for growth and development of the nervous system. TSH secreted from the pituitary gland by the action of TRH from hypothalamus regulates the synthesis and release of thyroid hormones. TSH secretion is regulated by the thyroid hormones by negative feedback mechanism.

3. **Adrenal cortex** produces glucocorticoids, mineralocorticoids and androgens. Mineralocorticoids, especially aldosterone, regulate reabsorption of sodium in the renal tubules and thus maintains the circulatory volume at a constant level. The renin angiotensin system inturn, regulates the aldosterone level. Excretion of potassium by the kidney, secretion of sodium as well as potassium through sweat and saliva and also the absorption of sodium in the large gut are under the control of aldosterone. Metabolic pathway of androgen production.

   Cortisol is the major glucocorticoid and increases the blood glucose concentration by promoting reactions leading to gluconeogenesis. It has also an important anti inflammatory action mimicked by drugs such as betamethasone.

4. **Chromaffin cells of the adrenal medulla** release the catecholamines (viz. dopamine, norepinephrine and epinephrine) which are amines of 3, 4-dihydroxy phenyl derivatives. During emergency situations these hormones are secreted by stimulation of the adrenal medualla by splanchnic nerves. They have different actions viz :
   - Heart rate is increased
   - Contractility of the heart is increased
   - Motility of the GI tract is decreased
   - Bronchodilatation occurs
   - Glycogenolysis is increased

5. **Insulin and glucagon** are two of the most important hormones produced by the islets of Langerhans of the pancreas. **Glucagon** is a peptide hormone with a single chain which has a stimulating effect on metabolic activities, thereby increasing blood levels of glucose and ketone bodies. **Insulin** is also a peptide hormone but has two chains or subunits. It has the following functions :
   - increases uptake of glucose by adipose tissue.
   - promotes storage of fatty acids.
   - increases synthesis of triglycerides.
   - increases glucose transport and glycogen synthesis in the muscle.

6. **Parathyroid hormone (PTH)** increases blood calcium level by :
   - increased mobilization of calcium from bone
   - increased tubular reabsorption of calcium by the kidney
   - increased absorption of calcium from the gastrointestinal tract indirectly by increasing the secretion of active vit. D.

   PTH also acts on proximal tubules of the nephron to decrease reabsorption of phosphate from the glomerular filtrate and thus lowers blood phosphate level.

7. **Calcitonin** is secreted by the ***parafollicular cells*** or the C cells of the thyroid gland. It decreases serum calcium level.

8. **Calcitriol** is the active form ***of vit. D*** and is important in the control of calcium metabolism. It increases calcium and phosphate absorption from the intestine and also increases mineralization of bone.

## ➤ 9.16 DISORDERS/CLINICAL CORRELATIONS

➤ **Tetany :** A disorder marked by intermittent tonic muscular contraction, accompanied by fibrillary tremors, paresthesia and muscular pain; the hands are usually first affected, the spasms occurring later in the face, trunk and sometimes the laryngeal muscles. There is increased irritability of the motor and sensory nerves to electrical and mechanical stimuli.

➤ **Pituitary dwarfism** : It is the ***failure of growth due to lack of GH during childhood***. Patients with pituitary dwarfism, when left untreated, may have heights of 1-1.5 m (3 to 4 feet).

➤ **Panhypopituitarism** : When ***deficiency in GH is associated with deficiency of other anterior pituitary hormones,*** this is termed as panhypopituitarism. It may result from trauma to the pituitary gland or a tumor that destroys pituitary cells or their connections to the hypothalamus. The patient may suffer from sexual disorders as well as hypofunction of the thyroid and adrenal glands.

*Causes of panhypopituitarism* : (i) pituitary tumors; (ii) pituitary surgery or irradiation; (iii) postpartum necrosis (Sheehan's syndrome).

*Treatment* : Pituitary tumor, if present, is removed surgically. Lifelong hormone replacement therapy is given, with corticosteroids, thyroid hormone, growth hormone and sex hormones.

➤ **Goiter** : The term goiter is used for any ***enlargement of the thyroid gland***. This may be associated with hypofunction, hyperfunction or, even, normal concentration of thyroid hormones in blood.

➤ **Simple goiter** : [Only gland enlargement (low $T_3$ & $T_4$)]. Deficiency of thyroid hormones ***due to iodine deficiency*** leads to thyroid enlargement because lack of thyroid hormones promotes pituitary release of TSH. Thyroid gland is enlarged (goiter) but its functions are below normal. Simple goitre may also be caused by a lower than normal amount of iodine in the diet. It may also develop when iodine intake is not increased during pregnancy. Manifests with a pot belly, protruding tongue and pigeon chest.

➤ **Hypothyroidism in infants (Cretinism)** : Stunted growth due to low metabolic rate; abnormal bone formation, mental retardation; lower body temperature. Toxic goitre → gland enlargement + hyperthyroidism. Hyposecretion of thyroid hormones during fetal life or infancy results in **cretinism**.

**Exophthalmic goiter** : Hypersecretion of thyroid hormones may be due to an autoimmune disease called Graves' disease. This disease, like myxedema, is more frequent in females. The enlargement of the thyroid gland **(goiter)** may be two or three times its original size. Thyroid gland enlarges, resulting in hypersecretion of thyroxine leading to increased metabolic rate.

➤ **Thyrotoxicosis** : Thyrotoxicosis occurs when tissues are exposed to high levels of the thyroid hormones. Used correctly, the term **'hyperthyroidism'** refers to the overactivity of the thyroid gland but thyrotoxicosis can also occur from ingestion of too much thyroxine or rarely, from increased pituitary stimulation of the thyroid.

Mental and sexual development are not affected but the patients lack alertness.

**Hypothyroidism** is a conditon of deficient thyroid hormone secretion. Hypofunction of the thyroid is usually the result of a primary thyroid disorder (primary hypothyroidism), although it is sometimes caused by reduced TSH production by the pituitary (secondary hypothyroidism).

➤ **Hypothyroidism in adult (Myxedema)** : (Hyposecretion of thyroid hormones in the adult). Hypothyroidism during adulthood produces myxedema. Low metabolic rate, sensitivity to cold, sluggishness, poor appetite, swollen tissue, depression, dry flaky skin and hair, alopecia, constipation, infertility, fluid retention, increased blood volume, and hypertension.

➤ **Hyperthyroidism** : Hyperthyroidism is a condition in which there is excessive secretory activity of the thyroid gland, as in exophthalmic goitre; the symptoms are produced by excessive amounts of endogenous or exogenous thyroid hormone. High metabolic rate; sensitivity to heat; restlessness; hyperactivity; weight loss, protruding eyes; goitre; menorrhagia; infertility.

*Features* :

CNS — characteristic eye changes, mood changes, Hyper-reflexia, muscle weakness.

Skin — rough, pigmentation, pruritus, increased sweating.

GIT — diarrhea.

Generalized — Feels exhausted, feverish at all times.

## ➤ 9.16 DISORDERS/CLINICAL CORRELATIONS

*Causes (of hyperthyroidism) :*

- Grave's disease (primary hyperthyroidism)
- Toxic multinodular goitre
- Toxic adenoma

➤ **Graves' disease** : This is the most common ***type of hyperthyroidism*** which may occur at any age (20-40 yrs.). Autoantibodies bind to TSH receptors on the thyroid cell membrane, mimicking the action of TSH, overstimulating the gland (hyperthyroidism). This is more common in females. Exophthalmos is a feature of this disease.

The overactivity is caused by circulating immunoglobulins of the IgG class, known collectively as thyroid stimulating immunoglobulins (TSI) or as thyroid stimulating antibodies (TSAb).

➤ **Dwarfism**

- It is caused by the ***deficiency of growth hormone in infants***.
- Growth of long bones stops prematurely.
- Dwarfs do not show any abnormal physical features.

➤ **Primary hyperparathyroidism** : It is a condition resulting from the ***primary over-production of parathyroid hormone*** from one or more of the parathyroid glands.

➤ **Hypoparathyroidism** : A condition of ***hyposecretion of parathyroid hormone*** by the parathyroid glands. The commonest form of hypoparathyroidism is seen following surgical removal of the thyroid gland. Idiopathic hypoparathyroidism is a rare condition. Serum calcium is low; serum phosphate is high.

➤ **Cushing's disease and Cushing's syndrome** : Generally when ***hypothalamic or pituitary disorder*** is the primary abnormality, the term used is **Cushing's disease**. When there is ***an adrenal tumour the name of the*** condition is *Cushing's* **syndrome**. It is a condition of hypersecretion of glucocorticoids, especially cortisol and cortisone. The condition is characterized by redistribution of fat accompanied by 'moon face', buffalo hump on the back and pendulous abdomen. Other symptoms are hyperglycaemia, osteoporosis, weakness and hypertension.

**Pituitary Cushing's syndrome is** caused by a small pituitary tumour (microadenoma) producing excessive amounts of adrenocorticotropic hormone (ACTH).

**Adrenal Cushing's syndrome is** caused by autonomous cortisol production by an adrenal tumour (adenoma; carcinoma) and is associated with suppressed plasma ACTH.

➤ **Syndrome of inappropriate ADH secretion (SIADH)**

It is characterised by an excessive or inappropriate secretion of ADH from the posterior lobe or from an ectopic source.

It is manifested by water retention, edema and increased urine osmolality.

➤ **Insulinoma (insulin-secreting tumor)** : ***These tumors arise from the B cell of the pancreatic islets*** and are usually encountered in middle life. The features of hypoglycemia are always associated with weight gain. Approximately 95% of insulinomas are benign and 5% are malignant. Severe hypoglycemia may result on fasting due to partial blocking of the action of hormones which raise blood agar by insulin (vide figure).

➤ **Adrenogenital syndrome** : There is ***deficiency of a group of enzymes that block the synthesis of glucocorticoids***. To compensate for this the anterior pituitary secretes more ACTH. As a result, excess androgens are produced causing virilism or masculinization. Tumours of the adrenal cortex result in production of androgenic hormones which lead to virilism in women and precocious puberty in boys.

➤ **Virilizing adenomas** : Virilism may result from tumors of the adrenal gland.

➤ **Pheochromocytoma** : Pheochromocytomas are catecholamine-producing tumours. They usually ***arise from the adrenal medulla*** but may develop in chromaffin tissue situated elsewhere. The patient complains of impending death during a typical attack which includes headache, palpitation, pallor, tremor and sweating. There is severe hypertension. It may occur outside the adrenal at any site along the sympathetic chain, including the bladder wall. These tumors secrete only noradrenalin. Urinary catecholamines, metanephrines and vanillyl mandelic acid are elevated. Serum ephinephrine is also elevated.

## ➤ 9.16 DISORDERS/CLINICAL CORRELATIONS

- **Diabetes mellitus** : Diabetes mellitus is a condition of ***impaired carbohydrate utilization caused*** by an absolute or relative deficiency of insulin. It is marked by the passage of excess glucose in urine. Metabolism of the body is disturbed. It is characterised by polyuria, polydipsia, polyphagia, weight loss, nocturnal enuresis. Fasting serum glucose level is more than 140 mg/dL.

- **Diabetes insipidus** : The principal abnormality associated with ***dysfunction of the neurohypophysis*** is diabetes insipidus. It is the result of hyposecretion of ADH, usually caused by damage to the neurohypophysis or the hypothalamic paraventricular and supraoptic nuclei. Symptoms are excretion of large amounts of urine and subsequent dehydration and thirst. A major problem associated with this condition is inability to concentrate urine. DI is treated by administering desmopressin, a synthetic ADH-analog. Diabetes insipidus is characterized by a complete or partial failure of either ADH secretion (central neurogenic diabetes insipidus) or the renal response to ADH (nephrogenic diabetes insipidus).

- **Gigantism** : When there is ***over-production of GH in children,*** this is termed as **gigantism**. Excessive growth of hands, feet, jaw, face and tongue occurs. Insulin like growth factor (IGF-I) is elevated.

- **Acromegaly** : When there is ***over-production of GH during adulthood,*** this is termed as **acromegaly**. This growth is due to stimulation of osteoblastic progenitor cells in the periosteum. The patient presents with thickening of the cranium, the mandible and also facial bones. The patient may present with typical barrel-chested appearance. There may be thickening of the skin and abnormal growth of some soft tissues in the spleen and liver.

- **Adrenal virilism** : ***Adrenal virilism*** is a condition of excessive secretion of androgens by the adrenal cortex.

- **Primary hyperaldosteronism (Conn's syndrome)** : It is rare. In most cases, the disease is due to a single adrenocortical adenoma. Patients may present with polydipsia and polyuria, symptoms of neuromuscular abnormalities such as weakness, paraesthesiae and tetany and hypertension.

# Reproductive Physiology

AGENDA :



10

## ➤ 10.1 CHAPTER OVERVIEW

The difference between males and females in the human species is primarily due to the Y chromosome and a pair of gonads (the testes in the male and the ovaries in the female). The primitive gonads differentiate into testes or ovaries during intrauterine life and the process is genetically determined. The presence of functioning testes is required for the development of male genitalia. During adolescence, the quiescent gonads are activated by gonadotropins secreted by the anterior pituitary. Appearance of typical male or female features depend on gonadal hormones; this transition to adulthood is known as **puberty**. The onset of the female sexual cycle is also dependent on gonadal hormones; these cycles cease (menopause) after a number of years with regression of ovarian function. Gonadal activity in males persist from puberty onward.

The functions of the gonads in both sexes are gametogenesis (production of sperm or ovum) and secretion of sex hormones.

**Testicular Leydig cells** secrete testosterone (an androgen) and Sertoli cells support spermatogenesis. **Testosterone** is the principal androgen having masculinizing effects. A small amount of estrogen is also secreted by the testis. The reproductive function in male is maintained by the hypothalamic-pituitary-testis axis. **Testicular function** is regulated by the gonadotropins (follicle stimulating hormone, FSH —and luteinizing hormone — LH) secreted by the anterior pituitary. Secretion of FSH and LH is under control of hypothalamic gonadotropin-releasing hormone (GnRH) as well as some testicular hormones including gonadal steroids and inhibin.

The **ovary** secretes a large amount of estrogen as well as progesterone. **Estrogen** has feminizing effects whereas **progesterone** prepares the uterus for pregnancy. Sequential secretion of gonadotropins (LH and FSH) from the anterior pituitary in postpubertal female is necessary for the menstrual cycles as well as for pregnancy and lactation. The 28-day (average) **menstrual cycle** is divided into the follicular phase (1-13 days), ovulation (14-15), and the luteal phase (16-28 days). Coordinated effects of LH and FSH stimulate the maturation of ovarian follicle in the follicular phase. After ovulation, estrogen and progesterone secreted by the ovarian corpus luteum (luteal phase) stimulate the growth and differentiation of the endometrium by acting sequentially on the uterus. **If fertilization of the oocyte** by sperm occurs, there is implantation of the embryo in the endometrium leading to pregnancy. In the **absence of fertilization,** a fall in estrogen and progesterone secretion results in endometrial breakdown and shedding (menstrual bleeding).

The hormone **relaxin** is secreted by the ovary during pregnancy. It facilitates childbirth by loosening the ligaments of the symphysis pubis and softening the cervix.

## ➤ 10.2 Sex Differentiation and Development of Gonads

The differentiation of genotypic sex is determined at the time of Fertilization when a sperm (22 + X/Y) unites with the ovum (22 + XX) to form zygote either male (44 + XY) or female (44 + XX) chromosome patterns, respectively [Figs. 10.1(a) and 10.1(b) (overleaf)].

Every nucleated somatic cell of human body contains 22 pairs of autosomes and two sex chromosomes (XX or XY). The chromosomes can be isolated and studied after staining. Nucleated cells can be grown in culture media and during mitosis, chromosomes can be readily identified. The cell division is arrested at metaphase by colchicine. Now the cells are lysed by hypotonic solution and the chromosomal materials are processed and stained appropriately. The chromosomes vary in length and position of centromeres and definite numbers are assigned to them except X and Y chromosomes (karyotypic classification). The centromere divides each chromosome into short (petit or p) arm and long (q) arm. The chromosomes are grouped into metacentric (1, 3, 16, 19, 20), acrocentric (13, 14, 15, 21, 22 and Y) and submetacentric (the rest). The sex determining (or testis-determining) region of Y chromosome is located at the tip of the p arm of Y chromosome.

The genotypic sex does not indicate always the development of phenotypic sexual characteristics. This is because the development of internal and external sexual organs along with gonads is dependent on information gathered not only from sex chromosomes but also from other related factors.

In the early days of embryogenesis in either sex primitive gonad arises at the genital ridge close to suprarenal gland. From the inception up to one and half months, the primitive gonads are similar in either sex.

The primitive gonad consists of outer cortex and inner medulla. Up to 6 weeks, there is no sexual differentiation, but between 6-8 weeks, the cortex of primitive gonad in genetic female gives rise to ovary and the medulla regresses. In genetic males, the medulla grows to develop a testis and the cortex degenerates. So in between one and half to two months the embryonic testis secretes testosterone and

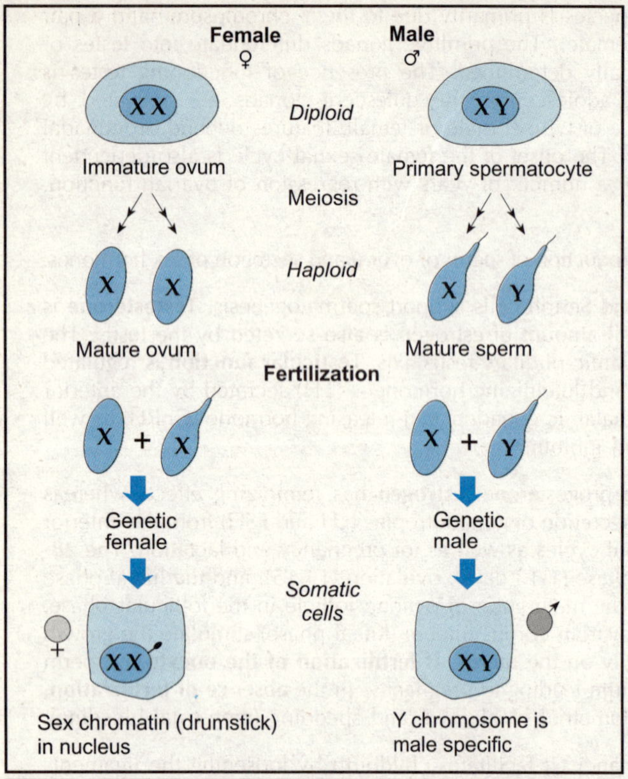


Fig. 10.1(a) : Genetic determination of sex

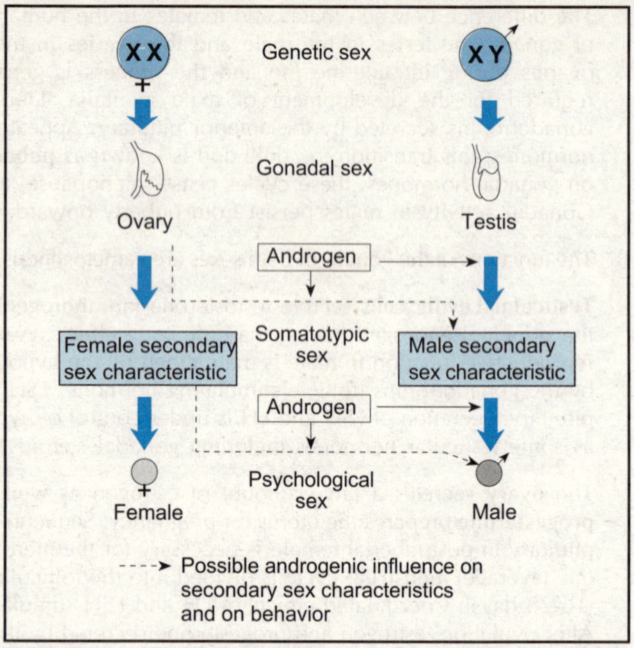


Fig. 10.1(b) : Influences on sexual differentiation

[The genetic sex determination (Fig. 10.1a) of the embryo is followed by the development of the specific gonads and by primary germ cells. Somatic sex development and differentiation in female in the absence of testosterone (Fig. 10.1b). Testosterone at both stages is essential for male sex development]

Müllerian inhibiting substance to have their appropriate effects unilaterally.

The primitive gonad consists of superficial cortex and deeper medulla similar to adult gonads. After this period of undifferentiated state, differentiation into the appropriate gonad starts due to influence of some factors directed by Y chromo-some (**testis determining factor** TDF). In presence of TDF, testis develops, and during its absence ovary develops from the primitive gonads.

***Closure of urogenital slit at 8 weeks indicates the onset of definitive sexual differentiation of external genital organs.*** In male fetuses, with deficient activity of testosterone, the urogenital slits fail to close resulting in male **pseudo-hermaphroditism**. But in female fetuses, if there appears inappropriate androgenic activity, within 3 months there is closure of urogenital slit without duevelopment of vaginal aperture **(female pseudohermaphroditism)**. But if androgenic exposure occurs later, then, the urogenital slit persists as external opening of vagina; however, virilization in the form of an enlarged clitoris occurs.

## Classification of intersexes

I. **Chromosomal level** :
- Turner's syndrome
- Klinefelter's syndrome
- XYY male
- Triple X female

II. **Gonadal level** :
- True hermaphrodite
- True gonadal agenesis
- Leydig cell hypoplasia

III. **Defective androgen receptors** :
- Testicular feminization
- Incomplete testicular feminization.

## Development of accessory organs of gonads

In either sex the conduits must develop to transport the definitive germ cells from gonads to be discharged to exterior or, in case of ovum, if fertilized, to be embedded at a site for growth of a fetus. Though the fertilized ovum bears the chromosomal sex characters, yet during development there occurs an undifferentiated bipotential state at the early stages. This undifferentiated state is characterized by development of *Wolffian* and *Müllerian ducts* on either side draining into a common *urogenital sinus* (Fig. 10.2).

In case of normal male, the Wolffian ducts persist and become converted to epididymis and vas deferens, but there is simultaneous regression of Müllerian ducts. Testosterone formed by interstitial cells of testis (Leydig cells) causes persistence of Wolffian ducts and also development of other parts of male genital system (prostate,

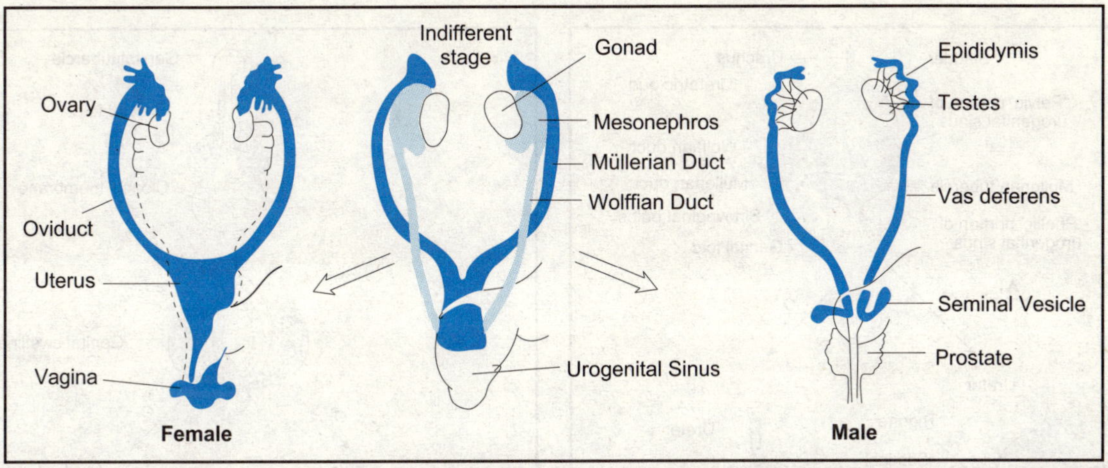


**Fig. 10.2 :** Sex differentiation of the gonad and the internal genitalia. The gonad is a bipotential structure (indifferent stage) up to 6 weeks of gestation. The Wolffian and Mullerian ducts and mesonephros terminate in urogenital sinus. **In the female :** (i) the gonad develops into an ovary; (ii) the Mullerian ducts – fallopian tube, uterus and upper vagina; (iii) the Wolffian ducts remain vestigial. **In the male :** (i) testis develops; (ii) the Wolffian duct—epididymis, vas deferens and seminal vesicle; (iii) the Mullerian ducts—regress

seminal vesicle, urethra, penis). Müllerian duct system is regressed under the influence of Müllerian inhibiting substance (MIS) secreted by Sertoli cells of seminiferous tubules of testes (see Fig. 10.3).

In **case of normal female,** due to absence of testosterone, the Wolffian duct system degenerates and the male internal and external genitalia fail to develop. Due to absence of testis, no MIS is available from this source; the concentration of MIS is negligible in female fetuses. So the Müllerian duct

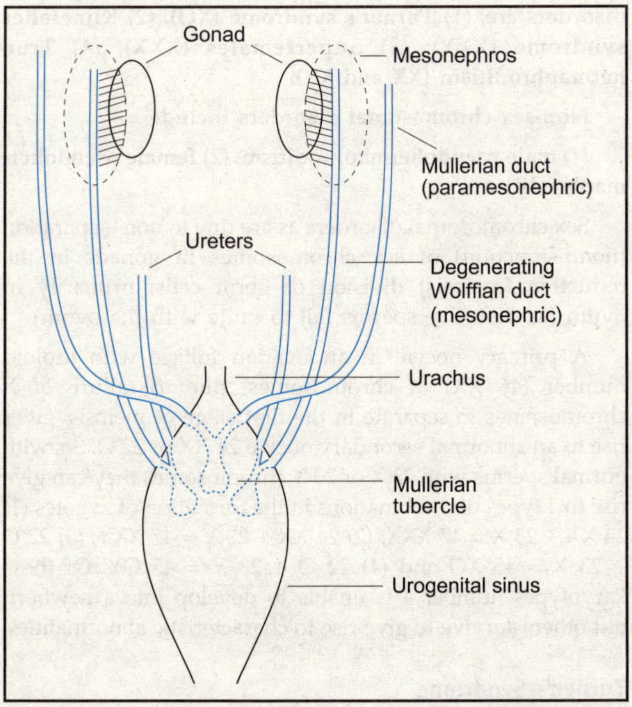


**Fig. 10.3 :** Formation of mullerian and Wolfian duct system

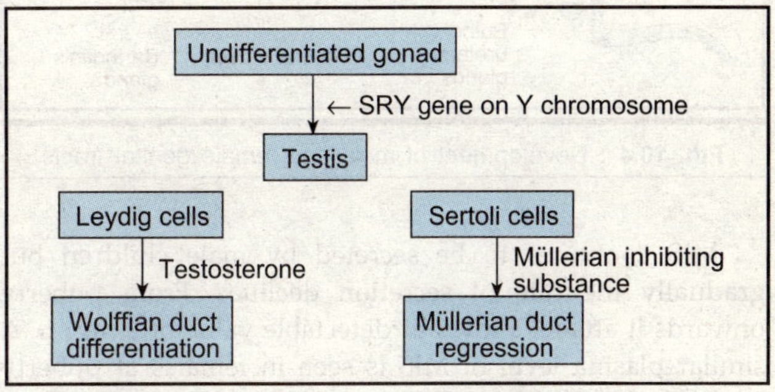


system develops and grows normally to form female internal genitalia in the form of uterine tubes and uterus. The lower portion of the Müllerian ducts fuse to form uterus and cervix while the upper portion remains separate as the fallopian tubes. Remnants of Wolffian duct system may be evident as cysts in the vagina (**Gartner's duct**); remnants of the Wolffian duct and mesonephric tubules may persist in the broad ligament (**paraovarian cysts**). Vagina develops from urogenital sinus in its lower fifth, the upper four-fifth being derived from the Müllerian duct (Fig. 10.4).

## Development of External genitalia

The urogenital sinus has three portions : ***The upper portion*** forms the bladder, the pelvic portion contributes to the urethra and forms the prostate gland in the male; the ***lower portion*** (phallic part) becomes increasingly shallow to form vestibule in the female and contribute to penile urethra in male.

Normal female development does not depend on any gonadal hormones; instead, it is a 'neutral' state that occurs in absence of testis, which, by its endocrine effects, stimulates development of male genitalia.

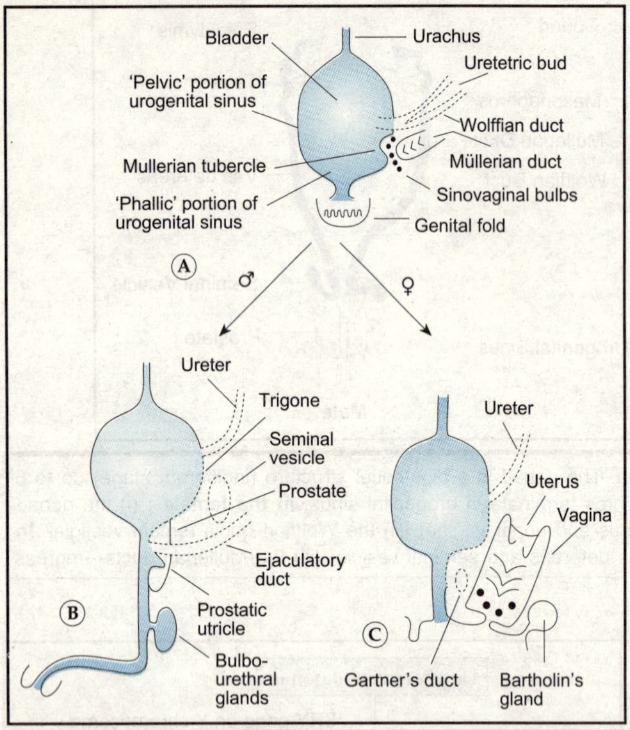


Fig. 10.4 : Development of male and female genital tracts

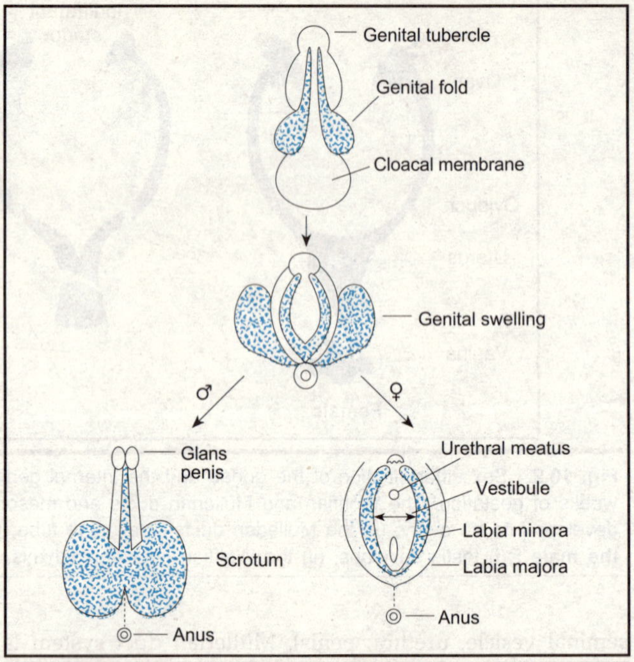


Fig. 10.5 : Development of external genitalia

MIS continues to be secreted by male children but gradually the rate of secretion declines. From puberty onwards it attains a low but detectable value of 2 mg/L. A similar plasma level of MIS is seen in females at puberty (undetectable earlier), MIS being secreted from ovaries.

It is interesting that in the development of internal genital organs in male and regression of Müllerian duct system, both testosterone and MIS act together on one side only (Fig. 10.5).

**Differentiation of primitive structures into male and female gonads and genitalia**

| *Primitive structure* | *Male* | *Female* |
|---|---|---|
| **Gonad** | Testis | Ovary |
| **Wolffian duct** | Epididymis; Vas deferns Trigone of bladder | Part of bladder and urethra |
| **Müllerian system** | Appendix; testis upper part of vagina | Uterus; tubes; |
| **Genital folds** | Penile urethra | Labia minora |
| **Genital swellings** | Scrotum | Labia majora |
| **Genital tubercle** | Penis | Clitoris |

## Abnormal sexual development

Sexual differentiation may take place in abnormal ways owing to defects that involve sex chromosomes or to aberrations further in the development processes. Defects involving sex chromosomes can be grouped under the heading of structural sex chromosomal aberrations and the rest as non-sex chromosomal disorders.

Structural sex chromosomal disorders include conditions where the normal chromosomal patterns (46 XX or 46 XY) are distorted in the affected individuals. **The important disorders are,** (1) **Turner's syndrome (XO)**; (2) **Klinefelter syndrome (XXY)**; (3) **Superfemales (XXX)**; (4) **True hermaphroditism (XX and XY).**

**Non-sex chromosomal disorders include**

(1) **male pseudohermaphroditism**; (2) **female pseudohermaphroditism.**

Sex chromosomal disorders as are due to non- separation (nondisjunction) of sex chromosomes in gonads in the reduction (meiosis) division of germ cells, primarily in ovum (as defective sperms fail to unite with the ovum).

A primary oocyte in an ovarian follicle with diploid number (46 XX) of chromosomes, due to failure of X chromosomes to separate in the first stage of meiosis, gives rise to an abnormal secondary oocyte 24 XX or 22 O. So, with normal sperms with 23 X or 23 Y chromosomes they can give rise to 4 types of combinations in the formation of zygotes (1) 24 XX + 23 X = 47 XXX; (2) 24 XX + 23 Y = 47 XXY; (3) 22 O + 23 X = 45 XO and (4) 22 O + 23 Y = 45 OY. Of these karyotypes number 4 is unable to develop into a newborn but others survive to give rise to characteristic abnormalities.

### Turner's Syndrome

Karyotype 45 X0, i.e. no sex chromatin body.

Incidence : 1 : 2000 live femalebirths

**Causes :**

- Non-dysjunction of sex chromosomes.
- Mosaicism (XO/XX, XO/XY or XO/XXX)

**Clinical features :**

- Phenotypically female, short stature, wide carrying angle, webbing of neck; short metacapals; sexual infantilism (lack of breast development with widely spaced nipples, scanty pubic and axillary hair).
- Primary amenorrhoea, high gonadotrophin levels, low estrogen level.
- Slight intellectual defect.
- Associated anomalies with coarctation of the aorta and renal abnormalities.

## Klinefelter's Syndrome

Karyotype 47 XXY, XXXYY or XXYY i.e. one or two sex chromatin bodies.

**Incidence :** 1 : 400-600 male births.

**Clinical features :**

- Tall, thin men with bilateral gynecomastia and infertility due to hypogonadism (small, azoospermic testes)
- Increased incidence of mental subnormality.
- High urinary gonadotrophins with 17-Ketosteroid content

## 47 XYY

**Incidence :** 1 : 2000 live female birth. Tall, aggressive males with increased tendency to psychiatric illness. More common in prison communities.

**True hermaphroditism** is extremely rare. The hermapro-dites are intersex individuals with testis on one side and ovary on the other, or the gonads on either side presents mixed testicular and ovarian tissues. The external genitalia resemble those of an indeterminate male. At the time of puberty, female secondary sex characteristies like breast development occurs. The chromosomal pattern in mosaics XX/XY, probably develops from faulty development of a (male) zygote or it may be 46XX with paternal X chromosome bearing sex determining short arm of Y chromosome arising out of translocation at the time of sperm formation.

**Male pseudohermaphrodites are karyotypically** normal 46 XY; their gonads are testes, but their external genitalia resemble those of females. ***The causes of pseudohermaphoditism are multiple*** :

(a) The testes in utero are functionally defective; lack of secretion of testosterone and MIS are responsible for development of external and internal genitalia of females.

(b) End organ unresponsiveness where the target cells fail to respond to testosterone due to genetically determined defects in the receptors. The extreme form of unresponsiveness leads to testicular feminization.

(c) Female external genitalia develops due to deficient androgen activity, but the activity of MIS (a protein heterodimer) go unsuppressed; so Müllerian duct system (internal female genitalia) regresses and vagina ends blindly. There are thus, primary amenorrhea and sterility. At puberty owing to unopposed activity of whatever estrogen that is available, there is development of breasts. Receptor defect is a X-linked recessive disorder.

(d) In some cases, androgen concentration and receptor activity is normal, but the active form of testosterone (dihydrostestosterone) is absent owing to congenital deficiency of 5α-reductase enzyme. Under the influence of testosterone, male internal genitalia are formed normally. The development of external genitals and pubertal growth of prostate and penis depends on dihydrotestosterone.

The children are considered girls, but at puberty increased pituitary gonadotropin (LH) causes increased testosterone secretion that can overcome DHT deficiency to some extent to cause enlargement of the clitoris resembling penis. The growth of skeletal muscles and sexual behaviour are normal as they depend upon testosterone.

**Male pseudohermaphroditism** is seen in cases of deficient pregnenolone formation from cholesterol (congenital adrenal hyperplasia) and congenital deficiency of 17α-hydroxylase because pregnenolone and 17α-hydroxypregnenolone are precursors of sex steroids including testosterone. So genetic males phenotypically resemble females owing to deficient androgen formation.

**Female pseudohermaphrodites** are genetically 46 XX. Their gonads are ovaries but have external genitalia resembling males. The virilism is due to the presence of excess androgen in early uterine life owing to inappropriate secretion of adrenal androgen, or androgen derived from maternal ovarian tumors or her consumption of androgens as drugs.

A child with indeterminate sex at birth is most probably female or male pseudohermaphrodite as true hermaphrodites are rare. Barr bodies (inactive X chromosome) in buccal smears in newborns will settle the issue.

## Puberty

Puberty is the stage in life at which reproductive capacity isachieved, and it is associated withthe various physiological, morphological, and behavirouralchanges of adolescence.

This requires a major change in the pattern of secretion of reproductive hormones. The maturation of the gonads is accompanied by the acceleration of growth (the **growth spurt**) and the development of **secondary sex characteristics** which are the most obvious physical changes during adolescence.

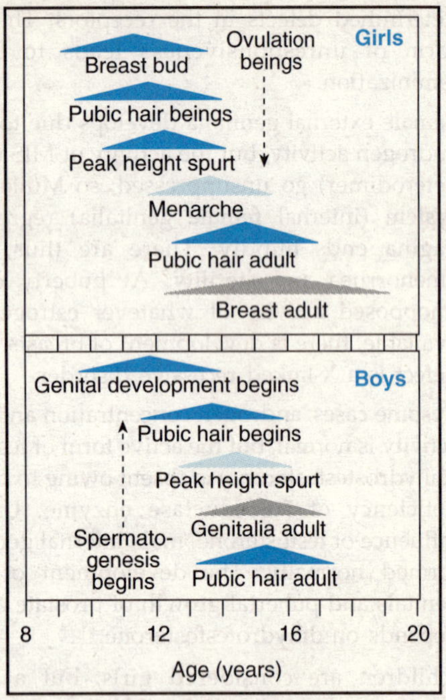


**Fig. 10.6 :** Peripubertal maturation of secondary sex characteristics in girls and boiys.

In general, girls reach puberty earlier **(10 to 16 years)** than boys **(14 to 18 years)**.

During puberty, the adrenal glands begin to secrete adrenal androgens, a process described as **Adrenarche**.

The acceleration of growth is mainly due to the increasing levels of **sex steroids** from the gonads acting with **somatotrophin** from the adenohypophysis. Other growth-promoting hormones such as **insulin** are probably necessary also for the normal growth spurt. Girls usually enter this 'growth spurt' phase some two years earlier than boys. During childhood, the FSH and LH concentrations are **low** despite the apparent lack of **negative feedback** by the **gonadal steroids** and **inhibin.**

This has been explained by two theories :

**The Gonadostat theory :** This theory states that during childhood the hypothalamus has a lower set point for inhibition by circulating gonadal steroids (it is more responsive to circulating FHS and LH). With progression to puberty, the hypothalamus becomes less responsive to circulating gonadal steroids (its set point then increases).

**The hypothalamic maturation theory :** This theory states that the hypothalamus simply does not work during childhood with maturation of the central nervous system, at around puberty, the adult pattern of GnRH gradually becomes established. Although it is not known what causes the change in the CNS evidences are in favour of this theory. During puberty, the gonadotrophin levels gradually increase towards adult levels. This is associated with a market rise in LH pulses (both in amplitude as well as frequency) at night. These are known as **sleep-augmented LH secretion**.

Once puberty is established, the daily variation in gonadotrophin secretion disappears. There is a market difference in the pattern of secretion of gonadotrophins in adult males and females. In females, the pattern of gonadotrophin secretion shows a monthly rhythmicity associated with the ovarian cycle. This pattern is established about two years into puberty, and is marked by the onset of menstruation (the **menarche**).

By contrast, plasma gonadotrophin levels in the adult male are stable. **Physical changes at puberty in boys and girls are given in the Fig. 10.6.**

## 10.3 The Male Reproductive System

The male reproductive system must perform two main functions :

- Spermatogenesis production of sperm (male gamete).
- Ejaculation expulsion of sperm into the vagina.

After puberty, the testes begin to produce sperm and they continue to do so until death. This process is regulated by three main homones :

- Follicle stimulating hormone (FSH);
- Luteinizing hormone (LH);
- Testosterone.

The male reproductive system consists of five main components (Fig. 10.7) :

- **Testes** produce the sperm.
- **Epididymis** store and mature the sperm.
- **Ductus deferens** transport the sperm from the epididymis to the penis.
- **Prostate** and **seminal vesicles** secrete seminal fluid to support and protect the ejaculated sperm.
- **Penis** becomes erect to penetrate the vagina and deposit the sperm at the cervix.

### The Testes

Each olive-sized testis is approximately 4 cm (1.5 inches) long and 2.5 cm (1 inch) in diameter and is surrounded by two tunics. The outer tonic is the two-layered tunica vaginalis, derived from the peritoneum. Deep to this is the tunica albuginea; ("**white coat**"), the fibrous capsule of the testis. Septal extensions of the tunica albuginea divide the testis into 250 to 300 wedge-shaped compartments or lobules. Each lobule contains one to four tightly coiled seminiferous tubules, the actual "**sperm factories**".

The connective tissue, which makes up about 20% of the testicular mass, contains Leydig cells, which make testosterone. The seminiferous tubules, constituting 80% of the testicular mass, generate the sperm. The tutules contain

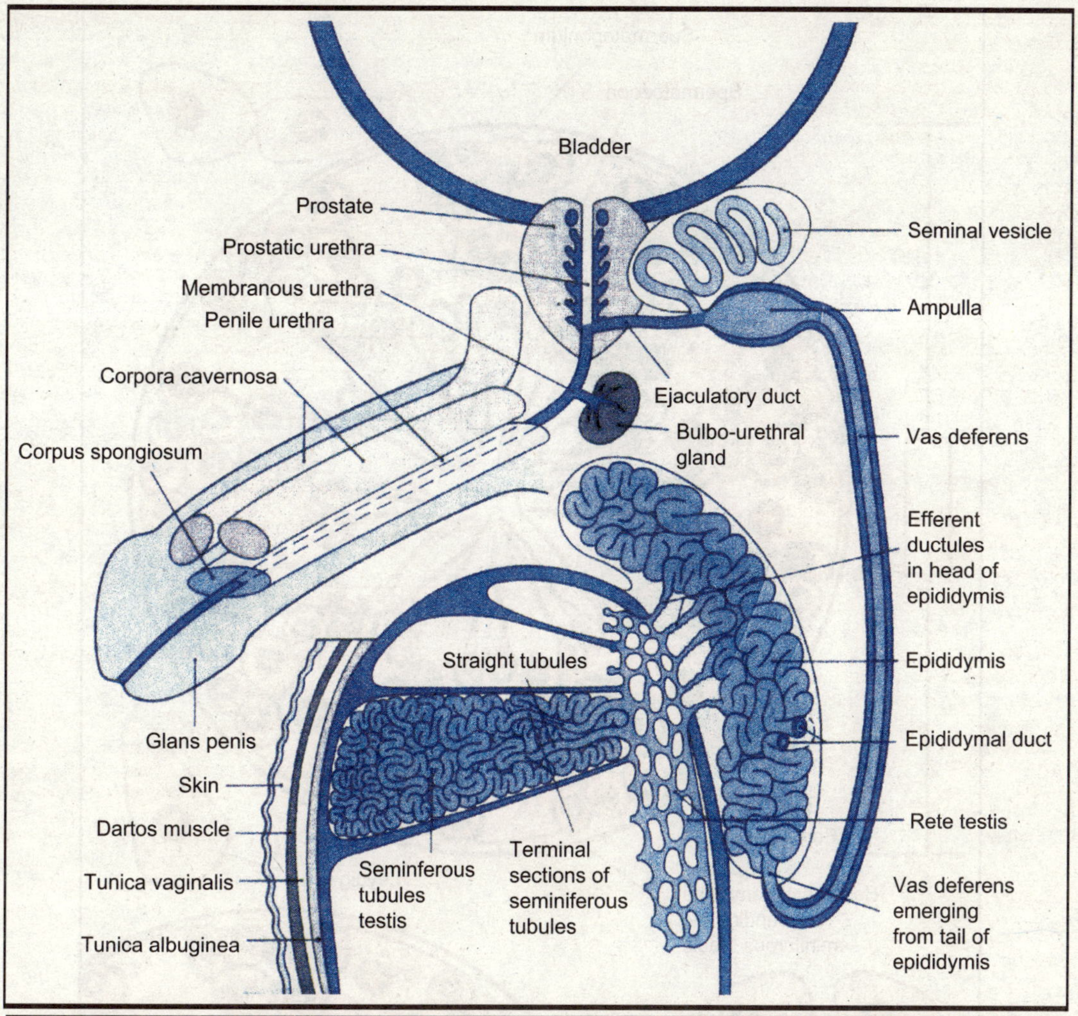


**Fig. 10.7 :** Arrangement of the male reproductive system. This diagram is not to scale

two main cell types: **spermatogonia** and **Sertoli** cells (Fig. 10.8). Spermatogonia are the germ cells that undergo miosis to give rise to spermatids, the immediate precursors to spermatozoa. The copious cytoplasm of the Sertoli cells completely envelops and protects the spermatids, sealing them off from any contact with the tubules outer basement membrane or blood supply. This Sertoli sheath hence forms a blood testis barrier to protect the male gametes from any harmful bloodborne agents, and to prevent the imune system from attacking the unique sperm-specific proteins as though they were foreign antigens. By virtue of their position between the blood and the spermatids, the Sertoli cells also transport nutrients, oxygen, and hormones, such as testosterone, to the spermatids.

The spermatogonia sit outside the blood-testis barrier near the basement membrane. Here, they continuously conduct mitosis. The products of mitosis are pushed toward the tubule lumen and undergo meiosis and differentiation into sperm cells. The testes make around 120 million sperm a day. As they differentiate, the sperm migrate into the tubulo lumen for transport distally to the **rete testis**, a plexus of ducts that collects sperm from each of roughly 900 seminiferous tubules. The **rete testis** empties into the epididymis, a single coiled tubule running from the top of the testis down its posterior aspect. In the epididymis, sperm are stored and undergo maturation before continuing their voyage outside the testis (Fig. 10.9).

## The Ducts and Penis

Each epididymis leads to a long, straight tube called the **vas deferens.** The vas deferens from the epididymis of each testis in the scrotum, ranges laterally through the inguinal canals, runs backwards, and descends along the posterior aspect of the bladder. Here the two vas deferens tubes widen into ampullae, which are attached to glands called **the seminal vesicles.** (There are two seminal vesicles, one for each vas deferens.) The seminal vesicles secrete more than half the volume of the semen. The two ampullae each send an ejaculatory duct through the prostate gland, and the ejaculatory ducts join the urethra inside the tissue of the

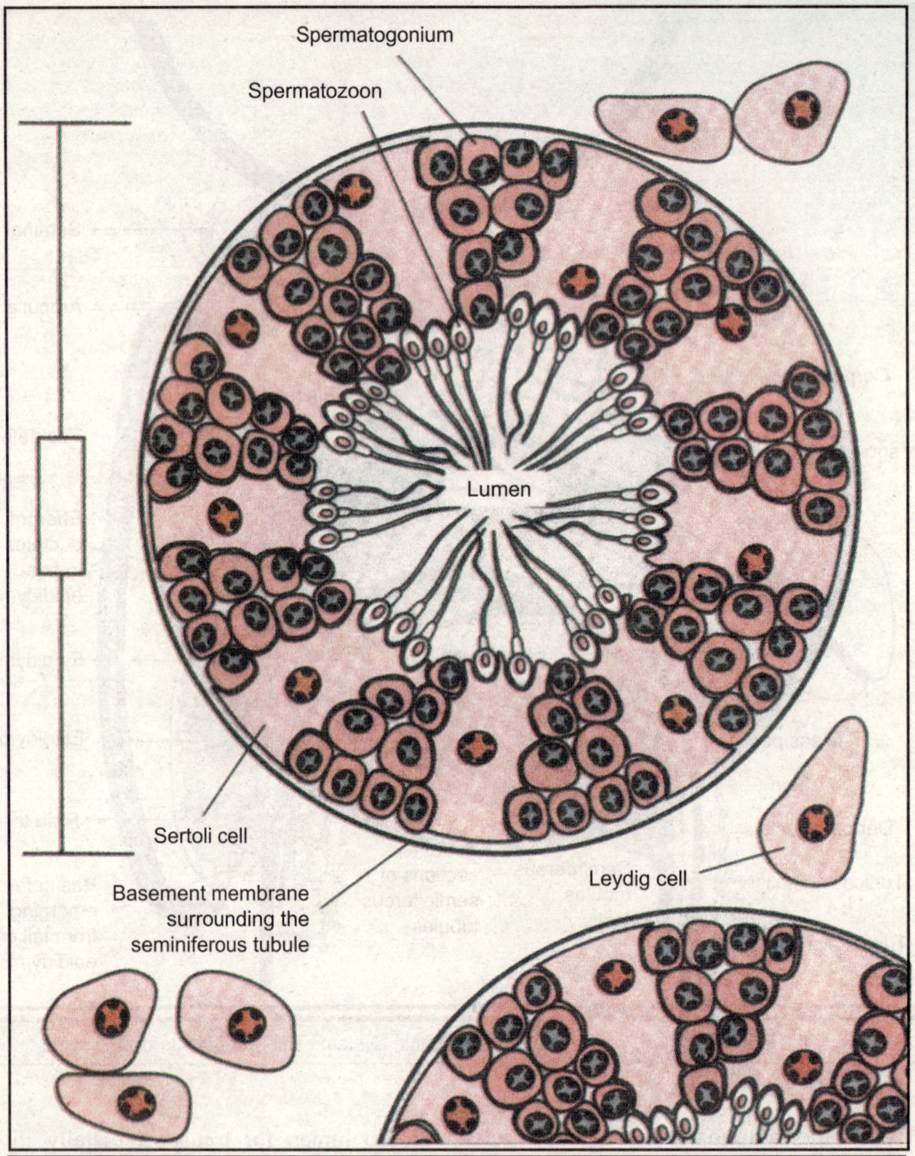


Fig. 10.8

prostate gland. From this point onward, the male penis serves as part of both the reproductive and urinary tracts, unlike female anatomy, in which the reproductive and urinary tracts are completely separate. Male physiology ensures that micturition and ejaculation do not occur simultaneously. The urethra next passes through the muscle tissue of the urogenital diaphragm a consciously controllable sphincter. Just under the urogenital diaphragm are the bulbourethral glands (also called **Cowper's glands**), which lubricate the urethra with mucus. Finally, the urethra enters the penis. The cylindrical penis houses the urethra in erectile tissue, which helps effect the transition between the excretory and reproductive functions of the urethra. This erectile tissue contains cavernous sinuses that fill with blood under circumstances of increased penile blood flow, leading to erection of the penis. The erectile tissue is present in three cylinders inside the penis, each called a **corpus cavernosum** and together called the **corpora cavernosa**. Two of the corpora lie dorsally and are sheathed by the ischio cavernosus muscles. One lies ventrally and is sheathed by the bulbospongiosus muscle. The ventral corpus cavernosum is also called the corpus spongiosum, and it is special in that it contains the urethra and forms the **glans penis**, the spongy head of the penis. The corpora are each supplied by a cavernous artery that gives out helicine arteries. The penis averages 8.8 cm (3.5 in) in length when flaccid and 12.9 cm (5.1 in) when erect. There is no correlation between flaccid and erect size.

### Hypothalamo-pituitary-testicular axis (Fig. 10.10) :

Just as the female reproductive system is co-ordinated by the hypothalamus and pituitary, the activities of the

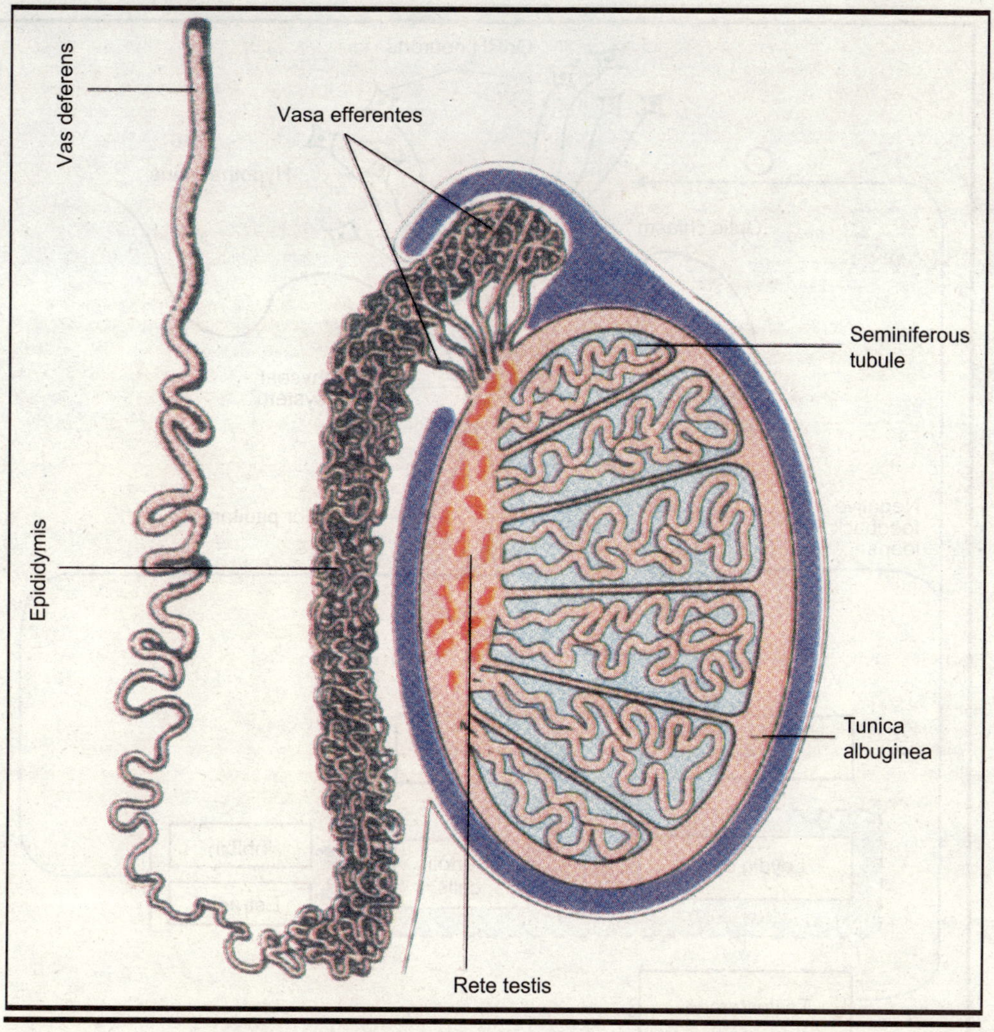


**Fig. 10.9 :** The adult testis, epididymis, and vas deferens

male reprodutive system are co-ordinated by the HPG axis, in this case the hypothalamic-putuitary-testicular (HPT) axis (FIG). (The gonadal HPT axis is not to be confused with the hypothalamic-pituitary-thyroid axis, also labelled **HPT**). The male axis shares with the female the exact same hypothalamic hormone, **gonadotropin-releasing hormone** (GnRH), and the same **pituitary gonadotropins**, **folicle-stimulating hormone** (FSH) and **luteinizing hormone** (LH). (The gonadotropins are named for their female reproductive functions, but they act in the male nonetheless). The same array of gonadal steroid hormones that is produced by the ovary is also synthesized by the male reproductive system, but in different proportions. Because of differential expression of enzymes in the steroid synthesis pathway, the female gonad makes predominantly progesterone and estrogen, while the male gonad predominantly makes the androgen steroid hormone **testosterone**. Testosterone inhibits the secretion of GnRH, LH, and FSH in a classic negative feedback loop.

## Spermatogenesis (Fig. 10.11) :

**Introduction :** The term **spermatogenesis** refers to the processes leading to the production of fully mature spermatozoa from the germinal epithelium of the seminiferous tubules in the foetus, meiotic division of the spermatogonia does not occur because of the presence of a meiosis-inhibiting factor. Its apperance between the ages of 12-14 years signals the onset of puberty; and from then on, goes to completion, producing spermatozoa throughout adult life and old age. Each spermatogonium ultimately gives rise to over 500 spermatozoa.

The phases of spermatogenesis can be divided into three :

**Spermatocytogenesis, meiosis, and spermiogenesis**. The duration of spermatogenesis varies in different species: in man it lasts about weeks, and in rabbits, six weeks. As the cells develop, they move over from the basal capartment (created by the cells of Sertoli) to the luminal compartment attaching to the sides of the Sertoli cells; the more mature

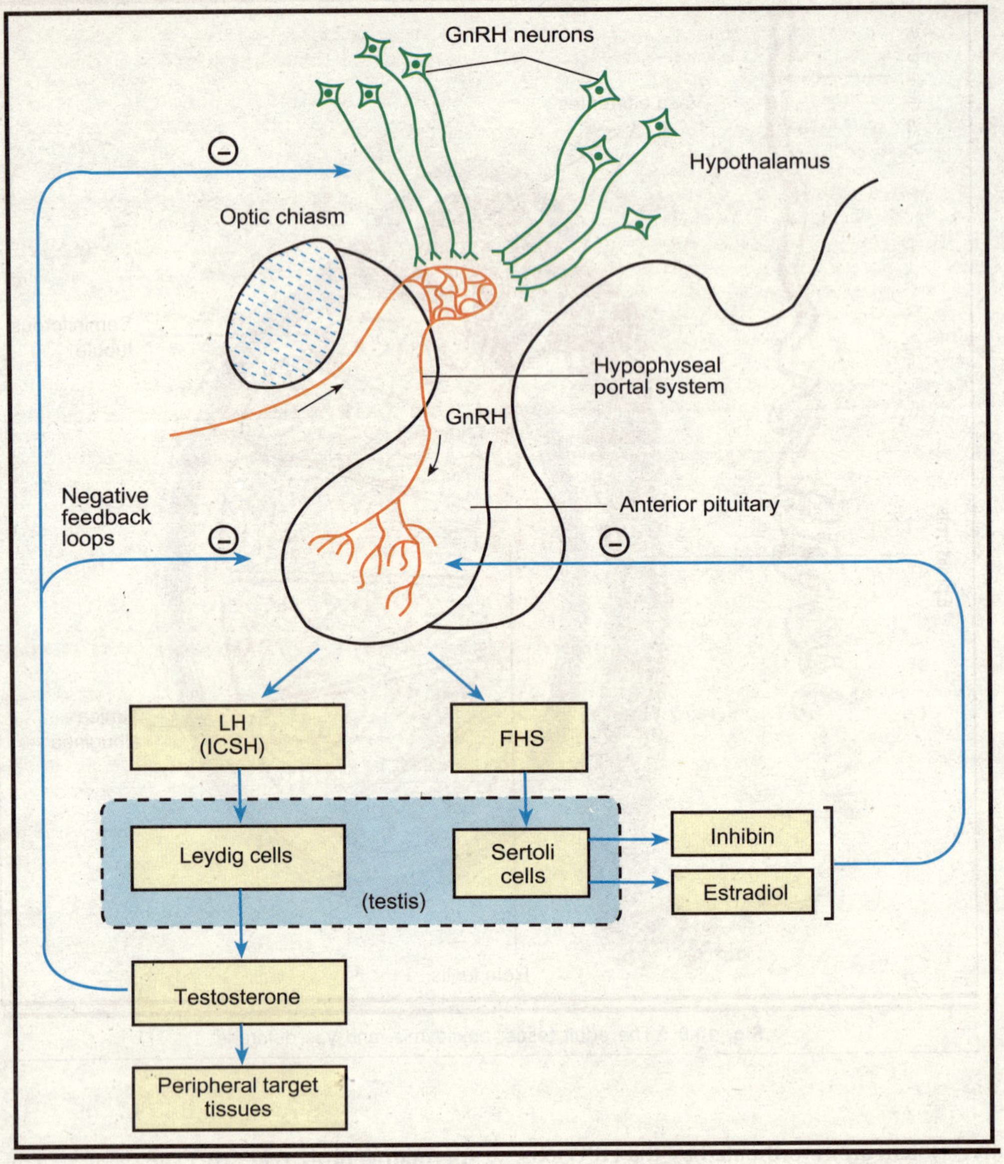


Fig. 10.10 : The relationship between the hormonal secretions of hypothalamus, pituitary gland, and testis.

forms are more deeply embedded in the apical cytoplasm of the Sertoli cells.

## Spermatocytogenesis (Mitosis)

Spermatocytogenesis refers to the division of the spermatogonia by mitosis to produce **primary spermatocytes**. The spermatogonia located next to the basal lamina multiply by successive mitosis and produce types of cells :

1. **Spermatogonia A cells :** Which retain the properties of the original cells, and provide a continuous source of spermatogonia.

2. **Spermatogonia B cells :** Which divide, grow larger than the orginal cell, and enter the first stage of meiosis with the condensation of chromosomes and replication of DNA. The chromosomes now consist of double-stranded chromatids joined at their centromeres, and the cells are known as **primary spermatocytes.**

## MEIOSIS

The primary spermatocytes undergo two successive meiotic divisions. The first division gives rise to diploid secondary spermatocytes, and the second gives rise to haploid cells known as spermatids.

The first meiotic division begins with a pairing of homologous chromosomes, followed by a crossing-over of the chromatids, and exchange of chromatid segments. The homologous chromosomes separate, and the cytoplasm divides giving rise to two cells, each with 23 double-standed

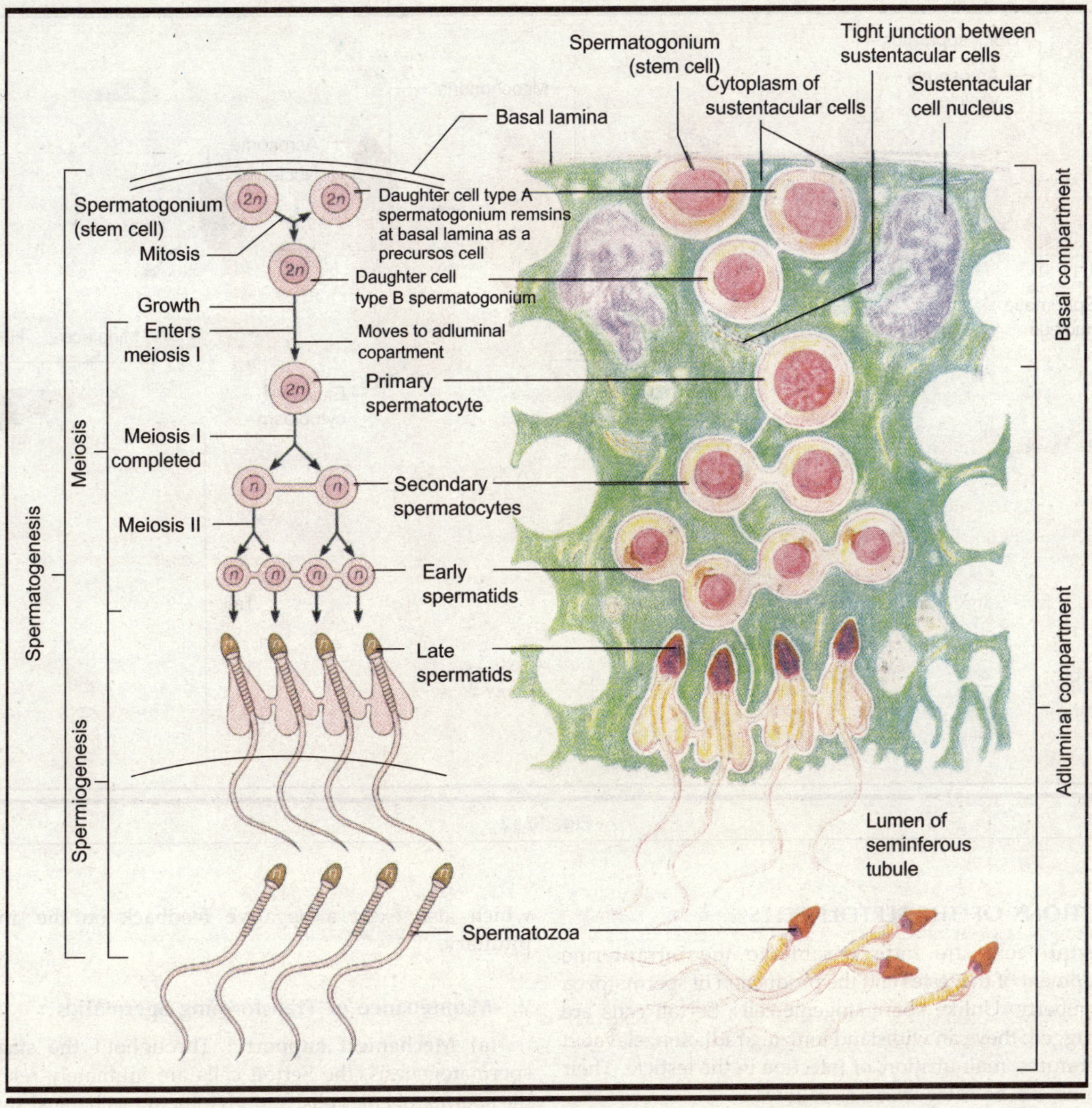


Fig. 10.11

chromatids, known as **secondary spermatocytes**. This is followed by the second or reduction division, in which the centromeres joining the chromatids, quickly split, resulting in the division of each secondary spermatocyte into two haploid cells called **spermatids**. As a result, each primary spermatocyte ultimately gives rise to four spermatids; two with 22+1X and two with 22+1Y chromosome structure.

## SPERMIOGENESIS

The term spermiogenesis refers to the structural changes which transform spermatids into spermatozoa (Fig. 10.12), and are summarized below :

The nucleus elongates to become the head of the spermatozoon and is capped by a product of Golgi apparatus rich in carbohydrates and hydrolytic enzymes, known as **the acrosomal cap**. The acrosome enables the spermatozoon to penetrate the ovum.

A **flagellum** or **tail** arises from a centriole at the pole opposite thecap. It has the typical features of true cilia: an inner core of a pair of microtubules surrounded by nine pairs of microtubules. It is further surrounded by nine longitudinal contractile fibrils, as well as annular rings of fibrils. The middle piece (first part of the tail) contains most of the cytoplsm and all the mitochondria, arranged around the flagellar structure. Later, much of the cytoplasm is cast off as residual bodies which are phagocytosed by Sertoli cells. Although there are wide variations in the shape and size of sperm cells among mammals, they all have the same structures located in the same relative positions within the cell.

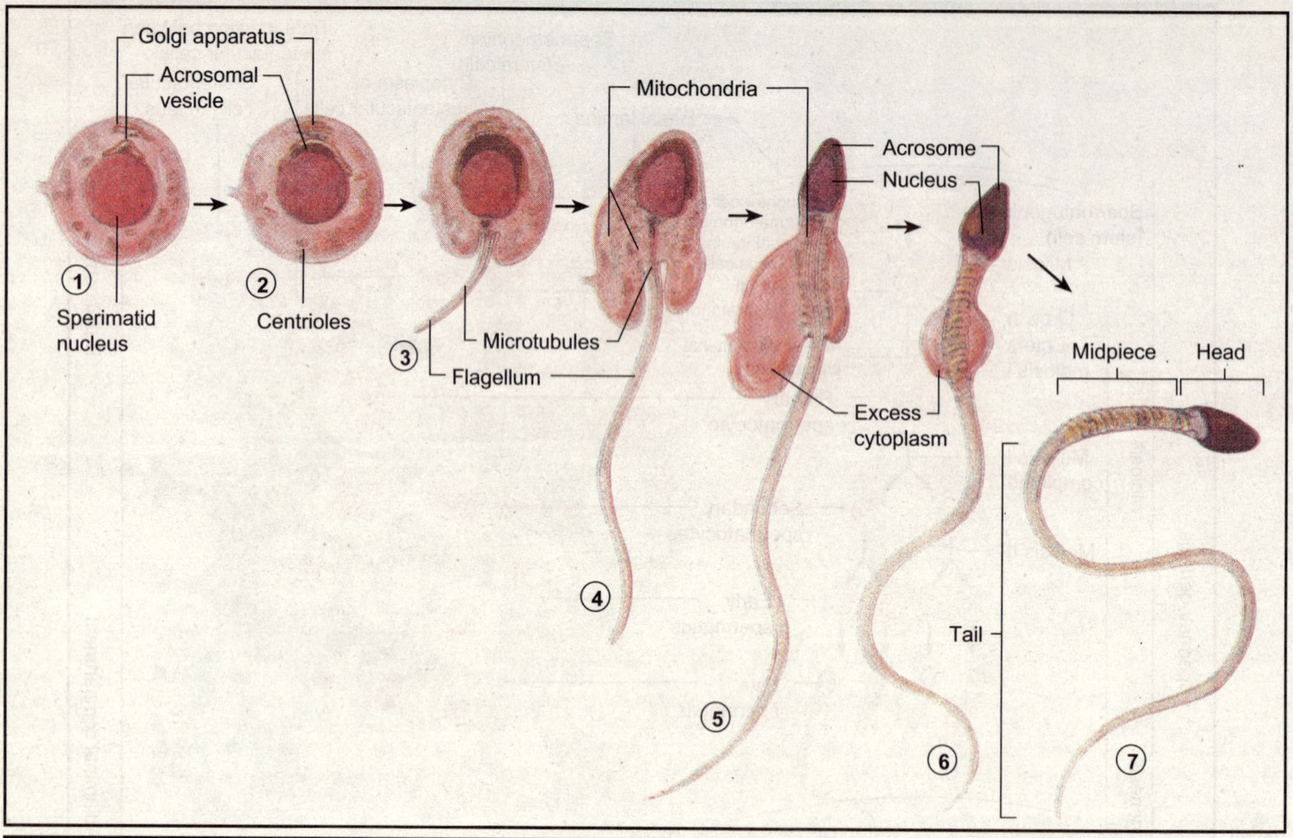


Fig. 10.12

## FUNCTIONS OF THE SERTOLI CELLS

**Sertoli** cells are indispensable to the intrauterine development of the testes and the production of spermatozoa after puberty. Unlike spermatogenic cells, Sertoli cells are very rugged; they can withstand ionizing radiation, elevated temperatures, malnutrition, or infection in the testicle. Their functions can be categorized as follows :

1. **Endocrine functions**
2. **Maintenance of transforming spermatids**
3. **Blood-testis barrier**
4. **Exocrine functions**

### 1. Endocrine functions :

(a) **Müllerian Regression Factor :** In uterus, the Sertoli cells secrete mulierian regressin factor, a glycoprotein which causes the regression of the female müllerian ducts in foetuses that are destined to be males.

(b) **Inhibin :** The Sertoli cells are under the control of the follicle-stimulating hormone (FSH) from anterior pituitary; and in turn, they secrete inhibin which by negative feedback regulates FSH (Fig. 10.13).

(c) **Oestrogens :** They contain the enzyme aromatase which converts some of the androgens into oestrogens, which also exert a negative feedback on the anterior pituitary.

### 2. Maintenance of Transforming Spermatids :

(a) **Mechanical support :** Throughout the stages of spermatogenesis, the Sertoli cells are intimately related to the spermatogenic cells, and give them mechanical support.

(b)**Nourishment :** Sertoli cells are rich in glycogen and presumably provide a source of nourishment for the developing spermatids. During spermiogenesis, the spermatids attach to the lateral membranes of Sertoli cells, and later, their heads and middle pieces are buried within infoldings of the membranes of the apical portion of the Sertoli cells. There is electron-microscopic evidence to suggest that transfer of materials occurs from Sertoli cells to the spermatids.

(c) **Phagocytosis of Cytoplasmic Fragments** detached from the transforming spermatozoa.

(d) **Release of Spermatozoa :** Sertoli cells participate in sperm release by extruding the axial component of spermatids, while holding and phagocytosing lobules of their cytoplasm.

### 3. Sertoli Cells Provide a Blood-testis Barrier for the Seminiferous Tubules :

The occluding tight junctions between Sertoli cells maintain a special fluid environment within the lumen of the seminiferous tubules. Substances such as androgens from the interstitial **cells of Leydig** can only enter the lumen by passing through the basal membrane of Sertoli cells, while many passively substances, including macromolecules and certain small ions, are prevented from passing from the blood into the lumen of the seminiferous tubules. This protects the spermatogenic cells from noxious substances in the blood.

It is possible that these tight junctions also serve as low resistance bridges for the direct electrical transmission between Sertoli cells, thereby co-ordinating their activity.

### 4. Exocrine Functions of Sertoli Cells :

(a) **Secretion of Seminal Fluid :** Sertoli cells secrete a fluid into the seminiferous lumen which is necessary for the onward transport of spermatozoa. The fluid is high in K and $HCO_3$ but low in Na and Cl, like intracellular fluid. It contains **androgen-binding protein** (ABP), **inhibin** and **steroids** (e.g. **testosterone**). The pressure of the fluid propels the spermatozoa along the genital ducts into the epididymis.

(b) **Synthesis and Secretion of Androgen-Binding Protein** : A high concentration of **androgens** is essential for the production and maturation of spermatozoa. Sertoli cells synthesize and secrete an ABP into the luminal fluid, which binds and concentrates the androgens secreted by the interstitial cells of Leydig for the benefit of the developing spermatozoa.

(c) **Secretion of the H-Y Antigen :** In the foetal testis, Sertoli cells secrete a protein known as the histocompatibility-Y (H-Y) antigen, formerly thought to be a product of the genes which is the development of the testis. However, the H-Y antigen is produced by a gene located in the long arm of the Y chromosome while the testis-development gene is located in the short arm of the Y chromosome.

### Mature spermatozoon (Fig. 10.13) :

**Mature spermatozoa** have a distinct head and tail. The had is composed largely of condensed chromatin in the pointed nucleus, the front is surrounded by a giant lysosome called the acrosome that allows the spermatozoa to penetrate the oocyte.

The tail is a long and specialized flagellum derived from one of the **centrioles**. It has the usual pattern of microtubules with nine outer pairs around a central pair. This structure is called the **axoneme**. There are four sections of the tail :

- **Neck**-this narrowing contains the centrioles connected to the axoneme.
- **Middle piece**-the axoneme is surrounded by elongated spiral mitochondria. These release energy to drive the axoneme by the anaerobic respiration of fructose.

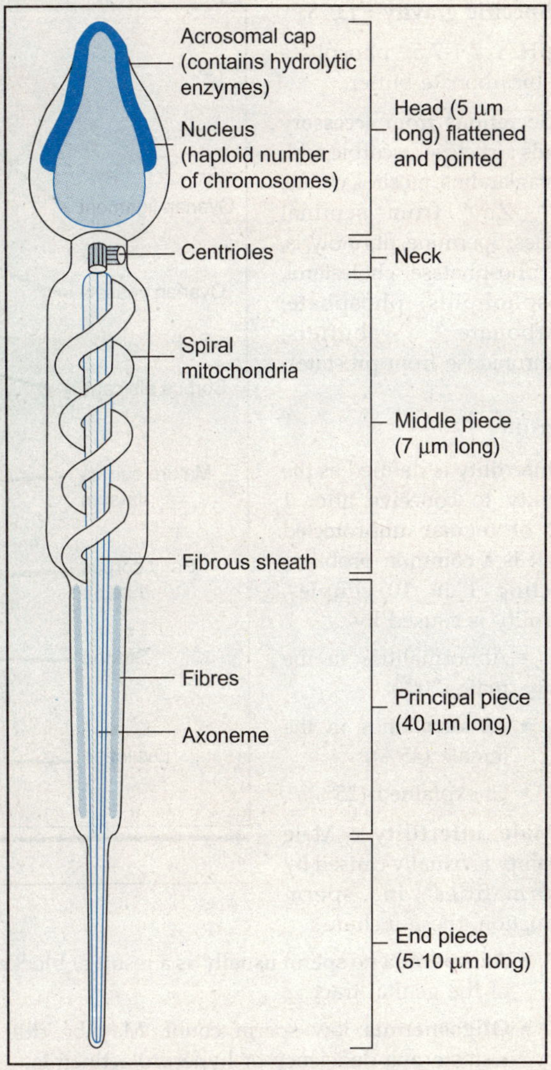


**Fig. 10.13 :** Microstructure of a mature spermatozoon. This gram is not to scale

- **Principal piece**-this forms the majority of the tail. It contains fibres, which are not present in the smaller end piece.
- **End piece.**

### Composition of semen :

**Volume :** After at least three of rest, the volume is 2-5 ml; It clots soon after ejaculation, presumably because of its fibrinogen content, and then luquefics shortly after by fibrinolysis.

**Colour :** White, opalescent.

**Sperm count :** 40-100 million spermatozoa per ml, of which at least 80% is normal in shape and motility. Men with a sperm count of les than 20 million per ml, or a higher percentage of abnormal forms are sterile.

**Specific gravity :** 1.028.

**pH :** 7.1-7.5; phosphate and bicarbonate buffer.

**Secretions from accessory glands :** fructose, ascorbic acid, prostaglandins, inositol, citrate, $Ca^{++}$, $Zn^{++}$ from seminal vesicles; Spermine, fibrinolysis, acid phosphatase, cholesterol, phospholipids, phosphate, bicarbonate buffers, hyaluronidase from prostate.

## Infertility :

Infertility is defined as the inability to conceive after 1 year of regular unprotected sex. It is a common problem, affecting 1 in 10 couples. Infertility is caused by :

- Abnormalities in the male (30%).
- Abnormalities in the female (45%).
- Unexplained (25%).

**Male infertility :** Male infertility is usually caused by abnormalities in sperm production, these include :

- **Azospermia** no sperm usually as a result of blockage of the genital tract.
- **Oligospermia** low sperm count. May be due to testosterone deficiency or hyperprolactinemia.
- **Asthenozoospermia** decreased sperm quality due to reduced motility or abnormal morphology. Occurs due to raised scrotal temperature e.g. **varicocoeleor** may be due to antisperm antibodies.

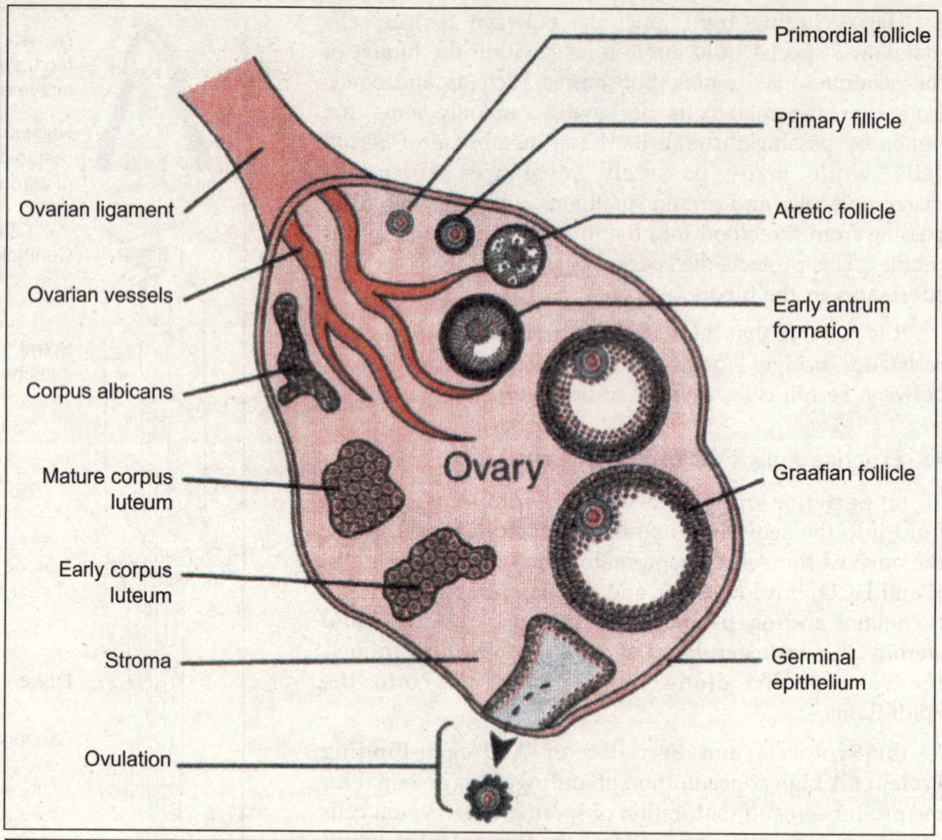


Fig. 10.14

## 10.4 The Female Reproductive System

The female reproductive system must perform five main functions :

- **Oogenesis** and ovulation-production and release of oocytes (female gametes).
- **Fertilization**-allowing the sperm and oocyte to meet and fuse.
- **Pregnancy**-providing a suitable environment for the fetus to grow.
- **Paturition**-expelling the fetus with minimal trauma to the mother and baby.
- **Lactation**-providing the baby with nutrition.

The female reproductive system consists of the six main coponents :

- **Ovaries**-produce oocytes and female sex steroids (e.g. oestrogens).
- **Fallopian tubes**-connect the ovaries to the uterus, they are the normal site of fertilization.
- **Uterus**-support the implantation and development of the fetus.
- **Vagina**-normal site for deposition of sperm.
- **Vulva**-the structures surrounding the introitus (external orifice of the vagina).
- **Breasts**-provide milk for the baby.

The ovaries are situated in the pelvic portion of the abdominal cavity on both sides of the uterus and are anchored by ligaments. An adult ovary weights 8 to 12 grams and consists of an outer cortex and an inner medulla without any sharp demarcation. The cortex is surrounded by a fibrous tissue, the tunica albuginea, covered by a single layer of surface epithelium continuous with the mesothelium covering the other organs in the abdominal cavity. The cortex contains oocytes enclosed in follicles of various sizes, corpora lutea, corpora albicantia, and stromal cells (Fig. 10.14). The medulla contains connective and interstitial tissues. Blood vessels, lymphatics, and nerves enter the medulla of the ovary through the hilus.

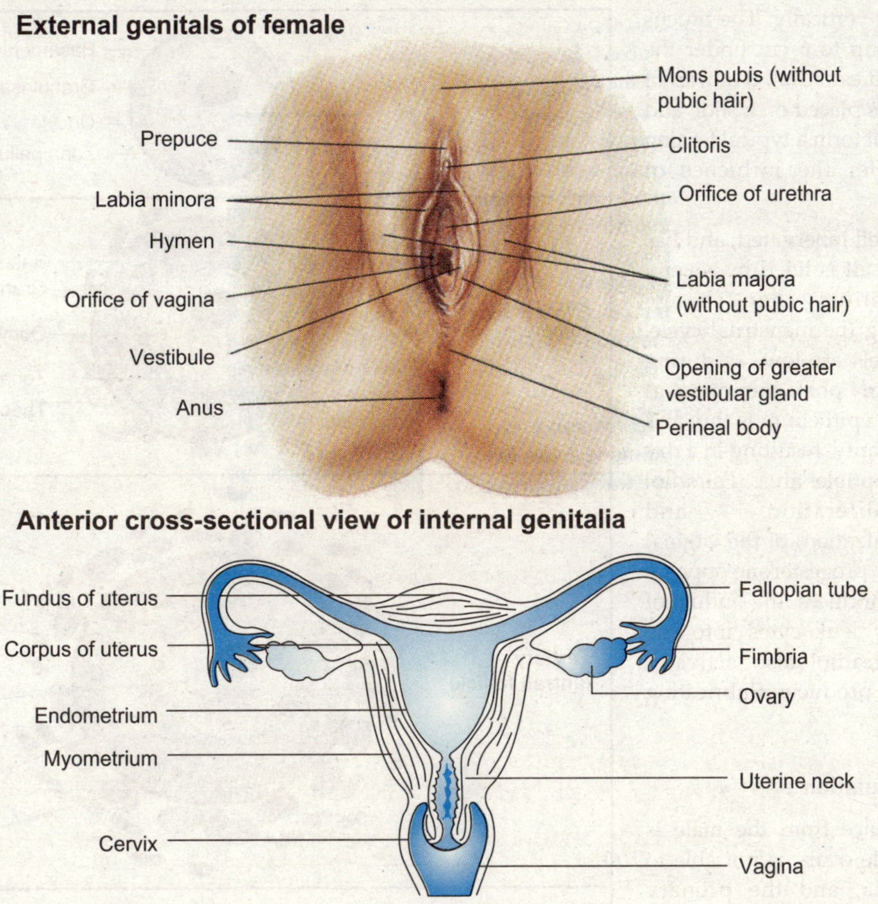


**Fig. 10.15**

The fallopian tubes are the site of fertilization and provide an environment for development of the earlky embryo. The tubes are 10 to 15 cm long and are composed of sequential regions called the **infundibulum, ampulla and isthmus** (Fig. 10.15). The infundibulum is adjacent to the ovary and opens into the peritoneal cavity. It is trumpet-shaped with finger-like projections called fimbria along its outer border that grasp the ovum at the time of follicular rupture. Its thin walls are covered withdensely ciliated projections, which facilitate ovum uptake and movement through this region. The ampulla is the site of fertilization. It has a thin musculature and well-developed mucosal surface. The isthmus is located at the uterotubal junction and has a narrow lumen surrounded by smooth muscles. It has sphincter-like properties and can serve as a barrier to the passage of germ cells. The oviducts transport the germ cells in two directions: sperm ascend toward the ampulla and the zygote descends toward the uterus. This requires coordination between smooth muscle contraction, ciliary movement, and fluid secretion, all of which are under hormonal and neuronal control.

The **uterus** is situated between the urinary bladder and rectum. On each upper side, an oviduct opens into the uterine lumen, and on the lower side, the uterus connects to the vagina. The uterus is composed of two types of tissue. The outer part is the **myometrium**, composed of multiple layers of smooth muscle. The inner part, lining the lumen of the uterus, is the **endometrium**, which contains a deep stromal layer next to the **myometrium** and a superficial epithelial layer. The stroma is permeated by spiral arteries and contains much connective tissue. The epithelial layer is interrupted by uterine galnds, which also penetrate the stromal layer and are lined by columnar secretory cells. The uterus provides an environment for the developing fetus, and eventually, the myometrium will generate rhythmic contractions that assist in expelling the fetus at delivery.

The **cervix** (neck) is a narrow muscular canal that connects the vagina and the body (corpus) of the uterus. It must dilate in response to hormones to allow the expulsion of the fetus. The cervix has numerous glands with a columnar epithelium that produces mucus under the ocntrol of estradiol. As more the more estradiol is produced during the follicular phase of the cycle, the cervical mucus changes from a scanty viscous material to a profuse watery and highly elastic substance called "**spinnbarkeit**". The viscosity os the spinnbarket can be tested by touching it with a piece of paper and lifting vertically. The mucus can form a thread up to 6 cm under the influence of elevated estradiol. If a drop of the cervical mucus is placed on a slide and allowed to dry, it will form a typical ferning pattern when under the influence of estradiol.

The **vagina** is well innervated, and has a rich blood supply. It is lined by several layers of epithelium that change histologically during the menstrual cycle. When estradiol levels are low, as during the prepubertal or post menopausal periods, the vaginal epithelium is thin and the secretions are scanty, resulting in a dry and infection-susceptible area. Estradiol induces proliferation and cornification(keratinization) of the vaginal epithelium, whereas progesterone opposes those actions and induces the influx of polymorphonuclear leukocytes into the vaginal fluids. Estradiol also activates vaginal glands that producing lubricating fluid during coitus.

## Oogenesis and Ovulation :

A major difference from the male is that the adult female ovary is not able to make new oogonia, and the primary oocytes present at birth represents an already declining population, from a maximum of some 7 million at 24 weeks' gestation, down to 2 million at birth, with a further decline to 400000 at puberty. All the germ cells prsent at birth are primary oocytes (equialent to primary spermatocytes) with a potential life span of 50 years.

The meiotic division is suspended in prophase, with the first meiotic division being completed only at ovulation.

The **primary oocytes** are contained in primordial follicles which are formed as a result of a single layer of mesonephric spindle cells from the stroma being induced to surrounded the oocyte. Those spindle cells are the precursors of the granulosea cells and they secrete a basement membrane, the membrane propria, to surround the primordial follicle (the primary oocyte with a single layer of flat **granulosa cells** surrounding it. (Fig. 10.16)

Each month a series of events asociated with the maturation of an ovum occurs. In the adult female this ovarian cycle has a average length of 28 days, although there is significant individual variation from 21-33 days. Physiologically the cycle can be divided into three phases :

- The **follicular phase**, during which follicle growth takes place, is timed from the start of the menstrual blood flow which signifies and end of the previoius

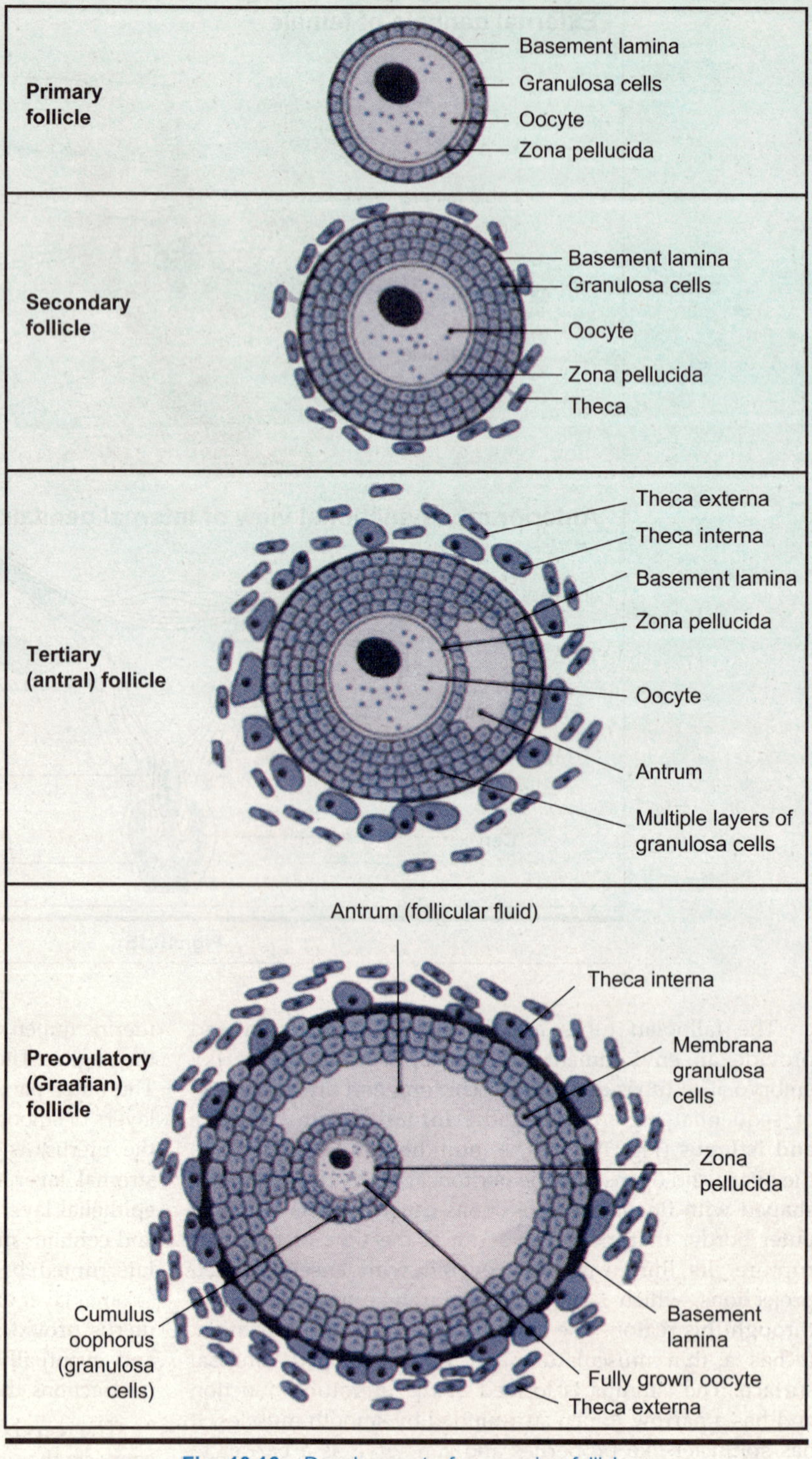


**Fig. 10.16 :** Development of an ovarian follicle through the follicular phase of the menstrual cycle.

cycle. This phase is of variable length, ranging from 1-13 days, although it tends to be reasonably constant for each individual.

- The **ovulatory phase** is 1-3 days in length and ends with ovulation.
- The **final luteal phase**, when the corpus luteum is active, is more consistent in length, averaging 14 days and ending with the menstrual bleed.

**The Follicular Phase :** As mentioned above, hundreds of thousands of follicles are embedded in the ovary with oocytes inside them arrested during meiosis prophase I. In fact, while the oocytes are all suspended at this meiotic stage, the primordial follicles have continued to develop throughout childhood. The granulosa cells have multipled, a thecal cell layer has developed around the granulosa, and the oocytes have increased in size. Eventually, the granulosa cells secrete a fluid into the middle of the follicle containing mucopolysaccharides, electrolytes, proteins, and numerous steroid and peptide hormones (including OMI-oocyte maturation inhibitor). The resultant lake of follicular fluid is called the antrum. The formation of antral follicles takes place continuously over the entire reproductive lifespan, but before puberty their destiny is atresia—**follicular apoptosis (programmed cell death)**.

At puberty, pulsatile GnRH secretion increases in amplitude and frequency (one pulse every 60 to 200 min), in turn increasing the size and frequency of LH and FSH pulses. This exposes the ovary to increased long-term blood concentrations of LH and FSH. Under the increased pubertal influence of LH and FSH, recruitment beging from among those follicles at the antral stage. In each cycle, a group of around 10 follicles is recruited to develop further. They grow large, while the antral follicles which are not recruited take the default path of atresia. The granulosa cells of the large recruited follicles make estrogen, which stimulates the uterine endometrium to grow.

Finally, for reasons not completely understood, 1 out of 10 folicles achieves a metabolic advantage and grows larger than the others. The process is sometimes referred to as **selection**. This single fully grown follicle is called the **Graafian follicle**. Perhaps due to increased expression of the FSH receptor, the Graafian follicle is especially sensitive to FSH from the pituitary, which enhances its advantage over the other follicles. As all the follicles pour estrogen and inhibin (a cytokine from the ovary which increases androgen output and reduces aromtizing activity) into the bloodstream, these ovarian hormones begin to inhibit FSH secretion from the pituitary gonadotrophs. Lacking the Graafian follicle's enhanced FSH sensitivity, and hence lacking the growth stimulus received by the Graafian follicle, the other follicles become atretic and die. This 2-week cultivation of a Graafian follicle is called the follicular phase of the ovarian cycle. Follicular estrogen production yields endometrial growth during these 2 weeks, so that the follicular phase of the ovarian cycle coincides with the proliferative phase of the uterine cycle.

**Ovulation :** By mechanisms that are also not precisely clear, the climbing estrogen level of the follicular phase has a remarkable effect on the hypothalamus and pituitary: once it reaches a concentration of more than 100 pg/mL in the blood for more than 36 hours, it no longer inhibits LH and FSH secretion, but rather stimulates it. The high estrogen level results in a shift from negative feedback to positve feedback. This results in the 48 hour midcycle surge of LH and FSH. (LH levels increase in excess of FSH levels). LH stimulates a burst of activity in the follicle, antagonizing the effects of OMI, and meiosis resumes. LH promotes follicular inflammation, activates proteolytic enzymes, and initiates ovarian contractions. The contractions, the pressure accumulated in the antrum by continued fluid secretion, and the weakening of the follicular wall together lead to follicular rupture. The oocyte inside the follicle is ejected into the peritoneal cavity and clings to the ovarian capsule until it is removed by the fallopian fimbria. It then begins its journey to the uterus via the fallopian tube. This is the process known as ovulation.

The **Luteal Phase :** FSH in the follicular phase has increased the expression of LH receptors on the granulosa of the follicle. THis, in combination with the LH surge, puts the follicle under the heavy influence of LH. Under this influence, the ruptured Graafian follicle transforms into a new tissue called the corpus luteum (Latin for yellow body). This transformation is called luteinization and accounts for LH's name, **luteinizing hormone**.

The two major leutinizign effects of LH are a shift in enzyme expression and an alteration in the proliferative characteristics of the follicular cells. The shift in enzyme expression diverts the cells' steroidogenic pathway away from estrogen production and toward progesterone production. (The corpus luteum does produce estrogen as well, however.) Meanwhile, the follicular cells begin proliferating at an enormous rate and become heavily vascularized. They receive a copious blood supply into which they pour progesterone, which cease the estrogen-mediated buildup of the uterus and over the next 2 weeks of the luteal phase renders the uterine lining secretory and supportive of a potential embryo. Thus, the luteal phase of the ovarian cycle corresponds with the secretary phase of the uterine cycle. (Fig. 10.17)

The **corpus luteum** is a transitory structure, fated for degeneration in 2 weeks' time unless rescued by the influence of a hormone called human chorionic gonadotropin (hCG). This hormone is produced only in the context of pregnancy. IT is structurally similar to, but distinct from, LH and stimulates theLH receptors of the corpus luteum, thereby enabling the survival of the corpus luteum. The corpus luteum continues to produce progesterone, maintaining the endometrial lining of the uterus in a condition supportive of a developing embryo. hCG is produced by a part of the embryo itself called the trophoblast cells, which will later develop into the placenta—the structure that will establish a vascular connection between mother and foetus in the

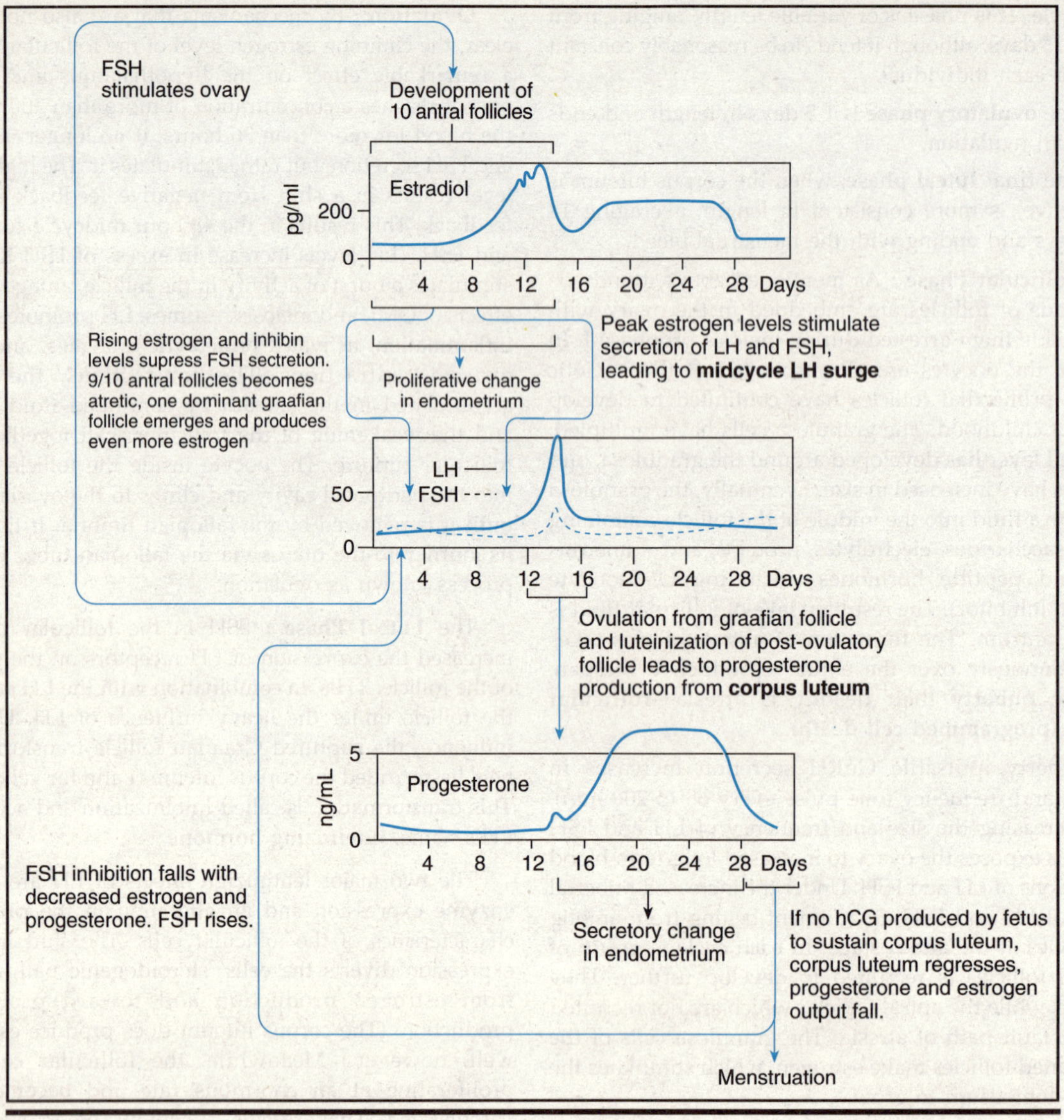


**Fig. 10.17 : Hormonal signaling in the menstrual cycle, under the control of follicular development.**

womb. Pregnancy tests measure the presence of hCG in the urine with impressive accuracy and can be confirmed with a blood test for the exact hCG level.

If pregnancy does not occur, no hCG is produced and the corpus luteum degenerates. The granulosa and theca cells become necrotic, and the corpus luteum is invaded by macrophages and leukocytes, a process called **luteolysis**. **Luteolysis** ends with the transformation of the corpus luteum into the corpus albicans, a scar-like structure in the ovary. As the corpus luteum degenerates, progesterone production falls and the endometrium degenerates, having lost its supporting hormone. It is sloughed off in the bleeding of menses.

Meanwhile, the decreased progesterone and estrogen production that follows luteolysis removes inhibition from the hypothalamus and pituitary. Estrogen and progesterone have been feeding back negatively on the brain during the luteal phse, suppressing LH and FSH. The removal of this negative feedback results in a peak in FSH secretion, which initiates recuritment of another 10 antral follicles for growth. A new follicular-proliferative phase has begun. This cycle repeats for all the reproductive years of a woman's life until the supply of antral follicles is exhausted.

**The Uterine Cycle :** The uterine cycle begins with the proliferative phse, in which endometrial growth occurs (Fig. 10.18). The proliferative phse coincides with the follicular phase of the oarian cycle and takes place under the influence of estrogen from the growing follicles. As basal endometrialk cells proliferate, the stratum functionalis grows and its glands and arteries elongate. The endometrium increases in thickness from 1 to 2 mm to 8 to 10 mm by day 14

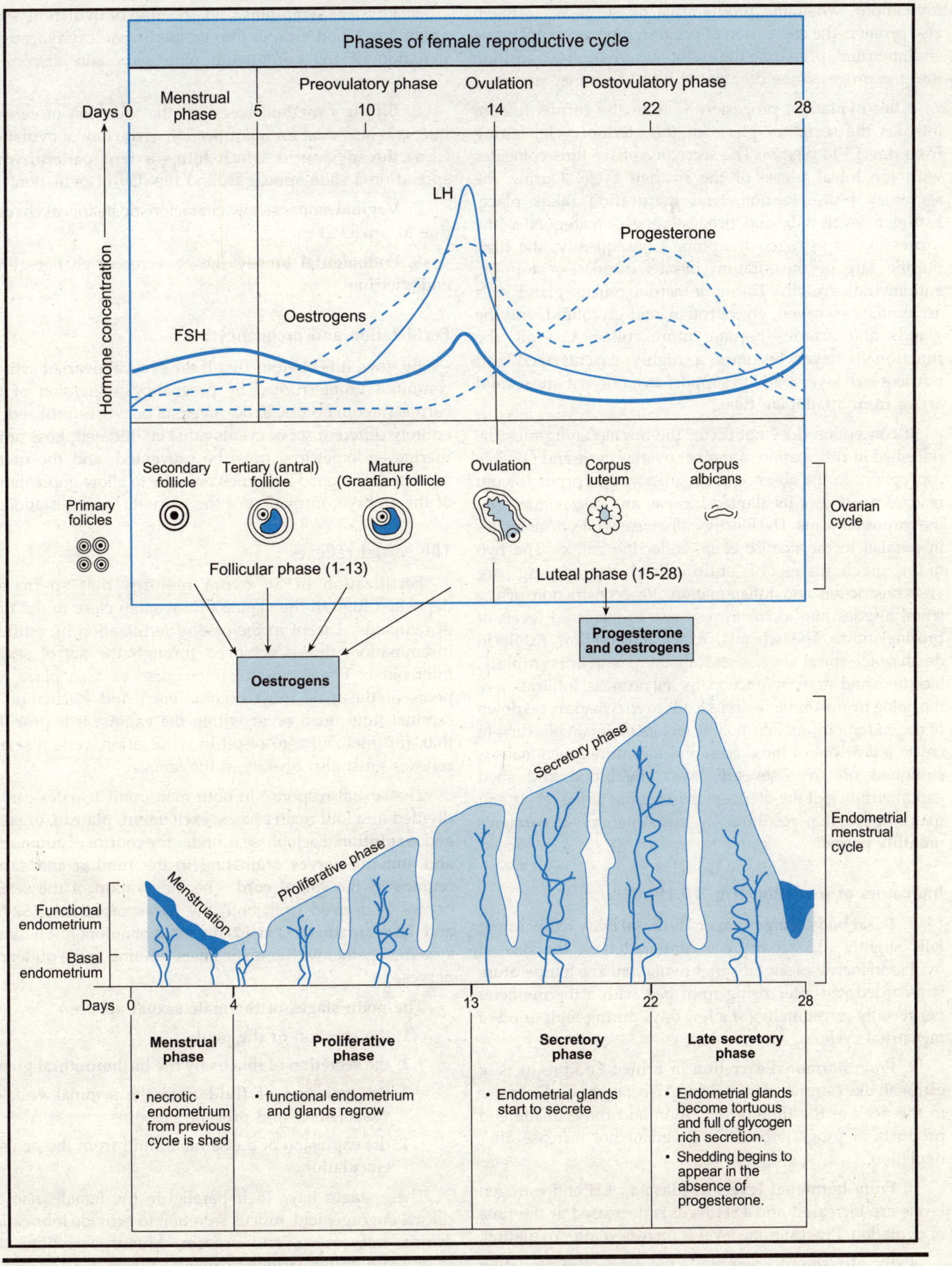


**Fig. 10.18 :** The hormonal, ovarian and endometrial changes during the menstrual cycle. (FSH, follicle stimulating hormone; LH, luteinizing hormone.)

(ovulation), when the proliferative phase ends. Estrogen also promots the expression of progesterone recepotrs int he endometrium, preparing the endometrium for the transition into the progesterone dominated luteal secretory phase.

After ovulation, progesterone from the corpus luteum initiates the secretory phase of the uterine cycle, lasting from day 15 to day 28. The secretory phase thus coincides with the luteal phase of the ovarian cycle. During the secretory phase, endometrial maturation takes place. Estrogen levels fall, and progesterone downregulates the expression of estrogen receptors. Consequently, the high mitotic rate of the stratum basalis decreases, stopping endometrial growth. The endometrial mucus gland cells accumulate glycogen, glycoprotein, and glycolipid, and the glands and arteries become more coiled. Overall, the functionalis layer becomes a highly vascularized and nutrient-rich layer ready to support an embryo if one should arrive from a fallopian tube.

If conception does not occur, the uterine lining must be refreshed in anticipation of another ovarian cycle and possible conception. In the absence of pregnancy, the corpus luteum reaches the end of its allotted lifespan and degenerates into the **corpus albicans**. The functiionalis, meanwhile, degenerates in parallel to the demise of its endocrine patron. The two main mechanisms of endometrial remodeling are vasoconstriction and inflammation. Vasoconstriction of the spiral arteries may occur in response to increased levels of prostaglandins. The ischemia, or lack of blood flow, results in death of the spiral arteries' endothelium, with arteryrupture, bleeding, and stratum functionalis cell necrosis. Infiltration of the lining by inflammatory cells leads to enzymatic breakdown of the endometrium. Fibrinolytic factors maintain bleeding to create a flow out of the uterus, and the entire functionalis is sloughed off over several days. The blood and shed endometrium exit the uterus by passing out of the cervix and then the vagina, resulting in menstruation—**a woman's monthly period.**

## Indicators of ovulation (Fig. 10.19) :

1. **Basal body temperature :** The basal body temperature falls slightly (0.3-0.5 degrees centigrade) on the day of ovulation increases slightly after ovulation. The temperature is recorded just after rising from bed with a thermometer per rectally or vaginally for a few days during midperiod of menstrual cycle.

2. **From hormonal excretion in urine :** End products of estrogen like estrone, estradiol and 17-beta estradiol increase to the peak at the time of ovulation and those of the end products of progesterone like pregnanediol increase after ovulation.

3. **From hormonal levels in plasma :** LH and estrogen levels are increased and FSH level is decreased at the time of ovulation. Progesterone level is increased after ovulation.

4. **By ultrasound scanning** – the process of ovulation can be recorded.

5. **Physical symptoms :** AT the time of ovulation, some amount of blood escapes into the peritoneal cavity, causing irritation of the peritoneum with pain and discomfort (Mittelschmerz).

6. **Billing's method** based on the secretion of cervical mucus is also used for identification of the day of ovulation. Clear thready mucus which forms a **fern pattern**, when spread on a slide appear around the day of ovulation.

7. **Vaginal smears** show characteristic histolical changes due to progesterone.

8. **Endometrial biopsy** shows secretory changes inthe endometrium.

## Fertilization and pregnancy :

By now, it is obvious that if the cyclical ovarian activity continues uninterrupted by pregnancy, regression of the corpus luteum occurs. If, however, an oocyte is fertilized, an entirely different set of events must be initiated. Loss of the uterine endometrium must be prevented, and the uterus must be maintained in a quiescent state to allow implantation of the embryo, formation of the placenta, and gestation.

## The sexual reflexes :

Fertilization of an ovum requires that sperm are deposited high in the vagina of a woman close to the time of ovulation. Except in the case of fertilization by artificial insemination, this is achieved through the act of sexual intercourse. For successful intercourse to take place, the penis of the male must become erect and ejaculation of seminal fluid must occur within the vagina. It is probable that, for intercourse to result in fertilization, certain sexual reflexes must also operate in the female.

The sexual response in both males and females can be divided into four main phases: **excitement, plateau, orgasm,** and **resulution**. Each phase is under the control of **autonomic** and **somatic nerves** orginating in the **lumbar** and **sacral regions** of the **spinal cord**. The innervation of the sexual organs is derived from both the **parasympathetic (S2-S4)** and the **sympathetic (T11-L2)** divisions of autonomic nervous system, together with somatic fibers running in the pudendal nerves.

**The main stages of the male sexual act are :**

1. the **erection of the penis.**
2. the **secretion of mucus by the bulbourethral gland**;
3. the **emission of fluid** from the seminal vesicles, vasdeferens, and prostate gland;
4. the expulsion of the seminal fluid from the penis—**ejaculation**.

These stages have their parallel in the female, namely clitoral engorgement, mucus secretion to provide lubrication during intercourse, and orgasm. Mucus secretions are provided both by Bartholin's glands, which are adjacent to the labia minora, and by the vaginal epithelium. These

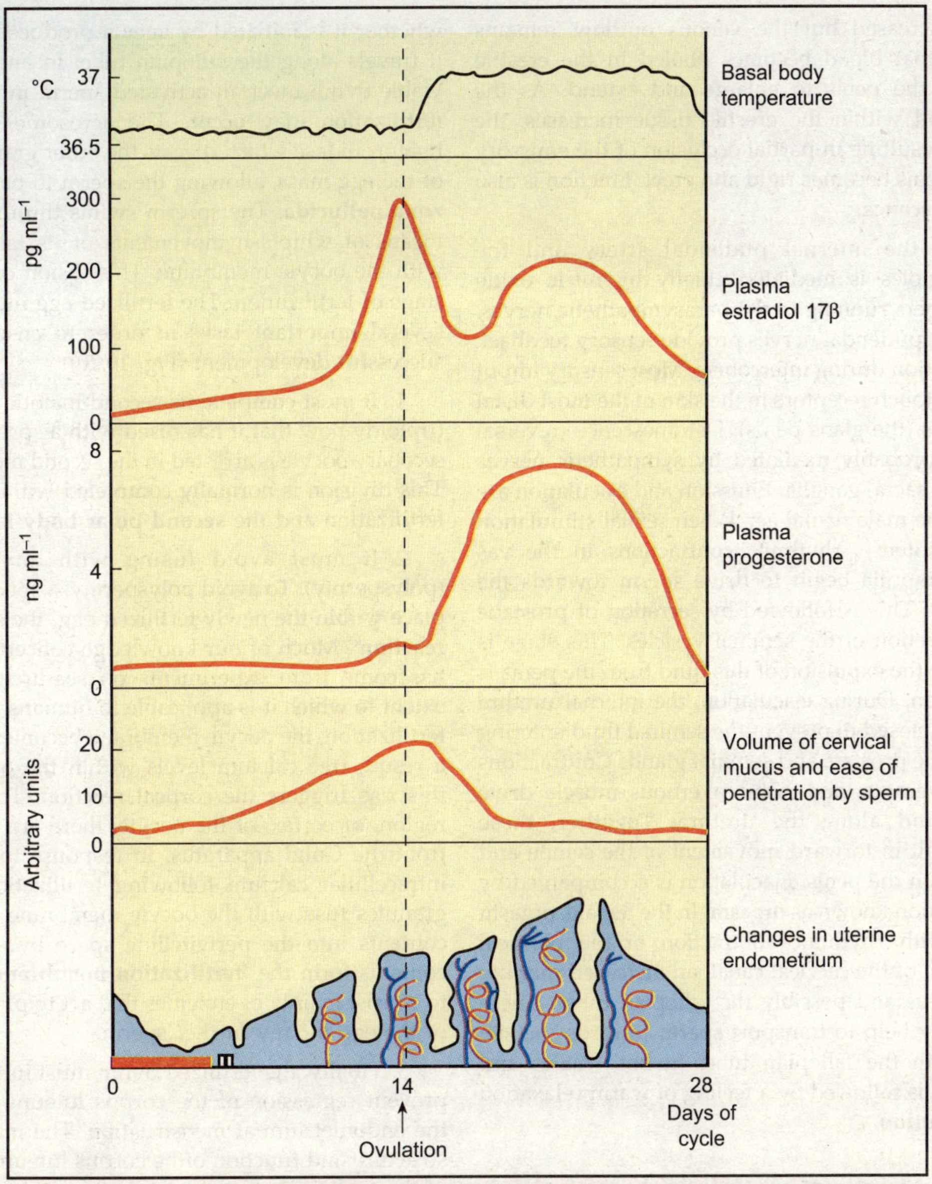


**Fig. 10.19 :** The cyclical changes shown by body temperature, cervical secretions, and the uterine endometrium in relation to the circulating levels of estradiol-17β and progesterone.

secretions ensure the intercourse is associated with a pleasurable massaging sensation rather than dry frictional irritation which can inhibit both ejaculation and the female climax.

## Penile erection–the result of a parasympathetic reflex :

Penile erection results from either descending nerve activity originating in the higher centers of the brain (psychogenic erection) or from stimulation of the skin in the genital region (reflexogenic erection). The afferent nerve fibers from the genital region run in the pudendal nerves to the sacral region of the spinal cord. The efferent fibers are parasympathetic in origin, derived from segments S2-S4. When they leave the spinal cord, the efferent fibers run in the pelvic nerve and synapse in the pelvic plexus. The neurons of the pelvic plexus also receive sympathetic fibers from the hypogastric nerves. The cavernous nerve provides the final limb of the efferent pathway.

The erectile tissue of the penis consists of the two corpora cavernosa and the corpus spongiosum which surrounds the urethra. The erectile tissues are essentially large venous sinusoids surrounded by a coat of strong fibrous tissue. Erection is a simple hydraulic process, mainly controlled by the parasympathetic nerves. Impulses in the cavernous nerve cause the internal pudendal artery and its main branches to dilate. Consequently, the blood flow to the penis is increased but the venous outflow remains unchanged so that blood becomes pooled in the erectile tissue, causing the penis to enlarge and extend. As the volume of blood within the erectile tissue increases, the pressure rises, resulting in partial occlusion of the emissory veins and the penis becomes rigid and erect. Erection is also known as **tumescence**.

Dilation of the internal pudendal artery and the associated arterioles is mediated chiefly by nitric oxide derived from fibers running in the parasympathetic nerves. Somatic afferent pudendal nerves provide sensory feedback to maintain erection during intercourse. Most sensory imput is derived from touch receptors in the skin of the most distal part of the penis (the glans penis). Detumescence (reversal of erection) is probably mediated by sympathetic nerves arising from the sacral ganglia. Emission and ejaculation are final stages of the male sexual act. When sexual stimulation becomes very intense, rhythmic contractions in the vas deferens and ampulla begin to drive sperm towards the ejaculatory duct. This is followed by secretion of prostatic fluid and ocntraction of the seminal vesicles. This stage is called **emission;** the expulsion of this fluid from the penis is called **ejaculation**. During ejaculation, the internal urethra becomes tightly closed to prevent the seminal fluid entering the bladder or the prostate and seminal glands Contractions of the bulbocavernous and ischiocavernous muscle drive the seminal fluid along the urethra. Together, these adaptations result in forward movement of the semen and its expulsion from the penis. Ejaculation is accompanied by an intense sensation known as **orgasm**. In the female, orgasm is associated with rhythmic contraction of the perineal muscles, dilation of the cervical canal, an increased motility of both the uterus and possibly the fallopian tubes. These contractions may help to transport sperm towards the site of fertilization in the fallopian tube. In both males and females, orgasm is followed by a feeling of warm relaxation known as **resolution.**

### Fertilization and Implantation of the embryo :

Around 3 ml of seminal fluid are released in each ejaculation and this will normally contain about 200 million sperm. Sperm deposited in the vagina during intercourse swim through the cervical mucus and through the uterus to the fallopian tube which is the site of fertilization. Both the male and female gamets have a limited period of viability within the female reproductive tract. Sperm are thought to retain their fertility for up to 48 hours while ovulated ova remain viable for only around 12-24 hours. There is therefore a relatively short time during each menstrual cycle in which intercourse must take place if pregnancy is to be achieved.

Before a sperm can fertilize an ovum it must undergo a process known as **cpacitation**. This is a calcium-dependent process, also termed the acrosome reaction, involving fusion of the surface membrane of the head of the sperm with the underlying acrosomal membrane. It is not clear whether this process occurs spontaneously within the female tract or whether it is initiated by agents produced by the ovum as it travels along the fallopian tube. In any event, should a viable ovum meet an activated sperm in the fallpian tube, fertilization may occur. The acrosome reaction releases hyaluronidase which digests the outer granulosa cell matrix of the egg mass, allowing the sperm to pass in towards the **zona pellucida**. The spserm swims through this region by means of whiplash movements of its tail and then fuses with the oocyte membrane. This fusion completes the first stage of fertilization. The fertilized egg must now complete several important tasks in order to ensure its continued successful development (Fig. 10.20).

1. It must complete its second meiotic division to avoid triploidy now that it has fused with a spserm (note that the seconary oocyte is arrested in the second meiotic metaphase). This division is normally completed within 2 or 3 hours of fertilization and the **second polar body** is extruded.

2. It must avoid fusing with any further sperm (polyspermy). To avoid polyspermy, a special reaction takes place within the newly fertilized egg, the so-called '**cortical reaction**'. Much of our knowledge concerning this reaction has come from experiments on sea-urchin eggs and the extent to which it is applicable to humans is not clear. After fertilization, the oocyte membrane becomes depolarized. As a result, free calcium levels within the ooplasm rise, and this rise triggers the cortical reaction. Towards the outer region, or cortex, of the oocyte, there are granules derived fromt he Golgi apparatus. In response to the elevation in intracellular calcium following fertilization, these cortical granules fuse with the oocyte membrane and release their contents into the perivitelline space by exocytosis. These contents form the '**fertilization membrane**' which appears to consist mainly of enzymes that act to prevent penetration of the egg by any further sperm.

3. Finally, the fertilized ovum must initiate changes that prevent regression of the corpus luteum and shedding of the endometrium at menstruation. The maintenance of the structure and function ofthe corpus luteum beyond the end of the cycle is dependent on the secretion of a glycoprotein hormone known as human chorionic gonadtrophin (hCG). This hormone is a potent luteotropic agent that is secreted by the zygote. By its luteotropic action, hCG is believed to maintain the corpus luteum beyond its normal life span so that it will continue to secrete the progesterone that is required for the continuation of pregnancy. Structurally, hCG is very similar to anterior pituitary LH but has a longer half-life. It appears in the maternal circulation within a few days of fertilization and may be detected in the urine by about 2 weeks after ovulation. Levels of hCG then continue to increase stedily up until 8-10 weeks of gestation before falling rather sharply over the next few weeks (Fig. 10.21). After 6 or 8 weeks, the placenta is well established and is able to produce sufficient progesterone itself to maintain the remaining gestation period. The pregnancy is then said to be autonomous, and the fall in hCG secretion seen after about 8 weeks probably reflects this diminishing requirement for the hormones of the corpus luteum.

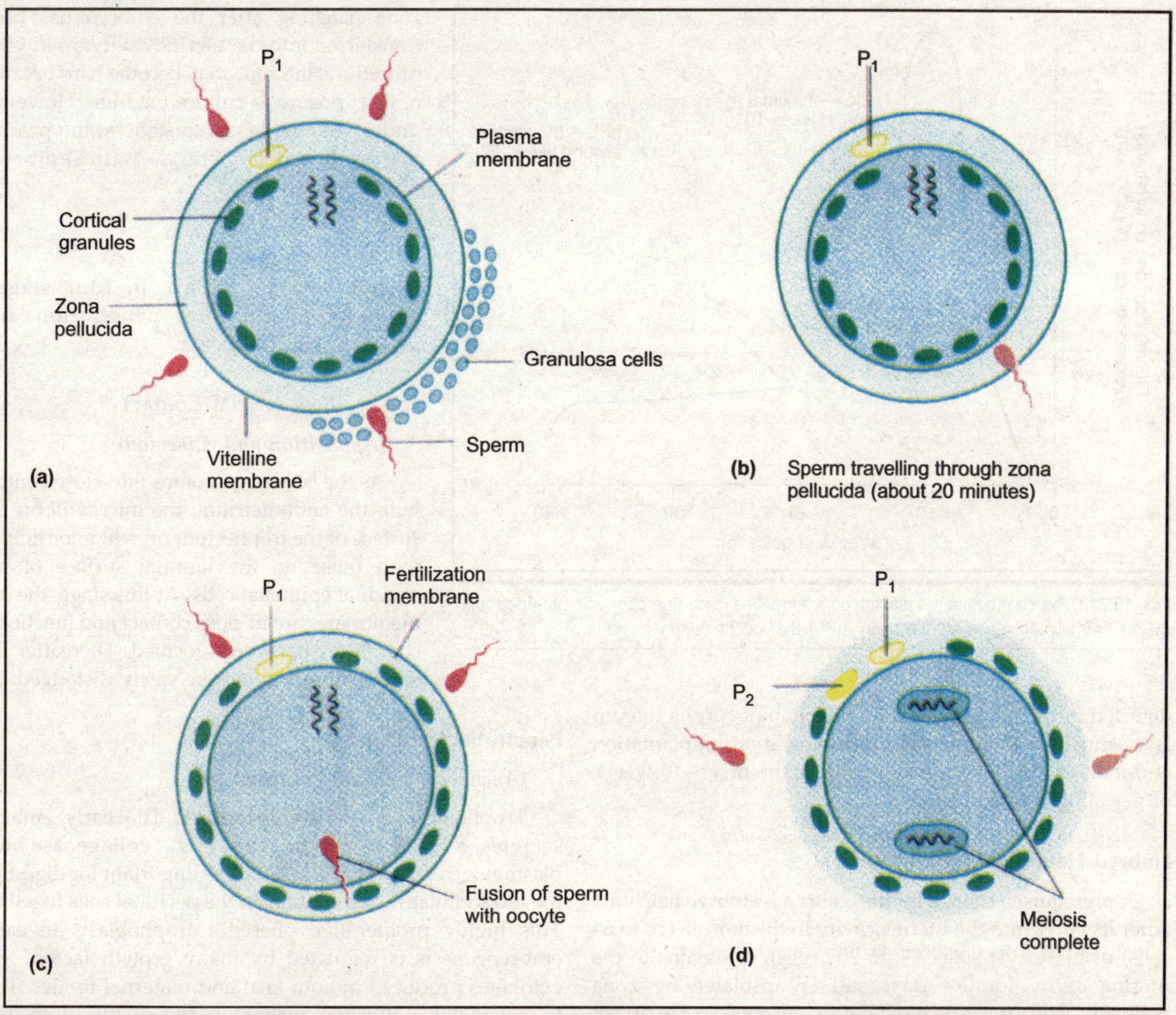


**Fig. 10.20 :** The changes that occur during fertilization. For a sperm to fuse with an egg it must first penetrate the layer of granulosa cells and the zona pellucida, as shown in (a) and (b). Fusion with the egg leads to the formation of the fertilization membrane. (c) and this is followed by the second meiotic division and the extrusion of the second polar bodies (d) $P_1$ and $P_2$ are the first and second polar bodies.

Clinically, hCG is a very important hormone, chiefly because of its early appearance in the maternal body fluids following fertilization. hCG can be detected in the maternal plasma as early as 7 days after ovulation. Its presence in the urine 2 weeks or so after ovulation is used as a reliable and simple test for pregnancy. More sophisticated assay techniques can also be used by clinicians to gain information about the pregnancy. Levels of hormone above the normal range, for example, suggest the presence of twins, a situation that may be confirmed later by ultrasound scans. In women who have suffered habitual miscarriages because of insensitivity of the corpus luteum to hCG, it may be useful to be able to detect the presence of an embryo within a few days of fertilization so that progesterone may be administered exogenously to prevent loss of the pregnancy when the corpus luteum regresses.

## ➤ 10.5 Embryonic Preparation for Implantation and Preimplantation Signals

### Signals

Embryo while still in the Fallopian tube, signals to the mother as it prepares for implantation. In response to this signal, mother produces. Early Pregnancy Factor (EPF). EPF has immunosuppressive property and is associated with cell proliferation and growth.

After reaching the uterine cavity in the compacted morula or blastocyst stage, the embryo produces CG (chronic gonadotrophin) which is essential for embryo hatching and embryonic implantation. hCG liberated by the embryo (even before implantation) will signal the corpus luteum to secrete higher levels of oestradiol and progesterone which can be

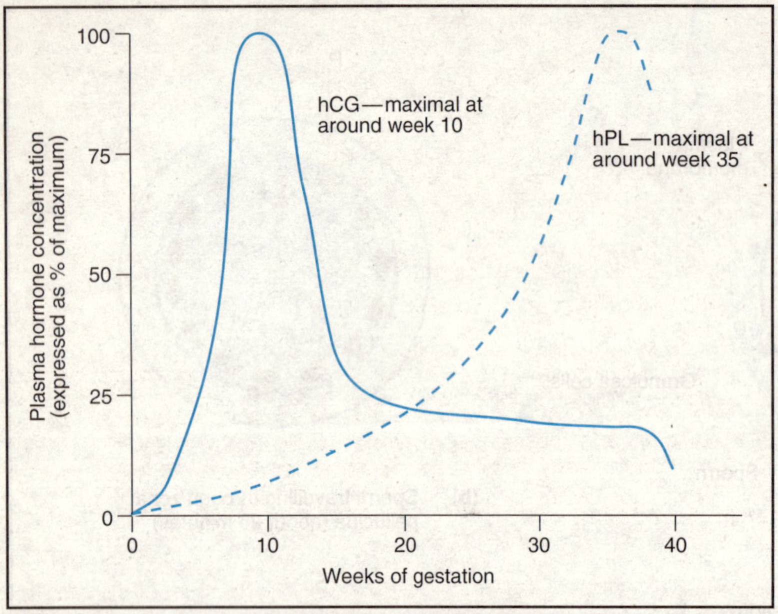


**Fig. 10.21 :** The changes in the plasma concentrations of human chorionic gonadotropin (hCG) and human placental lactogen (hPL) that occur during gestation

detected in the maternal serum. Function of corpus luteum is essential for endometrial bed preparation, implantation and maintenance of pregnancy during the first 9–10 weeks of gestation.

## Embryo Hatching

A prerequisite change for the embryo is embryo hatching. After its entry into the uterine cavity in the morula (16 to 64 cells) or blastocyst stage (30 to 200 cells), it remains in the uterine cavity for 2–4 days still encapsulated by zona pellucida. Zona must be lysed before the embryo can attach to the maternal decidua. Lysis of zona and escape of embryo is known as zona hatching. Zona hatching is accomplished by components of uterine fluid as well as by blastocyst movement. By this time, blastocyst has differentiated into inner cell mass (embryo) at one pole and trophectoderm (placenta) at the other pole with a cystic cavity (blastocele) in between. Zona pellucida becomes thin and ultimately disrupts through which the inner cell mass wriggles out to differentiate into three primitive layers of future foetus, namely ectoderm, mesoderm and endoderm. Initially, primitive embryonic plate is bilaminar consisting of ectoderm and endoderm. After certain period of growth, a third layer, mesoderm originating from ectoderm insinuates between ectoderm and endoderm so that the embryonic plate now becomes trilaminar. All tissues and organs of the growing foetus will develop from these three layers. Trophoectoderm and inner cell mass are essential for implantation. Even if the endometrial preparation is adequate for implantation, this may not occur if the embryo is not at the proper stage of development. This disparity is often observed in in-vitro fertilization procedures when there is a risk of failure of zona hatching after the embryo has been transferred into the uterine cavity. In in-vitro procedure, the zona may become hard because of its exposure to culture medium. However, under favourable circumstances, the process of implantation starts with embryo-endometrial contact.

## Implantation

Implantation occurs in four stages: apposition, adhesion, penetration and invasion (Fig. 10.22).

## Embryo-Endometrial Contact

**(*Apposition and Adhesion*)**

As the blastocyst comes into close contact with the endometrium, the microvilli on the surface of the trophectoderm will interdigitate with those on the luminal surface of the decidual epithelial cells. At this stage, the cell membranes are in close contact and junctional complexes have been formed. Thereafter the early embryo cannot be easily dislodged.

## Penetration and Invasion

**(*Anchorage and placentation*)**

Trophoblast is invasive in nature. The early embryo secretes a variety of enzymes (e.g., collagenase and plasminogen activators) and these are important for digesting the intracellular matrix that holds the decidual cells together. This highly proliferative phase of trophoblasts in early embryogenesis is regulated by many growth factors and cytokines produced in both fetal and maternal tissues. This is essential for effective anchorage and at the same time limiting the extent of trophoblastic invasion of maternal decidual tissue. Invasion requires the expression of integrins stimulated by insulin like growth factor II and inhibited by transforming growth factor-2.

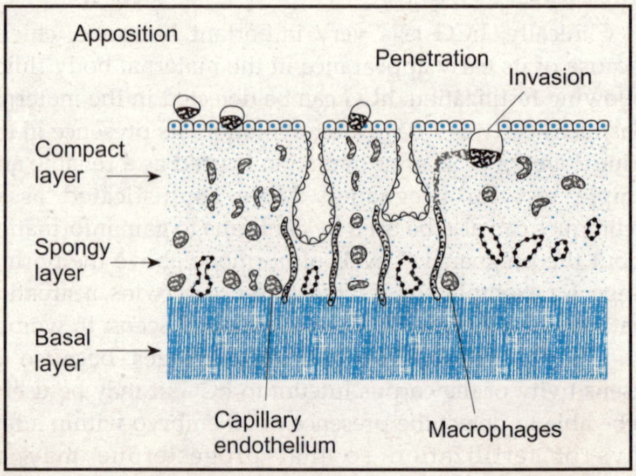


**Fig. 10.22**

The trophoblast differentiates into two layers—**cytotrophoblast** (the cellular layer) and the **syncitiotrophoblast** (the acellular layer). Cytotrophoblast invades the uterine spiral arterioles and allows the maternal blood to enter into the decidual lacunae created by trophoblastic invasion. These lacunae are built up by cytotrophoblastic cells which remain in contact and constantly bathed by maternal blood for foetal nutrition and exchange of gaseous materials.

Penetration of the maternal decidua will depend on factors which are capable of suppressing the maternal immune response to paternal antigens. The endometrial tissue is responsible for immune suppression by synthesizing proteins in response to the blastocyst even before implantation. Usually the genetically abnormal embryos are rejected by the decidua. It may be possible that the abnormal embryo cannot produce a signal in early pregnancy that can be recognized by the mother.

The fundamentals of normal reproduction involves the fulfilment of three basic requirements. These are; availability of male and female gametes, anatomically and functionally competent reproductive organs of both the partners and the ability of the gametes to achieve biological competence for fertilization and implantation in the female genital tract. The gametes, originating as germ cells in the hind gut and yolk sac, migrate to the genital ridge (future gonad) to become either oocyte or spermatocyte. Genital ridge differentiates into ovary or testis in response to chromosomal complement of the embryo. For spermatocyte, the maturational changes are nearly completed within the testis as the diploid spermatogonia are reduced to number haploid before leaving the testis. In case of oocytes, the first meiotic division which starts in intrauterine life remains arrested at prophase and is completed before ovulation. The maturational changes of gametes and their periodic release from testis and ovary are influenced by endocrine, autocrine and paracrine factors. DNA in the nucleus of the sperm head, centriole in the neck and release of mature haploid oocyte from the dominant follicle are the vital segments of gametes which are actively involved for successful fertilization.

Anatomically normal and physiologically active male and female reproductive organs are essential for further maturation and for accelerating fertilizing potential of the gametes. For this, sperm requires additional energy because it has to travel a long distance to penetrate the outer vestments of the oocyte namely the cumulus matrix and zona pellucida. The additional energy is acquired by the sperm in different phases. As it travels through the seminal pathway in the male genital tract, sperm acquires motility and other biochemical back up from secretion of epididymis, vas deferens, seminal vesicles and prostate. In the female genital tract, **fertilizing potential of the sperm** is completed by two very significant changes; namely **capacitation** and **hyperactivation**. Oocyte after ovulation, travels a relatively shorter distance before it reaches the sperm for sperm-ovum interaction. During this short journey, there is intracellular influx of calcium which accelerates its fertilizing potential.

The biological competence of gametes induces sperm-ovum interaction, fertilization, formation of pronucleus, cleavage into a two celled zygote. **Zygote** sends signals to the maternal tissues which now prepares to receive the incoming embryo for implantation.

**Implantation** occurs in four stages namely, **attachment, adhesion, penetration** and **anchorage**. Besides endometrial bed preparation under the influence of **steroid hormones** and **prostaglandins** ($PGE_2$) the process of implantation is additionally controlled by various members of the **endometrial cytokine family** and **growth factors**. These cytokines and growth factors are the biochemical vehicles through which the various phases of embryonic adhesion, trophoblastic invasion and placentation are completed.

## 10.6 The Reproductive Hormones

**The reproductive hormones are —**

(a) The **gonadal steroids,** eg, *estrogen (E), progesterone (P), testosterone (T), dehydroepiandrosterone (DHEA)* and *androstenedione (ASD).*

(b) The gonadotropic hormones (gonadotropins) released from the anterior pituitary are the most important gonadotropins although there are other important gona-dotropins like the **chorionic gonadotropin (CG)** or **pregnant mare serum (PMS).** There are two subclasses of pituitary gonadotropins; ***follicle stimulating hormone (FSH)*** and ***the luteinising hormone (LH).*** The CG of human female is called **human chorionic gonadotropin** (hCG). hCG has, largely, LH–like action but little or no FSH like action. All these gonadotropins have a peptide structure in contrast to the gonadal steroids.

(c) Gonadotropin releasing hormone, GnRH is a hypothalamic releasing hormone. GnRH stimulates the secretion of pituitary gonadotropins, both FSH and LH. Previously GnRH used to be called **LHRH** (luteinising hormone releasing hormone) or even **FSHRH**. Obviously, **GnRH = LHRH = FSHRH.**

### The ovarian hormones (Fig. 10.23)

The active hormones of the ovary are **steroids**. They are derived from cholesterol.

The two important ovarian hormones are **estrogen** and **progesterone**. The term **estrogen** means any substance capable of producing estrus. In the animal world, the females show cyclic patterns of sexual activity. That is, females develop desire for sex only in some highly specified periods of the year. The period when they develop sex desire is called **estrus**. Only during estrus, the female allows the

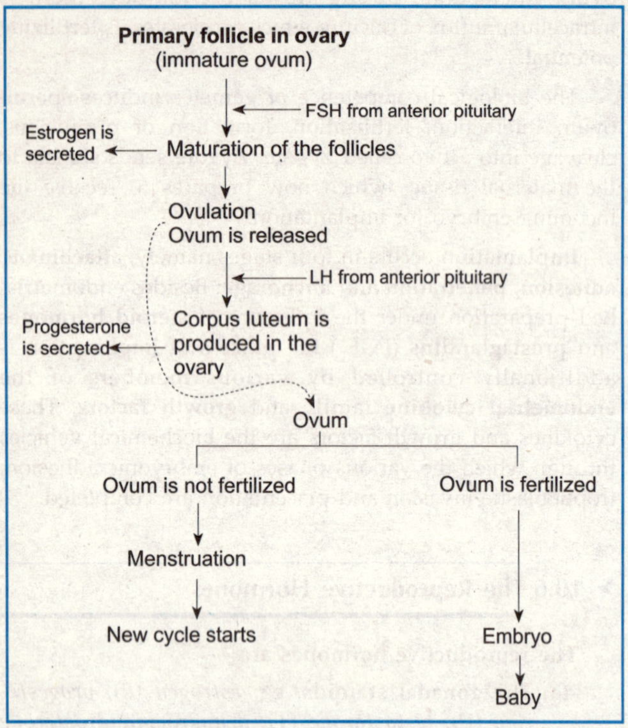


Fig. 10.23 : Stages of development of ovum and associated hormones

male (of its own species) to mount on herself (coitus). At other times, this is not permitted. The ovary produces female sex steroids particularly estrogen which prepares the female. Thus the endometrium is prepared (follicular or proliferative phase) and the endometrium proliferates.

Next occurs ovulation. The ovum (containing 'n' number of chromosomes) is now ready to be fertilized and is waiting at the outer end of the fallopian tube to unite with a spermatozoon.

The corpus luteum is formed, progesterone secretion occurs → the endometrium undergoes further changes (luteal or secretory phase) → now it is ready for implantation of a fertilized ovum.

If the fertilization does not occur in human species, the endometrium breaks down and blood and endometrium escape via the vaginal route to constitute menstrual flow.

## ESTROGENS

In medical literature, estrogens usually refer to (i) the naturally occurring estrogenic (steroid) compounds of the ovary, viz. estradiol, estrone and estriol or (ii) their synthetic (steroidal) analog (often used clinically) or (iii) some non-steroidal compounds (eg, diethylstilbesterol/stilbesterol and so forth) which, pharmacologically, behave like the naturally occurring or their synthetic congeners.

Natural estrogens are $C_{18}$ steroids. The main sources are theca and granulosa cells of Graafian follicles and corpus

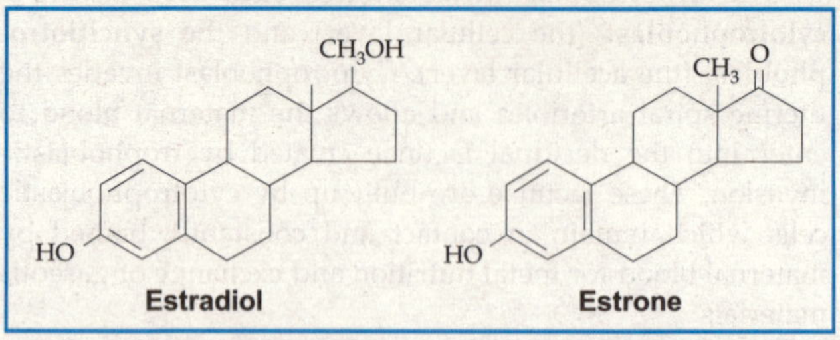


Fig. 10.24 : Structure of estradiol and estrone

luteum. However, adrenal cortex is the secondary source. Estrogen is secreted as estradiol. It is inactivated in the liver. It is excreted as conjugates of estrone, estradiol and estriol in the urine. The plasma estradiol level increases about 6-7 days before ovulation. The peak level is reached 2 days prior to ovulation.

### Chemistry

Three naturally occurring estrogens are (i) estradiol, (ii) estrone, (iii) estriol. Of the three, estradiol is the most potent and is present abundantly in the systems of young women of reproductive age. Estrone is the major estrogen in the post-menopausal woman whereas estriol is a metabolite of estradiol. All these three estrogens are steroidal structures but ring A is aromatized (ie, the ring A of the CPP structure contains three double bonds like the benzene ring). There is an OH at $C_3$ position (of ring A) and obviously this – OH is a phenolic – OH group. Estrogens are $C_{18}$ structures, that is, there is no side-chain at $C_{17}$, neither is there any angular methyl group ($-CH_3$) at $C_{19}$ position. In the Graafian follicle, estrogen is produced by theca interna cells (most important source) as well as by granulosa cells.

Estradiol is the primary estrogen produced by the ovary. Estradiol is the most potent and estriol is the least potent. Estradiol is free (2%) or bound to sex steroid binding globulin (37%), or to albumin (61%) in circulation (Fig. 10.24).

### Functions

The **functions of estrogens** can be divided into two cate-gories, (i) **the effects on reproductive organs** (eg, uterus, vagina, breast) and (ii) **extragenital effects.**

### Physiological actions of estrogens

***Puberty :***

- Broadening of pelvis
- Epiphyseal fusion
- Axillary and pubic hair development
- External genitalia development
- Breast enlargement
- Subcutaneous fat deposition
- Initiation and maintenance of menstruation.

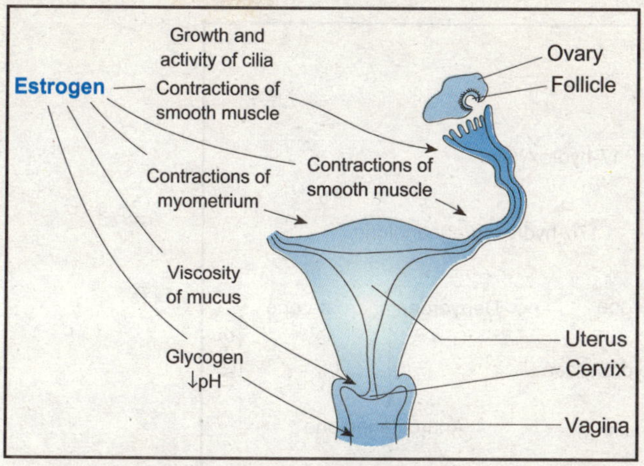


**Fig. 10.25 : Functions of estrogen**

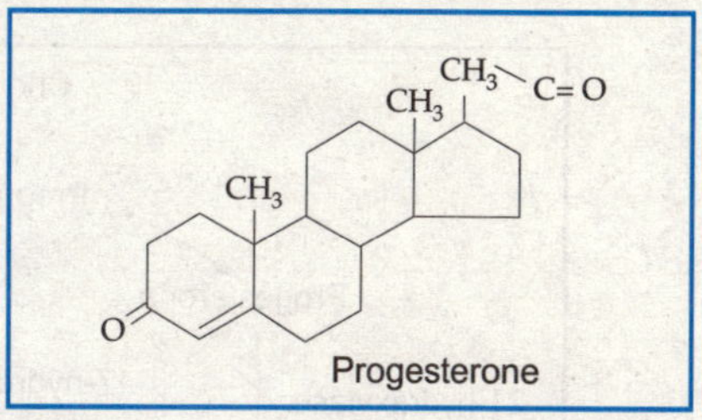


**Fig. 10.26 : Structure of progesterone**

*General actions :*

- Supports libido
- Growth of the ovarian follicle
- LH surge is promoted prior to ovulation
- Proliferation of the endometrium
- Secretion of endometrial glands
- Excitability of uterine myometrium is enhanced
- Development of vagina, uterus and oviducts
- Enlargement of mons pubis, labia majora and labia minora
- Ductal growth and stromal development of breasts and increased vascularity
- Fat is accumulated in breasts, buttocks and thighs
- Hepatic synthesis of a few hormone transport proteins
- Feedback inhibition of FSH secretion
- Causes growth of the skeleton by stimulating osteoblastic activity
- Protects against arterial disease
- Increases vascularity of the uterus, vulva and vagina
- Stimulates the tubal musculature
- Influences calcification of bone. Decalcification of bone is present in post-menopausal women due to estrogen deficiency
- Responsible for water and sodium retention
- Controls blood cholesterol level to some extent.

***Of the extragenital effects of estrogen, some have received extensive attention and some are beginning to draw attention :***

(a) Its effects on lipid metabolism, plasma lipids, coronary heart disease, coagulability of blood, thromboembolic phenomenon suggest that **estrogen** reduces the **risk of coronary heart disease.**

(b) Another extragenital effect of **estrogen** is its **carcino-genicity**. Numerous reports are available suggesting that estrogens can cause cancer while others find no concrete evidence of carcino-genicity of estrogens Endometrial cancer, breast cancer and some other cancers are said to be facilitated by estrogens. Further more, diethylstilbesterol (a non-steroidal synthetic estrogens preparation), if used during pregnancy, can cause (in a female fetus) and genital cancer in later life.

## PROGESTINS

Meaning of some terms need to be at first clarified. Usually, progesterone is used to mean the naturally occurring hormone but some authors also include synthetic progestin or gestagens to mean the naturally occurring hormone plus its synthetic analog.

### Chemistry

Progesterone is a $C_{21}$ steroid compound. Ring A of the progesterone, unlike that of estrogens, is not aromatized. It has, however, a double bond between $C_4$ and $C_5$. This makes progesterone a compound (unlike estrogens) which is, chemically, closer to other steroid hormones like glucocorticosteroids, mineralocorticosteroids, androgens and so forth.

Consequently, synthetic progesterone compounds can bind with the receptors of glucocorticoids, androgens, mineralocorticoids and so forth.

*The most common **natural source of progesterone*** is the **corpus luteum.** Lutein cells of corpus luteum secrete progesterone. Some **progesterone**, although very small in quantity, is secreted by the **Graafian follicle**. During pregnancy, large quantities of progesterone is synthesized by the fetoplacental unit. However, whereas, in the case of estrogen, both the fetus and the placenta (of the fetoplacental unit) contribute to the synthesis of estrogen, for synthesis of progesterone the fetal contribution is nil.

Therefore, during pregnancy, fall of estrogen concentration in the maternal blood signifies fetal distress or even death while progesterone concentration may not be affected. Progesterone is a major intermediary of the biosynthetic pathways of corticosteroids and androgens. Some spilling of progesterone from the suprarenal cortex or testis occurs, into the systemic circulation.

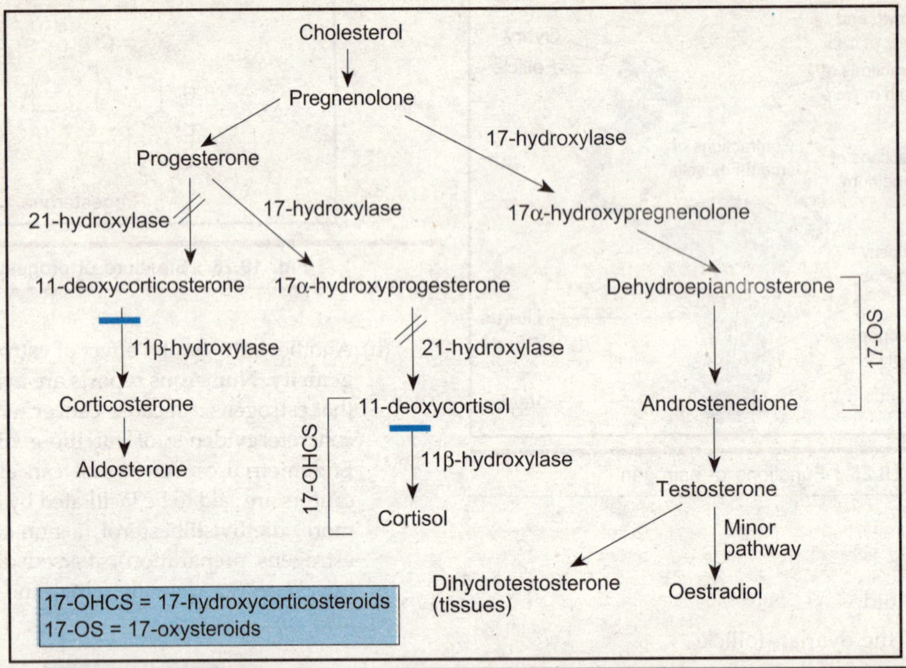


**Fig. 10.27 : Biosynthesis of Adrenal steroids**

## Functions

Very little progesterone secretion occurs from the ripe Graafian follicle just before ovulation. After ovulation, corpus luteum starts to secrete vigorously. However, if fertilization does not occur, the corpus luteum must degenerate completely on the 14th postovulatory day and the concentration of progesterone falls sharply (sharp fall of progesterone is the prime cause of menstrual bleeding).

### Effects of progesterone on the reproductive system

**Progesterone** is secreted by the **corpus luteum, placenta, adrenal cortex** and **testis.**

**Functions of progesterone :**

- Progesterone causes secretory changes in the uterine endometrium during the later half of the monthly cycle
- Reduces myometrial contractility
- Maintenance of pregnancy
- Decreases excitability of myometrium
- Development of the alveoli of breast lobules
- Increases body temperature
- Inhibition of gonadotropin secretion
- Causes thickening of endocervical mucosa (thus reducing the chances of any spermatozoal ascent through the cervical canal and subsequent fertilization)
- Causes water and sodium retention
- It relaxes smooth muscle. As such, uterine muscle relaxes during pregnancy
- Progesterone causes an upward resetting of the body temperature control system by about 0.5°F
- Exerts an anabolic effect.

***It should be understood that progesterone (P) has two specialities*** — (i) **progesterone** acts only after estrogen has primed the tissue and (ii) in general, **P** is **antiestrogenic**; it opposes the action of estrogen. ***There are several examples in reproductive physiology*** :

(i) **Estrogen** (E) makes the endocervical mucus thin (facilitates the spermatozoal entry) while **progesterone** makes it thick (opposes the entry).

(ii) **Estrogen** promotes **uterine contraction** (facilitates the suction of spermatozoa from the vaginal canal to the uterus → fertilization) while **Progesterone** makes the **uterus passive** (prevents the abortion of the products of conception).

(iii) **Estrogen** causes **endometrial proliferation** whereas, with progesterone, endometrial proliferation ceases (and the secretory phase begins). Incidentally, in *anovular menstruation*, progesterone synthesis is practically absent (as there is no corpus luteum) → due to continued action of estrogen the endometrium continues to grow → a time comes when the proliferated endometrium cannot be supported by arterial blood supply → breakdown of endometrium (anovular menstruation).

***The extragenital effects of Progesterone** are now beginning to be understood.* **Progesterone** has **effects on** (i) **CNS**, (ii) **respiratory system**, (iii) **metabolism** and (iv) **kidney**.

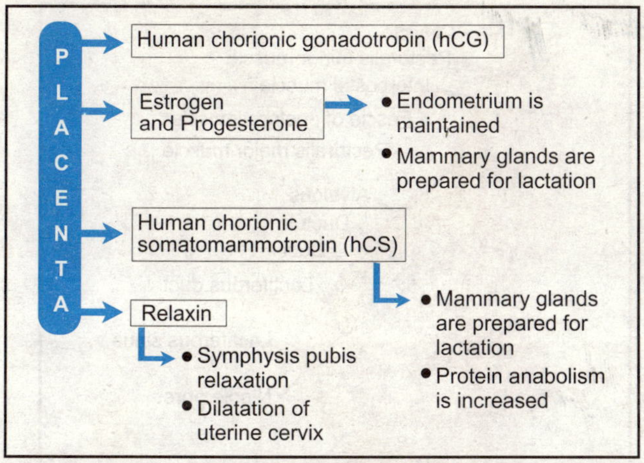


**Fig. 10.28 : Sources and functions of hormones of pregnancy**

## Other ovarian hormones

The ovary not only produces estrogen and progesterone but also many other hormone-like chemicals. Notable among them are :

(i) **OMS,** an inhibitor of oocyte maturation.

(ii) **Ovarian inhibin** also called *folliculostatin* or **inhibin** F or gonadostatin which blocks pituitary FSH in vitro as well as in vivo.

(iii) **A luteinisation inhibitor** that prevents LH receptor induction by FSH and reduces cAMP production and progesterone secretion from granulosa cells.

(iv) **Luteinisation stimulator (S)** that enhances induction of membrane receptors for LH in granulosa cells in the porcine species.

(v) **FSHBI (FSH binding inhibitor),** LHBI, which inhibits binding of LH is also known.

(vi) **Putative granulosa cell mitogens — somatomedin-** like peptides.

(vii) **An inhibitor of aromatization** extracted *from human follicle.*

(viii) **Relaxin,** which has structural similarities with insulin, is synthesized in the corpus luteum (CL). In addition, it can be synthesized by the placenta.

## Regulation of estrogen and progesterone

FSH and LH are responsible for ovarian follicle maturation during which estrogen is secreted. LH maintains the corpus luteum which secretes estrogen and progesterone in the luteal phase. FSH and LH secretion from the pituitary gland is stimulated by gonadotropin releasing hormone (GnRH). This is released from the hypothalamus in a pulsatile fashion. There is a negative feedback control of the gonadotropin secretion when there is a low level of estrogen. A positive feedback control occurs when there is a higher estrogen level. Gonadotropin secretion is inhibited by estrogen and progesterone during the luteal phase (Fig. 10.28).

**Effects of estrogen and progesterone on the reproductive tract**

| Organ | Estrogen | Progesterone |
|---|---|---|
| ***Oviducts*** – Muscular wall | ↑ Contractility | ↓ Contractility |
| ***Uterus*** – | | |
| Endometrium | ↑ Proliferation | ↓ Differentiation and secretion |
| Myometrium | ↑ Growth and contractility | ↓ Contractility |
| Cervical glands | Watery secretion | Dense, viscous secretion |
| ***Vagina*** | ↓ Epithelial proliferation | ↓ Differentiation |
| | ↓ Glycogen deposition | ↓ Proliferation |

## ➤ 10.7 Placenta as an Endocrine Organ

The placenta is an extremely important endocrine organ. It secretes a wide variety of different hormones, both peptideand steroid, which are important in the maintenance of pregnancy and for the preparation of the body for parturition and lactation.

**The major peptidehormones secreted by the placenta are :**

1. **Human chorionic gonadotropin (hCG)**
2. **Human placental lactogen (hPL)**

The major placental steroids are :

3. **Estrogen**
4. **Progesterone**

**1. Human chorionic gonadotropin (hCG) :** It is a powerfully luteotropic hormone that prolongs the life of the corpusluteum beyond the normal 12-14 days. As such progesterone secretion continues, shedding of uterine endometrium is prevented, and spontaneous contractile activity of the myometrium is inhibited. Luteal progesterone is required for about first 6-8 wks. of pregnancy. After this time, placenta takes over as the main source of progesterone and pregnancy is said to become autonomous. Levels of hCG output decline sharply after about 10 weeks, although the hormone continues to be producedby the placenta for the remainder of pregnancy.

- hCG may exert a direct effect on **maternal hypothalamus** to **inhibit** the synthesis of **FSH**. If so, this might contribute to the suppression of ovulation during pregnancy.

- **hCG** possesses **immunosuppressive activity** which may prevent the mother rejecting the fetus as foreign tissue.
- **hCG** exerts a stimulatory effect on the **leydig cells** of the testes in male fetuses and plays a part in the differentiation of the male reproductive tract. Plasma levels of hCG are high during the period of Wolffian duct development and the start of differentiation of the external genitalia.

**2. Human placental lactogen (hPL) :**

- hPL is secreted from approximately **10 wks.** of gestation.
- It contributes to **proliferative changes seen** in the **mammary tissue** in preparation for lactation and exerts important metabolic effects in the mother.
- It stimulates an increase in the **maternal plasma levels of glucose, aminoacids** and **free** fatty acids.

**3. Steroid hormones (estrogen and Progesterone)** are produced in large amounts by the placenta throughout gestation. Progesterone is essential for successful pregnancy and the placenta takes over from the corpusluteum as the major source of this steroid at around 10 weeks. Progesterone maintains the endometrium and reduces myometrial excitability as well as stimulating mammary development in readiness for lactation.

**Progesterone is important during pregnancy** because it maintains a quiescent myometrium and prevents endometrial shedding prior to placentation. Stimulation of breast development, suppression of ovulation and inhibition of immunorejection of the embryo may also be significant actions of this steroid.

**4. Placenta secretes** large amounts of a number of estrogenic hormones, including estrone, estriol and estradiol -17β. Their precise role in pregnancy is unclear, although they appear to prepare the body for labor and lactation. They seem to bring about relaxation of the symphysis pubis and to act along with hPL to stimulate proliferation of mammary tissue. They may also play a part in the initiation of parturition.

5. **Relaxin :** Relaxation of symphysis pubis and ligaments of sacroiliac and sacrococcygeal joints.

Helps in the dilatation of the uterine cervix prior to delivery of the baby.

## ➤ 10.8 Breast and Lactation

**Mammary glands** are responsible for production of milk for nourishment and antibodies for protection of the body. Estrogen, progesterone, cortisol, chorionic somatomammotro-phin and growth hormone are responsible for development of the alveoli and ducts. Prolactin is responsible for full maturation of mammary glands and milk production during late trimester of pregnancy. Prolactin stimulates the synthesis of calcitriol and, as such, calcium balance is maintained during pregnancy and lactation (Figs. 10.29 and 10.30).

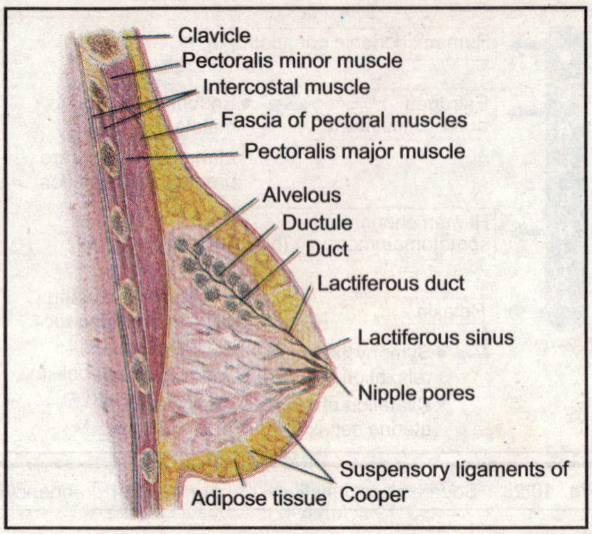


**Fig. 10.29 :** Structure of mammary gland

The mammary glands are accessory organs of the female reproductive system. They are also present in male but only in a rudimentary form.

The breasts are very small till puberty in case of female. They grow and mature in size under the influence of estrogen and progesterone.

During pregnancy, the breasts increase in size due to the actions of estrogen and progesterone. Following the birth of the baby, prolactin released from the anterior pituitary is responsible for the formation of milk in the breasts. Oxytocin released from posterior pituitary is responsible for release of milk in response to stimulation of the nipple by the sucking baby.

### Structure

The mammary glands consist of glandular tissue, fibrous tissue and fatty tissue. The areola is located at the centre of the breast. It is 2.5 cm in diameter and pigmented. Sebaceous glands are present over it. Involuntary muscles are also present. The nipple is a small conical eminence at the center of the breast which is surrounded by a pigmented area known as areola. There are numerous sebaceous glands (Montgomery's tubercles) present on the surface of the areola. Its function is to lubricate the nipple during lactation. The whole breast is embedded in the subcutaneous fat. The fat is absent beneath the nipple and areola. The breast tissue is composed of the following :

- Presence of 15-20 lobes by fibrous tissue septa which radiate from the center.
- Glandular tissue has duct system in non-lactating breast.

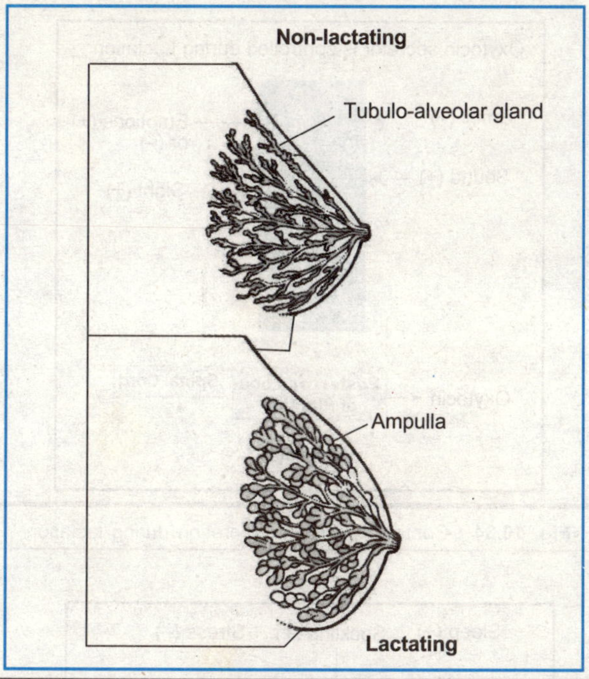


**Fig. 10.30 :** Non-lactating and lactating breast

- The lining epithelium of the duct is cubical.
- Each duct subdivides and terminates in alveoli (the total number is 10-100).
- Each alveolus is lined up with columnar epithelium.
- Myoepithelial cells surround the alveoli and smaller ducts. Milk is secreted and ejected from the breast due to contraction of myoepithelial cells.
- Main duct dilates to form ampulla.
- Suspensory ligaments (connective tissue forms dense strands) extend inward from the dermis of the breast to the fascia, helping support the weight of the breast.

## Development of breast

Male breasts remain nonfunctional. The male and female breasts are similar. When the children attain puberty, the male breasts remain normal, but ovarian hormones stimulate the female glands to develop. The alveolar glands and ducts enlarge. Fat is accumulated and adipose tissue surrounds the breast except the region of areola.

Progesterone, in combination with estrogen, promotes growth and branching of the lobuloalveolar tissue.

Estrogen stimulates female breast development during pregnancy. The breast is further enlarged. Ductal system is more enlarged due to estrogen. Alveolar glands are more developed due to progesterone. Prolactin is released during pregnancy. Progesterone inhibits milk production. When estrogen and progesterone levels are high, pituitary prolactin and hCS levels are also increased.

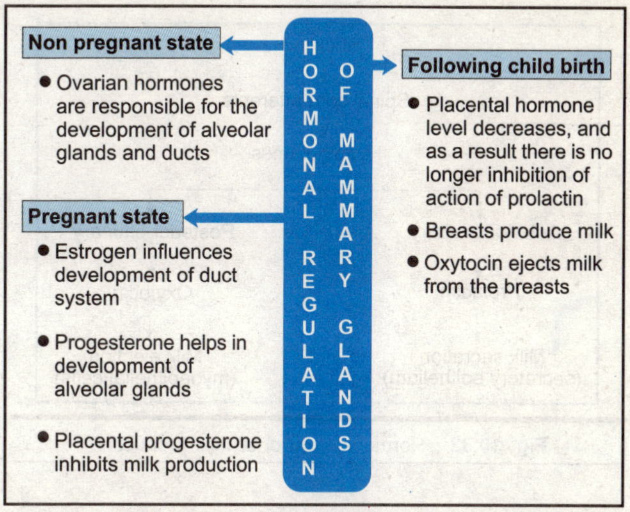


**Fig. 10.31 :** Hormonal regulation of mammary glands

## Histology of the lactating mammary gland

The alveolar epithelium has short columnar cells. Prominent endoplasmic reticulum and Golgi apparatus are present at the base of the cell. When lactation ceases, there is degeneration of lactogenic cells.

## Composition of milk

The most abundant protein is casein (iron-binding protein). Early breast milk contains relatively high levels of $I_gG$, $I_gM$ and $I_gA$.

| *Component* | *Human* | *Cow* |
|---|---|---|
| **Protein** | 1 – 1.5% | 3.3% |
| **Carbohydrate** | 7% | 4.5% |
| **Fat** | 4% | 4% |
| **Minerals** | 0.25% | 0.75% |
| **Vit A, B, C, D** | — | — |
| **Growth factors** | — | — |

## Hormonal control of breast growth and lactation (Fig. 10.31)

Estrogen, progesterone and prolactin from maternal pituitary are responsible for breast growth. Milk ejection is due to the contraction of myoepithelial cells around the alveoli and ducts under the influence of oxytocin. Oxytocin is released as a result of a neural reflex originating from the suckling stimulus to the nipple. Suckling inhibits the GnRH pulse generator. Probably, it is the cause of anovulation during breast feeding (see Figs. 10.32, 10.33 and 10.34).

## Hyperprolactinemia (Fig. 10.35)

The synthesis of prolactin is regulated mainly by the

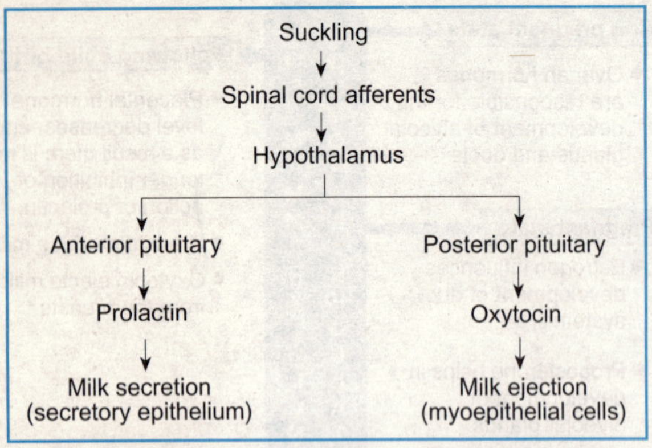


**Fig. 10.32 :** Hormonal control of milk production

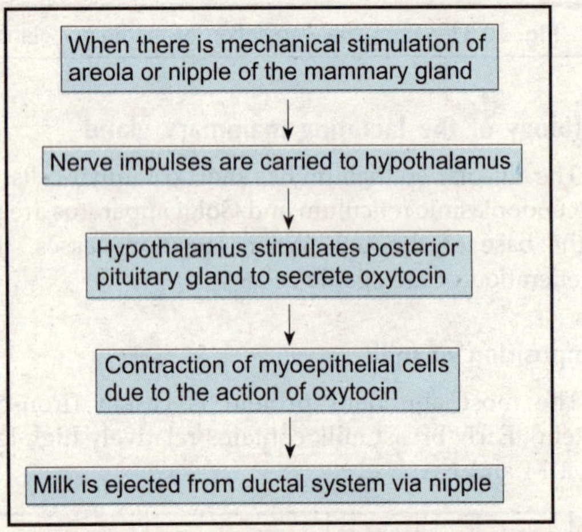


**Fig. 10.33 :** Pathway of ejection of milk

inhibitory influence of dopamine, stimulatory effect of thyrotropin releasing hormone and by estrogen during pregnancy. When prolactin secretion is more than enough (pituitary tumors, microadenoma) the condition is known as **hyperprolactinemia**. When there is increased prolactin in blood, it causes anovulation, amenorrhea in women, and impotency and infertility in men.

It is a common cause of infertility and abnormal or absent menstrual cycles. Bromocriptine (a drug) activates dopamine receptors and suppresses prolactin secretion.

## Maternal changes in pregnancy

The average duration is about 280 days or 40 weeks or 10 lumar months

**Uterus :** Enlarges in size and increases in weight from 30 gms to 1000 gms at full term. Enlargement is due to hyperplasia and hypertrophy of muscle cells. There is an increase in the conective tissue also. Endometrial thickness increases. Bloof flow increases appreciably. Uterine enlargement during the first trimester depends on oestrogen

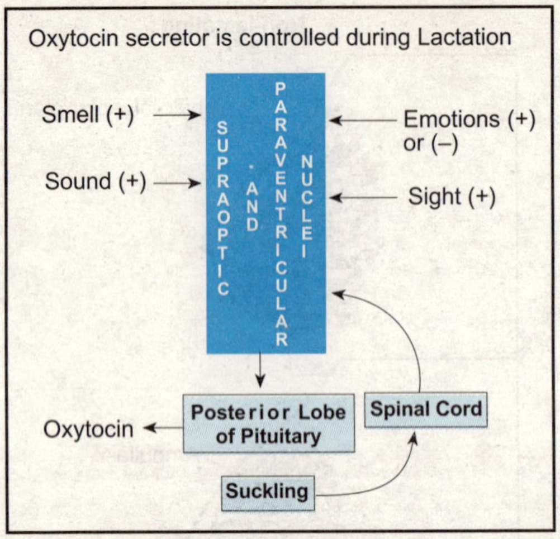


**Fig. 10.34 :** Control of oxytocin secretion during lactation

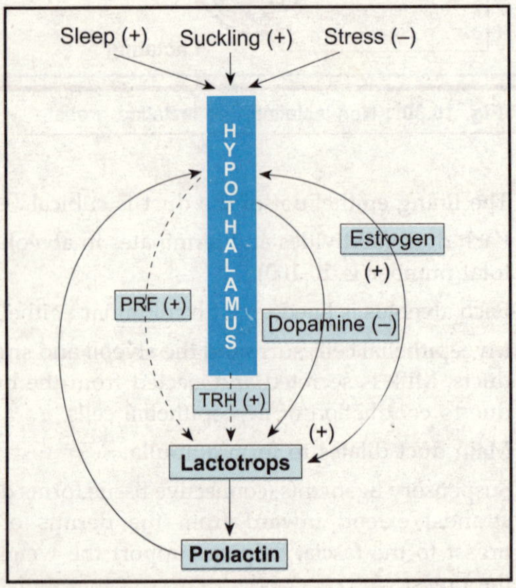


**Fig. 10.35 :** Control of prolactin secretion

and during the latter months is due to pressure exerted by the growing fetus.

**Blood :** The volume of bood increases by 30%. Both plasma and erythrocyte volume increase. But that of plasma is more as compared to RBC leading to a fall in RBC and HB concentration. Plasma iron levels fall but plasma iron binding capacity increases. There is an increase in demand for iron. If adequate iron is not suplemented, the subject may develop iron deficiency anaemia.

**Bone marrow :** It beomes hyperplastic involves all the cell elements.

**Nervous sytem :** Mild mental changes are common in pregnancy. Craving for unusual food and alterations inmood is seen in the first trimester.

**Plasma proteins :** Albumin falls, alpha and beta globulin rise due to oestrogen. Fibrinogen rises. Hence ESR rises in pregnancy.

**Heart :** Heart appears to be enlarged. Cardiac out put, stroke volume and heart rate all increase. At full term, cardiac output comes to prepregnant levels.

**Respiration :** Is stimulated due to progesterone. The respiratory rate rises with a fall in alveolar PCO2. The BMR rises with an increase in Oxygen consumption. The vital capacity does not change appreciably because a decrease in vertical dimension of the chest is compensated by an increase in the transverse dimension.

**GIT :** (1) Hypochlorhydria, with decreased motility of the stomach. Morning sickness and vomiting may be due to degraded products from the endometrium by the trophoblastic cells. Decreased colonic tone may be associated with constipation.

**Urinary system : increased GFR due to** a rise in cardiac output. At term the values come back within the normal range. Renal glycosuria may occur.

**Ureter :** Loss of tone of ureters may lead to urinary tract infection.

## Endocrine Glands :

**Pituitary gland :** Slight enlargement with an increase in secretion of its trophic hormone.

**Thyroid gland :** Moderate enlargement as a result of hyperplasia with an increase in thyroxine secretion. Thyroxine binding glubulin is also increased. As a result, symptoms of hyperthyroidism is not commonly seen.

**Parathyoids :** Increased secretion of parathormone, facilitating the mobilization of Calcium from the maternal bones to the fetal bones.

**Adrenal cortex :** Enlarges during pregnancy particularly Zona fasciculata. Cortisol secretion and C.B.G. (transcortin) are increased. So, there are no symptoms of adrenal hypersecretion.

**Skin :** Pigmentation of the nipple and the areola **occur**. The linea alba becomes pigmented also. There may also be brownish patches on the neck and face as a result of increased secretion of ACTH or MSH or both.

**Metabolism :** Weight of the body increase by an average of about 12 kilograms.

**Water metabolism :** There is an increase in water retention in the tissue. This may be due to reduction in colloidal osmotic pressure as there is a fall in the plasma protein levels or secondary to sodium retention underthe influence of sex steroids.

**Mineral metabolism :** There is a retention of Na, K, Cl due to increased secretion of mineralocorticoids, glucocorticoids and sex hormones.

**Carbohydrate metabolism :** There is a tendency to glycosuria during pregnancy. This is due into lowered level of renal thereshold for glucose. There is hyperglycemia due to H.P.L.

**Protein metabolism :** There is a positive nitrogen balance. Amino acids are converted into proteins. These are necessary for the growing fetus.

**Fat metabolims :** In pregnancy there is an increase in blood cholesterol, phospholipids and neutral fats. Adipose tissue depot fat increases and provides a large energy store for use in the latter stages of pregnancy and during lactation.

**Breast gland : There is growth of the duct system and the alveoli :** The hormones responsible are estrogen, progesterone, and prolactin. Thyroxine, growth hormone, ACTH, HCG and Insulin also play a role.

## Pregnancy diagnostic tests :

**Principle :** During pregnancy, Human chorionic gonadotrophin (HCG) is secreted by the placenta. Its secretion during the first trimester is maximum and during the rest of the pregnancy is low. Peak blood levels are attained between the 60-70th day leading to excretion in urine. Detection of the presence of this hormone in urine confirms pregnancy. HCG can be detected in the urine as early as the 9th day after conception by radioimmunoassy.

There are two types of tests :

1. **Biological tests :** In these test either male or female animals are used. HCG has LH activity. In male animals it brings about release of spermatozoa. I females, it brings about ovulatory changes in the ovary or release eggs. Morning urine samples of women with doubtful pregnancy is collected around the 60-70th day of amenorrhoea 3-5 ml of urine is injected daily for specified periods into the dorsal lymph sac (frog) or peritoneal cavity (rabbit, mice and rats).

| | | | |
|---|---|---|---|
| Ascheim–Zondek test | Immature female mice | 5 days | Hemorrhagic collicles in ovary |
| Kupperman test | Immature female rat | 6-12 hours | Hemorrhagic follicles |
| Friedman test | Immature female rabbit | 2 days | Ovulatory changes |
| Hogben test | Female toad | 6-12 hours | Eggs in urine |
| GalliMainini test | Male frog | 3 hours | Spermatozoa in urine |

2. **Immunological test :** Anti bodies can be produced against HCG by injecting this hormone into some animals. These antibodies are available in the form of commercial preparations. There are two types of tests.

(a) *Haemagglutination test :* Urine containing HCG is mixed with antiserum. Antibodies agglutinate with HCG. To this mixture, add sheep coated with HCG → no agglutination occurs in pregnancy (negative test). A positive test is seen in women who are not pregnant.

(b) *Latex agglutination test :* Latex coated particles are taken. Principle is the same as inthe haemagglutination test. Test requires 2 hours.

## ➤ 10.9 Parturirition and Labor

**Labor** is the process whereby the fetus and placenta are expelled from the uterus and normally occurs between 37 and 42 weeks' gestation.

**Partuirition** is the formal term for birth, and labor is the sequence of events that occurs during birth. The average gestation period is 40 weeks (280 days), with a normal range of 37 to 42 weeks.

### Initiation of Labor

The basic trigger for human labor is still unknown. Labor appears to be a self-perpetuating process once it is initiated. Type 2 and 3 factors are important in this respect :

**Type 1** : Fetal oxytocin, ACTH and related peptides.

**Type 2** : Estrogen; Progesterone; Cortisol; maternal oxytocin; oxytocin receptors, relaxin.

**Type 3** : Prostaglandins.

The process by which the child is born is referred to as parturition. Parturition is a sequence of events, termed labor. Some factors which are responsible for the onset of labour :

(i) Muscles of uterus contract rhythmically and forcefully.

(ii) Placental and ovarian hormones play an important role.

(iii) Progesterone inhibits uterine contractions.

(iv) Some factors released from placenta, fetus or mother inhibit the effect of progesterone. As a result, there will be pronounced effect of estrogen.

(v) Oxytocin released from posterior pituitary gland stimulates uterine contractions.

(vi) Relaxin helps by relaxing the symphysis pubis and dilatation of uterine cervix.

Uterine contraction is enhanced due to fall in progesterone secretion but uterine contractions are stimulated when the stretch receptors in the uterus and cervix are stimulated due to increased release of oxytocin from posterior pituitary. When the stretch receptors located in the uterus and cervix are stimulated at the time of parturition, oxytocin is also released. Prostaglandin induces labor. There is initiation of uterine contractions due to release of prostaglandin. There is also change in placental steroid synthesis when there is increase in fetal cortisol secretion.

Relaxin (a polypeptide hormone) is released from ovary, uterus and placenta during the late trimester of pregnancy. It helps in parturition by enhancing the relaxation of birth canal.

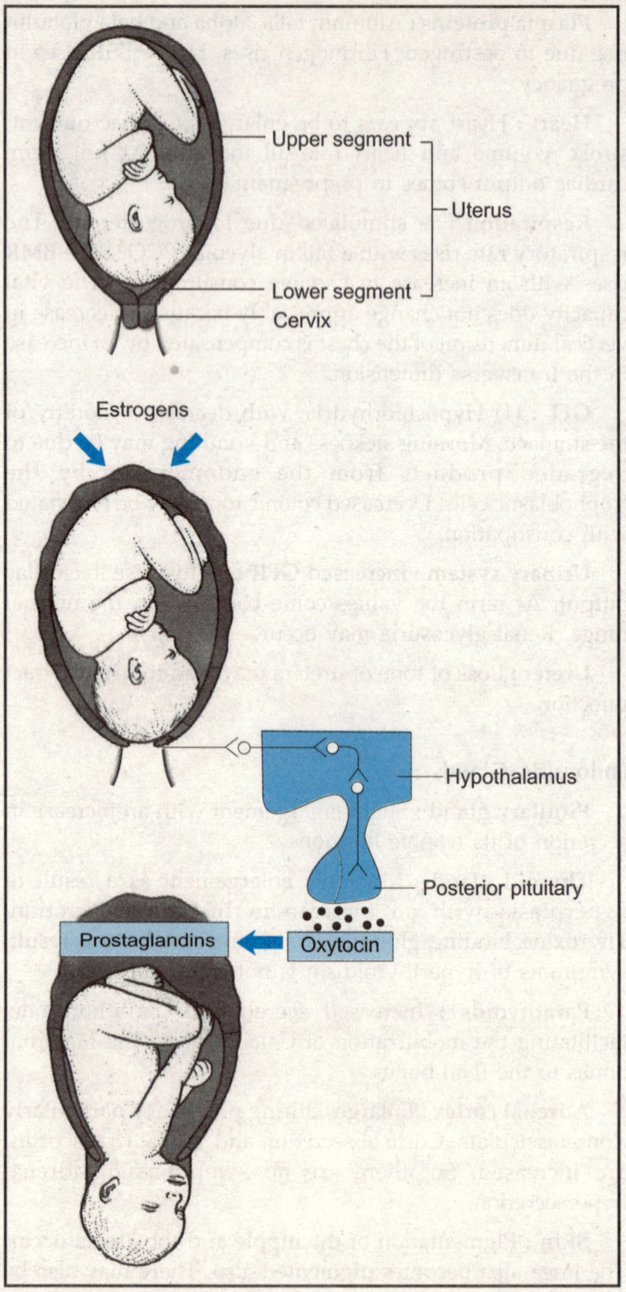


**Fig. 10.36 : Birth process involves positive feedback mechanism**

**Labor is divided into three stages :**

- *First stage of labor*
- *Second stage of labor*
- *Third stage of labor*

The figure (Fig. 10.36) shows the process of birth that involves a positive feedback mechanism.

***First stage of labor :*** This lasts from the diagnosis of labor until the cervix is dilated by 10 cm (fully dilated). The cervix often dilates slowly for the first 3 cm; this is the 'latent phase of labor'. Thereafter, average cervical dilatation is at the rate of 1 cm/hour in nulliparous women and about 2 cm/hour in multiparous women. The first stage should not be normally last longer than 12 hours. When the cervix is stretched, a nervous reflex is initiated → posterior pituitary gland is stimulated → stimulation of uterine contracton. Oxytocin enhances the onset of labor.

Figure 10.37 shows how positive feedback helps in increasing the force, frequency and duration of contractions with advancement of labor.

***Second stage of labor*** : This lasts from full dilatation of the cervix to delivery. This stage can be much quicker but should not last longer than one hour.

***Third stage of labor*** : This is the time from delivery of the fetus to delivery of the placenta. It normally lasts about 15 minutes, and normal blood loss is up to 500 ml.

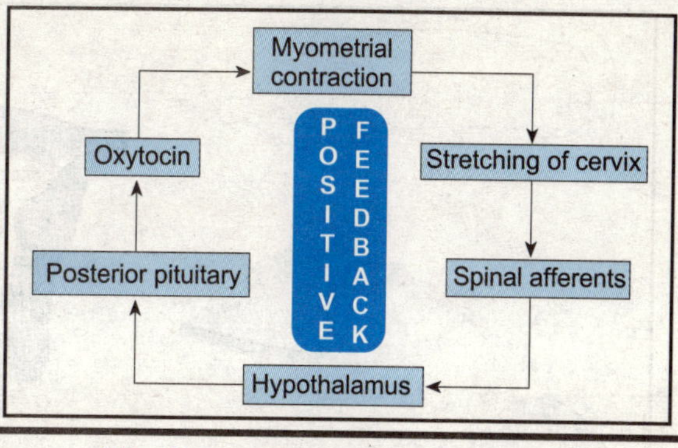


**Fig. 10.37 :** Effect of oxytocin on uterus

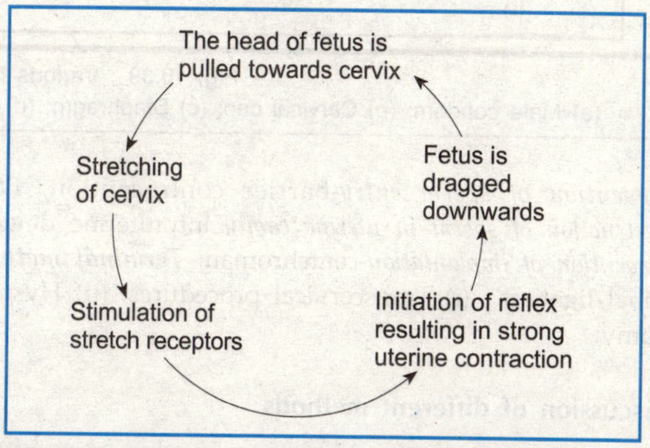


**Fig. 10.38 :** Positive feedback mechanism

### Factors helping labor (Fig. 10.38)

(a) Progesterone level declines as the time of birth approaches.

(b) Synthesis of prostaglandins are stimulated when there is fall in the progesterone concentration . As a result there will be initiation of labor.

(c) Oxytocin, released from posterior pituitary gland, stimulates uterine contractions.

(d) When the head stretches the cervix or positive feedback mechanism initiates stronger uterine contractions, the fetus is forced out via the birth canal.

## ➤ 10.10 Contraception (Fig. 10.39)

**Contraception is** the prevention of pregnancy. On an individual basis it is important to ensure that an unwanted pregnancy is prevented. Most methods of contraception have been the subject of adverse publicity. **The efficacy of contraception** is measured as the risk of pregnancy per 100 woman years of using the given method and is called the PEARL index. If the PEARL index (PI) of a contraceptive is 2, then of 100 women using it for a year, two will be pregnant by the end.

### Hormonal contraception

Estrogens and progestogens can be used for contraception in the following ways :

(1) *Progestogen as a tablet* : The progesterone only pill (mini pill).

(2) *Progestogen as a depot* : Norplant, Depo-Provera, or in the progestogen containing IUD. (3) *Estrogen and progestogen* : The combined oral contraceptive (the pill) : mono/bi/tri-phasic.

### Physiology

For an effective pregnancy, a healthy sperm and a healthy ovum in a healthy environment of cervical mucus and uterine cavity and tube should be able to unite. Also, the zygote must be able to implant itself in the uterine wall with effective formation of embryo and placenta.

The various processes of oogenesis, spermatogenesis, ovulation, fertilization, embryogenesis and implantation are influenced by hormonal conditions and various physicochemical factors.

Thus, blockade in any of the above processes leads to failure of conception, i.e., contraception.

**Male factor :** Very few methods have been described for spacing of births.

*Condom* prevents sperm entry during coitus.

*Male pill (gossypol)* destroys and immobilizes sperm.

*GnRH analogues* prevent sperm production but not much effective.

**Terminal method** : Vasectomy is safe and effective.

Vas occlusion methods : Vasoocclude; Injection of polyurethrane or silicon into vas; Contraceptive plugs; Clips; Intravasal Contraceptive Device (IVCD); Vas valves.

**Female factor :** Prevention of ovulation by *oral contraceptive pill (OCP), GnRH, estrogen; Natural methods* abstinence during fertile period of menstrual cycle, i.e., 10-17 days;

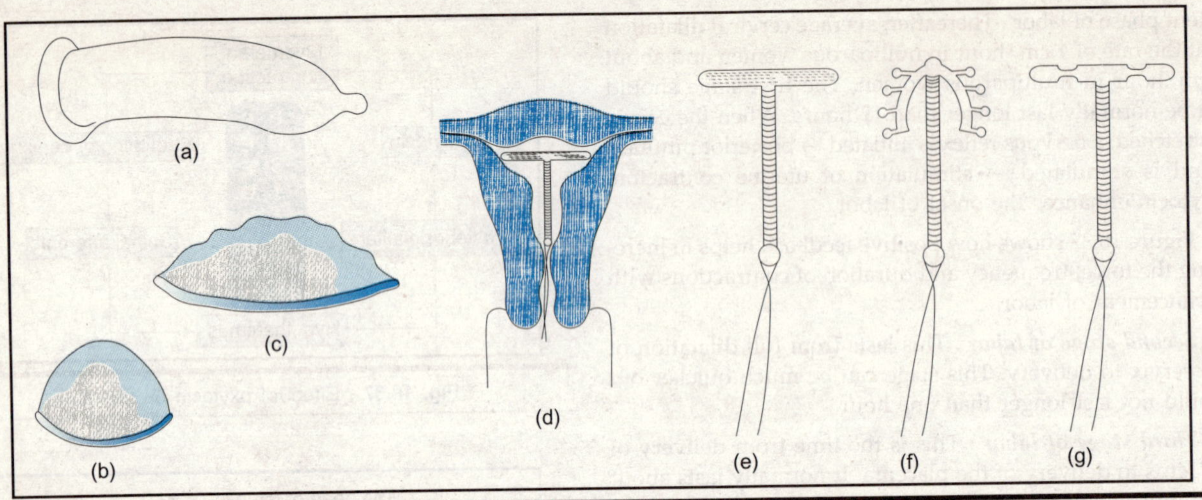


Fig. 10.39 : Various types of contraceptive devices — (a) Male condom; (b) Cervical cap; (c) Diaphragm; (d) Copper T in uterus; (e), (f) and (g) — different types of I U C D.

*Prevention of sperm entry*-barrier contraception, POP; *Destruction of sperm in uterine cavity* intrauterine devices; *Prevention of implantation*-centchroman; ***Terminal methods*** Tubal ligation : (i) Transcervical procedures, (ii) Hysterectomy.

## Discussion of different methods

**Natural family planning** entails planning or avoiding pregnancies by abstaining from sexual intercourse during the fertile phase of the menstrual cycle without the use of drugs, devices and surgical procedures.

*Rhythm method :* Calendar method (safe period/Ogino-Knaus method); Mucus method (Billing's or ovulation method); Basal body temperature method; Symptothermal method.

*Coitus interruptus* (withdrawal method).

*Breast feeding* : A physiological phenomenon.

## Barrier contraceptives

Oldest, simplest, reversible, effective, prevent the users from developing STD, hepatitis B, HIV, herpes, chlamydia, cytomegalovirus infections.

*For female :* Occlusive caps, spermicides, intratubal mechanical device, intracervical device, vaginal rings, female condoms, home-made barrier.

*For male* : Condom (dry type, prelubricated, skin condom, short/glans condom).

**Advantages :** No prescription needed; No medical help needed; Easily available over the counter; Suitable for teenage, aged, during lactation, couples with infrequent coitus; Intolerant to IUCD pills; Protection against STD, PID, amnionitis.

**Disadvantages :** Reduction in sexual pleasure; Low effectiveness; Hypersensitivity to latex rubber.

**Other uses :** McIndoe's vaginoplasty; Infertility due to sperm antibody; Semen allergy; Collection of semen for analysis.

## Intrauterine contraceptive device (IUD or the Coil)

These devices are inserted into the uterine cavity, without anaesthetic. Thin plastic strings protrude through the cervix and are pulled to remove the device.

**Classification :** 1. 1st generation or unmedicated IUCD – Lippes loop, Sa/T-coil. 2. Second generation or medicated IUCDs (i) IUCD containing Cu, Zn, Silver; (ii) IUCD containing hormones progestasert; (iii) IUCD containing drugs Tranexamic acid, EACA

Commonly used ones are CuT 380A, CuT 220C, Nova T, Multiload 375.

## Mechanism of action

IUCDs act as contraceptives primarily by preventing fertilization, decreasing the numbers of sperms reaching fallopian tubes and inactivating them.

This is effected by formation of a biological foam within the uterine cavity with strands of fibrin, proteolytic enzymes, phagocytic cells → altered environment.

Progesterone containing devices → allow sustained slow release of hormone → atrophic endometrial lining.

**Advantages :** Highly effective; Easy to use; Continuous protection; Convenient, reversible; Very little user-compliance.

**Complication :** Bleeding; Pelvic infection; Pregnancy; Perforation; Complete/Partial expulsion; Allergy.

**Absolute :** Endometrial or cervical cancer; undiagnosed vaginal bleeding; Active or recent pelvic infection; pregnancy.

**Relative :** Previous ectopic pregnancy; Excessive menstrual loss; Multiple sexual partners; Immuno compromised including HIV-positive.

**Effective life :** Cu T 200 – 3 years; Progestasert – 1 year.

**Table 10.2 : Classification of Contraception**

| | | |
|---|---|---|
| **Spacing methods** | | |
| A. ***Natural methods*** | • Rhythm method<br>• Coitus interruptus (20-30/100 wy)*<br>• Breast feeding (27-30/100 wy)* | • Calendar of safe period (14-47/100 wy)*<br>• Basal body temp. charting (8-20/100 wy)*<br>• Billing's cervical mucus method (2-25/100 wy)*<br>• Symptothermal method |
| B. ***Barrier contraceptives*** | • Condom<br>• Occlusive caps<br>• Spermicides<br>• Intratubal mechanical device | PI 3.5<br>PI upto 20 |
| C. ***Intrauterine contraceptive device (IUCD)*** | | • 1st generation – Lippes loop<br>• 2nd generation – CuT<br>• 3rd generation – progestasert<br>PI 0.2 – 2.0 depending on type |
| D. ***Hormonal contraceptives*** | | |
| (i) **Combined oral contraceptive** | Women : | Any women except listed under major side effects/lactation. |
| | Failure : | PI 0.2 |
| | Action : | Inhibits ovulation by suppressing LH and FSH release |
| | Major problems : | Deep vein Thrombosis, Ischemic heart disease, cerebro vascular accident, hypertension; breast and cervix carcinoma. |
| | Side effects : | Breast tenderness; weight gain; nausea. |
| (ii) **Progestogen only pill** | Women : | Any |
| | Failure : | PI 1.0 |
| | Action : | Cervical mucus and sometimes inhibition of ovulation |
| | Side effects : | Vaginal spotting. |
| (iii) **Depot progestogens** | Women : | Any |
| | Failure : | PI < 1.0 |
| | Action : | Ovulation usually inhibited |
| | Side effects : with Depo-Provera | Progestogenic prolonged amenorrhoea |
| E. ***Post-coital contraceptives*** | • High dose estrogens<br>• Combined contraceptive pills<br>• Cu IUCD<br>• Danazol<br>• Mifepristone | |
| F. ***Miscellaneous*** | • Nonsteroidal contraceptive pill<br>• Male pill – Gossypol<br>• Immunological contraceptive (eg, hCG vaccine, LHRH vaccine, FSH) | |
| **Terminal methods** | • Male – vasectomy<br>• Female | • Mini lap } tubectomy<br>• Laparoscopic } tubectomy<br>• Transcervical procedures<br>• Hysterectomy |

**Note :** Figures in parentheses are failure rate per 100 woman-year of use

## Hormonal contraceptives

**Oral contraceptive pills :** (a) **Single agent** minipill; (b) **Combination pills** (i) Monophasic; (ii) Bi- or triphasic; (iii) Sequential pills.

**Monophasic :** A fixed concentration of estrogen and progesterone throughout the cycle.

**Multiphasic :** 2 or 3 variations of concentrations of estrogen and progesterone.

### Mechanism of action

(i) Combined contraceptive pills are the most effective reversible contraception available.

(ii) Due to pharmacologic synergism, ovulation is inhibited at lower dose of each agent.

(iii) Combined pill suppresses basal FSH and LH levels.

(iv) Diminishes the ability of pituitary glands to synthesize gonadotropin when stimulated by hypothalamic GnRH.

Thus ovarian follicles do not mature → ↓ estradiol → No midcycle LH surge → no ovulation → no corpus luteum → no progesterone (Table 10.3).

### Contraindications

**Absolute contraindications :** History of oligomenorrhea; Delayed periods; Thrombophlebitis and coronary heart disease; Impaired liver function; Estrogen dependent tumour; Known or suspected pregnancy; Age 35 or more, Heavy smoker, Obese; Juvenile diabetes; Infective hepatitis; Chlamydial infection; Focal migraine; History of cholestatic jaundice (during pregnancy); Hirsuitism; Immobilization.

**Relative contraindications :** History of migraine; History of bouts of depression; Elective surgery; Hypertension, PIH, History of diabetes; Breast-feeding; Suspected breast carcinoma; taking rifampicin/medication for epilepsy; Obstructive jaundice; Sickle-cell disease, Hyperprolactinemia.

### Mechanism of action

With implants releasing levonorgestrel there is some follicular maturation + estrogen production but LH peak levels are low and ovulation does not occur.

Low dose progesterone affects cervical mucus, endometrium and tubal motility.

- Progestin :

↓Nuclear estrogen receptor

↓Progesterone receptor

Induces 17 hydroxy steroid dehydrogenase that metabolizes natural estrogen.

**Injectables** : Based on interaction of central + peripheral mechanism :

(a) Ovulation is inhibited during 1st 5-7 weeks after injection.

(b) Peripheral progestational effects change cervical secretion.

### Failure rate

1. DMPA 150 mg every 90 days 0.01/100 w-yr.

2. NET EN 200 mg within 1st 5 days of cycle repeated at 8 weeks for 1st six months and then 12 weeks – 0-1.2/100 w-year.

**Table 10.3 : Adverse effects of oral contraceptives :**

| General | Metabolic |
|---|---|
| Nausea | Precipitate porphyria in susceptible individuals. |
| Headache | Impaired glucose tolerance. |
| Fluid retention and weight gain. | Increase in Cholesterol and triglycerides. |
| Hypertension | Increase in gall bladder disease. |
| Depression | |
| Loss of libido | |
| Urinary tract infection. | |
| Genital candidiasis. | |
| Persisting amenorrhoea after stopping pill. | |
| Venous thrombosis and embolism. | |
| Thrombotic and hemorrhagic stroke. | |
| Myocardial infarction. | |
| Jaundice (rare) | |

### Subdermal implants

6 rods — 34 mm length — 2-4 mm diameter with 36 mg levonorgestrel.

80 mg/day for 1st 6-12 months, then 30-35 mg/day (effective life 5 years) — 0.7 to 1/100 wm/3 years.

**Disadvantages** : Ectopic gestation; Menstrual abnormalities; Progestational side-effects.

### Post-coital contraceptives/emergency contraception

A method of contraception which is required when a woman has had sexual intercourse without any contraceptive protection, and does not wish to have a pregnancy.

**Indications :** Rape; Unplanned sexual activity; Rupture of condom.

**Prerequisites :**

1. There must not be any sexual activity prior to this one in this menstrual cycle.
2. Couple willing to accept MTP if postcoital method fails.
3. Couple should realize that postcoital methods should only be used during emergency, **not as a regular method**.

### Methods

I. Estrogen administration as soon as possible (within 24 hours – 72 hrs)

(i) Ethinyl estradiol – 5 mg/day;

(ii) Conjugated estrogen 30-50 mg/day;

(iii) Estradiol benzoate 30 mg/day;

(iv) Diethylstilbestrol 50 mg/day.

II. Yuzpe method : Use of estrogen-progestin combination.

Multifactorial action produces asynchronous development of glandular and stromal elements of endometrium. Suppresses pituitary hormones → inhibiting ovulation → suppresses corpus luteum function.

III. Copper IUD, failure rate – 0.1%

**Disadvantages :**

(i) Difficulty in young, multipara;

(ii) Abdomen discomfort;

(iii) Risk of infection – rape, multiple partner;

(iv) Long term contraception not desired.

IV. Danazol – 400 mg orally soon after coitus; repeat after 12 hrs.

V. Mifepristone (RU 486) — 50-100 mg/day for 4 days at midluteal phase irrespective of time of coitus.

### Miscellaneous

1. Centchroman – nonhormonal oral pill. It is 3, 4 trans 2, 2 dimethyl 3-phenyl 4 [P (Betapyrroledinoethoxy) phenyl (methoxychroman hydrochloride).

- Has weak estrogenic and strong anti-estrogen actions
- Binds to estradiol receptors and exerts its action by suppression of endometrial proliferation and making it unfavourable for implantation.
- Accelerates transport of the embryo.

**Side effects :** 8% of the menstrual cycles are longer than usual. No effect in amount and duration of menstrual flow. Reversible; subsequent pregnancies are normal. Useful against breast cancer.

**Male pill :** Oral estrogen + methyl testosterone; DMPA + androgen; GnRH analogues; Gossypol.

Search for an acceptable male pill is still going on.

### Immmunological contraceptive

(1) hCG birth control vaccine :

(i) most advanced;

(ii) birth control vaccine;

(2) LHRH vaccine;

(3) FSH and FSH derived vaccine;

(4) Using sperm antigen;

(5) Vaccine against egg antigen. But all these are under trial.

### Terminal methods

***Male sterilization*** : Vasectomy involves ligation and removal of a small segment of the vasdeferens, thereby preventing release of sperm. It can be performed under local anaesthetic.

**Advantages :** Highly effective; Simple OPD procedure; Local anesthesia; Minimal personnel; Minimal surgical facilities required; Minimal surgical expertise; Low complication rate; Low failure rate; Success can be proved by a postoperative semen examination; Does not affect sexual performance.

**Disadvantages :** Being a male method needs more persuasion; Psychological features of castration.

**Complication :** Minor side-effect pain; Serious complications – hematoma, epididymitis; Death – tetanus; Long term – psychological.

**Efficacy :** Failure rate is less than 1% due to : Unprotected coitus before azoospermia; Spontaneous recanalisation; Surgeon's error – vas. intact.

**Female sterilization** being a one time method does not require sustained motivation and provides the most effective protection against pregnancy.

**Timing :**

(a) Interval case 6 weeks post partum or when not pregnant. Done immediately post-menstrual.

(b) Post-MTP.

(c) Puerperium.

**Eligibility criteria :** Women are certain that they deserve no more children; Women have no contraindication to surgical/anesthetic; Should be married and spouse living; Women above 22 years and below 45.

***Written consent*** of the woman and her husband mandatory.

**Methods :** Laparotomy large abdominal incision (obsolete now); Mini lap widely used; Colpotomy; Laparoscopy; Trans-cervical approaches (hysteroscopy occlusion of tubal lumen with hysteroscope), Hysterectomy in presence of pathological condition like recurrent menorrhagia, uterine descent, multiple fibroids (Fig. 10.40).

**Technique of tubectomy :** Pomeroy technique 0-0.4% failure rate, low morbidity; Uchida technique complicated; Irving technique 100% effective but complicated.

**Complications :**

(i) Injury to intraabdominal viscera and blood vessels;

(ii) Respiratory depression or arrest;

(iii) Cardiac arrest;

(iv) Cardiorespiratory embarrassment, mediastinal emphysema, pneumothorax;

(v) Injury to urinary bladder;

(vi) Uterus perforation due to introduction of uterus elevator from below;

(vii) Bleeding from mesosalpinx;

(viii) Gas or air embolism;

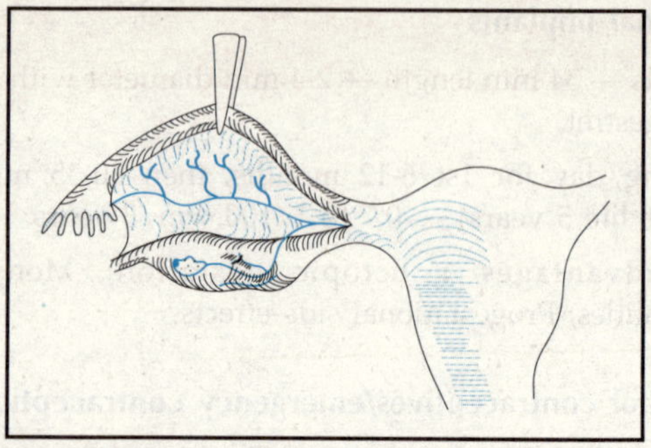

Fig. 10.40

(ix) Vasovagal attack;

(x) Convulsion and toxic reaction to local anesthetic.

**Immediate postoperative :** Internal obstructive paralytic ileus; Hematoma in abdominal wall; Wound sepsis; Tetanus.

**Delayed :** Menstrual irregularities; Incisional hernia; Chronic pelvic inflammatory disease; Psychological problem; Ectopic pregnancy.

## Conclusion

There is no ideal contraceptive in the true sense. That is why so many methods are available with their advantages and disadvantages. As such, there are difficulties in selection of a particular method.

## ➤ 10.11 KEY CONCEPTS

1. The **male reproductive organs** are :
   • the testes • the penis • several glands.
2. There are two testes, one is slightly larger than the other. Each testis consists of many seminiferous tubules (site of sperm production) and interstitial cells of Leydig (site of production of hormone testosterone).
3. **Sperm production is** enhanced by :
   (a) Follicle stimulating hormone (FSH) [Its secretion is stimulated by luteinizing hormone releasing hormone (LHRH) from the hypothalamus.];
   (b) Testosterone [The main androgen, testosterone, is produced by Leydig cells of testis. Androgens are responsible for the development, maintenance and function of the male reproductive organs and male secondary sex characteristics such as the ability to form and deliver sperm, low pitch of the male voice and the pattern of hair distribution. They have profound anabolic activity increasing bone mass and muscle.]
4. The **main structures of the female reproductive tract are** :
   • ovaries • uterus • fallopian tubes • vagina • vulva.
5. The **ovaries** are responsible for the production of ova and ovarian hormones. Inhibin is secreted by granulosa cells and the corpus luteum.
6. The **function of estrogen is proliferation of the** endometrium, excitability of the endometrium, excitability of the myometrium and development of genitalia and breast. Estrogen promotes growth of glands.

   **Functions of progesterone :**
   • promotes endometrial differentiation
   • pregnancy is maintained
   • myometrial excitability is decreased
   • thick cervical mucus is produced
   • relaxation of uterine smooth muscle.

   Estrogens together with progesterone are produced by cells of Graafian follicles in the ovary. They are responsible for the development, maintenance and functions of the reproductive organs, sexual activity cycles and secondary sex characteristics in the female.
7. **The menstrual cycle** is divided into two phases —

   (i) **The follicular phase** (starts from first day of menstruation and ends with ovulation). (ii) **The luteal phase** (from ovulation to the beginning of menstruation). Hormonal changes in the menstrual cycle.

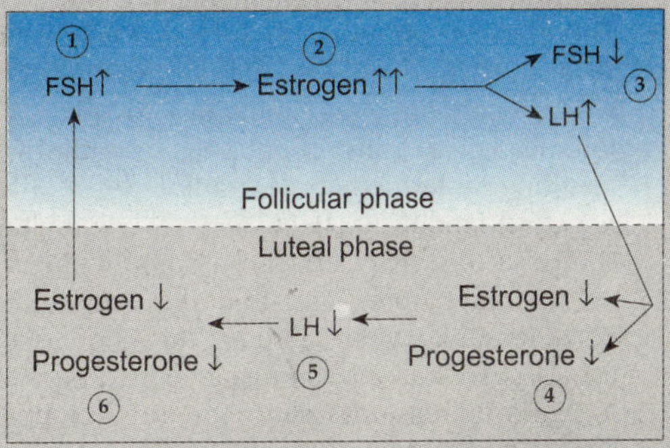


   ***Hormonal alterations during the menstrual cycle*** (1) Loss of inhibitory influence of estrogen in the beginning of the cycle (2) Highly increased release of estrogen from the ovarian follicle due to stimulation by FSH (3) Stimulation of release of LH and inhibition of release of FSH by estrogen leading to ovulation. A point to be noted here is that the FSH level almost doubles just before ovulation, reason of which is uncertain. (4) Release of estrogen and progesterone from corpus luteum stimulated by LH. (5) Inhibition of LH by lower estrogen levels. (6) Regression of corpus luteum.

   **Regulation of male reproductive system**. Leydig cells are stimulated by LH to produce testosterone which is bound by androgen-binding protein (ABP) produced by Sertoli cells on stimulation by FSH. LH release by anterior pituitary is inhibited by testosterone feedback. Inhibin produced by Sertoli cells inhibits FSH from anterior pituitary.

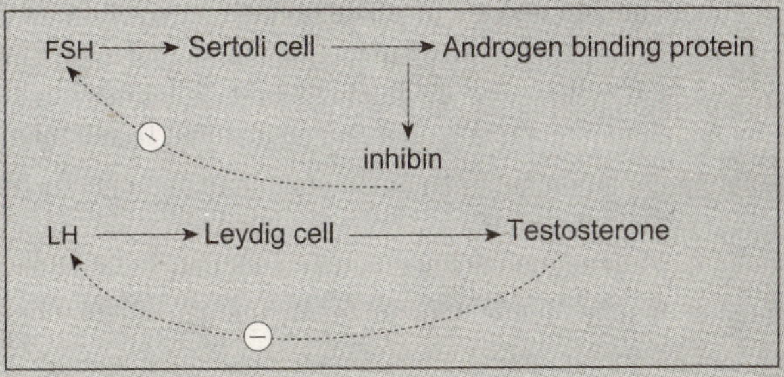

## ➤ 10.11 KEY CONCEPTS

8. **Follicle stimulating hormone** promotes spermatogenesis. Luteinizing hormone stimulates the secretion of the androgens from the interstitial cells of the testis. The principal androgen is testosterone. The androgen has a depressant action on the secretion of gonadotropins from the anterior pituitary gland. Testosterone is fully metabolized in the body. The urinary excretion products are 17-ketosteroids, the most important of which is the weakly androgenic androsterone.

   Follicle stimulating hormone causes development of the ovarian follicles and luteinizing hormone stimulates the secretion of estrogen and estradiol from the follicle. During the menstrual cycle, the release of estrogen inhibits the pituitary secretion of FSH and stimulates that of LH.

   At this stage, LH becomes the principal gonadotropin and the **follicle matures** to become the corpus luteum, which secretes progesterone under the stimulation of LTH. The **fall** in the level of circulating estrogen and rise in **progesterone** cause menstrual bleeding, stimulate secretion of FSH, and depress secretion of LH; the cycle recommences.

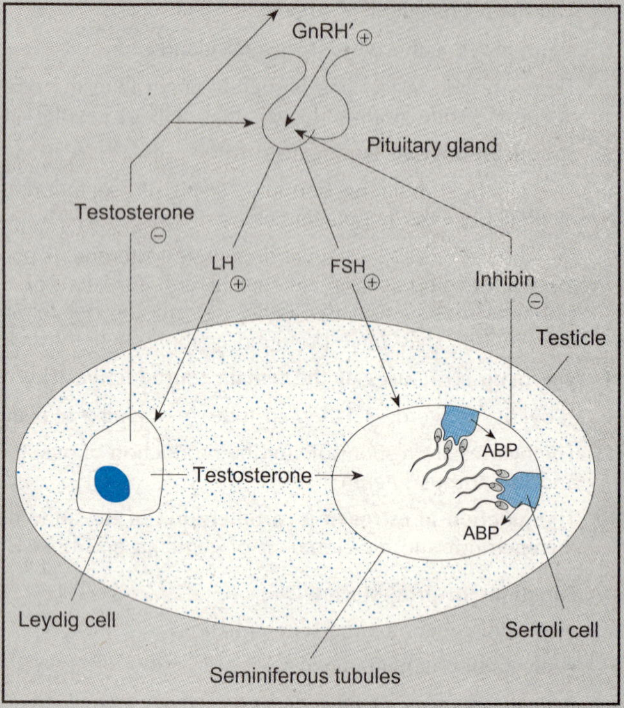


9. **The physiology of ovulation :** At the beginning of each cycle, low estrogen levels exert a positive feed back to cause hypothalamic gonadotropin **releasing hormone (GnRH)** pulses to stimulate the anterior pituitary gland to produce gonadotropins : follicle – **stimulating hormone (FSH)** and **luteinizing hormone (LH)**. These cause growth and initiate maturation of several of the follicles of the ovary, each of which contains an immature ovum. These follicles also start producing estradiol. The resulting intermediate estradiol level has a negative feedback effect on the hypothalamus, such that less FSH and LH is produced. When the follicle matures, its estradiol output increases considerably. When a high 'thresold' level of estradiol is attained, the negative feed back is reversed and positive feed back now causes LH and FSH levels to again increase dramatically : it is the peak of LH that ultimately leads to rupture of the now ripe follicle. This is **ovulation** and the egg spills on to the ovarian surface where it can be picked up by the fallopian tube.

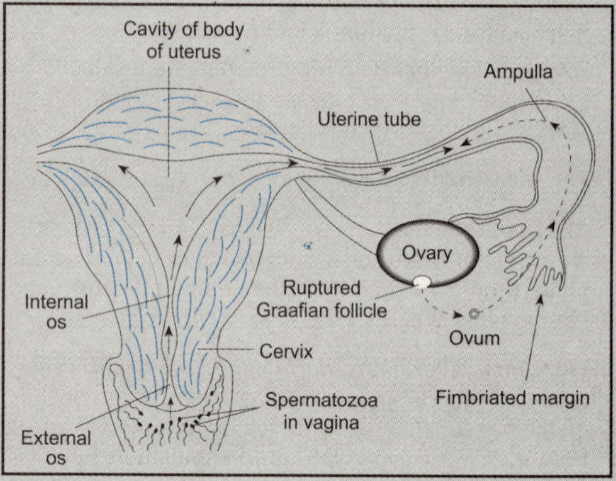


10. **The physiology of fertilization :** At ovulation, the fallopian tube moves so that the fimbrial end collects the ovum from the ovaries. The tube must have adequate mobility to move on to the ovary to achieve this. Peristaltic contractions and cilia in the tube help sweep the ovum along toward the sperm. Blockage or ciliary damage will impair this. At ejaculation, the millions of sperm enter the vagina. The cervical mucus helps them get through the cervix.

11. The **placenta** is a complex and vascular organ which is responsible for exchange of gases, nutrients and electrolytes between maternal and fetal circulations. The placental hormones are — human chorionic gonadotropin; human chorionic somatomammotropin; progesterone and estrogen.

## ➤ 10.11 KEY CONCEPTS

12. **Human chorionic gonadotropin (hCG)** is secreted by the early trophoblast. It maintains progesterone production by the corpus luteum. Human chorionic somatomammotropin (hCS) is produced in late trimester of pregnancy. The fetal pituitary gland drives placental estrogen and progesterone production by stimulating adrenal production of androgen precursors for estrogens which, in turn, increase uptake of the cholesterol needed for progesterone synthesis.

13. **Oxytocin** is a neurohormone secreted by nerve endings in the posterior lobe of the pituitary gland in response to neural stimulation received by cell bodies in the supraoptic and paraventricular nuclei. During parturition, oxytocin receptors increase in both the endometrium and myometrium. Oxytocin hastens expulsion of fetus and the placenta.

14. **Prolactin** acts directly on the alveolar epithelium to synthesize and secrete milk. Suckling plays a key role for secretion of prolactin. Prolactin concentration in blood may increase 10-fold or more during suckling. It is secreted continuously at low basal rates throughout life regardless of sex.

15. **Hyperprolactinemia** results from a small prolactin-secreting pituitary tumor. It is a common cause of infertility. It is associated with abnormal or absent menstrual cycles. **Treatment** is done by *bromocriptine.* Bromocriptine activates dopamine receptors and suppresses prolactin secretion. Normal reproductive function is restored.

16. **Mechanism of normal labor at a glance.**

| | |
|---|---|
| **When occurs** | 37–42 weeks |
| **Diagnosis** | Contraction with effacement and dilatation of the cervix. |
| **1st Stage** | Average duration 8 hours; nulliparous; 4 hours multiparous. Uterus contracts 2-3 minutes cervix dilates until the widest diameter of head passes through. Head descends remaining flexed to maintain the smallest diameter. |
| **2nd Stage** | Contractions continue. Head descends and flexes further, rotation usually completed. Pushing starts when head reaches pelvic floor. |
| **Delivery** | Head now extends as it is delivered over perineum. |
| **3rd Stage** | Placenta is delivered. Average duration 15 minutes. |

17. **Assisted conception** — Recent advances have greatly increased the success of fertility treatment. The current methods are (i) in **vitro fertilization** (IVF) (ii) **intra-uterine-insemination (IUI)** and **gamete intrafallopian transfer (GIFT)**. The most frequently and currently practiced assisted reproductive technologies are : (a) In—vitro fertilization and embryo transfer (IVE-ET) (b) Intracytoplasmic sperm injection (ICS) and (c) Intrauterine Insemination (IUI).

    **In vitro fertilization (IVF) :** The eggs are procured under local anaesthesia by aspirating follicles under ultrasound control. They are then incubated with washed sperm and then transferred to a growth medium. The fallopian tubes need not be patent. The procedure involves six essential steps : (a) Indication and selection of cases (b) stimulation and monitoring (c) Ultrasound guided oocyte retrieval (d) Fertilization and cleavage in laboratory under optimum environment (e) Embryo transfer and (f) Post transfer hormonal support.

    **Intra uterine insemination (IUI) :** Sperms are injected directly into the cavity of the uterus at the time of ovulation. The tubes should be patent because the ovum is required to pass from the ovary to the sperm.

    **Zygote intrafallopian transfer ZIFT) :** The embryo is transferred laparoscopically into the fallopian tube. Oocyte retrieval and fertilization occur in vitro.

    **Intracytoplasmic–sperm injection (ICSI) :** This is the injection with a very fine needle of one sperm right into the ooplasma. It is indicated for male factor infertility, allowing use of poor quality sperm that would normally be unable to penetrate the ovum.

    **Gamete intrafallopian transfer (GIFT) :** The eggs are collected laparoscopically, mixed with sperm and transferred back to the fallopian tube straight away. For this method atleast one tube is functional.

## ➤ 10.12 DISORDERS/CLINICAL CORRELATIONS

➤ **Gynecomastia** : Excessive development of male mammary glands, sometimes secreting milk. Investigations : Chest X-ray; liver function tests; karyotype; measurement of plasma concentration of prolactin; hCG; testosterone and estradiol. It is common in puberty and among elderly men. Treatment is by removing offending drug or treating the underlying condition. Reassurance is given if idiopathic. Surgical interference is considered in severe cases.

➤ **Hirsutism** : Hirsutism is male pattern of excessive hair growth in women. Androgens are the major determinants of body hair distribution in both sexes. The three principal circulating androgens among the women are dehydroepiandosterone (adrenal) and androstenedione, andtestosterone (ovarian and adrenal). Menstrual abnormalities is almost invariable. In the majority of cases, hirsutism will have a racial or familial basis and, in them, it is believed that the hair follicles have become excessively sensitive to normal circulating levels of androgen.

➤ **Female hypogonadism** : There is failure of ovum production with or without diminished hormone secretion by the ovary. It may be due to a primary ovarian disorder, impaired gonadotropin secretion or increased prolactin secretion by the pituitary.

➤ **Klinefelter's syndrome** : It is seen in males who display variable degrees of eunuchoidism and gynecomastia and who have azoospermia, elevated urinary gonadotropins and atrophic testes, some have a female sex chromatin pattern.

➤ **Testicular feminization** : This is a rare condition characterized by patients of female phenotype with absent pubic and axillary hair. Testes are present. The condition is actually a failure of virilization rather than a feminizing process. The usual mode of inheritance is as an X-linked recessive trait. The subjects have a 46 XY karyotype and their gonads are histologically testes, although there is no spermatogenesis. They first present with primary amenorrhea but few other complaints. They have normal breasts but they have no pubic or axillary hair.

➤ **Sterility and Infertility** : In the female, **sterility** may be defined as inability to conceive because of some inherent fault; in **the male**, as inability to procreate. **Infertility** is the inability to achieve pregnancy within a stipulated period of time, usually 1 year, or repeated failure to carry a pregnancy to term. Primary infertility is a term used to designate those couples who have never conceived. Secondary infertility indicates that she had previously conceived even if the pregnancy culminated in a miscarriage or abortion.

➤ **Male infertility** : Male infertility : the inability of sperm to fertilize an egg has several causes. If, during fetal development, the testes do not descend into scrotum, the higher temperature of abdominal cavity or inguinal canal causes the developing sperm cells in the seminiferous tubules to degenerate. Certain diseases such as mumps may inflame the testes producing infertility by destroying cells in the seminiferous tubules.

**Causes of male infertility :** (i) Endocrine disorders; (ii) Obstruction of the vas deferens; (iii) Failure of ejaculation during intercourse; (iv) Failure of erection during intercourse; (v) Vasectomy operation.

**Oligospermia :** Disruption of sperm producing function of seminiferous tubules can result in decreased sperm production.

**Cryptorchidism :** Occasionally a baby is born with undescended testes.

**Phimosis :** A condition in which the foreskin fits so tightly over the glass that it cannot retract treatment—circumcision.

➤ **Dysfunctional uterine bleeding (DUB)** is irregular or excessive uterine bleeding that results from a hormonal imbalance rather than from an infection or other disease condition. In DUB, hormonal imbalances may cause excessive growth (hyperplasia) of the endometrium or abnormally frequent menstrual flow.

➤ **Premenstrual syndrome (PMS)** is a condition that involves a collection of symptoms that regularly occur in many women during the premenstrual phase of their reproduction cycles symptoms like irritability, fatigue, nervousness depression are present.

➤ **Female infertility :**

*Infertility* (in the female) : Coitus may be difficult due to local factors such as (a) intact hymen, vaginismus, undue dryness of the vagina, gross obesity; (b) cervical mucus may be hostile to the spermatozoa; (c) failure of ovulation is an important cause of infertility; (d) inflammatory disease of the fallopian tube; (e) emotional factors.

➤ **Hyperprolactinemia** : Hyperprolactinemia is a consequence of excessive prolactin secretion by the pituitary. It may be due to drugs (phenothiazines); hormones (estrogens) or thyroid deficiency. It may be due to a prolactin producing pituitary tumor, a prolactinoma.

## ➤ 10.12 DISORDERS/CLINICAL CORRELATIONS

➤ **Ectopic pregnancy** : An ectopic pregnancy occurs when the embryo implants outside the uterine cavity. It is more common with advancing maternal age and lower social class. The most common site is in the fallopian tube (95%) although implantation can occur in the cornu, cervix, ovary and abdominal cavity.

➤ **Failure of lactation** : It is due to inadequate suckling or to emotional factors. It is due to inhibition of the reflex secretion of oxytocin by increasing sympathetic activity.

➤ **Persistent lactation** : It may persist for many years following confinement. It may be due to some hypothalamic disturbance which prevents the normal inhibition of lactogenic hormones from anterior pituitary.

➤ **Adolescence** : **Adolescence** is the period of time during which the developing human undergoes his/her final stages of physical maturation.

➤ **Puberty** : Puberty is the onset of sexual maturity. It is marked by the development of secondary sex characteristics.

➤ **Precocious puberty** : Menstruation occurs before the age of 10, or other secondary sexual characteristics are evident before 8 years. It is very rare. The growth spurt occurs early and final height is reduced due to early fusion of the epiphysis.

➤ **Delayed puberty** : Puberty may be delayed for as long as five years. Assurance should be given to the patient. Laparoscopic visualization of pelvis will confirm the diagnosis.

➤ **Menopause (Climacteric) :** The menopause is the last menstruation and is a natural, universal phenomenon of age — the **average age** is 45-50 years. There is reduction in the level of estrogen. So the negative feedback effect on pituitary hormone production is reduced and LH & FSH levels rise as a result. There will be atrophy of the breasts, skin and genitalia. Consequently, the follicles no longer mature, ovulation does not occur. About 50% of menopausal women experience unpleasant vasomotor symptoms which are due to changes in the rhythmic secretion of GnRH by the hypothalamus. There is reduction in the sex hormones. Menopausal women are treated with estrogen replacement therapy.

➤ **Imperforate hymen** : The vagina acts as a passage for spermatozoa and menstrual flow. Vaginal orifice is located at the lower end of the vaginal opening. A thin fold of vascularised mucous membrane, hymen forms a border around the orifice. Sometimes hymen completely covers the orifice. This condition is called **imperforate hymen**. Treatment is surgery.

➤ **Impotence** : Lack of power in the male to copulate. Primary impotence is rare. Secondary impotence may have organic causes or may be followed by drugs or alcohol. Stress, and depression are also possible causes.

➤ **Amenorrhea** : Amenorrhoea is the absence of menstruation. It may be physiological or pathological.

*Physiological* **:** It occurs before the menarche, after the menopause, during pregnancy and in about 70 per cent of women during lactation.

*Pathological* : This may be of two kinds : primary or secondary. Primary : when menstruation has never occurred and may be due to disorders of pituitary gland, severe systemic illness or underdevelopment of the uterus and ovaries. Secondary : when menstruation has occurred and then ceased and most common cause is pregnancy.

➤ **Dysmenorrhea** : It is difficult and painful menstruation.

*Types of dysmenorrhea* • Congestive; • Spasmodic; • Membranous.

Primary dysmenorrhea occurs in 50-70% of women at some time or other. It generally begins within 1-2 years after menarche. Secondary dysmenorrhea is menstrual pain for which an organic cause exists.

➤ **Menorrhagia** : The duration of the bleeding phase of the menstrual cycle may be normal or prolonged but the amount of blood lost is excessive and will eventually lead to anemia. It can be due to pelvic inflammatory disease or fibromyoma of the uterus.

➤ **Metrorrhagia** : It means bleeding from the uterus independent of the menstrual period. It is irregular, acyclical bleeding from uterus.

➤ **Epimenorrhea** (Polymenorrhea) : It is very frequent. The cycles are short. The patient menstruates too frequently but the periods are not prolonged or excessive. The menstrual cycle is reduced to 2 or 3 weeks.

## ➤ 10.12 DISORDERS/CLINICAL CORRELATIONS

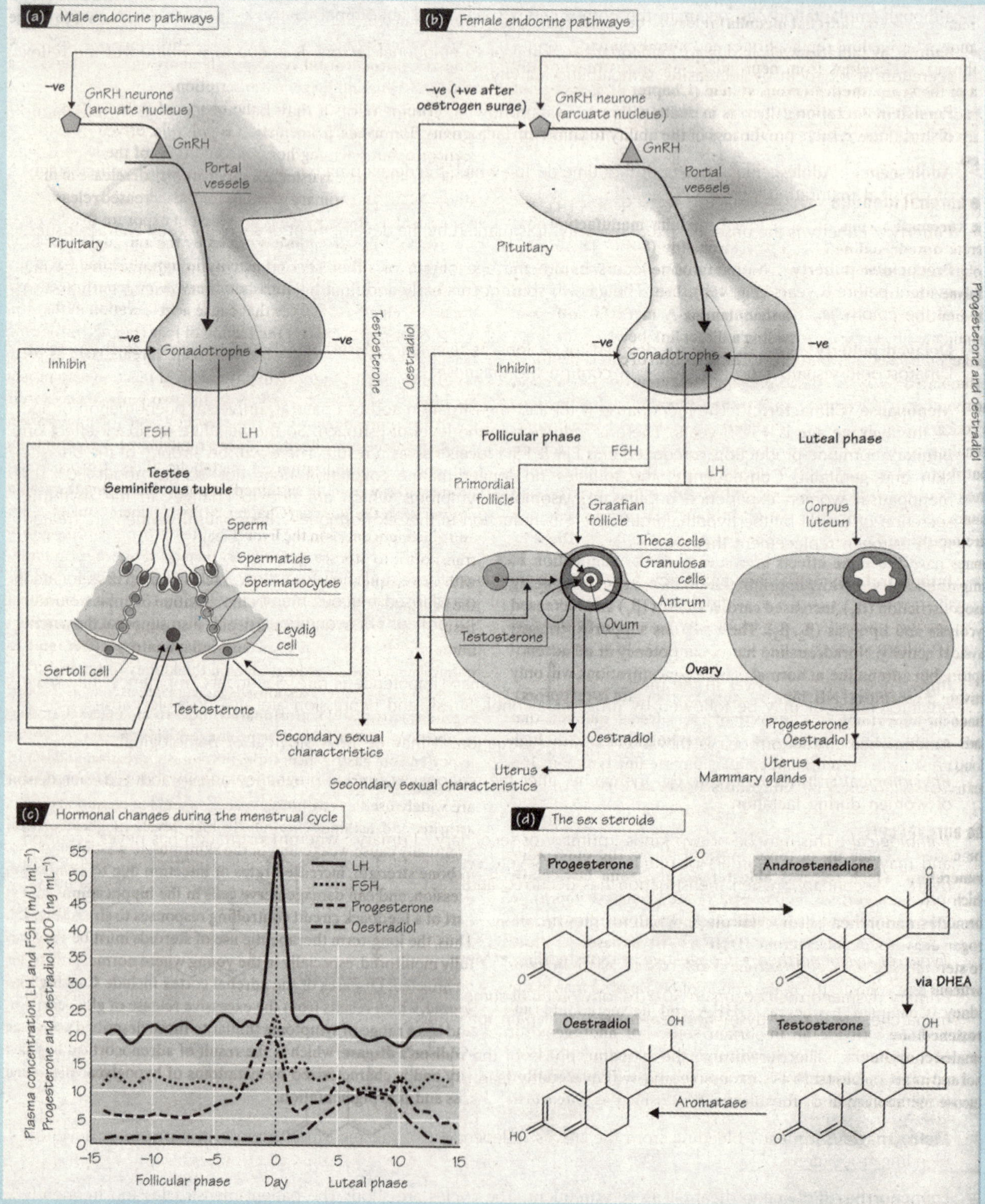

# Neurophysiology

14 July 2006 19:09:53

AGENDA :



11

## ➤ 11.1 CHAPTER OVERVIEW

**Nervous system** through sophisticated signalling acts as a control network within the body. Information about the internal and external environments are converted into action potentials by sensory receptors. **Neuron** is the structural and functional unit of the nervous system. About *20 billion neurons* are present in the human nervous system. They are linked together in motor and sensory pathways which have distinctive anatomic, biochemical and electrophysiologic properties. The **central nervous system (CNS)** receives information about the environment (both external and internal) through *sensory pathways. Motor pathways* from the cerebral cortex control the movements of skeletal muscles. The sympathetic and parasympathetic divisions of the nervous system are concerned with autonomic control of smooth muscles and glands. These two divisions together is called the **autonomic nervous system** (ANS). Sensory tracts ascend in the lateral and dorsal columns of the spinal cord, whereas motor tracts descend in the ventral column. The motor commands from the cortex are co-ordinated and refined by the basal ganglia loop system as well as by the cerebellum. The ANS has influence on the general emotional state of an individual. The cingulate cortex is the site of emotional awareness.

**Cerebellum** plays a significant role in motor control. Basal ganglia have similar role in planning and organization of voluntary movements.

Various parts of the **limbic system** have been implicated in emotional and motivational behavior. The brain stem **reticular activating system** (RAS)switches the functional status of the brain between wakefulness and sleep. **Electroencephalogram (EEG)** is the surface recording of the electrical activity of the brain that reflects the functional state of brain. The parts of the brain involved in learning and memory include the medial temporal lobe and diencephalon.

## ➤ 11.2 Organisation and Major Divisions of Nervous System

The nervous system is composed basically of cells whose function is to receive sensory stimuli and to transmit them to effector organs.

It is divided into 2 main parts : (ANATOMICALLY)

(a) Central Nervous System (C.N.S.) → Brain + Spinal cord

(b) Peripheral Nervous System (P.N.S.) → Cranial and spinal nerves and associated ganglia.

It is also divided into 2 parts on a FUNCTIONAL BASIS

(a) Somatic Nervous System : This system collects information about changes in the external environment, interprets their meaning and utilises skeletal muscles to make an appropriate response.

(b) Autonomic nervous system : This system collects information about changes in the "milieu interieur" i.e. in the internal environment and guides the action of smooth muscles, secretory epithelium and cardiac muscles in response to internal changes.

### Afferents and Efferents

These are components of the Peripheral Nervous System. The former deals with neurons carrying information from peripheral tissues to C.N.S.

### Autonomic nervous system

It has two components :

(a) **Sympathetic Nervous System**

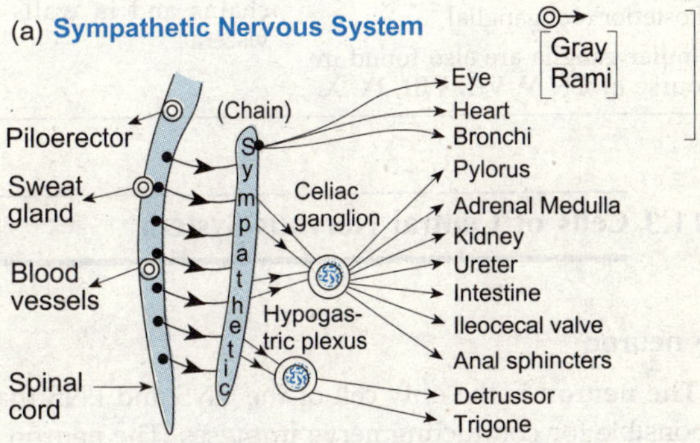


(b) **Parasympathetic Nervous System**

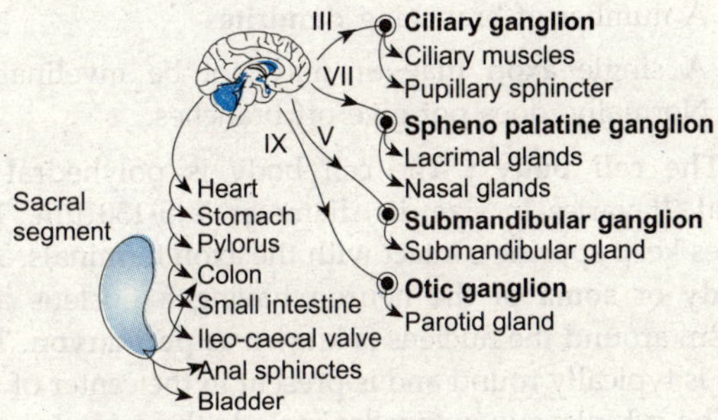

## The Brain

It lies surrounded by 3 meninges in the cranial cavity :

(i) Duramater
(ii) Arachnoid mater — From outside inwards
(iii) Piamater

**Divisions of brain**

- 1. Rhombencephalon (Hind brain)
  - Myelenecephalon (Medulla)
  - Metencephalon (Pons)
  - Cerebellum
- 2. Mesencephalon (Mid brain)
- 3. Prosencephalon (Fore brain)
  - Diencephalon (Central part of forebrain)
  - Telencephalon (Cerebrum)

**BRAIN** : (Cerebellum + Cerebral hemispheres) = Brain Stem.

**Ganglia**

| **Sensory** | **Autonomic** |
|---|---|
| There are dilatations on posterior root of each spinal nerve just proximal to the root's junction with a corresponding anterior root. [Posterior root ganglia] Similar ganglia are also found in course of CN V, VII, VIII, IX, X. | There are irregular and located along efferent fibers of ANS. e.g. in paravertebral sympathetic chains and in walls of viscera. |

## ➤ 11.3 Cells of Central Nervous System

### The neuron

**The neuron** is the only cell of the CNS and PNS that is responsible for conducting nerve impulses. The neuron has got three distinct regions :

- The **cell body** or **soma**
- A number of branching **dendrites**
- A single **axon** may or may not be myelinated. Normally, does not give off branches.

1. **The cell body :** The cell body is polyhedral or spherical. It varies in size, its diameter is 5-130 μm. The dendrites keep specific contact with the axon terminals. The **cell body** or **soma** of the neuron having a nucleus and cytoplasm around the nucleus is known as **perikaryon**. The nucleus is typically round and is present in the center of the soma. The cytoplasmic organelles include the granular and agranular endoplasmic reticulum, the Golgi bodies, mitochondria, lysosomes; multivesicular bodies,

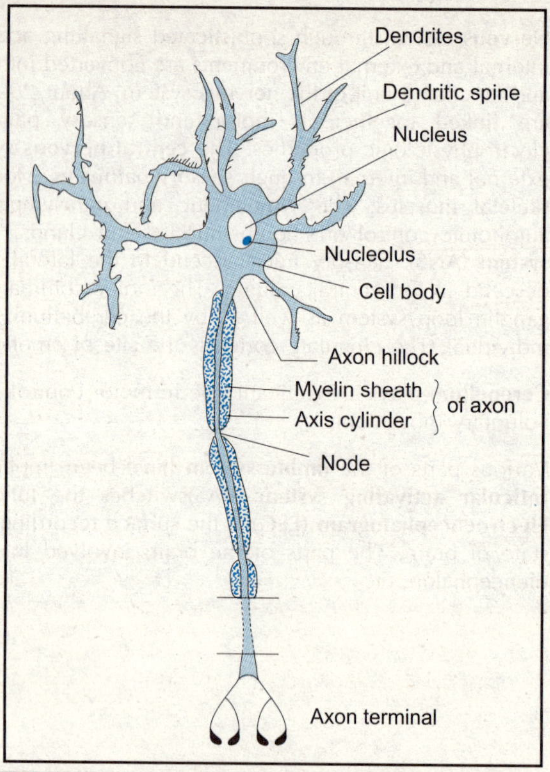


**Fig. 11.1 :** Various parts of neuron

neurofilaments, cilia and centrioles. The inclusion bodies are lipofuscin, melanin granules and glycogen particles (Fig. 11.1).

The Nissl substance looks like basophilic blocks or granules in the perikaryon. The **Golgi apparatus** was first discovered in nerve cells by Camillo Golgi. **Mitochondria** are also prominent organelles in the nerve cell and play vital role in cellular activities. **Lysosomes** are sufficiently present and are responsible for the breakdown of endogenous and exogenous cytosolic ingredients. **Microtubules** and **neurofilaments** are present in bundles and extend from the cell body to the cell processes. The yellowish-brown **lipofuscin** granules are present in all neurons. **Melanin pigment** is also present in a few cell groups.

2. **The axon :** Most of the organelles are present in the cytoplasm of the cell body. ***There is no Nissl bodies in the initial segment of axon.*** However, a small amount of free ribosomes may be present. As such, the axon is incapable of synthesizing protein. The axons may or may not be covered with myelin sheath. In myelinated axons, myelin sheath covers the axon close to the origin of the axon to a point just short of its terminal branching. But the myelin sheaths in peripheral nerve fibers are interrupted at regular intervals known as **Nodes of Ranvier**. The term *internode* is the area between two consecutive nodes of Ranvier.

***Nonmyelinated central axons*** are devoid of individual sheaths and may be isolated into groups by glial cell

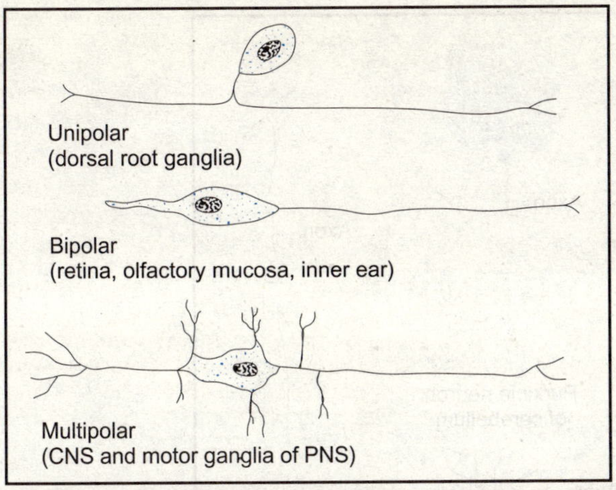


**Fig. 11.2 :** Different types of neurons

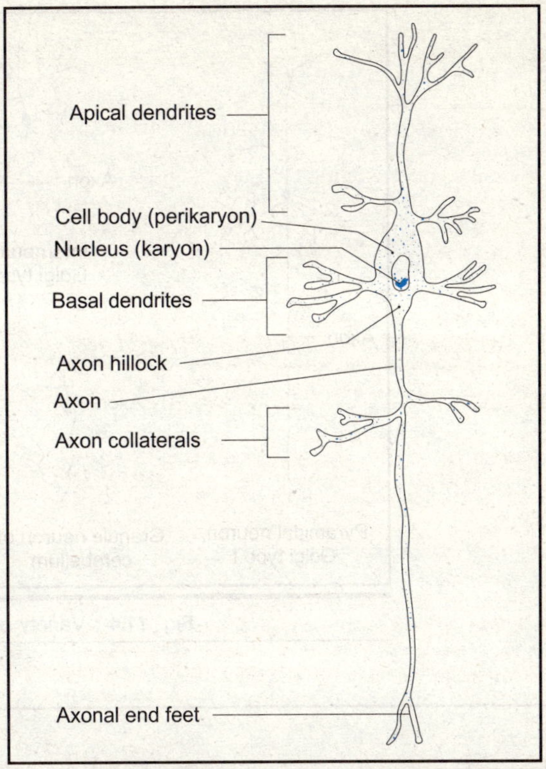


**Fig. 11.3 :** A multipolar neuron

processes but ***nonmyelinated peripheral axons*** are embedded in separate invaginations of Schwann cell surface.

**Conduction of nerve impulse :** Conduction of a nerve impulse along a nerve fiber follows a transient depolarisation of its membrane due to inflow of sodium ions and outflow of potassium ions. The influx and efflus of ions generally occur at the node of Ranvier in a myelinated fiber. This is **saltatory conduction**. It is a quicker process in contrast to continuous conduction along a nonmyelinated fiber.

**The terminal bouton** is the bulbous expansion where the axon terminates. The bouton terminal may synapse on the cell body or the process of a second neuron.

3. **Dendrites :** The organelles are less conspicuous as the dendrites are further away from the cell body. Dendrites are not myelinated.

## Classification of neurons

Morphologically, neurons are classified as unipolar, bipolar or multipolar depending mainly on the pattern of ramification of their processes. Neurons are also classified by axon length, eg, (a) Golgi type I neuron, (b) Golgi type II neuron and (c) amacrine neuron.

***Unipolar neuron*** : It contains a single myelinated trunk that divides into peripheral and central processes. The peripheral process supplies the periphery and the central process enters the central nervous system. Unipolar neurons are present in the craniospinal ganglia (Figs. 11.2 and 11.3).

***Bipolar neurons*** : They have two processes extending from the two ends of the neurons. Examples are the retinal bipolar cells; olfactory cells; vestibular and spiral ganglion cells.

***Multipolar neuron*** : Consists of several dendrites radiating from cell bodies. Most of the neurons in the central nervous system are of multipolar type.

***Golgi type-I neuron*** : It is a larger neuron with long axon. For example, the neurons extending from brain to tip of spinal cord or those extending from spinal cord to peripheral parts of limbs (lower motor neurons).

***Golgi type-II neuron*** : It is a small neuron having relatively short axon extending to its immediate vicinity (see Fig.11.4).

## Supporting cells

These are the nonexcitable cells of the nervous system and include the neuroglial cells and ependymal cells in the central nervous system. These cells line the cavities of the brain and spinal cord. Satellite or capsular cells and Schwann cells belong to this category.

***Neuroglia*** : Neuroglial cells are simply called **glial cells**. They are comprised of ***macroglia*** and ***microglia***. The **macroglia** consists of ***astrocytes*** and ***oligodendrocytes***.

***Astrocytes*** : These cells form the main supporting tissue of the central nervous system. They are star-shaped with fine branching processes. At the free ends of some of the processes, there are small swellings called **foot processes**. Astrocytes are present in large amounts close to blood vessels with their foot processes forming a sleeve round them. The processes are shorter and thicker in the protoplasmic astrocytes which are located in the gray matter. The processes of fibrous astrocytes are longer and more slender and are present in the white matter. Astrocytes may be identified from other glial cells by the presence of fibrils (see Fig.11.5).

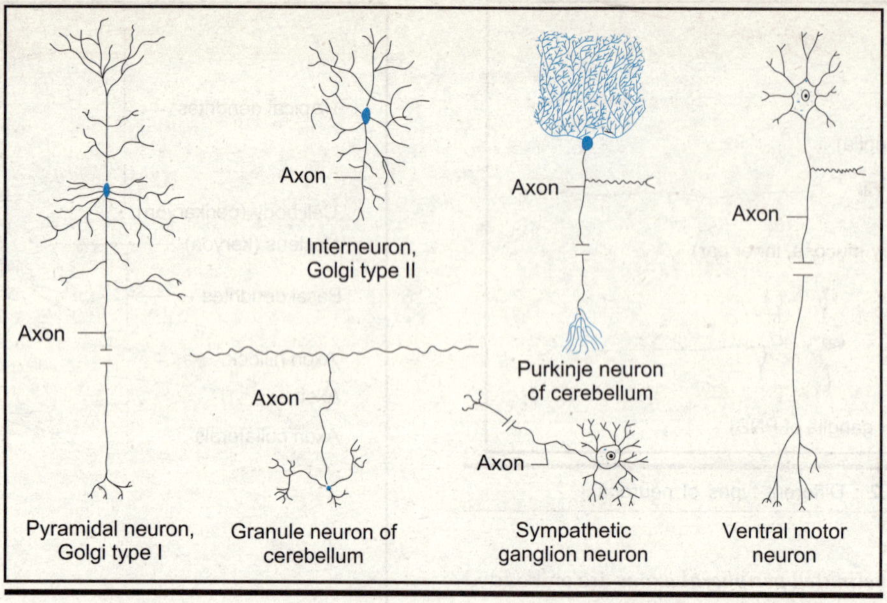


Fig. 11.4 : Variety of shapes of multipolar neurons

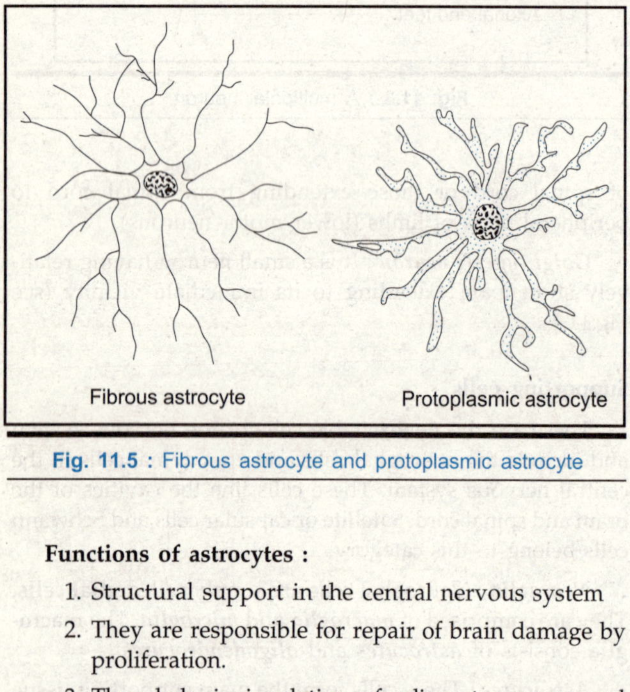


Fig. 11.5 : Fibrous astrocyte and protoplasmic astrocyte

**Functions of astrocytes :**

1. Structural support in the central nervous system
2. They are responsible for repair of brain damage by proliferation.
3. They help in insulation of adjacent neurons and maintain homeostasis of brain ISF.

## Oligodendrocytes

These cells are smaller than astrocytes. They are generally present in clusters surrounding the neuron cell bodies in the grey matter. The **oligodendrocytes** are responsible for the formation and maintenance of myelin sheath in the central nervous system and are also responsible for nutrition and maintenance of neurons in case of the perineuronal satellite cells.

## Microglia

These are the ***smallest of glial cells*** and are derived from monocytes that migrate from the blood into the nervous system. They are present particularly in the area of blood vessels. They enlarge and become phagocytic in the area of inflammation and destroy cell when activated. The microglial cells contain many lysosomes in addition to the usual organelles

## Ependymal cells

**Ependymal cells** are arranged as a single layer of columnar cells which are present around the cavities of the brain and spinal cord. The free surfaces of the ependymal cells contain numerous villi and cilia.

## Schwann cells and satellite cells

The Schwann cells surround the peripheral axons and satellite cells surround neurons in the craniospinal ganglia.

***Schwann cells*** : The cell bodies are irregular in outline, sending out sheet-like processes. **Schwann cells** are involved in myelination in PNS. They are indispensable for maintenance and proper function of the axon. They are phagocytic and play a vital role in axonal regeneration following injury.

***Satellite cells*** : They are present in the craniospinal and the autonomic ganglia which are surrounded by a single layer of flattened satellite cells. The cytoplasm of **satellite cells** is similar to that of Schwann cells. The functions of the satellite cells are not clearly understood. They are also phagocytic.

**Table 11.1 : Types of neuroglial cells**

| Type | Morphology | Functions |
|---|---|---|
| **Astrocytes** | • Star-shaped cells located between neurons and blood vessels | • Production of substances trophic to neurons and removal of compounds and ions to maintain the normal composition of brain ISF.<br>• Structural support |
| **Oligodendrocytes** | • Star-shaped<br>• Cellular processes are less in number<br>• Present in nerve fibres | • Produce nerve growth factor<br>• Myelination |
| **Microglia** | • Cell size is small<br>• Cellular processes are few<br>• Present in CNS | • Structural support<br>• Phagocytosis |
| **Ependyma** | • Cuboidal and columnar cells<br>• Present in the central canal of the spinal cord and lining of ventricles | • Structural support |

## 11.4 The Spinal Cord

The spinal cord is a roughly elongated cylindrical portion of C.N.S. extending beyond medulla oblongata at level of foramen magnum of skull and ends below (in adults) at level of lower border of first lumbar vertebra. Inside the upper 2/3 of vertebral canal it lies surrounded by 3 meninges corresponding to those of brain. It acts as a conduct for nerve tracts and as a site for neurons where synapses (of reflexes) and nerve fibres find their seat.

**Gross Anatomical Features :**

(i) Cervical and lumbar fusiform enlargements in cervical and lower thoracic cum lumbar regions respectively.

(ii) Tapering inferior end conus medullaris

(iii) Pial prolongation (filum terminale) from apex of (ii) to its attachment at posterior surface of coccyx.

(iv) Anterior median fissure in midline anteriorly.

(v) A furrow like posterior median sulcus on posterior surface.

(vi) Anterior and posterior roots which join 31 pains of spinal nerves to spinal cord.

(vii) Posterior root ganglion in each posterior nerve root.

### Gross Structure

It is composed of gray matter and white matter. The gray matter forms the core and white matter its outer covering.

**Contents :**

(i) Multipolar nerve cells and processes.

(ii) Neuroglia

(iii) Blood vessels

### A. Gray Matter

(a) **Features :** It is seen as an H shaped pillar with anterior and posterior horns or pillar joined by a thin commissure containing the central canal. A small lateral horn is seen in thoracic and lumbar regions. Size of gray matter is proportional to amount of muscles innervated at that level. Thus it is greatest in cervical and lumbar dilatations for muscles of upper and lower limbs respectively.

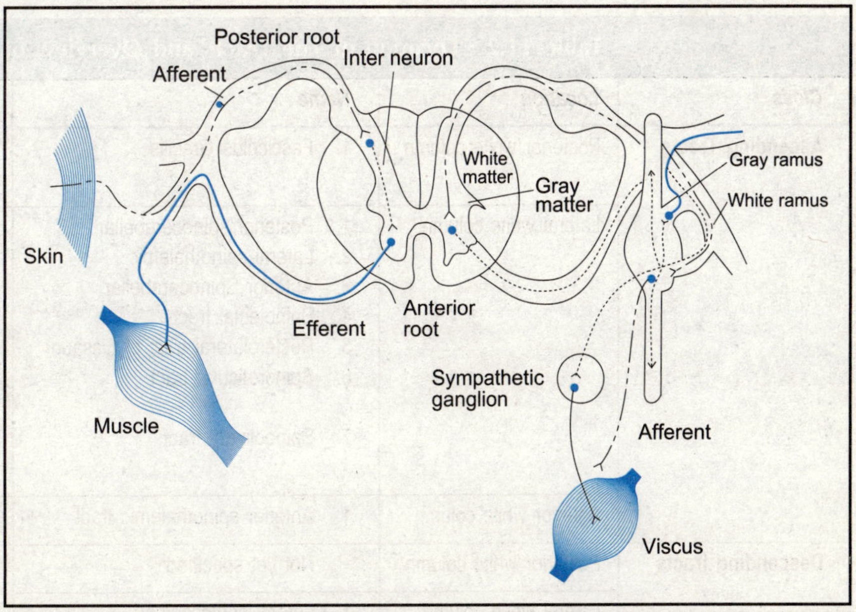


**Fig. 11.6 :** Role of spinal cord in somatic nervous system and ANS

(i) **Anterior gray column :** The axons of multipolar cells form α or γ efferents.

| *Medial Group* | *Central group* | *Lateral Group* |
|---|---|---|
| Innervate muscles of neck and trunk. | ($C_{3,4,5}$) Phrenic nucleus<br>Accessory nucleus ($C_{1-6}$) lumbosacral nucleus ($L_2 \rightarrow S_1$) | In cervical and lumbosacral regions and innervates the limbs. |

- The phrenic nucleus innervates the diaphragm.
- The accessory nucleus innervates sternocleido mastoid and trapezius.
- Supply of Lumbosacral nucleus is unknown.

(ii) Nerve cell groups in **Posterior gray column :**

| *Substantia Gelatinosa group [Most segments]* | *Nucleus proprius group [Most segments] (Main bulk)* | *Nucleus dorsalis (Clark's column) [$C_8$ to $L_4$]* | *Visceral afferent nucleus group [$T_1$ to $L_3$]* |
|---|---|---|---|
| Receives afferents conveying (i) Pain (ii) Temperature (iii) Touch (iv) Supraspinal descending fibres | Receives fibres from posterior white column that are associated with the senses of proprioception, two point discrimination and vibration. | Associated with proprioceptive endings. | Associated with visceral afferents. |

(iii) **Nerve cell groups in lateral column :** Comprised of intermediolateral cells in $T_1$ to $L_2$ or $L_3$. These give rise to preganglionic sympathetic fibres.

$S_{2,3,4}$ segments comprises of neurons which give rise to pre-ganglionic parasympathetic fibres.

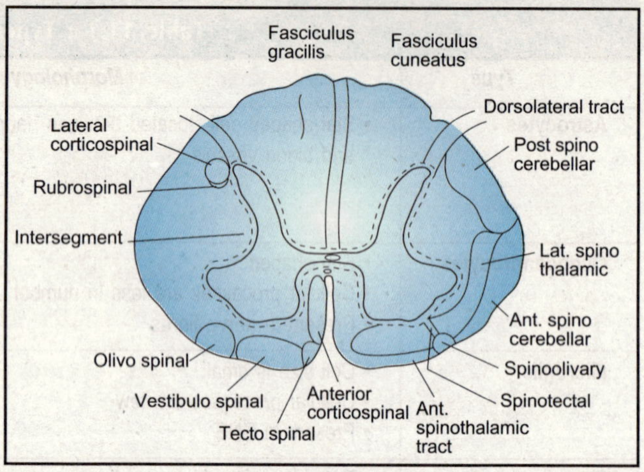


**Fig. 11.7 : General arrangement of tracts**

### B. White Matter

It is divisible into anterior, lateral and posterior white funiculi or columns.

It is comprised of nervefibres, neuroglia and blood vessels and the white color is due to high percentage of myelinated nerve processes.

**Arrangement of Nerve Fibre Tracts :** Three classes of tracts exist in white matter of spinal cord :

(i) Ascending tracts.

(ii) Descending tracts.

(iv) Intersegmental tracts.

**Table 11.2 : Location of The Tracts and Overview of their Functions**

| *Class* | *Location* | *Name* | *Role* |
|---|---|---|---|
| **Ascending Tracts** | Posterior white column | 1. Fasciculus Gracilis | Proprioceptive sensibility, vibration, tactile discrimination. |
| | Lateral white column | 1. Posterior spinocerebellar | Proprioception, touch, pressure. |
| | | 2. Lateral spinothalamic | Pain and temperature. |
| | | 3. Anterior Spinocerebellar | Proprioception, touch, pressure. |
| | | 4. Spinotectal tract | Spinovisual reflexes. |
| | | 5. Posterolateral tract of Lissauer | Involved in pathway of spinothalamic tracts. |
| | | 6. Spinoreticular tract | Afferent pathway for reticular formation which has role in 'consciousness' |
| | | 7. Spinoolivary tract | Conveys information from cutaneous and proprioceptive organs. |
| | Anterior white column | 1. Anterior spinothalamic tract | Tactile and pressure sensibilities. |
| **Descending tracts** | Posterior white column | Not yet specified | — |
| | Lateral white column | 1. Lateral corticospinal | Voluntary motor activity |
| | | 2. Rubrospinal | Muscular activity |

| Class | Location | Name | Role |
|---|---|---|---|
| | | 3. Lateral reticulospinal<br>4. Descending autonomic<br>5. Olivospinal tract | Muscular activity<br>Control of visceral functions<br>Muscular activity. |
| | Anterior white column | 1. Anterior corticospinal<br>2. Vestibulospinal<br>3. Tectospinal<br>4. Reticulospinal | Voluntary movements.<br>Equilibrium and muscle tone.<br>Reflex response to visual cues.<br>Motor function. |
| **Intersegmental Tracts** | Posterior white column | Posterior intersegmental tract | Intersegmental spinal reflexes. |
| | Lateral white column | Lateral intersegmental tract | Intersegmental + some descending tract fibres. |
| | Anterior white column | Anterior intersegmental tract | Intersegmental reflexes. |

## Meninges of Spinal cord

(From outside inwards)

(a) Dura mater : (i) Dense (ii) Strong (iii) Fibrous membrane.

(The extra dural space contains loose areolar tissue and internal vertebral venous plexus)

(b) Arachnoid mater : (i) Delicate (ii) Impermeable membrane.

(Subarachnoid space contains C.S.F. and strands of connective tissue.)

(c) Pia mater : (i) Thin (ii) Highly vascular membrane.

(Thickened on either side between anterior and posterior nerve roots to form ligamentum denticulatum)

## Blood Supply (an over view)

**Arteries : Three arteries** provide the bulk of blood supply :

(i) 2 posterior spinal arteries

(ii) 1 anterior spinal artery.

These are reinforced by segmental arteries entering through intervertebral formina.

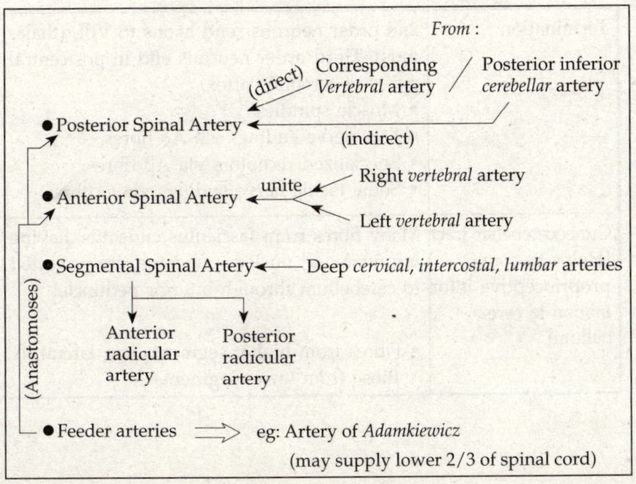


## Veins

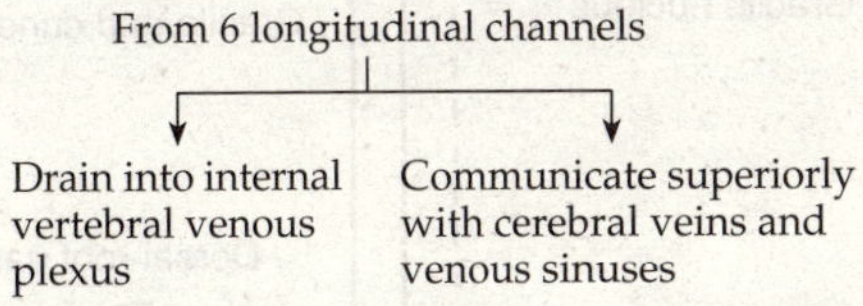


## The ascending tracts

The spinothalamic tracts (Important features)

| *(a) Lateral STT* | *Lateral STT* | *Anterior STT* |
|---|---|---|
| Receptors : | Free nerve endings | Various |
| Sensations : | Pain, temperature | Crude touch, pressure |
| Nerve fibres : | Aδ, C | Aβ,C |
| Neurotransmitter at synapse in spinal cord | Substance P | Not known |
| Arrangement of fibres | Higher fibres are added anteromedially | Higher fibres are added medially. |
| Role of thalamus | Crude interpretation and relay centre | |
| Role of cerebral cortex | Conscious appreciation | |
| Other terminations | Reticular nuclei | Insignificant |
| Location of 2nd order neuron (i.e. first synapse) | Cells of posterior gray horn including. Substantia gelatinosa. | |

The axons entering spinal cord from dorsal ganglion proceeds to tip of posterior gray horn and divides into ascending and descending branches for one or two segments forming tract of Lissauer.

**Spinotectal tract :** Helps to bring about movements of eyes and heads towards source of visual stimulation via SPINO VISUAL REFLEXES.

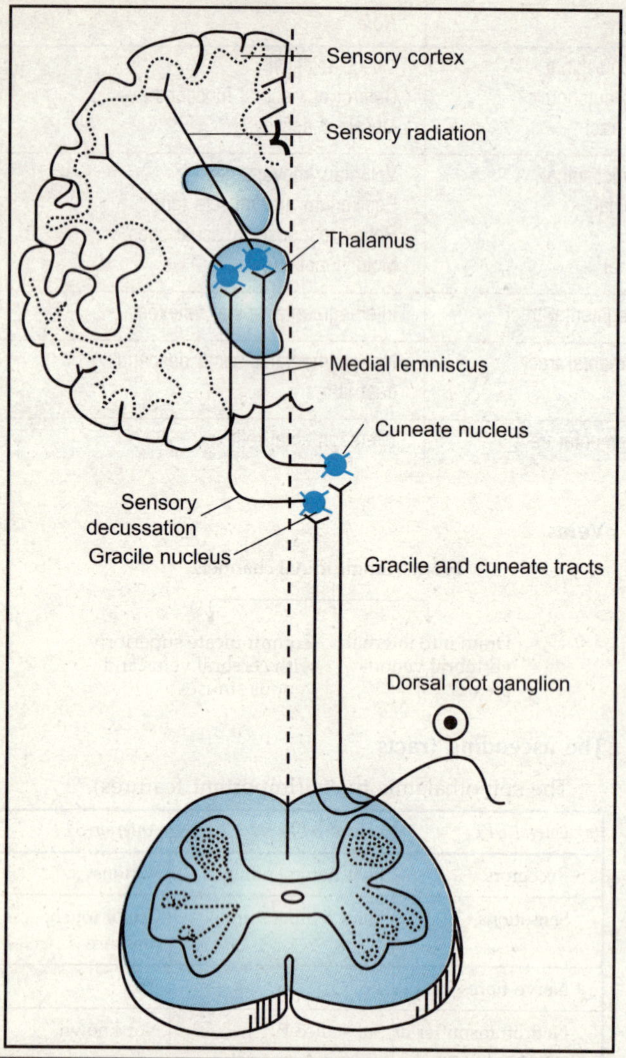


Fig. 11.8 : Scheme of posterior column pathway

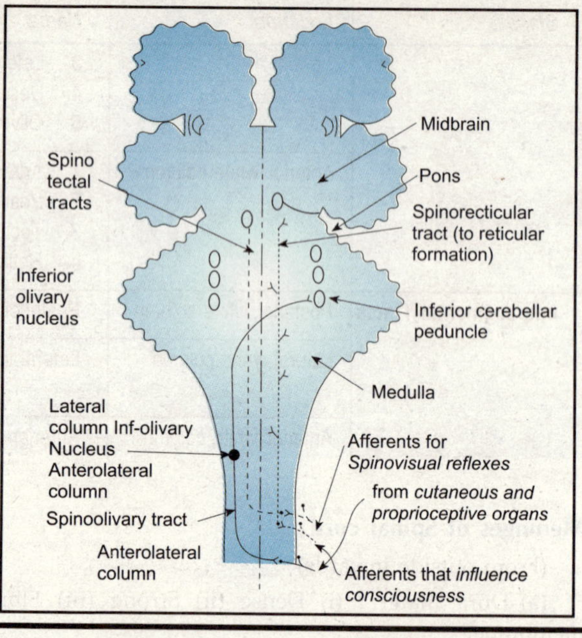


Fig. 11.9 : Spinoreticular tract

**Spinoolivary tract :** Conveys cutaneous and proprioceptor information to cerebellum.

**Spinoreticular tract :** Helps the afferents to influence consciousness.

- The fibres of spinotectal and spinothalamic tracts while ascending through medulla oblongata, form the **spinal lemniscus**.
- Fibres carrying pain are slightly anterior to those carrying temperature sensation.
- The fibres carrying pain cross closest to midline to the opposite side at almost the same segment as that of the site of the second order neuron. The temperature and crude touch fibres cross further away from midline at higher segments in that order respectively.

| | *Fasciculus Cuneatus* | *Fasciculus Gracilis* |
|---|---|---|
| Sensations : | Fine touch, tactile discrimination, vibratory sense, conscious muscle joint sense. | |
| Second order Neurons : | Nucleus (inmedulla) cuneatus. | Nucleus gracilis. |
| Role in intersegmental reflexes : | The axons from posterior root ganglia divide into ascending and descending branches some of which synapse with posterior horn cells interneurons and anterior horn cells. | |
| Location | Upper thoracic and cervical segments. | Throughout spinal cord. |
| Formation of Medial lemniscus | Axons of 2nd order neurons sweep around midline and 3rd order neuron processes form sensory decussation and ascend as **medial lemniscus** through brain stem. | |
| Termination : | 2nd order neurons send axons to VPL (thalamus). Third order neurons end in postcentral gyrus of cerebral cortex.<br>• Muscle spindles.<br>• Free nerve endings via Aδ fibres.<br>• Specialized receptors via Aβ fibres.<br>• Some tactile nerve endings via C fibres. | |
| Cuneocerebellar tract [Helps to convey proprioceptive information to cerebellum] | Many fibres from fasciculus cuneatus, having terminated at nucleus cuneatus, are projected to cerebellum through inferior peduncle.<br>• Fibres from higher segments join lateral to those from lower segments. | |

## The Spinocerebellar tracts

**Features :**

| *Property* | *Posterior (Dorsal)* | *Anterior (Ventral)* |
|---|---|---|
| Impulses for | Muscle joint information | Muscle joint information |
| Receptors | Muscle spindles, tendon organ, joint receptors. | |
| Location of 2nd order neurons | Nucleus dorsalis of posterior gray column | |
| Arrangement of fibres | Shown in the figure. | |
| Termination of the tract | The tract joins the inferior cerebellar peduncle at level of medulla and terminates into cerebellar cortex on same side. | Fibres enter cerebellum through superior peduncle. Those fibres that crossed the midline cross back with in cerebellum. |

**Spinocerebellar Tracts :**

- The nucleus dorsalis extends from segments $C_8$ to $L_4$ of spinal cord.
- The information carried by these tracts is used by cerebellum in coordination of limb movements and maintenance of muscle tone.
- Probably, the anterior spinocerebellar tract also sends information from skin and superficial fascia to cerebellum.

## Descending Tracts

The **corticospinal tracts** form **pyramidal tract system**. The **extrapyramidal tracts** are :

(a) Rubrospinal tract

(b) Lateral and medial vestibulospinal tracts.

(c) Reticulospinal tract

(d) Olivospinal tract

(e) Tectospinal tract

(f) Interstitiospinal tract.

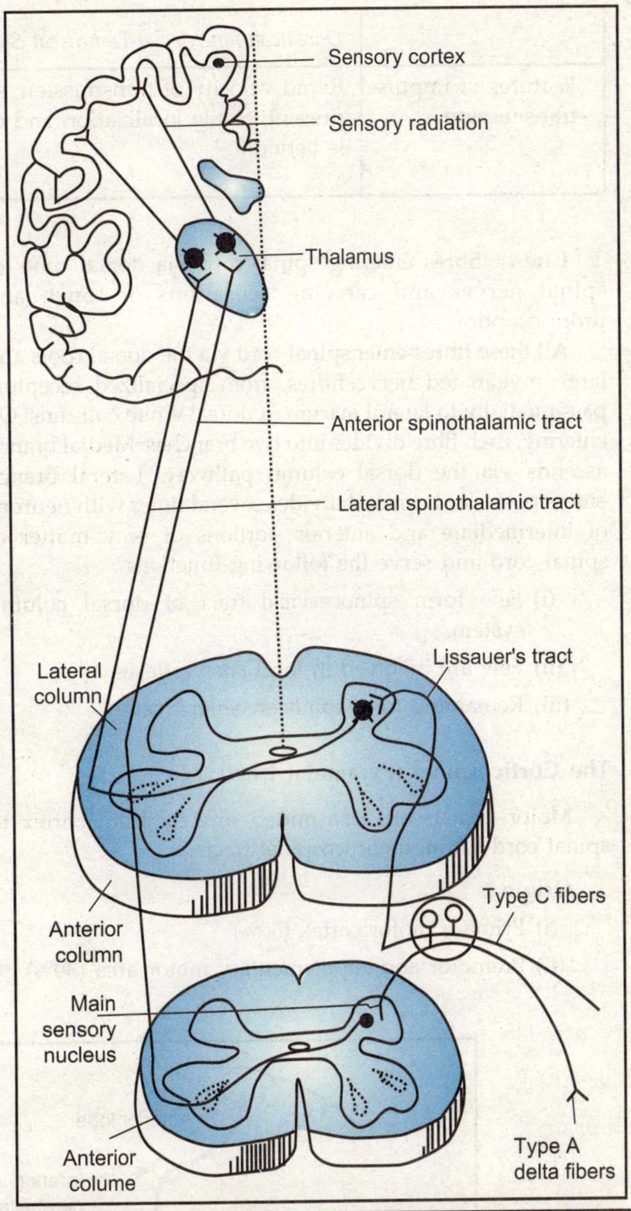


**Fig. 11.10 : Spinothalamic pathways**

**Features of Anterolateral Pathway and Dorsal Column-Medial Lemniscal System.**

| | *Dorsalcolumn-Medial-Lemniscal System.* | *Anterolateral System* |
|---|---|---|
| Components | Fasciculi cuneatus, gracili. | Spinothalamic tracts; spinoreticular and spinotectal tracts. |
| Functions | Carries sensation of fine touch, vibration and proprioception. Helps as detecting rapidly changing peripheral conditions and intensity of stimulus over a wide range. | Carries sensation of crude touch, pain, heat, cold, tickle, itch etc. |
| Effect of damage | Sensory ataxia (on closing the eyes) and loss of fine touch, tactile discrimination and vibration sense on affected side. | Loss of sensitivity to pain and temperature etc. e.g. in tabesdorsalis or syringomyelia. |

| | *Dorsalcolumn-Medial-Lemniscal System.* | *Anterolateral System* |
|---|---|---|
| Features of impulse transmission | Rapid velocity of transmission; spatial organization present; tactile localization and discrimination is better. | Velocity of transmission is 1/3 of dorsal column system. Spatial organization is poor. Gradations of intensities judged is far less accurate. |

Fate of fibres entering spinal cord via dorsal roots of spinal nerves and carrying sensations of touch and proprioception :

All these fibres enter spinal cord via the dorsal roots and large myelinated nerve fibres, from specialized receptors pass medially to lateral margin of dorsal white columns. On entering, each fibre divides into two branches. Medial branch ascends via the dorsal column pathway. Lateral branch enters posterior horn and divides several times with neurons of intermediate and anterior portions of gray matter of spinal cord and serve the following functions :

(i) Few form spinocervical tract of dorsal column system.

(ii) Few are involved in local cord reflexes.

(iii) Remaining form spinocerebellar tracts.

## The Corticospinal (Pyramidal tract)

Motor signals are transmitted directly from cortex to spinal cord through corticospinal tracts.

**Origin :**

(i) Primary motor cortex (30%)

(ii) Premotor and supplementary motor area (30%)

(ii) Somatic sensory area (40%)

**Course of Tract :** After leaving the cortex, fibers passes through the posterior limb of internal capsule and then through the brain stem. Most of the fibres cross the midline and descend in **lateral corticospinal tract** (at level of Medulla). Rest of the fibres do not cross and descend as **anterior corticospinal tract**.

**Termination :** The anterior corticospinal tract eventually cross midline and terminate in the anterior gray column of the cervical and upper thoracic region. The lateral corticospinal tract ends on all cord segments' anterior horn. (Type of Fibres : 3% are large, myelinated. 97% are of diameter less than 4 micron.)

Fibres end mostly on interneurons of intermediate gray matter or cells of dorsal and anterior horn.

**Other Branches :**

(i) Branches to cortex to inhibit activity of adjacent regions.

(ii) Branches to caudate, lentiform, red, olivary and reticular nuclei.

**Functions :** It causes initiation of movements by cortex. Mostly distal muscles are influenced for movements requiring precision.

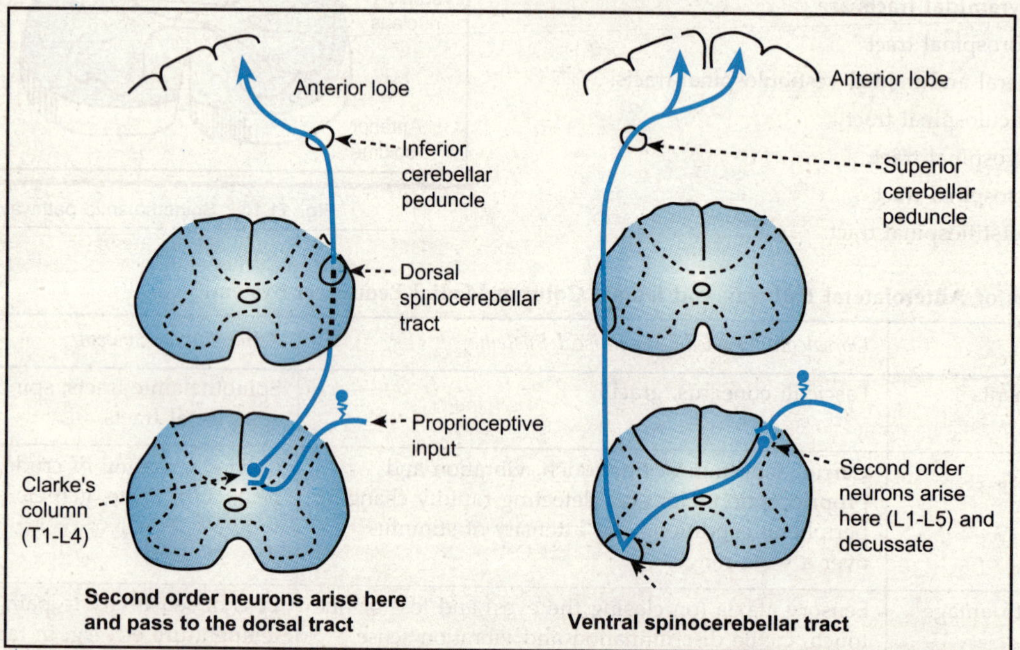


**Fig. 11.11 :** The cerebellar peduncles

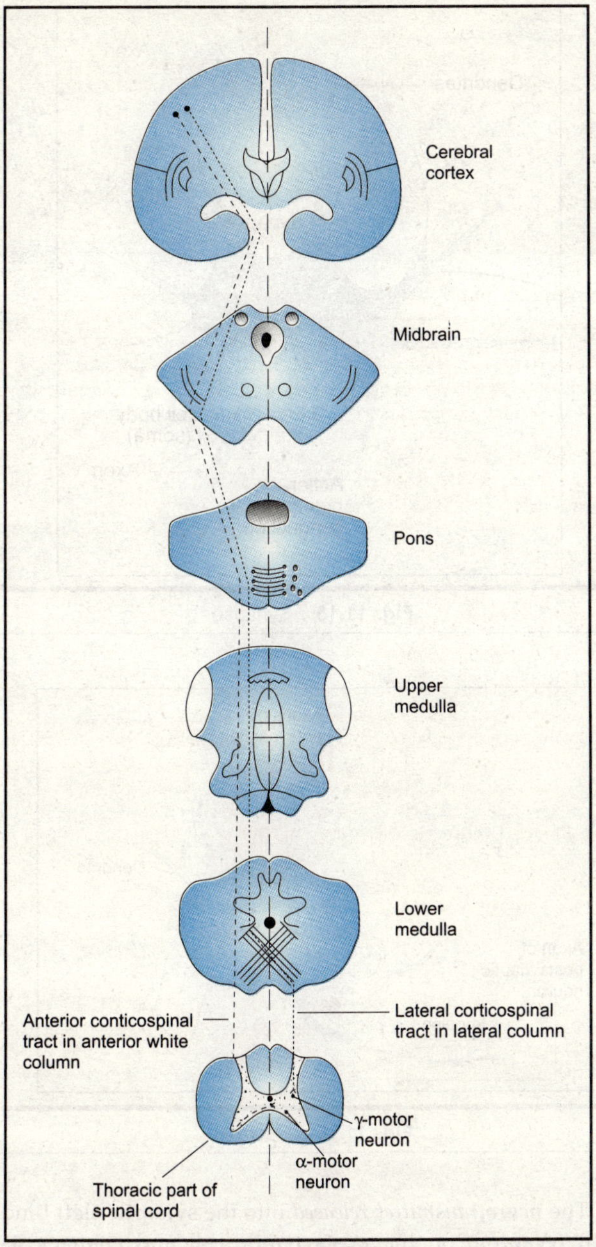


Fig. 11.12 : Corticospinal tract

**Effect of Lesion :** Major effect is weakness and loss of precise movements especially of distal parts of limbs; Babinski sign, etc.

## Extrapyramidal Tracts

**Rubrospinal Tract :** The red nucleus receives direct fibres from cerebellum and primary motor cortex through the pyramidal tract and its branches which synapse at magnocellular nucleus which has large neurons and give rise to the rubrospinal tract which crosses the midline in lower part of brain stem and descends similar to pyramidal tract.

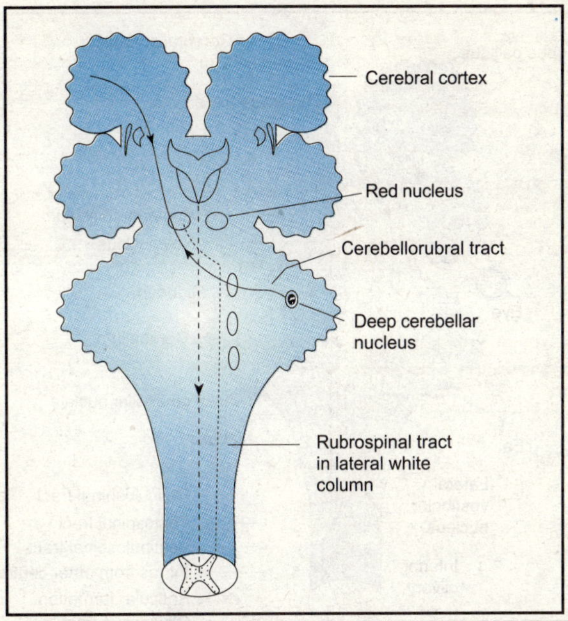


Fig. 11.13 : Rubrospinal tract

Fibres end on interneurons.

Along with pyramidal tract helps in precision movements.

**Reticulospinal Tracts :** This originates from the reticular formation. The arrangement of fibres is shown. The pontine reticulospinal tract is mainly uncrossed but just before termination, crosses midline and ends on interneurons. Medullary reticulospinal fibres descend both in ipsilateral and contralateral manner and ends on motor neurons.

**Pontine :** Excitatory to motor neurons of proximal extensors.

**Medullary :** Inhibitory to proximal limb motor neurons.

**Vestibulospinal Tract :** These excite antigravity muscles.

These are two parts. (i) Lateral and (ii) Medial

**Lateral :** Originates from lateral vestibular nuclei and does not cross. Ends on extensor motor neurons of proximal postural muscles. Vestibular nuclei receives afferents from vestibular apparates and this tracts helps in adjustment of postural muscle

**Medial :** Originates from the inferior part of vestibular nucleus to receives afferents from the semicircular canal.

**Tectospinal Tract :** Fibres arise from superior colliculus and cross the midline. This mediates visually guidedhead movements.

**Olivospinal Tract :** Originates from the inferior olivary nucleus. Descends and terminates on anterior horn cells to influence motor activity.

**Interstitiospinal Tract** mediates movement of head and body about a longitudinal axis and originates from interstitial nucleus of Cajal in rostral midbrain. Descends without crossing.

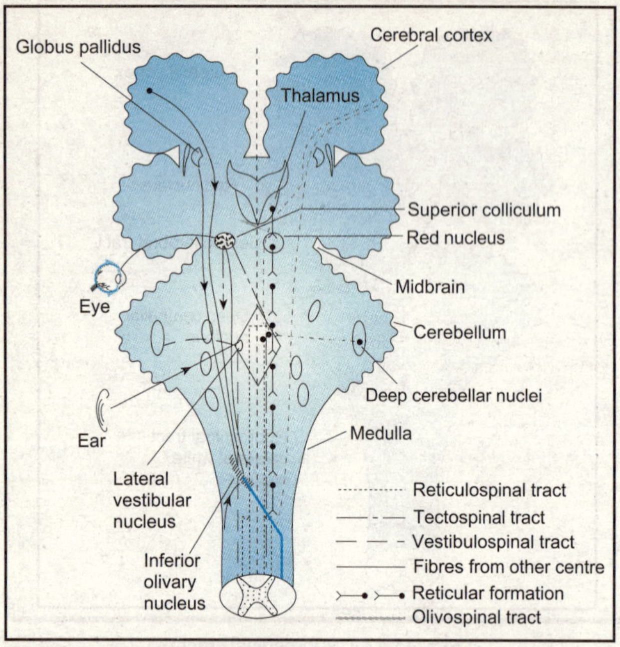


Fig. 11.14 : Extrapyramidal tracts

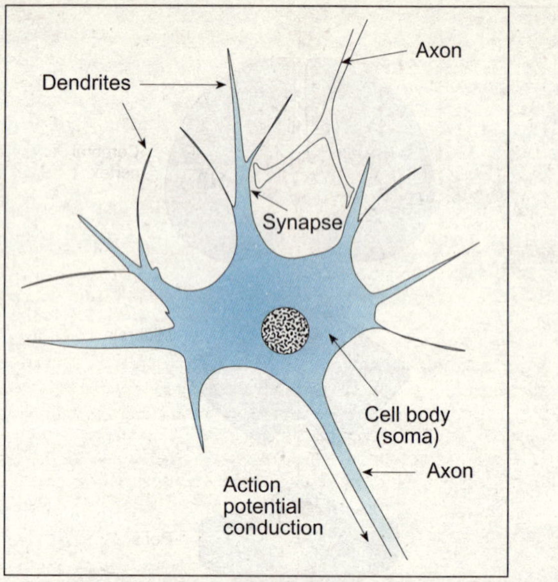


Fig. 11.15 : Synapse

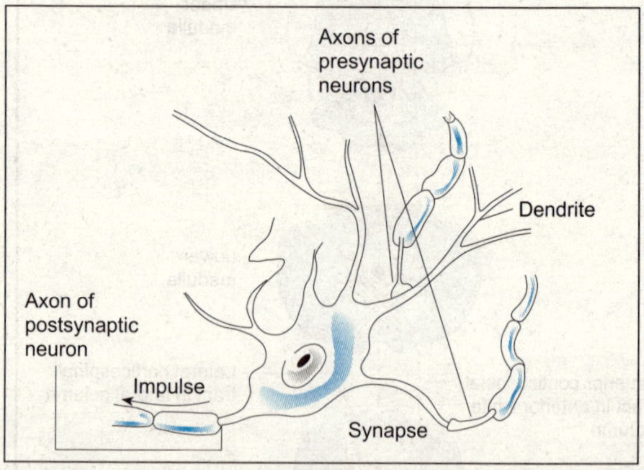


Fig. 11.16 : Neurone

## ➤ 11.5 Mechanism of Synaptic Transmission, EPSP, IPSP

**Synapse** (Gr. *synapsis*, point of contact) (Fig. 11.15&11.16) is the junction between two nerve cells. The axon of a presynaptic neuron may form single or multiple (via branches) synapses to contact one or more postsynaptic neurons. Barring a few exceptions where the transmission is electrical via gap jun-ctions, the mode of transmission is chemical. In a few conjoint synapses both types of transmission take place. There are a good number of **neurotransmitters**; *acetylcholine, catechola-mines, serotonin, glycine,* and *substance P are a few among them.*

According to their site of termination, the synapses may be *axosomatic, axodendritic* and *axoaxonic* types. The axon of a presynaptic neuron branches into axon telodendria, ends of which enlarge to form **terminal boutons** or **synaptic knobs**. The synaptic knobs abut against the dendrite spines, body or axon of the postsynaptic neuron, there is no gap junction or cytoplasmic continuity between the two. There remains a space of 30-50 nm width (**synaptic cleft**) separating the two.

With the help of an electron microscope the synaptic knob is shown to contain membrane-limited vesicles or granules containing neurotransmitters close to synaptic cleft besides numerous mitochondria. The granules differ morphologically according to their contents.

When a action potential reaches the synaptic knob of the presynaptic neuron voltage-gated $Ca^{2+}$-channels open and $Ca^{2+}$ causes fusion of granules with the cell membrane and exocytosis of granule contents into the synaptic cleft.

The *neurotransmitter released* into the synaptic cleft bind with receptors on the postsynaptic cell and changes its potential to have *physiologic effects*, either *stimulation* or *inhibition*. Receptors are specific in that they bind with particular ligand, but the same ligand may bind to a family of receptors to have different functions, eg, acetylcholine has nicotinic and muscarinic receptors. In some cases, there may be also subgroups of receptor types eg, $\alpha_1$, $\alpha_2$ and $\beta_1$, $\beta_2$ adrenergic receptors (Fig. 11.17 & 11.18).

The morphology of the synapses vary at different sites. Climbing fibers of cerebellar cortex interwine with dendrites of postsynaptic cells or basket cells of the same area have a network or basket formed by branches of presynaptic cells. Number of synapses received by a particular neuron vary widely. A spinal motor neuron may bear about ten thousand synapses converging on it.

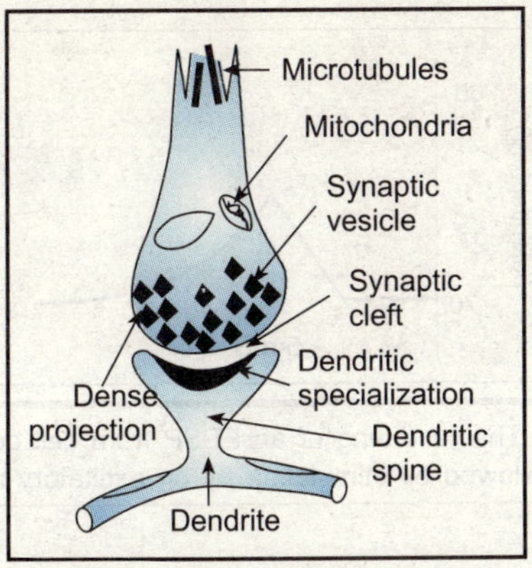


**Fig. 11.17 :** Basic features of a synapse

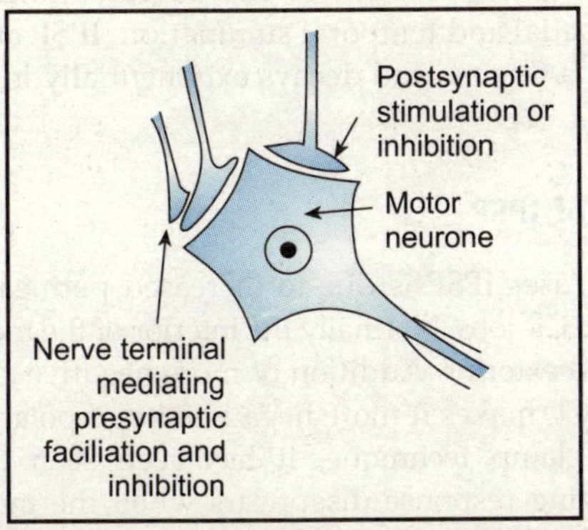


**Fig. 11.18 :** Arrangement for presynaptic stimulation or inhibition

A synapse is formed by the junction of a presynaptic neuron with a postsynaptic neuron, but the presynaptic neuron may receive a third neuron close to the former synapse and the neurotransmitter released from the third neuron may facilitate or inhibit neurotransmitter discharge from the presynaptic neuron and, in this way, can secondarily stimulate or suppress the post-synaptic cell. This mode of influencing synaptic transmission is called **presynaptic inhibition or facilitation (Fig. 11.19).**

## EPSP

When an impulse is carried by a presynaptic neuron, there is release of neurotransmitter that affects the postsynaptic cell, but some time is required for the release and effect of the chemical on the postsynaptic cell **synaptic delay** (less than one millisecond). But the binding of neurotransmitter to postsynaptic cell does not mean development of action potential in it but there is transient localized depolarization of the membrane, which reaches its peak within 2 ms and then decays exponentially. This transient depolarization which is localized, non-propagated, but is the forerunner of action potential of postsynaptic neuron by means of spatial or temporal summation is called **excitatory postsynaptic potential (EPSP)** (Fig. 11.20).

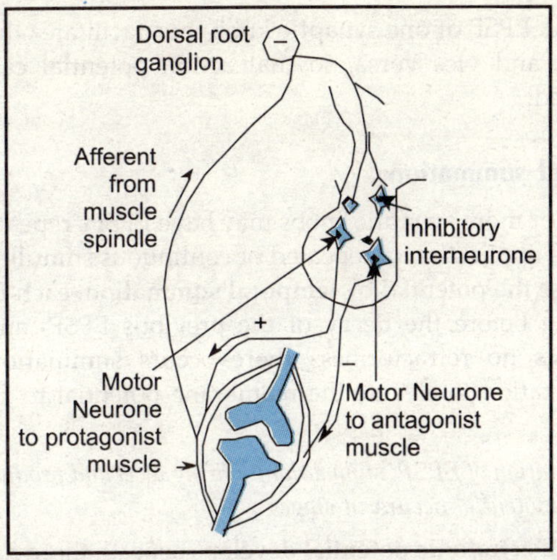


**Fig. 11.19 :** Illustration of simultaneous stimulation and inhibition

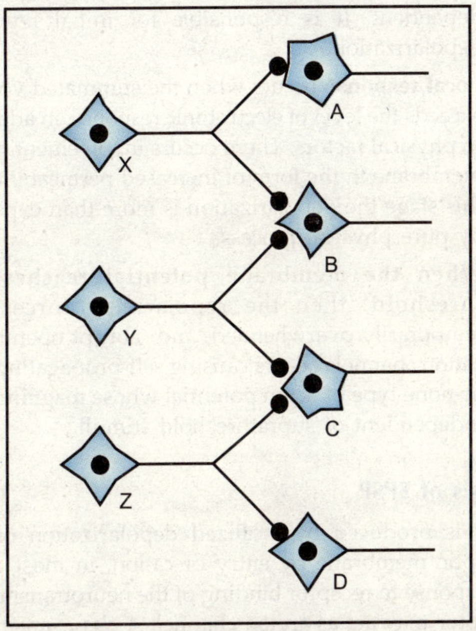


**Fig. 11.20**

(1) **X or Y or Z stimulated EPSP in** A, B or B, C or C.D. (2) When X, Y stimulated simultaneously, B will fire by spatial summation and A,C with partial depolarization will be in subliminal fringe of B. (3) When X is stimulated repeatedly A & B will fire (temporal summation), but C will not be influenced and retrograde transmission via Y is not possible. (4) When X, Y, Z fire repeatedly at a time, combined tempo-ral and spatial summation discharge A, B, C, D — 4 neurons — less than 6 neurons if stimulation of two neurons each, in case of X, Y, Z considered separately. X & Y shared B; Y & Z shared C. This is occlusion.

## Spatial summation

The magnitude of potential under one synaptic knob is subthreshold. But when multiple synaptic knobs ending on a particular neuron activate it one at a time, there is addition or summation of EPSP of all of them, lifting the potential to threshold value, generating propagated action potential. EPSP of one synaptic knob thus facilitates that of another, and vice versa, so that action potential can be generated.

### Temporal summation

One or more synaptic knobs may have EPSPs repeatedly owing to application of repeated or continuous stimuli. This may raise the potential by **temporal summation**, each EPSP occurring before the decay of the previous EPSP, and as EPSP has no refractoriness there occurs summation of depolarization to elevate the membrane potential to firing level.

*Generation of EPSP, summation to firing level and production of action potential occurs in stages :*

(a) **Electrotonic potential** develops beneath the synaptic knob upon stimulation. It is a purely physical process, magnitude depends upon capacitance and conductivity of the membrane and is dose-dependent. It is responsible for initial few mV depolarization.

(b) **Local response** occurs when the summated voltage exceeds the level of electrotonic response, in addition to physical factors. There occurs involvement of the membrane in the form of increased permeability. In this stage the depolarization is more than expected by pure physical process.

(c) **When the membrane potential reaches the threshold,** then the repolarizing forces get temporarily overwhelmed, and abrupt opening of cation channels occurs causing self-propagating, all-or-none type of acton potential whose magnitude is independent of suprathreshold stimuli.

### Ionic basis of EPSP

**EPSP** is produced by localized depolarization of the postsynaptic membrane by entry of cation, in most cases $Na^+$ in response to receptor binding of the neurotransmitter. The receptor may act as an ion-channel. *A classic example is the nicotinic receptor of acetylcholine* which increases $Na^+$ permeability when it binds to the receptor. The amount of $Na^+$ ion entering through a synaptic knob at one time is small but, on summation, spatial or temporal, the depolarization becomes sufficient to attain the firing level.

**EPSP** may be due to diminished permeability to $K^+$. If a nerve membrane is made less permeable to $K^+$ ion during stimulation, depolarization occurs and, on summation, the depolarization may attain firing level generating action potential.

### IPSP

In contrast to EPSP, in some synapses the neurotransmitter released binds to its receptors to cause hyperpolarization and the firing level is brought farther from the then membrane potential — stimulus threshold increases. This response (hyperpolarization), which

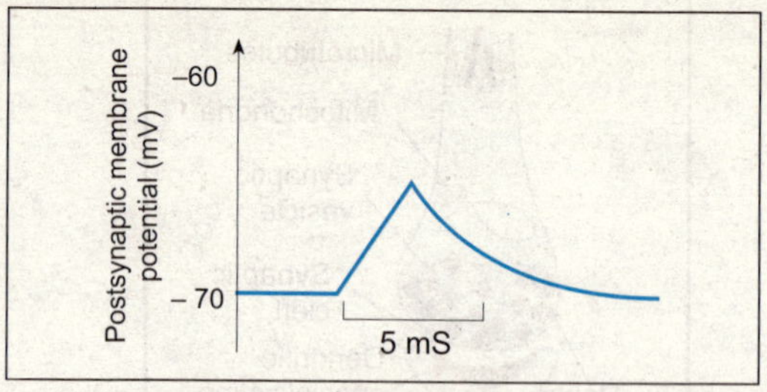


**Fig. 11.21 :** The recording of an EPSP from cell body of a neuron followed by stimulation by an excitatory nerve

diminishes the excitability of a neuron, is called **inhibitory postsynaptic potential**. The magnitude of IPSP is dependent on the strength of the stimulus and is also subject to spatial and temporal summation. IPSP attains its peak within a few ms and decays exponentially in another few ms.

### Ionic basis of IPSP

In most cases IPSP is due to increased permeability of membrane to $Cl^-$ ions. Normally the interior of the membrane is negative to exterior. Addition of more negative charge in the form of $Cl^-$ makes it more negative (hyperpolarization). By voltage clamp technique, it has been seen that this hyperpolarizing response disappears when the membrane potential is fixed at equilibrium potential of $Cl^-$, proving the role of this ion in IPSP. Repolarization is favored by increased $Cl^-$ permeability. Depolarizing stimuli must be bigger than normal.

Closure of $Na^+$ and $Ca^{2+}$ channels may increase the negativity of membrane potential and IPSP is also produced in this way by some neurotransmitters.

### Examples of EPSP and IPSP (Fig. 11.21)

The neural circuitry of stretch reflex involving spinal cord provides example of EPSP at the synapses formed by the afferent neuron and anterior horn cells of the protagonist muscle and IPSP at the junction between the interneuron (Golgi bottle neuron) and the anterior horn cell sending axon to the antagonist muscle.

### Presynaptic inhibition and facilitation

The axo-axonic synapse in case of *presynaptic inhibition release* some neurotransmitters eg, *GABA* (Gamma amino-butyric acid) which increases $Cl^-$ conductance in the pre-synaptic neuron, by which it reduces the size of action potential of the neuron, lessening entry of $Ca^{2+}$ via voltage gated channels and reducing transmitter secretion. The neurotransmitter may itself inhibit $Ca^{2+}$ channel in the presynaptic neuron, hindering its entry when action potential reaches it and thus diminishes neurotransmitter secretion.

In presynaptic facilitation the neurotransmitter will increase the duration of action potential in the presynaptic neuron, so the voltagegated $Ca^{2+}$ channels can remain open for a prolonged period, liberating more neurotransmitter by exocytosis from the presynaptic neuron. In this way the postsynaptic neuron can get prolonged exposure to the chemical stimulating it. In the sea snail aplysia, serotonin released at axo-axonic synapse has its effect via G-protein, adenylate cyclase, cyclic AMP, protein kinase A – phosphorylation and inactivation of $K^+$ channels in presynaptic knob – prolonging its action potential – increasing $Ca^{2+}$ influx and enhancing neurotransmitter release.

Descending pathways from higher level of CNS may end on the afferent neurons carrying pain sensation to second order neurons of posterior horn. These descending pathways may inhibit presynaptically the transmission of pain sensation via the second order neuron.

### Particular features of synaptic transmission :

1. **One-way propagation** : The synapses act as valves so that transmission occurs from presynaptic to postsynaptic neuron only as the presynaptic neuron itself is unresponsive to the chemical it releases.

2. **Convergence and divergence** : Synapses may converge on a neuron which gives rise to branches to supply multiple neurons (divergence).

3. **Facilitation and inhibition of neurons** via synapses.

4. **Summation, occlusion** and **subliminal fringe** effect (Fig. 11.22, 11.23).

5. **Synaptic plasticity** and **learning**, eg, posttetanic potentiation, low frequency depression, habituation and sensitization (Fig. 11.24).

## ➤ 11.6 The Somatic Sensory System

### Receptors

Receptors are non neuronal specialized cells present at the afferent nerve endings. They are capable of transforming stimulus energy into electrical energy, which leads to transmission of nerve impulses along afferent nerve fibres.

**Classification of Receptors :**

1. Based on **Source of Stimulus.**

**Based on Source of stimulus**

| Exteroceptors | Interoceptors | Teleceptors | Proprioceptors |
|---|---|---|---|
| Receive stimuli from immediate external surrounding e.g. : cutaneous receptors | Receive stimuli within body e.g. : chemoreceptors Baroreceptors | Receive stimuli coming from a distance e.g. : visual receptors, cochlear receptors | There detect changes in muscle length, tension and movement of joints |

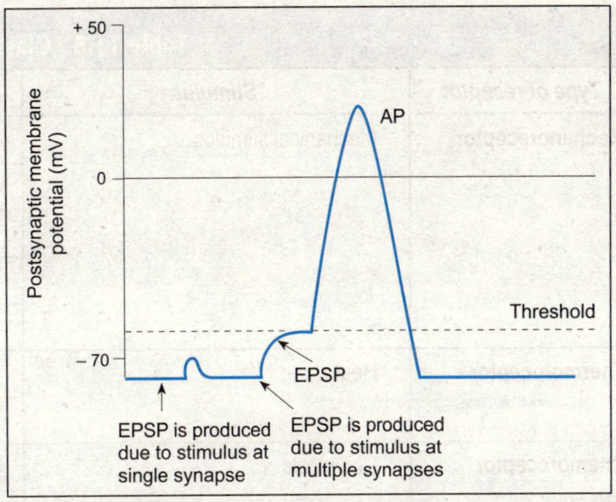


**Fig. 11.22 :** EPSP summation resulting in AP when threshold is reached (spatial summation)

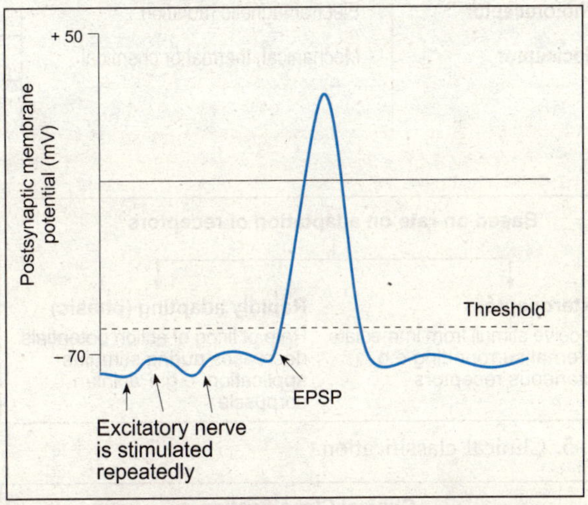


**Fig. 11.23 :** EPSP summation resulting in AP when threshold is reached (Temporal summation)

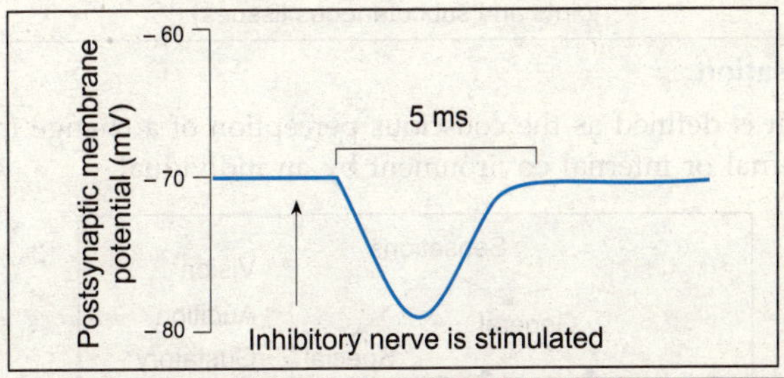


**Fig. 11.24 :** Postsynaptic inhibitory effects

2. Based on **type of stimulus energy** (See table 11.5).
3. Based on **type of sensation** e.g. touch, cold, heat, pain, light, smell, taste.
4. Based on **rate on adaptation of receptors.**

**Table 11.5 : Classification of receptors**

| *Type of receptor* | *Stimulus* | *Location* | *Effective stimulus* |
|---|---|---|---|
| **Mechanoreceptor** | Mechanical stimulus | Skin | Touch, pressure, vibration |
| | | Muscle and tendon | Change in muscle length and tension |
| | | Joints | Joint position and movement |
| | | Cochlea | Sound vibrations |
| | | Vestibule | Linear and angular acceleration |
| **Thermoreceptor** | Heat | Skin | Warming or cooling |
| | | Hypothalamus | Warming or cooling |
| **Chemoreceptor** | Chemicals | Carotid and aortic bodies | Changes in plasma $P_{O_2}$; $P_{CO_2}$ and pH |
| | | Medulla | Change of pH locally |
| | | Tongue | Acid, salt and sugar |
| | | Hypothalamus | Plasma osmolality changes |
| **Photoreceptor** | Electromagnetic radiation | Eye | Light |
| **Nociceptor** | Mechanical, thermal or chemical | Skin | Pinch; crush |
| | | Muscle, joint and viscera | Excessive stretch |

**Based on rate on adaptation of receptors**

- **Exteroceptors**: Receive stimuli from immediate external surrounding e.g. : cutaneous receptors
- **Rapidly adapting (phasic)**: Rate of firing of action potentials decreases during stimulus application. e.g. Pacinian corpuscle

5. Clinical classification.

**Clinical Classification**

- **Superficial** (In skin, mucosa)
- **Deep** (In muscles, tendons, joints and subcutaneous tissues)
- **Visceral** (Visceral organs)

## Sensation

It is defined as the conscious perception of a change in external or internal environment by an individual.

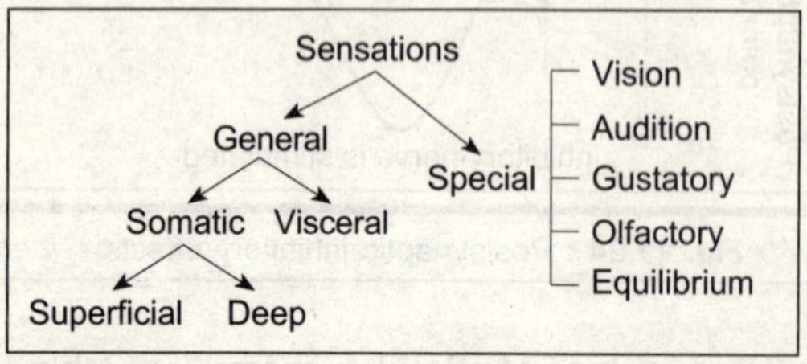


## Properties of Receptors

1. **Specificity of response :** Each receptor has lowest threshold for only one type of sensation.

2. **Generation of generator or receptor potential on stimulation :** When a stimulus excites the receptor, it changes the potential across the membrane of receptor. This is known as receptor potential.When receptor potential rises above the threshold for eliciting action potential in the nerve fibre, action potential is generated in nerve fibre attached to receptor.

**Properties :**

(i) Amplitude of receptor potential increases with increasing frequency of stimulus application and increasing strength of stimulus.

(ii) Can be added, if second stimulus arrives before previous receptor potential fades out.

(iii) Adaptation when a continuous sensory stimulus is applied, receptors respond at very high impulse rate initially, then at a progressively lower rate until response falls to nil.

3. **Adaptation :** Adaptation is a property of receptors and all sensory receptors adapt either partially or completely. However nociceptors never adapt.

The function of adaptation is to decrease the amount of sensory information to the brain.

4. **Intensity discrimination :**

(i) Gradations of stimulus strength are discriminated approximately in proportion to log of stimulus strength. This holds for higher intensities of visual, auditory and cutaneous sensations

Interpreted intensity = Log (Stimulus strength + Constant)

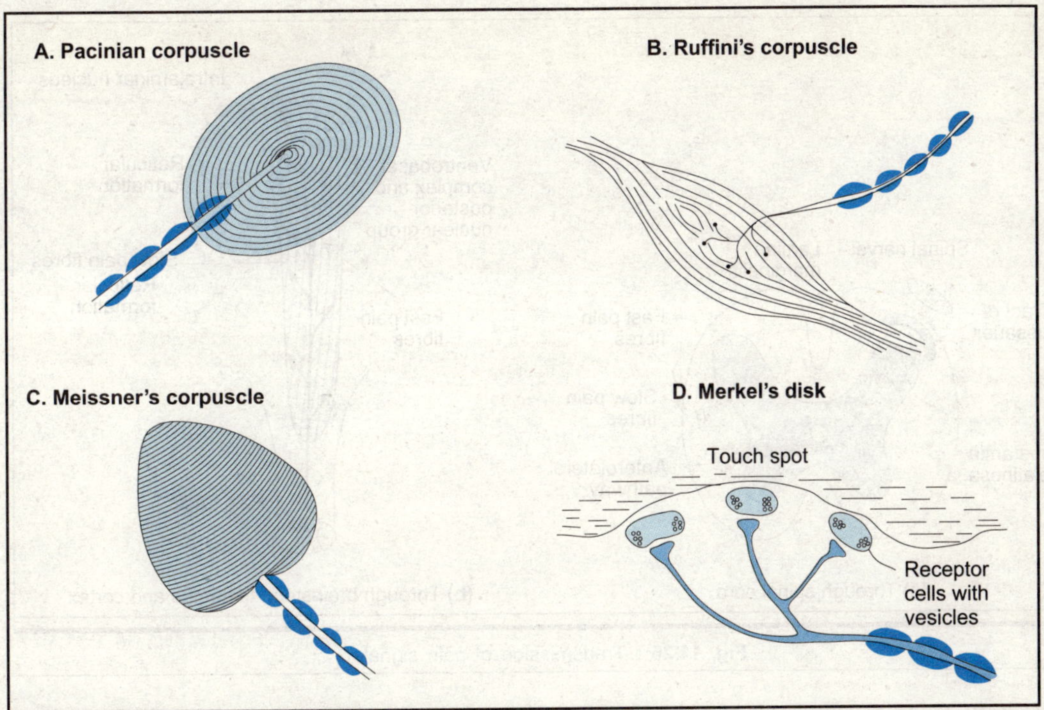


Fig. 11.25 : Different types of receptors

(ii) Gradations of stimulus strength are discriminated approximately in proportion to the power to which the stimulus strength is raised.

Fails at very high or low intensities.

Interpreted intensity = K (Stimulus strength — $K_i)^{\gamma}$

K, $K_i$ are constants.

'$\gamma$ is the power to which stimulus strength is raised.

5. **Projection :** When any part of sensory path is stimulated, conscious sensation is referred to the location of the receptor.

## Tactile Receptors

1. **Free Nerve Endings :** These are abundant in skin and other tissues. They detect touch and pressure.

2. **Meissner's corpuscles :** These are encapsulated receptors (supplied by Aβ fibres). They are present in non-hairy parts of skin and abundant at fingertips and lips. They are rapidly adapting and detect low pressure vibration.

3. **Merkel's disc :** There are always grouped inside receptor organs called Iggodome receptors. Only a single large myelinated fibre supplies all receptors of the Iggodome. They are present along with Meissner's corpuscles and are slowly adapting. They help in localization of sensation and Stereognosis i.e. by determining texture of objects and help in detecting movement of light objects over the surface of skin.

4. **Hair end organ :** It consists of hair and a basal nerve fibre encireling the basal part of hair. These detect movements of objects on surface body.

5. **Ruffini's end organs :** They are present in deeper layers of skin and also in the deeper tissues. They are multibranched encapsulated endings and adapt very little. They thus signal the state of continuous deformation of skin and deeper tissues. They are present in joint capsule where they detect the degree of joint rotation.

6. **Pacinian Corpuscles :** They are present immediately beneath skin in subcutaneous layer. These are rapidly adapting. These detect rapid changes in mechanical state of tissue.

## PAIN AND PURPOSE OF PAIN

Its function is not to indicate the quality of stimulus, but to indicate that the stimulus is physically damaging.

It apprises the C.N.S. that a harmful agent is in close contact with the body. This information causes the individual to react to the pain stimulus to prevent tissue damage.

As the receptors are non-adaptable, the person is conscious of the noxious stimulus as long as it is present.

Thus pain has a **Protective Function.**

## Receptors (Nociceptors)

Receptors are NON ADAPTABLE free nerve endings in skin as well as other tissues. These are stimulated by excessive mechanical stretch; extremes of temperature or damaging chemicals.

Thus, Nociceptors → Thermal / Mechanical / Chemical

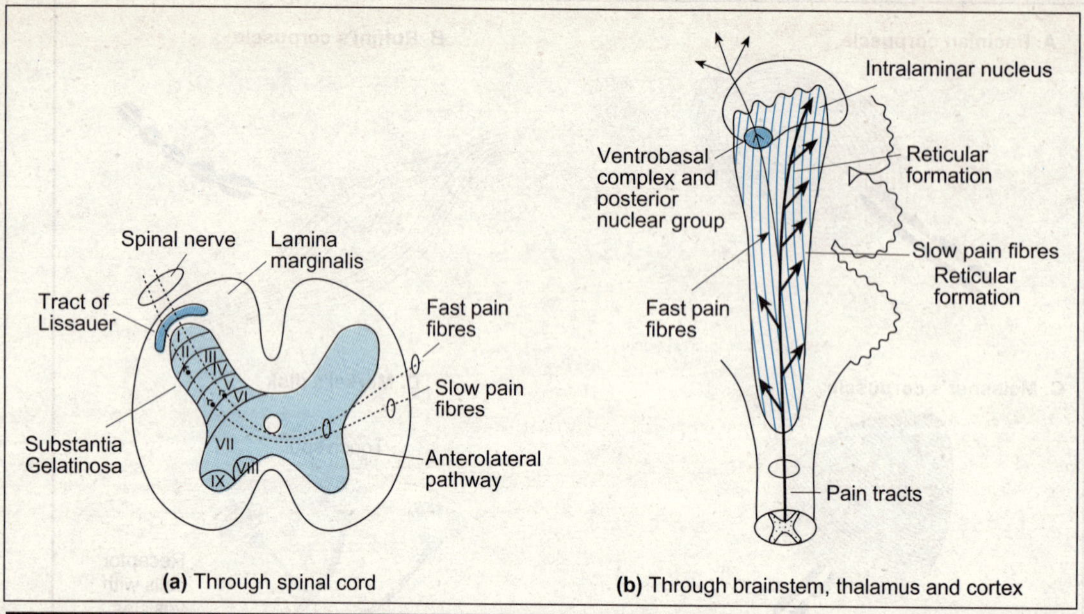


**Fig. 11.26 :** Transmission of pain signals

Some of the chemicals exciting chemical nociceptors are : (i) Bradykinin, (ii) Serotonin, (iii) Histamine, (iv) $K^+$ ions, (v) ATP, ADP, (vi) Acids, (vii) Ach

**Neurotransmitter** in primary pain fibres is substance P.

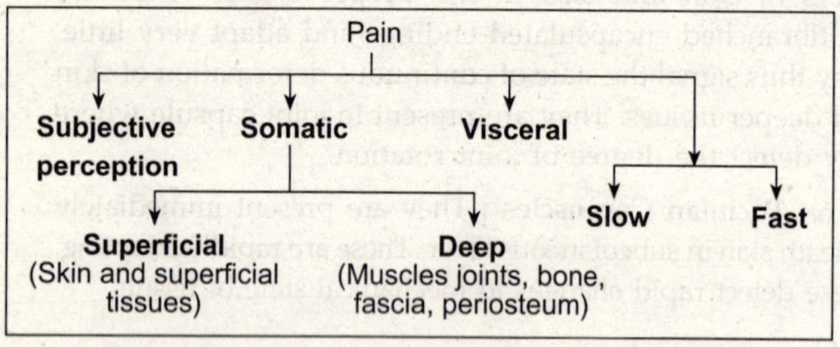


## Causes of Pain Sensation

1. **Tissue trauma :** This leads to release of various chemicals of which bradykinin is most potent in causing pain. Other chemicals include serotonin, histamine, $K^+$ ions, ATP, ADP etc.

These chemicals stimulate chemical nociceptors.

They also reduce the threshold for excitation of mechanical and thermal nociceptors.

2. **Ischemia :** Ischemia leads to accumulation of lactic acid in tissues due to anerobic reactions due to lack of blood supply. The role of bradykinin and enzymes released during ischemia is uncertain.

3. **Muscle spasm :** It causes pain by stimulating mechanical nociceptors and also excites pain receptors indirectly due to vasospasm leading to ischaemia.

**Causes of Visceral Pain :** The viscera insensitive to pain are parenchyma of liver and alveoli of lungs.

(i) *Inflammation.*

(ii) *Ischemia :* Due to release of metabolites or products of tissue destruction (bradykinin, enzymes etc.)

(iii) *Chemical stimuli :* e.g. gastric acid leaking through perforated ulcer.

(iv) *Spasm of hollow viscus :* Via stimulation of mechanosensitive nociceptors and ischemia.

(v) *Over distension.*

(vi) *Parietal pain :* The parietal walls of viscus (e.g. parietal pleura or peritoneum). These parietal walls are innervated by somatic nerves. True visceral pain is carried by autonomic nerves and referred to distant areas. However parietal pain is localised over the viscus.

## Slow and Fast Pain

Slow pain is the pain which begins after a second or more, after application of stimulus, but it slowly increases and also lasts for a longer time.

It leads to prolonged consciousness of pain and a burning sensation.

Slow pain can arise from both skin and deep tissues and viscera. Fast pain appears within 0.1 ms after application of stimulus. It is sharp, pricking acute pain and felt generally from superficial tissues (Fig. 11.26).

## Effect of Ablation of Somatic Sensory Area

- Perception of pain is not destroyed.
- Localisation of pain is lost.

This is due to involvement of the thalamus and reticular formation in conscious perception of pain.

**Table 11.6 : Classification of receptors**

| | *Slow Pain* | *Fast Pain* |
|---|---|---|
| **Characteristic of pain** | Burning, throbbing | Pricking, sharp |
| **Fibres carrying pain** | C[unmyelinated] | A-δ |
| **Localisation** | Poorly localised. | Well localised. Localisation is better if tactile receptors are concomitantly stimulated. |
| **Physiological responses** | Nausea, vomiting, hypotension, hypotonia | Withdrawal response, sympathetic response. |
| **Tissues involved** | Skin and deep tissues | Superficial tissues. |
| **Time lapse between application and perception of stimulus noxious** | 1 second or more | 0.1 ms. |
| **Path way** | Mostly 'C' unmyelinated fibres and flow A-δ fibres carry impulses to dorsal root ganglion and then axons of latter form dorsal root which terminate on Ia, II and III of dorsal horn of spinal cord. (Substantia Gelatinosa). From here fibres reach lamina V of dorsal horn. Last neurons in the series provide long axons which cross midline and join the fibres of fast path as PALEO spinothalamic tract and terminates at (i) Reticular nuclei (ii) Tectal area (iii) Periaqueductal gray. From reticular areas impulses are sent to thalamus, hypothalamus and basal parts of brain. | A-δ fibres (6-30m/s) carry impulses for nocicepton to dorsal root ganglion and then enter the spinal cord as dorsal root of spinal nerve. On entering the spinal cord, the fibres ascend on descend for few segments its tract of Lissauer and then terminate on neurons (lamina I) of dorsal horn. The second order neurons cross the midline at once and ascend as NEO spin othalmic tract. Few fibres terminate in reticular formation and rest in posterior nuclear group of thalamus. From thalamus fibres pass basal part of brain and to somatic sensory cortex. |

**Properties of Sensation of Pain :**

(i) ***Threshold and intensity :*** Pain is not felt if intensity of stimulus is subthreshold. As the intensity increases, more pain is felt. When intensity rises, pain also spreads to neighbouring areas due to recruitment of nerve fibres.

(ii) ***Adaptation :*** Nociceptors are non-adaptable.

(iii) ***Localization :*** Superficial pain is better localised. Visceral pain is mostly expressed as referred pain.

(iv) ***Emotional accompaniment :*** Leads to unpleasant feeling (affect)

(v) ***Role of damage :*** Rate of damage feeling proportionately raises intensity of pain.

(vi) ***Types :*** Classification given earlier.

**General Reaction to Pain :**

(i) ***Emotional :*** Pain generally leads to feeling of unpleasantness. Slow pain (prolonged) causes irritation and frustration.

(ii) ***Muscular :*** Muscle spasm occurs in affected areas. This helps in immobilizing the area.

(iii) *Reflex response :* Slow pain leads to lowering of blood pressure, nausea etc.

## Referred Pain

Pain originating in a visceral organ is referred to sites on skin or other somatic structure. These locations are innervated by nerves arising from the **same spinal segment** as the nerve innervating the visceral organ. The skin is topograpically mapped, thus pain is identified as originating on the skin.

**Cause of referred pain :**

(a) Sympathetic afferent nerves from viscus and the somatic afferent nerves from same dermatome converge on to a common neuron of next order. (CONVERGENCE)

(b) Afferent sympathetic nerve bringing pain sensation from viscus, terminates on second order neuron but at same time via collaterals on another second order neuron, which is a somatic neuron of corresponding dermatome. (FACILITATION)

(c) Previous trauma in the vicinity of a viscus makes the previously traumatized region more susceptible to be the site of referred pain (ROLE OF EXPERIENCE)

Pain is referred usually to a structure developing from same embryonic segment (dermatome) as the structure in which pain originates (DERMATOMAL RULE)

**Application :** Because of this anatomic relationship, diagnosis of visceral diseases is based on location of referred pain. e.g. Ischemic cardiac pain to chest wall and inside of left arm.

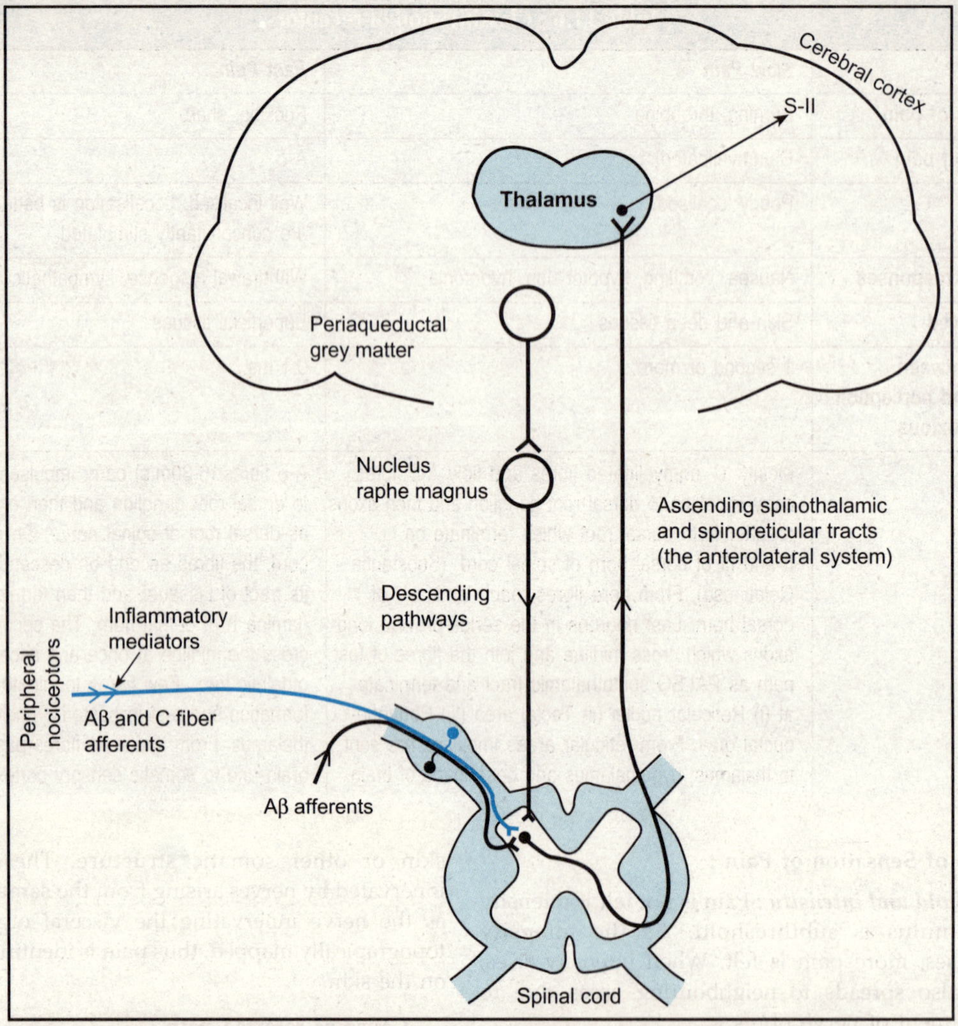


**Fig. 11.27 :** C.N.S. analgesia system

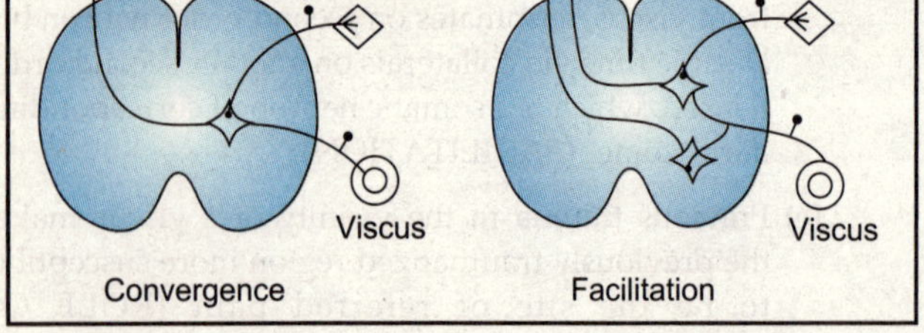


**Hyperalgesia :** Hypersensitivity to pain is known as hyperalgesia.

It may be due to :

(i) Hypersensitivity of pain receptors themselves (Primary hyperalgesia)

(ii) Facilitation of sensory transmission (Secondary hyperalgesia)

## Pain Modulation

**C.N.S. Analgesia System :** There is a pain suppression (analgesia) system in the brain.

The major components of this are :

Periaqueductal gray area of midbrain and upper pons surrounding aqueduct of Sylvius. From here, neurons send impulses to raphe magnus nucleus.

The raphe magnus nucleus is a midline structure in lower pons and upper medulla. Signals are then transmitted via dorsolateral columns to the spinal cord.

Pain inhibitory complex located in dorsal horn of the spinal cord. Here pain is blocked before its relay to brain.

The periventricular nucleus of hypothalamus and medial forebrain bundle also participate.

Fibres from periventricular area and periaqueductal gray area release enkephalin. Fibres originating in raphe magnus release serotonin. This **serotonin** acts on **local**

**spinal cord neurons** that secrete **enkephalin** which causes **presynaptic inhibition** of incoming Aδ and C fibres synapsing in dorsal horn by blocking calcium channels. This also **blocks local reflex responses** to pain e.g. withdrawal reflex.

**Another explanation is inhibition of release of substance P at posterior horn due to release of enkephalin.**

**Central Inhibition and Counter irritants :** Extreme stress helps in masking perception of pain. This is called stress analgesia. This is due to C.N.S. inhibition and opiates (enkephalin and endorphin). Pain transmission is susceptible to inhibition as well as facilitation in C.N.S. This inhibition explains efficacy of counterirritants.

Projected pain is not the same as referred pain. **Projected pain** is due to true stimulation of a pain pathway anywhere along the path, which causes that pain to manifest as if it were occurring at the periphery of pain pathway. **Phantom limb pain** or chronic back pain after a herniated disk are the common examples of projected pain.

### Phantom limb pain

It is an excellent example of law of projection, a primary concept of neurophysiology which explains that involvement of any part of sensory pathways up to cortex produces sensation at the site of receptor.

In case of amputated limbs, the receptors are absent but the peripheral and central pathways remain intact and, if the amputated stump gets hurt, then the individual perceives pain in the peripheral part that was cut off (phantom limb).

It is due to conduction of impulses by the remaining sensory pathways which are responsible for the projection.

But sectioning of the sensory part (posterior root) of the affected limb may not abolish the pain permanently due to some poorly understood central facilitation.

### Gate control theory of pain

The nerve impulses pass into the nervous system → via a 'gate' in the spinal cord. The gate can be blocked by nerve impulses from above or by impulses from adjacent nerves. The **intensity of a painful stimulus** may be modified e.g. : *(i) pain nerves can be blocked by local anesthetic; (ii) gate can be blocked by mental activity and, lastly, the stimulation of other nerves may close the gate and pain is reduced.*

### The Gating theory

Massage and liniments to painful areas is effective in suppression of pain. Acupuncture and low frequency electrical stimulus or vibrations also provide relief. To explain this, the gating theory was proposed. Connector neurons excited by large myelinated fibres (Aβ) carrying touch and pressure sensations may inhibit pain fibres at the site of their entry in spinal cord i.e. the 'gate' is closed. The role of C.N.S. Analgesia System is also suggested.

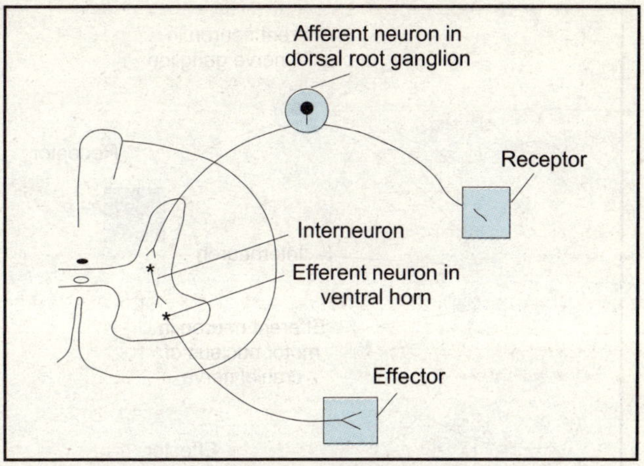


Fig. 11.28 : Basic components of a reflex arc

## 11.7 Somatic Motor System

A **motor unit** is a motor neuron and all the muscle fibers it innervates. **Lower motor neurons** are the cells and fibers of motor cranial and spinal nerves. The **upper motor neurons** are the motor cells and fibers from cortex to cranial nerve nuclei and anterior horn cells.

**Table 11.7 : Motor neuron lesions**

| | *Upper motor neuron* | *Lower motor neuron* |
|---|---|---|
| **Tone** | Increased | Decreased |
| **Reflexes** | Hyperreflexic | Areflexic |
| **Muscle mass** | Slight decrease | Atrophy |

### Reflexes

**Reflexes** are the involuntary spontaneous/automatic responses occurring without volition, independent of cerebral cortex but mostly produced by a part of central nervous system. They help maintain homeostasis by controlling many involuntary processes (heart rate, breathing rate, blood pressure and digestion). **Reflexes** are responsible for carrying out automatic actions of swallowing, sneezing, coughing and vomiting. A neural reflex arc is behind an involuntary response to a stimulus. The reflex arc originates in a receptor and via central integrating stations returns to the site of response. **The basic components of the reflex arc (Fig. 11.28) :**

- receptor
- an afferent neuron
- an interneuron (may or may not be present)
- an efferent neuron
- an effector.

The peripheral part of the afferent neurons are modified to form the sensory receptors (exteroceptors; interoceptors or proprioceptors). See Fig. 11.29.

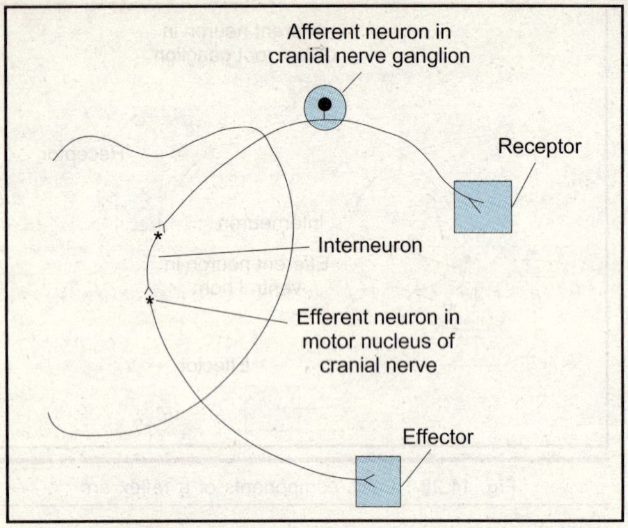


Fig. 11.29 : Basic components of a reflex arc at the level of brain stem

A **reflex** is said to be **somatic reflex** when the effector is a skeletal muscle and **autonomic reflex** when the effector is the smooth muscle of a visceral organ, cardiac muscle, a gland or a vessel.

## The Muscle Spindle (Fig. 11.31)

It is a spindle shaped receptor whose tapering ends are attached to the endomysium. There are 8-10 intrafusal fibres parallel to extrafusal fibre. The central portion of intrafusal fibres lack contractile elements and is sensory. The nuclei may be arranged so as to form nuclear bags or nuclear chains. Each spindle has 1-3 nuclear bagfibres and 3-9 nuclear chain fibres.

**Sensory Supply :** Group Ia fibres supply nuclear bag and nuclear chain fibres and end in annulospiral or primary endings.

Group II fibres innervate nuclear chain fibres on one side of primary endings as secondary or flower spray endings.

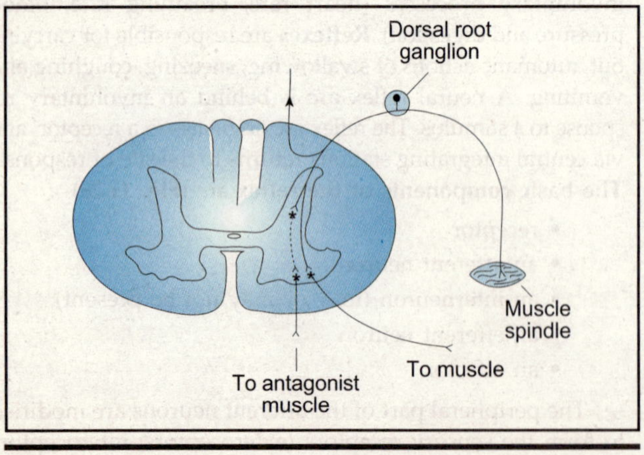


Fig. 11.30 : Stretch reflex arc

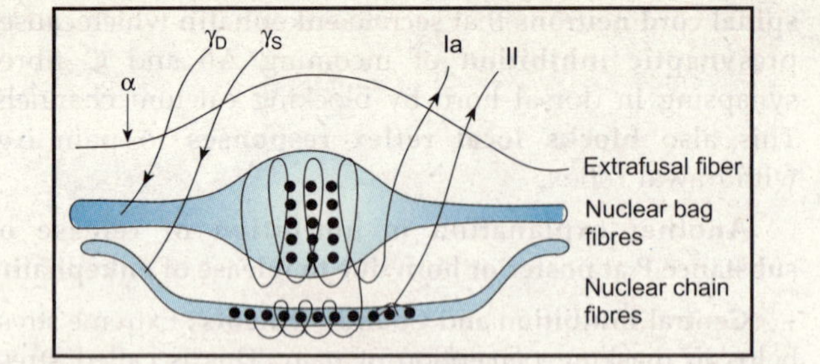


Fig. 11.31 : Muscle spindle

**Motor Supply :** γ-D and γ-S fibres innervate nuclear bag fibres and nuclear chain fibres at the striated poles respectively and control dynamic and static responses respectively.

**The Stretch Reflex :** The muscle spindle is stimulated when the central portion of intrafusal fibres are stretched either due to stretch of entire muscle or stimulation of γ-motor fibres.

Stretching of musclespindles results in reflex contraction of the muscle.

**Dynamic Response :** When length of muscle spindle is increased suddenly, primary endings are stimulated and strong reflex contraction of muscle occurs.

**Static Response e.g. :** Action of antigravity muscles during standing. When muscle is slowly stretched, signals are sent through both primary and secondary endings of nuclear chain and fibres causes reflex contraction of muscle as long as the stretch is maintained.

**Function of Stretch Reflex :**

1. Maintenance of muscle tone. (via activation of γ-motor neurons)
2. Maintenance of posture (Via static component of stretch reflex)
3. Control of voluntary movements : via afferents to motor command systems (via Iafibres) regarding changes in muscle length which in turn provides α-motor neuron with a source of excitatory input.

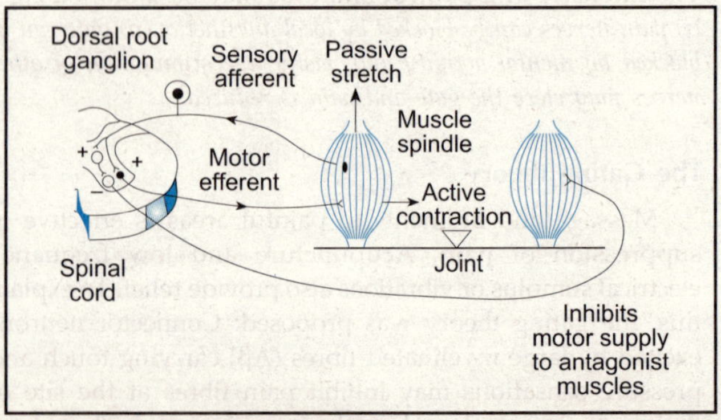


Fig. 11.32 : Stretch reflex (monosynaptic reflex arc)

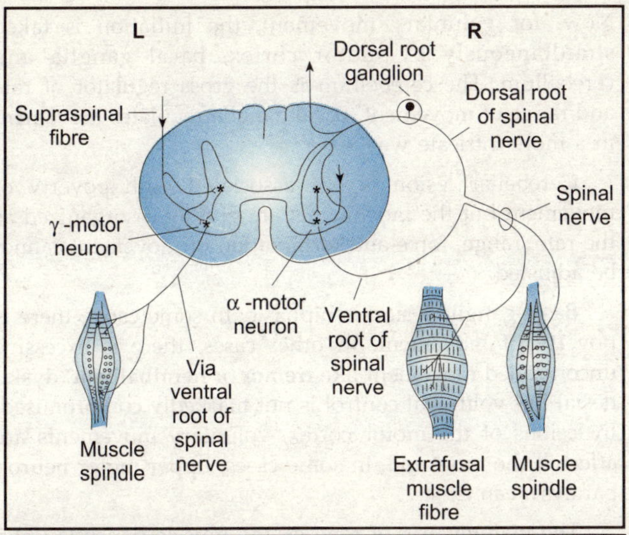


**Fig. 11.33** : γ-motor neuron acting on the intrafusal muscle fibres

**Negative Stretch Reflex :** When muscle is suddenly shortened negative signals from muscle spindles cause reflex inhibition of muscle either as a dynamic or static response.

**Inverse Stretch Reflex (Golgitendon) :** It is a protective reflex in which strong force reflexly causes muscle inhibition.

**Gamma Loop :** C.N.S. is capable of initiating movements directly by stimulating γ-efferents using the gamma loop :

Increase in γ-motor activity causes intrafusal fibres to contract, which stretches the sensory portion of receptors and stretch reflex is initiated which increases γ-motor discharge.

γ-loop is normally activated only during α–γ coactivation.

## Maintenance of Muscle Tone (Fig. 11.34)

Muscle tone is chiefly maintained by stretch (myotatic) reflex. It is reinforced by non-myotatic way due to asynchronous discharge of impulses in motor neurons and the cerebellum also plays an important role in maintaining muscle tone. The descending reticular formation has 2 parts : facilitatory and inhibitory in upper medulla, pons, midbrain and in ventromedial side of lower medulla respectively. Activity of descending facilitatory component is maintained by impulses from vestibular nucleus, cerebral cortex's facilitatory portion, cerebellum and basal ganglia. The descending inhibitory component is controlled by cerebral and cerebellar inputs and it inturn inhibits facilitatory components.

Cerebellum is site for α–γ linkage. In absence of cerebellum, muscle tone is maintained by α-motor neuron activity only.

Nuclear bag fibers are meant for phasic or transient response to increase in length, whereas the nuclear chain fibers are primarily utilized for tonic or sustained stretch. Gamma efferents are, accordingly, of two types those supplying nuclear bag fibers are dynamic (plate ending)

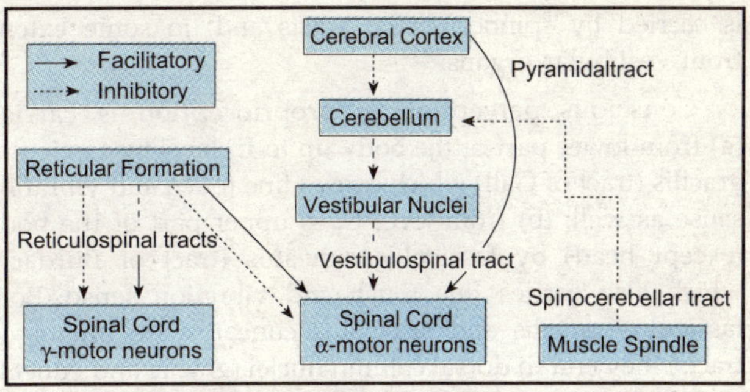


**Fig. 11.34** : Maintenance of muscle tone

and those supplying nuclear chain fibers are static (trail endings) functionally.

***Golgi tendon organ and inverse stretch reflex*** : The **golgi tendon organ (GTO)** is a specialized sensory receptor found in muscle tissue which is in series with the muscle connected with the tendon. It is stimulated by either passive stretch or active contraction of a muscle. When GTO is strongly stretched → Ib fibers to the spinal cord are activated → there is inhibitory input to the α-motor neurons to the same muscle causing relaxation. They are sensitive to muscle tension rather than length and initiate an inhibitory response. This reflex seems to be protective, limiting tension so as to avoid permanent damage to muscle or tendon. **In short,** ***its function is to signal the amount of tension generated by muscle contraction.*** The golgi tendon organ also regulates muscle length but it elicits reflexes (the reverse myotatic reflex) that are opposite to those of the muscle spindle (Fig. 11.35).

## Proprioception pathway

Proprioception is the awareness of position, movement and posture relating to any limb or whole body. The proprioceptive senses are carried by fibers around joints and muscles by means of receptors like muscle spindles, Pacinian corpuscles, golgi tendon organs, and mechanoreceptors of skin. Proprioception is both conscious and, at the same time, unconscious. Proprioceptive sensation

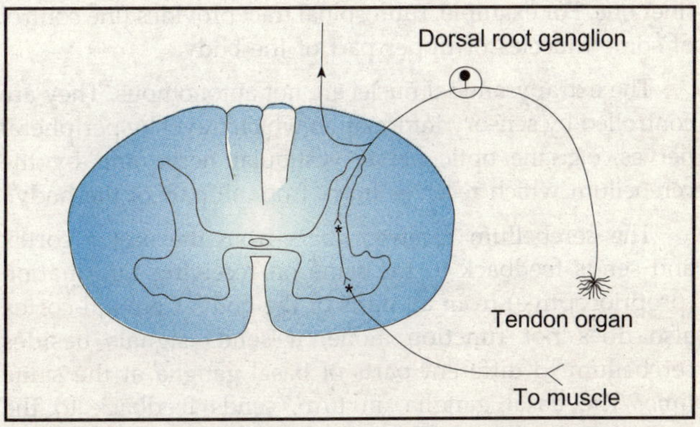


**Fig. 11.35** : Reflex arc involving tendon organ

is carried by spinocerebellar tracts and, to some extent, from vestibular organs.

Conscious perception of proprioception is carried (a) from lower part of the body up to $L_4$ level by fasciculus gracilis (tract of Gall) which carries fine touch and vibration sense as well; (b) from level $L_3$ to upper part of the body (except head) by fasciculus cuneatus (tract of Burdach) which also carries fine touch and vibration sense. Both fasciculus gracilis and fasciculus cuneatus are uncrossed tracts, they end in dorsal column nuclei (gracile and cuneate nuclei). Second order neuron crosses to opposite side and travels via medial lemniscus to terminate at ventral posterolateral nucleus of thalamus from which fibers ultimately reach the primary somatosensory cortex.

From head, proprioceptive fibers along with pain, temperature and touch travel through trigeminal nerve. The proprioceptive fibers end in the principal and also mesencephalic part of trigeminal nucleus. From there, second order neurons cross to opposite side to ventroposteromedial nucleus of thalamus from where fibers reach the somatosensory cortex.

### Control of posture and movement

Control of posture, gait and movements in general are made useful and appropriate by the components of motor system which receives feedback from sensory system.

The final operation is done by motor neurons of anterior horn cells of spinal cord and homologous neurons of cranial nerve nuclei (lower motor neurone) But they are continuously controlled by fibers from higher centers. The fibers are components of corticospinal tract (pyramidal tract and corticomedullary tract).

Besides the corticospinal control, the lower motor neurons receive fibers which arise from the brain stem. They are called **extrapyramidal fibers** (rubrospinal tract, reticulospinal tract, vestibulospinal tract, tectospinal tract, olivospinal tract, etc.). ***The extrapyramidal fibers are involved in both voluntary and involuntary control of movement and posture.*** As for example, an unexpected noise or a visual signal can reflexly control the posture. On the other hand, extrapyramidal control may be gross or it may be a finer one. For example, rubrospinal tract provides fine control of some muscles of upper part of the body.

The extrapyramidal nuclei are not autonomous. They are controlled by sensory information which travel by peripheral nerves, e.g. the optic nerve, vestibular nerve and by the cerebellum which receives fibers from all part of the body.

The cerebellum receives fibers from the motor cortex and sends feedback to the same on receiving information (proprioceptive) from all parts of the body. Cerebral cortex also does not function alone, it sends signals besides cerebellum to different parts of basal ganglia at the same time. The basal ganglia, in turn, sends feedback to the cortical motor areas. The basal ganglia is also connected with substantia nigra, subthalamic nucleus and brain stem. Now, for voluntary movement, the initiation is taken simultaneously by motor cortex, basal ganglia and cerebellum. The cerebellum is the gross regulator of rate and range of movement. Basal ganglia regulates movement in a more intricate way.

Cerebellar lesion is not associated with poverty of movement but the movements are grossly disorganized as the rate, range, force and termination of movement cannot be adjusted.

Basal ganglia lesion is biphasic. In some cases, there is poverty of movement. In other cases, there is excessive uncontrolled movement like **tremor** or **hemiballism** (dyskinesia) but volitional control is not markedly compromised. In lesions of the motor cortex, voluntary movements are affected the most and, in some cases, upper motor neuron paralysis can exist.

The maintenance of tone of any muscle depends upon the reflex arc starting from muscle spindle. Gamma motor neuron increases the spindle sensitivity to stretch. The gamma motor neurons are controlled by both extrapyramidal and pyramidal fibers. For this reason, in upper motor neuron lesion there may be hypertonicity (**clasp knife rigidity or spasticity**) and, in extrapyramidal lesions (**parkinsonism**), there is hypertonicity in the form of rigidity which may be of **cog wheel** or **lead pipe varieties**.

As the lower motor neuron acts at the "grass root level" and all information from "headquarters" funnel into them for execution, non functioning of lower motor neurons means complete disruption of all motor movements.

## ➤ 11.8 The Basal Ganglia

**The basal nuclei** (also called basal ganglia) are located in ***the ventral (basal) part of the cerebral hemispheres***. **The basal nuclei** consist of ***caudate nucleus, lentiform nucleus, amygdaloid nuclear complex*** and ***claustrum***. Caudate nucleus and putamen together form the corpus striatum. **The lentiform nucleus** has an ***external part (putamen) and an internal part (globus pallidus)***. (Fig. 11.36).

The basal ganglia are responsible for regulating the function of the cerebral cortex. Most of the areas of the cortex project to basal ganglia which then project via thalamus back to prefrontal and premotor cortex. The net effect of this loop is excitatory to the cortex. This activity is modulated by a circuitry within the basal ganglia (Fig.11.37).

**Caudate nucleus** is arch shaped and consists of the head, the body and the tail which is continuous with amygdaloid nuclear complex. **The putamen** is located deep to the *insula* and is isolated from claustrum by external capsule (Figs. 11.38 and Fig. 11.39).

The **globus pallidus** is identified laterally from the putamen by a layer of white matter. Medially, it is separated by internal capsule from the thalamus behind and caudate nucleus in front.

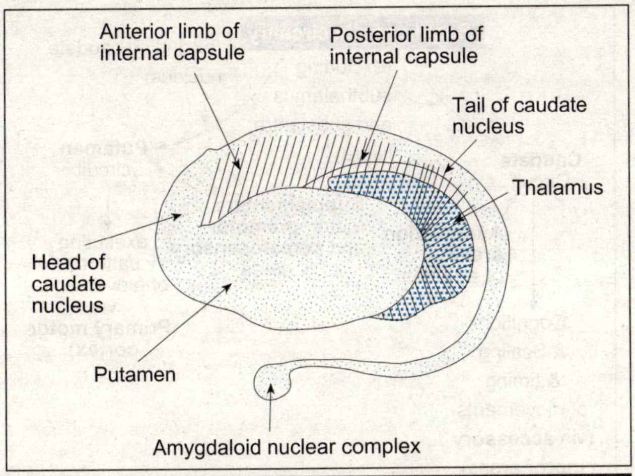


**Fig. 11.36 : Basal ganglia**

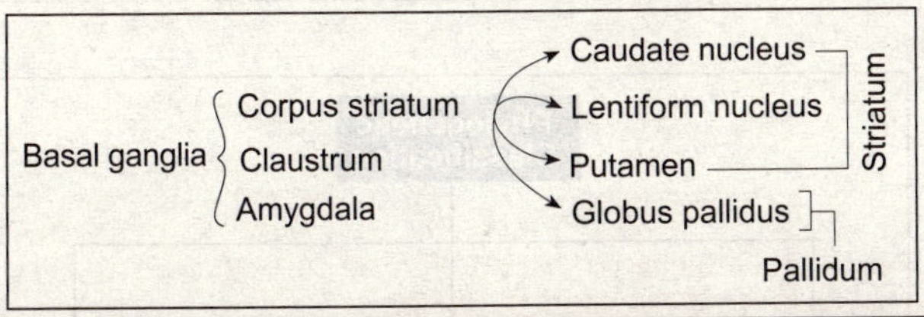


**Fig. 11.37 : The nomenclature of the components of basal ganglia**

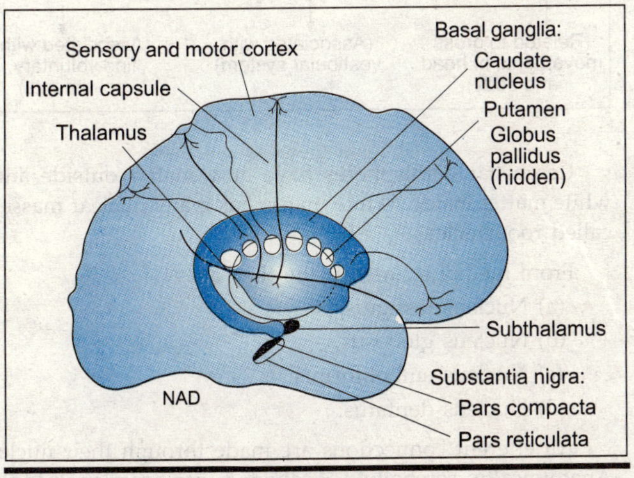


**Fig. 11.38 : Anatomy of basal ganglia and associated structures** *(lateral view)*

## Connections of basal ganglia

***The connections of the basal nuclei are extremely complex and their functional role in motor control is still primitive.***

The impulses from cerebral cortex, thalamus, subthalamus, substantia nigra and a number of brain stem centers (red nucleus and reticular formation) reach the corpus striatum where they are integrated and diverge

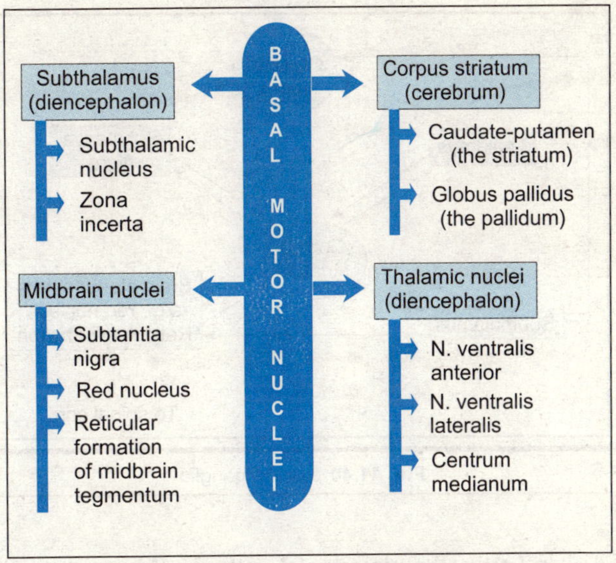


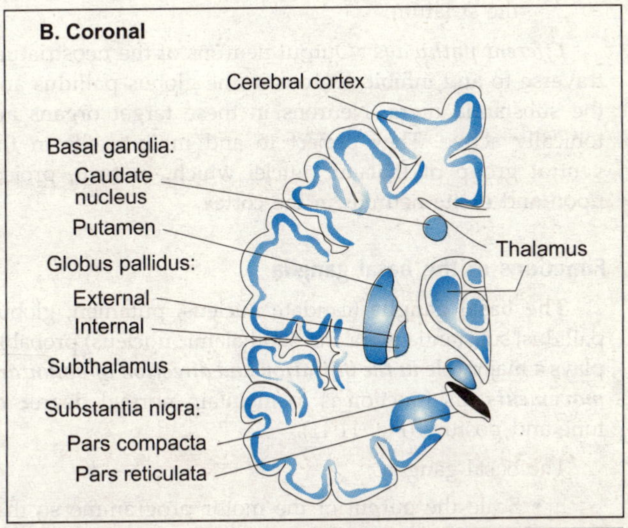


**Fig. 11.39 : Anatomy of basal ganglia and associated structures** *(coronal section)*

again to the thalamus, subthalamus, substantia nigra and the brain stem centers ( Fig. 11.40).

## Circuits within the basal ganglia

***Afferent pathways*** : The neostriatum is the input structure of the basal ganglia. It receives projections from all regions of the cortex. Inputs also come from the intralaminar nuclei of the thalamus and the substantia nigra.

- The output cells influence each other via recurrent axon collaterals. They are inhibitory to neighbouring output cells eg, γ-aminobutyric acid (GABA).
- Local interneurons are present in few number and they contain acetylcholine.

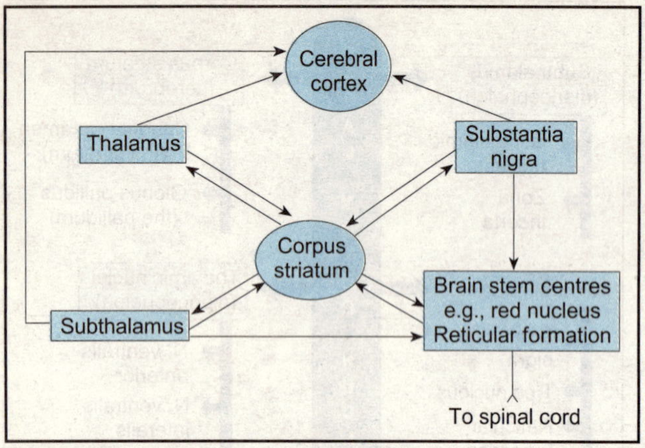


**Fig. 11.40 :** Basal ganglia

- Lastly, the nigrostriatal pathway (from substantia nigra to the neostriatum) releases dopamine into the striatum.

***Efferent pathways*** : Output neurons of the neostriatum traverse to and inhibit neurons in the globus pallidus and the substantia nigra. Neurons in these target organs are tonically active. They project to and inhibit cells in the ventral group of thalamic nuclei which, in turn, project upon and excite neurons in the cortex.

### Functions of the basal ganglia

**The basal ganglia** (caudate nucleus, putamen, globus pallidus, substantia nigra and subthalamic nucleus) probably plays a major role ***in the initiation and direction of voluntary movements.*** Its function is to maintain normal degree of tone and posture (Fig. 11.41).

The basal ganglia :

- Scale the output of the motor programme so that appropriate movements are made. This is particularly important in motor programmes with fine movement (e.g. handwriting) and also where similar repetitive movements are needed (e.g. in locomotion);
- Project to the frontal eyefields via the thalamus, and have a role in saccadic eye movements;
- Has a circuit with the prefrontal and other association areas which may have a role in memory relating to body orientation;
- Connects with the orbitofrontal cortex which many indicate a role in modulating behaviour.

## 11.9 Structure of Cerebellum

Cerebellum is made up of two cerebellar hemispheres connected with each other by vermis.

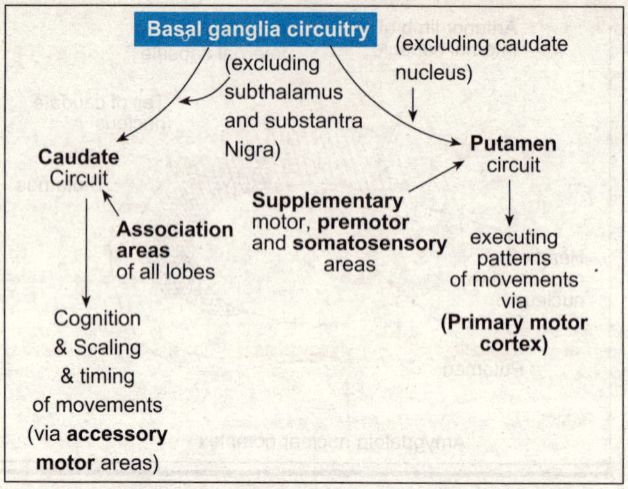


**Fig. 11.41 :** The connections among motor cortex, basal ganglia and thalamus

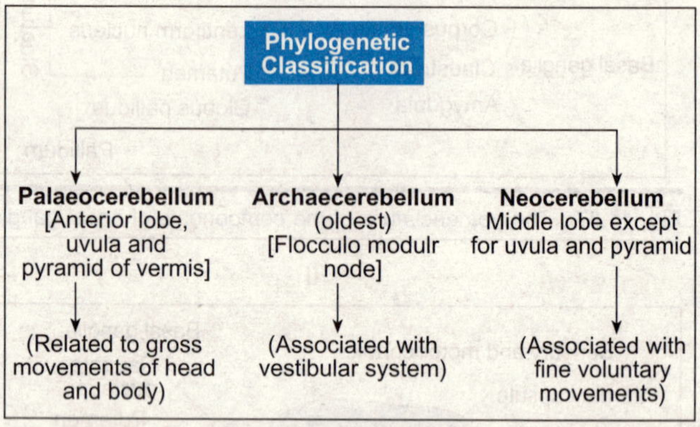


Cerebellar hemispheres have gray matter outside and white matter inside. White matter has many nuclear masses called roof nuclei.

From medial to lateral side they are :

(a) Nucleus fastigius,

(b) Nucleus globosus,

(c) Nucleus emboliformis,

(d) Nucleus dentatus.

All efferent connections are made through their nuclei Anatomically, cerebellum is divided into anterior, middle and flocculonodular lobes. Anterior and middle lobes are separated by fissura prima.

The main cerebellar lobes, lobules and fissures are :

**Cerebellum is connected to brainstem by three pairs of cerebellar peduncles :** Superior, middle and inferior connected with midbrain, pons and medulla respectively.

All afferents and efferents travel via these peduncles.

The outer gray matter of cerebellar hemisphere is called cerebellar cortex. It has three layers.

(a) Outer molecular,

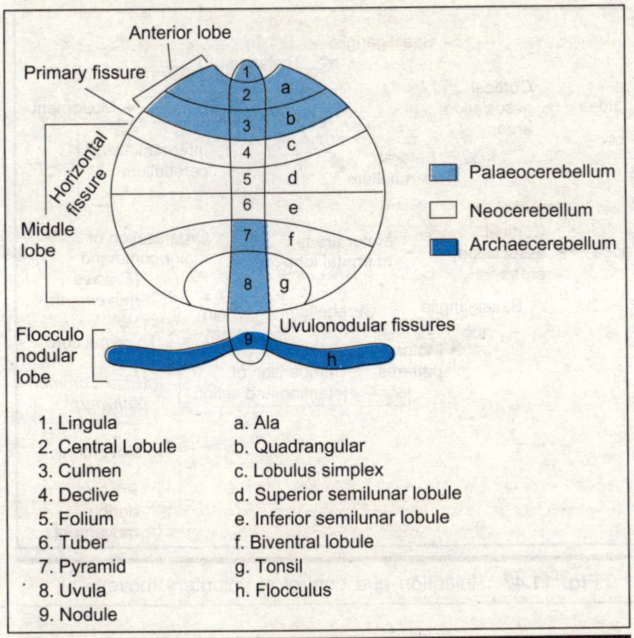


**Fig. 11.42**

(b) Middle purkinje cell layer,

(c) Inner granular cell layer.

Most afferents relay at granular layer and fibres then climb to molecular layer. From there, they form basket like network around Purkinje cells which in turn send axons to roof nuclei from where impulses are relayed to different parts of neural axis.

## Afferent connections of cerebellum :

| *Passing through* | *Name of tracts* | *Features* |
|---|---|---|
| Inferior peduncle | Dorsal spinocerebellar | Bring proprioceptive and exteroceptive information |
| | External arcuate fibers | Bring cutaneous and deep sensations. |
| | Reticulocerebellar fiber | |
| | Vestibulocerebellar tract | Come from vestibular nuclei which in turn receive information from vestibular apparatus. |
| | Olivocerebellar fibers | From inferior olive which in turn receives afferents from basal ganglia and collaterals from pyramidal tract. |
| Middle peduncle | Cerebropontocerebellar fibres | |
| Superior peduncle | Ventrospinocerebellar tract | Bring proprioceptive and exteroceptive information |
| | Tectocerebellar | Auditory and visual information via inferior and superior colliculi respectively. |

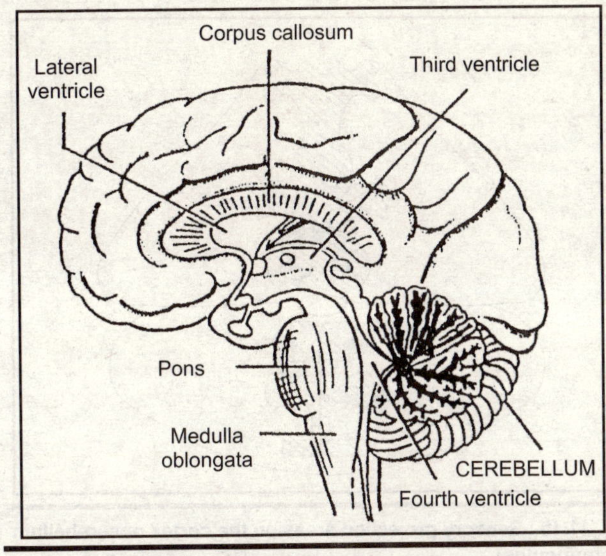


**Fig. 11.43 : Cerebellum and associated structures**

The olivocerebellar fibres are climbing type and reach the molecular layer. All other afferents are mossy type and synapse with granular cells Axons of granule cells and climbing fibre synapse with Purkinje cells.

Impulses fromgranular cells excite Purkinje cells subminimally whereas climbing fibres immediately activate purkinje cells which are in turn inhibitory to roof nuclei.

Collaterals from all fibres send facilitatory impulses to roof nuclei.

## Efferents of Cerebellum (Fig. 11.44) :

| *Via* | *Fibres* | *Features* |
|---|---|---|
| Superior peduncle | Dentatorubrothalamo cortical fibres to motor cortex | Influences motor cortex. |
| | Cerebello thalamo cortical fibres | Influence motor cortex. |
| | To reticular nuclei | Role in control over anterior horn cells via reticulospinal tracts. |
| Inferior peduncle | Cerebello vestibular fibres to vesticular nuclei. | Role in control over anterior horn cells via vestibulospinal tract. |

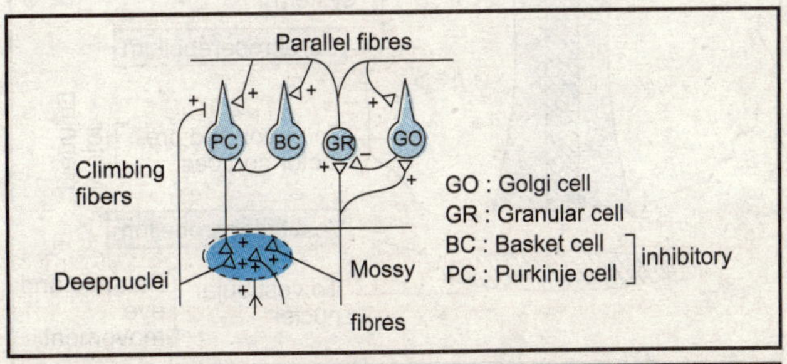


**Fig. 11.44 : Synaptic relations in cerebellum**

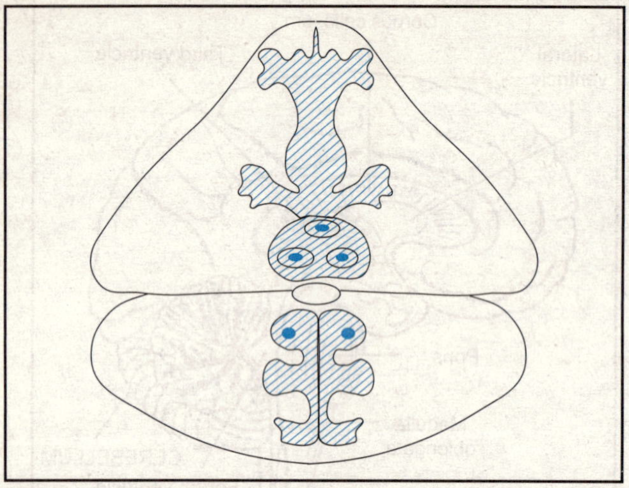

Fig. 11.45 : Sensory projection areas on the cortex of cerebellum [homunculus]

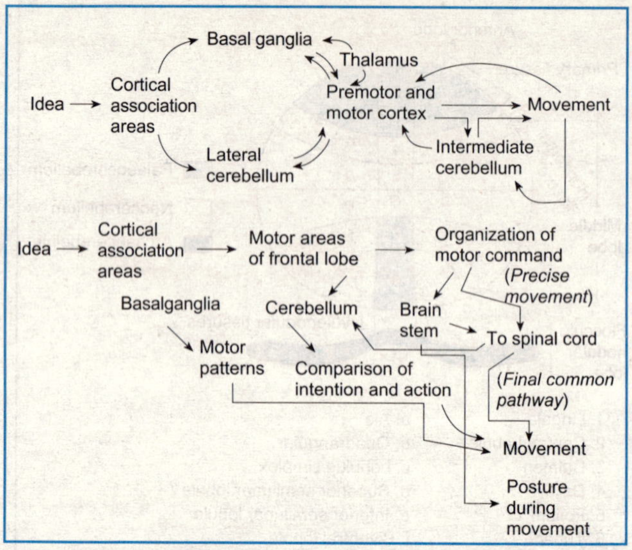


Fig. 11.47 : Initiation and control of voluntary movement

Functional divisions of cerebellum on basis of efferents. (Fig. 11.46)

## Functions of Cerebellum

1. It controls voluntary and involuntary motor activity though it is unable to initiate any motor activity.

2. Control over voluntary movements : This is possible by 2 feedback circuits between cerebellum and periphery and cerebellum and motor cortex. This serves 2 functions :

(i) It helps in precise and complicated movements of distal parts of limbs.

Once cerebellum learns its role in a pattern of movement, it provides rapid turning on-off of agonist muscle activity and inhibition of antagonist muscles at beginning of a movement. At end of a movement, it plays a role in rapid turn off of agonist muscles and turn on of antagonist muscles.

(ii) It helps the cerebral cortex to plan and execute movements.

Lateral zone of cerebellum and dentate nuclei are involved.

(iii) Cerebellum also has role in predicting events.

3. It can correct errors in execution of voluntary movements

4. Cerebellum and brain stem along with spinal cord help in regulation of posture and equilibrium. Flocculonodular lobes and vermis are responsible for this.

## Cerebellar control is IPSILATERAL (Fig. 11.48)

## Circuits of cerebellum

The structure of cerebellar cortex is more uniform than that of cerebral cortex. ***From superficial to deep***, it can be divided **histologically** into three layers (a) ***molecular layer***; (b) ***middle Purkinje cell layer***; (c) ***granular layer***.

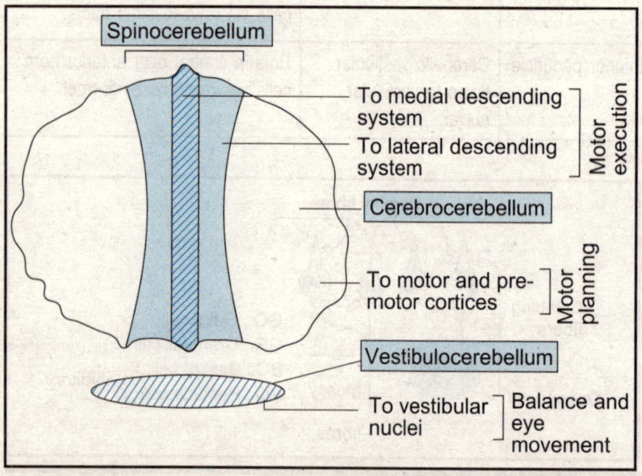


Fig. 11.46

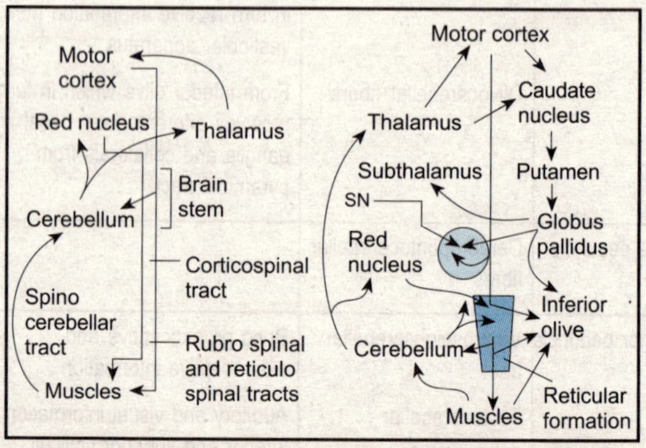


Fig. 11.48 : SN – Substantia nigra

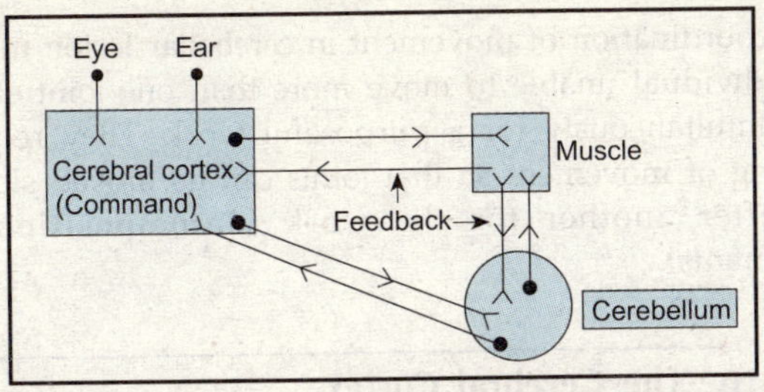


**Fig. 11.49 :** Cerebellum as comparator

**Purkinje cell** layer is an one-cell layer composed of the largest neurons of CNS–Purkinje cells. These cells extend their dendritic tree through superficial molecular layer. This layer also harbors the axons of granule cells (cell bodies are in granular layer). **Each granule cell** sends its axon to molecular layer where it undergoes bifurcation like T. Each branch then runs in the molecular layer and form parallel fibers with similar branches of other axons. These parallel fibers make contact with the dendrites of Purkinje cells. There is a regular arrangement of the disposition of dendrites of Purkinje cells and parallel fibers similar to the orientation of electrical iwires installed with repeated posts.

Besides these two types of cells, **the cerebellar cortex** contain three other varieties of cells (a) *basket cells* in the molecular layer; (b) *stellate cells* in the molecular layer superficial to basket cells; (c) *Golgi cells* in the granular layer.

All three neurons are inhibitory. *Basket cells* have afferent input from parallel fibers (granular cells) and send their axons around individual Purkinje cells where each axon branches to form a basket-like structure surrounding soma and axon hillock of each Purkinje cell.

*Stellate cells* also receive afferents from parallel fibers and project to Purkinje cells.

*Golgi cells*, via their bodies, receive afferent from mossy fibers and Purkinje cell axon (collaterals) and send their dendrites to molecular layer to make contact with parallel fibers. Their axons end on dendrites of granule cells.

The basket cells, stellate cells and golgi cells are stimulated by their afferents but they are inhibited by their efferent conne-ctions. The first two inhibit Purkinje cells and the third inhibits granule cells.

The fibers that form the afferent input to the cerebellar cortex can be divided into two groups **climbing fibers** and **mossy fibers**. The source of climbing fibers are neurons of inferior olivary nuclei of medulla. Each climbing fiber (axon) terminates in the primary dendrite of a Purkinje cell which it encircles like a climbing plant.

All other afferents form the mossy fibers which terminate mainly on the dendrites of granule cells forming complex structures called *glomeruli* — the site where the Golgi cells also make contact. Mossy fibers also send collaterals to Golgi cells and nuclear cells of cerebellum (Figs. 11.50 and 11.51).

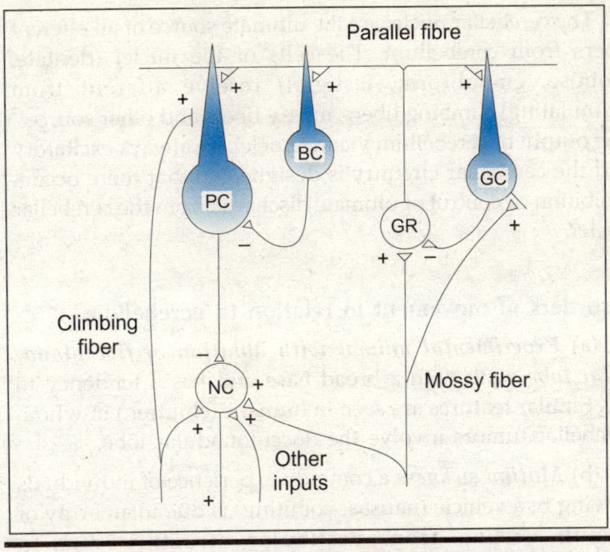


**Fig. 11.50 :** Cerebellar circuitry. BC = Basket cell. GC = Golgi cell, GR = Granule cell, NC = Nuclear cell, PC = Purkinje cell

From the description of the connections, it is apparent that a climbing fiber is able to stimulate strongly a Purkinje cell but a mossy fiber is capable of weaker stimulation via granular cell – parallel fiber circuit.

**Golgi cells** are stimulated by all its afferents (mossy fiber, parallel fiber, Purkinje fiber collaterals) and send inhibitory impulse to glomeruli of granule cells to inhibit stimulation of the same by mossy fibers. It is to be mentioned in this connection that all the afferents derived from mossy fibers and climbing fibers are stimulatory, but **Purkinje cell** discharge is always inhibitory to deep cerebellar nuclei.

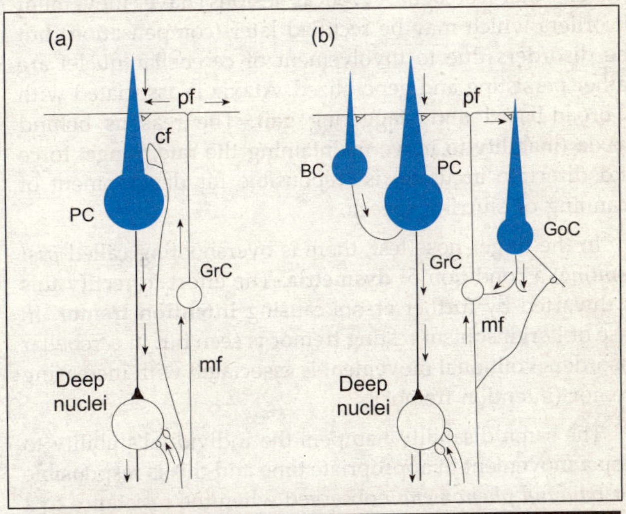


**Fig. 11.51 :** Synaptic relationship in cerebellum

(a) Input-output circuits. (b) Inhibitory circuits. BC =Basket cell. cf = climbing fiber. GoC = golgi cell. GrC = granule cell. mf = mossy fiber. PC = Purkinje cell. pf = Parallel fiber.

The cerebellar nuclei are the ultimate source of all efferent fibers from cerebellum. The cells of the nuclei (dentate, globose, emboliform, fastigial) receive afferent from (stimulating) climbing fibers, mossy fibers and other sources. The output of cerebellum via the nuclei are always excitatory and the cerebellar circuitry is designed so that there occurs inhibition or control of ultimate discharge from the cerebellar nuclei.

### Disorders of movement in relation to cerebellum

(a) ***Experimental animal with ablation of flocculonodular lobe*** walk with a broad base and has a tendency to fall. Similar features are seen in humans (children) in whom cerebellar tumors involve the flocculonodular lobe.

(b) ***Motion sickness*** a common experience of individuals moving in a vehicle (nausea; vomiting) is due to an array of stimuli arising from vestibular structure due to unaccustomed type of movement in the vehicle. There is involvement of all the structures having vestibular connections including the flocculonodular lobe. They can be controlled by some antiemetic drugs.

(c) ***In experimental animals, ablation of anterior lobe of cerebellum*** causes hypertonia of corresponding parts of the body but, in human beings, hypotonia is seen in cerebellar lesion.

(d) ***The manifestation of cerebellar involvement in human beings*** and in experimental animals have common features in that the disability appears on movement and there is no sensory impairment.

The movements called **ataxia** are awkward in nature and are due to incoordination of different groups of muscles involved in maintaining accuracy in the force, range, direction and rate of movement if it is repetitive. It is of interest that cerebellar cortical lesions have movement disorders which may be rectified later (compensation) but the disorders due to involvement of cerebellar nuclei are rather persisting and generalized. **Ataxia** is associated with a broad-based and staggering gait. The reasons behind ataxia (inability to move maintaining the rate, range, force and direction accurate) is responsible for development of scanning or slurring speech.

In the finger nose test, there is overshooting called *past pointing*, a condition of **dysmetria**. The effort to rectify this is thwarted by further errors causing **intention tremor**. In case of Parkinsonism resting tremor is seen but in cerebellar disorders volitional movement is associated with increasing tremor (intention tremor).

The same disability hampers the individual's ability to stop a movement in appropriate time and this is responsible for ***rebound phenomenon*** observed when the resistance to a pressing limb of the patient is suddenly withdrawn. Now it is understandable how it is impossible for patients with cerebellar lesion to perform rapidly repeated movements like alternate pronation and supination of forearm (keeping the upper arm apposed to the body) – **adiadochokinesia**.

Incoordination of movement in cerebellar lesion makes the individual unable to move more than one joint easily and simultaneously for a purposeful work. They require splitting of movement so that joints can be moved slowly one after another for the work (**decomposition of movements**).

## ➤ 11.10 The Cerebral Cortex

**Cerebrum** is the largest part of the brain. The superficial part of the cerebrum is composed of nerve cell bodies or gray matter, forming **cerebral cortex** and the deeper layers consist of nerve fibers or white matter. The cerebral cortex consists of many foldings. The exposed areas of the folds are the gyri or convolutions and these are separated by sulci or fissures. These convolutions increase the surface area of the cerebrum. The cerebral cortex is composed of thin horizontal layers of neuron and nerve fibers.

### Histology of cerebral cortex

**Layer I (molecular layer)** is rich in fibers but the cellular contents are very poor. The fibers are principally dendrites of the deeper lying cells. The cells are very small and stellate in appearance, termed as horizontal **cells of Cajal**.

**Layer II** (external granular layer) contains plerty of small **pyramidal** and **stellate cells**.

**Layer III** (external pyramidal layer) consists of typically pyramidal cells of varying sizes. The axons of the pyramidal neurons pass into the white matter of the cerebral hemisphere.

**Layer IV** (internal granular layer) having closely packed **stellate cells**.

**Layer V** (internal pyramidal layer) consists of **giant pyramidal cells, Betz cells**. Axon of the pyramidal neurons in layer V form pyramidal tract.

**Layer VI** (fusiform or multiform layer) consists of different forms of several cell types including pyramidal cells (Fig. 11.52).

### Fibers of cerebral cortex (see Chart 2)

The **projection fibers** may be corticofugal or corticopetal.

The **association fibers** are present in large numbers. They function to correlate activities of different cortical areas.

The **commissural fibers** the anterior commissural fibers connect the olfactory bulb and parts of the temporal lobe of the two cerebral hemispheres. The corpus callosum connects thecerebral cortex of the two hemispheres.

**Functional localisation in the cerebral cortex** : The neocortex may be classified into cortex of the frontal, parietal, occipital and temporal lobes.

1. **Cortex of the frontal lobe (Fig. 11.53) :** ***The neocortex of the frontal lobe is responsible for motor activities, higher mental functions and emotions.***

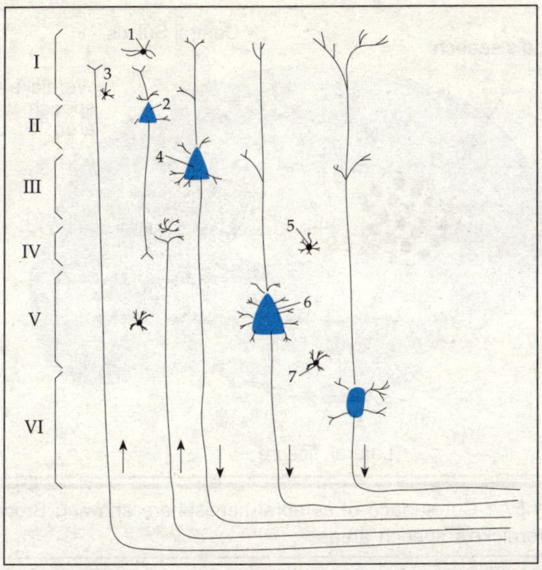


Fig. 11.52 : Types of cells present in six layers of cerebral cortex

(a) The **portion of the cortex** which is responsible for movements is the motor and premotor area, corresponds to *Brodmann's areas 4 and 6, respectively*.

Axons of the pyramidal neurons in areas 4 and 6 contribute 60 per cent of the pyramidal tract fibers, the other pyramidal fibers arise from somatosensory area, the occipital and temporal lobes (Figs. 11.54 and 11.55).

(b) The **frontal eye field** is located in the anterior part of area 6, area 8 and a small part of area 9. Neurons located in these areas influence the cranial nerve nuclei of III, IV and VI via interneurons. They are related to voluntary movements of the eye (Fig. 11.56).

(c) **The Broca's speech area** (in dominant hemisphere) is located in front of the face region of motor cortex. It plays a dominant role in language functions.

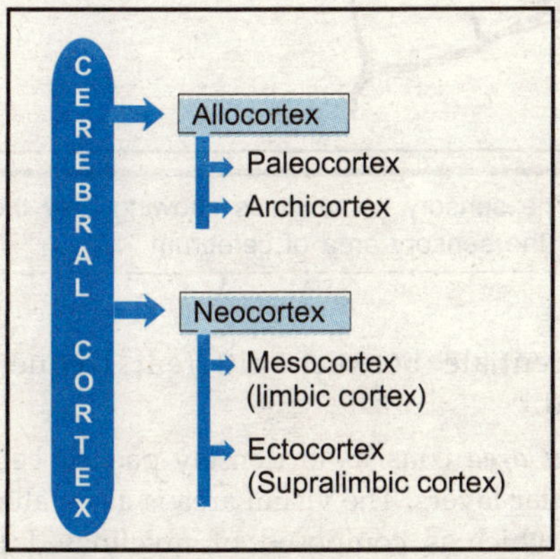


Chart 2

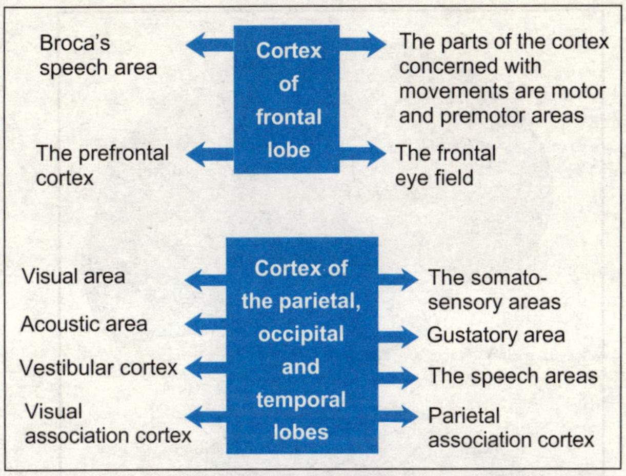


Fig. 11.53 : Fibers of cerebral cortex

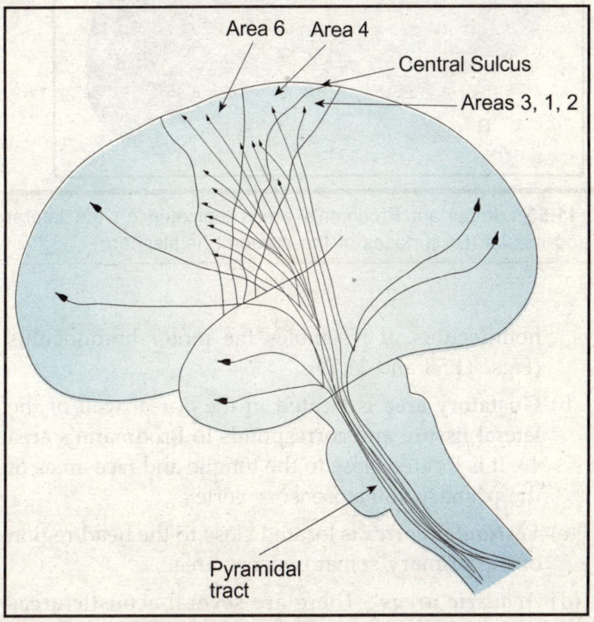


Fig. 11.54 : Origin of pyramidal tract

There is motor aphasia in addition to contralateral hemiplegia following a lesion affecting this area and areas 4 and 6 (see Fig. 11.57).

(d) **The prefrontal cortex** is located in front of the area 4, 6 and 8 and is connected with all the lobes of the cerebrum and with the thalamus. The intellect and judgements are reduced following a lesion affecting the prefrontal cortex as occurs in neurosyphilis.

2. **Cortex of the parietal, occipital and temporal lobes (Fig. 11.50) :**

(a) ***Somatosensory areas :*** The primary area of reception of sensory data is located in Brodmann's areas 3, 1 and 2. The body representations in the primary somatosensory area are known as the sensory

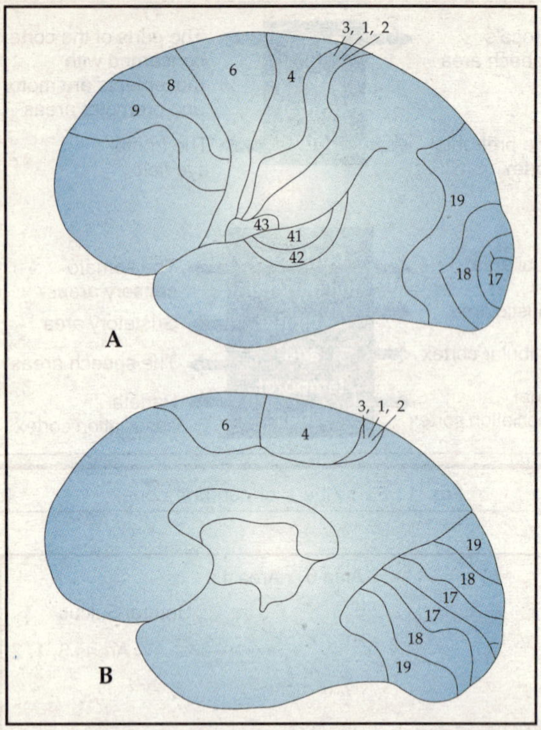


Fig. 11.55 : Important Brodman's areas indicated on the lateral (A) and medial (B) surfaces of the cerebral hemisphere

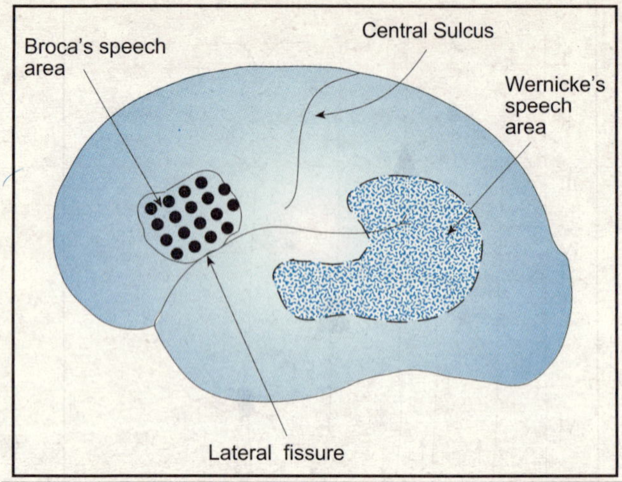


Fig. 11.57 : Cut surface of cerebral hemisphere showing Broca's and Wernicke's speech areas

homunculus. It resembles the motor homunculus (Figs. 11.58 and 11.59).

(b) **Gustatory area** is located in the dorsal wall of the lateral fissure and corresponds to Brodmann's area 43. It is located close to the tongue and face areas of the primary somatosensory cortex.

(c) ***Vestibular cortex*** is located close to the head region of the primary somatosensory area.

(d) ***Acoustic areas*** : There are several acoustic areas and one important acoustic area is located in the *transverse gyri of Heschl* which corresponds to Brodmann's areas 41 and 42. Its function is to differentiate between different frequencies of sound.

(e) ***Visual area*** consists of densely packed cells in the granular layers. The visual area is also called striate area which is composed of myelinated fibers. It corresponds to area 17 around calcarine sulcus of the occipital lobe.

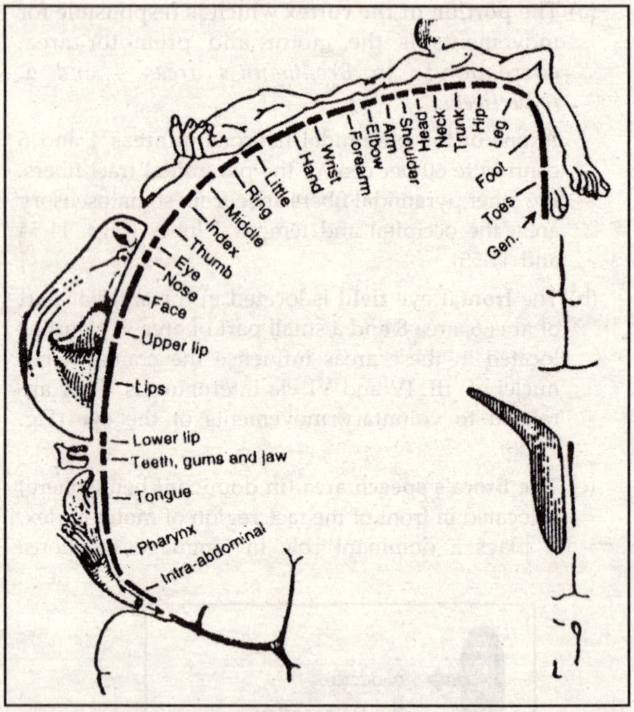


Fig. 11.58 : The sensory homunculus showing how the body is represented in the sensory area of cerebrum

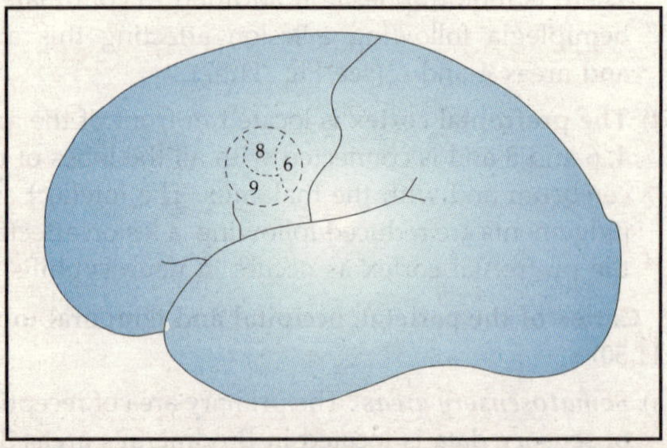


Fig. 11.56 : Lateral surface of cerebral hemisphere showing frontal eye field which includes parts of areas 6, 8 and 9.

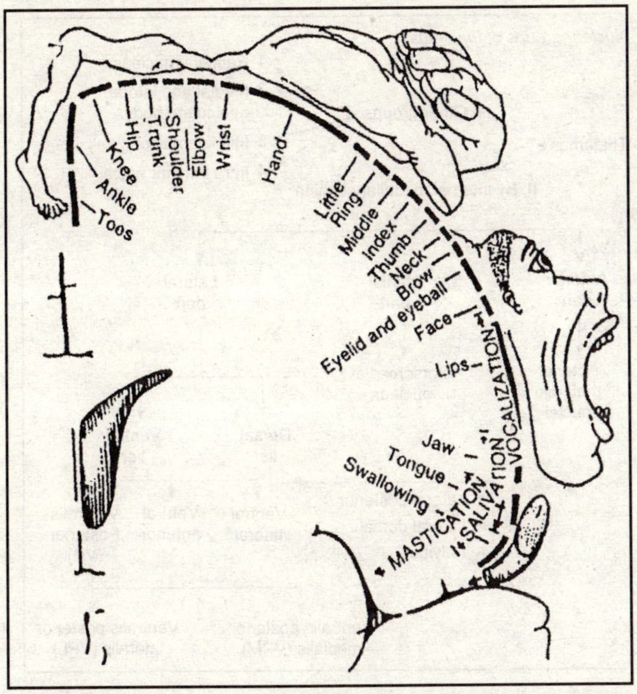


**Fig. 11.59 :** The motor homunculus showing how the body is represented in the motor area of the cerebrum

(f) ***Visual association cortex*** : It is located in areas 18 and 19 which surround area 17. It occupies the whole of the medial surface of the occipital lobe and extends up to part of its lateral surface. If there is a lesion of areas 18 and 19, there will be visual agnosia.

(g) ***Parietal association cortex*** : It is located in between the primary somatosensory and visual areas and includes part of Wernicke's speech area. This area is responsible for performing complex and integrated activities.

(h) ***Speech area*** : The motor speech area is located in the frontal lobe. However, a sensory speech area has also been described by Wernicke. Sensory aphasia develops following destruction of the speech area. Wernicke's area is situated at the posterior part of superior temporal gyrus (categorical hemisphere).

## 11.11 The Cerebral Hemisphere

The **cerebrum** occupies the anterior and middle cranial fossae. The cerebellum is separated from the cerebrum by the tentorium cerebelli. The cerebral hemisphere is lined with an outer layer of gray matter. The white matter and the basal nuclei are located beneath the cortex.

Each **cerebral hemisphere** has got three surfaces (medial, lateral and inferior) and four lobes (frontal, parietal, occipital and temporal). See Fig. 11.60.

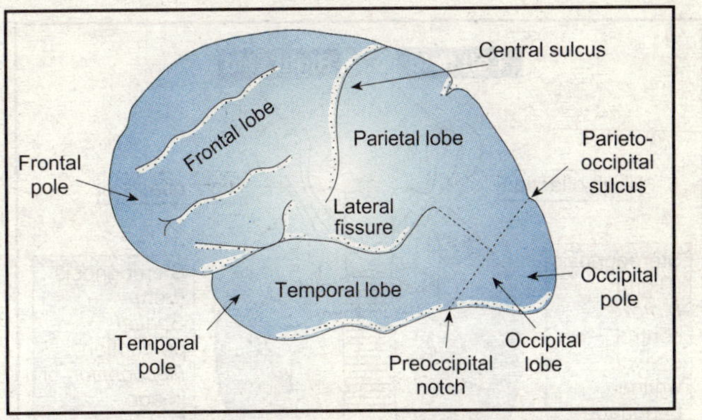


**Fig. 11.60 :** The frontal, parietal, temporal and occipital lobes, demarcated on the lateral surface of the cerebral hemisphere

The lateral surface of the hemisphere shows two important features, the lateral fissure and the central sulcus.

*Temporal lobe* is located below the lateral fissure. The *parietal lobe* is isolated by the central sulcus. Only a small part of the *occipital lobe* appears on the lateral surface of the hemisphere.

The lateral surface of the hemisphere contains many other sulci and their related gyri such as precentral sulcus, postcentral sulcus, precentral gyrus and postcentral gyrus, respectively (Fig. 11.61).

The medial surface of one hemisphere is separated from the other by the longitudinal fissure. Corpus callosumwhich contains commissural fibers interconnecting corresponding parts of the two hemispheres bridges the fissure. Septum pellucidum; fornix, anterior commissure, thalamus, hypo-thalamus, paraterminal gyrus and cingulate gyrus (Fig. 11.62) are the structures situated close to the corpus callosum.

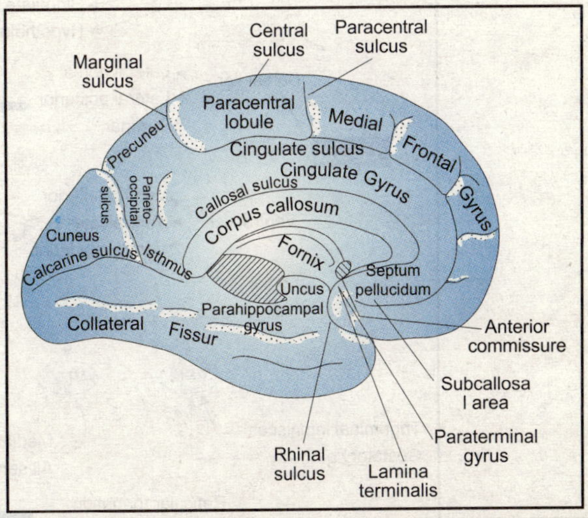


**Fig. 11.61 :** Sulci and gyri on the medial and part of the inferior surface of the cerebral hemisphere

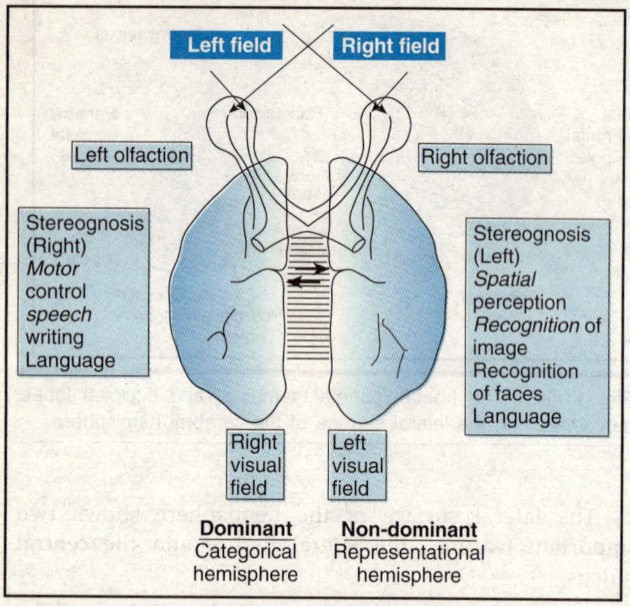


Fig. 11.62 : Concept of cerebral dominance

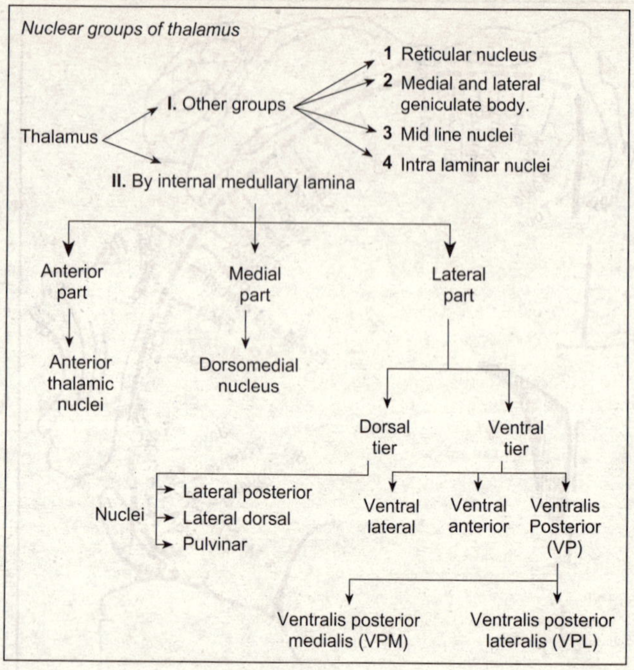


## ➤ 11.12 The Thalamus

The thalamus is located medial to the posterior limb of the internal capsule. The two thalami form the lateral walls of the third ventricle, superior to the hypothalamic sulcus. A sulcus of different depth located in the lateral wall of the third ventricle (hypothalamic sulcus) divides the diencephalon into a dorsal part called **thalamus** and a

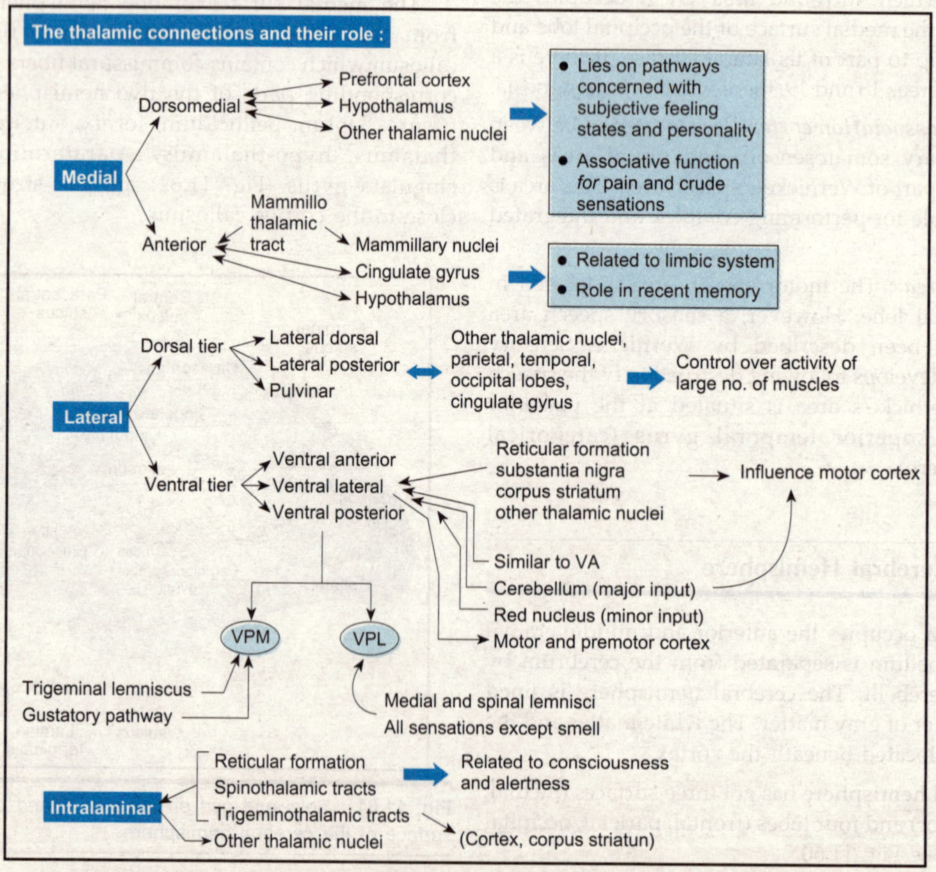

ventral part called **hypothalamus**. There are two small swellings, known as the **medial and lateral geniculate bodies** which are located in the inferior part of the caudal end of the thalamus.

The lateral surface of the thalamus is lined by a layer of white matter called **external medullary lamina**. It is isolated by a layer of gray matter, the reticular thalamic nucleus. There is another distinct lamina of white matter, called the **internal medullary lamina**.

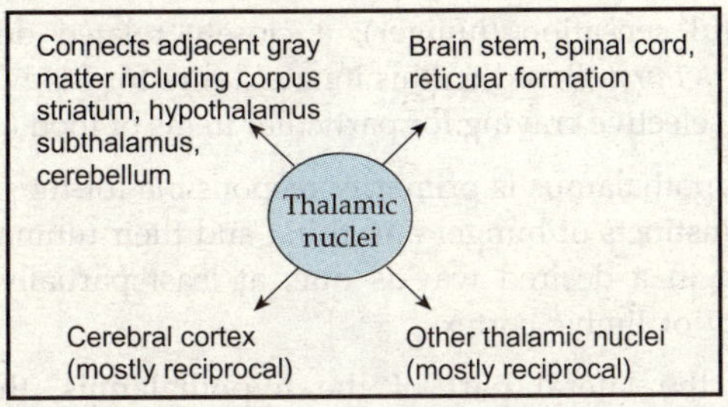


**Features of thalamic connections :**

(i) Every thalamic nucleus (except reticular) sends axons to different parts of cerebral cortex and the latter sends projections to thalamus.

(ii) The cerebello-rubro-thalamo-cortico-ponto-cerebellar loop and cortical-striatal-pallidal-thalamo-cortical loop are involved in meaningful, voluntary movements.

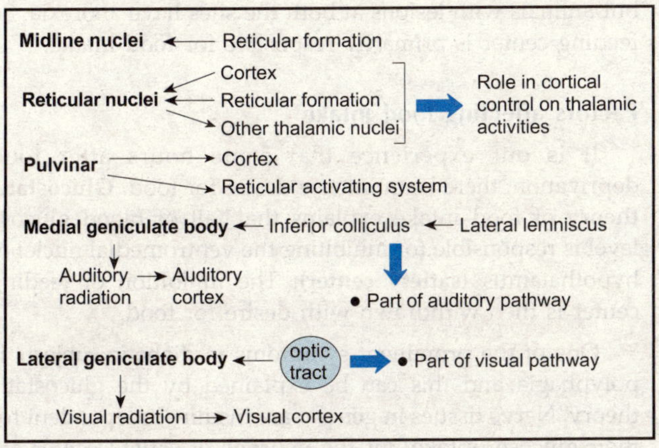


## General Functions of thalamus

Functionally, it is the first centre for coordination of sensory, motor and autonomic information. In lower animals it is the highest centre for sensory coordination while hypothalamus and basal ganglia act as highest autonomic and motor centres respectively.

Functions :

(i) Acts a major relay station for sensory impulses destined for cerebral cortex. It acts as a crude centre for sensory perception.

(ii) Connections with RAS and cortex cause wakefulness, alertness and consciousness.

(iii) It forms part of the limbic system.

(iv) Acts as a relay point for dentatothalamic tract which then passes to cortex and provides information for motor activity.

## Thalamic Syndrome

When a branch of posterior cerebral artery supplying posteroventral nucleus of thalamus is blocked, nuclei of this area only degenerate.

The thalamic syndrome has the following features :

(i) Loss of all sensations on the opposite side.

(ii) Sensory ataxia.

(iii) Affective qualities are abnormal.

(iv) After some weeks, some of the sensations on opposite side return, but are poorly localized and very painful (always).

# ➤ 11.13 Function of Limbic Cortex—Emotion, Behavior and Mood

## Introduction

It is an universal truth that basic instincts of life like feeding, protective movements, sexual activities, silent or vocal responses to pleasant or irritating stimuli are common throughout the animal kingdom. Cerebral cortex is highly developed in mammals only. Cerebral cortex of human beings has an old part that is concerned with basic instinct like emotion and other vegetative functions supplemented by a highly developed part which is meant for speech, intelligence, judgement by which man has acquired the highest seat among all living beings.

The older part of the cerebral cortex is the **allocortex** which is histologically simpler than the newly developed **neocortex.** Anatomically, allocortex is situated like an annulus (or ring or border) surrounding the hilum of each cerebral hemisphere – *limbic cortex*. The cortical part which joins the limbic cortex with neocortex is histologically transitional between them. It is called *juxta-allocortex*. The limbic cortex is connected with the hypothalamus which the plays an effective role in response to emotion etc. The limbic system regulates inborn and acquired behaviour and is the site of origin of instinctive behavior, motivation and emotion.

The anatomical connections of the limbic cortex is called **Papez circuit**. The limbic system has cortical (hippocampus, parahippocampal gyrus, cingulate gyrus, parts of the olfactory cortex) and subcortical divisions (amygdaloid body, septal area, anterior thalamic nucleus). The limbic system governs the expressions of emotions. It is important also in the regulation of behavior and in memory.

Starting from the hippocampus situated at the floor of the lateral ventricle, fibers travel via fornix to the mamillary bodies of the base of the brain. From mammillary bodies fibers project via mamillothalamic tract to anterior nuclei of thalamus. From the anterior nucleus of thalamus fibers project to cingulate gyrus on each side; cingulate cortex sends signals back to hippocampus forming the Papez circuit. From different parts of this basic circuit there are connections with septum, olfactory striae, olfactory tubercle, olfactory cortex and hypothalamus. The hippocampus is related to dentate gyrus and parahippocampal gyrus.

From the description, it is apparent that neocortex is connected rather poorly to the limbic cortex. Neocortex has definitely some control over limbic cortical functions like emotion and behavior but the control can be overridden by the limbic cortex. We are all familiar with experiences of emotional outbursts overriding our constant desire of restraining it.

### Overview of Functions of Important Components of Limbic System

| *Area* | *Function(s)* |
|---|---|
| 1. **Hypothalamus** | Discussed under "HYPOTHALAMUS". |
| 2. **Hippocampus** | It has profuse connections with widespread areas of cerebral cortex |
| | It acts as an area where incoming signals are channelised to appropriate behavioural patterns |
| | It is also responsible for consolidation of long-term memories of verbal and symbolic type. |
| | It is association area for behavioural control. Anterior temporal cortex causes gustatory and olfactory associations. Auditory associations and thought association from Wernicke's area occurs at Parahippocampal gyri. Sensory motor associations occur in posterior cingulate cortex |
| 3. **Limbic cortex** | A ring of cerebral cortex beginning in orbitofrontal area on ventral surface of frontal lobe, extending upward in subcallosal gyrus, extending over top of corpuscallosum and downward onto medial aspect of cerebral hemisphere in cingulate gyrus and passing behind and below corpus callosum on ventromedial surface of temporal lobe to parahippocampal gyrus and uncus. |
| 4. **Amygdala** | Olfactory association in lower animals. Receives neuronal signals from limbic cortex as well as neocortex and transmits impulses to same cortical areas and subcortical structures. It is a behavioural awareness area at subconscious level. It projects to the limbic system one's present status in relation to both surroundings and thought and decides behaviour accordingly. |

## FUNCTIONS OF LIMBIC SYSTEM

### A. Food intake

One of the primary and essential instinct of each animal is to acquire food and the limbic cortex is intimately related with hypothalamus in this behavior. It is our common experience that food deprivation makes us anxious and often over reactive to minor stimuli and there occurs changes in autonomic functions like heart rate, blood pressure etc.

Deprivation of food is responsible for a subjective stressful sensation (hunger); a closely related desire for water is *thirst*. Based on this innate desire for food (hunger) is our selective craving for particular items of food (*appetite*).

Hypothalamus is primarily responsible for the origin of basic instincts of hunger and thirst and their ultimate satisfaction in a desired way is due, at least partially, to the activity of limbic cortex.

In the lateral part of the hypothalamus, there are collections of neurons which form hunger or feeding centers. These neurons are tonically active and they are responsible for the desire for food. But they are inhibited by neurons in ventromedial nuclei of hypothalamus called **satiety center.**

In experimental animals (mice) it has been observed that lesions of the lateral hypothalamus bilaterally make the animals reluctant to take food. They lose weight and may even die. Animals with lesions of the ventromedial nuclei on both sides become voracious eaters and become obese but animals with lesions at both the sites have anorexia. So feeding center is primarily resposible for food intake.

### Factors affecting food intake

It is our experience that some hours after food deprivation, there is an intense desire for food. **Glucostatic theory** of food intake explains that fall of blood glucose level is responsible for inhibiting the ventromedial nuclei of hypothalamus **(satiety center)**. The inhibition of feeding center is then withdrawn with desire for food.

One of the prominent symptoms in diabetic subjects is polyphagia and this can be explained by the glucostatic theory. Nerve tissues in general are insulin–independent for their glucose uptake but the neurons of satiety center are insulin- dependent for glucose uptake. So, in diabetic individuals, lack of insulin makes this area glucose depleted and their function remains suppressed in presence of normal or elevated blood sugar level.

Feeding center thus remains uninhibited for considerably longer time causing hyperphagia.

Sometimes, individuals cannot restrain their food intake even if they want to lose weight; their body fat store may not send signals suppressing appetite **(lipostatic hypothesis)**.

There are some other regulators of appetite. Cold environment stimulates and hot environment suppresses appetite, an appropriate response to metabolic needs and body temperature regulation.

Some gastrointestinal hormones like CCK inhibits appetite. Probably they help in keeping our appetite suppressed along with other factors.

Gastric emptiness is a common feeling and it may be associated with painful contractions **(hunger contractions)** and sensation of hunger. Distension of stomach and other parts of the GI tract also inhibits appetite by humoral or neural mecha-nisms. So, after a heavy meal, rise of blood glucose level, GI hormones and other humoral and nervous stimuli suppress desire of feeding for a considerable length of time.

Food intake is also related to the activity of *brown fat.* **Brown fat** has a limited distribution in adult individuals but considerable amount of brown fat are present around the scapulae, nape of the neck and large blood vessels of thorax and abdomen in infants and children.

**Brown fat** differs from ordinary storage form of white fat in that within them (brown fat) lipid is distributed (cellular) in small globules rather than a single large bolus as in white adipose tissue. The brown fat is more vascular and has more sympathetic innervation. They are also rich in mitochondria. Cytochrome enzymes of mitochondria are responsible for their brown color.

The brown fat adipocytes have, at their inner mitochondrial membrane, a leak protein for $H^+$ movement. Normally, when $H^+$ enters across the inner mitochondrial membrane there is generation of ATP, but when $H^+$ enters through the leak channels there is no generation of ATP. Generation of ATP with entry of $H^+$ is a manifestation of oxidation-phosphorylation coupling but the leak channels provide for uncoupling of oxidation and phosphorylation.

Thus, it is responsible for liberation of large amount of energy as there is no recovery of energy in the form of ATP. So, if brown fat becomes active, substrates are broken down rather than being stored.

Unlike white fat, brown fat cells along with blood vessels receive sympathetic innervation. So sympathetic stimulation in response to food intake stimulates their activity contributing to specific dynamic action (SDA) after food intake.

During cold, by sympathetic stimulation, brown fat under-goes quicker degradation liberating increased heat energy. It is a response (nonshivering) to cold and an attempt to raise body temperature.

Defects of neural control of brown fat is probably a cause of **obesity**. In experimental animals with lesions of satiety center, sympathetic stimulation of brown fat is diminished after feeding. So breakdown of foodstuff by brown fat is absent. So food is utilized in such a way that accumulation of redundant energy can take place more efficiently. In humans, similar defective brown fat activity may impair proper utilisation of foodstuff and deposition of their excess amount.

### B. Thirst

Thirst, like hunger, is also controlled primarily by hypothalamus. Evidence in hypothalamus of cells regulating fluid intake independent of food intake has been observed. These neurons of anterior hypothalamus are called thirst centers on either side.

**Factors regulating water intake :**

- Predominant stimulus for thirst is an increase in osmolality of plasma or extracellular fluid. When an individual is not taking water, there is constant loss of water from skin and respiratory system (insensible perspiration) and sweating in hot environment.
- Angiotensin II generated stimulates thirst by acting on subfornical organ and vascular organ of lamina terminalis.
- Loss of blood, eg hemorrhage, stimulates drinking in response to diminished discharge from baroreceptors.
- Dryness of mouth and irritation stimulates drinking. Considerable relief is often obtained by simply keeping the mouth moist at short intervals.
- Drinking may also be psychogenic in some cases. Compulsive water drinking is seen in some mentally unstable individuals. They have diuresis and it is required to distinguish them from diabetes insipidus by water deprivation test. In compulsive water drinking, urinary concentration increases and there is no loss of body weight but, in diabetes insipidus, water deprivation fails to increase urinary concentration and body weight gets reduced.

The limbic cortex is associated with the psychological aspects of hunger and thirst. It also influences the motor activity which is dependent on neocortex. Bilateral lesions of the temporal lobe involving the amygdala causes hyperphagia and intake of anything as food without discrimination and is also associated with hypersexuality **(Klüver Bucy syndrome)**.

## Emotion

Emotion is a mental state or feeling such as love, hate, anger, joy, fear, grief arising from within or in response to external stimuli. Emotion has a physical component in addition to subjective sensations, like alteration in heart rate, respiratory rate, vasomotor reactions and changes in muscle tone.

The mental and physical effects related to emotion are described by several terms which appear synonymous but are distinct in the true sense. As for example, when we hear an explosive sound we try to trace its origin (whether from a cracker or a deadly bomb); this faculty is **cognition** (L. cognoscere, to know), the mental process by which know-ledge is acquired. The feeling may be of fear or of nothing as the case may be. ***Affect*** (L. affectus, exerting influence) is the emotional reaction associated with an experience. According to ***affect*** an individual may try to escape from the spot or ignore it. This urge is called ***conation*** (L. connatio, an attempt), the impulse and drive an individual takes, in response to a particular incidence. The cognition, affect and conation are associated with physical changes mostly from autonomic nervous discharge like tachycardia, tachypnea, sweating etc. The hypothalamus and limbic cortex are concerned both with the mental and the physical changes in relation to emotion.

## Fear, rage and sham rage

**Fear** or **fright** is an universal emotional perception (affect) to situations threatening life or other stressful conditions of any kind. It is the psychological basis of avoidance reaction. When one happens to come across a snake all on a sudden, he experiences a typical fear response. He stops moving, withdraws his legs, gets seriously alarmed in mind and take care to flee from the animal. Fear induces anxiety and is associated with physical changes like palpitation etc. The changes vary considerably among individuals. It is not uncommon to see students suffering from anorexia, malaise, and even fever, prior to examination. The avoidance reaction is protective, reflexive and partly conscious response.

**Rage** or **violent anger** is a feeling with which we all are familiar. It is also a protective response like fear to adverse circumstances. **Rage** is a fighting response intending to destroy the cause of irritation. Angry individuals commonly use loud abusive languages and then hit their opponents to overpower them. There is tachypnea, tachycardia, other autonomic and motor reactions associated with rage. Quality and degree of rage reaction vary among individuals. While hungry anger commonly increases and it is not uncommon to learn cases of assault and even murder when a hungry individual is denied food or even the quality of food he wants.

Lateral hypothalamus contains both the feeding center as well as areas involved in rage reaction. Stimulation of lateral hypothalamus and some part of the brain stem in experimental animals causes rage reaction. On the other hand, ventromedial nuclei of hypothalamus and septal nuclei appear to inhibit rage, similar to satiety-hunger phenomenon.

In experimental animals, the ablation of neocortex and part of amygdaloid nuclei exacerbates rage response. On the other hand, bilateral amygdaloid nuclei destruction makes an animal calm. It deserves mention that both the rage and pacidity produced by separate areas of amygdaloid nuclei can be changed by destruction of ventromedial and ventrolateral nuclei of hypothalamus; amygdaloid nuclei probably have their effects via hypothalamus.

It is a common observation that males of most mammals are more aggressive than females. But in human society the ultimate response is governed by cultural and social restrictions. To reduce aggressiveness animals are castrated, and utilised for cultivation of land and transport.

**Sham rage** : The rage reaction produced by stimuli in decorticated animals was called **sham rage** on the assumption that psychological and physical manifestations are different or dissociated in comparison to anger reactions in intact animals. But careful observations after destruction of neocortical and hypothalamic areas producing rage reaction, it was impossible to separate mental and physical aspects of the anger response. So sham rage can be taken as a term synonymous with experimentally produced anger phenomenon.

## Motivation

The desire arising in the mind and also that provoked by any external stimulus to do something physical or mental is called **motivation.**

All our short term and long term efforts are guided by some sort of motivation. Motivation is intimately associated with the feelings of reward or punishment. It is due to reward in the form of a regular income that individuals take up occupations involving immense risks, even with loss of life. Similarly, we do not hesitate to part with a portion of our income in apprehension of punishment from tax collecting authorities. Criminals resort to the same phenomenon of motivation to extract money from their victims by intimidation.

The physical adjunct of these emotional reactions are beginning to be explored by animal experiments in which different areas of brain are stimulated by some motor activity like bar-pressing.

It has been observed that stimulation of certain areas of the brain near the midline causes repeated bar pressing. It indicates that it leads to some psychological gratification in the animal but its subjective character is difficult to interpret in absolute terms. The areas involved include part of forebrain, medial forebrain bundle, tegmentum of midbrain and septal nuclei.

On the contrary, stimulation of other areas of the brain produces avoidance reaction i.e., if the animal happens to stimulate such areas it will never repeat the bar pressing. The areas include the posterolateral hypothalamus, part of dorsal mid-brain, olfactory cortex and elsewhere. The avoidance response inducing area is much less extensive than areas associated with pleasure. However, areas where neither type of response is seen are enormous.

It has been observed that reward producing area is sometimes close to punishment inflicting sites. There must be interaction between two opposing systems of reward and punishment. It is evident from our experience that kleptomaniacs and alcoholics are difficult to rectify in spite of punishment. On the other hand, if the degree of punishment can be made more severe the behavioral change can be done with permanently. Imprisonment or other forms of punish-ment do rectify some errant individuals, eg. imposing fine on ticketless travellers. When there occurs interaction of reward and punishment systems, the motivation is appropriately modified, eg. if some food intake is associated with illness we regularly avoid the food.

As expected, some chemical mediators can affect the behavioral responses in the bar-pressing tests because transmission across the synapses are chemical almost universally. Dopamine acts as an inducer of reward system.

## ➤ 11.14 Hypothalamus

It is a diffuse nuclear mass which is separated from the thalamus by the hypothalamic sulcus and forms anteroinferior wall of third ventricle.

Nuclear masses are classified as :

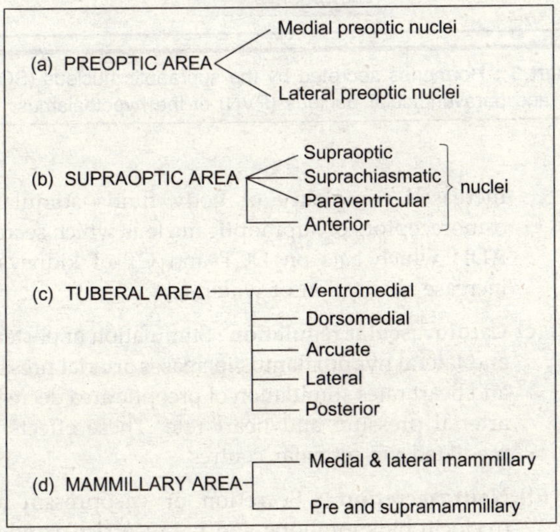


### Connections of hypothalamus

**The main AFFERENT connections are :**

1. From other parts of limbic system :
   (i) Pyriform cortex.
   (ii) Amygdaloid complex.
   (iii) From Amygaloid nucleus to stria terminalis.
   (iv) From hippocampus and post-commissural fornix to mammillary body other hippocampal fibres to medial forebrain bundle bundle.
   (v) From cingulate gyrus via hippocampus.
   (vi) From restricted region of hippocampus, the medial hypothalamic tract reaches arcuate nucleus.
2. From midbrain tegmentum to mammillary nuclei and medial forebrain bundle (Through these routes visceral sensations project to hypothalamus).
3. From frontal cortex and dorsomedial nucleus of thalamus to medial forebrain bundle.
4. Olfactory impulses through medial forebrain bundle.

### Summary of Afferent Coonections

1. Receives information from (a) viscera (b) Limbic cortex.
2. It has its own receptor systems like glucoreceptors, osmoreceptors, thermoreceptors, etc.
3. Ill-defined connections with reticular formation, basal ganglia and cortex.

**The main efferent connections are :**

(a) To amygdaloid nuclei and thence to pyriform cortex.
(b) To septal nuclei (via medial forebrain bundle) and then to hippocampus
(c) Mammillo-thalamic tract.
(d) To reticular formation, bulbar nuclei and spinal cord. These contribute to extrapyramidal facilitatory pathway. These fibres also establish connections to brain stem autonomic nuclei and lateral horn cells of thoracolumbar segments and thus control sympathetic outflow. These fibres also establish connections with cranial and sacral parasympathetic outflow.

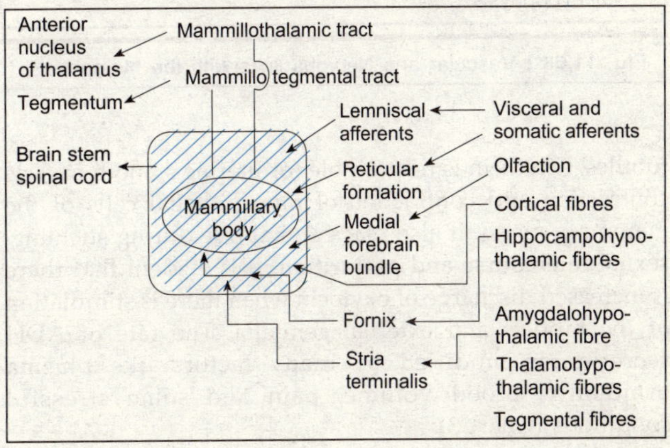


(e) From supraoptic and paraventricular nuclei hypothalamo-hypophyseal tract runs to posterior pituitary.

### Vascular and Nervous links with the hypophysis

***Vascular link*** is maintained by the hypothalamo-hypohyseal portal vessels that connect plexuses of sinusoids in the median eminence and infundibulum of the hypothalamus with the sinusoids of the anterior lobe of the hypophysis. The releasing hormones are produced in the neurons in the infundibular and adjacent nuclei. Then they are conveyed along their axons and discharged into hypothalamic sinusoids (Fig. 11.63).

***Nervous link*** : Hypothalamohypophyseal tracts originate in the supraoptic and paraventricular nuclei and terminate in the capillaries in the posterior lobe of hypophysis. *The supraoptic and paraventricular nuclei are concerned with the production and release of hormones oxytocin and vasopressin (ADH) and related transport proteins, the neurophysins.* The neurosecretory materials released at the nerve terminals are taken up by the blood percolating through the adjacent capillaries. ADH is predominantly a product of the supraoptic nucleus whereas oxytocin is a product of the paraventricular nucleus. ADH plays a vital role in maintaining the body water balance by exerting a powerful effect on the reabsorption of water by the kidney

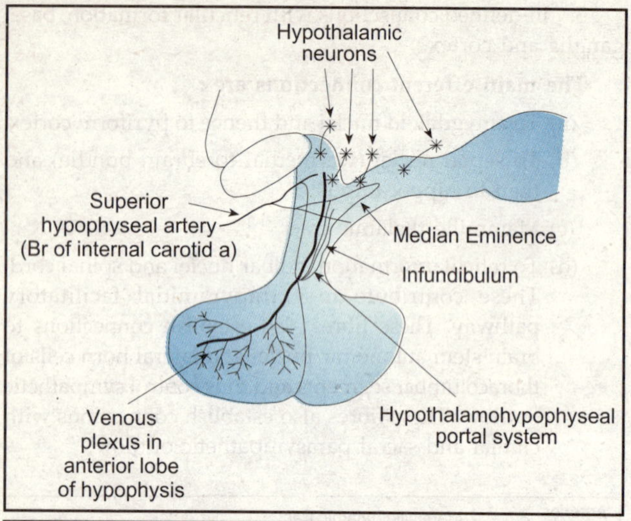


**Fig. 11.63 :** Vascular and Nervous links with the hypophysis

tubules. Oxytocin is responsible for uterine smooth muscle contraction and contraction of myoepithelial cells of the mammary gland. It also plays a vital role during suckling, sexual intercourse and parturition. It is evident that there is increased discharge of oxytocin when there is stimulation of the nipples and external genitalia. The rate of ADH secretion is modified by many factors like plasma osmolality, blood volume, pain and some stressful conditions (Chart 3).

The condition **diabetes insipidus** is produced due to the destruction of the supraoptic nucleus. Diabetes insipidus is manifested by increased secretion of urine *(polyuria)* resulting in excessive thirst and water intake *(polydipsia)*.

## Functions of Hypothalamus

A. Vegetative and endocrine functions and

B. Behavioural functions.

A. **Vegetative and endocrine functions :**

(a) **Regulation of body temperature :** Anterior hypothalamus controls heat loss mechanisms. Increase in temperature of blood flowing through the area increases activity of thermo-sensitive neurons. Posterior hypothalamus controls heat gain mechanisms. Thus body temperature is maintained at 37°C.

(b) **Regulation of food and water intake :** Stimulation of lateral region of hypothalamus initiates eating and increases food intake (Hunger centre). Stimulation of ventromedial nucleus produces **satiety (Satiety Centre).**

Stimulation of **thirst centre** of lateral hypothalamus causes increase in water intake.

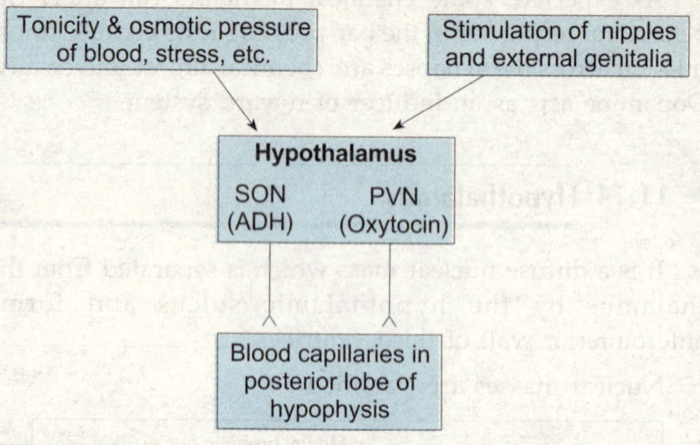


**Chart 3 :** Hormones secreted by the supraoptic nucleus (SON) and paraventricular nucleus (PVN) of the hypothalamus.

Increased osmolality of body fluids stimulates-osmoreceptors of supraoptic nucleus which secretes ADH which acts on DCT and CT of kidneys to increase absorption of water.

(c) **Cardiovascular regulation :** Stimulation of posterior and lateral hypothalamus increases arterial pressure and heart rates stimulation of preoptic area decreases arterial pressure and heart rate. These effects are mediated via reticular centres.

(d) **Neurosecretion :** Secretion of vasopressin and oxytocin by supraoptic and paraventricular nuclei.

(e) **Endocrine control :** Neurons of hypothalamus produce various releasing factors or release inhibiting factors and control production of ACTH, FSH, LH, TSH, GH, MSH, LTH. There are positive and negative feedback regulations.

(f) **Control of circadian rhythms :** These include temperature, adrenocortical activity, eosinophil count and hormone levels. Hypothalamus also has role in sleep and wakefulness. The suprachiasmatic nucleus receives retinohypothalamic fibres and this modulates biological rhythms in response to time of day by using light intensities as signals.

B. **Behavioural functions :** Emotion and behavioural function of hypothalamus, limbic system, prefrontal cortex. Hypothalamus is integrator of afferent information from other parts of nervous system and brings about physical expression of emotion.

(a) **Lateral hypothalamus** is centre for rage; Ventro medial nucleus is placidity centre.

(b) **Sexual drive** is under control of most anterior and posterior portion of hypothalamus.

(c) **Hypothalamus** and limbic system are concerned with affective nature of sensations i.e. reward and punishment.

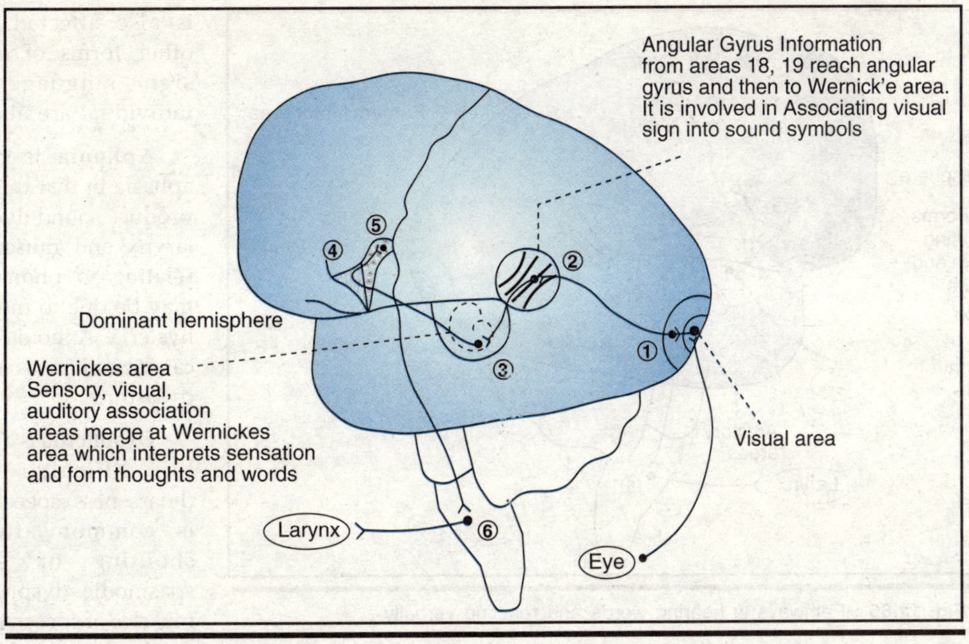


**Fig. 11.64 : Pathways in seeing written words and reading aloud**

## ➤ 11.15 Language and Speech, Learning and Memory

### Language and speech

Literally, language means any manner of expressing thoughts. It may be symbolic as in written objects or auditory that is sound arising from any source. Naturally, it has both afferent (receptive) and efferent (expressive) components. When we read a newspaper the afferent part is the visual pathway and the meaning may or may not be expressed by speech. When we hear a radio programme we can understand by auditory pathways and may or may not express it by speech. The visual or auditory symbols can be expressed by meaningful words (speech) or they may be expressed by writing.

In the production of articulated sound or speech the categorical cerebral hemisphere is primarily involved. Left hemisphere is categorical or dominant in 90% of right-handed individuals. But in left-handed individuals, left cerebral hemisphere is dominant in 70%. The production of sound requires the higher centers, the brain stem and the muscles supplying mouth, pharynx and larynx. If there is paralysis of some muscles or if there is tongue tie or deficient salivary secretion, speech is affected. This condition is called *dysarthria*.

Disorder of language function when there is no defect in the anatomy of nerves and muscles and the special senses are intact is called **aphasia**. In other terms, aphasia can be defined as the impairment of ability to communicate through speech due to dysfunction of brain centers affecting comprehension of written or verbal symbols or their ultimate vocal expression (Figs. 11.64 and 11.65).

Aphasias develop due to lesions affecting the afferent, integrating and efferent centers for articulation. A simplified list of aphasias is given below :

- If there is involvement of the angular gyrus of the dominant hemisphere, then the individual cannot clearly recognize an object seen and becomes unable to utter its name. Similarly, written materials cannot be reproduced by speech. The condition is called **'anomic aphasia'**. Word blindness is also a term applied to this state. These individuals can speak normally by themselves and can repeat what is heard.
- If there is disruption of auditory association areas from Wernicke's area, the individual can hear spoken words but fail to understand their meaning just as we listen to the audio programme of an unknown language. So it is not possible to repeat the matter heard. This is called **'auditory aphasia'** or word deafness. The lesion is definitely on the temporal lobe of categorical hemisphere. They can recognize visual objects and written instructions and able to utter them in words.
- If there is involvement of Wernicke's area, there is inability to comprehend matters both seen and heard. They can hear the spoken words and see the written subjects but cannot make out the idea in them, naturally they suffer from severe language deficit. They can speak fluently by themselves but as they cannot understand their own utterances, they introduce self-made words *(neologisms)* and the speech is unintelligible *(jargon)*.

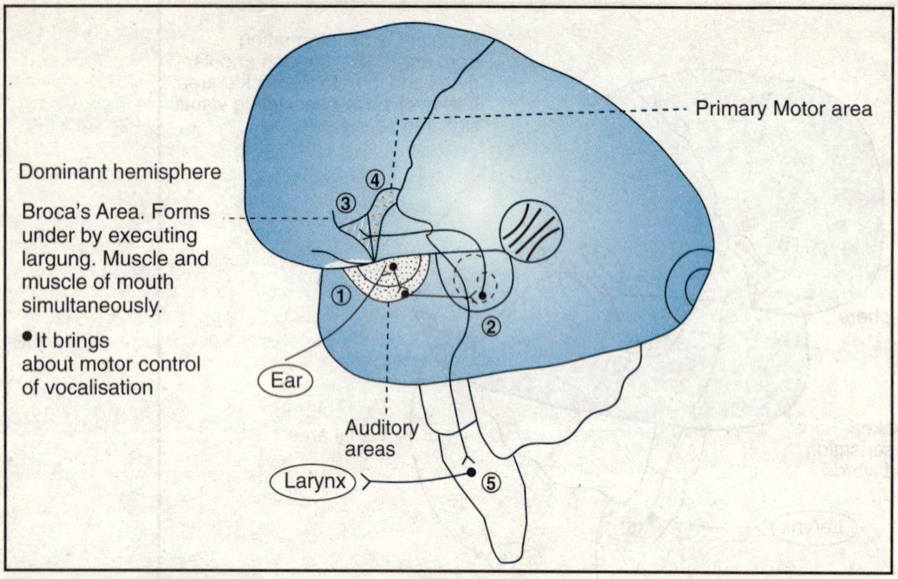


**Fig. 11.65 :** Pathways in hearing words and reacting verbally

- Lesions involving the conduction pathway between the motor and speech centers, i.e., interruption of the arcuate fasciculus joining Wernicke's area with Broca's area causes **'conduction aphasia'**. Here, comprehension is intact but the individual cannot find the word to name an object seen or anything heard. It seems similar to anomic aphasia, but, in the latter, there is inability to recognize the object seen but, in conduction aphasia, understanding is perfect.
- Broca's area, when involved, produces motor aphasia. Here, the understanding of any form of communication is normal, but, due to the lesion, the individual cannot use muscles of speech correctly. Here the subject has equal disability in spontaneous speech and also expressing verbally in response to sensory signals. Speech is non-fluent and the stock of words is poor. The disability is complete or partial according to the extent of involvement of Broca's area for coordination of movement of muscles related to speech.
- Most forms of aphasia are a sequelae to vascular catastrophies. If there is extensive involvement of the categorical hemisphere compromising its receptive, integrative and expressive functions severe language deficiency in the form of **'global aphasia'** takes place.
- Writing in response to visual or auditory stimulation or spontaneously is an important mode of communication. The motor system of writing is linked definitely with speech centers (Wernicke's area). So in most forms of aphasia, due to lesions of categorical hemisphere, writing is also affected. As expected, other forms of expression like sign language in a deaf individual are also affected.

**Aphonia** is different from aphasia in that the subject cannot produce sound due to affection of larynx and muscles and nerves relating to phonation. Aphonia may be due to mental illness, eg. hysteria. Aphonia due to organic causes is almost synonymous with dysarthria.

**Dysphonia** is a term that refers to difficult or defective (hoarseness) speech production. It is common after prolonged shouting or speaking. In spasmodic dysphonia spasm of muscles of speech prohibits sound production, but the same muscles function normally in swallowing or singing.

**Stammering** or **stuttering** is a common functional disorder of speech characterised by hesitation, mispronunciation and repetition. The condition is made worse by emotions like fear and anxiety. The individual is aware of his defect but cannot rectify the incoordination behind the defective phonation. The condition is amenable to speech therapy.

## LEARNING AND MEMORY

### Learning

**Learning** is the process of acquisition of new information of every sort and new skills of all kinds. Learning is a prerequisite to changing our behaviour and life style. So the term learning is applied in a wider sense. We may learn cycling, singing or any professional expertise.

**Basic Modes of Learning Are :**

(a) **Conditional learning :** This implies learning from past experiences such as any mistakes etc. It is present only in higher animals to a substantial degree.

(b) **Conceptional learning :** Here, information is stored in genetic code and can be passed from one generation to another in any particular form such as visual signals etc. This is present only in human beings.

(c) **Contemplation :** In this mode, there is analysis of existing information leading to a more developed and varied learning via elaboration of thoughts in prefrontal lobe.

Some forms of learning are described below to understand the mechanisms behind the process :

- ***Habituation*** : It is our common experience that a new stimulus moves us to a considerable extent but if the stimulus is repeated and if the stimulus is unexciting, it fails to stimulate us any more. For example, a music which becomes popular for a time gradually loses its popularity, or a political slogan gradually loses its attraction, or a particular dress material/style gradually loses its market.
- ***Sensitization*** : It is also a response to repeated stimulus. But here, the response increases with repetition because the stimulus here is either rewarding or punishing. So an individual becomes sensitized to the stimulus. As for example, in a locality an incidence of theft alarms its inhabitants but if such happenings recur, the inhibitants become very much annoyed and anxious. This is **sensitization.**

  Sensitization is often beneficial e.g. as a mother gets sensitized to its baby's crying, a low cry of her baby in the midst of loud noise alerts her.

  Both habituation and sensitization are related to particular stimuli. But, in most cases of learning, association between different stimuli and response is in the form of conditioned reflex.
- ***Conditioned reflex*** : **Conditioned reflex** is the most important of all the forms of learning and behavior. An **unconditioned stimulus** (US) has its effect that is innate when it is adequate. As for example, sugar put into the mouth always causes salivation. So sugar is an unconditioned stimulus. But, if a sound is made before the unconditioned stimulus and they are combined together for a length of time, it is seen that the sound in absence of sugar can stimulate salivation. Sound normally does not cause salivation. So it is a **conditioned stimulus (CS)** that has association with the unconditioned stimulus regarding the response. A common example of conditioned stimulus is that on changing from red to green signal we hurry to catch a train.

The conditioning of a stimulus is possible when there is chance of reward or fear of punishment. The conditioned stimulus *must precede the unconditioned stimulus within a short time* (seconds or minutes). If the time interval is prolonged, this association or conditioning does not take place. If, after development of conditioning, the unconditioned stimulus is withdrawn on repeated occasions, the reflex disappears. It is called **extinction or inhibition of the conditioned reflex.**

External inhibition of conditioned reflex takes place when a disturbing stimulus is applied just after the conditioned stimulus. Here, if the disturbing stimulus is withdrawn, the conditioned reflex reappears. So it is different from internal inhibition.

After abolition of conditioned reflex by internal inhibition, if US and CS are repeated together then the conditioned reflex is again established.

When conditioned reflex is initially established, then a similar stimulus will evoke response but with repeated application of CS with US, the reflex becomes more specific in the sense that it can distinguish between a stimulus from its close ones. As for example, small differences between frequency of sound signal and wavelength of light can be appreciated. This is called **discriminative conditioning.**

Conditioned reflex may force an animal or human being to perform movements in response to properly designed unconditioned stimulus. Soldiers at a battle-field take safe shelter in response to alarming siren; a typical example of **operant conditioning.**

The stimulus must be rewarding or punishing for its **(operant conditioning)** development. Most of our behavior in the family and society can be explained in terms of operant conditioning. It includes avoidance responses as we avoid the food which caused some illness before or in response to cautions regarding its intake.

Withdrawal from alcohol is tried in chronic alcoholics by drugs which cause unpleasant sensations after taking alcohol. These are ***useful applications of the avoidance response***.

Brain which is required for the development of conditioned reflexes or any form of learning consists of right and left halves. Two sides are connected by commissural fibers, anterior commissure, posterior commissure and corpus callosum. Even optic chiasma can transmit information from one side to another. If, in an experimental animal, the optic chiasma is sectioned, then conditioned reflex developed by right eye can be elicited from left eye because commissural fibers will transfer information from one cortex to another. But when all the connections are snapped then this type of transfer is not possible. Then the conditioned reflex becomes ipsilateral and in such state, either site can be stimulated simultaneously by different stimuli having appropriate separate responses. But, in intact condition, such type of selective unilateral response is never possible.

## Memory

**Memory** is the faculty by which we can recall past experiences. Like learning, it is also used in a wide sense. As for example, we can remember our date of birth, prominent political figures in recent or remote past, or even identify the name and functioning of a machine or an apparatus we use. It can be divided into **reflexive memory** and **declarative** or **recognition memory** (Chart 4).

The **reflexive memory**, as its name implies, is unconscious or automatic recall. As for example, during typing or driving or cycling, after some period of training, we use appropriate parts of the machine automatically. And it does not require conscious recall of where and how it functions. A student of type school initially has to remember consciously the position of the different letters and numbers and operate the machine consciously, utilizing *declarative* form of memory, but with passage of days and weeks, he

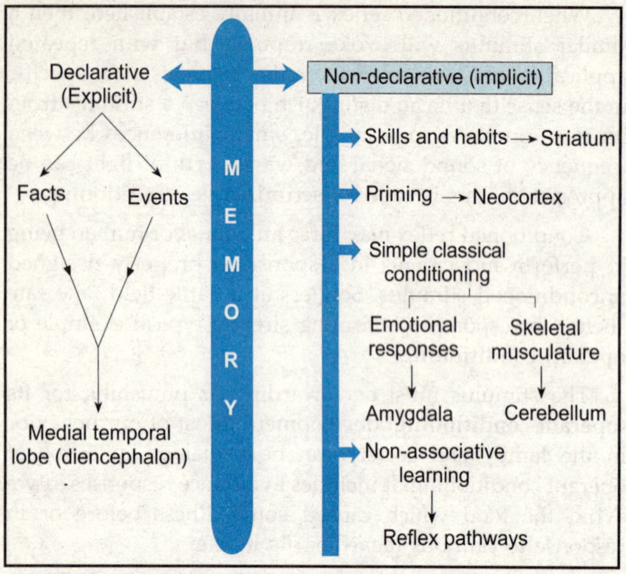


Chart 4 : Different types of memory

becomes habituated so that without any conscious knowledge of the keys he can type correctly. Thus ***declarative memory*** is converted into ***reflexive type.***

**Declarative memory** is the memory that requires conscious recall. It can be divided into (i) immediate recall, (ii) intermediate or short term memory; (iii) long term memory.

(i) **Immediate recall** : We frequently utilize this memory, e.g. a telephone number used for once by picking up from the telephone directory. This memory is very evasive.

(ii) **Intermediate or short term memory** : Here the persistence of events in memory is more than the above. It can last for days. The important or even less important matters that happened hours or days earlier can be appropriately recalled. But not the events occurring much earlier. As for example, a student can recall the hours and classes taken for a few days from the day of interview but not those taken weeks or months earlier.

(iii) **Long term memory** : It is a faculty by which we can recall experiences or information acquired in the distant past.

Any information that is repeated for a good number of times can enter the store of long term memory by passing through the other two stages of memory. It also applies to very important personal or national incidents because, due to their importance, they get rehearsed within our mind repeatedly. The memorable things like date and place of our birth, names of parents, the independence day and occurrence of great wars remain alive in our mind till death.

In some cases of long term memories, we have to search our mind to remember a name, place or incidence and in some cases it can be partially retrieved. In some cases, an associated event helps to recall the subject. Incidence of very remote past events can be completely forgotten. But it is surprising that occurrence of any incidence related to the past or even sight, or smell related to past incidents can bring back to the mind or the happenings of the remote past.

## Mechanism of Immediate Memory

This lasts for few seconds such as 7-10 digits of a phone number and lasts as long as person continues to think about the numbers.

**Suggested mechanisms :**

1. Continuous neuronal activity due to reverberation of signals through a maze of neurons.
2. Presynaptic facilitation or inhibition which occurs at synapses on presynaptic terminals and not in the subsequent neuron.
3. Synaptic potentiation : When a train of impulses passes along a presynaptic terminal, the amount of intracellular $Ca^{++}$ ion increases with each impulses and this leads to more prolonged release of neurotransmiter at the synapse.

## Mechanism of Intermediate Term Memory

This lastsfor as much as few weeks and results from terminal temporary physicochemical changes at the presynaptic.

1. One terminal is from the primary input sensory neuron and terminates on the neuron that is to be stimulated. This is the **'sensory' terminal**. The is the 'facilitation' terminal lies on the **'sensory' terminal** and following occurs :

   (a) **Facilitatory and sensory neuron** are simultaneously stimulated causing serotonin release at facilitatory synapse on sensory presynaptic terminals.

   (b) **Serotonin** acts on receptors on sensory terminal surface and adenylyl cyclase is activated. Thus cAMP is formed.

   (c) **cAMP** activates protein kinase which phosphorylates a protein component of $K^+$ channels, thus blocking the channels.

   (d) **Blocking of $K^+$ channels prolongs** the action potential leading to activation of $Ca^{+2}$ channels. Influx of $Ca^{+2}$ causes release of transmitter at the sensory terminal. This produces a memory trace (Fig. 11.66).

2. **Second mechanism is change the membrane properties of postsynaptic neuron** when stimuli from two different sources act on a single sensory neuron.

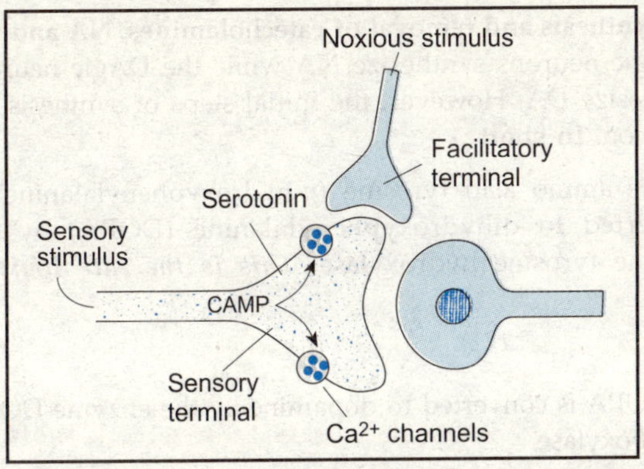


**Fig. 11.66**

### Mechanism for Long-Term Memory

This is due to actual structural changes at synapse which alters signal conduction.

**Suggested mechanisms :**

1. Increase in total area of vesicular release site in presynaptic terminal.
2. Increase in number of transmitter vesicles in presynaptic terminal.
3. Increase in number of terminals.

### Consolidation

For transfer of immediate and intermediate term memories to long term memory, it must be consolidation i.e. chemical, physical and anatomical changes at synapses. About 5 to 60 min. are needed for consolidation via repetition (rehearsal) of information.

New memories are stored in direct association with other memories by help of Wernicke's area. Hippocampus (output pathway of reward and punishment) is an important site of storage of long term memory by providing drive for remembering pleasant or unpleasant experiences.

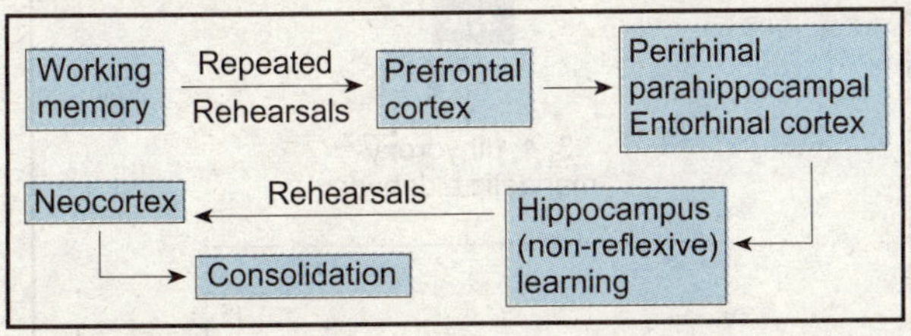


**Amnesia** and other phenomena related to memory, learning and other higher functions are performed at the cortical level. Temporal cortex is very much involved in formation of declarative memory and, specially, long term memory. Epileptic focus arising from temporal lobe may produce feelings of familiarity in strange circumstances. This is called **deja vu phenomenon**. It is also seen in perfectly normal individuals who even exploit this feeling arising in them in different situations of life.

**Hippocampus** of the temporal lobe along with mammilary body and amygdala are related to important aspects of memory. Bilateral lesions of hippocampus deprive an individual or animal of short term memory but they have immediate recall and long term memory unimpaired. Hippo-campus is somehow related to consolidation of memory from its short lasting stage to long lasting form. They cannot form any new long term memory. Acquired ones, of course, are retained.

Lesions of the mamillary body and its projections through the thalamus (mammilothalamic tract) cause impairment of short term memory. Alcoholism is associated with memory loss when it involves the mamillary bodies. These bodies receive extensive input from the hippocampus.

**Amygdala** is related to the hippocampus and hypothalamus and, by the connections, memories are colored with emotion. Simultaneous involvement of hippocampus and amygdala produce more profound loss of memory than the hippocam-pus itself. Loss of any grade of memory will hamper the process of learning because memory and learning are two sides of the same coin.

Basal part of the forebrain is intimately related to memory. It is related diffusely to other parts of the neocortex including amygdala and hippocampus by cholinergic fibers and, at the same time, it receives input from the prefrontal cortex and elsewhere. In **Alzheimer's disease** (a form of presenile or senile dementia) there is loss of these cholinergic neurons. It is characterized by progressive loss of memory and intellectual functions. This disease is commoner in women between ages of 40-60 years. Besides loss of memory and dementia disorders of gait, speech and abnormal psyche (apathy) also occur. This chronic progressive disease may lead to complete loss of intellectual functions. Anticholinesterase drugs can sometimes improve the condition temporarily by increasing acetylcholine in the affected regions.

## ➤ 11.16 Neurotransmitter

**Neurotransmitter (NT)** is released by the presynaptic cell whenever there occurs chemical transmission. Then NT diffuses across the synaptic cleft and binds with receptors present on the postsynaptic cell. The NTs include acetyl-choline, several different amines, a number of amino acids and a variety of peptides.

### Action of Neurotransmitters

When the neurotransmitters reach the synaptic cleft, they attain their goal by either depolarising or hyperpolarising the post synaptic membrane for an instant.

The receptors on postsynaptic membrane bind the neurotransmitter. This alters the membrane permeability to specific ions.

For excitatory synapses, the permeability to most ions increases.

Depolarisation and excitation are concomitant while hyperpolarisation and inhibition are concomitant.

The net excitation and inhibition, however, depends on summation of postsynaptic responses at different synapses.

## Different Neurotransmitters (5 classes)

**(i) *Small Molecules* (Rapid response)**

(a) Acetyl choline

(b) Amines → Norepinephrine, Dopamine, Serotonin, Epinephrine

(c) Gases → NO, CO

(d) Amino acids → γ-Aminobutyric acid (GABA), Glycine, Glutamate, Aspartate, Leucine, Methionine

**(ii) *Neuropeptides* (Slow acting and prolonged response)**

(a) Neuroactive peptides – Releasing hormones from hypothalamus → TRH, LHRH, Somatostatin

(b) Pituitary peptides → ACTH, β-endorphin, Vasopressin, Oxytocin

(c) Peptides common to enteric nervous system and brain → Insulin, Enkephalin (opioid peptides), Substance P, CCK, VIP, Glucagon, Neurotensin

(d) Other tissues → Carnosine, Angiotensin II, Bradykinin, Bombesin

**(iii) *Purines*** → Adenosine (Brain), ATP (Autonomic ganglion brain)

**(iv) *Lipids*** → Prostaglandins, Anandamide (Brain)

**(v) *Neurosteroids***

**Synthesis and removal of catecholamines, NA and DA** : NAgic neurons synthesize NA while the DAgic neurons synthesize DA. However, the initial steps of synthesis are common. **In short** :

the amino acid tyrosine (*p*-hydroxyphenylalanine) is converted to dihydroxyphenylalanine (DOPA) by the enzyme tyrosine hydroxylase. ***This is the rate limiting step.***

↓

DOPA is converted to dopamine by the enzyme DOPA decarboxylase.

In DAgic neurons no further chemical reactions (conversion of DA into other products) occur but in NAgic neurons dopamine is converted to noradrenalin by dopamine β hydroxylase. This dopamine β hydroxylase is absent in the DAgic neurons so that in them DA → NA conversion does not occur.

**Removal of DA and NA** : Most NA that is released by the NAgic neurons is taken as the same neurons that secrete the NA, a process called **reuptake**. This reuptake is thus a major mechanism of removal of NA. The reuptake NA reenters the NAgic neuron where it binds with $\alpha_2$-receptor (situated within the neuron that has takenup the NA) → this binding suppresses further NA release. In short it is a negative feedback (in this instance, also called, **'autofeedback'**) mechanism which ensures that sudden massive release of NA from these NAgic neurons does not occur (by stoppage of further NA secretion) thus avoiding disaster.

A small part of the released NA is chemically degraded. The major steps of the degradation are outlined (Chart 5) :

### Some highlights are emphasized :

Many NTs (eg, NA, DA, 5 HT, GABA but not acetylcholine, ACh) are removed primarily by the reuptake mechanism. Many drugs, collectively known as MARI

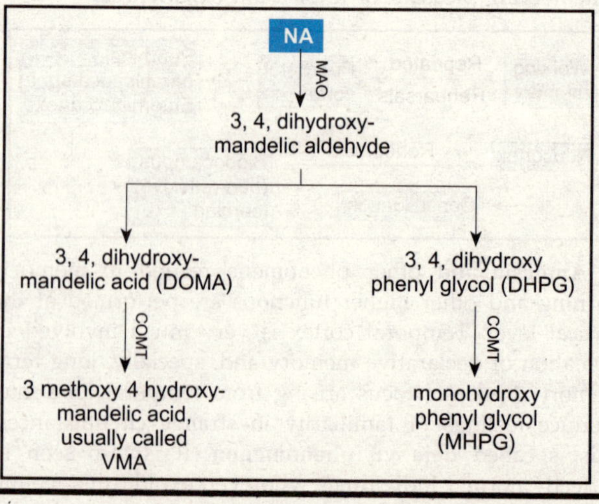


**Chart 5**

**Table 11.8 : Roles of Major Neurotransmitter Systems**

| *Neurotransmitter* | *Site of release* | *Role* | *Receptors* | *Second messengers* | *ionic effect* |
|---|---|---|---|---|---|
| **Acetylcholine** | (i) Pyramidal cells<br>(ii) Basal ganglia<br>(iii) Motor neurons innervating skeletal muscles<br>(iv) Preganglionic neurons in ANS<br>(v) Postganglionic neurons of parasympathetic and some neurons of sympathetic nervous system.<br>(vi) Muscle vasodilator endings<br>(vii) Endings of some amacrine cells of retina. | • In most places, excitatory<br>• At few places (viz-heart), inhibitory | Nicotinic<br>$M_1$<br>$M_2$(Heart)<br>$M_3$<br>$M_4$ (Glandular)<br>$M_5$ | —<br>$\uparrow IP_3$, $DAG_1$<br>$\downarrow$cAMP<br>$\downarrow$cAMP<br>$\uparrow IP_3$, DAG<br>$\uparrow IP_3$, DAG | $\uparrow Na^+$<br>$\uparrow Ca^{+2}$<br>$\uparrow K^+$ |
| **Norepineplrine** | (i) Locus ceruleus (related to arousal, dreaming, mood)<br>(ii) Postganglionic sympathetic endings<br>(iii) Tegmentum<br>(iv) Hypothalamus | • Mainly excitatory<br>• Inhibitory at very few places, e.g. gut musculature | $\alpha_{1A,B,C}$<br>$\alpha_{2A,B,C}$<br>$\beta_1$<br>$\beta_2$<br>$\beta_3$ | $\uparrow IP_3$,DAG<br>$\downarrow$cAMP<br>$\uparrow$cAMP<br>$\uparrow$cAMP<br>$\uparrow$cAMP | $\downarrow K^+$<br>$\uparrow K^+$ $\downarrow Ca^{+2}$ |
| **GABA (Deficient in corpus striatum in Huntington's Chorea)** | (i) Most common neurotransmitter in brain<br>(ii) Retina<br>(iii) Presynaptic inhibition mediating neurons | • Inhibitory | $GABA_A$<br>$GABA_B$ | .........<br>$IP_3$, DAG | $\uparrow Cl^-$<br>$\uparrow K^+$, $\downarrow Ca^{+2}$ |
| **Glutamate** | (i) Presynaptic terminals in many sensory pathway<br>(ii) Cortical neurons, brain stem | • Excitatory | Metabotropic<br>Ionotropic | $\downarrow$cAMP or $\uparrow IP_3$<br>$\longrightarrow$ | <br>$\uparrow Na^+$, $\uparrow Ca^{+2}$ |
| **Dopamine (Deficient in nigrostriatal pathways in Parkinsonism)** | (i) Substantia Nigra<br>(ii) Ventral tegmentum<br>(iii) Corpus striatum<br>(iv) Sympathetic ganglia<br>(v) Retinal interneurons<br>(vi) Limbic system & hypothalamus | • Inhibitory<br>• Tranquilizer<br>• Stimulates reward system<br>• Increased availability induced by agents causes addiction | $D_{1,5}$<br>$D_2$<br>$D_{3,4}$<br>$\downarrow$cAMP | $\uparrow$cAMP<br>$\downarrow$cAMP | $\uparrow K^+$, $\downarrow Ca^{+2}$ |
| **Substance P** | (i) Pain fibreterminals of spinal cord, basal ganglia,<br>(ii) Hypothalamus<br>(iii) Retina | • Excitatory | Serpentine | $\downarrow IP_3$, $\uparrow$DAG | $K^+$ |
| **Nitric oxide** | (i) CNS<br>(ii) Memory | • Long term behaviour<br>• Memory | Directly Guanyl cyclase | cGMP | |
| **Enkephalin** | (i) Spinal cord (Substantia Gelatinosa)<br>(ii) Basal ganglia<br>(iii) Brain stem<br>(iv) Thalamus<br>(v) Hypothalamus<br>(vi) Retina | • Excitatory to inhibitory systems for pain | Opioid receptors | cAMP | Various |

| Neurotransmitter | Site of release | Role | Receptors | Second messengers | ionic effect |
|---|---|---|---|---|---|
| Glycine | (i) Spinal cord, retina | • Excitation, in brain (Excitation NMDA)<br>• Inhibitory (mainly) | Inhibition of $Cl^-$ channel | ↓Cl(inhibition) | |
| Serotonin | (i) Median raphe nucleus | • Inhibitory to pain pathway<br>• Controls mood<br>• Cause sleep(?)<br>• Temperature regulation.<br>• Activation of serotonergic neurons (e.g. by LSD) causes hallucination | $5\text{-HT}_{1,2,3,4,5,6,7}$<br>$5\text{-HT}_3$ | cAMP<br>IP3, DAG(Ionic) | Various |

(monoamine reuptake inhibitor) group of drugs (eg, imipramine), inhibit the reuptake and thus prolongs the stay of the NA molecule outside the neuron effect of NA becomes longer.

- MAO inhibitors, abbreviated MAOI, are also used as drugs in clinical medicine. Use of such drugs also increases the stay of the NA outside the neuron.
- For the reuptake, a *transport protein* is necessary. That is, NA reuptake takes place by a transport protein. Similarly, transport proteins for the reuptake of 5 HT, DA and GABA have been identified and cloned. These transport proteins are different from each other, although it is possible that they belong to a single family of proteins.

## Serotonergic neurons

***The ultimate source of 5 HT is the dietary amino acid tryptophan.*** Tryptophan is ultimately taken up by the neurons where it is converted into 5 hydroxytryptophan by a (rate limiting) enzyme, tryptophan hydroxylase; this step can be inhibited by p-chlorphenylalanine, PCPA.

↓

Subsequently, 5 hydroxytryptophan is decarboxylated to 5 hydroxytryptamine, 5 HT by an enzyme decarboxylase which closely resembles (or may even be identical to) DOPA decarboxylase.

After release from the neuronal ending, most of the 5 HT is takenup by the neurons themselves and a small part (which escapes the reuptake) is degraded by MAO (monoamine oxidase) which converts 5 HT into 5 hydroxyindoleacetic acid, 5 HIAA. 5 HIAA escapes via urine.

The reuptake of 5 HT mentioned above is dependent upon a specific transport protein. These transport proteins are different from each other. Various drugs of the class of MARI (monoamine reuptake inhibitors) inhibit reuptake of the monoamines. Amitryptiline blocks the reuptake of both NA and 5 HT powerfully, while clomipramine blocks, rather selectively, the reuptake of 5 HT. These are useful information for clinicians who use it successfully in the treatment of depression.

***Functions. Clinical correlates*** : Like most other CNS NTs, our knowledge about the functions of 5 HT in the brain remains largely woolly, speculative and even enigmatic. Serotonin is strongly suspected to be involved in the causation of sleep-wake cycle, mood (depression), endogenous pain inhibition and endocrinal control.

## GABAergic neurons

***Synthesis and removal*** : GABA is synthesized in the GABAergic neurons. Glutamic acid is decarboxylated by an enzyme called ***glutamate decarboxylase (GAD)*** into gamma aminobutyrate, GABA.

## Histaminergic nerves

***Synthesis and removal*** : **Histidine**, an amino acid, is decarboxylated (by the enzyme histamine decarboxylase) to histamine. Most of the histamine is converted to methylhistamine by the enzyme ***histamine N methyl transferase***.

A small part of histamine, however, is attacked by diamine oxidase (also called, histaminase) to form imidazole acetic acid. This path does not require involvement of MAO.

## Cholinergic Neurons

**Acetylcholine** is secreted in widespread areas but specifically by large pyramidal cells (motor cortex), nuclei of basal ganglia, myoneural junctions, preganglionic neurons of ANSand postganglionic neurons of parasympathetic system and some postganglionic neurons of sympathetic nervous systems.

It is mainly **excitatory**, exceptions include heart, where role is **inhibitory**.

**Receptors :** Nicotinic and Muscarinic classes exist
(N) (M)

Muscarinic receptors may be $M_1$, $M_2$, $M_3$, $M_4$, $M_5$.

Role of these receptors is explained in chapter on ANS)

### Synthesis and Removal

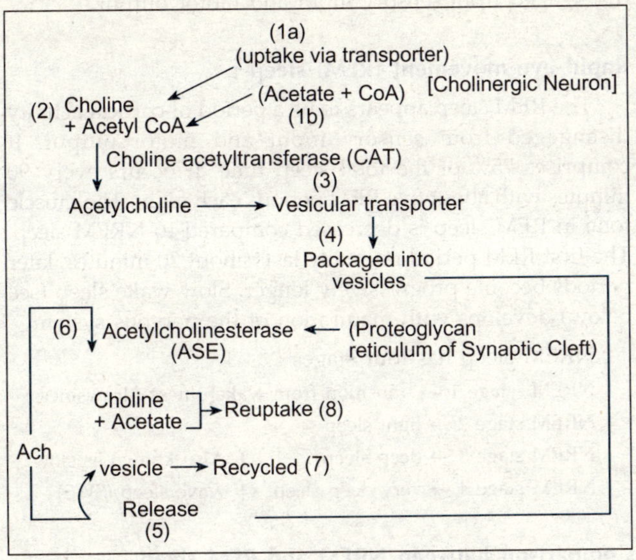


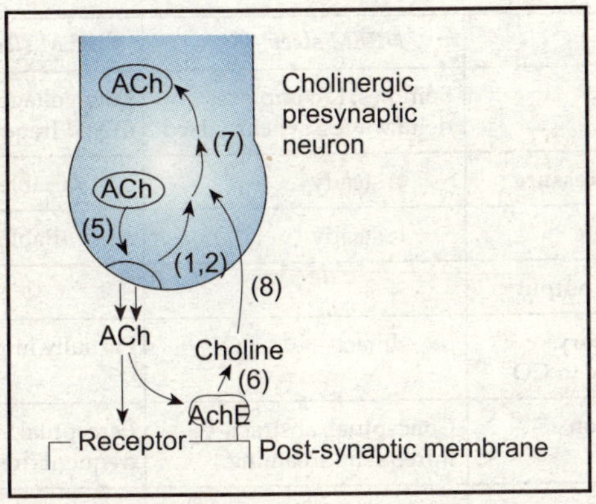


## 11.17 Reticular Activating System (RAS)

**The reticular activating system (RAS)** is a complex and diffuse network of neurons located in the reticular formation of the brain stem. The term **'reticular formation'** (*formatio reticularis*) means a dense network of nerve fibers that extend from the ventromedial part of medulla to the mid brain. This network consists mostly of innumrable short neurons making large number of synapses on their way (multi-synaptic).

The neurons which constitute the specific modalities of sensation (eg, touch, pain, temperature and so forth) climb up via the brain stem (= medulla + pons + mid brain) via specific tracts spinal lemniscus, medial lemniscus and so on to end in the thalamus. Apart from these specific sensory (= ascending) paths there is another system, called the **reticular activating system, RAS**, which also ascends but, anatomically as well as physiologically, these two systems, viz, the specific ascending pathways and the RAS, are quite distinct.

While, **anatomically**, the specific pathways are laterally situated, the RAS is more centrally placed. **Functionally**, the specific ascending fibers convey the sensations of specific senses (eg, touch/pain/temperature) while the RAS is concerned with (nonspecific) general alertness, wakefulness and sleep. In addition, the RAS strongly influences the EEG.

The terms formation reticularis and RAS are identical, i.e, interchangeable terms. **The reticular formation consists of the following types of fibers** :

- the aminergic fibers like the NAgic, adrenergic, DAgic and GABAergic fibers;
- some descending fibers (eg, reticulospinal tracts) which descend to the anterior horn cells. They control the basic stretch reflex, thus controlling the tone of the skeletal muscles;
- the reticular formation also contains many 'centers' for visceral regulations, eg, vasomotor center (VMC), respiratory center and so on;
- The reticular formation projects excitatory fibers to higher levels of CNS.

The reticular formation contains many serotonergic, noradrenergic and adrenergic cell bodies and fibers.

The RAS receives inputs from all sensory modalities directly or via collaterals as well as retrograde from the cerebrum. It receives outputs from all portions of the cortex either directly or through thalamic relays. When there is permanent damage in the RAS, coma develops. But the temporary inhibition produces sleep. Unconsciousness may be produced by depressing conduction in the RAS via activation of $GABA_A$ receptors with resultant hyperpolarization of neurons.

## 11.18 Sleep

Sleep is defined as a state of unconsciousness from which the person can be aroused by sensory stimuli :

There are 2 different types of sleep :

1. Slow wave sleep (Non REM) "SWS"
2. Rapid Eye Movement (REM) sleep.

### The Sleep Cycle

This implies the progressive states during a typical sleep period.

(i) Initially light stage of NonREM or SWS sleep is present.

(ii) During next hour or so, deeper stages of sleep occur till the deep stage of sleep is reached. The NonREM sleep thus has 4 successive stages.

(iii) After about 15 min. of deep sleep, depth of sleep begins to wane till the person reenters light sleep about 90 min. after the initiation of first sleep cycle.

(iv) Then REM sleep takes over from nonREM sleep.

(v) This cycle occurs about 5 times during night at intervals of about 90 mins.

(vi) As the duration of sleeping acute increases, REM sleep periods are lengthened and become more frequent and subject awakens periodically.

**The progressive changes in brain waves during different stages of sleep and wakefulness.**

1. **Alert wakefulness** → β waves
2. **Quiet wakefulness** → α waves
3. **NREM sleep**
   - Stage 1 → Low amplitude, high frequency and low voltage
   - Stage 2 → presence of bursts of α-like, 10-14/s, 50μv waves (Sleep spindles)
   - Stage 3 → lower frequency, increased amplitude (θ waves)
   - Stage 4 → Maximum δ slowing of waves (δ waves)
4. **REM sleep** → β waves, PGO spikes (PGO : Ponto geniculo occipital)

## Slow wave sleep (SWS)/NonREM (NREM) sleep

This is a restful sleep occurring during the first hour of falling asleep after substantial physical exertion. It progresses in an orderly way from light to deep sleep.

The EEG characteristics are given under the "sleep cycle".

Important features are progressive reduction in consciousness and increasing resistance to awakening. Muscle tone is reduced. Heart and respiratory rates and body metabolism are lowered.

## REM (Rapid eye movement) sleep (Paradoxical sleep)

This is characterised by rapid movements of eyeball. This is associated with frequent dreaming.

It is called **paradoxical sleep** because, the cortex is obviously active as shown by high frequency and low amplitude fast waves (as in the waking state) apart from occasional PGO spikes. The subject is however unresponsive to external stimuli. **Other features** are :

(i) Middle ear muscles are active.

(ii) Penile erection may occur.

(iii) Heart rate and respiration are irregular

(iv) Occasional twitching of limbs.

(v) Muscle tone is tremendously reduced.

The REM sleep appears to be a period of cortical activity disengaged from sensory input and motor output.

## Rapid eye movement (REM) sleep :

The REM sleep appears to be a period of cortical activity disengaged from sensory input and motor output. It comprises 25% of the total sleep time. It occurs every 90 minutes with about five REM periods each night. The muscle tone in REM sleep is decreased compared to NREM sleep. The first REM period normally lasts about 20 minutes, later periods become progressively longer. Slow wake sleep (see below) develops with maturation of the nervous system.

NREM sleep has four stages :

NREM stage 1 → transition from wakefulness (drowsiness)

NREM stage 2 → light sleep.

NREM stage 3 → deep sleep.
NREM stage 4 → very deep sleep. } Also known as slow wave sleep (SWS)

## Comparison between NREM and REM sleep (Figs. 11.67 and 11.68)

| | *NREM sleep* | *REM sleep* |
|---|---|---|
| **EEG** | Spindles; K complexes; delta waves; synchronized | Low voltage; mixed frequency |
| **Blood pressure** | ↓; steady | Variable |
| **Heart rate** | ↓; steady | Variable |
| **Cardiac output** | ↓ | ↓ |
| **Ventilatory response to $CO_2$** | Intact | Partially impaired |
| **Mentation** | Conceptual, abstract, infrequent dreaming. | Perceptual, frequent dreaming. |
| **Pathology** | Night terrors; somnambulism; panic attacks | Nightmares; REM sleep behavior disorder |

## Neurotransmitters and neuromodulators related with sleep-wake states :

| *Substance* | *Possible Roles* |
|---|---|
| **Serotonin** | L–tryptophan has hypnotic effect; ↑ delta sleep |
| **Noradrenaline** | REM sleep inhibition; Arousal. |
| **Acetyl choline** | Orchestrates REM sleep. Inhibits cortical EEG synchronization |
| **Dopamine** | Mediates alerting effect of amphetamine/cocaine. |
| | Mediates sedative effect of anti-psychotics. |
| **GABA** | Mediates hypnotic effects of benzodiazepines. |
| **Adenosine** | Promotes sleep. Caffeine blocks adenosine receptors. |

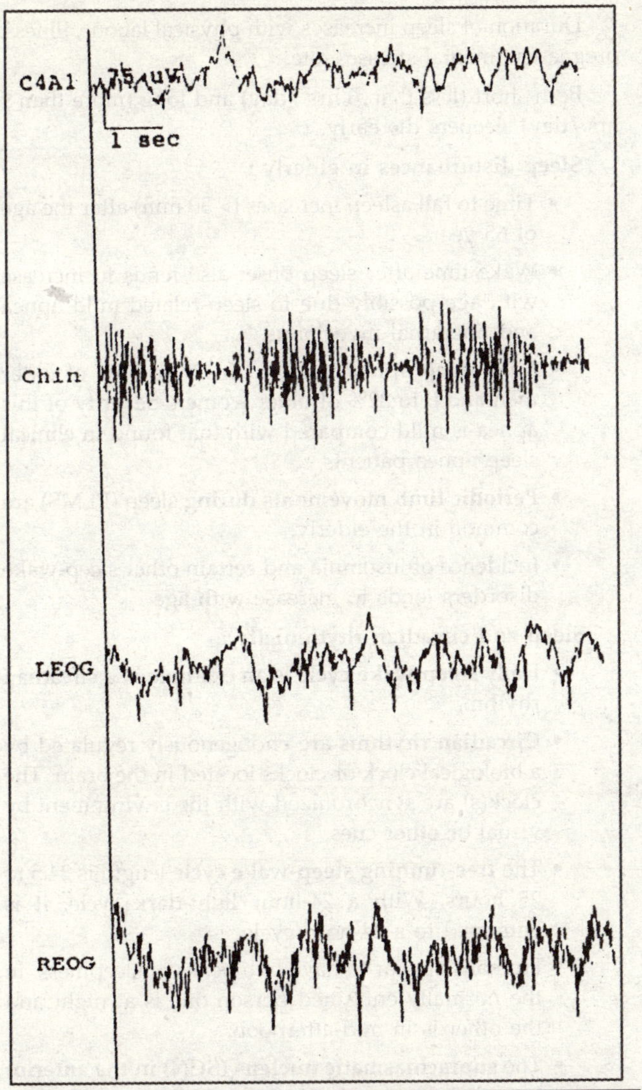


**Fig. 11.67 :** Stage 4 NREM sleep. **Note** : (1) Abundance of delta waves in EEG, (2) Tonic chin EMG, (3) Absence of REM. Compare with Fig.12.82(REM sleep).

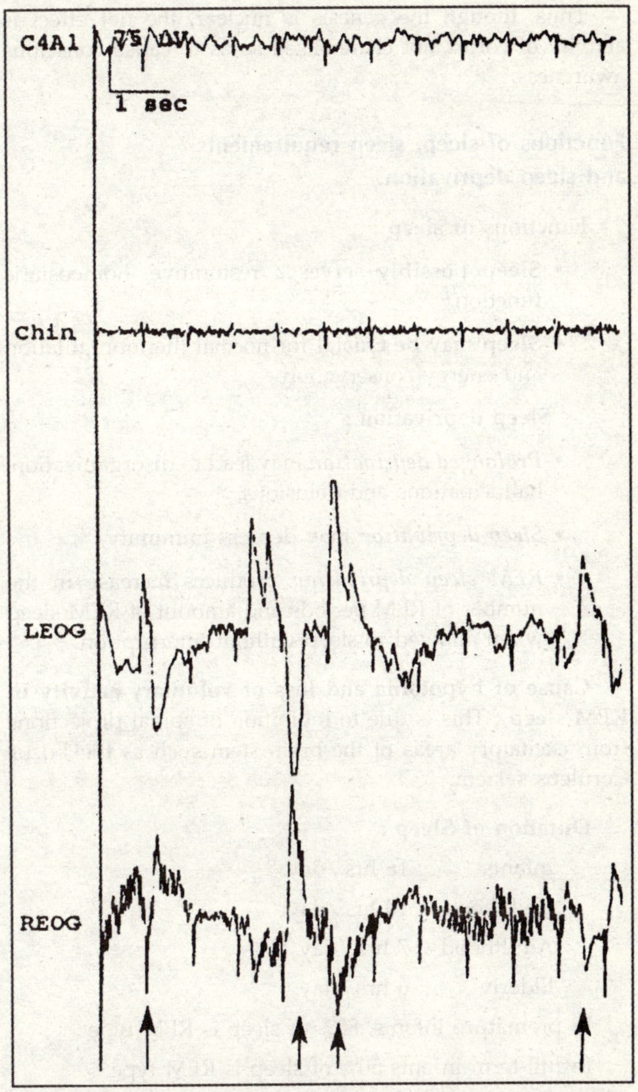


**Fig. 11.68 :** REM sleep. **Note** : (1) Mixed frequency, low amplitude EEG, (2) Low chin EMG, (3) REMs (≠). Compare with Fig. 12.81.

## Genesis of slow waves/Non REM sleep

There are three mechanisms.

(a) Activity of three subcortical regions produce synchronization of cortical electrical activity.

This is the **basis of Non-REM sleep**.

The **regions** are :

(i) Diencephalic sleep zone (Posterior hypothalamus and intra-laminar and anterior thalamic nucleus)

(ii) Medullary synchronising zone. at the level of NTS

(iii) Basal forebrain zone (Preoptic area and diagonal band of Broca)

The role of (i) & (ii) are discussed in "wakefulness and sleep mechanisms".

(b) Afferents from mechanoreceptors in skin at rates of 10/s or less, produce sleep via brain stem.

(c) Activity of serotonin antagonists.

## Genesis of REM Sleep

The exact mechanism is not clear but according to one theory it is caused by **genesis** and **progression of PGO spikes while** the locus ceruleus and midbrain raphe area are silent. PGO spikes progress from pons to LGB to occipital cortex.

However during REM sleep, there is intense activation of certain areas of brain which can be explained by activity of locus ceruleus.

Thus, though the genesis is nuclear, the net effect is activity of cortex not channelised so as to cause conscious awareness.

## Functions of sleep, sleep requirements and sleep deprivation.

**Functions of sleep :**

- **Sleep possibly serves** a restorative, homeostatic function.
- **Sleep may be crucial** for normal thermoregulation and energy conservation.

**Sleep deprivation :**

- ***Prolonged deprivation*** may lead to disorganization, hallucinations and delusions.
- ***Sleep deprivation*** may depress immunity.
- ***REM sleep deprivation*** produces increase in the number of REM periods and amount of REM sleep when allowed to sleep without interruption.

**Cause of hypotonia and loss of voluntary activity in REM sleep :** This is due to inhibition of spinal projections from excitatory areas of the brain stem such as the Locus Ceruleus system.

**Duration of Sleep :**

Infants : 16 hrs./day

Childhood : 10 hrs./day

Adulthood : 7 hrs./day

Elderly : 6 hrs./day.

In premature infants, 80% of sleep is REM type

In full-term infants 50% of sleep is REM type

Total time of REM sleep is reduced by 1.5-2 hrs at puberty and remains at this constant level.

Duration of sleep increases with physical labour, illness, pregnancy, mental stresses, etc.

Both short (less than 6 hrs./day) and long (more than 9 hrs./day) sleepers die early.

**Sleep disturbances in elderly :**

- Time to fall asleep increases (> 30 min) after the age of 65 years.
- Wake time after sleep onset also tends to increase with age possibly due to sleep-related mild apnea and nocturnal myoclonus.
- Mild **sleep apnea** is found in 27 to 75% of older men and 0 to 32% of older women. Severity of this apnea is mild compared with that found in clinical sleep apnea patients.
- **Periodic limb movements during** sleep (PLMS) are common in the elderly.
- Incidence of insomnia and certain other sleep-wake disorders tends to increase with age.

**Sleep and circadian rhythmicity :**

- Daily **sleep-wake cycle** is an example of a circadian rhythm.
- **Circadian rhythms** are endogenously regulated by a biological clock or clocks located in the brain. The clock(s) are synchronized with the environment by visual or other cues.
- The **free-running sleep-wake cycle** length is 24.5 to 25 hours. With a 24-hour light-dark cycle, it is entrained to a 24-hour cycle.
- Humans appear to have two peaks of sleepiness in the normally entrained person one is at night and the other is in mid-afternoon.
- The **suprachiasmatic nucleus (SCN) in the anterior** hypothalamus maintains the 24-hour sleep-wake cycle and synchronizes it with the environmental light-dark cycle (Table 11.9).

**Table 11.9**

| *Waves* | *Frequency* | *Feature* | *Origin* | *Remarks* |
|---|---|---|---|---|
| **Alpha (α)** | 8-13/S | Rhythmic 50 microvolts | Due to spontaneous thalamocortical activity (nonspecific). Occur intensely in occipital region and in parietal and frontal regions. | Present in quiet resting state of the cerebrum. Disappear during sleep or mental activity of specific nature. |
| **Beta (β)** | >14/S to 25-50/S | Associated with fast occipital and slow occipital rhythms in children and infants respectively | Recorded in parietal and frontal region during activation of CNS. | During REM sleep, alert wakefulness. |
| **Theta (θ)** | 4-7/S | | Probably in hippocampus | Seen during emotional stress frustration and brain disorders. |
| **Delta (δ)** | <4/S | | Due to background cortical activity irrespective of subcortical activity. | In slow wave sleep, infancy serious organic brain damage. |

## Maintenance of Waking state and sleep mechanisms

The waking state is maintained by signals from RAS to the cortex which are reinforced by positive feedback by cortex and peripheral nervous system in the waking state.

**Passive theory of sleep :** Fatigue of RAS reverts the waking state and causes sleep.

**Active theory of sleep**

(i) Centres located in midpons cause sleep by inhibition of other parts of brain.

(ii) Activity of raphe nuclei in lower pons and medulla causes sleep. Nerve fibres from these nuclei reach upto reticular formation, thalamus, neocortex, hypothalamus and most of limbic system.

Descending fibres terminate on posterior horn cells to inhibit incoming pain signals. Most endings are serotonergic which induces sleep.

(iii) Serotonergic areas of tractus solitarius cause sleep.

(iv) Stimulation of regions of diencephalon like SCN i.e. suprachiasmatic nucleus of hypothalamus and diffuse nuclei of thalamus also produce sleep

(v) Several substances such as sleep peptides like muramyl peptide accumulate in blood and CSF during wakefulness and may be sleep inducers.

## ➤ 11.19 Electroencephalogram (EEG)

In the 1930s **Hans Berger**, a German psychiatrist, developed what is now known as **electroencephalography**. EEG recordings are, therefore, also called **'Berger rhythm'**. EEG is a recording of the surface potentials of cortical cells. It is clinically important as the normal patterns are changed in the brain areas when they are injured, damaged and diseased.

Widespread alpha waves (8-12 Hz) of wakefulness are found along with beta waves (18-30 Hz) at places under resting condition with eyes closed. Theta (4-7 Hz) and delta (less than 4 Hz) are seen in deep sleep (Fig.11.69).

When a pair of electrodes are placed on suitable areas of the scalp, records of electrophysiological activities of the underlying brain structures can be obtained. When the eyes are closed and the mind wandering, **α-rhythm**, characterised by about 8-12 Hz frequency and amplitude of about 50 mV are obtained, mostly from the parietal and occipital regions of the brain. α-rhythm is also called **'synchronisation wave'**.

Now, if the person opens his eyes or starts to work his mind, the α-rhythm is replaced by a rhythm, variously called **'α-block'**, **'desynchronization'** etc. characterised by faster rate and lower voltage. Desynchronization, therefore, occurs when the brain is alert and working.

During sleep, EEG records show characteristic changes. During the alert and wakeful state, EEG waves show desynchronization. As alert and wakeful state progresses into dozing, the EEG records show synchronization. As sleep supervenes, the EEG waves develop very slow rate but high amplitude (slow wave sleep, SWS).

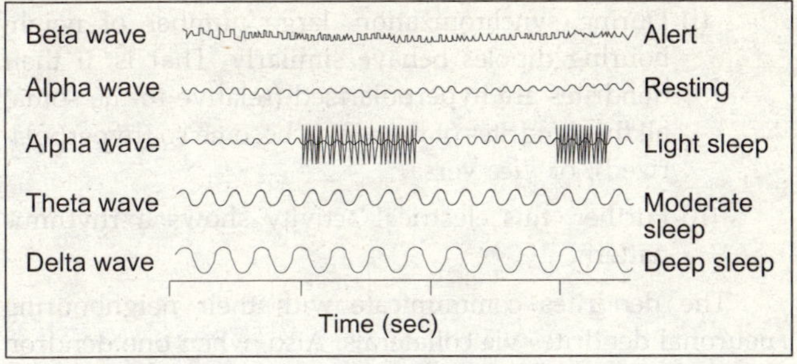


**Fig. 11.69 :** EEG waves during different conditions (from wakefulness to deep sleep)

During a sleep cycle of 8 hrs, several (say 5) bouts of REM (rapid eye movement, also called paradoxical) sleep appear, each lasting for about 20 minutes, when, although the subject remains asleep, desynchronization of EEG and other features can appear. This (REM) is the period when the subject dreams. His eyes move to follow the events of the dream (and hence the rapid eye movements); his mind becomes engaged in seeing the events of the dream which explains the desynchronization. The level of sleep is deep (or even deeper) although EEG and the rapid eye movements can (falsely) give the impression that the person is awake. Hence the name **paradoxical sleep**. The important thing to note is that although, behaviorally, the person is asleep (ie, his CNS, in general, is sedated) there is EEG desynchronization.

***Genesis of EEG waves*** : Mechanism of the development of EEG waves are poorly understood. On the whole, it appears to be like this :

In the most superficial layer of cerebral cortex, there are mostly dendrites and only few cell bodies (soma). Now, dendrites are different from the axons in the sense that when an electrical activity develops in the dendron, the activity unlike that of the axon remains local, ie, is non-propagated. Therefore, an electrical activity of dendron is not an action potential (AP) like that of an axon.

The dendron and the soma (nerve cell body) of the neuron together can be considered to be the two poles (dipole). The dendron can be hyperpolarized relative to its soma, or vice versa.

Further, large number of dendrons become concomitantly depolarized/hyperpolarized relative to their own soma, the effect becomes additive. Eventually this summed up record is recorded as EEG tracings via electrodes placed on the scalp. Obviously, such a record must show ups and downs, because, at a given instance, the dendrites may be hypopolarized and in the next moment they become hyperpolarized. These ups and downs of the summed up values of the dendritic potentials (see below) produce the typical EEG waves.

***Synchronization mechanism*** : The potential difference between the dendron and its own nerve cell body is called (by the physiologists) **'dendritic potential'**.

(i) During synchronization, large number of neighbouring dipoles behave similarly. That is, if their dendrites are hyperpolarized (relative to the soma) all the dendrites of the region become so (hyperpolarized), or vice versa.

(ii) Further, this electrical activity shows a rhythmic pattern.

The dendrites communicate with their neighbouring neuronal dendrites via collaterals. Also, when one dendron becomes electrically activated, some changes occur in the local extracellular fluid (ECF) and this leads to changes in the neighbouring neuron. The changes are (qualitatively) similar when these neighbouring dendrons are parallel and running in the same direction.

The dendritic (or the synaptic) potential fluctuates rhythmi-cally (when the rhythm is 8-12 Hz it is called **α-rhythm**). There are three different areas lower down in the brain which send fibers (carrying signals) to the cerebral cortex. These **three centers discharge** rhythmically and the EEG waves follow. The centers are :

- diencephalic sleep zone;
- medullary synchronizing zone;
- basal forebrain sleep zone.

- **Diencephalic sleep zone** is situated in the posterior hypothalamus and part of the thalamus. Apparently, fibers ascend from this zone, conveying impulses of this zone to the cerebral cortex. When this zone is stimulated at the rate of 8 per second (low frequency), the EEG shows α-rhythym with 8 per second frequency. However, if this zone is stimulated with higher frequency, the EEG develops faster rhythm and wakefulness results.
- A similar zone called the **medullary synchronization zone** is present in the medulla near the ***nucleus tractus solitarius (NTS).*** Probably fibers from this zone ascend up to end in the thalamus.
- The third zone, **the basal forebrain sleep zone** is present in the preoptic area (a part of the hypothalamus) and the diagonal band of Broca. All frequencies of stimulation of this zone, however, produce ***desynchronization***.

***Desynchronization mechanism*** : Stimulation of the RAS causes the behavioral pattern of awakening as well as EEG desynchronization. Because the upward prolongation of the spinothalamic tract (STT) in the brain gives collaterals to the RAS, pain and crude touch sensation also stimulates RAS.

## 11.20 The Neuronal Environment

### Analysis of cerebrospinal fluid

The chemical components of CSF which are commonly estimated are protein, glucose and chloride. The chemical composition of a sample of CSF, drawn from a normal subject, depends on the site of withdrawal of the fluid. **The normal composition of the lumbar CSF and ventricular CSF of an adult :**

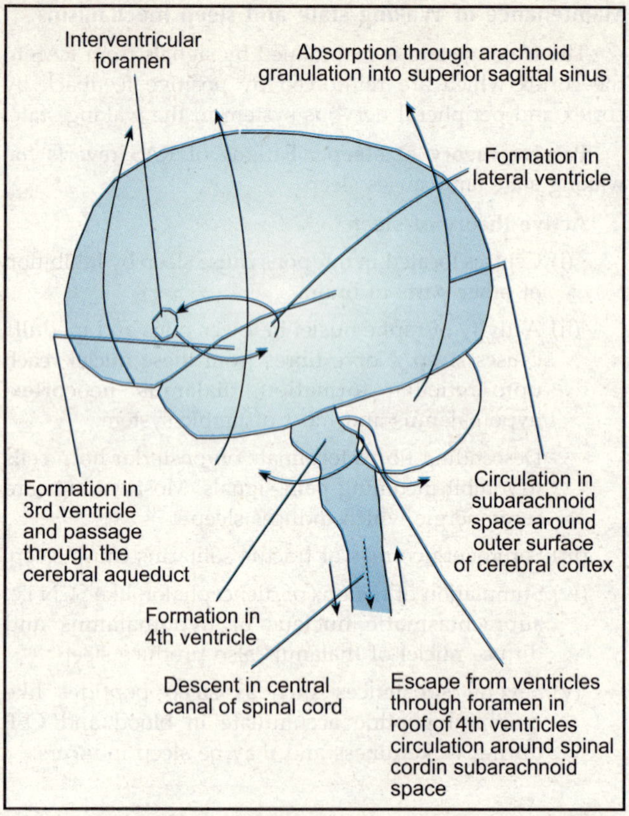


**Fig. 11.70 :** Circulation of CSF

| | *Lumbar* | *Ventricular* |
|---|---|---|
| Total protein | 10-40 | 5-75 mg/100 ml |
| Glucose | 50-80 | 60-100 mg/100 ml |
| Chloride | 710-750 | 710-750 mg/100 ml (as NaCl) |

A count of 1-5 cells per cubic millimeter is said to be within normal limits. A count of more than 10 cells per cubic millimeter indicates disease.

### Formation of C.S.F. (100-250 ml/day)

C.S.F. is mainly formed in the choroid plexuses of lateral and to some extent third ventricles of brain. It is formed by filtration and secretion and strictly speaking, it is not an ultrafiltrate of plasma.

**Circulation :** C.S.F. is formed in the lateral ventricle. Through the foramen of Monro enters third ventricle and then to 4th ventricle via aqueduct of Sylvius. C.S.F. passes then to foramina Lushka and Magendie and occupies subarachnoid space and is distributed all over the brain and central canal of spinal cord.

**Absorption :** Arachnoid villi of the Sagittal sinus project from the arachnoid matter. These villi come in contact with venous blood of the Sagittal sinus. Pressure within sinuses is low, colloid osmotic pressure of venous blood is high whereas that of C.S.F. is low. These help to transfer C.S.F. into venous blood.

The average volume of CSF is about 125 ml in adults. It is regulated by a balance between daily production and absorption of CSF. In sitting position, the normal CSF pressure is 200-300 mm of water. It is raised due to an excessive amount of CSF resulting in the condition termed **hydrocephalus.**

## Functions of the CSF

- It **supports the brain and spinal cord** and provides protection against trauma.
- It regulates **intracranial pressure** by changing its normal amounts in response to changes in blood and brain volume.
- There are no lymphatics in the brain parenchyma. CSF **maintains a fluid pathway to enable chemical substances** to reach the brain and neural metabolites to be returned to the blood stream.

## Blood-brain barrier

It is intuitive to think that composition of brain ECF needs vigorous maintenance as the controlled excitability of the neurons of brain is important for the overall well-being of an individual. It was observed in histological experiment on animals that certain dyes (e.g. trypan blue) fail to penetrate CNS when it stains tissues elsewhere.

Brain (and spinal cord) are supplied by two sets of capillaries, the first and most abundant are those that supply structural elements and the second that supply choroid plexus from where CSF is secreted. Brain and spinal cord are surrounded by a layer of CSF intervened by pia mater, but fluid immediately surrounding the brain neurons (ISF) is, in fact, in free communication with CSF functionally. For this reason, though the two sets of capillaries are anatomically distinct, functionally they form blood-brain barriers regarding passage of substances from plasma to brain cells.

The anatomical components of the barriers include the nonfenestrated capillaries of CNS in general in which the endothelial cells are closely set (tight junctions) restricting passage of substances across them considerably. In case of choroid plexus, ependymal lining epithelium also contributes to the barrier. Immediately adjoining the neurons and their processes, the expansions of processes of glial cells also serve as elements of the partition.

It is to be considered in this context that capillary endothe-lium provides restriction of substances crossing across it, more or less in any tissue site. So the permeability across tissue capillary is different at different organs. But certain generalization exists, as for example, lipid soluble molecules and molecules of small effective diameter that are nonpolar cross the capillary barriers readily. Charged molecules (polar) are transported with difficulty in every site. ***The physical processes operating behind the transport*** is (a) filtration through intercellular spaces along hydrostatic pressure gradient (b) diffusion along concentration and electrical gradient (c) endocytosis and exocytosis. Tissue/plasma concentration ratio of most substances is below unity in any organ but in CNS the ratio is lower in most cases as compared to other sites.

Water, $O_2$, $CO_2$, anesthetic gases and alcohol cross the blood-brain barrier readily.

Charged molecules like $Na^+$, $K^+$, $Cl^-$, $HCO^-_3$, $Ca^{2+}$, $Mg^{2+}$, $HPO_4^{2-}$ equilibrate with CSF and brain ISF slowly.

Small organic molecules like urea and glucose are also slow to equilibrate. Urea infusion thus causes osmotic gradient to draw fluid out of brain ISF similar to mannitol (infusion) which is used clinically to reduce brain edema.

The transport is not one way; it is bidirectional and, necessarily, there exists restriction in the passage of molecules from brain ISF and CSF to venous ends of the capillaries. So, in some cases, the tissue/plasma concentration ratio is more than unity. $H^+$ is a typical example. Continuous cellular activity raises $H^+$ in brain ISF and CSF but, as its transport is restricted, the pH of CSF is lower than arterial or venous plasma.

$HCO^-_3$ is also slow to equilibrate. During metabolic acidosis, hyperventilation reduces $CO_2$ content and its partial pressure everywhere because $CO_2$ is freely permeable to any boundary, so CSF pH rises in spite of fall in pH elsewhere (primary defect).

Dopamine cannot penetrate the barrier but its precursor L-Dopa (dihydroxyphenylalanine) can cross readily and is used in **Parkinsonism**.

**Kernicterus** is a condition of bilirubin staining of basal ganglia of brain in jaundiced newborn infants. In jaundiced adults, basal ganglia involvement is absent. This proves that development of blood-brain barrier continues after birth.

Some hormones are elaborated from the posterior pituitary (vasopressin and oxytocin). Hypothalamis factors influence the anterior pituitary (releasing hormones). This indicates that some parts of CNS are outside the blood-brain barrier. The other sites (besides posterior pituitary and median eminence of hypothalamus) are the ***area postrema of medulla, vascular organ of lamina terminalis at supraoptic region and subfornical organ.*** All the areas are close to different sites of cerebral ventricles bilaterally. These circumventricular vascular structures are designed for specific functions. They have receptors for blood-borne substances to give appropriate reactions. As for example, some compounds like apomorphine or emetine act upon area postrema to initiate vomiting (chemoreceptor trigger zone).

**Angiotensin II** stimulates **thirst center of hypothalamus via the subfornical organ and vascular organ of lamina terminalis bypassing the blood-brain barrier.**

Besides these well recognized functions, the circumventricular organs mediate drinking and ADH release. These are responses to raised plasma osmolality or raised body temperature by influencing hypothalamic heat conserving zone. Histologically, the circumventricular organs have fenestrated capillaries and are highly permeant. Anterior lobe of pituitary and pineal gland are close to brain anatomically, but they are distinct organs and, in spite of their fenestrated capillaries, they are outside the purview of blood-brain barrier.

Maintenance of composition of extracellular fluid surrounding every organ is essential for their proper function and, accordingly, homoestatic mechanisms have been devised by nature to rectify any deviation that may occur. For example, if water is taken in excess, the urine flow increases; if $K^+$ intake is high, aldosterone secretion rises excreting $K^+$ at higher rate. But, as normal brain function is dependent on right ionic composition of brain ISF or CSF ($Na^+$, $K^+$, $Ca^{2+}$, $Mg^{2+}$, $H^+$ etc.), their concentrations are regulated more cautiously by the blood-brain barrier.

Besides the restriction imposed by the barrier, homeostasis is helped by glial cells and by the operation of some reflexes. Due to the existence of this barrier most of the endogenous compounds (metabolites, hormones) and exogenous substances like drugs cannot have harmful effects on CNS. Conversely, the neurotransmitters of diverse functions cannot enter into circulation in sufficient amount to affect other organs.

Certain drugs can penetrate the blood-brain barrier with more ease than others. Sulphonamides have better penetrating power than other antimicrobials like penicillin or tetracyclines. Inflammation of brain and meninges due to infection or any other cause tends to breach the banor less permeant drugs can then traverse blood-brain barrier in adequate amounts. Tumors are associated with permeant vascular supply and may be labelled with albumin bound radioactive iodine.

## Intracranial pressure

It has been observed that cerebrospinal fluid (CSF) in recumbent individuals has a pressure above atmospheric (70–180 mm of CSF) and the level increases during straining and compression of jugular veins of neck. There occurs continuous formation of CSF at choroid plexus and its reabsorption by arachnoid villi. In both formation and reabsorption of CSF, primary driving force is hydrostatic pressure gradient (filtration). CSF formation can occur at a normal rate in the face of CSF pressure exceeding the upper range (of normal pressure) and also its reabsorption depends upon the pressure difference between CSF and veins of arachnoid villi.

With rise of CSF pressure, reabsorption increases linearly if there is no obstruction at the site of reabsorption. When the CSF pressure is near 70 mm Hg, reabsorption stops and, at 110 mm of Hg pressure, both secretion and reabsorption are the same.

**Hydrocephalus** is a condition of excess accumulation of fluid within the cavities of brain. CSF is formed mainly at ventricles from choroid plexus and arrive at subarachnoid space around CNS via median foramina of Magendie and lateral formina of Luschka of roof of 4th ventricle. When the reabsorption of CSF at arachnoid granulations is defective, excess CSF accumulates both outside and inside CNS (communicating or external hydrocephalus). On the other hand, when there is obstruction at exit foramina of Magendie and Luschka or elsewhere proximally (cerebral aqueduct), accumulation of CSF occurs within whole or part of CNS (noncommunicating or internal hydrocephalus).

Inside the rigid structure of cranium and vertebral canal, the volume of brain, CSF and blood remains constant altogether **(Monro-Kellie doctrine)**. Both the blood perfusing brain and CSF ultimately drain into venous system of CVS. So, during straining (forced expiration with closed glottis), when venous return diminishes due to raised intrathoracic pressure blood flow through brain decreases as pressure gradient (arterial-venous) diminishes and raised intracranial pressure, through CSF and ISF (CSF volume increases due to diminished reabsorption), compresses blood vessels. Thus, capillary pressure does not increase much so that the vessels are protected. During acceleration upwards (positive G), similar events occur.

When blood goes towards the lower extremities, there should be much fall of cerebral blood flow. But along with fall of intracranial pressure, blood vessels are exposed to lower pressure to make them more dilated and adequate flow can be maintained. So cerebral ischemia is prevented till the G force is very high. During deceleration downwards (negative G), blood moves headward and cerebral blood kept near normal level in the face of raised cerebral arterial pressure and small vessels are protected by measures as in straining during defecation. Thus, changed level of intracranial pressure during physiological conditions tend to regulate cerebral blood flow and protect its microcirculation.

But if the rise in intracranial pressure is substantial during any pathological condition, cerebral ischemia develops. It stimulates the vasomotor center to raise systemic arterial blood pressure that via baroreceptor reflex causes bradycardia and lower respiratory rate. This pressure elevating response is called **Cushing reflex** that tries to maintain perfusion in the face of raised intracranial pressure.

## Lumbar Puncture

Sampling of CSF is done by lumbar puncture from subarachnoid space below the **lower end of spinal cord** that tapers in the lower end of the body of 1st lumbar vertebra.

**Technique :**

- The patient is kept near the edge of the bed and bent forward as far as possible.
- The **4th lumbar spine is identified** as it lies at the level of highest point of iliac crest.
- At the space **between 3rd and 4th lumbar spines**, taking proper asepsis, skin and deep tissues are anesthetized locally with 2% lignocaine.
- The lumbar puncture needle is then inserted through the anesthetized part at midline–forwards and slightly upwards.
- When the needle is felt to enter the subarachnoid space (loss of resistance), the stylet is withdrawn. CSF appears through the needle due to its pressure (normal 60-150 mm of CSF).
- The pressure exerted by CSF can be **measured** with **suitable manometer and samples collected** in sterile tubes for cytological, biochemical and bacteriological studies.
- The puncture site is dressed and the patient is asked to remain in lying position for some time to **avoid headache**.

The needle passes through following structures before entering the subarachnoid space :

(i) Skin,
(ii) Superficial fascia
(iii) Supraspinous ligament
(iv) Interspinous ligament
(v) Ligamentum flavum
(vi) Areolar tissue containing internal vertebral venous plexus
(vii) Duramater
(viii) Arachnoid mater.

## Queckenstedt's Sign

A block of subarachnoid space in vertebral canal (due to any cancerous growth) may be tested by compressing the internal jugular veins in the neck. This raises cerebral venous pressure which in turn retards the absorption of C.S.F. in arachnoid granulations; thus an increased C.S.F. pressure reading. A failure to do so indicates a block of subarachnoid space and this is the positive **QUECKENSTEDT'S SIGN**.

## Indications for lumbar puncture

- Diagnosis of **meningitis, encephalitis, multiple sclerosis, neurosyphilis** etc.
- Diagnosis of **subarachnoid hemorrhage.**
- Intrathecal injection of drugs.
- Measurement of intracranial pressure, draining of CSF as treatment in selected cases of raised intracranial tension.

## Contraindications for lumbar puncture

- Raised **intracranial tension** and **space occupying lesions** in cranium as fall in CSF pressure may cause herniation of **cerebellar tonsils** through foramen magnum and compress brain stem structures.
- Infection at the puncture site, coagulation disorders (e.g. thrombocytopenia).

Finding of papilledema by ophthalmoscopy indicates raised intracranial tension.

## ➤ 11.21 KEY CONCEPTS

1. There are about 20 billion neurons in the nervous system. They are ,linked together in sensory and motor pathways. Movement of skeletal muscle is controlled by motor tracts from the cerebral cortex; sympathetic and parasympathetic nerves are concerned with autonomic control of smooth muscles and glands; sensory pathways send information to the receiving areas in the central nervous system (CNS).

2. Nerve impulses are conveyed from one neuron to another through electrical and chemical synapses of which chemical synapses are more common in the nervous system. Acetylcholine is released into the synaptic cleft in presence of $Ca^{2+}$ followed by the diffusion of acetylcholine and subsequent hydrolysis by cholinesterase enzyme. The action potential reaching the presynaptic terminal activates the voltage gated $Ca^{2+}$ channels leading to influx

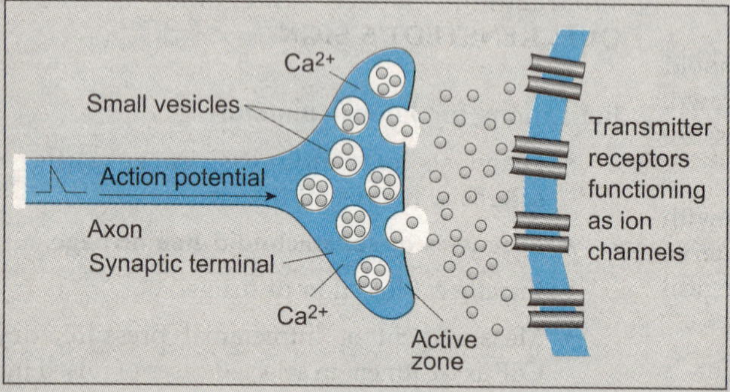


A nerve ending and neuromuscular junction to show the release of so-called 'fast' neurotransmitters into neuromuscular junction

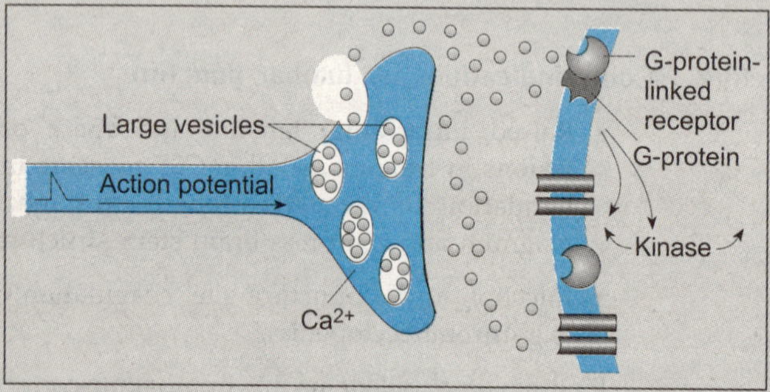


There is release of 'slow' neurotransmitters from around the neuromuscular junction

of $Ca^{2+}$ which, in turn, stimulates the exocytosis of the vesicles of the neurotransmitter. Ionotropic and metabotropic receptors are responsible for regulation of both excitatory and inhibitory type of synaptic potentials. Release of acetylcholine from presynaptic terminals generates end plate potential. Neurotransmitter (NT) is released by the presynapatic cell whenever there occurs chemical transmission. Then NT diffuses across the synaptic cleft and binds with receptors present on the post synaptic cell. The NTs are acetylcholine, several different amines, a number of aminoacids and a variety of peptides.

3. Sensation can be of two types **general somatosensory sensation** (touch, pain, temperature and proprioception) and **special sensation** (vision, hearing, equilibrium, taste and olfaction). Several types of somatosensory mechanoreceptors have been identified. Pacinian corpuscles are rapidly adapting mechanoreceptors with large receptive fields. Ruffini's endings also have large receptive fields and have sustained responses. Meissner's corpuscles adapt rapidly but Merkel's disks adapt slowly; both have small receptive fields. Nociceptors convey pain sensation while thermoreceptors convey the sensation of temperature. Position sense is mediated through proprioceptors in muscles and joints. Visceral sensory afferents provide information about the internal environment of the body.

4. **Stimulation of sensory receptors** with adequate stimuli initiate action potential leading to transmission of sensory impulse to the CNS. The neurotransmitter released from somatosensory neurons at their axon terminals is **glutamate**. There are discrete pathways in the dorsal and lateral parts of the spinal cord for different modalities of somatosensory sensation. The motor tracts pass through the ventral part of the spinal cord.

5. **The sensory pathway** for fine touch and proprioception passes through the dorsal column of the spinal cord and projects to the thalamus after crossing the midline in the lower medulla. The pathways for crude touch and pain reach the thalamus via the lateral column of the spinal cord. Fibers from thalamus project to the **somatosensory cortex**.

## ➤ 11.21 KEY CONCEPTS

6. **Lower motor neurons (LMN)** link the nervous system to the appropriate muscle group. Reciprocal connections among groups of LMN innervating antagonistic and synergistic muscles are made by excitatory and inhibitory interneurons. Input to LMN and interneurons is provided by **upper motor neurons (UMN)** which reside at a higher level in the hierarchy of the motor system.

7. Nerve endings in the ***muscle spindles*** monitor the length of a muscle and are responsible for **stretch reflex** (reflex contraction of the muscle when it is stretched). The tension on the muscle spindle is regulated by the $\gamma$ motor neurons innervating the infrafusal muscle fibers within the spindle. The Golgi tendon organ elicits inverse stretch reflex which is opposite to the reflex elicited by the muscle spindle. Thus, these organs are also responsible for monitoring muscle length. Alpha and gamma motor neurons receive instructions from the cerebral cortex and the brain stem for complex voluntary and involuntary movements.

8. **Pyramidal cells** in frontal motor cortex (M–I) send command for conscious motor activity. M–I area receives input from adjacent motor association area (M–II), prefrontal cortex, thalamic motor nuclei, primary sensory cortex (S–I), and sensory association area (S–II). The premotor area (a part of M–II) is concerned with orientation of the body for upcoming movement while the supplemental motor area (another part of M–II) is related with coordination of bilaterally coordinated movements.

9. The cortical motor commands are coordinated via motor loop pathways involving the **basal ganglia**. The information passes from the cerebral cortex to the basal ganglia and thalamic nuclei; and from there back to the cortex. Both excitatory (direct) and inhibitory (indirect) pathways are present in this loop; they provide counter balancing influences on the activity of the motor cortex. The dopaminergic nigrostriatal pathway plays a crucial role in modulating activity in these direct and indirect pathways.

   **Parkinson's disease** is produced by deficit in the nigrostriatal pathway while **Huntington's chorea** occurs due to loss of GABAergic neurons of corpus striatum. Lesion in the subthalamus leads to involuntary movements called **hemiballismus**.

10. The **cerebellum** provides another motor loop pathway for refining motor commands from the cortex especially when the movements involve multiple joints and learning new motor skills. Spinocerebellum sends information to the spinal cord for control of limb movements. Vestibulocerebellum is concerned with postural movements in response to gravity, and cerebrocerebellum smoothens complex motor activities. Input to cerebellum comes from the spinal cord via climbing fibers originating from the inferior olivary complex in the medulla, and from the cerebral cortex via mossy fibers and parallel fibers. Activity of mossy fiber is modulated by the inputs from the climbing fiber. Cerebellar lesion cause defects in coordination of motor activities (ataxia).

11. The emotional status of an individual is influenced by the **autonomic nervous system (ANS)**. The feelings of pleasure are associated with the parasympathetic division of the ANS while feelings of anxiety are related with the sympathetic. The cingulate cortex, the site of emotional awareness, is linked to appropriate parts of the ANS by the papez circuit. The aggresive behavioral pattern is generated by the hypothalamus which receives input from the papez circuit and the amygdala.

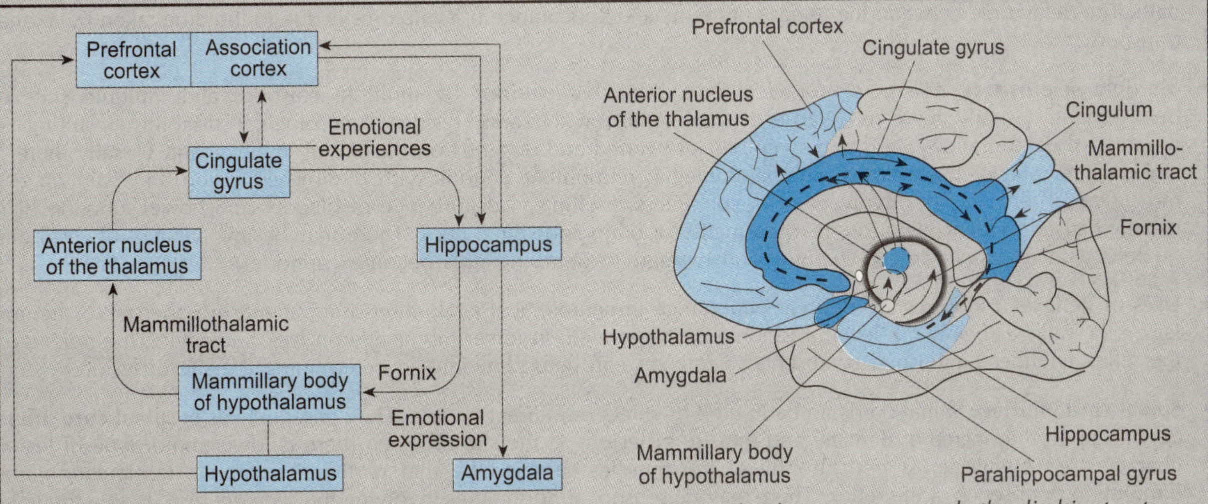


*Papez circuit components and other limbic structures*

## ➤ 11.21 KEY CONCEPTS

**Papez circuit** is the proposed anatomical basis of emotion. The cingulate gyrus is connected with the parahippocampal gyrus and piriform area of the temporal lobe via the cingulum. The temporoammonic tract connects the temporal lobe with hippocampus (Ammon's horn). The hippocampus is connected to the mamillary body by the fornix. The mamillothalamic tract connects the mamillary body with the anterior nucleus of the thalamus which is connected with cingulate gyrus via the superior thalamic peduncle, completing the circuit.

The diffuse modulatory system in the brainstem that influence emotional behavior and motivation utilize dopamine, noradrenalin, and serotonin as neurotransmitter; they also establish the general state of awareness of an individual. The **reticular activating system (RAS)** in the brain stem is concerned with different functional states (such as aroused or sleep state) of the brain which are reflected in the electroencephalogram (EEG).

12. There are distinct areas in the brain that are responsible for learning and memory. **Learning** is the process of acquisition of new information of every sort and skills of all kinds. Learning is prerequisite to change of our behaviour and life style. ***Memory*** is the faculty by which we can recall past experiences. Like learning it is also used in a wide sense. As for example, we can remember our date of birth, prominent political figures in recent or remote past or even identify the name and use of the function of a machine or an apparatus we use. It can be divided into reflexive or non declarative or implict memory and declarative or recognition memory.

The medial temporal lobe and diencephalon play crucial role in declarative or recognition (explicit) memory (memory for facts, concepts and events). Various parts of the brain appear to be involved in non declarative or implicit or reflexive memory (memory for skills, habits etc.) that operates at an unconscious level. Alternations in the properties of membrane channels have been correlated with learning and memory. Long-term memory needs synthesis of new proteins and growth, whereas short-term memory is related with changes in existing neuronal circuits.

## ➤ 11.22 DISORDERS/CLINICAL CORRELATIONS

- **Migraine :** A symptom complex occurring periodically and characterized by pain in the head usually unilateral, vertigo, nausea and vomiting, photophobia and scintillating appearances of light.
- **Meniere's disease :** An affection characterized clinically by vertigo, nausea, vomiting, tinnitus and progressive deafness : due probably to an effusion of blood into the semicircular canal.
- **Neuralgias:** It is described as sharp, brief and lancinating pain along the distribution of the particular nerve. It is mainly due to disease of sensory nerves in the face and scalp e.g. Trigeminal neuralgia.
- **Axonal transport :** It is the mechanism by which materials are transported back to the cell body of a neuron. Viruses like Herpes and Rabies and bacteriotoxins, eg. Tetanus bacteria, are transported to the cell body of neurons via this path. The delay time between the release of toxins and appearance of symptoms is due to the time taken by axonal transport.
- **Multiple sclerosis :** It is a neurological condition characterized by multiple episodes and multiple sites of involvement. Usually there is relapse and remission with some residual neurological disability resulting in progressive deterioration. Signs and symptoms are varied and depends on the site of involvement. Usually there is weakness in one or more limbs; ophthalmoplegia; retrobulbar neuritis with diminished vision and pain on eye movement. There may be involvement of sphincters resulting in disturbance of bladder and bowel function. It is usually caused by demyelination in white matter of brain and spinal cord. There may be involvement of vestibular nucleus with resultant vertigo, vomiting and nystagmus. Some patients become euphoric.
- **Uses of Reflexes : Reflexes** are of great importance in neurological evaluation of a patient. In upper motor neuron lesion the reflexes below the level of lesion are exaggerated. In lower motor neuron lesion involving the reflex arc, the reflex is either diminished or absent. So reflexes can help clinicians in determining the site of lesion.
- **Spinal cord injuries :** Spinal cord can be injured by direct or indirect trauma. The consequences of **spinal cord injury** depend upon the degree of damage and the site of lesion. At the site of lesion there is lower motor type of lesion characterized by weakness and atrophy of the muscles supplied by that particular segment, fasciculation and diminution or absence of the reflex. There may be sensory abnormalities involving the segment also. Below the level of lesion there is sign of upper motor neurone involving with bladder and bowel involvement.

## ➤ 11.22 DISORDERS/CLINICAL CORRELATIONS

➤ **Cerebral injuries :** A **stroke** or **cerebrovascular accident** can be due to hemorrhage or ischemia. Usually the lenticulostriate branch of middle cerebral artery ruptures resulting in a hematoma in the basal ganglia region with consequent contralateral complete hemiplegia. In ischemic stroke, either due to the thrombosis or embolism, the sign and symptoms depend upon the area of supply of the affected artery.

➤ **Cerebrospinal fluid pressure : Cerebrospinal fluid** is constantly secreted from the choroid plexuses of the lateral ventricles and it is constantly reabsorbed from the arachnoid villi. Consequently, the pressure of CSF within the ventricular septum of brain remains constant. The pressure of CSF can be increased if there is any space occupying lesion in the brain; if there is increased formation of CSF, as in meningitis, or if there is diminished reabsorption of CSF, as in sagittal sinus thrombosis or if there is obstruction to the outflow of CSF from the 4th ventricle due to organized exudate in tubercular or any other form of chronic meningitis. The increased intracranial pressure can cause displacement of brainstem through the cerebellar tentorium resulting in features of **brainstem compression**.

➤ **Factors affecting impulse conduction :** Some substances are responsible for alteration of the nerve fiber membrane permeability to ions. Calcium ions cause closing of sodium channels in the nerve fiber membrane during an action potential. If calcium ions are deficient, sodium channels remain open, as such sodium ions diffuse through the membrane again and again. As a result the impulses are transmitted repeatedly.

➤ **Brain waves :** These are the recordings of the fluctuating electrical changes in the brain. Electrodes are located on the surface of surgically exposed brain (electrocorticogram) or on the outer surface of the head (electroencephalogram). These electrodes are responsible for detecting electrical changes in the extracellular fluid of the brain in response to changes in potential among large group of neurons.

➤ **Spinal nerve injuries :** Spinal nerve injuries may result from birth injuries, dislocations, vertebral fractures, stabs, gun shot wounds and the pressure from tumors.

Sudden bending of the neck can compress the nerves of the cervical plexuses causing peristent headache and pain in the neck and skin which the cervical nerves supply.

➤ **Cancer pain and chronic pain :** The patient with cancer suffers pain at the time of their diagnosis and 90% of those are in advanced stages. Generally, chronic pain can be classified as lower back pain, migraines and myofascial syndrome.

➤ **Alzheimer's disease :** It is presenile dementia occurring usually in persons under fifty years of age associated with sclerosis and neurofibril degeneration.

➤ **Phantom pain :** It is an excellent example of law of projection, a primary concept of neurophysiology which explains that involvement of any part of sensory pathways up to cortex produces sensation at the site of receptor.

In case of amputed limbs, the receptors are absent but the peripheral and central pathways remain intact and if the amputed stump gets hurt then the individual perceives pain in the peripheral part that was cut off (**Phantom limb**).

➤ **Cerebellar disorder :** Cerebellar disorders are characterized by the cardinal features like —

- Swaying away from the line of walking.
- Loss of motor coordination.
- Characteristic speech disorder.
- Nystagmus.
- Patient walks with his legs wide apart to ensure his stability on the ground (ataxic gait).
- Hypotonia of the limbs.

➤ **Wallerian degeneration :** Neuron has got an unique cytoplasmic architecture. Neurons lack ribosomes. Therefore, all protein biosynthesis is essentially done by the smooth endoplasmic reticulum. The axons lack any such capacity of protein synthesis even. They solely depend on the Golgi apparatus of the cell body; which — apart from doing the posttranslational potentiation of the proteins — take part in their transport to the extreme nerve endings. Not only for the structural protein but also for the enzymes, the axons are totally dependent on the cell body and unable to continue if this primary supply line is disrupted. This orthograde cytoplasmic transport is grossly interrupted by the trauma to the neurilemma. Injury to a particular site on the axon leads to the orthograde degeneration and lysis of the distal segment (Wallerian degeneration).

## ➤ 11.22 DISORDERS/CLINICAL CORRELATIONS

➤ **Transverse section of spinal cord :**

| *Type of lesion* | *Tracts involved* | *Level of decussation* | *Improvements* |
|---|---|---|---|
| **Hemisection** | Dorsal | Brain stem | Touch, vibration and joint sense, lost in the ipsilateral side below the level. |
| | Ascending (Spinothalamic) | Cord | Loss of pain and temperature of contra-lateral side. |

Hemisection of the spinal cord refers to a partial transection. It is characterized below the hemisection by a loss of proprioception, tactile discrimination and vibration on the same side as the injury; paralysis on the same side and loss of pain and temperature sensations on the opposite side.

Hemisection (upper cervical cord) hemiplegia.

Hemisection (thoracic cord) monoplegia (paralysis of one lower extremity).

*Complete transection :* involves all tracts and total loss of all sensations and voluntary movements below the level of transection. (upper cervical cord is transected quadriplegia transection is between the **cervical** and **lumbar paraplegia**).

*Spinal Shock* : There is an initial period of spinal shock following transection. It lasts from a few days to several weeks. All reflexes are lost **(areflexia)**. There is also hypotonia.

➤ **Chromatolysis :** The disintegration of the granules of **Nissl's substance** in a nerve cell body which may occur after exhaustion of the cell or damage to its peripheral process.

➤ **Sleep disorders :** About one-third of the adults experience sleep disorders in some form or the other. Two neurobiologic systems govern the sleep wake cycle in a 24 hour clock system (i) that initiates sleep (ii) timing of sleep in 24 hours clock. Both intrinsic and extrinsic factors modulate and interfere with these systems :

I. *Dyssomnias* — (a) Intrinsic sleep disorders : (i) Insomnia (Idiopathic, Psychological); (ii) Narcolepsy; (iii) Sleep apnea syndrome. (b) Extrinsic sleep disorders (trauma; altitude; temperature; noise; alcohol; drug).

II. *Parasomnias* — (a) arousal disorders; (b) sleep-wake transition disorders; (c) associated phenomena.

III. *Associated* — Neurological; Psychological; Psychiatric.

➤ **Brain injuries :** *Concussion* : An abrupt but temporary loss of consciousness following a blow to the head or a sudden stopping of a moving head.

*Contusion* : A visible bruising of the brain due to trauma and blood leaking from microscopic vessels. The pia mater is stripped from the brain over the injured area and may be torn, allowing blood to enter the subarachnoid space. A contusion usually results in an extended loss of consciousness, ranging from several minutes to many hours.

➤ **Speech area injuries :** Damage to the cerebellum through trauma or disease is characterised by certain symptoms involving skeletal muscles on the same side of the body. The effects are on the same side of the body as the damaged side of the cerebellum because of a double-crossing of tracts within the cerebellum. There may be lack of muscle coordination called ataxia.

Cerebellar damage may also result in disturbances of gait in which the subject staggers or cannot coordinate normal walking movements and severe dizzines results.

➤ **Motor Neuron Disease :** It is a **degenerative disorder** in which there is degeneration of spinal and cranial motor neurons and pyramidal neurons in the motor cortex. The disease is characterized by the wasting and fasciculation of muscles and weakness of muscles of limbs, tongue, face and palate. Detailed study of this disease has been done in recent years especially to cure the famous theoretical physicist Stephen Hawking who has been suffering from progressive motor neurone disease since the 1960s.

➤ **Basal Ganglia :** The most common disorder of the basal ganglia is Parkinson's disease (parkinsonism). Less common disorders include chorea, athetosis and ballismus.

➤ **Parkinsonism** (Paralysis Agitans, i.e. the shaking palsy) : This condition, first described by James Parkinson in 1817, is characterized by a triad of rigidity, hypokinesia or bradykinesia, and tremor. Most of the patients are over the age of 50.

## ➤ 11.22 DISORDERS/CLINICAL CORRELATIONS

**Cause :** In over 75 per cent of cases, the cause is unknown (idiopathic Parkinsonism). Known causes include drug toxicity, notably phenothiazines which block dopamine receptors. This is supported by the fact that parkinsonism has been produced experimentally in monkeys, by the injection of the chemical methyl-phenyl-tetrahydropyridine (MPTP) which destroys the neurons in the substantia nigra. Other causes include: viral encephalitis, head injury: especially repeated trauma as in boxers, and cerebral tumours.

➤ **Pathophysiology of Parkinson's disease :** The common pathological finding in Parkinson's disease is a cellular loss and depigmentation of the substantia nigra, with a degeneration of its dopaminergic projection to the striatum. Sometimes there is also an atrophy of the globus pallidus and a patchy cortical atrophy. Neurochemical studies show that in parkinsonism, there is a depletion of the dopamine content of the striatum and the substantia nigra.

It has been found that the rigidity, hypokinesia and to a lesser extent the tremor, can be reduced by the administration of levodopa, L-DOPA. Prior to this discovery, it had been known that the symptoms could be relieved by the administration of drugs which decrease the effects of acetylcholine on the triatum i.e. anticholineric drugs. There is also a reduction of serotonin in the brains of Parkinsonian patients, and administration of serotonin relieves the tremor, although it has little effect on the hypokinesia and rigidity. These observations have led to the belief that normally, there is a balance between the inhibition of the striatum by dopamine from substantia nigra, and its facilitation by acetylcholine from the cortex and the thalamus.

➤ **Clinical features of Parkinsonism :**

**Tremor :** An early symptom is tremor of the fingers spreading to the proximal parts of the arm, the tongue, and later the legs.

**The characteristics of the tremor are** :

The **tremor in parkinsonism** is present at rest and often lessened during purposeful activity. This is unlike the intentiion tremor of cerebellar disease.

It is **regular** in rhythm, about 4 cycles per second.

It consists of alternation between agonist and antagonist muscles presenting as: the hands are flexed at the metacarpo-phalangeal joints with the thumb adducted across the palm. Then there is an alternation of ab duction and adduction of the thumb, combined with a flexion and extension of the fingers which has been likened to 'pill-rolling'. Pronation and supination of the forearm follows.

The **tremor** commonly reduces as rigidity progresses, and is absent during sleep.

It has been found that the neurons in the ventrolateral nucleus of the thalamus fire impulses synchronously with the tremor, and a surgical damage of this nucleus abolishes the tremor.

**Muscular rigidity :** There is increased resistance to passive movement in both agonist and antagonist muscles which is dominant in the flexors and lasting throughout the are immobile giving a mark-like facial appearance, and the eyes stare with little blinking. Emotiional expressions of the face are slow in onset, limited and prolonged. Speech is low in starting, of low volume, and difficult in execution (dysarthria); and so is writing, the letters become smaller and illegible (micrographia). When the rigidity is fully developed, the patient assumes a fixed hunched (flexion) posture with the hips, elbows, and knees flexed.

Unlike spasticity, passive flexion does not culminate in the clasp-knife reflex, instead a cog-wheel phenomenon commonly occurs in which the resistance to passive movement is interrupted by a series of 'catch' and 'give'. This phenomenon is probably the result of the superimposition of tremor, but some view it as a response the Golgi tendon reflex. In some patients the cog-wheel phenomenon is not demonstrable; instead, the muscles offer a continuous resistance to stretch, like a plastic or lead pipe. It is not clear whether rigidity is due to alpha-motor neuron or gamma-efferent facilitation.

➤ **Hypokinesia (poverty of movement) :** Movements are infrequent, slow in initiation and execution, and are lacking in precision. The gait is reduced to short shuffling steps, with uncontrolled acceleration when walking downhill, which leads to frequent falls. Loss of arm swinging when walking occurs early; fine movements like fastening buttons are difficult.

➤ **Drug treatment of Parknisonism :** The aim of drug treatment is to restore the dopamine acetylcholine balance which seems to govern the extrapyramidal control of motor activity at the level of the corpus striatum and substantia nigra. The drugs used can thus be classified as follows :

## ➤ 11.22 DISORDERS/CLINICAL CORRELATIONS

1. **Anticholinergics** e.g. **orphenadrine**. They ameliorate the tremor and rigidity, but not the hypokinesia.
2. Dopamine precursors e.g. **L-DOPA**. Dopamine itself cannot be used since it does not pass through the blood-brain barrier to reach the corpus striatum. It is effective against the rigidity and hypokinesia, and to a lesser extent, the tremor. In order to enable the administered L-DOPA to reach the brain without peripheral destruction, selective MAO inhibitos e.g. L-deprenyl are also administered. They act by inhibiting the breakdown of levodopa in the peripheral tissues only, but not in the CNS.
3. **Dopamine** agonists which stimulate dopamine receptors in the corpus striatum e.g. bromocriptine.
4. Drugs that release dopamine from stores and inhibit re-uptake e.g. **amantadine**.
5. **Transplantation of fetal** substantia nigra neurons into the caudate nucleus and putamen-has been tried in an attempt to increase dopamine levels, but it has shown only limited success.
6. **Cultured cell lines** (e.g.—fibroblasts) that have been genetically altered to produce dopamine are beginning to show promise as a fetal transplantation alternative.
7. **Pallidotomy** by placing an electrode in the globus pallidus near its output pathways and making a destructive lesion that interrupts the projection to the thalamus.
8. **Electrode implantation** here a stimulating electrode is implanted in the globus pallidus. When activated by the patient, signals are generated by the electrode that disrupt the flow of impulses from the pallidum to the thalamus; the effect is the same as that of pallidomy.

➤ **Chorea :** Chorea is a disease **characterized by involuntary non-repetitive** jerky movements of the distal extremities, with spasmodic contortions of the facial muscles. It is associated with damage to the corpus striatum, mainly the caudate nucleus. The case may be hereditary (Huntington's chorea) or infective (Sydenham's chorea).

Unlike parkinsonism, administration of L-DOPA worsens the symptoms. Treatment is with dopamine receptor antagonists e.g. phenothiazines or GABA- enhancing agents such sodium valproate.

➤ **Athetosis :** Athetosis is a disorder which presents as frequent slow, writhing (sinuous) movements of the limb, with forced axial rotations of the trunk and neck, and is associated with damage to teh striatum.

➤ **Hemiballismus :** It is a syndrome characterized by spontaneous, wild, flinging movements of the limbs, due to a lesion in the subthalamic nucleus. The common cause of damage is hemorrhage in the nucleus. Damage to the subthalamic nucleus reduces inhibitory output from the GpiSNpc to halamus. This leads to disinhibition of thalamic output, resulting in hyperkinetic movements mediated by the corticospinal tracts.

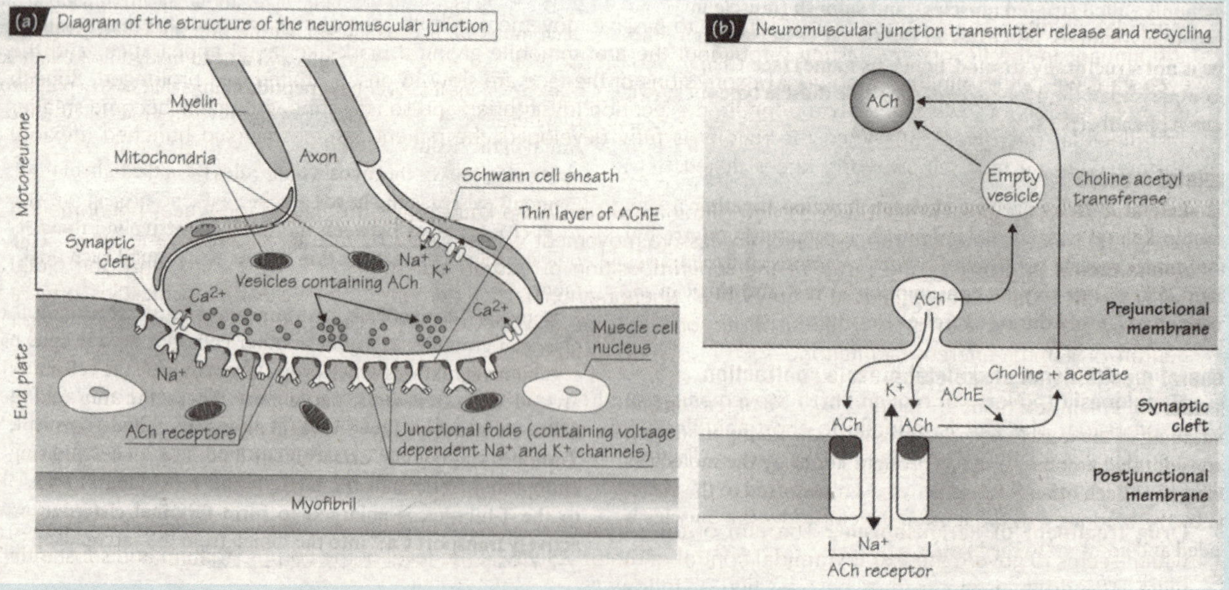

# The Special Senses

AGENDA :



12

## ➤ 12.1 CHAPTER OVERVIEW

**Special senses or somatic senses** are physical apparatuses by which stimuli are received, transduced, and conducted as impulses to be interpreted in the brain.

The **eye** contains lens, pupil and retina for recording visual images. **Vision** is closely related to a complex receptor organ, the eye. The eye contains important optical elements and the photoreceptors. These receptors are present in the retina. They are responsible for converting the incoming signal into an electrical signal in the optic nerve.

**Refraction** of the eye is measured in **diopters** and is the reciprocal value of the anterior focal length in meters when the eye is accommodated for distant vision.

**Visual acuity** is a measure of the resolving power of the eye. **Rods** and **cones** are the light sensitive receptors of the retina.

The cones are specialized for discriminating color in bright light, the rods are for vision in poor light. The **rods** and **cones** contain the visual pigments in their disk membranes. They are responsible for conversion of a light stimulus into a chemical signal and, ultimately, into electrical stimulation of the receptor.

The image is formed on the retina and the image is inverted and reversed. It is due to the path of the light rays entering the eye. The readjustment of the power of the crystalline lens along with some other changes are called **accommodation**.

The photosensitive compounds decompose on exposure to produce a change in the permeability and, subsequently, there is a change in potential in the receptor cell.

Visible light has a wave length ranging between 400 nm to more than 700 nm. Prismatic dispersion of white light gives rise to seven coloured ray. So white light is a compound of monochromatic lights recognized from the acronym 'vibgyor', violet (430 nm), indigo (480 nm), blue (505 nm), green (530 nm), yellow (580 nm), orange (630 nm) and red (680 nm).

Red, green and blue are called **primary colors** because by mixing suitable amounts of them any colour, even white, can be created. Leaves of a tree is green, blood looks red – this perception is called **hue** or **color**.

**Taste buds** are present in the papillae of the tongue. They are scattered throughout the epithelium of the tongue, soft palate, pharynx and epiglottis. The taste receptors are stimulated by molecules in solution in the fluids of the mouth. The receptors consists of 40-50 chemosensitive cells which are exposed to chemicals.

The relation between the molecular structure of compounds and modalities of taste is very loose and substances of wildly different structure can elicit same sensation. **Olfactory cells** are located in a specialized region in the roof of the nasal cavity. The basic mechanism for olfactory discrimination is not known. Olfactory cells are located in the olfactory epithelium. These are specialised bipolar cells.

The **ear** is the organ of hearing. The ear has got external, middle and inner compartments. It is supplied by eighth cranial nerve which is stimulated by vibrations produced by sound waves.

**Sound** is transmitted from external ear through ossicular chain. When tympanic membrane vibrates with sound, ossicular system also vibrates and conducts the vibrations to the fluid in inner ear.

**The vestibular apparatus** contains three semicircular canals and the two otolith organs (the utricle and saccule). It is located in the membranous labyrinth. The semicircular canals detect angular acceleration but the utricle and saccule detect linear acceleration.

## ➤ 12.2 The Eye

The eye is located in the orbital cavity and it is innervated by 2nd cranial nerve, the optic nerve. It is the sense organ of light. It is more or less spherical in shape and is about 2.5 cm in diameter.

### Functional anatomy of eye (Fig. 12.1)

There are three layers of tissue in the walls of the eye :

- outer fibrous coat – **sclera** and **cornea**
- middle vascular coat – **choroid**, **ciliary body** and **iris**
- inner nervous tissue coat – **retina**.

The lens, aqueous fluid (humor) and vitreous body are located inside the eyeball.

The outer coat is composed of tough, connective tissue layer termed sclera. Some portion of the **sclera** is normally seen as the white of the eye. Anteriorly, it is continuous with cornea. The middle layer is composed of vascular **choroid** and muscular ciliary body and iris. The inner coat is the **retina**. Nerve fibers are emerging out of the optic disc and the blood vessels supplying the retina pass and leave the eye at this point.

The space located between the back of the cornea and the lens of the eye is filled with clear fluid known as **aqueous humor**. The lens is attached with ciliary body by the suspensory ligament. These ciliary smooth muscles are responsible for alteration of the shape of the lens and, as such the eye is allowed to alter its focal distance to accommodate vision to objects at different distances. Gelatinous **vitreous humor** is located just behind the lens. The shape of the lens is maintained by intraocular pressure (15 mm Hg).

**Optic disc** is the area where retinal axons enter the optic nerve.

**Macula** is located very close to the visual axis of the eye. Fovea is the depressed portion in the centre of the macula. This region is produces the sharpest vision.

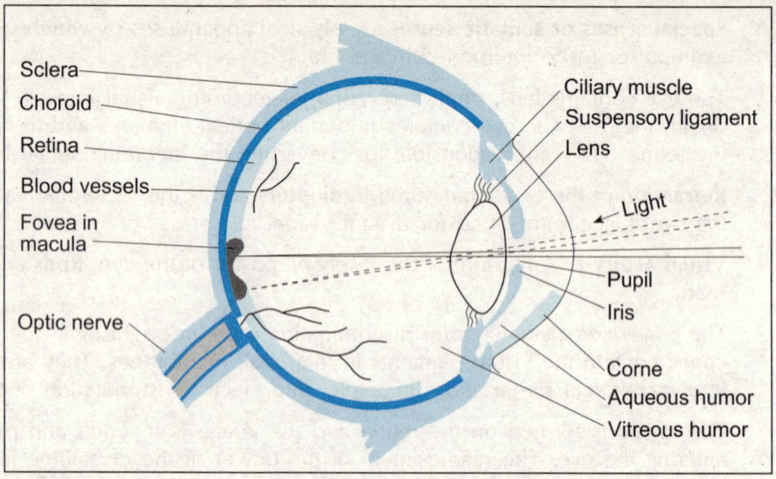


**Fig. 12.1 :** Functional anatomy of eye

**Iris** is the colored part of the eye which extends anteriorly from the ciliary body and is located behind the cornea and in front of the lens. There is an aperture in the center known as **pupil**. The size of the pupil is variable depending on the intensity of light. The iris is supplied by parasympathetic and sympathetic nerves. Parasympathetic stimulation constricts pupil and sympathetic stimulation dilates the pupil. Light enters the eye through the cornea → via aqueous humour → lens → vitreous humor → finally neural elements of the retina to reach the photoreceptors of the posterior surface of the retina.

**Smooth muscles**

| Name | Nerve supply | Action |
|---|---|---|
| Ciliary muscles | III CN, oculomotor nerve– parasympathetic fibers | Relaxation of suspensory ligaments |
| Iris, circular muscles | III CN, oculomotor nerve, parasympathetic fibers | Constriction of pupil |
| Iris, radial muscles | Sympathetic fibers | Dilatation of pupil |

**Muscles of the eyelids and eyes**

**Table 12.1 : Skeletal muscle**

| Name | Nerve supply | Action |
|---|---|---|
| **Extrinsic muscles of the eyes** Superior rectus | III CN, oculomotor nerve | Upward rotation of eye and towards midline |
| Inferior rectus | III CN, oculomotor nerve | Downward rotation of the eye and towards midline |
| Medial rectus | III CN, oculomotor nerve | Eye is rotated towards midline |
| Lateral rectus | VI CN abducens nerve | Eye is rotated away from midline |
| Superior oblique | IV CN, trochlear nerve | Eye is rotated downwards and away from midline |
| Inferior oblique | III CN, oculomotor nerve | Eye is rotated upwards and away from the midline |
| **Muscles of the eyelids** Orbicularis oculi | VII CN, facial nerve | Eye is closed |
| Levator palpebrae superiors | III CN, oculomotor nerve | Eye is opened |

## ➤ 12.3 The Lens and Image Formation

The **image** is formed on the retina and the image is inverted and reversed. It is due to the path of the light rays entering the eye. The readjustment of the power of the crystalline lens (plus some other changes) are called **accommodation**. **Accommodation** is a reflex process which is regulated by the cortex. It allows one to focus on a nearby object voluntarily. There are some events in accommodation (a) ciliary muscles are contracted which reduces the tension of the lens ligaments thereby refraction is increased; (b) constriction of pupil helps to decrease stray light rays and depth of the focus is increased.

The ***power of the accommodation is about 10 diopters,*** but is constantly reduced with the advancement of age (presbyopia). Accommodation occurs due to contraction of ciliary muscles under the control of CN III, oculomotor nerve (parasympathetic nerve fibers).

### Pathway of accommodation (Fig. 12.2)

Retina → optic nerve → optic tract → lateral geniculate body → area 17 of occipital lobe → area 8 (frontal eyefield)

**Table 12.2 : Layers of the eye with their functions**

| *Layer* | *Posterior portion* | *Function* | *Anterior portion* | *Function* |
|---|---|---|---|---|
| **Outer layer** | Sclera | Protective function | Cornea | • Transmission of light<br>• Refraction |
| **Middle layer** | Choroid | • Blood supply<br>• Reflection is prevented | Ciliary body; iris | • Accommodation<br>• Light intensity is controlled |
| **Inner layer** | Retina | • Photoreception<br>• Transmission of impulses | — | — |

→ fibers from area 8 intermingle with corticospinal tract → turns back on the midbrain → EWN (Edinger-Westphal nucleus) and motor nuclei of III CN → effects are produced.

## Accommodation for near vision (Fig. 12.3)

*Events* (a) constriction of circular muscles of the pupil,

(b) relaxation of fibers of zonule,

(c) curvature of the lens is increased.

## Accommodation for distant vision (Fig. 12.4)

**Events** (a) relaxation of the circular muscles of the ciliary body. (b) Zonule fibers become taut.

**Normal eye** : The point of focus is on the retina (Fig. 12.5).

**Myopia or near-sightedness** : When axial length of the eyeball is long in respect to refractive power, the image of the objects will be focused in front of the retina. ***It is corrected by diverging lens placed in front of the eye* (Fig. 12.6).**

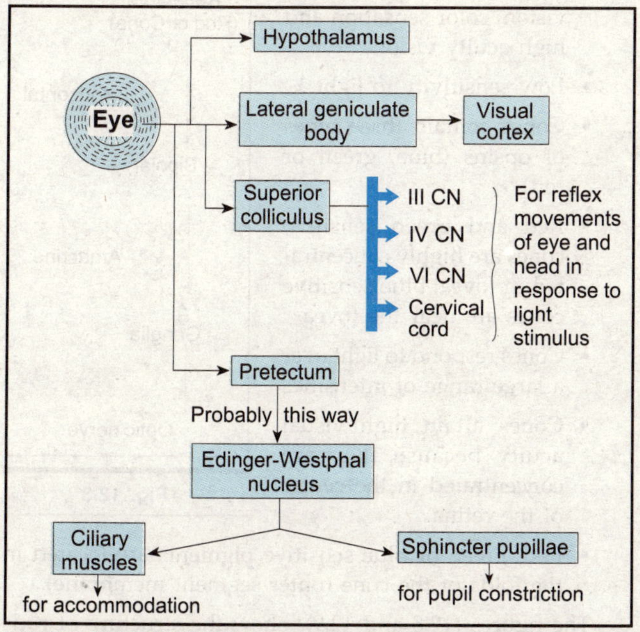


**Fig. 12.2 : Pathway of accommodation**

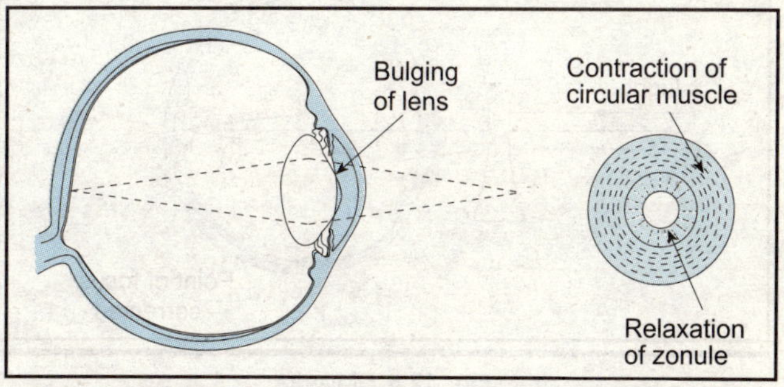


**Fig. 12.3 : Accommodation for near vision**

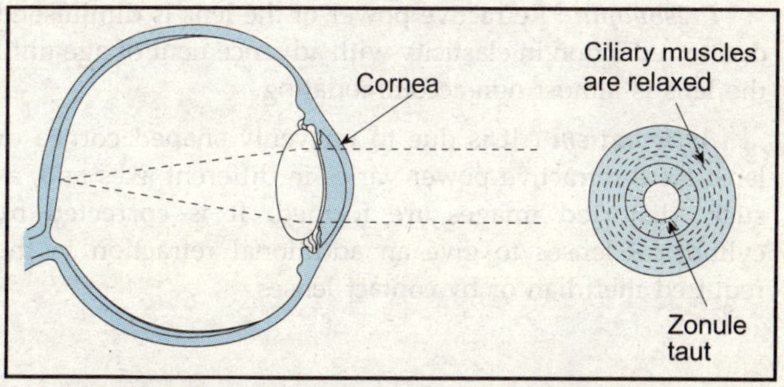


**Fig. 12.4 : Accommodation for distant vision**

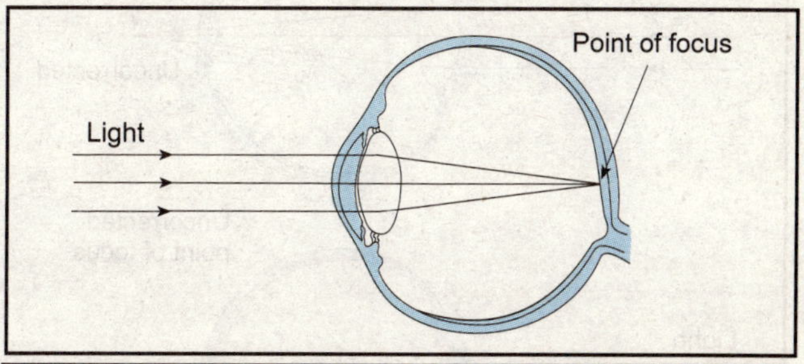


**Fig. 12.5 : Normal eye**

## Hyperopia or far-sightedness

Near objects will be focused behind the retina when the eye-ball is too short. ***It is corrected by a converging lens*** (Fig. 12.7).

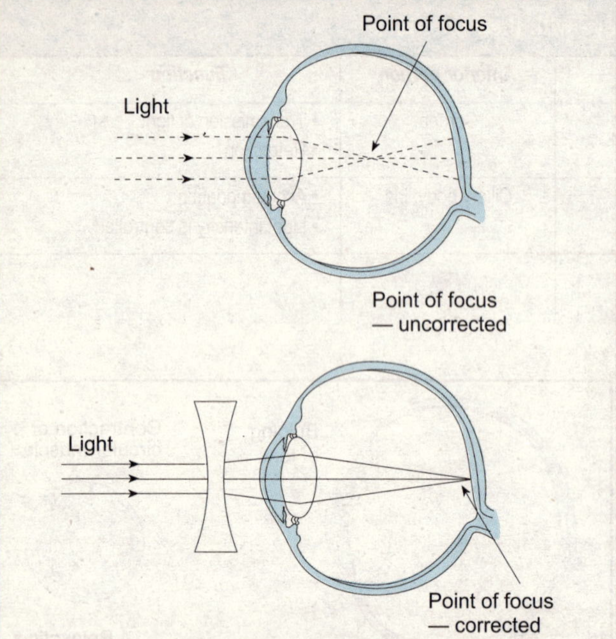


Fig. 12.6 : Myopia

*Presbyopia* : Refractive power of the lens is diminished due to reduction in elasticity with advancement of age until the lens is almost non-accommodating.

*Astigmatism* : It is due to unevenly shaped cornea or lens. Here refractive power varies in different axes and, as such, distorted images are formed. It is corrected by cylindrical lenses to give an additional refraction in the required meridian or by contact lenses.

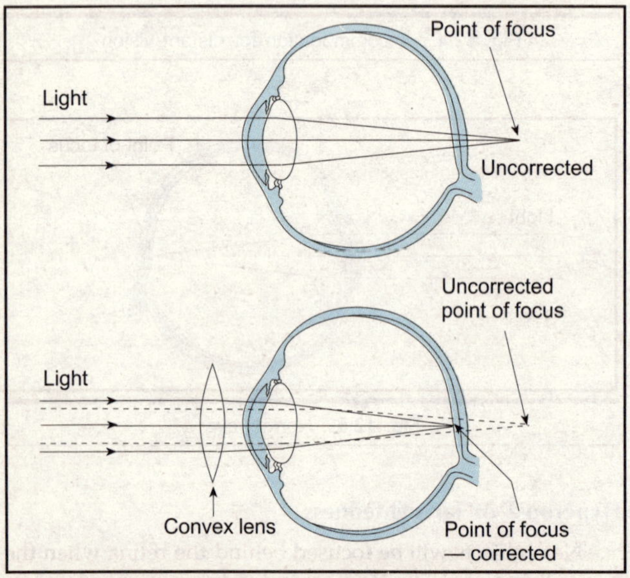


Fig. 12.7 : Hyperopia

## 12.4 Photoreceptor Cells and the Retina

When light is focused on the retina, it is absorbed by the visual pigments located in the photoreceptors. The rod and cone photoreceptor cells of the retina contain photosensitive compounds which are stored in the membrane disks in the outer segments. **Rods** ***are responsible for monochromatic and night vision.*** **Cones** ***are for day vision and color vision.*** Pigment rhodopsin is present in the rod receptors and three color pigments (red, green and blue-sensitive opsins) are present in the cones.

### Salient features of rods

- It is distributed throughout the eye except the fovea
- Outer segment is longer
- High sensitivity to light
- Responsible for night vision
- Do not produce color sensation
- Rhodopsin pigment is located in the membranous disks inside the outer segment of the rod
- Rhodopsin contains a protein called opsin and 11-cis retinal, a light absorbing analogue of vitamin A.
- Rods contain a single type of opsin
- Rods can absorb more light than cones
- Rods may polarize for a good length of time than cones. As such , the response from several photons of light can stimulate more easily in rods than in cones.

### Features of the cones

- Responsible for daylight vision, color sensation and high acuity vision
- Low sensitivity to light
- Cones contain three types of opsins (blue, green or red)
- Red and green sensitive cones are highly concentrated in fovea; bluc sensitive cones are near the fovea
- Cones respond to light over a large range of intensities
- Cones attain high visual acuity because they are concentrated in the center of the retina.
- Red, green or blue sensitive pigments are located in the folds of the cone (outer segment membrane).

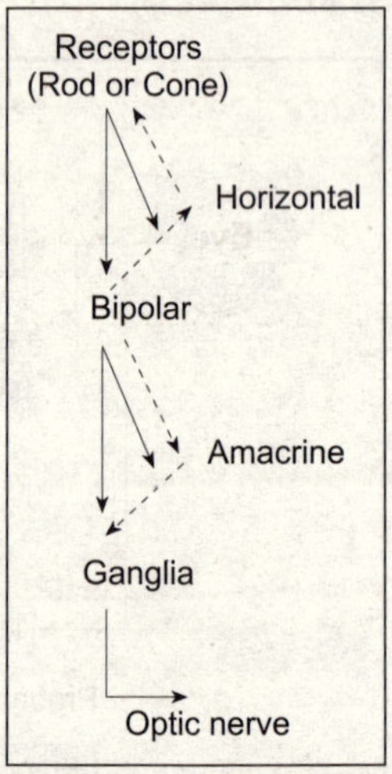


Fig. 12.8

The figures (12.8 and 12.9) show the structure of rods and functional connections of the layers of retina.

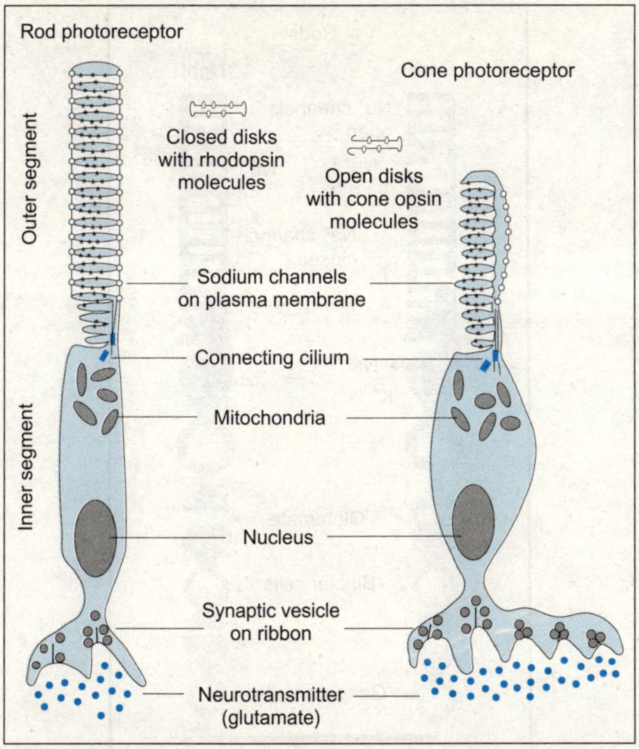


**Fig. 12.9 :** Cellular structure of rod and cone photoreceptors

## 12.5 Photopigments

The photosensitive compounds decompose on exposure to light to produce a change in the permeability and, subsequently, there is a change in potential in the receptor cell .

The scotopic spectral luminosity curve has got maximum sensitivity to light of 507 nm wavelength and shows the absor-ption of spectrum of rhodopsin. ***But the photopic spectral luminority curve shows a peak at 555 nm and is responsible for combined absorption of three cone pigments.*** The eye is most sensitive to blue in scotopic (night) vision and is sensitive to yellow during photopic (day) vision. **Purkinje shift** is the shift from scotopic vision to photopic vision.

### Events between light hitting a rod or cone and change in membrane potential of the receptor

In darkness the photoreceptors remain depolarized due to open state of $Na^+$ channels. When light wave hits them they get hyperpolarized by closure of sodium channels and a train of events lead to excitation of ganglion cell axons.

### Stimulation of photoreceptors

***Excitation of rods*** : Light energy is converted into nerve impulses when an image is formed on the retina. The photopigment present in the rods is rhodopsin which is

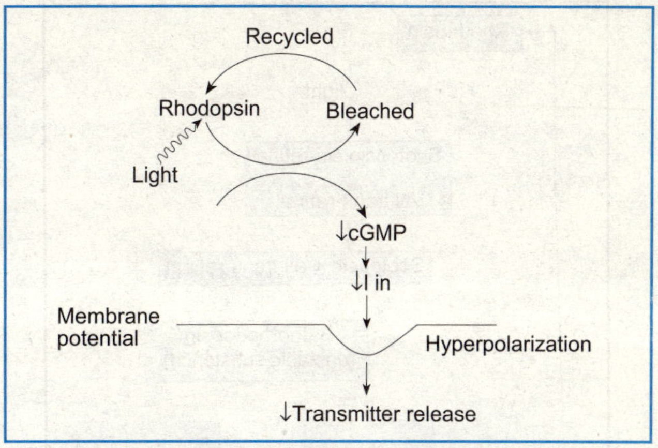


**Fig. 12.10 :** Stimulation of photoreceptors

sensitive to low level of illumination. **Rhodopsin** is formed from scotopsin (a protein) plus retinal (a derivative of vitamin A). The retinal can occur in two forms (absence of light or presence of light).

Retinal occurs as cis-retinal in the absence of light. Cis-retinal converts to all trans-retinal in presence of light. The structure of the all trans-retinal does not fit the scotopsin part of the rhodopsin and form an unstable substance **bathorhodopsin**. The bathorhodopsin converts to lumirhodopsin, metarhodopsin-I, metarhodopsin-II and pararhodopsin. The pararhodopsin splits into scotopsin and all trans-retinal. The receptor potential is initiated in rods when metarhodopsin-I is converted to metarhodopsin II. Rhodopsin is reformed following decomposition of rhodopsin into scotopsin and all trans-retinal in presence of light. All trans-retinal is converted to cis-retinal in the absence of light but in the presence of an enzyme. The rhodopsin (stable form) is reformed when cis-retinal combines with scotopsin (Figs. 12.10 and 12.11).

***Excitation of the cones*** : **Cones** are responsible for vision in bright light, color vision and visual acuity. Photopigment of cones decompose to produce receptor potential due to hyperpolarisation. **Rods** contain the pigment rhodopsin having an opsin (a large protein molecule) and a chromophore molecule, retinene (11-cis-retinal, an aldehyde of vitamin A). The three cone pigments also contain retinene, but the opsin is of a different variety.

## 12.6 Photo Transduction Cascade

Light is detected by the rods and cones contained in the retina of the eye. The retina contains five types of neurons : photoreceptors (rods & cones); bipolar cells, ganglion cells horizontal cells and amacrine cells.

Light rays from distant objects are normally focused on the photoreceptors by the cornea and relaxed lens. When objects are brought closer to the eye, they are kept focused

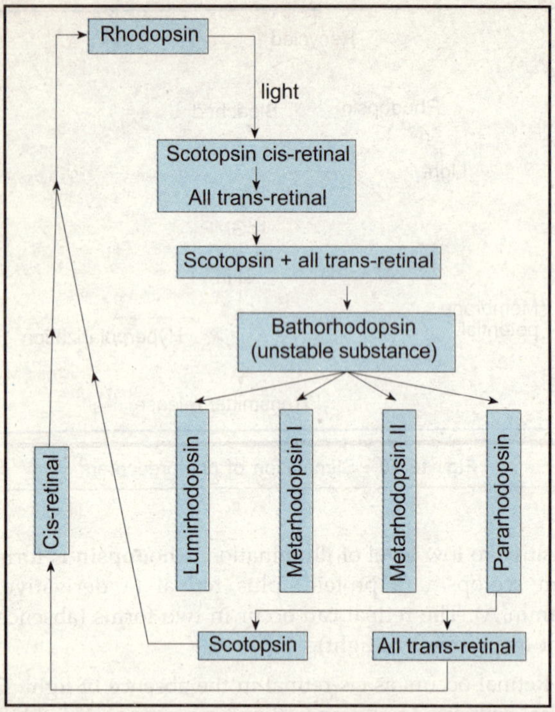


Fig. 12.11 : Rhodopsin cycle

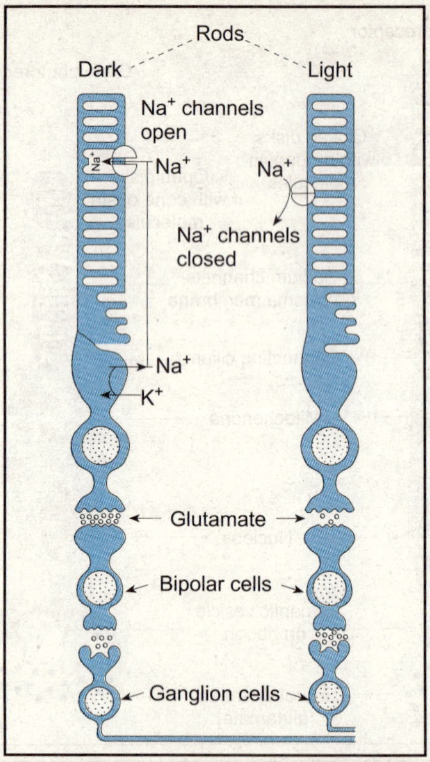


Fig. 12.12 : Cellular anatomy of retina

on the retina by accommodation reflex, which causes the refractive power of the lens to increase. The rods and cones contain a visual pigment called rhodopsin, which absorbs light energy. Rhodopsin contains two components : opsin which determines the wavelength of light absorbed by rhodopsin and retinal, which undergoes isomerization by light.

The photoreceptors are unusual because they hyperpolarize when they are stimulated by light. When the rods and cones are not stimulated, they are depolarized by the flow of $Na^+$ into the cell through $Na^+$ channels held in the open state by cGMP.

The photoisomerization of retinal from its 11-cis form to its all transform activatesrhodopsin, which in turn activates a G-protein called transducin. Activated transducin activates a cGMP esterase. Hydrolysis of cGMP causes $Na^+$ channels on the rod and cone outer segments to close, which produces the membrane hyperpolarization.

The neurotransmitter keeps the bipolar cells and therefore, the ganglion cells in a polarized and relatively quiescent state. Hyperpolarization of the photoreceptors stops the release of an inhibitory neurotransmitter, which in turn causes bipolar cells to depolarize. The bipolar cells stimulate ganglion cells, which in turn convey information about the light stimulus to the visual cortex. The ganglion cells are the only cells in the retina to produce an action potential. Their axons form the optic nerve.

## ➤ 12.7 The Retina (Fig. 12.12)

### Retinal processing of visual information

Like other modalities of sensation, the faculty of all sorts of discrimination, eg, size, shape, color in relation to vision is due to involvement of all its cellular components from retinal receptors to cortical neurons.

**Rods** and **cones** are the photoreceptors, but their functions are not homogeneous. Cones respond to bright light and colors. Rods, being more sensitive as well as more in number (human eye has 120 million rods but only 6-7 million cones), respond to weak illumination. **Rods** and **cones** synapse and converge on ***bipolar cells*** at the level of external plexiform layer where there is modulator role of ***horizontal cells***. ***Bipolar cells*** synapse and converge on ganglion cells whose axons ultimately form the optic nerve to synapse on lateral geniculate nucleus, the penultimate station to primary visual cortex (area 17).

From the fovea, the centripetal pathways have minimal convergence at every step so that finer and detailed information can reach the center. More peripherally, there occurs increasing convergence and the visual system becomes more sensitive to light but deficient in acuity.

***At the external plexiform layer***, the horizontal cells, after being stimulated by a photoreceptor, inhibits neighbouring bipolar cells. They thus help to enhance the contrast between excited and nonexcited zones of neural tracts, similar to other sensory modalities. ***Retinal receptors are always hyperpolarizing on stimulation, but bipolar cells can be divided functionally into (a) depolarizing and (b) hyperpolarizing types.*** On activation by light, the depolarizing bipolar cells will excite ganglion cells; but hyperpolarizing cells will inhibit ganglion cells they make contact with.

***At the inner plexiform layer,*** amacrine cells have modulating influence. On stimulation by bipolar cells they stimulate nearby ganglion cells, thus accentuating their excitatory activity. So their actions differ from inhibitory horizontal cells which dictate the route of transmission of impulse (excitation) in the midst of inhibition, but amacrine cells ensure further propagation.

Ganglion cells are the ones that regularly send action potentials on stimulation, but other retinal interneurons show non-propagated graded responses. Amacrine cells (axon-less) generate action potential in addition to local potentials. They respond by quick onset and offset of activity. So, like rapidly adapting touch receptors, they help to send information in response to rapid fluctuation of light intensities.

**Photic stimulation** has ***depolarizing and hyperpolarizing responses on two varieties of bipolar cells.*** In darkness, bipolar cells remain depolarized and stimulate horizontal cells to inhibit neighbouring bipolar cells. So, if there is uniform darkness, the mutual inhibition of bipolar cells by horizontal cells will make the former functionally silent. But if there is illumination nearby, the dark responsive bipolar cells there become hyperpolarized due to feedback inhibition by horizontal cells of lighted retinae. So the dark response to non-illuminated field gets potentiated.

The visual fields of receptors, bipolar cells and ganglion cells vary; get progressively bigger along with convergence. ***Ganglion cells of lateral geniculate nucleus and cells of the primary visual cortex exhibit center-surround relation*** due primarily to the behaviour of bipolar cells. A dark responsive (depolarising during darkness) bipolar cell (along with its link neurons) has a circular visual field which can stimulate the cell most if the center is dark, but the surrounding is lighted (off-center cell). But this type of cell receives maximum inhibition when the center is illuminated, but the surrounding is dark. The bipolar cell together with adjacent horizontal cells produce this response.

Light responsive bipolar cells which get depolarized on photic stimulation stimulate horizontal cells to produce **lateral inhibition**. The bipolar cell along with its centrally relaying neurons have a circular visual field that stimulates it most when the center is illuminated, but periphery remains dark (on-center cell). ***This type of cell is inhibited maximally when the center is dark but periphery is bright.*** Bipolar and hori-zontal cells come together to produce this response.

The convergence of same type of bipolar cells (on-center or off-center) on ganglion cells and more central neurons exhibit similar center-surround relations. It can be exploited by cortical neurons in differentiating the border or edge of areas of different illumination. In fact, this is done by simple cells of visual cortex, where further analysis of visual information takes place.

***Ganglion cells*** can be divided structurally and also functionally into two groups ***parvocellular (small)*** and ***magnocellular (large) types.*** **The parvocellular types,** having restricted visual field with fewer convergence of bipolar cells, secondary mostly to cone cells, are responsible for deciphering minute details of size, shape and color. **The magnocellular ganglion cells,** on the other hand, have large visual field, formed by convergence of hundreds of bipolar cells, secondary both to rods and cones and are concerned more with existence, location and movement of stimulus rather than its particulars. They are more sensitive, though less elaborative.

There is **a third type of ganglion cells** which are movement-sensitive. They appraise us about a moving object, even in darkness. The details of their structure, functions and connections are not known.

## ➤ 12.8 The Visual Pathways

The retina of each eye has a point to point representation in the ***lateral geniculate body (LGB)*** and ***primary visual cortex bilaterally.*** The axons of ganglion cells come together to form the optic nerve. The point of exit from the eye forms the optic disc at the medial aspect of the fovea centralis. At the optic disc, optic nerve fibers acquire myelin and there are no photoreceptors here. This constitutes the **physiological blind spot,** whose existence can be known experimentally and its extent can be mapped with a perimeter. Normally we are not conscious of its presence because unresponsiveness of small area is obscured (cortically) by much larger, light- sensitive area having widespread connections. Similarly, we are ignorant of the opaque retinal vessels overlying the retinal receptors.

**Retina** of either side can be divided into ***nasal*** and ***temporal halves*** and each half into upper and lower quadrants, optic nerve fibers arising from the nasal side decussate at the ***optic chiasma*** to join the ***optic tract of opposite side,*** but the fibers from temporal half remain on the same side. So optic tract of each side comprises fibers from contralateral nasal hemiretina and ipsilateral temporal hemi-retina. Thus right optic tract carries sensation from left halves of visual fields of both eyes, reminiscent of cortical projection to other sensory modalities like touch.

**Optic tract** on each side terminates ultimately at lateral geniculate bodies. Before termination at LGB some fibers leave the tract to enter pretectal area of brain stem to mediate visual reflexes. Some fibers from chiasma travel to the suprachiasmatic nuclei of hypothalamus to be associated with the circadian rhythm of hormonal and other changes. ***Optic tract*** fibers that terminate at LGB on each side

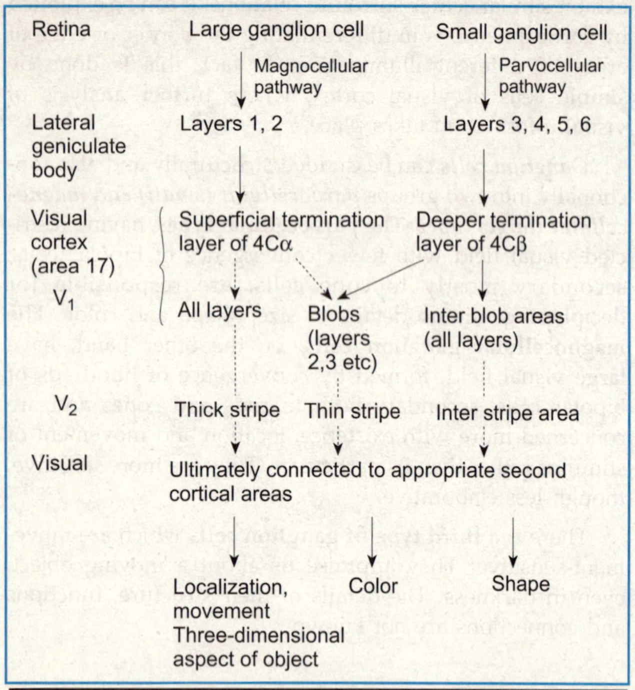


**Fig. 12.13 :** The visual pathways

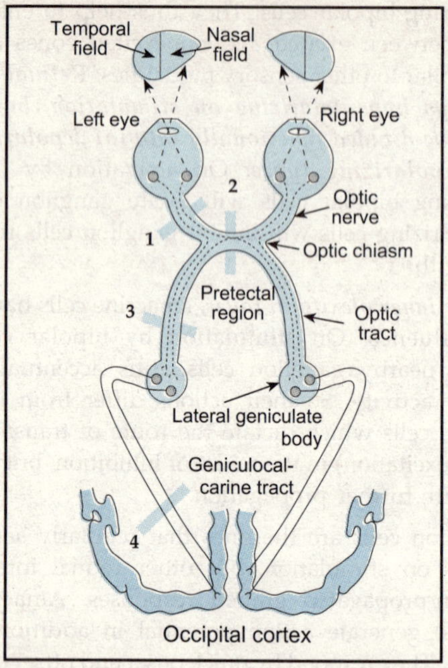


**Fig. 12.14(a) :** Visual pathways *(diagrammatic)*

comprises fibers arising from both sides. ***The LGB can be divided into six layers : layers 1, 4, 6 receives ganglion cell axons from contralateral side and 2, 3, 5 receive afferent from ipsilateral side.*** **Magnocellular pathway** arising from large ganglion cells end on similar cells of LGB at layers 1 and 2. The layers 3, 4, 5 and 6 are concerned with parvocellular pathway. **Parvocellular pathways** represent smaller fields and are involved in color vision and shape detection. Magnocellular pathway represents larger fields. Their acuity may be less yet they are involved in location, movement and, to some extent, color vision (Fig. 12.13).

***From the LGB, geniculo-calcarine fibers*** proceed to primary visual cortex on either side of calcarine sulcus at the occipital pole. ***The macular fibers*** have more extensive distribution starting from the tip of occipital lobe; the peripheral retina has moderate representation anteriorly. The fibers from LGB terminate at deep part of 4th layer (4C); ***magnocellular pathway at relatively superficial (4Ca) and parvocellular at deeper (4Cb) levels.*** From that layer 4C, there arises extensive communication to all other layers of primary visual cortex (area 17), particularly 4B, III and II. Further communication to other visual areas have been discussed in the section on visual cortex.

Not only ***primary*** and ***secondary visual areas,*** connections made out by radioactive 2-deoxyglucose methods is seen to extend to ***posteroinferior temporal cortex, posteroinferior parietal cortex*** and also with frontal cortex. These extensive communications is in conformity to the interaction of visual sensations with other sensory and motor functions, as in the development of language.

Primary visual cortex is connected with frontal eye field (area 8) which is concerned with voluntary eye movements (conjugate deviation). Frontal eye field projects to superior colliculus which receives fibers from layer V of primary visual cortex and also extensively from nonvisual cortex like primary sensorimotor cortex, secondary somatosensory area and auditory cortex. ***Superior colliculus is the principal brain stem reflex center for visual signals.***

**Primary visual cortex** is also connected to subcortical structures besides superior colliculus, claustrum, parts of basal ganglia like caudate nucleus, putamen and limbic structures like amygdala. Connections with basal ganglia influence movement (voluntary) in response to visual signals; those with limbic structures relate with emotional overtones.

**Claustrum** is a thin layer of gray matter deep to insular cortex but outside the lentiform nucleus. It receives and transmits fibers from all parts of primary visual cortex. The efferents from claustrum influences the input of visual information at the striate cortex (layer IV) and also centrifugal output from the cortex to the LGB (layer VI of visual cortex). See Figs. 12.14a, b, c.

***Lesions affecting visual pathways will develop predictable disability according to the site of lesion*** [Fig. 12.14(a)] :

(i) **at the level of optic nerve** – visual loss of the eye concerned;

(ii) **at the decussation of optic chiasm** – ***bitemporal hemianopia***

(iii) **uncrossed fiber at optic chiasm** – ***nasal hemianopia of visual field of an eye.***

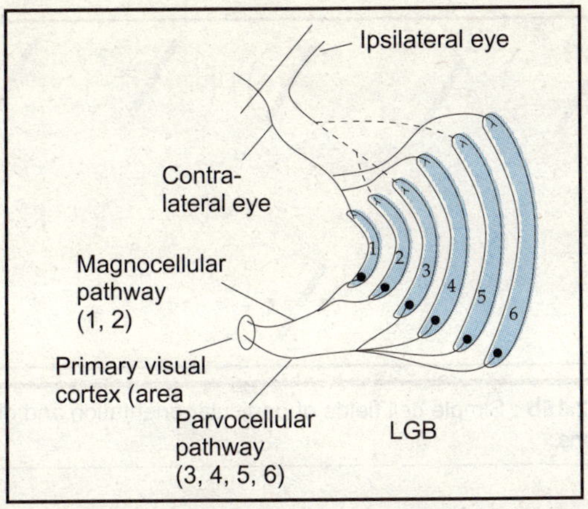


**Fig. 12.14(b) : Magnocellular and parvocellular pathways**

(iv) **optic tract** – ***homonynous hemianopia,*** eg, if left optic tract is sectioned there is loss of right visual half field of each eye. If the lesion is beyond (central) emergent fibers to the pretectal nucleus, the light reflex persists in the anopic field.

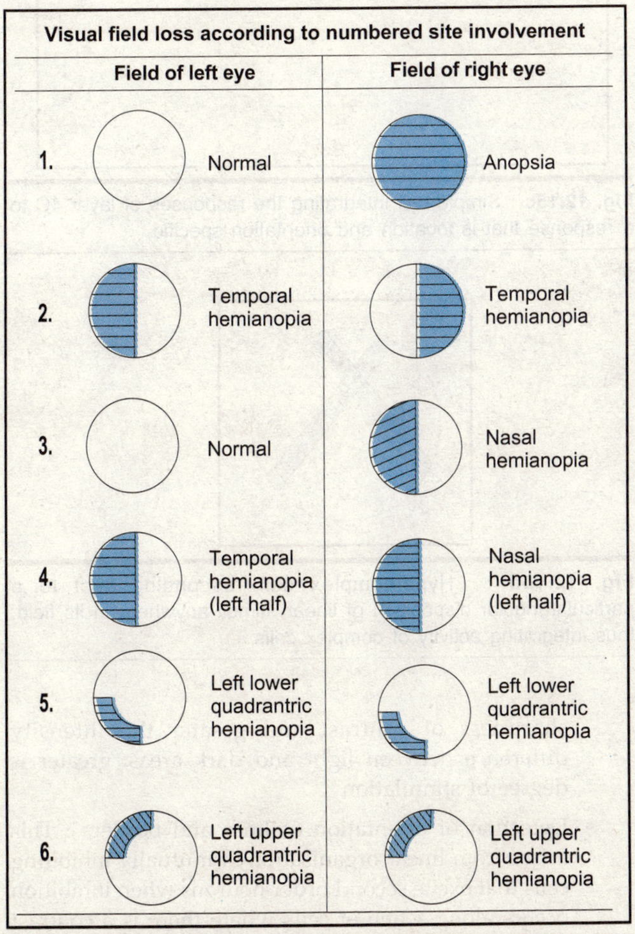


**Fig. 12.14(c) : Different types of visual field defects**

(v) **LGB unilateral lesion** shows ***homonynous hemianopia*** similar to optic tract lesion;

(vi) **geniculocalcarine fibers' involvement** shows ***homonymous hemianopic*** or ***quadrantanopic defects*** but partial macular sparing is there because of the extensive distribution of macular fibers.

(vii) **occipital cortex lesions show** more restricted ***homonymous hemianopic*** or ***quadrantanopic lesions.*** Lesion above upper bank of the calcarine sulcus exhibits lower quadrantic defect and that below calcarine sulcus produces upper quadrantic visual loss.

## 12.9 The Visual Cortex

The analysis of visual information starts from the level of photo-receptors. Final processing occurs at the cortical level. Like other neocortical areas, the visual cortex, both primary and secondary areas has six layers, starting from the surface towards white matter.

An extensive area of the cerebral cortex is devoted to visual perception. They are at present numbered according to the anatomical position and function from $V_1$ through $V_5$. ***$V_1$ is the striate cortex,*** immediately around calcarine sulcus or primary visual area where the geniculocalcarine tracts end. ***From $V_2$-$V_5$, the areas are peristriate areas progressing anteriorly from $V_1$. $V_1$ is essential for visual perception; $V_2$ is the relay station of parvocellular (color, shape) and magnocellular (movement, stereoscopy) pathways; $V_3$ for shape; $V_4$ contains the color columns and $V_5$ is for movement.***

All the information of entire visual field is carried from each retina by ganglion cells (having overlapping visual fields) to both lateral geniculate bodies. ***Each LGB has six alternate layers, three (1, 4, 6) receive ganglion cells of contralateral side and other three (2, 3, 5) from those of ipsilateral*** side. Geniculocalcarine tract on either side then terminates in the stellate cells of deep part of 4th layer of primary visual cortex. The parvocellular pathway of LGN terminates at further deeper **(4 Cβ) layer,** whereas the magnocellular pathway end at relatively superficial **(4 Cα) layer**.

Processes from the stellate cells of layer 4C (α and β) connect with pyramidal cells of superficial layers overlying them more importantly to 4 B, 3 and 2. The parvocellular pathway carrying color sensation from either eye synapse with pyramidal cell clusters in layers 3 and 2 which form **color blobs.** The cells have high mitochondrial cytochrome oxidase activity.

From the blobs, the parvocellular pathway for color discrimination end at thin strips (cytochrome oxidase stained feature) of $V_2$. From $V_2$ fibers pass anteriorly to color columns for detailed analysis of color ($V_4$).

The parvocellular pathway transmitting information regarding size, shape, etc. also terminate similarly at 4 Cβ and from these to 4 B,3, 2 and elsewhere. But in layers 2 and

3 they connect at inter blob areas and then via interstripe area of $V_2$. They ultimately relay to the association areas. This occurs diffusely but specially to inferotemporal and occipital cortices on either side. Large areas of the inferotemporal occipital region of brain is devoted to detailed meaningful interpretation of visual information, specially recognition of human faces a vital information for our existence. Bilateral lesions involving this area is responsible for inability to recognise faces **prosopagnosia.**

The magnocellular pathway of visual recognition has the cortical termination area 4 Cα of primary visual cortex ($V_1$) then via 4 B, 3 and 2 to thick stripe of $V_2$ and then to extensive areas of visual association cortex, area 18 ($V_2$, $V_3$) and area 19 ($V_4$, $V_5$). ***Magnocellular pathways are concerned with localization, movement and three-dimensional aspect of objects.*** Whatever may be the specificity of termination of particular pathways, the secondary visual areas have extensive communication with all visual areas and also with other sensory modalities. These connections enable us to name a object after looking at it and experience all the sensory and emotive aspects of its recognition. ***Primary visual cortical area ($V_1$, layer 5) is connected with brain stem areas involved in visual reflexes,*** eg, superior colliculus. Centrifugal fibers also arise from $V_1$ (layer 6) to LGB.

From the bipolar cells of the retina to stellate cells of layer 4C of primary visual cortex all show center-surround relation regarding their sensitivity of individual visual fields. But the cortical cells other than initial receptor cells (stellate cells of 4C) show integrated activity. A ganglion cell (LGB and 4C) has a visual field with either on-center or off-center in response. But a linear stimulus, light among dark, or dark among light will stimulate an on-center and an off-center cell, respectively, wherever it is placed in the visual field. Now, corresponding to a specific orientation of a linear stimulus exciting a number of on-center or off-center ganglion cell, there exists a simple cell which responds to the particular orientation.

## Neuronal patterns of Analysis of visual image

- Analysis of contrast in visual image : The areas of maximum excitation of cortical neurons occur along sharp borders of visual pattern. The greater the sharpness of contrast and greater the intensity difference between light and dark areas, greater is degree of stimulation

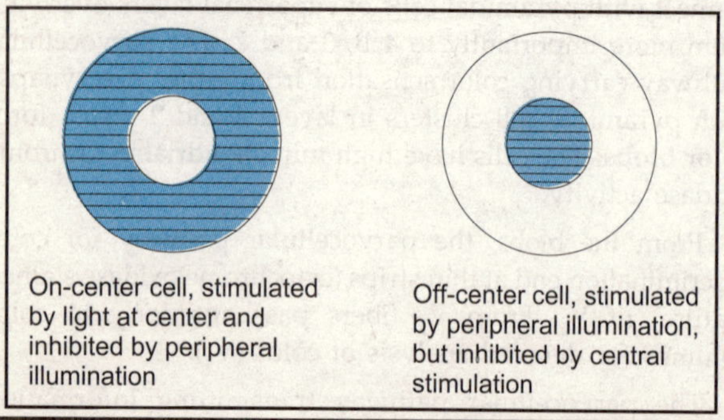


**Fig. 12.15a :** Receptive fields of ganglionic, geniculate cells and those of 4th layer of visual cortex

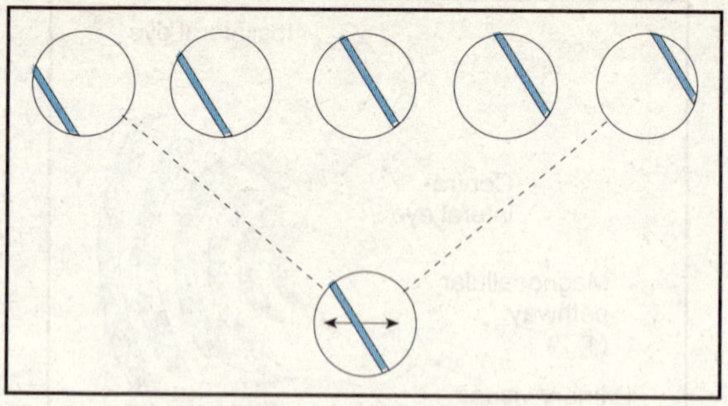

**Fig. 12.15b :** Simple cell fields of particular orientation and different locations

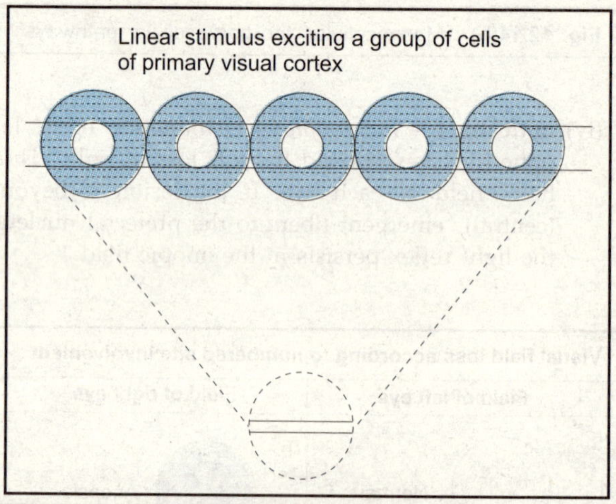


**Fig. 12.15c :** Simple cell integrating the responses of layer 4C to a response that is location and orientation specific

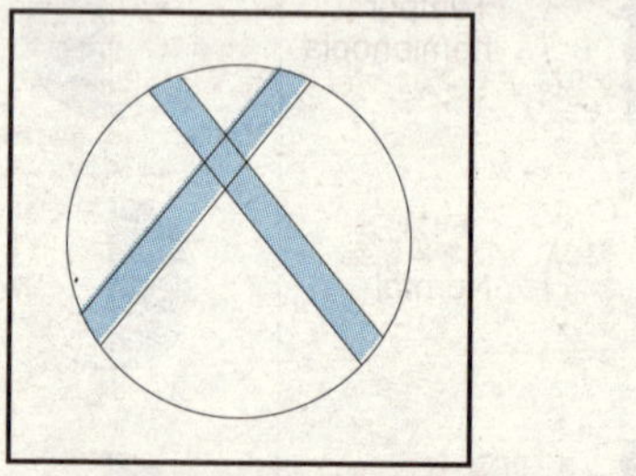

**Fig. 12.15d :** Hypercomplex cell responding best to a particularangular disposition of linear stimuli anywhere in its field, thus integrating activity of complex cells

- Detection of orientation of lines and borders : This arises from linear organisation of mutually inhibiting cells that excite second order neurons when inhibition occurs along a line of cells where there is a contrast edge. A specific orientation excites a specific 'Simple cell' in layer 4 of $V_1$.

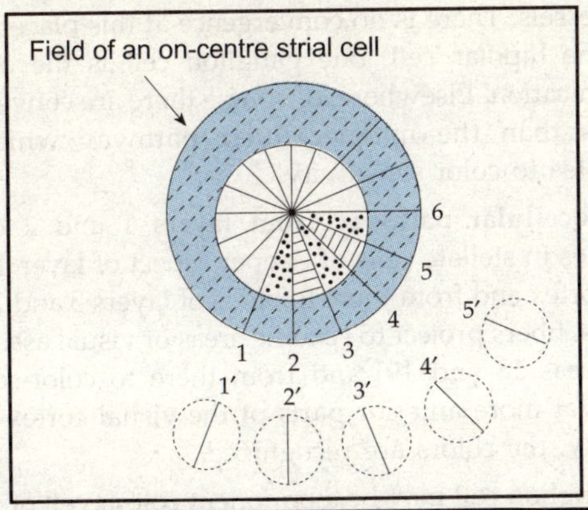


Fig. 12.15e : 1′, 2′ etc. are the orientation columns corresponding to the orientations 1, 2, etc. of a linear stimulus exciting in the field of a striatal (ganglion) cell

- Detection of orientation of lines when they are positionally displaced : If the direction of a line (whose image is analysed as in detection of orientation of lines and borders) remains the same but position is changed; complex cells are stimulated as signal moves away from layer 4.
- Detection of lines of specific lengths, angles or shapes : This is done by hypercomplex cells in $V_1$ or secondary visual areas.
  (a) The speed of information into different brain locations involves the so called parallel processing.
  (b) The sequence of progression of analysis from simple to complex to hyper complex cells is serial analysis.

Both (a) and (b) interact to give full interpretation of signals.

Second order neurons of color-sensitive cortical cells of layers 2 and 3 of primary visual area (blobs) do not show orientation specificity. Thus, recognition of orientation of a linear colored stimulus requires involvement of color responsive elements and simultaneous action of color independent orientation columns.

**Complex (and hypercomplex) cells of striate cortex** exhibit ocular dominance. LGN, stellate cells of 4C, simple cells respond to photic stimulation to either eye, but complex cells vary in their ocular dominance, so that some responds to stimuli from corresponding areas of both retinae, some exclusively to either ipsilateral or contralateral eyes. Those that respond to bilateral stimuli differ regarding their strength from either eye, figuratively, between R, Rl RL, rL, rL, L in this fashion.

They form complex stripes alternating with ocular dominance columns of other eye. The ocular dominance column incorporates the functional orientation columns and are different from them. The stripes of orientation column do cross the bands of ocular dominance column. Complex cells responding to stimuli from both eyes add more to the information than monocular vision. **Binocular vision** is superior to monocular vision regarding localization and distance perception.

## ➤12.10 Color Vision and Development of Vision

### Color vision

Visible light has a wave length ranging between 400 nm to 700 nm. Prismatic dispersion of white light gives rise to seven colored rays. So, white light is a compound of monochromatic lights recognized from the acronym **'vibgyor'** : violet (430 nm), indigo (480 nm), blue (505 nm), green (530 nm), yellow (580 nm), orange (630 nm), red (680 nm).

Red, green and blue are called **primary colors,** because by mixing suitable amounts of them any color, even white, can be created. Any two colors are called **mutually complementary** if, with mixing, they give rise to white color, eg, yellow and indigo, or orange and blue.

Leaves of a tree is green, blood looks red. This perception is called **hue or color.** Hundreds of hues can be produced by mixing primary colors. If we dilute blue dye with white it still remains blue but paler in appearance. We estimate degrees of **saturation**. A color may appear more intense as undiluted blood is more red than diluted one, it is different from saturation – a sensation that is called **brightness.** Hue, saturation and brightness are criteria by which *human beings can distinguish nearly a million shades.*

This subjective sense of color recognition is due to the action of cone cells of retina and its higher connections, principally visual cortex. **Young Helmholtz theory** of ***color vision accepts the existence of three types of cone cells for 3 primary colors.*** The photopigments in three cones are also of different composition (protein part). Blue sensitive cone cells contain pigments that absorb light of short wave length, maximum at 430 nm. Green sensitive cones contain pigments that absorb light at intermediate range of wave length with maximum absorption at 530 nm. The red sensitive cones contain pigments that absorb light of large wave lengths, maximum at yellow 570 nm, spreading widely to include rays of wave length up to 730 nm (red). See Fig. 12.16.

The particular hue that is seen depend upon the relative activity (frequency of impulse) of three types of cones. When 700 nm light falls on retina only the long wave sensitive cones are excited and the color is red. When 400 nm light falls the blue sensitive cones are stimulated only. But in most cases of intermediate wave lengths all the three cones will be stimulated at varying rates. Orange color is seen when there is more stimulation of long wave cones than green color cones. Equivalent stimulation of long and intermediate sensitive cones produce yellow color.

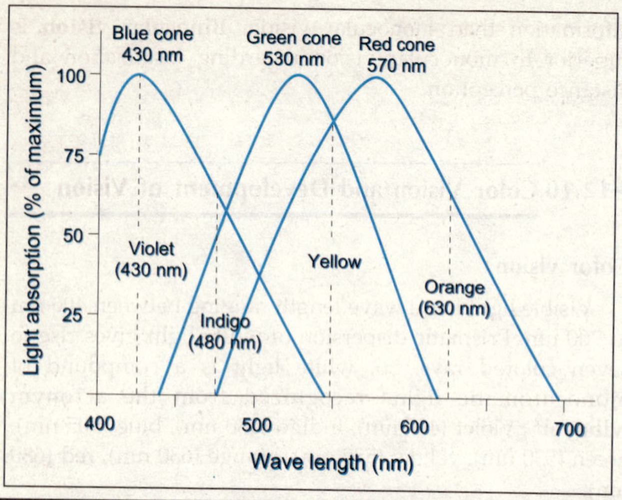


**Fig. 12.16 :** Light absorption by different color specific cones also denotes their efficiency in impulse transmission. Dashed lines indicate how they are affected by different monochromatic lights. Equal stimulation of green and red cones produces yellow sensation

Retinal distribution of red, green and blue sensitive cones are different. ***Macula lutea contains yellow pigment that absorbs light rays of short wave length and fovea centralis does not contain blue cones.*** Thus central part of retina contains more red and green cones and the periphery contains blue sensitive cones and rods (peak absorption at 500 nm), but at extreme periphery only rods are present. Congruent with the distribution it is seen that visual field of an eye for green, red, yellow, blue to white increases progressively.

***It is widely known that cones are responsible for photopic (bright light) vision along with color detection.*** Blue cones have some similarities to rods, their peak wave length sensitivity is closer, their threshold intensity lower than other cones and they are distributed along with rods at more peripheral level. For this reason in a garden with diminution of intensity of day light, the red or green flowers appear darker than the blue flowers as the intensity of light becomes unable to stimulate the red, green cones but adequate enough to stimulate the blue cones and rods **Purkinje shift phenomenon.**

Adequate dark adaptation requires 10 minutes or more. So persons like radiologists who have to work alternately in bright and dim illumination can use red glasses in light to avoid delay in dark adaptation as red spectrum of large wave length rays stimulate the rods only weakly (peak sensitivity at 500 nm), enabling them to take up their usual scotopic visual function early.

## Neural pathways of color vision

Sense of color is carried from the cone cells primarily by the parvocellular pathway. In the fovea centralis, there are only cone cells (longer, thinner and closely packed) and no blood vessels. There is no convergence at this place i.e., one cone, one bipolar cell, one ganglion cell is the order of communication. Elsewhere, of course there are convergence, but less than the magnocellular pathway which also contributes to color sensitivity.

**Parvocellular pathway from layers** 1 and 2 of LGB terminates in stellate cells of deeper aspect of layer 4C(β) of striate cortex and from there to blobs of layers 3 and 2. From the blobs, fibers project to specific areas of visual association areas (areas 18 and 19) and from there to color-sensitive columns at more anterior parts of the visual cortex where, ultimately, the colors are recognized.

A ganglion cell may be a opponent colour cell or double opponent colour cell.

***Opponent colour cell*** - excited by one colour (e.g. red) and inhibited by another colour (e.g. green) and vice-versa. These are responsible for successie colour contrast (a phenomenon of coloured after-images).

***Double opponent colour cell*** - these have a receptive field with a centre and surround. The response on ON to one colour (e.g. red) in the centre and OFF to it in the surround. These cells are responsible for simultaneous colour contrastia phenomenon ofperception of parcitular coloured spot against a coloured background a grey spot arrears greenish in a red surround and reddish in a green surround.

**Color sensitive neurons lack** orientation specificity. Spatial and temporal resolution power is lower in colored rays than in color independent illumination.

**Double opponent character of blobs** signify **integration of activity of ganglion cell descendants**. Similar further integration occurs at other sites of visual cortex. Thus equal intensity of green and red colors, on mixing, gives yellow color. Mixing of yellow and indigo may remove the colors leaving the photopic sense intact. The color specific columns are more sensitive to color contrasts than uniform color. Thus a red object appears colorless in red surroundings but prominent in green surroundings.

## Color blindness

The occurrence of **color blindness** points towards accuracy of the concept of three cone systems. The protein part of visual pigment differs in different types of photoreceptors. The genes of opsins of red and green sensitive cones are X-linked, but those of rod and blue cones are autosomal having genes on 3 and 7, respectively. The amino acid composition of opsins of green and red are very similar; their genes are derived by splitting of ancestral long wave sensitive opsin gene. But the amino acid composition of other opsins differ markedly.

Man and higher mammals are trichromats, i.e., they have cones with short, medium and long wavelength sensitive pigments and can differentiate and match any color with one or more of all the primary colors. Subhuman mammals are mostly dichromats whose subjective sense of color is due to two pigments, one for short wave length and another for long wave length. Defects in development may leave an individual with only one type of cone system (monochromats). These individuals have poor or absent color sense and differentiate objects by their saturation and brightness — as in black and white telecasting.

In the classification of color blindness, the suffix ***anopia*** means absence and ***anomaly*** means weakness in color recognition. Anopic individuals are mostly dichromats whereas anomalic ones, like normal individuals, are trichro-mats. Thus the classification can be summarized as :

1. *Trichromats* — Deuteranomaly (green weakness)
   Protanomaly (red weakness)
   Tritanomaly (blue weakness)
2. *Dichromats* — Protanopia
   Deuteranopia
   Tritanopia
3. *Monochromats*

**Color blindness** can be detected by ***(a) Ishihara pseudo-isochromatic chart, (b) Holmgren's skeins of colored wool, (c) Edridge green lantern.***

Among the European population, 8% of males and 0.4% of females show color deficiencies; but in dark races the incidence is lower (less than 5%). As the genes for blue cones are autosomal, the ***incidence of tritanomaly and tritanopia is very low*** but is equally distributed between the sexes. But **red-green color blindness is relatively common and is found almost exclusively in males** due to the presence of genes on X-chromosome.

A heterozygous woman with defective/deficient gene on a X-chromosome is phenotypically normal, but half of her sons has a chance of developing red-green blindness and half of her daughters will be carriers, as Y-chromosome cannot make up the deficit. All the sons of an affected male are normal and all the daughters are carriers of the defect. So the disability skips one generation (color blind father → normal sons and carrier daughters → color blind grandson). This is the same type of inheritence as in hemophilia A or B. **Incidence of deuteranomaly is the highest** among all sorts of color blindnesses.

As expected, tests for color blindness are done meticulously for persons opting for driving motor vehicles etc. and those found deficient in color perception are denied entry into the profession.

## Physiological explanations behind some well-known optical illusions and sensations

1. Everyone is familar with sound echoes, in which the reflector must be more than 1/20th the velocity of sound (per second) apart from the person to detect any sound he produces to be heard again, because more than 1/10th second must elapse to distinguish between sounds. This proves that auditory receptive elements continue activity for some time beyond the termination of the stimulus. This phenomenon is seen also with vision. When one looks to an object for some time and then closes his eyes or the object is removed, the object is seen for a few moments in the same color. It is due to persistence of chemical and electrical events after the withdrawal of stimulus. The sensation is called **positive after image** because the same receptors are implicated. But if one, after looking at a colored object, quickly stares at a white surface, the object is seen in complementary color.

When the object is of red color the red cones become maximally stimulated, but on looking at a white surface emitting mixed colors, the less affected cones of the other end of spectrum are stimulated most and the brain recognizes the object as if stained in complementary color (green) **negative after image**. This is due to fatigue of original red-sensitive receptors.

If an individual looks at a white object, retinal receptors corresponding to the retinal image get stimulated. But when one looks at a generalized white surface, the retinal receptors outside the original image is stimulated better because the object-stimulated receptors are fatigued this pattern of stimulation is perceived as the object looking black. Negative afterimage also indirectly points to persistence of the receptive activity, because if the reception had vanished with the stimulus, no positive or negative after image would be seen.

These positive and negative images do play a role in the visualization of repeated similar and dissimilar stimuli. For example, if a disc of seven colors (vibgyor) is rotated quickly the perceptions fuse to give rise to white color. If a drum with different shades of one color is rotated, the positive after images give rise to the sense of a particular shade, every shade intermingling the next consecutive shade. But if contrasting colors e.g. white and black, red and green are rotated slowly the negative after image of one will enhance the other. The phenomenon of **flickering** (an unpleasant glittering sensation when alternate black and white colors are presented in slow succession) occurs due to the same reason.

The **physico-chemical mechanisms** that operate in the case of after images also explain contrast phenomenon with which every one is familiar. As for example, red flowers in the back ground of green leaves make both vivid, similarly black and white form good combination for distinction **simultaneous contrast.** It is clear that negative after image is responsible for this contrast. If one looks at a well-illuminated colored object for some time and then looks at another of complementary color eg. after observing a yellow object, if one looks to a blue one, the second object appears brighter. It is also due to the physico-chemical effects mediating negative after image.

## ➤ 12.11 Taste and Taste Afferent Pathways (Fig. 12.18)

Taste buds are located in the papillae of the tongue. They are scattered throughout the epithelium of the tongue, soft palate, pharynx and epiglottis. The **taste receptors** are stimulated by molecules in solutions in the fluids of the mouth. The receptors consist of 40-50 chemosensitive cells which are exposed to chemicals. **Four fundamental sensations of taste are :**

**Sweet** (organic compounds);
**Sour** (due to hydrogen ion concentration);
**Bitter** (alkaloids); and
**Salt** (anions of ionizable salts).

**Taste cells** are shed all the time (half life is 10-14 days) and is replaced by underlying basal cells. Receptors for taste sensation are taste cells located in taste buds.

### Taste buds

- Barrel shaped structures
- 50-70 mm in diameter
- Contain 40-50 taste cells per bud
- Contain sustentacular cells
- Basal replacement cells are located at the bottom of the taste buds.
- Outer tip of the taste cells are covered with microvilli.
- Taste pores are present.
- Taste pores contain microvilli of the taste cells smeared with salivary secretion.

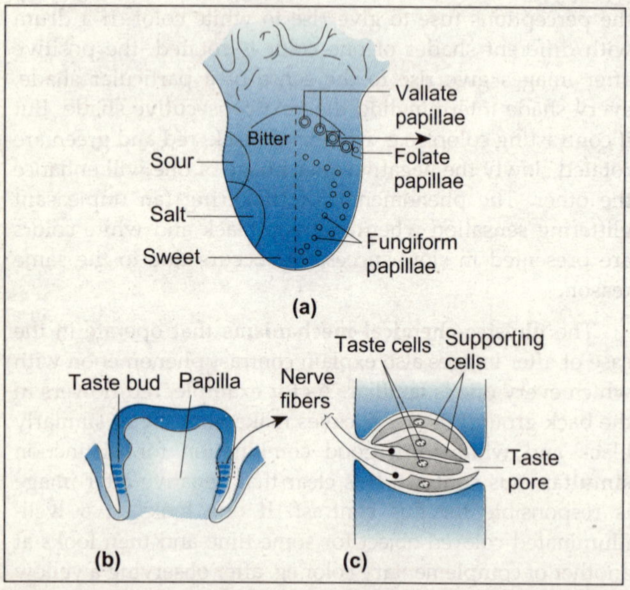


Fig. 12.18 : (a) The region of the tongue to show four modalities taste. (b) Cross sectional views of a vallate papilla showing locations of taste buds. (c) Structure of a single taste bud.

**Papillae**

**Gustatory papillae**
- Fungiform papillae
  - Located at anterior 2/3 of the tongue.
  - Contains 8-10 taste buds.
- Circumvallate papillae
  - Located at the posterior surface of tongue.
  - Contains 200 taste buds.
- Foliate papillae
  - Located at lateral border of tongue.
  - Contains numerous taste buds.

**Mechanical papillae**
- Located at internal border of tongue.
- Has got the role of breaking up food particles.

Fig. 12.19 : Papillae

- Taste buds are present in circumvallate, fungiform and foliate papillae (Fig. 12.19).
- Taste buds contain several cell types. Apart from sensory cells, there are basal and supporting cells. Basal cells replace taste cells.

**Transduction in taste receptors**

When a substance is dissolved in saliva, only then taste sensation can be evoked. Sensations from tongue are carried as follows : **(a) the anterior 2/3rd of the tongue**

General sensation (touch, pain and temperature)
Carried initially by lingual nerve, a branch of VCN

Taste fibers enter the chorda tympani nerve, a branch of VII CN

(b) Posterior 1/3rd of the tongue
↓
Taste fibers are carried by IX CN along with general sensation

(c) From epiglottis, palate and pharynx
↓
XCN

All the taste fibers that pass in different cranial nerves join tractus solitarius to synapse with neurons in the nucleus of tractus solitarius.

↓

2nd order of neurons cross the midline and join medial lemniscus and relay in ventroposterior medial nucleus (VPM nucleus) of thalamus from where 3rd order of neurons pass to inferior part of **postcentral gyrus.**

Taste cells are chemoreceptors. The chemicals traverse the pores of the taste buds and react with microvilli at the apical surface of the receptor cells. Transduction process is not clearly understood. There is evidence for different mechanisms for different variety of chemicals.

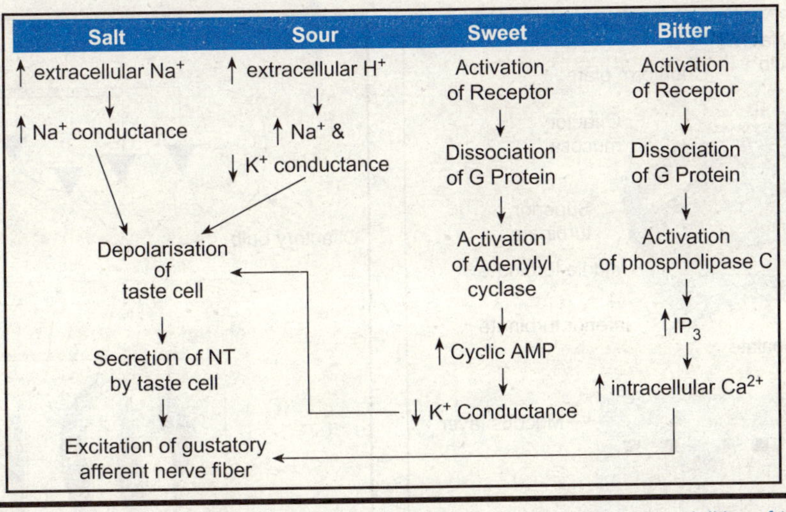


**Fig. 12.20 :** The cellular mechanism that allow the direction of the principal modalities of taste

There is production of generator potential. Depolarization of taste cells occurs by different mechanisms.

The cellular mechanism that allow the detection of the principal modalities of taste (Fig. 12.20).

### Subjective aspects of taste sensation

The relation between the molecular structure of compounds and modalities of taste is very loose and substances of widely different structure can elicit some sensation. As for example, lead salts, chloroform, beryllium salts taste sweet in common with sucrose, glucose, glycerol, some alcohols and ketones. It has been observed by immunological studies that there is a correspondence between three-dimensional structural configuration of a molecule and the taste modality it elicits. Of course, the threshold concentrations vary widely. Saccharin, a non-calorigenic sweetner for diabetics, has threshold concentration about 1/500th of sucrose.

Of all the taste eliciting compounds, bitter substances have lowest threshold concentrations in conformity to the fact that deadly natural poisons are bitter and non-human animals mostly select edibles on the basis of taste. Nicotine, strychnine, morphine, caffeine, quinine are a few bitter harmful substances having low threshold. Strychine has a threshold concentration below 2 mmol/L, whereas that of glucose is $10^4$ mmol/L. It is of interest that certain inorganic compounds like salts of calcium, magnesium etc. taste bitter, their cations are responsible in this regard.

Though there is overall site specifity over tongue surface for taste modalities, every site can perceive all of them more or less. The taste cells vary in their capacity to respond to a particular modality even if they are indistinguishable morphologically.

The complete satisfaction of a particular item of food depends upon its smell, taste, consistency and temperature. A combination is loosely termed **'flavour'**. For example, tea or coffee is taken when hot but a bottle of soft drink is chilled before opening.

It is our common experience that after taking sweets, a cup of tea appears less sweet. Prior application of a tasty material raises the threshold to a particular modality. Some compounds may even modify the taste of a substance. Acids are normally sour, but they may taste sweet by prior application of 'miraculin', a plant derived protein. Individuals also vary in their capacity regarding gustation eg, phenylthiocarbamide is tasted sour by some and tasteless by others !

## ➤ 12.12 The Smell

**Olfactory cells** are located in a specialized region in the roof of the nasal cavity. Human nose can identify between 2,000-4,000 odors. The basic mechanism for olfactory discrimination is not known. Smell receptors are chemoreceptors which are stimulated by the molecules in solution in the fluids of nose and generate receptor potential resulting ultimately in action potential in nerves of olfaction in the olfactory mucous membrane. Histologically, olfactory mucous membrane contain 10-20 million **olfactory cells** located between sustentacular cells. In contrast to taste buds, where the chemoreceptor taste cells are distinct from the afferent nerves, the receptive element here is modified (dilated) peripheral part of nerve **cell process** (dendrite) in **olactory mucosa** (Fig. 12.21).

### Olfactory systems (Fig. 12.22)

(i) the **olfactory receptors** (dendrites) and cell bodies are located in the olfactory mucosa

(ii) the **olfactory bulb** covers the anterior part of the olfactory sulcus on each side of the brain

(iii) the **olfactory tract** is the caudal termination of the olfactory bulb

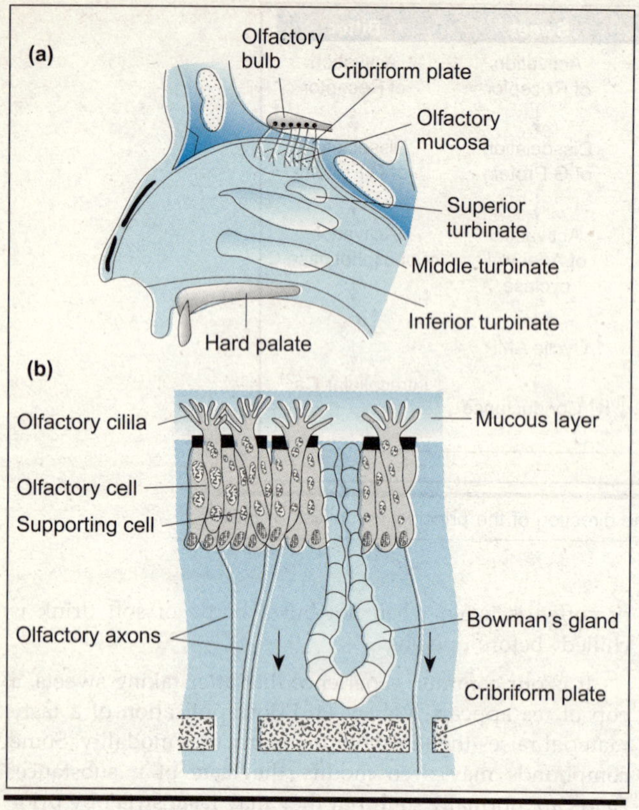


**Fig. 12.21 : (a)** Sectional view of the nose, **(b)** Olfactory epithelium

(iv) the cerebral cortex serves olfactory functions

(v) projections of the olfactory tract to some brain stem centers.

## Olfactory receptors (Figs. 12.23 and 12.24)

Primary smell sensations proposed are : Putrid, pepper mint, pungent, ethereal, musky, camphoraceous and floral.

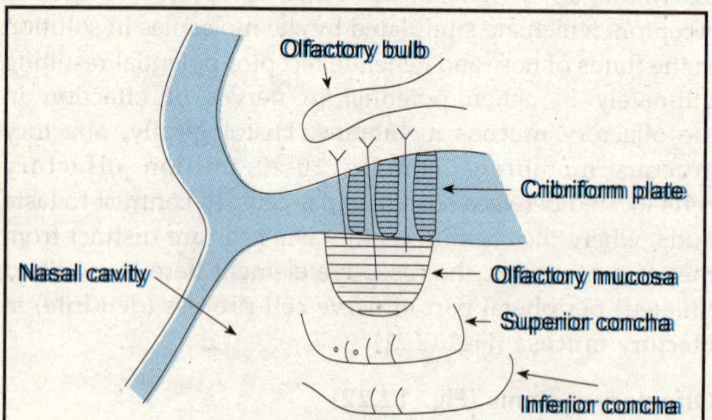


**Fig. 12.22 :** Olfactory systems

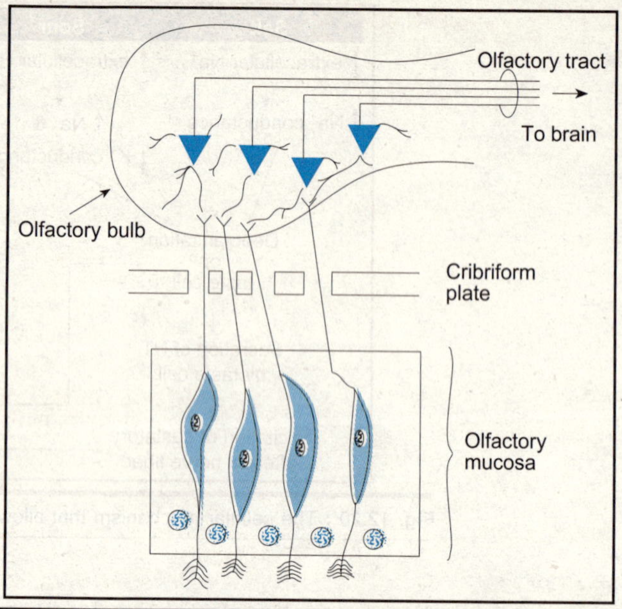


**Fig. 12.23 :** Components of olfactory system

**Olfactory cells** are located in the olfactory epithelium. These are the specialized bipolar cells. The cells bear modified dendrite at the apical region and terminate on the surface with nonmotile cilia which are embedded in the mucosa. The hundreds of different membrane receptors are excited. The initiation of olfaction is probably via guanosine triphosphate binding protein, adenylyl cyclase and cyclic adenosine monophosphate → there is increase in conductance to $Na^+$ → generator potential is established. cAMP acts as a major second messenger in olfactory transduction. Still there is involvement of phosphoinositide derived second messengers.

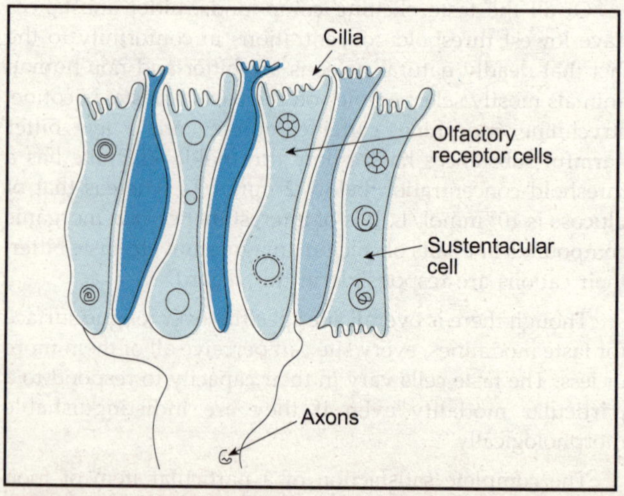


**Fig. 12.24 :** Olfactory mucosa

## 12.13 Central Pathways in Olfaction

The **olfactory bulbs** contain mitral cells as well as tufted cells. The axon terminals of the olfactory neurons form synapse with the dendrites of mitral cells and tufted cells to constitute complex globular masses called **olfactory glomeruli** → the mitral or tufted cells constitute 2nd order of neurons. The periglomerular cells also participitate in the formation of olfactory glomeruli → the axons of mitral and tufted cell run in the olfactory tract. Posteriorly, the tract divides into medial and lateral striae, and occasionally an intermediate stria. The intermediate stria when present terminates in the anterior perforated substance.

The medial stria carries fibers that cross the median plane in the anterior commissure to pass to contralateral olfactory bulb.

The lateral stria conveys fibers to olfactory cortical regions.

**Pathway :**

(a) **Very old pathway :** Fibers → Medial olfactory area (mid basal portion of brain, anterosuperior to hypothalamus) → hypothalamus and limbic system → primitive responses like licking lips, salivation, etc. caused by smell of food.

(b) **Old path way :** Fibers → Lateral olfactory area (primary olfactory cortex i.e. prepiriform and periamygdaloid)

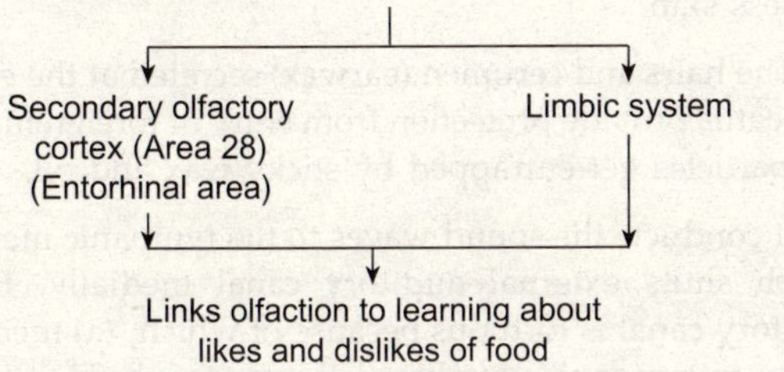


(c) **New pathways :** Fibers → Dorsomedial nucleus of thalamus → orbitofrontal cortex (Tertiary olfactory cortex) → conscious perception of smell.

### Subjective aspects of smell sensation

It is our common experience that some substances emit intense smell even if present in trace amounts eg, garlic, ie, olfactory threshold varies widely between odorants. Methylmercaptan the odorant in case of garlic has a threshold concentration of 0.5 ng/L, whereas it is about 6 mg/L in case of ether. Small, volatile, high lipid and water soluble compounds emit intense smell.

Structural isomers have different odors owing to differing functional groups. Olfactory receptors are housed in the most suitable site. The olfactory neurons have their efficiency heightened (threshold lowered) by the fluid part of the mucus which helps to dissolve odoriferous molecules and also increase their local concentration by odorant-binding proteins secreted by mucous glands.

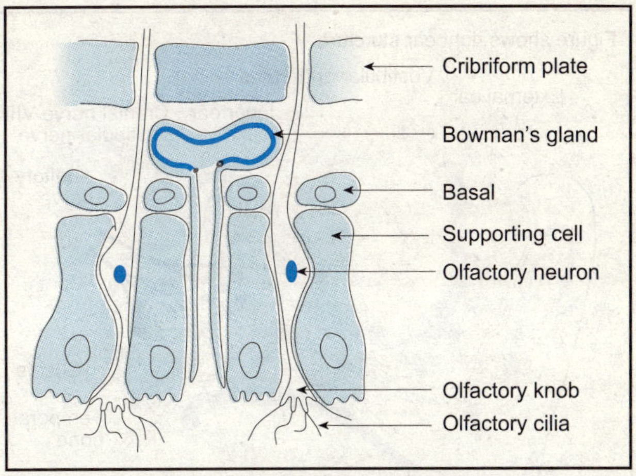


**Fig. 12.25 :** The structure of olfactory epithelium

The **sense of smell** in human beings is inferior to dogs and other mammals in whom the olfactory mucous membrane is more extensive. Women excel men in olfaction. Olfactory cortex is part and parcel of limbic cortex and as expected sexual sensations are intimately related with odors. Smell —and, to some extent, taste — is related inextricably to memory and we frequently associate a familiar smell with an apparently forgotten evidence.

Normally, some air ventilates the roof of the nose by bulk flow, diffusion and convection current out of temperature difference in the nasal cavity, but, by sniffing a larger volume, can be deflected to the olfactory epithelium for increasing the concentration of odorants and detecting their characters.

The power of judging the concentration of odorants is poorly developed in men, a change of nearly 30% of concentration is required to detect change in intensity.

It is also universally known that on continuous exposure we gradually become insensitive to a particular odor, as for example, we are ignorant of our own body odors. This phenomenon is called **adaptation** It is specially observed in case of smell sensation and is beneficial in many occupations associated with disagreeable odor. This adaptation is specific, making this faculty even more beneficial. The adaptation or desensitization takes place both at peripheral and central levels. The olfactory dendrites (cilia) mediate smell sensation by binding of odorant to G-protein-adenylyl cyclase → cAMP → $Na^+$ channel activation pathway.

The desensitization is due to simultaneous operation of receptors which somehow blocks the train of activation by the generation of some inhibiting enzyme or enzymatically modifying the configuration of odorant concerned. Though poorly developed, we can somehow point to the site of origin of smell. As the faculty of intensity discrimination is poor in olfaction, the differences of time of arrival in two nostrils indicate the location of odorant.

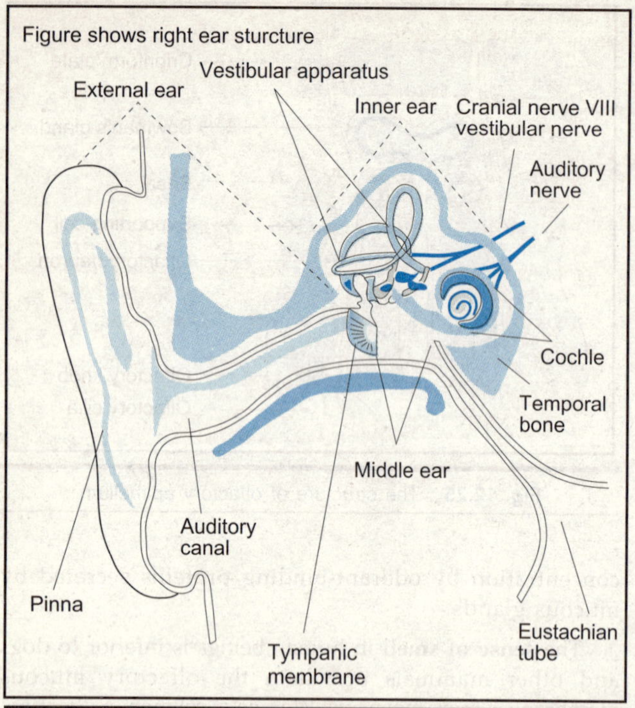


Fig. 12.26 : Structure of right ear

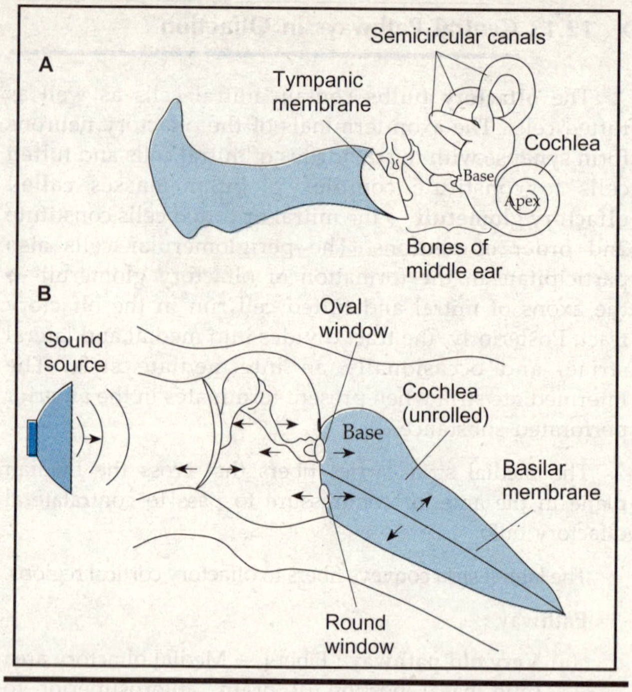


Fig. 12.27 : (A) The outer ear is separated from the middle ear by the tympanic membrane whose fibrations are transmitted to the cochlea via the bones of the inner ear. (B) The cochlea the separation between the upper and lower compartments of the cochlea.

**Olfactory neurons** undergo continuous loss and simultaneous replacement similar to taste cells in taste buds. As age advances, the acuity of olfaction gradually subsides, almost all of individuals above 80 years of age show some deficiency in olfaction.

## 12.14 The Hearing

The ear is the organ of hearing. The ear has got external, middle and inner compartments. It is supplied by the eighth cranial nerve (cochlear part of vestibulocochlear nerve) which is stimulated by the vibrations, produced by sound waves (Fig. 12.26).

### External ear

- *Pinna* : It is the expanded portion projecting from the head and is composed of fibroelastic cartilage. Lobule is the soft lower part of ear and is composed of fibrous and adipose tissue. It collects and reflects the sound waves into **external auditory canal.**
- ***External acoustic meatus (auditory canal)*** : It is 'S' shaped tube (2.5 cm long). Tympanic membrane separates the external acoustic meatus from the middle ear. The shape of the tympanic membrane is oval.

**External acoustic meatus** is formed of elastic cartilage at its outer third and bony tympanic plate at inner two-thirds. Outer third is lined by hairy skin, that also bears sebaceous and ceruminous glands; the inner two-thirds are lined by hairless skin.

The hairs and cerumen (earwax) secreted at the entrance of meatus provide protection from entry of foreign materials; the particles get entrapped by sticky wax and oil.

It conducts the sound waves to the tympanic membrane which shuts external auditory canal medially. External auditory canal is tortuous because of which (a) mechanical injury to tympanic membrane is prevented; (b) it helps in maintaining favorable temperature and humidity for normal functioning of the tympanic membrane.

### Tympanic cavity or middle ear

The middle ear is a small air sac which has an opening into pharynx through the auditory tube (eustachian tube). The boundary of the middle ear is formed laterally by tympanic membrane, posteriorly by temporal bone, medially by a thin layer of temporal bone in which oval window and round window are located and the roof and floor are formed by temporal bone.

***Auditory ossicles*** are three very small bones that extend across the cavity from tympanic membrane to oval window. The bones are malleus, incus and stapes.

The **malleus** (lateral hammer-shaped bone) : The handle lies with tympanic membrane and head forms a movable joint with the incus.

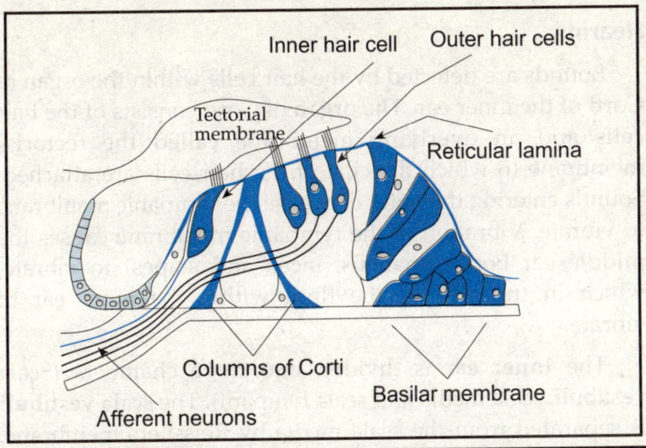


**Fig. 12.28 :** Organ of corti

The **incus** (middle anvil-shaped bone) : The body of the incus articulates with malleus.

The **stapes** (medial stirrup-shaped bone) : The head of the stapes articulates with the incus.

## Functions of middle ear

Sound is transmitted from external ear to inner ear thorugh ossicular chain when tympanic membrane vibrates with sound, ossicular system also vibrates and conducts the vibrations to fluid filled inner ear.

There are two muscles in the middle ear. The ***stapedius*** and ***tensor tympani muscles.*** They can reduce the intensity of transmission of low frequency sound to the cochlea to some extent. Probably they are also responsible for the reflex maintenance of a constant intensity of this reduced sound, protection against very loud sounds and vibrations in the middle ear. The tensor tympani (supplied by CN V) pulls the manubrium of the malleus medially. The stapedius muscle (supplied by CN VII) pulls the footplate of the stapes out of the oval window.

Middle ear muscles of both sides contract reflexly in response to sound to either ear and non-reflexly with vocali-zation, chewing, swallowing, yawning, stimulation of ear and face and also with movement. The latency of reflex response makes them incapable of taking a protective role if the sound is sudden and short. Their principal function besides protection of organ of Corti and ossicles is to eliminate the effect of relatively low or high frequency sounds so that tone (1-2 $kH_Z$) of speech can be better appreciated.

## The internal ear

The internal ear is also called the **labyrinth**. It contains two main divisions : an outer ***bony labyrinth*** and an inner ***mem-branous labyrinth***. The labyrinths contain cochlea which is concerned with hearing and three semicircular canals which are responsible for the sense of equilibrium.

The cochlea is a coil-shaped structure. It contains a bony core and a spiral lamina. Three chambers are present separated by two membranes which are ***Reissner's membrane and basilar membrane.***

The central tube is filled with endolymph and is known as scala media. It is accompanied on one side by scala vestibuli which starts at the oval window and on the other by the scala tympani. Both contain perilymph and run with the scala media to the summit of the helix, helicotrema where they connect with each other. The scala tympani ends at the membrane of the round window in the wall of the middle ear.

Sound waves set the basilar membrane in motion that is detected by hair cells in the organ of Corti → generate auditory signal.

## Bels and Decibels

**Decibel** is one tenth of a **bel**. Unit for expressing the loudness of sound on a logarithmic scale.

The softest sound that is just audible to a normal ear under ideal conditions is used as a reference level against which the intensity of all other sounds is compared.

$$\text{Intensity (bels)} = \log_{10} \frac{\text{Intensity of the sound}}{\text{Intensity of the reference sound}}$$

If the intensity of the sound being measured is exactly the same as the reference sound (0.0002 dynes/$cm^2$) then

$$\text{Number of bels} = \log_{10} \frac{0.0002}{0.0002} = \log_{10} 1 = 0$$

The intensity of every day sounds ranges between 0 and about 100 dB. Sounds of greater intensity may be painful and can cause permanent damage.

***Frequency and pitch :*** The frequency of sound waves is the number of cycles of compression and rarefaction occurring per second.

One cycle per second = 1 Hertz ($H_z$)

100 cycles per second = 1000 $H_z$

= 1 Kilo Hertz ($kH_z$)

## The Organ of Corti (Fig. 12.28)

**This organ** contains about twenty thousand receptor cells for hearing. It is located on the upper surface of basilar membrane and stretches from the apex to the base of the cochlea. The receptor cells are known as **hair cells** which are arranged in four parallel rows. There is a row of plump **inner hair cells** and three rows of outer hair cells; the space inter-vening is formed of rods of Corti on either side enclosing the tunnel of Corti. The hair cells bear long hair-like processes at the free ends which extend into the endolymph of the cochlear duct. The basal end of the hair cells lie with the fibers of the cochlear branch of the vestibulo-cochlear nerve. The projecting cilia of hair cells pierce the tough reticular lamina supported by rods of Corti and come

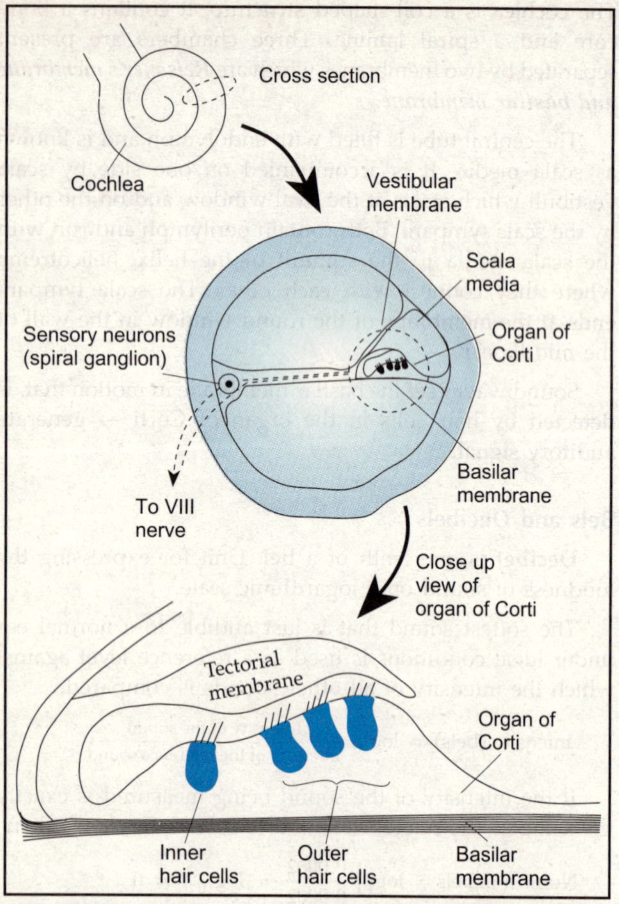


**Fig. 12.29 :** The internal structure of the cochlea viewed in cross section

in contact with thin visco-elastic tectorial membrane projecting from the spiral lamina.

In short, hair cells are embedded on the basilar membrane and has a bundle of hairs known as **stereocilia** each of which projects from its tip and is embedded in the shelf known as **tectorial membrane** (Fig. 12.29).

**Sound waves** : Sound waves are the alternate compression and rarefaction of the air molecules. Sound is heard most clearly by the human ear at a frequency of 1,000-4,000 cycles/sec. The sound intensities are easily measured in **decibel** unit. Sound waves enter the external auditory meatus and cause the eardrum to reproduce the vibrations.

Vibrations reach the stapes. Each sound wave causes inward and outward movement of stapes. When stapes moves inwards, because of movement of fluid, basilar fibers bulge through the round window. Inward and outward movement of stapes (1 sound wave) leads to 4 waves in basilar membrane

- When stapes move in
- When stapes moves back to original position.
- When stapes moves out
- When stapes comes back to original position.

## Hearing

Sounds are detected by the hair cells within the organ of Corti of the inner ear. The organ of Corti consists of the hair cells and an overlying membrane called the tectorial membrane to which the cilia of the hair cells are attached. Sounds entering the outer ear cause the tympanic membrane to vibrate. Vibration of the tympanic membrane causes the middle ear bones (malleus, incus and stapes) to vibrate, which in turn causes the fluid within the inner ear to vibrate.

The **inner ear** is divided into three chambers (Scala vestibuli, scala media and scala tympani). The **scala vestibuli** is separated from the scala media by Reissners membrane, the scala media and the scala tympani are separated by the basilar membrane. The **stapes** is attached to the membrane of the oval window, which separates the middle ear from the scala vestibuli. The **scala tympani** is separated from the middle ear by the round window. The **organ of Cortisits** on the basilar membrane. The fluid within the scala vestibuli and scalatympani (perilymph) is similar to interstitial fluid, the fluid within the scala media (**endolymph** resembles intracellular fluid in that it contains a high concentration of $K^+$). Vibration of the stapes causes the fluid within the scala tympani to vibrate which in turn causes the basilar membrane to vibrate. Vibration of the basilar membrane causes the cilia to bend back and forth. Bending the stereocilia toward the Kinocilium causes $K^+$ channels on the hair cells to open; bending the stereocilia away from Kinocilium causes $K^+$ channels to close. **Auditory hair cells** are unusual because they are depolarized by the flow of $K^+$ into the cell. $K^+$ can flow into the hair cells because the endolymph surrounding the apical portions of the hair cells contains a high $K^+$ concentration.

The **basilar membrane** is most stiff at the base of the cochlea (near the middle ear) and most compliant at the apex of the cochlea. High frequency sounds cause a greater vibration of the stiff portion of the cochlea, and therefore hair cells located near the base of the cochlea transmit information about high frequency sounds to the auditory cortex. Similarly, low frequency sounds are transmitted to the **auditory cortex** by the hair cells near the base of the cochlea, which are located on the more compliant portions of the basilar membrane.

Vibrations enter the endolymph of the cochlear duct → depolarization (and also repolarization) of the receptors occurs with phases of displacement of basilar membrane. During depolarization, $Ca^{2+}$ permeability rises → calcium ions → release of neurotransmitter → which stimulates the ends of sensory neurons → the fibers of the cochlear branch of the vestibulo-cochlear nerve are stimulated → travel to the cochlear nuclei in the medulla oblongata → auditory pathways ascend to the medial geniculate nuclei in both the contralateral and ipsilateral thalamus → they send some collaterals to the reticular activating system → the thalamus connects the auditory cortex in the temporal lobe.

### Subjective aspects of hearing

In human individuals, faculty of hearing is highly developed. We can differentiate loudness and pitch of sounds within wide ranges of intensity and frequency, respectively. It is also possible to find out the direction from which sound waves are coming.

The capacity of judging loudness of individual sound and the comparison between the two, arises from activities extend-ing from periphery to center (auditory cortex). At the cochlea-auditory nerve level, an intense sound causes (a) **involvement of a more extensive area of the cochlear partition** and (b) **increased frequency of impulse in individual afferent neurons**. At the cortical level, there is simultaneous involvement of larger areas and recruitment of neurons associated with high-toned activity in general.

Detection and differentiation of frequency depends upon operation of various mechanisms from the cochlea to cortex. There is a point-for-point representation of organ of Corti to relay nuclei and to auditory cortex. The basal turn of cochlea is sensitive to higher frequency and lower tones involve more and more of anterior part of basilar membrane as the physical character of fibers differ from base to apex of cochlea. So high frequency sound stimulates basal part of cochlea and the appropriate part of auditory cortex and the tone is appreciated. But when the frequency is very low, as most of the basilar membrane gets involved, site principle of detection cannot be depended upon. Here 'volley' principle, i.e., rate of impulse or action potential corresponds to the frequency of sound wave.

We can localize the source of sound more or less accurately. Sound waves are collected and reflected by the pinna, the character of sound differs whether they are either in front of or behind an individual. The head acts as an **obstacle**. In a horizontal plane, if we move our head, sound arrives directly to one ear. The other ear will have delayed arrival of sound of reduced intensity. The delay in the arrival of sound wave is detected by cortical neurons on the basis of analysis of bilateral information that occurs at relay stations. But this mechanism is more efficient at relatively lower frequency sound (below 3,000 Hz). In sound of higher pitch, where the wave length is shorter, the role of the head as a sound shadow becomes less apparent and then difference of loudness is a better guide than the time lag. Sound localization, thus, is better with both the ears than a single one and is also markedly compromised with lesions of auditory cortex.

The complicated bilateral input to nuclei related to **auditory pathways enables** brain stem nuclei to analyze the characteristics of sound received by the ears. The first important site is the superior olivary nucleus. The lateral part of superior olivary nucleus contains cells that sense the differences of time of arrival of sound waves in the ears. When the sound source is directly in front of the time lag is zero, but when it deviates from the midline the time difference widens the response of those neurons also change with delay. Similarly, there are some units in **Superior Olivary Complex** (SOC) which detect the differences of intensity between two sites.

The second-most important site is the **inferior colliculus**. Neurons show differential sensitivity to monoaural or binaural stimuli. Some are excited from either ear, some by both ears, some stimulated by one and inhibited by other. These neurons in combination thus helps in detecting sound source.

**Table 12.3 : Functions of the structures of the ear**

| *Structure* | *Function* |
|---|---|
| **External ear** | |
| a. Pinna | Sound waves are collected |
| b. External auditory canal | Sound waves are directed to the tympanic membrane |
| c. Tympanic membrane | Vibrations of the sound wave cause the malleus to vibrate. |
| **Middle ear** | |
| a. Auditory tube | The pressure is equalized on both sides of the tympanic membrane. |
| b. Auditory ossicles | Sound waves are transmitted to oval window from tympanic membrane. |
| **Internal ear** | |
| a. Utricle | Receptors present are known as **maculae** — responsible for static equilibrium. Respond to horizontal acceleration. |
| b. Saccule | Same as utricle. Responds to vertical acceleration. |
| c. Semicircular canals | Cristae are responsible for dynamic equilibrium. Responds to rotational acceleration. |
| **Cochlea** | Hair cells of the organ of Corti produce nerve impulses and transmit them to the cochlear branch of the vestibulocochlear nerve. |

Threshold of hearing rises in presence of background noise. In a moving vehicle, passengers have to speak loudly to overcome the noise present. This phenomenon is called **masking** and it is due to affection of some receptors of the organ of Corti by the environmental sounds that make their afferent nerves refractory. As there is site selection of a particular frequency along the organ of Corti, the sound of similar frequency will mask a particular sound better. As low frequency sound involves whole of the basilar membrane, its capacity of masking is better.

### Further details on receptive aspects of inner ear up to auditory cortex

Inner ear bears the sound receptive epithelium (organ of Corti) over the basilar membrane, that stretches from inner bony spiral lamina to outer spiral lamina and extends from the base to apical part of cochlea (30 mm) and gradually enlarging from base to apical part of cochlea. The basal fibers are more stiff than apical fibers.

The bony spiral lamina winds around bony modiolus. The inner ear comprises three spiral channels; from above down-wards they are scala vestibuli, scala media (or cochlear duct) and scala tympani, respectively. The scala vestibuli starts from oval window and scala tympani from round window, they communicate with each other at the apex of cochlea by helicotrema. The scala media is the space between **Reissner's membrane** above and **basilar membrane** bearing organ of Corti below. The outer wall is formed of stria vascularis.

The **scala media** is filled up with **endolymph** and the other two scalae contain **perilymph**. The composition of endolymph resembles intracellular fluid regarding electrolytes. Electrolyte composition of perilymph is like that of interstitial fluid.

The basilar membrane in adult extends 32 mm from the base of the stapes. The pattern of vibration depends upon tone (frequency) and loudness (amplitude). The lower frequency waves cause movement of the entire basilar membrane but the site of maximum displacement depends upon the frequency concerned.

The high frequency sound vibrates less than the entire length of membrane; the peak of displacement is near the stapes, high frequencies crowd densely near the base. The height and extent of waveform of a particular tone depends upon loudness, keeping its point of maximum displacement fixed.

The movement of the cochlear membrane is responsible for the shearing motion between the hairs and tectorial membrane that is responsible for mechanical opening of cation channels over the hairs. The hair cells get depolarized and secrete neurotransmitter to stimulate the afferent nerves synapsing with the cells. The inner hair cells, of course, respond to fluid movement as their hairs are not embedded in the tectorial membrane.

There is a potential difference between endolymph, hair cells and perilymph of scala tympani even in the absence of motion of basilar membrane. But when sound waves make the basilar membrane vibrate additional potentials are recorded. Their source of origin differs. Cochlear microphonics is a dynamic response recorded across cochlear partition and its characteristics indicate its origin by integration of the activity of receptors concerned with vibration of cochlear partition. It shows no latency, refractoriness, fatiguability, but follows sound intensity in magnitude. Thus **cochlear microphonics** resemble receptor potential or post-synaptic potential as a forerunner of propagated action potential of the afferent nerve.

As the **hair cells** respond to mechanical distortion of the stereocilia, the cochlear microphonics are secondary to activity of the receptors and initiation of nerve impulse (short of action potential) of the afferent nerves. The combined electrical activity of the receptors underlie **positive summation potential (+SP)** and that of initiation of neural impulse as **negative summation potential (–SP)**. When action potentials do develop in the afferents their combined effect can be recorded as large multipeaked action potential.

The potential recorded from round window or elsewhere shows cochlear **microphonics** and components of action potential are separated temporally. The cochlear microphonics can be distinguished from action potential by sound stimuli applied in such a way that action potential is suppressed, but the cochlear microphonics remain unchanged. By the same manner, negative summation potential (–SP) can be suppressed (neural component), but not the +SP (receptor component) comprising cochlear microphonics.

The hair cells of inner ear are innervated by peripheral processes of bipolar cells whose cell bodies lie within the bony modiolus forming the spiral ganglion. The (hair) cells form synapses with the unmyelinated terminal parts of peripheral axons that aquire myelin on leaving the organ of Corti. The distribution of receptor and afferents are not in simple 1 : 1 ratio. Inner hair cells, numbering 3,000-3,500 in a cochlea, receive more than 90% of 30,000 afferent processes.

Each peripheral process divides into 8-10 branches. Each branch supplies an individual inner hair cell. In this way, each inner hair cell receives processes of 8-10 bipolar cells. Less than 10% of peripheral processes of spiral ganglion cells cross the tunnel of Corti and each divides to supply 8-10 outer hair cells (20,000 in a cochlea). So the ratio of inner hair cells and innervating bipolar cells is around 1 : 10 and that between outer hair cells and innervating bipolar cells approximates to 10 : 1. So inner hair cells are primarily responsible for sound reception per se, outer hair cells are for modulation and other finer aspects of hearing.

**Action potential** in individual cochlear afferents has been recorded in experimental animals in response to sound of particular frequencies. It has been observed that a particular afferent has a range of frequencies through which it can respond. But there is a particular frequency at which the loudness or intensity requirement is minimum, **critical frequency.** If the intensity is gradually increased, it is seen that a particular afferent can respond to relatively wider range of a lower frequency than those of higher frequency.

Cochlear afferents unlike cutaneous mechanoreceptors (touch, pressure) are spontaneously active with a low rate of impulse formation (mostly below 100/sec). But with a sound stimulus, impulse frequency increases to thousands/sec changing in the direction of intensity of stimulus at a particular tone. The critical frequency of afferent auditory neurons differ but their ranges overlap and, anatomically, their distribution differs over the cochlear partition.

For a particular afferent neuron, critical frequency (intensity) threshold is variable according to the changes in metabolic functions, as for example hypoxia. In an individual, if the auditory threshold is measured at different tones (frequency) the acuity will differ in tones and if a plot of frequency-loudness threshold is done it will definitely express the frequency dependency of the afferents in respect to sensitivity.

In all the sensory modalities, there is a feature of lateral inhibition to sharpen the edge of the stimulating zone, and hearing is no exception, but where and how it is executed is not clear.

The extent of involvement of cochlear partition helps in tone differentiation. With change in frequency, there is inactivation of some afferents, but recruitment of additional ones. So, the change in the patterns of afferent activity gives conscious appreciation of alteration of tone.

It is our common experience that we ignore irrevalent sounds. It is primarily a cortical phenomenon but partly at the first order afferents. In response to repeated sounds the afferent gradually shows a diminution of response (reduction in action potential frequency) and irregular response at some particular point of the sound wave (**phase-locking**).

From just audible sound (zero decibel) to most loud sound (120 decibel), there is $10^{12}$ times increase in intensity. But individual afferents have a dynamic range below 70 dB, but some may have higher range. The site, extent and amplitude of involvement of cochlear partition as well as characteristics of response like activation rate, phase selectivity, all operate together to help us to listen such intense sounds. Like taste where a sweet tasting substance increases the threshold temporarily a loud sound temporarily shifts the intensity threshold. It is more applicable to sounds of higher frequencies.

Even if the metabolic state of receptors and afferents remain unaltered, sound intensity can shift the critical frequency of a particular afferent. Intense sounds shift critical frequencies from either side to some extent to approach the speech frequency around 1,000 Hz.

**Efferent control of the cochlea** : Both the vestibule and the cochlea are provided with efferent fibers that run along with the VIIIth nerve. The final station of efferent output to cochlea is the superior olivary complex on either side. Olivo-cochlear bundle on each side consists of fibers from both sides. Superior olivary complex, on the other hand, is connected bilaterally, directly or indirectly with cochlear nuclei, inferior colliculi and nuclei of lateral lemniscus. Thus both the uncrossed and crossed bundles of olivo-cochlear tract receive bilateral input from brain stem nuclei. The brain stem nuclei are connected, ultimately, on each side with medial geniculate bodies and auditory cortex.

The efferents comprising the olivocochlear bundle (1,200 on each side) branch extensively to innervate the outer hair cells directly and the afferent neurons of inner hair cells. It has been observed that stimulation of cochlear efferents inhibit simultaneously stimulated cochlear afferents. But the inhibition is discriminatory, ie, it increases the sensitivity to a particular tone at the expense of another.

The outer hair cells move in the process. The function resembles to some extent that of middle ear muscles, which contract to obscure unwanted tones highlighting the wanted one. The olivocochlear bundle and middle ear muscles together make hearing faculty more selective and purpose-oriented.

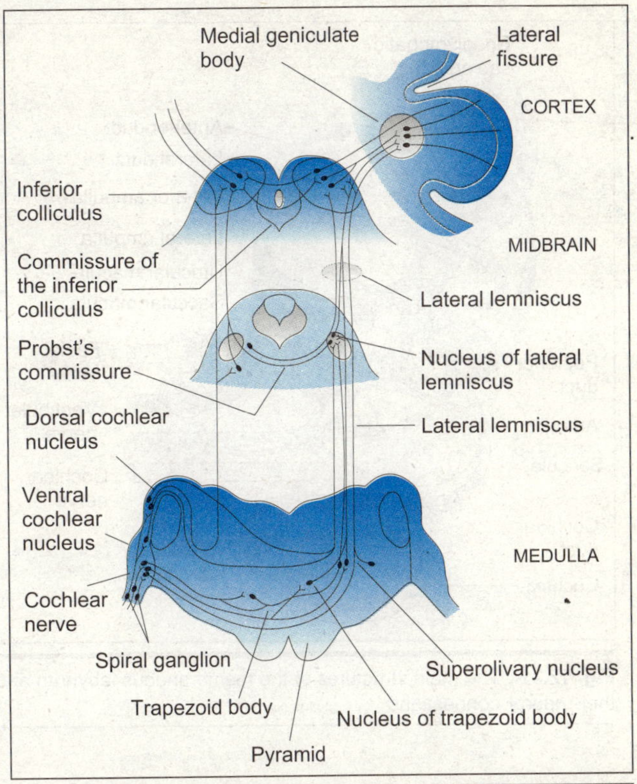


**Fig. 12.30 :** The ascending pathways of the auditory system

## Central auditory pathways

Primary auditory afferents bifurcate to form terminals in both the ventral (VCN) and dorsal (DCN) cochlear nuclei. From teh VCN, fibres run to the superior olivary complex (SOC) on both sides and the contralateral inferior colliculus (IC). The auditory fibres that cross the pons constitute the trapezoid body (TB). The SOC compares input from the two ears to compute the whereabouts of a sound source. The SOC projects to the nucleus of the lateral lemniscus. The dorsal cochlear nucleus sends axons directly to the contralateral nucleus of the lateral lemniscus.

The nucleus of the lateral lemniscus projects to the Inferior colliculus (IC). From IC medial geniculate nucleus (MGN) of the thalamus primary cortex via the auditory radiation. The primary auditory cortex (areas 41, 42) is located in the superior temporal gyrus.

The pathway via the MGN and auditory cortex mediates conscious auditory perception. The bigger auditory pathway is contralateral. But reciprocal connections between the nuclei of the lateral lemniscus (via Probst's commissure) and between the IC, (via the commissure of the inferior colliculus) ensures extensive interactions between the input from both ears.

The ascending sensory pathways are matched by descending projections. The auditory cortex sends axons back to both the MGN and IC and the latter in turn projects

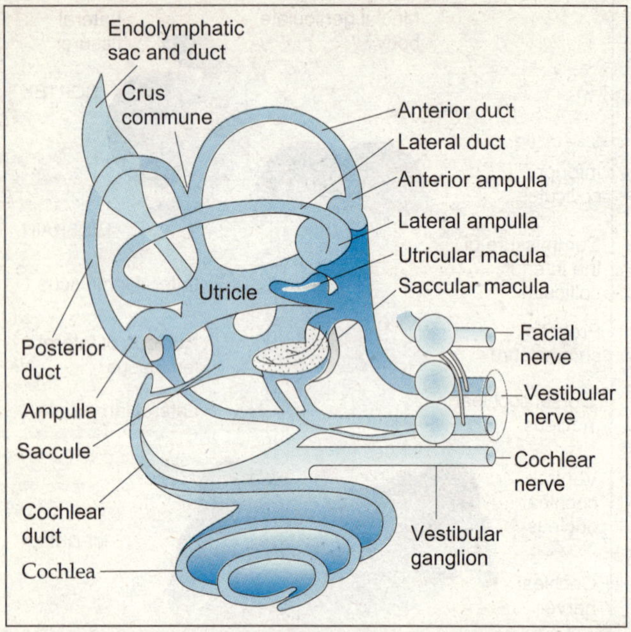


Fig. 12.31 : The main structures of the membraneous labyrinth and their neural connections

to the SOC and the cochlear nuclei. The SOC sends effeents to teh spiral organ which modify the output of cochlear hair cells.

## ➤ 12.15 The Vestibular System

### The Vestibular Pathways

The vestibular system provides information about the position and movement of the head, coordinates head and eye movements and initiates reflexes that keep the head and body erect,. Lesions to the vestibular system result in loss of balance and Nystagmus.

### Structure of the vestibular system

The vestibular portion of the membranous labyrinth is the organ of balance. It consists of two chambers, the utricle and saccule and three semicircular canals. The nerve supply is via the vestibular branch of the eighth cranial nerve and Scarpa's ganglion (Fig. 12.31).

The utricle and sacule are arranged horizontally and vertically, respectively, while the three semicircular canals are arranged at right angles to each other, with the lateral canal inclined at an angle of about 30° from the horizontal. The other two canals lie in vertical planes. Near the utricle, each canal has an enlargement known as the ampulla. The fluid within the semicircular canals, utricle and saccule is endolymph, and the whole structure floats in the perilymph that is contained within the bony labyrinth. The sensory portion of the semicircular canals is located within the ampulla. The wall of the canal projects inward to form the crista ampullaris. The hair cells are located on the epithelial layer that covers the crista and the hairs that project from their upper surface are embedded in a large gelatinous mass, the cupula, which is in loose contact with the wall of the ampulla at its free end. As a result, it forms a compliant seal that closes the lumen of the canal, preventing free circulation of the endolymph. The sensory epithelium of the utricle is in the horizontal plane, while that of the saccula lies in the vertical plane. As in the crista ampullaris the sensory cells are hair cells. Afferent axons from the vestibular nerve terminate on the hair cells via synaptic contacts similar to those seen in the cochlea (Fig. 12.32 & 12.33).

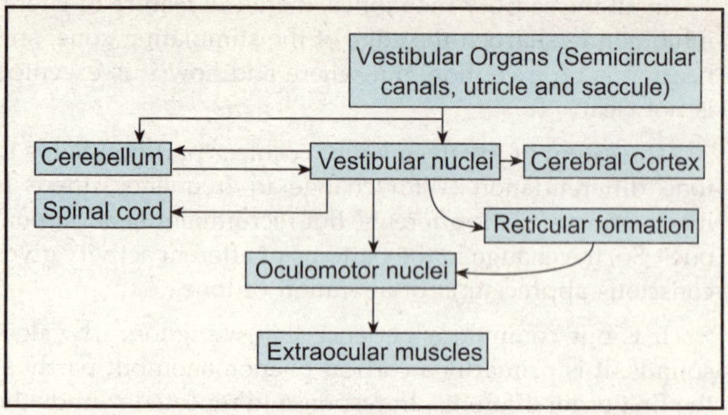


Fig. 12.32

The cilia of the hair cells consist of a single large hair known as **Kinocilium** and several rows of smaller **stereocilia**. The orientation of the haircells is rather specific for different parts of the vestibular apparatus. In the crista ampullaris, the hair cells are oriented so that they all have their kinocilium pointing in the same direction. In the utricle and saculle the orientation of the hair cells in rather more complex. This morphological polarization, coupled with saccule, enables the vestibular system to interprer any movement of the head.

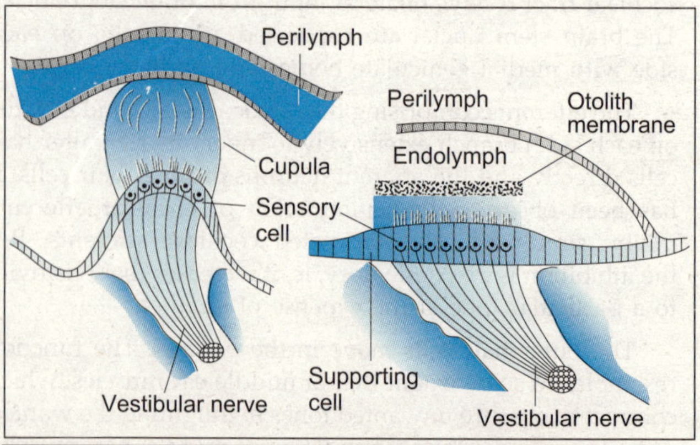


Fig. 12.33 : The structure of the ampulla of the semicircular canals (left) and of the saccule (right)

Bending of the hairs towards the Kinocilium opens transduction channels and since the upper surface of the hair cells is bathed in a high potassum medium (endolymph). This results in depolarization of the hair cells and excitation of the vestibular afferent fibers. Bending of the hairs away from the kinocilium leads to closure of transduction channels and hyper polarization of the hair cells; resulting in inhibition of the vestibular afferent fiber discharge.

**The receptors of the utricle and saccule signal linear accelerations such as gravity —**

The sensory epithelium of the utricle and sacule consists of a layer of hair cells covered by a gelatinous membrane containing small crystals of Calcium Carbonate called **otoliths**. The otolith membrane can move relative to the hair cells as the orientation of the head is changed. The movement of this membrane can cause deflection of the stereocilia and excitation of the vestibular afferents which ultimately provides the brain with sufficient information to define the position of the head with respect to gravity.

Information from the utricle and saccule is important in the control of posture unlike those of the semicircular canals, the afferents of the utricle and saccule continuously relay information to the brain about the position of the head. The nervous connections that permit the postural and oculomotor adjustments are complex.

(a) **Horizontal Motion :** Head rotates on left side → fluid in canal lags behind due to inertia

↓

Pushes cupula in left horizontal canal towards utricle

depolarization →

Hair cells in right horizontal canal are pushed away from utricle.

↓

hyperpolarized →

After some time, fluid catches up with head movement → Background discharge level reestablished.

Head Stops → fluid continues to move (inertia).

↓

opposite sequence of events

↓

receptors in left canal hyperpolarize and those in right canal depolarize

After sometimeendolymph stops and back ground discharge reestablished.

(b) **Vertical Motion :** Both vertical canals work in pairs

- When anterior canal is stimulated on one side → to CNS
- Posterior vertical canal is inhibited on opposite side → to CNS

## Disorders of the vestibular system

The information derived from the semicircular canals is used to control eye movements via the vestibulo-ocular reflexes, whose role is to stabilize the visual field on the retina. Information from the utricle and sacule plays an important role in the maintenance of posture.

- People with unilateral damage to the vestibular system have a sense of turning and of vertigo and associated with abnormal eye movements. First of all they have difficulty in maintaining their balance, ultimately they learn to compensate.
- If the vestibular system is damaged on both sides, affected subjects are unware of having sensory deficit.

**Motion Sickness :** It is not due to the damage to the vestibular system and caused by a conflict between the information arising from the vestibular system and that provided from other sensory systems such as vision and proprioception. Subjects with bilateral damage tothe vestibular system do not appear to suffer from motion sickness. It is characterized by cold sweats, hyperventilation nausea and vomiting-when the person is exposed to a repetitive motion of some kind.

**Meniere's disease :** It is progressive impairment of hearing due to abnormalcirculation of vestibular endolymph. There is a loss of sensitivity to low frequency sounds accompanied by attacks of dizziness or vertigo that may be so severe that the patient is unable to stand. These attacks are frequently accompanied by nausea and vomiting. Vertigo occurs due to vestibular damage with loss of balance having profound sense of dizziness.

## ➤ 12.16 KEY CONCEPTS

1. The **eye** is the receptor organ for vision. It is located in the orbital cavity and it is supplied by the optic nerve (2nd cranial nerve).
2. **Vision** involves the formation of an image by a refractive mechanism on the photosensitive retina. Light enters the eye through the pupil and is focussed by the cornea.
3. The **rods** and **cones** contain photosensitive pigments responsible for the conversion of light rays into nerve impulses. Rhodopsin is present in rods. **Cone photoreceptors** are responsible for high acuity color vision. **Rod photoreceptors** have more sensitivity but less acuity. They are responsible for dim light vision. Rods have more photopigments than cones. Rods respond more slowly than cones. **Cones** are mainly concerned with day (photopic) vision. **Rods** are sensitive to scattered light and have poor spatial resolution but cones are sensitive to direct axial light and have good spatial resolution. Like other modalities of sensation, the faculty of all sorts of discrimination, eg, size, shape, color in relation to vision is due to involvement of all its cellular components from retinal receptors to cortical neurons.
4. It is a common experience that when we enter a dark room from well-illuminated outside, initially it becomes difficult to see anything but as time passes on vision improves a lot. Though the acuity and color perception is poor, yet the power of sight is adequate for normal activities. This phenomenon is called **dark adaptation**.
5. Leaving aside the first five minutes for cone adaptation, all the rest of threshold lowering is due to adaptation of rods. The ratio between the luminosities of light adapted eye to completely dark adapted one is more that $10^{12}$.
6. Vitamin A, via one or more of its derivatives, is required for growth and differentiation of epithelial, osseous and nervous tissues. Its deficiency is associated with dryness (xerosis) and softness of cornea (keratomalacia), its subsequent ulcer, deformity and opacity.
7. **Light adaptation** : When one enters a well-illuminated area after passing some time in the dark, the light initially appears dazzling but within a few minutes, the tolerance occurs. Photopic vision is the function of cones. Increased sensitivity of rods and also of cones due to dark adaptation is responsible for initial intolerance. On sudden exposure to bright light but within a short interval the rods cease to function, cones start their usual function and retinal threshold rises.
8. When one looks at an object for some time and then closes his eyes or the object is removed, the object is seen for a few moments in the same color. It is due to persistence of chemical and electrical events after the withdrawal of stimulus, the sensation is called **positive afterimage** because the same receptors are implicated.
9. If one, after looking at a colored object, quickly stares at a white surface, the object is seen in complementary color. When the object is of red color the red cones become maximally stimulated, but on looking at a white surface emitting mixed colors, the less affected cones of the other end of the spectrum are stimulated most and the brain recognizes the object as if stained in complementary color (green) **negative afterimage**. This is due to fatigue of original red-sensitive receptors.
10. The physico-chemical mechanisms that operate in the case of after images also explain **contrast phenomena.** As for example, red flowers in the background of green leaves make both vivid, similarly black and white form good combination for distinction **simultaneous contrast.** It is clear that negative after image is responsible for this contrast.

    If one looks at a well-illuminated colored object for some time and then looks at another complimentary color eg, if after observing a yellow object one looks at a blue one the second object appears brighter. It is also due to the physico-chemical effects mediating negative after image.
11. Visual field defects due to lesions in different parts of the visual pathway (Fig. 1). At least six different types of characteristic visual field defects can be produced by discrete lesions in the primary visual pathway. Left visual field is shown in dark shades; right visual field is shown in light shade. Central or macular visual field projections are shown as solid lines while peripheral visual field projectioins are shown as interrupted lines. **Figure (1)** shows visual *pathways with normal visual fields and six possible sites where lesions may be located (viewed from above).* (2) **The figure 2** shows the lateral view and **figure 3** shows the *medial view (after removal of cerebellum) of the human brain depicting the sites of the same lesions.* **Figure 4** *visual field defects (shown in dark shade) that arise from those lesions.* Field of vision of both the eye are affected in all the cases except when the lesion is in the optic nerve. Also note that the visual field defect is contralateral to the side of brain injured. The pattern of visual field defect due to lesion in the crossing fibers of the optic chiasma is unique and can occur due to the pressure of an expanding pituitary tumor.
12. The **auditory system** is responsible for analysis of energy emitted or reflected from objects when they are located at a considerable distance from the body. Sound waves are transmitted through the ear drum and pass via the three ossicles of the middle ear. Sound vibrations are transduced into nerve action potentials by the hair cells in the cochlea. The cochlea consists of fluid-filled ducts that conduct sound waves. As a result, displacement of stereocilia of auditory hair cells occurs. The basilar membrane in the cochlea causes, tonotopic mapping of sound pitch.

## ➤ 12.16 KEY CONCEPTS

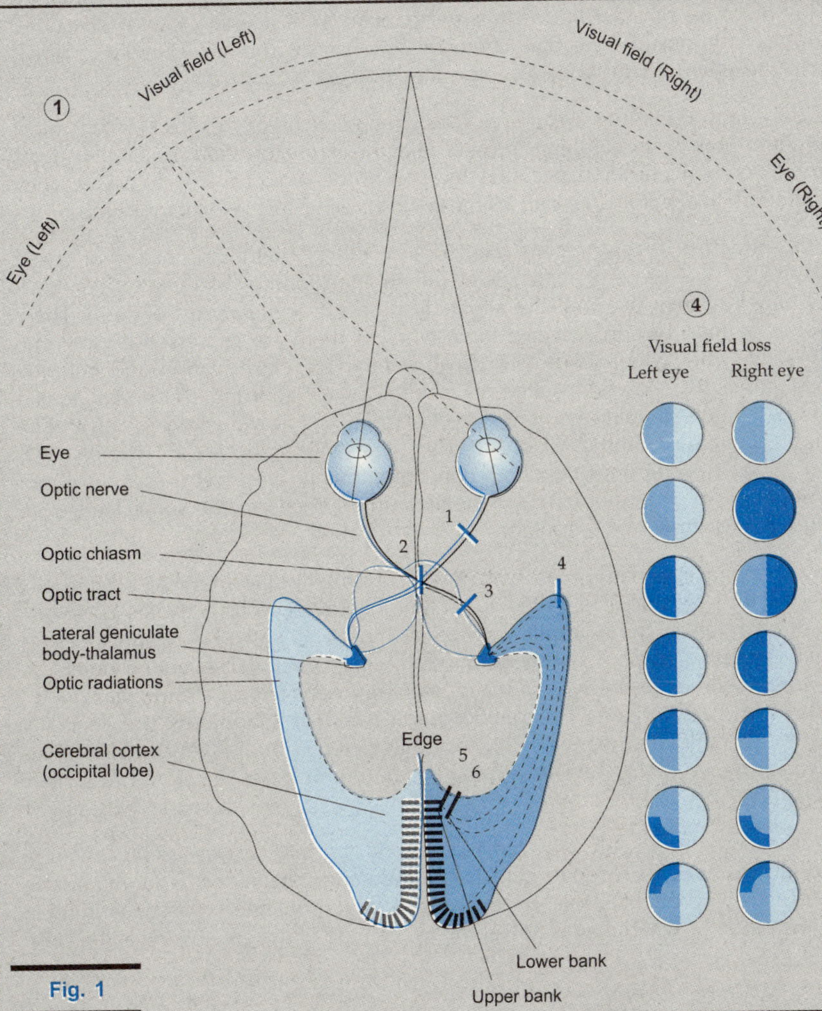


Fig. 1

| Name of deficit | Site of lesion |
|---|---|
| **0** Normal vision | No lesion |
| **1** Anopsia of right eye | Optic nerve |
| **2** Heteronymous hemianopsia | Optic chiasma |
| **3** Homonymous hemianopsia | Optic tract |
| **4** Upper quadrant anopsia | Meyer's loop |
| **5** Lower quadrantia anopsia having macular sparing | Upper bank calcarine fissure |
| **6** Upper quadrantic anopsia having macular sparing | Lower bank calcarine fissure |

Fig. 2

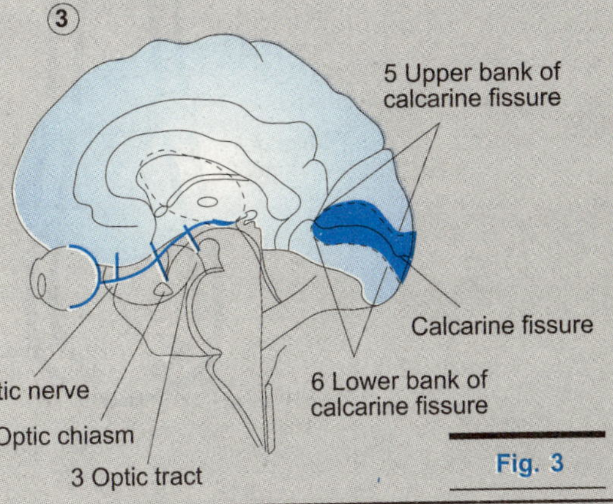


Fig. 3

## ➤ 12.16 KEY CONCEPTS

13. The outer and inner **auditory hair cells** in the organ of Corti are responsible for transmission of sound information to the primary auditory neurons. Multiple rows of outer hair cells are separated from a single row of inner hair cells by a supporting structure called the columns of Corti. The chemical senses taste and smell involve a direct interaction of chemical substances in the environment with receptor sites on sensory cells.

14. **Olfactory receptor neurons** are the only central nervous system neurons which are directly exposed to chemical substances in the environment. There are three main cell types present olfactory receptor neurons, supporting or sustentacular cells and basal cells. Olfactory cells lie in a specialized region in the roof of the nasal cavity. They are specialized neurons having a superficial receptor area and a fine axon passing to the olfactory bulb.

    **Generation of action potential in the olfactory receptor cells (Fig. 5):** The ciliary membrane of the olfactory neurons contain olfactory receptors which are proteins with seven membrane-spanning domains. The odor-specificity of these receptors is determined by their binding sites situated in the extracellular part of them. There are about 1000 different odor receptors in man but only one to three types of them are expressed by any one cell. The left panel (A) shows an inactive cilia where G-protein ($G_{olf}$), adenylyl cyclase, cation and chloride channels are all quiescent. The right panel (B) shows the effect of binding of an appropriate odorant to the receptor. $G_{olf}$ gets activated to bind GTP which stimulates adenylyl cyclase leading to production of cAMP. The cilium is depolarized due to opening of cation channels of cAMP. $Ca^{2+}$ that enters opens $Ca^{2+}$-sensitive $Cl^-$ channels through which intracellular $Cl^-$ (present in unusually high concentrations in these cells) escapes out of the cell; this leads to further depolarization of the cilium. This depolarization spreads to the soma leading to generation of action potential in the initial segment of the axon.

15. **Odorant receptors** are members of a receptor superfamily, all with seven transmembrane-spanning alpha helix regions. The specific G protein in olfactory receptors is called $G_{olf}$. Binding to receptor activates $G_{olf}$ → ↑ adenylyl cyclase → cAMP → calcium channels in the neuronal membrane bind to cAMP → ↑ conductance → calcium influx → ↑ chloride channel → depolarization → generation of receptor potential → action potential. It is also universally known that on continuous exposure we gradually become insensitive to a particular odour, as for example we are ignorant of our own body odours. This phenomenon is called **adaptation**. It is specially observed in case of smell sensation and is beneficial in many occupations associated with disagreeable odor. This adaptation is specific that makes this faculty even more beneficial. The adaptation or desensitization takes place both at peripheral and central levels.

16. **Taste receptors** and mechanisms for transdu-ction for salt, sour, umami, sweet, and bitter tastes are illustrated in Figs. 7–10. An increase in intracellu-lar $Ca^{2+}$ causes receptor cells to release neurotransmitters. The increase in intracyto-solic $Ca^{2+}$ concentration is usually brought about by opening of $Ca^{2+}$ channels consequent upon depolarization (of the receptor cells) the cause of which varies according to the type of the specific receptor cells.

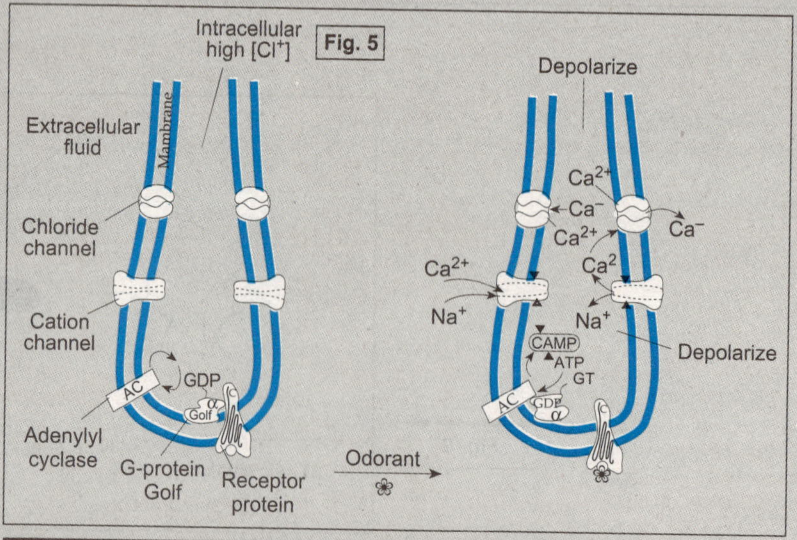


Fig. 5 : The olfactory bulb

## ➤ 12.16 KEY CONCEPTS

**Figure 7 :** Receptors for salty taste contain amiloride-sensitive $Na^+$ channels that are always open. Increases $Na^+$ concentration near the surface of the microvilli of these receptors cause $Na^+$ influx into the cells and there is depolarization. Hydrogen ions in acidic food can also pass through these channels and thus, acidic food tastes salty.

**Figure 8 :** Closure of $K^+$ channels that are present on the receptors for sour taste leads to depolarization. The $K^+$ channels are closed by direct action of $H^+$ ions on these channels.

**Figure 9 :** Umami taste, a recently recognized additional basic taste associated with some amino acids such as glutamate, is mediated by receptor cells containing cation channels that are similar to CNS glutamate receptors. Binding of glutamate to these receptors allows entry of small cations like $Na^+$, $K^+$, $Ca^{2+}$ etc. into the cell and leads to depolarization.

**Figure 10 :** Activation of the receptor proteins on the receptor cells for sweet taste causes G-protein mediated stimulation of adenylyl cyclase to produce cAMP which releases protein kinase A (PKA) from its regulator proteins. PKA causes closure of $K^+$ channels present on the receptor cell by phosphorylating them. The net effect is depolarization of the receptor cell.

**Figure 11 :** Receptors responsible for bitter taste elicited by quinine (bitter 1 receptors) are depolarized by closure of $K^+$ channels on them.

**Figure 12 :** Bitter substances other than quinine stimulate bitter 2 receptors that are G-protein dependent. G-protein mediated production of inositol triphosphate (IP3) leads to release of $Ca^{2+}$ from intracellular organelles and there is neurotransmitter release without depolarization.

17. The **vestibular function** plays an important role in regulating movement of the body and limbs. In addition, the body posture is maintained. The hair cells in the semicircular canals detect the rotatory movement of the head. The linear acceleration and the direction of gravity are detected by hair cells present in the otolith organs. There are two kinds of equilibrium, one is **static equilibrium**

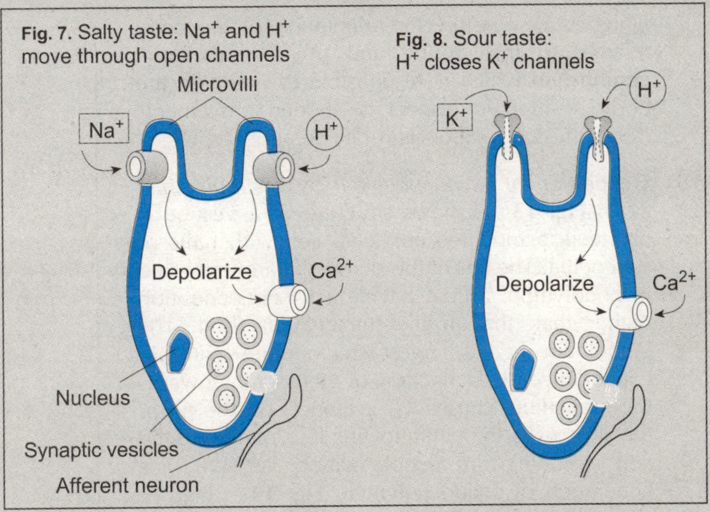


**Fig. 7.** Salty taste: $Na^+$ and $H^+$ move through open channels

**Fig. 8.** Sour taste: $H^+$ closes $K^+$ channels

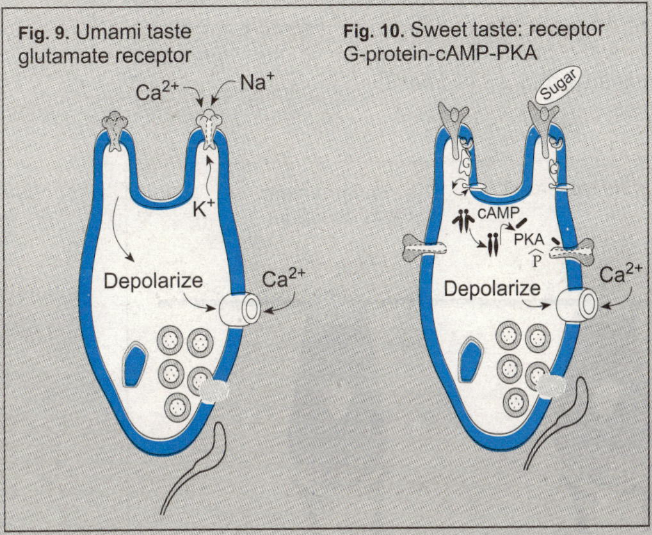


**Fig. 9.** Umami taste glutamate receptor

**Fig. 10.** Sweet taste: receptor G-protein-cAMP-PKA

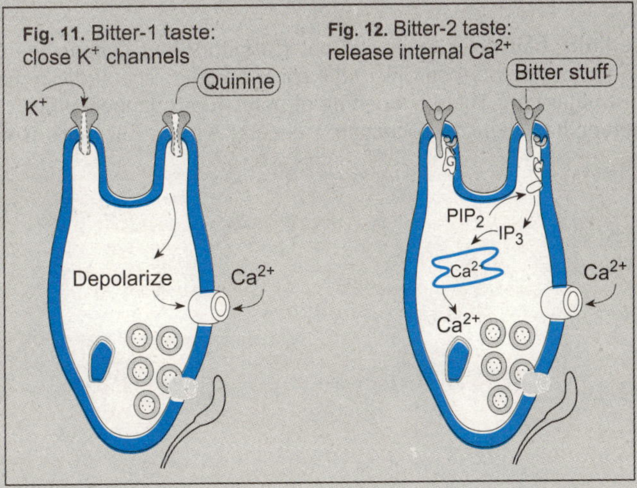


**Fig. 11.** Bitter-1 taste: close $K^+$ channels

**Fig. 12.** Bitter-2 taste: release internal $Ca^{2+}$

## ➤ 12.16 KEY CONCEPTS

which is responsible for orientation of the body relative to the ground and other is **dynamic equilibrium** which is responsible to maintain the body position in respect to sudden movements (rotation, acceleration and deceleration).

18. *Generation of action potential by vestibular hair cells.* **Fig. 13** — shows structure of a vestibular hair cell, a modified epithelial cell with hairs or stereocilia. The tips of the stereocilia are immersed in endolymph, a fluid having a $K^+$ concentration higher than that in the intracellular fluid. The kinocilium is the largest stereocilium with an expanded end. Deflection of stereocilia towards the kinocilium causes $K^+$ channels on the tip of the stereocilia to open allowing $K^+$ influx into the cell resulting in depolarization as well as generation of action potential. **Fig. 14 – Fig. 16** shows the changes in the frequency of action potential in the afferent neurons due to regulation of the release of glutamate (neuro-transmitter) brought about by movement of the stereocilia towards and away from the kinocilium.

**Fig. 13.** Vestibular hair cell

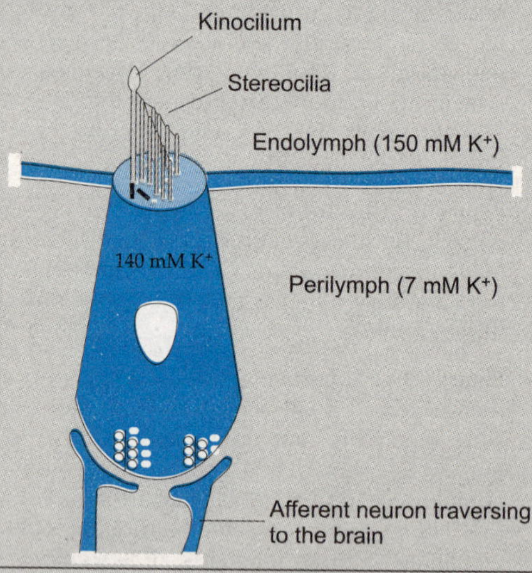


**Fig. 14.** No movement

**Fig. 15.** Movement towards kinocilium

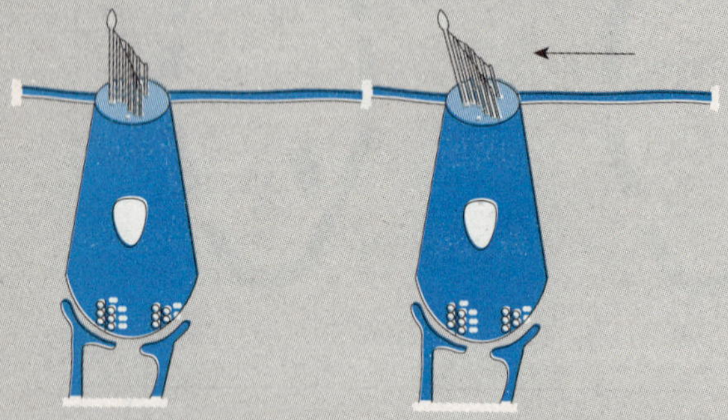

**Fig. 16.** Movement away from kinocilium

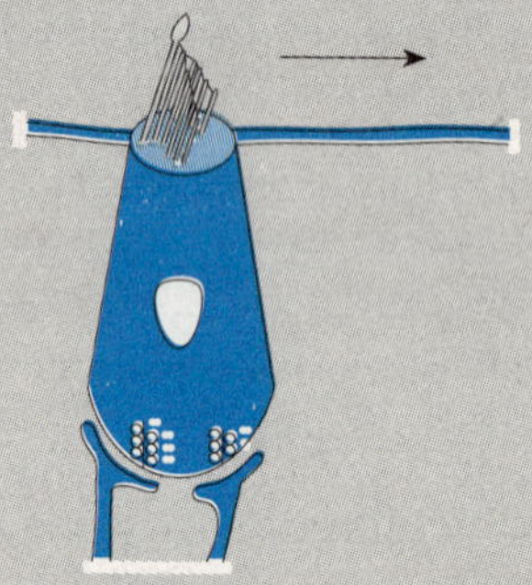

19. **Auditory hair cell :** Inner and outer auditory hair cells in the organs of Corti transmit sound information to the primary audi-tory neurons in the spiral ganglia. The auditory hair cell responds to much higher frequencies than vestibular cell. There is opening of potassium channels when the stereocilia bend in the direction of the longest stereocilia. Then depo-larization occurs. As a result there is release of neurotransmitter.

## ➤ 12.17 DISORDERS/CLINICAL CORRELATIONS

➤ **Astigmatism** : Astigmatism is a condition caused by the differential refraction of light rays in different meridians of cornea and/or lens making it impossible to focus light rays in the same plane or retina. In the majority of cases, astigmatism is the result of the cornea having different radii of curvature in different meridians. This is ***corneal astigmatism***. Less common is lenticular astigmatism which occurs when there are unequal radii of curvature in the lens. In either case, the eye acts as a spherocylindrical lens.

The condition in which correction can be achieved by use of a cylindrical lens is **regular astigmatism.** Astigmatism may be combined with hyper-opia or myopia.

When the cornea is of irregular shape due to irregular orientation of the principal meridians at different spots on the surface of cornea, the condition is called **irregular astigmatism**. This condition needs contact lenses for correction of refractive error.

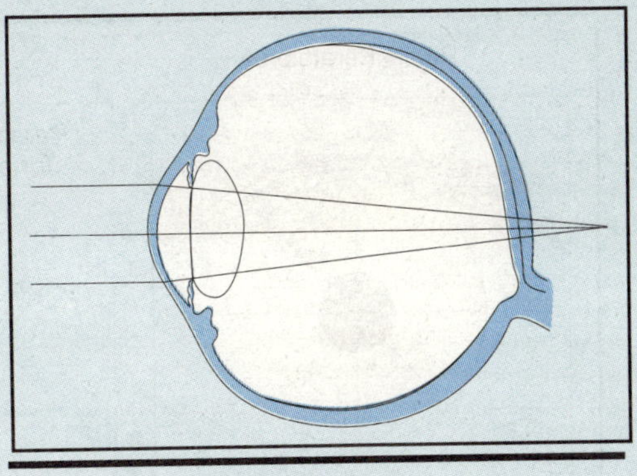

Fig. 1 : Hyperopia

➤ **Hyperopia (Far-sightedness)** : Here the eye lacks sufficient refractive power to focus light rays from a distant object on the retina. Instead, the focal point lies behind the retina. Hyperopia may be axial, curvature or index. In the ***axial type*** the eye is shortened relative to the emmetropic eye. In ***curvature*** hyperopia the cornea and/or lens is not curved enough to focus parallel right rays on the retina. ***Index* hyperopia** may result from the total decrease in index of refraction of the lens in old age. Hyperopia may be corrected by using plus (convex) lenses (Fig. 1).

➤ **Myopia** : The condition in which parallel light rays come to a focus before reaching the retina is **myopia.** There are three main types of myopia. The most common is **axial myopia,** which is the result of the eye being longer than normal. **Curvature myopia** is caused by excessive plus power due to the shape of the cornea and/or lens. Finally, **index myopia** is caused by an increase in the index of refraction of the lens. This can occur when the lens is hardened as a result of a cataract or because of lens dehydration related to diabetes. Correction is achieved by using minus (concave) lenses to compensate for the excess converging power of the eye (Fig. 2).

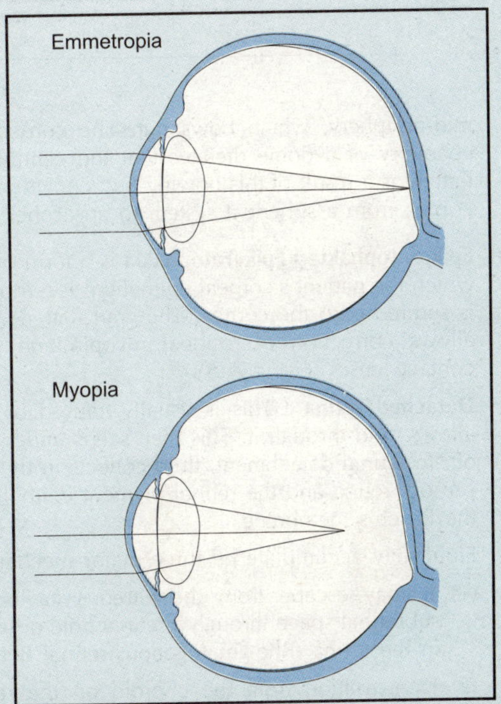


Fig. 2

➤ **Presbyopia** : Objects closer than about 6 meters (20 feet) away require accommodation to be brought into focus. Objects further away can be brought into focus with the lens remaining in its normal or flattened position. A young child can focus on a point as close as 7 cm from the eye. With aging the ability of accommodation reduces. The term for this progressive loss of accommodation is **presbyopia.** It becomes symptomatic after about age 40, when activities requiring accommodation such as reading or sewing become more and more difficult. Reading glasses, bifocal spectacles and contact lenses are used as remedy for presbyopia.

➤ **Watery eyes (chronic tearing or epiphora)** : The causes of epiphora can be divided into :

- Partial or complete obstruction of the nasolacrimal duct.
- Increased lacrimal secretion.
- Decreased lacrimal secretion with secondary reflex tearing.

Tear excretion involves the pumping action of the lids and good anatomic apposition of the patent punctal openings against the globe.

➤ **Radial keratotomy** : Radial keratotomy treats myopia by reducing the refractive power of the central cornea. This reduction in central corneal refractive power is achieved by weakening the dome-shaped corneal structure in the

## ➤ 12.17 DISORDERS/CLINICAL CORRELATIONS

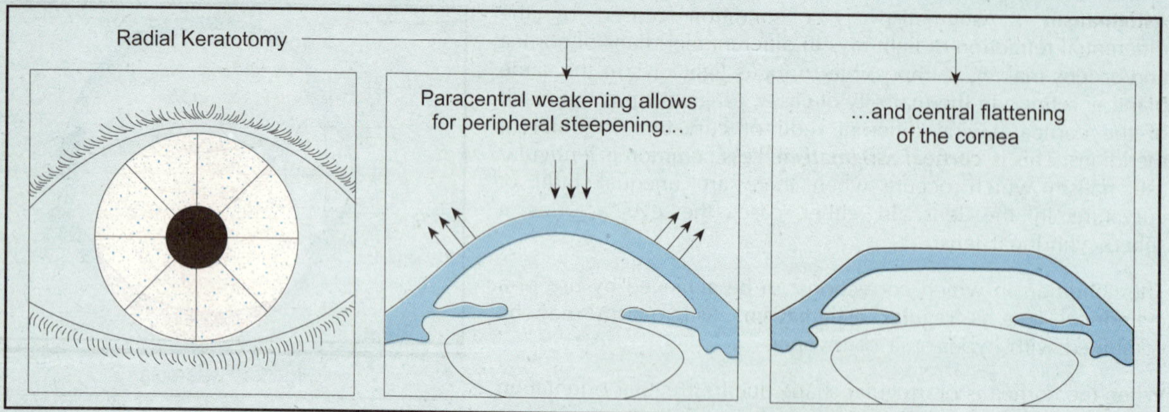


Fig. 3

mid-periphery, which bows out. The cornea is fixed at the limbus, the geometry of a dome dictates that the central portion of the cornea must flatten as a result of this bowing out, converting the central and paracentral cornea from a spherical system to an aspheric system (see Fig. 3).

➤ **Epikeratophakia** : **Epikeratophakia** is a form of refractive corneal surgery in which the patient's corneal epithelium is removed and a donor corneal disc is sutured onto the cornea. The graft flattens the cone in keratoconus and allows correction of residual myopia and astigmatism with glasses or contact lenses (Fig. 4 & 5).

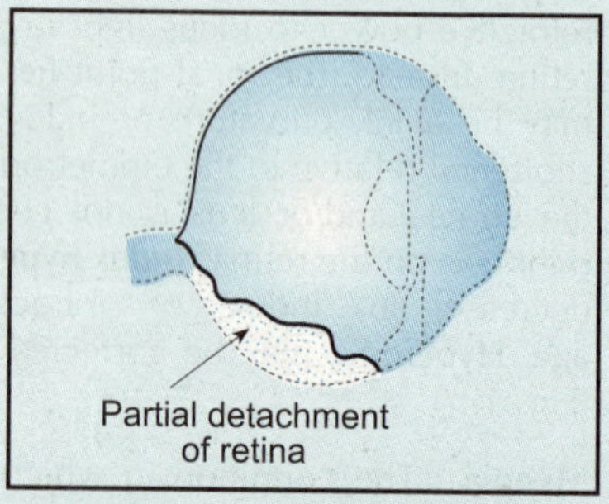


Fig. 4 : Retinal detachment

➤ **Detached retina** : This is usually caused by a hole in the retina which allows fluid through it. This then seeps under the retina and lifts the retina off. In retinal detachment, fluid collects in the potential space between the sensory retina and the retinal pigment epithelium that remains attached to the Bruch's membrane.

Fluid may accumulate by three major mechanisms :

(1) It may escape from the vitreous cavity into the subretinal space through a retinal hole or tear (break) in the retina (Rhe-gmatogenous retinal detachment).

(2) Extravasation from the choroid on the retina may result in retinal detachment (exudative retinal detachment).

(3) Retina can be detached from its normal position by fiborus bands in the vitreous (traction retinal detachment). Treatment is surgical.

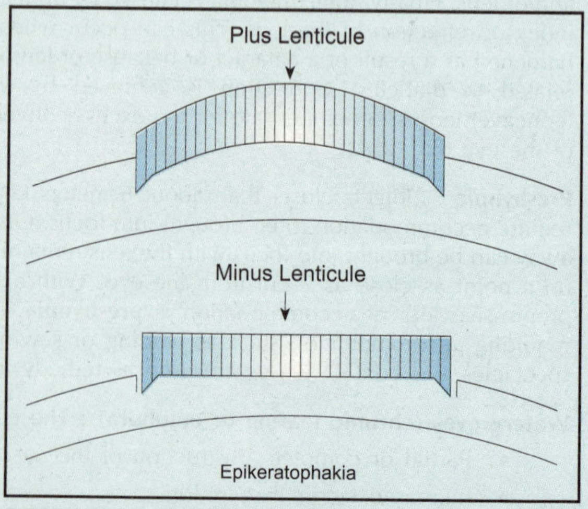


Fig. 5

➤ **Senile macular degeneration** : This condition is due to arterio-sclerotic changes at the macula, with chronic choroidal ischemia giving rise to degenerative changes in the retinal pigment epithelium, Bruch's membrane, and the choroid. Varying degrees of retinochoroidal atrophy may be seen, with minor atrophy of the retinal pigment epithelium to large punched out areas of complete loss of the choroid and the overlying retinal pigment epithelium and sensory retina.

➤ **Contact lens** : Contact lenses rest on the surface of the cornea. The same principles of refraction and optics apply to contact lenses as to spectacle lenses. They correct the amount of ametropia present by replacing the corneal curvature with a contact lens surface that is calculated to correct the degree of myopia or hyperopia. Since most

## ➤ 12.17 DISORDERS/CLINICAL CORRELATIONS

astigmatism is a result of the tonicity of the front corneal surface, rigid (hard) contact lenses usually eliminate the astigmatism. Soft lenses mould to the surface of the cornea. However, the front surface of the soft lens also becomes tonic, and the astigmatism will persist.

➤ **Conjunctivitis** : **Conjunctivitis** is an inflammation of the conjunctiva characterized by vascular dilation, cellular infiltration and exudation. It may be **bacterial, viral, allergic** or due to **some toxic factors**.

➤ **Diplopia** : Diplopia means double vision. It may be monoocular or binocular. **Binocular diplopia** occurs when the visual axes are not parallel, causing the image of the fixation object to fall on peripheral retina. The image is projected according to the visual direction of the retinal area stimulated. It may occur in various forms of paralistic strabismus. Monocular diplopia may occur in cases of polycoria, partially dislocated lens and occasionally in cataract.

➤ **Ptosis** : ***Ptosis*** means drooping of upper eyelids. Most ptosis are congenital and are caused by deficiency of the striated fibers in the levator muscle. ***Acquired ptosis*** is usually associated with good levator muscle, function and may be senile, myogenic (eg, in myasthenia gravis), neurogenic (deficient innervation of third cranial nerve to the levator muscle or deficient sympathetic innervation to Muller's muscle), traumatic and mechanical (eg, neurofibroma).

➤ **Glaucoma** : **Glaucoma** is a disorder in which the intraocular pressure is sufficiently elevated to damage vision. The main types of glaucoma are classified, primarily, as being of the **open angle** or **angle closure** types, according to the manner in which aqueous outflow is impaired. **In open angle glaucoma** the elevation of intraocular pressure is caused by increased resistance in the drainage channels, whereas in **angle-closure glaucoma** the obstruction to aqueous outflow is caused by closure of the anatomically narrow chamber angle by the peripheral iris.

➤ **Corneal transplants** : **Corneal transplanation** or **keratoplasty** is an operation in which abnormal host tissue is replaced by donor corneal tissue taken from cadaver eye. The eyes should be removed within 6 hours following death. The graft may be partial thickness (lamellar) or full thickness (penetrating) (Fig. 6).

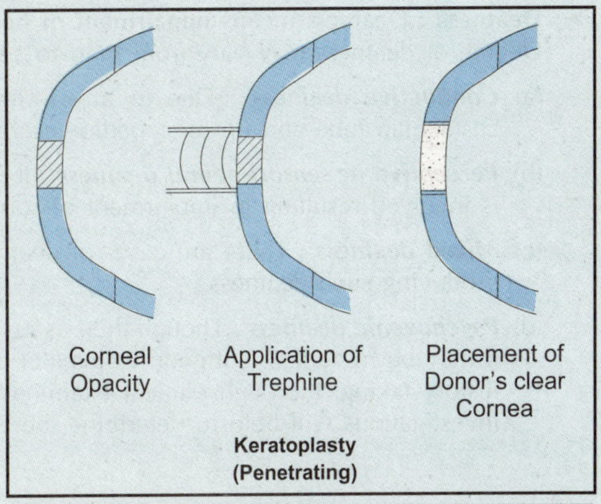


Fig. 6

➤ **Cataract : A cataract** is broadly defined as an opacity on or within the lens. It may be senile, metabolic (diabetes, hypoglycemia, galactosemia, galactokinase deficiency, Wilson's disease, hypocalcemia etc.), traumatic (including infrared irradiation, electric shock, ionizing irradiation etc.), toxic (corticosteroids, chlorpromazine, miotics), secondary (anterior uveitis, hereditary retinal and infraretinal disorder, high myopia), due to maternal infection (rubella, toxoplasmosis, cytomegalic inclusion disease), due to maternal drug ingestion (thalidomide, corticosteroids) etc.

➤ **Keratitis :** Inflammation of the cornea which may be caused by bacterial or viral infection, or may follow injury by a allergic reaction or mechanical cause. A common viral cause is herpes simplex which may result in a dendritic ulcer being formed on the cornea.

➤ **Blepharitis :** Inflammation of the eyelids, especially of the margins of the lids ciliary or marginal.

➤ **Ectropion :** Eversion of the eyelid due to infection, injury or degeneration.

➤ **Entropion :** Inversion of the eyelid due to injury and spasm in the elderly.

➤ **Color blindness** : **Color blindness** is a genetic disorder in which one of the three sets of cones is lacking or nonfunctional. **Total color blindness** — the inability to see any colors at all — is very rare. The normal person who needs a minimum of three primary color is a **trichromat**. Those who need two primary color are **dichromat** and those who need only one are **monochromat**. In the anomalous thichomat, the color mixture differ from those of the normal trichromat.

They may be classified into :

**A. Anomalous trichromats** *:* (a) Protanomalous; (b) Deuteranomalous; (c) Tritanomalous.

**B. Dichromats** *:* (a) Protanopia : One color is defective, red–blind, confusion of blue-green with red. (b) Deuteronopia : Two colors are defective, green – blind, confusing blue-green with purple. (c) Tritanopia : Three colors are defective, confusing yellow with blue.

## ➤ 12.17 DISORDERS/CLINICAL CORRELATIONS

**C. Monochromats** : They are very rare; there may be rod monochromatism and core monochromatism.

➤ **Cerumen or Wax :** Usually brown in color, it is a mixture of secretions of the ceruminous and sebaceous glands situated only in the cartilaginous part of the external auditory canal. Produces conductive deafness, especially when the whole canal is occluded. Considerable pain may occur due to impaction on the surrounding canal wall.

➤ **Acute suppurative otitis media :** One of the commonest diseases of infancy and childhood and is the **acute inflammation** of the muco-periosteal lining membrane of the whole middle ear cleft. *H. influenzae* and *Streptococcus penumoniae* are the most common causative organisms in children under the age of 5 yrs, while other causative organisms are *Staph aureus, N. catarrhalis, Streptococcus hemolyticus* etc.

➤ **Motion sickness :** It is due to the excessive stimulation of maculae. It is characterised by cold sweats, hyper ventilation, nausea and vomiting when the person is exposed to repetitive motion of some kind.

➤ **Meniere's disease :** It is defined as symptom complex of unknown etiology, the symptoms of which originate in the labyrinth and typically presents as a triad consisting of fluctuating deafness, tinnitus and episodes of vertigo. The disease is usually unilateral to start with and the common age of onset is **35-50 yrs**. It is characterized by **episodic attacks of rotatory vertigo, nausea, vomiting, fullness of ear, fluctuating deafness** and **tinnitus.** The giddiness and vomiting may be most disabling. The attacks last for a number of hours or days and then pass off completely leaving the patient normal. The deafness is of sensorineural type. The deafness and giddiness increase with subsequent attacks. Tinnitus is very troublesome and increases during the attack.

➤ **Bell's Palsy (Idiopathetic facial palsy) :** It is the commonest cause of **facial palsy**. Exact etiology is unknown. This is usually unilateral and of sudden onset. There is often history of exposure to cold. Individual cannot close the eye on the affected side which the patient notices after getting up from bed or while washing the face.

➤ **Deafness :** Deafness means **impairment of hearing**. It can occur at any age and may be congenital or acquired. Degree of deafness may vary from mild to severe loss. Clinically it can be divided into **four main categories** :

(a) ***Conductive deafness*** : Due to any lesion of the external auditory canal and middle ear cleft including Eustachian tube and up to stapedio-vestibular joint producing impaired sound conduction.

(b) ***Perceptive or sensori-neural deafness*** : It is the type of deafness where the inner ear or the VIII cranial nerve is involved resulting in impairment of sound perception in the cochlea and higher center.

(c) ***Mixed deafness*** : There are cases of deafness where both conductive apparatus and end organs are affected producing such deafness.

(d) ***Psychogenic deafness*** : Though there is no organic cause of deafness the patient complains of hearing loss and it may be hysterical (common in female) or malingering where the patient is conscious of deception. Careful history taking, thorough clinical examination of the ear including tuning fork tests and various audiological investigations will help to determine the type of deafness.

# Index

## A

## B



## C

## D



## E

## F



## G



## H

## I



## J



## K



## L

## M



## N

## O



## P

## Q



## R



## S

## T

## U



## V



## W



## Z